Progress in
Neural Information Processing

Springer

Berlin
Heidelberg
New York
Barcelona
Budapest
Hong Kong
London
Milan
Paris
Santa Clara
Singapore
Tokyo

Progress in
Neural Information Processing

Proceedings of the International Conference on Neural Information Processing
Hong Kong, September 24-27, 1996

Editors: Shun-ichi Amari, Lei Xu, Lai-Wan Chan, Irwin King and Kwong-Sak Leung

Volume 2

Springer

Editors

Shun-ichi Amari
RIEKN
Frontier Research Program
Wako-shi, Hirosawa 2-1
Saitama 351-01
Japan

Lei Xu, Lai-Wan Chan, Irwin King and
  Kwong-Sak Leung
Department of Computer Science & Engineering
The Chinese University of Hong Kong
Shatin, New Territories
Hong Kong

Co-sponsors of the conference:

Library of Congress Cataloging-in-Publication Data

International Conference on Neural Information Processing (3rd : 1996
  : Hong Kong)
    Progress in neural information processing : ICONIP'96 :
proceedings of the International Conference on Neural Information Processing,
Hong Kong, 24-27 September 1996 / Shun-ichi Ameri ... [et al.].
        p.   cm.
    "Third annual conference of the Asian Pacific Neural Network Assembly"--
    ISBN 9813083034 (vol. 1 - softcover)
        9813083042 (vol. 2 - softcover)
    1. Neural networks (Computer science)--Congresses. I. Amari, Shun'ichi.
II. Asian Pacific Neural Network Assembly. III. Title.
QA76.87.I573   1996
006.3--dc20   96–27442
                                                 CIP

ISBN 981-3083-04-2 (Volume 2)
ISBN 981 3083-05-0 (Set)

Cover designed by Dr. LOW Boon Toh

Typesetting: Camera-ready by authors
5 4 3 2 1 0

Foreword

The 1996 International Conference on Neural Information Processing is the third annual conference of the Asian Pacific Neural Network Assembly. For the first time, it is held in Hong Kong.

Hong Kong is known to the world as a bustling city where free enterprise is practiced to its extremes and competition goes almost uninhibited. It is a financial center, a communications center, and a shipping center in the Asian pacific region. It is becoming an information technology center as well.

To stay competitive, businesses and industries must adopt the latest technologies not only to make their operations more efficient and their staff more productive, but also to help their leaders make decisions based on predictive models constructed from information gathered over the world. Hong Kong businesses and industries are no exception. Indeed, Hong Kong is always among the first to acquire the newest computer, communication and information processing systems, and to use the most up-to-date technology, including neural network techniques, to improve a company's bottom line.

It is therefore most appropriate that the Asian Pacific Neural Network Assembly chose Hong Kong as the site of its 1996 annual conference. The subject matter will be of interest not only to academics and engineers but also to persons in the business and industrial sectors. More important, Hong Kong now has a broadly-based core of neural network enthusiasts among the universities, who constituted the organizing committee of the conference. We are also fortunate to have recruited a large number of supporters all over the world to serve on the various committees. It was their hard work, often over sleepless nights, that had brought about the conference. We want to take this opportunity to thank them all. Their names and affiliations are shown in the Conference Program.

We especially want to express our appreciation to the staff of the Chinese University of Hong Kong for their boundless contributions to the organization of this conference: Professor Lei Xu for his leadership of the Program Committee; Professor Lai-wan Chan and Professor K. S. Leung as co-chairs and Professor Irwin King as Secretary of the Organizing Committee.

Lastly, we want to invite you all to come to Hong Kong, to experience the energy and fervor that is Hong Kong, and to see for yourselves what is happening as she transforms herself from a Crown colony of United Kingdom to a Special Administrative Region of China.

<table>
<tr><td>Omar Wing</td><td>Shun-ichi Amari</td></tr>
<tr><td>General Co-chair</td><td>General Co-chair</td></tr>
<tr><td>Chinese University of Hong Kong</td><td>Tokyo University</td></tr>
</table>

Preface

The 1996 International Conference on Neural Information Processing (ICONIP'96) is organized by The Engineering Faculty of the Chinese University of Hong Kong, IEEE Computer Chapter (Hong Kong Section), Hong Kong Computer Society, ACM; and in cooperation with IEEE Neural Networks Council, International Neural Network Society, European Neural Network Society, Japanese Neural Network Society, China Neural Networks Council. On behave of the Organizing Committee of the we would like to thank their support to this conference. In addition, we acknowledge the distinguished sponsors of ICONIP'96; Silicon Graphics Ltd, Sun Microsystems, Automated Systems (HK) Ltd. Mr Fritz Chiu and Ms Mary Chan of the Hong Kong Productivity Council have provided their expertise in the management of the conference, which we like to acknowledge here.

We would like to specially thank the following people. The General Co-chairs of the conference, Professors Omar Wing and Shun-ichi Amari have been very supportive and have provided a lot of helpful advice to us from the early beginning. The Conference Program Co-chairs, Professors Lei Xu, Michael Jordan, Erkki Oja and Mitsuo Kawato, have been spent a lot of efforts to make this conference a qualitative one. Professor Lei Xu is also the source of the driving force to bring ICONIP'96 to Hong Kong. Professor Ke Chen gave us much help on the conference program and on the preparation of this book, whom we like to acknowledge.

Last but not the least, thanks should also be given to all members of the Organizing Committee, especially our secretary, Professor Irwin King. They, whom we like to give our special acknowledgement, have devoted many days of their precious time to this conference Without their voluntary help, ICONIP'96 would not be a success.

<table>
<tr><td>Kwong-Sak Leung
Organizing Co-chair
Chinese University of Hong Kong</td><td>Lai-Wan Chan
Organizing Co-chair
Chinese University of Hong Kong</td></tr>
</table>

A Message from the Program Committee

The goal of ICONIP'96 is to provide a forum for researchers and engineers from academia and industry to meet and to exchange ideas on the latest developments in neural information processing. The conference consists of one-day tutorial focusing on Financial Engineering by well known experts in the field and a three-day program with only four parallel sessions. The overall program covers the major topics in neural information processing and reflects the latest progress with a good balance between scientific studies and industrial applications, as well as featured neural information processing approaches on Financial Engineering.

The conference contains a high quality contributed program and a very strong invited program. For the contributed program, we received 314 submissions from 33 countries, including Asia-Pacific areas, Europe, North and South America. Each submitted paper has been sent to three experts in the related fields from all over the world for reviewing. With their rigorously and timely efforts, a high quality technical program has been achieved with around 60% overall acceptance rate (20% in oral presentation, 20% in spotlight presentations, 20% in poster presentation). The spotlight presentation is a poster presentation plus a 5 minutes oral presentation which highlights the contribution of the poster paper. For the invited program, we have 5 keynote speakers, 3 honored speakers, and 22 invited speakers by well known international neural information processing scientists and experts. The invited program is also featured by 8 special sessions on current interesting topics. Each special session organizer is invited by the Program Committee and the success of each special session is completely due to the hard efforts of each organizer.

Using this chance, we would like to specially thank our general chairs, Professors Omar Wing and Shun-ichi Amari, for their leadership and support. We also would like to specially thank our keynote speakers, Professors Shun-ichi Amari, Yaser Abu-Mostafa, Leo Breiman, Christoph von der Malsburg, Erkki Oja; our honored speakers, Professors Rolf Eckmiller, Mitsuo Kawato, Kunihiko Fukushima; our tutorial lecturers, Professors John Moody, A-P. N. Refenes, Halbert White, our 22 invited speakers and 8 special session organizers as well as all the advisory committee members, program committee members, and reviewers for their invaluable contributions and strong efforts to the ICONIP'96 program. Particularly, we would like to express our heartfelt gratitude to the organizing committee co-chairs, Professors Lai-wan Chan and K. S. Leung, and secretary, Professor Irwin King, for their great efforts on many laborious jobs.

Last but not least, we greatly appreciate all the authors, speakers, session chairs as well as all the members of the organizing committee—it is them who make the conference a success.

Lei Xu   Michael Jordan   Erkki Oja   Mitsuo Kawato
Program Co-chair   Program Co-chair   Program Co-chair   Program Co-chair
Chinese U. of HK   MIT   Helsinki U. of Tech.   ATR

General Co-Chairs

Omar Wing, CUHK
Shun-ichi Amari, Tokyo University

Advisory Committee

International
Yaser Abu-Mostafa, Caltech
Michael Arbib, University of Southern California
Leo Breiman, UC Berkeley
Jack Cowan, University of Chicago
Rolf Eckmiller, University Bonn
Jerome Friedman, Stanford University
Stephen Grossberg, Boston University
Robert Hecht-Nielsen, HNC
Geoffrey Hinton, University of Toronto
Anil Jain, Michigan State University
Teuvo Kohonen, Helsinki University of Tech.
Sun-Yuan Kung, Princeton University
Robert Marks, II, University of Washington
Thomas Poggio, MIT
Harold Szu, US Naval SWC
John Taylor, King's College London
David Touretzky, CMU
Christopher von der Malsburg, Ruhr-University of Bochum
David Willshaw, Edinburgh University
Lofti Zadeh, UC Berkeley

Asia-Pacific Region
Marcelo H. Ang Jr, NUS, Singapore
Sung-Yang Bang, POSTECH, Pohang
Hsin-Chia Fu, NCTU, Hsinchu
Toshio Fukuda, Nagoya University, Nagoya
Kunihiko Fukushima, Osaka University, Osaka
Zhenya He, Southeastern University, Nanjing
Marwan Jabri, University of Sydney, Sydney
Nikola Kasabov, University of Otago, Dunedin
Yousou Wu, Tsinghua University, Beijing

Hong Kong Region
N.V. Balasubramanian, CityU
Richard Chen, CityU
Paul Cheung, HKU
Francis Chin, HKU
Ernest Lam, HKBU
Agnes Mak, HKCS
Vincent Shen, HKUST

Wan Chi Siu, HKPU
Chak-Kuen Wong, CUHK
Kam Fai Wong, CUHK
Daniel Yeung, HKPU

Organizing Committee

L.W. Chan (Co-Chair), CUHK
K.S. Leung (Co-Chair), CUHK
D.Y. Yeung (Finance), HKUST
C.K. Ng (Publication), CityUHK
A. Wu (Publication), CityUHK
B.T. Low (Publicity), CUHK
M.W. Mak (Local Arr.), HKPU
C.S. Tong (Local Arr.), HKBU
T. Lee (Registration), CUHK
K.P. Chan (Tutorial), HKU
H.T. Tsui (Industry Liaison), CUHK
I. King (Secretary), CUHK

Program Committee

Co-Chairs
Lei Xu, CUHK
Michael Jordan, MIT
Erkki Oja, Helsinki University of Technology
Mitsuo Kawato, ATR

Members
Yoshua Bengio, University of Montreal
Jim Bezdek, University of West Florida
Chris Bishop, Aston University
Leon Bottou, Neuristique
Gail Carpenter, Boston University
Laiwan Chan, CUHK
Huishen Chi, Peking University
Peter Dayan, MIT
Kenji Doya, ATR
Scott Fahlman, CMU
Francoise Fogelman, SLIGOS
Lee Giles, NEC Research Institute
Michael Hasselmo, Harvard University
Kurt Hornik, Technical University of Wien
Yu Hen Hu, University of Wisconsin - Madison
Jeng-Neng Hwang, University of Washington
Nathan Intrator, Tel-Aviv University

List of Reviewers

Most of the 44 program committee members and the following additional reviewers:

Andreas Andreou	Oliver Mihatsch
Sung-Yang Bang	Itraru Nagayama
Ke Chen	Ralph Neuneier
Yizong Cheng	Klaus Obermayer
Richard Coggins	Dirk Ormoneit
Bernd Fritzke	Joel Ratsaby
Kunihiko Fukushima	Steve Rehfuss
Michael Haft	Jiong Ruan
Michael Herrmann	Matt Saffell
Lester Ingber	Juergen Schmidhuber
Masumi Ishikawa	Sara A. Solla
Marwan Jabri	Ah-Hwee Tan
Arun Jagota	Michiaki Taniguchi
Fan Jin	Chong Sze Tong
Nikola Kasabov	Hung Tat Tsui
Dmitri Kaznachey	Jun Wang
Irwin King	Chris Williams
Kai Pui Lam	Kam Fai Wong
Chi-Sing Leung	Lizhong Wu
Kwong Sak Leung	Youshou Wu
Tsungnan Lin	Yeung Yam
Boon Toh Low	Howard Hua Yang
Bao-Liang Lu	Dit-Yan Yeung
Jinwen Ma	Bai-ling Zhang
Jianchang Mao	David Dapeng Zhang
Ronny Meir	Jieyu Zhao
Igor Milosavlevich	Yi Xin Zhong

Contents, Volume 1

Recurrent Networks, Automata and Dynamics *(Poster Presentation)* . . 555

Associative Memory *(Oral Presentation)* 579

Contents, Volume 2

Financial Engineering
and
Time Series Forecasting

(Oral Presentation)

Biasing Towards Integer Solutions

A-P. N. Refenes
`prefenes@lbs.lon.ac.uk`

J. T. Connor
`jconnor@lbs.lon.ac.uk`

London Business School
Sussex Place, Regent's Park,
London NW1 4SA, England.

Abstract

Because of their ability to fit complex *non-linear* relationships between dependent and explanatory variables under relatively weak assumptions, Neural Networks have attracted considerable interest. Although this approach often leads to better *non-parametric* estimators, neural networks are not readily acceptable in a good deal of applications and particularly by the statistics/econometrics community; they are perceived as "black-boxes' which attempt to bypass, rather than support the step of theory formulation.

In this paper we formulate neural learning in a framework similar to non-linear, non-parametric regression. The formulation provides an *explicit (closed-form)* representation of the models estimated by the neural learning procedure. We derive an algorithm for making the closed-form representation more transparent, and discuss its convergence properties. We evaluate the procedure using synthetic data under controlled simulation to verify that it is capable of reconstructing the true data generating processes and more importantly, that it is capable of separating the stochastic from the deterministic component in the unknown data generating process.

1. INTRODUCTION

Neural Networks are the subject of increasing interest from practitioners in quantitative asset management They can provide a more reliable method of modelling asset returns, because, unlike conventional models they make few (if any) **a priori** assumptions about the nature of the relationship between the return of an asset (R_i) and its exposure to changes in market, financial and economic factors (f_j). It is generally assumed that variations in R_i are only partially due to a deterministic processes and mostly due to stochastic effects *i.e.*

$$R_i^{t+\tau} = g_i(f_1^t,..,f_n^t) + \varepsilon_i \tag{1}$$

where: $R_i^{t+\tau}$ is the return of asset i at time $t+\tau$ (the investment horizon); $g_i()$ is a deterministic but unknown function relating return to factor exposure, f_j^t the exposure of asset i to factor j at time t, and ε_i is a stochastic (and often dominant) effect.

The task of the learning procedure is to estimate the function $g_i()$ and its derivatives (c.f. β's) from the available data but without overfitting the noise.

Neural networks are being applied to a number of "live" systems in financial engineering and have shown promising results with many researchers claiming that they signal the beginning of a new era in the evolution of forecasting and decision support systems. Various performance figures are being quoted to support these claims but there is rarely a comprehensive investigation of the nature of the relationship, $g_i()$, that has been captured between asset prices and their determinants. The absence of an explicit representation of $g_i()$, makes it difficult to assess the significance of the estimated model and the possibility that any short term success is due to "data mining". This is preventing us from using financial economics theory on market dynamics to investigate the plausibility of the estimated models $g_i()$, and from analysing them in order to separate the non-linear components of the models which are invariant through time from those that reflect temporary (and probably unrepeatable) market imperfections.

The aim of this paper is to formulate neural learning in a way that provides an explicit representation for g_i (). Although our motivation accrues from the requirements of financial engineering the same requirement prevails a wide range of applications, where the stochastic component in (1) dominates the data generating process.

In section 2, we derive a closed-form representation for two-layer neural networks which we use to illustrate the full power of neural modelling and some of the potential drawbacks. This formulation provides the basis for an econometric representation of neural models. In section 3, we derive an algorithm for making the closed form representation of $g_i()$ more transparent and we discuss its convergence implications. The basic idea is to penalise complexity in $g_i()$ through the use of integer priors. In section 4, we show that the closed form representation, in conjunction with the new learning algorithm is capable of reconstructing unknown data generating processes and more importantly, that it is capable of separating the stochastic from the deterministic component in the data generating process.

2. AN ECONOMETRIC REPRESENTATION OF NEURAL MODELS

For the purposes of elucidating the capabilities of neural networks as non-linear nonparametric regression models, it suffices to consider a rather simplified form of connectivity whereby neurons are arranged in layers with each neuron in the layer is connected to all neurons in the layer before and after. Let us consider a network consisting of two input units a layer of two *hidden* neurons and one output neuron. The non-linear transfer function is the common logistic, and we ignore the constant connections for clarity. Let A and B denote input variables, y denote the output variable and α_0, α_1, β_0, β_1 are the connection weights from the input units to the hidden layer with γ_0, γ_1 denoting connections from the hidden units to the output unit.

The task of the training procedure is to estimate a function between input and output which minimises the ordinary least squares error. This function is parameterised by the network weights and the non-linear transfer function and (ignoring the bias terms) takes the form:

$$y' = \frac{1}{1 + e^{-(\gamma_0 \frac{1}{1+e^{-(\alpha_0 A + \beta_0 B)}} + \gamma_1 \frac{1}{1+e^{-(\alpha_1 A + \beta_1 B)}})}} \tag{2}$$

This representation is rather too complex to understand intuitively. Let us try to work out a simpler version that is easier to understand and to compare with traditional econometric approaches. To do so we make two rather weak simplifications. The first assumes that at the output level we use a linear energy transfer function. Thus,

$$y' = \gamma_0 v_0 + \gamma_1 v_1 = \gamma_0 \frac{1}{1 + e^{-(\alpha_0 A + \beta_0 B)}} + \gamma_1 \frac{1}{1 + e^{-(\alpha_1 A + \beta_1 B)}} \tag{3}$$

The second assumption is even weaker. In investment management applications, it is common to apply smoothing transformations to the input and output variables prior to training, in order for example to remove the effect of statistical outliers. A common transformation is the logarithmic operation. Typically instead of estimating $y = f(A, B)$ one would use the reversible transformation $y = f(ln(A), ln(B))$. Using this transformation, the exponential term can be rewritten as:

$$e^{(\alpha_0 \ln(A) + \beta_0 \ln(B))} = A^{\alpha_0} B^{\beta_0} \tag{4}$$

Using (4) it is easy to show that (3) can be rewritten as the sum of two products:

$$y' = \gamma_0 \frac{A^{\alpha_0} B^{\beta_0}}{A^{\alpha_0} B^{\beta_0} + 1} + \gamma_1 \frac{A^{\alpha_1} B^{\beta_1}}{A^{\alpha_1} B^{\beta_1} + 1} \tag{5}$$

Overall we have six parameters $\{\alpha_0, \alpha_1, \beta_0, \beta_1$ and $\gamma_0, \gamma_1\}$ ignoring the constants. The task of the learning procedure is to estimate the parameters in a way that minimise the residual least square error. In the general case for networks with n hidden neurons and m input variables (5) takes the form

$$y' = \gamma_0 \frac{A^{\alpha_0} B^{\beta_0} \dots M^{\mu_0}}{A^{\alpha_0} B^{\beta_0} \dots M^{\mu_0} + 1} + \gamma_1 \frac{A^{\alpha_1} B^{\beta_1} \dots M^{\mu_1}}{A^{\alpha_1} B^{\beta_1} \dots M^{\mu_1} + 1} + , \dots, + \gamma_n \frac{A^{\alpha_n} B^{\beta_n} \dots M^{\mu_n}}{A^{\alpha_n} B^{\beta_n} \dots M^{\mu_n} + 1} \tag{6}$$

Thus, neural learning is analogous to searching the function space defined by the terms of equation (6) and the range of the permissible values for the parameters ($\alpha_0, \alpha_1, \beta_0, \beta_1$ and γ_0, γ_1). This formulation is strikingly similar to the formulation of additive non-linear nonparametric regression (e.g. ACE and AVAS) [Hardle 1989] but it differs in many respects. Let us explore some of the implications of the estimation procedure and how it differs from traditional statistical models.

In theory, the parameters (α_i, β_i) can take any value which minimises the residual error (starting from a random point). Since they raise the corresponding variable to a power, we are effectively searching through function space to find the best combination of functions to fit the data. For example, suppose that the initial value of α_0 is equal to 0.5 (i.e. $A^{0.5} = \sqrt{A}$) and by gradient descent we end-up with say $\alpha_0 = 2$ (i.e. A^2). In the process we have tried all intermediate functions (the learning rate λ controls the step-size through this search).

The procedure, under certain conditions, can be shown to produce a universal approximator (e.g. given enough parameters it will always find a composite function that minimises the residual error). This is a very powerful property. Neural networks derive one of their main advantages from this property, but also one of their most important weaknesses, particularly in applications where the stochastic component in the data generating process (i.e. ε_i in equation (1)) is generally believed to be responsible for explaining a larger proportion of the variability in (1) than the deterministic component $g_i()$. This is certainly the case not only in financial engineering but also in most business and commercial applications.

Critics argue that this property makes neural networks perfect 'curve fitters' and epitomises the 'data mining' syndrome. It may also produce relationships which are counter intuitive and the whole process is competitive rather than synergetic with theory formulation. To the defence of neural networks, advocates will argue that this is definitely true but we can control the complexity of the search space in several ways. For example we may introduce complexity penalty terms in the fitness function which penalises over-parameterised networks (models), constrains the search space, and drives redundant parameters to values near or at zero. Alternatively we may introduce **a priori** constraints. For example if financial economics theory suggests that there is a quadratic relationship between, say changes in spot and changes in implied volatility (with spot being one of our independent variables) we may freeze that particular weight (or group of weights) to the value 2. In any case by letting the data speak for themselves not only about the co-efficient of a parametric model but also about the nature of the relationship we have a much more powerful tool.

The use of the closed-form representation in equation (6) (or similar) makes neural networks synergetic to theory formulation. It enables us to examine the nature of the estimated relationship and conclude for ourselves as to whether it represents some temporary financial anomaly or it is invariant through time.

Within typical statistical and econometric applications, any interactions between independent variables have to be assumed away (to enable matrix inversion). This is generally a crucial but common failing. Variables which are commonly used to explain asset returns (such as interest rates, unanticipated inflation, financial ratios, etc.) are hardly ever truly independent variables. Neural Network modelling as is evident from the closed form in equation (6) takes the exact opposite perspective. We start by assuming that all variables might interact with all others in n different ways (n being the number of hidden units). If the data does not support this hypothesis, we expect that the gradient descent procedure will, at least in theory, produce estimates for the parameters α_i, β_i which are equal (or close) to zero. Similarly if there are no strong direct non-linear relationships between independent and dependent variables the estimation procedure should produce estimates for α_i, β_i which are equal (or close) to one.

In general, non-linear dependencies in financial markets may arise partially because of **interactions** between independent variables and partially because of **direct** non-linearities between independent and dependent variables. Neural network models provide an elegant way to deal with both cases. Note that it is always possible and in many cases desirable to constrain the search space by using complexity penalty terms in the error function and/or incorporating sensible **a priori** knowledge in the model. For example, by freezing the α_i, β_i parameters to zero values between variables that are known to be truly independent.

Let us turn our attention to equation (6) which will serve as the basis for obtaining an econometric interpretation of the estimated $g_i()$. In theory the parameters α_i, β_i can take any **real** value that minimises the residual error. In order to facilitate a transparent representation of the equation in (6) it would be desirable to encourage the estimation procedure to produce **integer** values for these parameters. In the next section we describe an extension to the gradient descent procedure designed to "drag" weights towards integer values.

3. MINIMISING COMPLEXITY WITH INTEGER PRIORS

The procedure we shall use is best described in terms of Bayesian estimation but it has a straightforward OLS interpretation. We start by giving a brief overview of Bayes law on estimating neural network parameters and introduce the notion of prior bias in favour of integer values. We then convert this formulation into a gradient descent implementation.

The weights of a neural network are estimated by maximising the probability of the weights, w, given the data, $y_1, \cdots, y_n$, which by Bayes Law is given by

$$P(w|y_1, \cdots y_N) = P(\frac{y_1, \cdots y_N|w)P(w)}{P(y_1, \cdots y_N)}. \tag{7}$$

The probability of the data, $P(y_1, \cdots, y_N)$, is unknown and assumed constant reducing (7) to

$$P(w|y_1, \cdots, y_N) \approx P(y_1, \cdots, y_N|w)P(w). \tag{8}$$

The quantity $P(y_1, \cdots, y_N|w)$ is defined by the model and $P(w)$ denotes the prior knowledge (preference) of the weight parameters. If $P(w)$ is assumed constant, this Bayesian estimation procedure will reduce to maximum likelihood. We now present an integer prior which reflects our preference that the weights are close to integer values. To keep the models as simple as possible we also introduce an additional prior: weights are "more likely to be zero than not". In other words we shall always assume that the independent variable follows a random walk and will only revise this view if there is overwhelming evidence in the data to the contrary.

One possible prior which gives higher probability to a parameter (neural network weight), w, which is close to an integer value is given by

$$P(w) = \frac{1}{2N+1} \sum_{j=-N}^{N} \frac{1}{\sqrt{2\pi\sigma^2}} e^{-\frac{(w-j)^2}{2\sigma^2}}. \tag{9}$$

This prior is a summation of Gaussian distributions centred around each integer in the range $\pm N$. As the variance, σ^2, of the individual Gaussians is decreased, the probable range of w will be constrained to be closer to an integer value. The Ordinary Least Squares (OLS) estimator is a special case: when $\sigma > .5$ and $N \to \infty$ the effect is to give the same weight to all values for the parameter.

Another desirable property is to have a prior which smoothly goes to zero as w goes to infinity reflecting our preference that weights closer to zero ought to take precedence unless there is strong evidence in the data to the contrary. Such a prior is obtained by windowing the prior in (9) as $N \to \infty$ by an exponential decay factor

$$P(w) = \frac{1}{Z_w} e^{-\frac{w^2}{2\Sigma^2}} \sum_{j=-\infty}^{\infty} e^{-\frac{(w-j)^2}{2\sigma^2}} \quad \text{with} \quad Z_w = \int_{-\infty}^{\infty} e^{-\frac{w^2}{2\Sigma^2}} \sum_{j=-\infty}^{\infty} e^{-\frac{(w-j)^2}{2\sigma^2}} dw. \tag{10}$$

This prior is shown in figure 1 for σ equal to 0.2 and Σ equal to 3. Note the strong peaks in prior probabilities at integer values and the small prior probabilities for all large values of $|w|$. Since the prior probability is never zero, given enough data any weight can be estimated, but there will always be a disposition toward small integers.

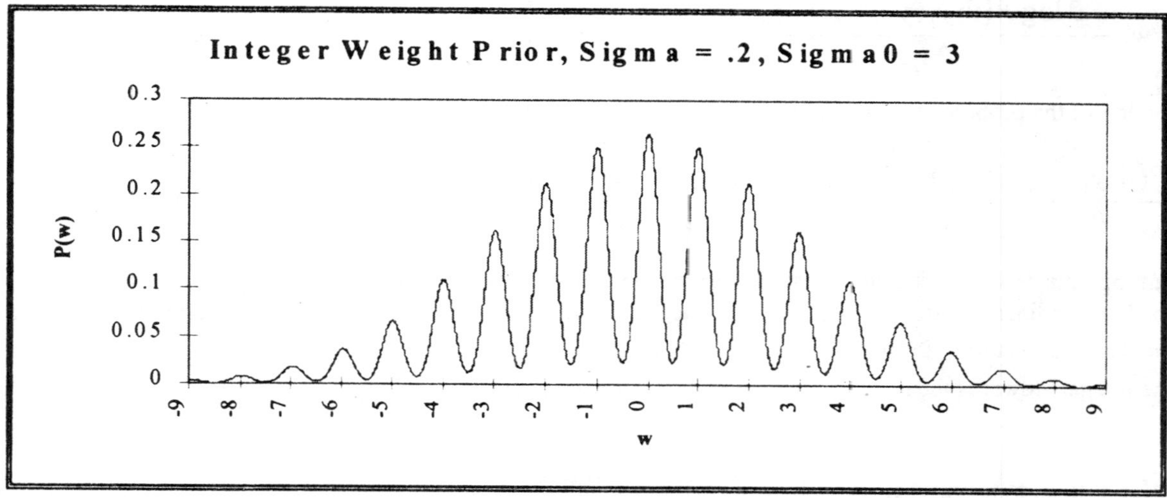

Figure 1: Integer prior with $\sigma = 0.2$ and $\Sigma = 3$; simple models are preferable to complex models.

Setting w_{int} equal to the closest integer to w, the infinite sum in (10) can be expressed as

$$\sum_{j=-\infty}^{\infty} e^{-\frac{(w-j)^2}{2\sigma^2}} = e^{-\frac{(w-w_{\text{int}})^2}{2\sigma^2}} + \sum_{k=1}^{\infty} e^{-\frac{(w-w_{\text{int}}+k)^2}{2\sigma^2}} + \sum_{k=1}^{\infty} e^{-\frac{(w-w_{\text{int}}-k)^2}{2\sigma^2}}$$

$$= e^{-\frac{(w-w_{\text{int}})^2}{2\sigma^2}} \left\{ 1 + \frac{1}{2}\sum_{k=1}^{\infty} e^{-\frac{k^2}{2\sigma^2}} \cosh(k\frac{w-w_{\text{int}}}{\sigma^2}) \right\} = g(w-w_{\text{int}},\sigma) \tag{11}$$

Combining (10) and (11) results in a prior

$$P(w) = \frac{1}{Z_w} e^{-\frac{w^2}{2\Sigma^2}} g(w-w_{\text{int}},\sigma). \tag{12}$$

which is expressed as a function of the distance to the nearest integer The prior will both give small but non-zero probabilities for large w and will give integer weights a higher probability than non-integer weights. Note the windowing factor, $\exp(-w^2/2\Sigma^2)$, has been used often before as a prior in its own right [4][5]. The log of the probability is proportional to $\log(g(w-w_{\text{int}},\sigma))$. Note the maximum at integer values, corresponding to $w-w_{\text{int}}=0$. The log of the probability falls much more for the smaller value of σ. Note also the flattening out of the log of the probability at $w-w_{\text{int}}=\pm0.5$. This corresponds to midway points between neighbouring integers.

A weight vector can be chosen to maximise the probability of $\vec{w}$ given the observed data, from Bayes rule: $w = \max_{w'} P(w'|y_1,\cdots,y_N)$ and with the use of (8) and some independence assumptions the Bayes rule for estimating weights becomes

$$w = \max_{w'} \prod_{i=1}^{N} P(y_i|w')P(w') \tag{13}$$

where, $P(y_i|\vec{w}) = \left(2\pi s^2\right)^{-1/2} \exp(-(y_i - \hat{y}_i)^2 / 2s^2)$ and $P(\vec{w}) = \prod_{i=1}^{M} P(w_i)$. Maximising the probability is equivalent to maximising the log of the probability. An iterative learning rule based on gradient descent which maximises the log of the probability is given by:

$$w_j^{i+1} = w_j^i + \frac{\partial \log P(\vec{w}|y_1, y_2, \ldots, y_N)}{\partial w_i}. \tag{14}$$

where the log of the probability is given by

$$\frac{\partial \log P(\vec{w}|y_1, y_2, \ldots, y_N)}{\partial w_i} = -\sum_{j=1}^{N} \frac{(y_j - \hat{y}_j)}{s^2}\frac{\partial \hat{y}_j}{\partial w_i} - \frac{w_i}{\Sigma^2} + \frac{\partial \log g(w - w_{\text{int}}, \sigma)}{\partial w_i} \tag{15}$$

This learning rule is composed of several understandable parts. The first term on the right hand side of (15) corresponds to Ordinary Least Squares "Backpropagation" which in turn corresponds to the maximum likelihood estimator. The second term, $\Sigma^{-2} w_j$, forces weights to be closer to zero. Lastly final term, $\partial \log g(w - w_{\text{int}}, \sigma)/\partial w_i$, forces the integers towards the nearest integer. This is easy to compute by:

$$\frac{\partial \log g(w - w_{\text{int}}, \sigma)}{\partial w_i} = \frac{w - w_{\text{int}}}{\sigma^2} - \frac{1}{\sigma^2} \frac{\frac{1}{2}\sum_{k=1}^{\infty} k e^{-\frac{k^2}{2\sigma^2}} \sinh(k \frac{w - w_{\text{int}}}{\sigma^2})}{1 + \frac{1}{2}\sum_{k=1}^{\infty} e^{-\frac{k^2}{2\sigma^2}} \cosh(k \frac{w - w_{\text{int}}}{\sigma^2})} \tag{16}$$

Observe that for $\sigma \ll 1$ and $|w - w_{\text{int}}| \ll \sigma^2$, $\partial \log g(w - w_{\text{int}}, \sigma)/\partial w_i \approx \sigma^{-2}(w - w_{\text{int}})$, which represents the desired push to the nearest integer w_{int}. At the mid-way point between integers, the prior will have no effect on the gradient, $\partial \log g(w - w_{\text{int}} = \pm.5, \sigma)/\partial w_i = 0$. To speed-up the computation time, for a given value of σ, a table of $\partial \log g(w - w_{\text{int}}, \sigma)/\partial w_i$ can be calculated for $w - w_{\text{int}}$ ranging between ± 0.5 Various shapes of these derivatives are plotted in figure 2. Note the sensitivity to non-integer values for small σ and the near flatness of the curves for large σ. Only the smaller σ will automatically give rise to integer solutions; the larger σ values will have no effect on the algorithm.

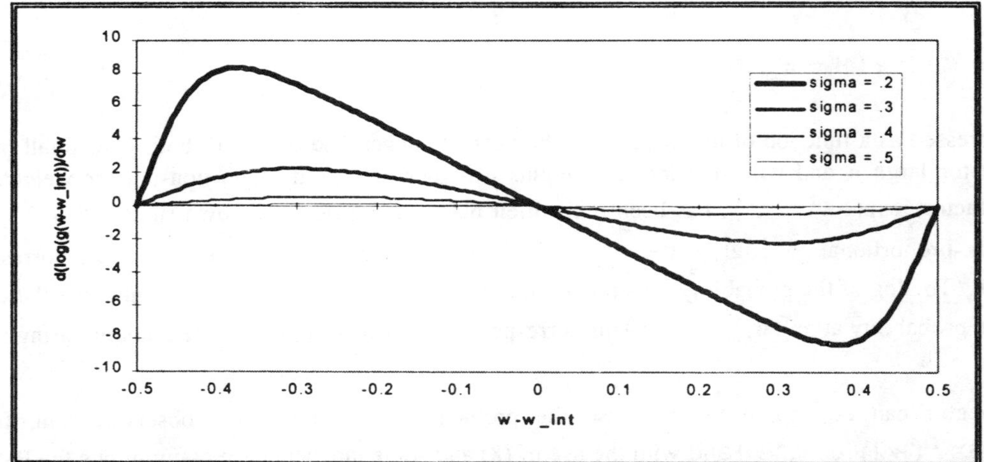

Figure 2: The gradient term due to distance of a parameter from the nearest integer, $\partial \log\big(g(w - w_{\text{int}}, \sigma)\big)/\partial w_i$.

This learning rule has three unknown, s^2, σ^2, and Σ^2 which are either known before hand or estimated from the data. Since the modeller may have a strong idea of what parameters are acceptable, σ^2 and Σ^2 are chosen explicitly. For instance, if parameters corresponding to an exponent of 4 or greater are unlikely or undesirable, the modeller can express this prior information/preference by setting Σ equal to say two or three. Alternatively, Bayesian estimation procedures for hyperparameters of similar problems can be found in [McKay, 92].

Exact integer parameter estimates are obtained by slowly reducing the value of σ toward zero. This is similar to simulated annealing. An example of the convergence of parameters to integers is shown in the next section.

4. SIMULATION RESULTS

We now examine the algorithms performance by trying to reconstruct a known data generating process comprised of non-linear terms, interacting variables and random noise. We identify the parameters of underlying following system governing y_i which is a function of the explanatory variables $x_{i,1}$ and $x_{i,2}$ and some additive noise e_i,

$$y_i = \frac{2x_{i,1}^2 x_{i,1}^3}{1 + x_{i,1}^2 x_{i,2}^3} + e_i .$$ (17)

As stated earlier in (6), the system in (17) can be put into an equivalent neural network form

$$\hat{y}_i = \sum_{j=1}^{M} W^j f\left(w_0^j + \sum_{k=1}^{P} w_k^j \log x_{i,k} \right)$$ (18)

with $M = 1$ and the associated parameter values $W = 2$, $w_0 = 0$, $w_1 = 2$, and $w_2 = 3$. This system is interesting because of the non-linear interaction between input variables. In general, the forecaster is not likely to know the correct value of M in (18).

A dataset is generated from (17) with no additive noise, $e_i = 0$. For the first demonstration, a relative large dataset is used, a 100 by 100 grid of x_1 and x_2 and the corresponding value of y is obtained by sampling evenly between 0 and 5 at steps of .05 for both x_1 and x_2.

For this first benchmark we use neural networks with an architecture as described by (18) with $M = 1$ and $P = 2$. The exact values for the parameters (i.e. weights in (18)) should be: $W = 2$, $w_0 = 0$, $w_1 = 2$, and $w_2 = 3$. The actual estimated values are sufficiently close as, shown in the top row of Table 1. The algorithm used the annealing schedule described above with a final $\sigma = .02$.

There are two criticisms with this first experiment that we will address. The first is that most problems are stochastic in nature, that is $e_i \neq 0$. We generate the same dataset as before but with e_i drawn from a Gaussian distribution of mean zero and a standard deviation of 0.1. As the second row of Table 1 shows, the procedure still correctly identifies all underlying system parameters within ±.05. The second criticism we address is that while the large amount of data used is good to illustrate the identification properties of the algorithm, in practice the data sets available are much smaller. The following rows of the Table 1 show the estimated parameters from varying sizes of data sets randomly drawn from the original 100000 data points.

Sample Size	Noise	$\hat{W}^1$ ($W^1 = 3$)	$\hat{w}_0^1$ ($w_0^1 = 0$)	$\hat{w}_1^1$ ($w_1^1 = 2$)	$\hat{w}_2^1$ ($w_2^1 = 3$)
10000	NO	3.000121	0.000097	1.999699	2.999549
10000	YES	3.000425	-0.004734	1.993826	2.989253
1000	YES	3.000815	0.0123971	1.984865	2.965046
100	YES	3.005318	0.041223	1.978176	3.005641
50	YES	2.965761	0.003232	2.005719	3.004969

Table 1: Estimated system parameters. The columns represent estimated weights against actual weights (in brackets at the top row).

To test the integer optimisation algorithm further, we try a neural net given by (18) with $P = 2$ as before, but this time with $M = 2$. In effect, we are testing the assumption that an over-parameterised model (i.e. a neural network with more complexity than is necessary to solve the problem) will estimate the redundant parameters to their true (zero) value. The procedure gives the easily interpretable results, $\hat{W}^1 = 0.000298$ and $\hat{W}^2 = 2.999791$ which are sufficiently close to zero and three respectively. The estimation procedure has reduced the complexity of the neural network by setting the effect of the first (excessive) hidden unit to zero. The remaining hidden unit performs in the same way as described earlier for the one hidden unit case, that is $\hat{w}_0^2 = -.000047$, $\hat{w}_1^2 = 2.000275$ and $\hat{w}_2^2 = 3.000191$. Because $\hat{W}^1$ is effectively zero, the values of $\hat{w}_0^1$, $\hat{w}_1^1$ and $\hat{w}_2^1$ have no impact on the model and are thus irrelevant.

Finally, the result of estimation algorithm depends on the value of σ used in the integer prior. In the limit as $\sigma \to 0$ the estimated parameters will be dragged towards integer values. The convergence of algorithm is demonstrated on the one hidden unit neural network estimated from 50 examples with additive noise in figure 3. As the value of σ goes to zero, the individual parameter values converge to integer values.

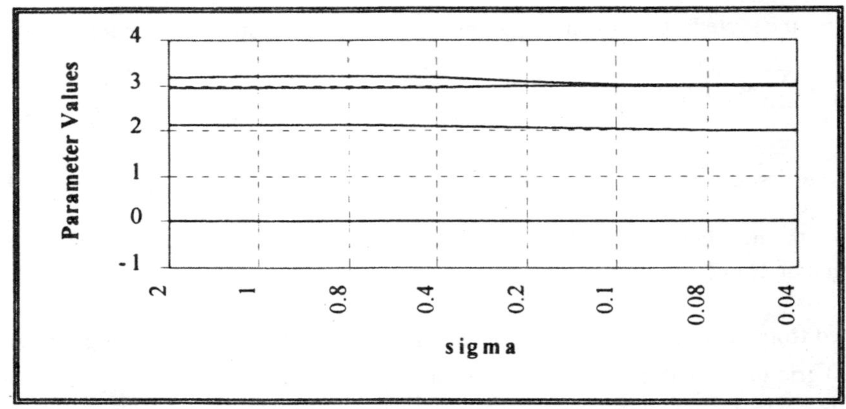

Figure 3: Estimated parameters for a dataset of 50 examples as a function of σ.

5. CONCLUSIONS AND FURTHER WORK

We have given a closed form representation of neural networks which enables us to use them as econometric models. This representation highlights the main strengths of neural networks with respect to their assumptions on normality, nonlinear causality and nonlinear interactions between independent variables. It also highlights some of their main weaknesses, and particularly the dangers of overfitting. We have devised a novel estimation procedure which uses integer priors to minimise complexity by dragging parameters towards the nearest integer. The procedure also penalises complexity by starting with the random walk hypothesis in its strong form and gradually selects linear (and higher order) terms if there is overwhelming evidence in the data to the contrary. We have used controlled simulation to demonstrate that the procedure is capable of reconstructing an unknown data generating process with varying degrees of random noise and also in the case that the initial model is overparameterised.

REFERENCES

[1] Hardle, W. "Applied Nonparametric Regression", Econ. Soc. Monographs, Cambridge Univ. Press (1989).

[2] LeCunn, Y., Denker, J.S., and Solla, S. S. (1990) "Optimal Brain Damage", *in Advances in Neural Information Processing Systems 2*, ed. David S. Touretzky, pp. 598-605.

[3] McKay, D. J. C. "Bayesian Interpolation", *Neural Computation*, 4, 448-472, (1992).

[4] Nowlan, S. J. "Adaptive Soft Weight-Tying using Gaussian Mixtures", *in Advances in Neural Information Processing Systems 4*, ed. Moody, J.E., Hanson, S.J., and Lippmann, R.P., pp. 993-1000.

[5] Refenes, A. N. *Neural Networks in the Capital Markets*, Wiley & Sons, Chichester (1994).

Modeling of Scholastic Aptitude Tests

Claudia Perlich[1]
Department of
Computer Science
University of Colorado
Boulder, USA
`perlich@cs.colorado.edu`

Matthias Brehler[2]
Department of Electrical &
Computer Engineering
University of Colorado
Boulder, USA
`brehler@colorado.edu`

Andreas S. Weigend
Department of Computer Science &
Institute of Cognitive Science
University of Colorado
Boulder, USA
`andreas@cs.colorado.edu`

Abstract— **We categorize nonlinearities and present some simple non-connectionist and connectionist methods of dealing with the different kinds of nonlinearities. In a case study we apply these methods to predict the result of a medical exam from a pre-university aptitude test. This seems to be a feasible task for a neural network model. A linear model fit to about one third of the 26,000 data points reaches a linear correlation coefficient of about 0.6 uniformly over the whole data set. A network trained on the residual error of the linear model does not manage to outperform the linear model. To simplify the problem, we reduce it to a pass/fail prediction of the exam. A three-step architecture, known as boosting, is especially suited for hard classification problems with many data points. Applying this technique to the data set, the final percentage of correct decisions is not higher than the one of the linear baseline. We analyze the learning process and give reasons for the 'failure' of the connectionist model for this data.**

1   Introduction

For many problems linear models perform well. However, the world is not always linear. For solving, e.g., regression tasks, we have to consider nonlinear dependencies between the input(s) and the output(s). One way of categorizing nonlinearities is the following:

· Strictly monotonic nonlinearities

· Non-monotonic nonlinearities (having minima/maxima or plateaus)

· Interactive nonlinearities (between two or more inputs and the output)

The first two kinds consider only one input at a time, whereas for interactive nonlinearities a combination of at least two inputs is necessary. Strictly monotonic here refers to the definition known from mathematics, i.e., an increasing input leads to an increasing (or decreasing) output in the whole definition range of the input. Considering a simple single input single output system, the distribution of the input is (nonlinearly) scaled to form the output distribution.

Non-monotonic behavior includes at least one plateau and/or minima/maxima. The decisive difference to the strictly monotonic case is that two or more different input values may lead to the same output value. This may lead to a completely different distribution of the output compared with the one of the input.

Interactive nonlinearities differ from the ones above by considering two or more inputs that have a combined, but non-additive, influence on the output. For example, the output can be the product of two inputs.

There are many possible ways to model nonlinearities. In the following we will present some simple conventional approaches for this as well as some connectionist approaches. As we think that evaluation and comparison of methods is an important part of modeling, the traditional models may be used as simple baselines to evaluate the new approaches. Section three of this paper presents some connectionist approaches. In our case study these are applied to a specific problem and their performance with regards to the baselines is evaluated and finally discussed.

---

[1]Permanent address: TH Darmstadt, `pdoerice@rbg.informatik.th-darmstadt.de`

[2]Permanent address: TU München, `brehler@eikon.e-technik.tu-muenchen.de`

2   Simple Non-connectionist Approaches

The presented approaches are all more or less variations of linear regression and are easily implemented. They deal with both, regression and classification. We introduce them here mainly as baselines for our connectionist approaches explored in section four.

2.1   Scaling

The standard method for solving regression problems (linear regression) cannot deal directly with nonlinearities. However, a proper scaling of the inputs and/or outputs might make the problem suitable. If both the input and output are noise free, the scaling of the input with some function, which also represents the nonlinear dependencies converts the problem into a linear mapping. Equivalently one could also scale the output with the inverse function. Still, there is the problem of choosing the right scaling function. But one can always find a scaling that transforms the input and output distributions into normal distributions, respectively the given histograms into histograms derived from a normal distribution. This can be done in two ways:

  · Pointwise: First one has to reorder all points according to their values. The desired histogram is fully specified by the mean and variance of the desired Gaussian distribution. As the number of points is given by the data, the number of points that have to be assigned to each bin of the desired histogram is known. So, one starts with the lowest values of the ordered data points and assigns as many points as necessary to the lowest valued bin (the very left one). This procedure is continued until all bins are filled. Shrinking the size of the bins of the histogram further and further leads to an almost continuous mapping.

  · Functional: Similarly, a function that transforms the original histogram into a histogram derived from a normal distribution can be found, but calculating this function may be computationally difficult.

Without loss of generality, we can assume the mean and standard deviation of the normal distributions to be zero and one.

In the case of a monotonic nonlinear dependence and no noise, linear regression will now solve the task. The solution is just a linear mapping of the order of the data-points. For example, considering only one input and a monotonic increasing nonlinear function, the nth smallest output value must correspond to the nth smallest input value. Adding noise to the output (or input) would in almost all cases change the order of the points, hence the scaling/reordering could not work properly.

2.2   Using higher order terms

Another way of preprocessing would be to raise the input to some power and then either use the new value as an additional input or replace the original value with the new value. Extending this idea leads to the adding of all possible crossproducts between the original inputs as new input variables. This empowers linear regression to take care of some interactive dependencies. Unfortunately, using all possible second order crossproducts leads to a total of $n*(n+1)/2$ new inputs. Dimensionality becomes a problem for models designed for generalization. In high dimensional spaces it becomes easier to fit any data with a hyperplane. This hyperplane, however, need not correspond to the underlying structure of the data. A correlation analysis between the inputs and the output can support the choice of the relevant terms. Performing a linear regression on several parts of the data set gives a feeling how stable the individual parameters of the hyperplane are and exposes those crossproducts whose parameters are unstable.

2.3   Logit

The methods presented so far are designed for regression problems in which the output can take any real value in a specified range. A large set of problems, namely classification, cannot be attacked by these methods, because the output is supposed to be either zero or one (or any two discrete values). So, a hyperplane, which that is a continuous function without bounds on the output range, cannot be used. In the logit approach, the output range is limited by a sigmoid function, whose output ranges from zero to one. Then, one can interpret thenumbers between zero and one as the probability of the input pattern belonging to the class given the input and the model (details in [6]). Such a 'continuous' classification is also called a soft classification.

Assigning one pattern completely to one class (or not) is called a hard classification (for two possible classes giving a binary output, like zero and one, and no intermediate values).

3 Connectionist Approaches

Connectionist models are very flexible, being able to fit almost any function. They are inherently nonlinear. On the other hand, they are also able to fit the measurement noise (overfitting), leading to poor generalizations. Therefore focusing on the dynamics of learning becomes an issue, for instance to avoid overfitting with early stopping, as one of the most simple methods.

As this minimization procedure does not lead to a unique solution for the weights of the neural network, evaluating different solutions and methods becomes important in choosing the best possible model. For regression, the correlation coefficient(s) R between the output(s) of the model and the desired output(s) is a suitable measure for comparing different models. The normalized mean square error, i.e., the mean squared error divided by the overall variance of the desired value, is often closely related to R (precisely $1-R^2$, if the variances of the desired values and the model output are close).

For hard classifiers the percentage of correct decisions is a suitable measure, whereas for a soft classifier the relative entropy (or Kullback-Leibler distance) between the probability mass functions of the desired and the model output is a good measure.

3.1 Standard Net

We like to call a neural network with two layers (one hidden unit layer and one output layer) a standard net. For the transfer functions of the hidden units usually the tanh function is used. The choice of the output function depends on the problem. For example, a linear output is appropriate for most regression problems and a sigmoid function is suitable for classification. Equally dependent on the problem a cost function is chosen (usually sum squared error for regression), which is minimized using back-propagation for updating the weights.

The inherent nonlinear properties of a neural network are due to the nonlinear transfer function in the hidden units. A superposition of a sufficient number of these functions can fit almost any function.

3.2 Residual Error Net

Training a network on the residual error focuses the network on the nonlinear properties of a regression task. The residual error is the difference between the desired output and the output of a linear regression. This error is the target for training the network, which is done with standard methods.

3.3 Boosting for Classification

The analog method to the residual net but for classification is boosting [3]. This method requires many data points because it requires to split them in at least four sets (maybe more if a crossvalidation set is necessary to control overfitting).

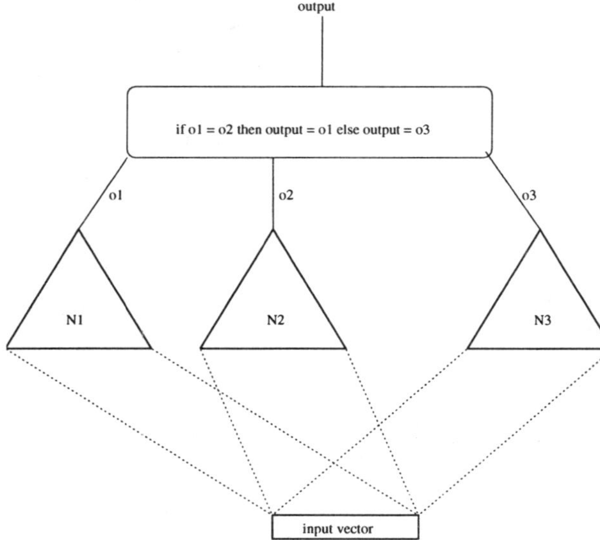

Figure 1 How a decision is made in a boosting network.

The architecture consists of three independent nets N1, N2, N3. First, N1 is trained on the first data set. N2 is then trained on a specific data set: 50% of this data out of set two was correctly classified by N1 and 50% was incorrectly classified. Depending on the problem N1 may do many more right decisions than wrong ones (or vice versa). This would require many data points in set two in order to have sufficient training data for N2. N3 is trained on the data points taken from set three, on which N1 and N2 disagree (make the opposite decision). This procedure leaves set four untouched to be used as test and evaluation set. The final output is defined by N1 and N2, if they agree, and N3 if they do not (see figure 1).

In this classification case sigmoid output functions are chosen, giving values between zero and one. To find the disagreements these values must be rounded to zero and one, resulting in a hard classifier.

4 Case Study

Most of the methods presented are now applied to a specific problem. The task is to predict the result of a medical exam, taken by German medical students after usually two years at the university. Typically all of these students will try to achieve a degree in medicine (M.D.), which will require about another three years of university education. The inputs contain the Abitur (German final high school examination) grade and the results of a pre-university aptitude test, required to study medicine. The pre-university test can be compared to the American CMAT. However, it consists of nine sub-tests, whose single scores are given.

4.1 The data

The data consists of approximately 27,000 student records. The students did not all take the same exam, so that there is also a number ("cohort") indicating which exam date they attended. We used the cohorts to split the data into training, crossvalidation, and test set. The analysis of the data yielded that all variables are approximately normally distributed, except the 5th input (a concentration test).

All our variables are orderable. In order to make similar things close in the input space we normalize the variables by their means and standard deviations (we do this for each cohort separately, because they represent different populations). Except the Abitur, higher values mean better results in the tests. The normalization results in a mean of zero and a standard deviation of one for all 10 inputs and the target. Roughly speaking, before normalization, the means and standard deviations for each cohort vary by less 10%.

4.2 Regression

The linear correlation coefficient between the output of the linear regression and the actual value of the exam's grade is slightly below 0.6 (out-of-sample, meaning on data that was not used for the linear regression). The German *Institut für Test- und Begabungsforschung der Studienstiftung des deutschten Volkes* also yields this result. The question we want to answer is whether we can improve this correlation coefficient using some of the above nonlinear methods.

4.2.1 *Scaling of the data*

We apply different functions to the inputs and the desired output (target) in order to find out about their influence on the data.

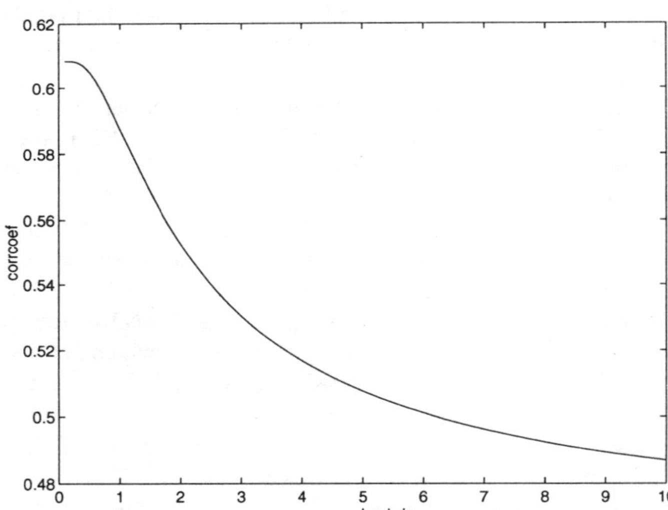

Figure 2 Resulting correlation coefficients between target and output of linear regression for different values of λ.

The arctan function, corresponding to a squashing of the data (everything between $\pm\infty$ is mapped to $\pm\pi$) is implemented with a parameter λ (arctan(λx)). λ controls how strong the squashing is. An increasing λ corresponds to a telescope focusing on the interval around zero of the input. In figure 2 the resulting correlation coefficients are plotted with respect to λ. The largest values for the correlation (0.61) are found for small values of λ, which lead to a linear map of the argument through the squashing function (arctan has an almost linear range around x=0). These correlation coefficients are not larger than without scaling.

Raising inputs and target to the third power and multiplying with a coefficient leads to a small linear correlation coefficient of 0.47 independent of the value of the coefficient. Hence, we could not improve the linear results using functional scaling.

4.2.2   Adding second-order terms

Adding all 55 possible cross products between the inputs (first with first, first with second,..) to the input vector, the linear correlation coefficient increases slightly above 0.61 (for fit and evaluation on the same cohort). Before this calculation, the products are also normalized to have standard deviation one and mean zero. An entry α_i (from $y=\alpha \cdot x$) becomes the correlation coefficient between input I and the output. Although the input space is increased by the second order terms to 65 dimensions, the linear correlation coefficient for the data on which the hyperplane is fit (in-sample) is still only 0.61 and 0.6 for the out-of-sample evaluation (correlation between model output and desired output). These results suggest that there are no dependencies between the second order terms of the input and the target.

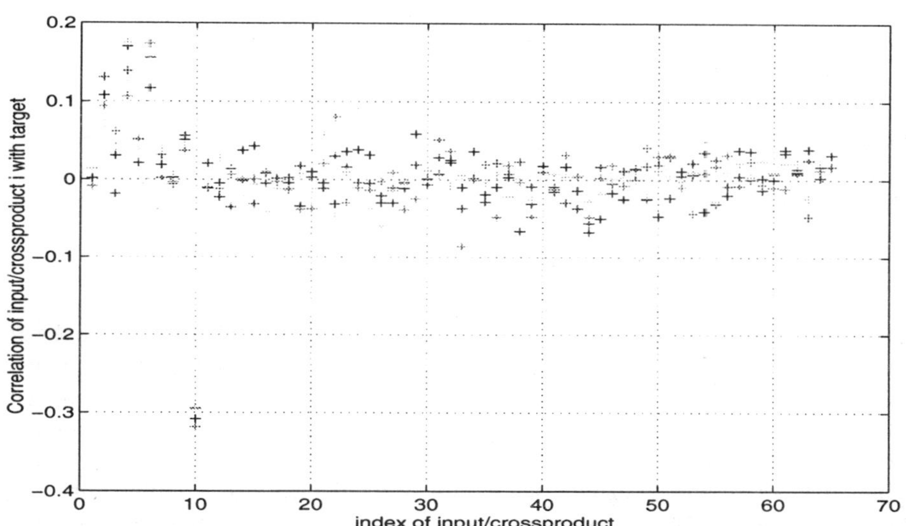

To get a feeling for the error bars of the different correlations of the now 65 inputs, we divided a cohort into four (and eight) groups and calculated the vectors α for each group separately and plotted their values versus their indices (figure 3). As mentioned above, because of the normalization (zero mean, variance one) these correlations are the entries in the vector α. Figure 3 suggests that there is a rather large variance in these entries, especially for the second order terms, meaning they have little significance.

Figure 3 Values of α bootstrapped from four different data sets. Input 10 is the Abitur with heigh (negative) correlation of 0.3. Inputs higher than 10 are crossproducts (input 11=input1^2, etc.)

4.2.3   Standard Regression Net

All networks presented here use 15 inputs (the 10 given plus the 5 most significant cross-products). Gradient descent is used as search method and the cost function is the summed square error of the output versus the target. The weights are updated after presentation of a group of patterns, in contrast to batch updates (accumulating the changes for all patterns and updating after presenting all training patterns once) or pattern updates (updating weights after presenting each single pattern). The presentation of all training patterns once and the corresponding update(s) of weights is called an epoch.

Our first model (in the following referred to as the standard net) features 84 tanh hidden units and one linear output, according to the regression task. The highest correlation coefficients on the test and cross validation sets between the output and the target are reached after 9 epochs. A surprising result is that with values of 0.61 and 0.60 they are not better then the results of the linear regression. Even on the training data the correlation coefficient does not exceed 0.60 after 80 epochs. Only slight overfitting is observed, i.e., the error on the training set does not decrease significantly and the error on the cross validation set does not increase.

The correlation coefficient between the linear regression and the network output is a measure of the degree of nonlinearity in the net: If it is close to one, the net and the linear regression almost yield the same results. For this net it stays about 0.99.

Even after 466 training epochs, the correlation coefficient with the linear model is still very high (0.965). The correlation coefficient on the training set stays at 0.61 (with slight overfitting, the errors and correlation coefficients almost keep the same value after epoch 5).

Hence, with a naive neural net approach we cannot improve over the standard linear regression. In the next step we change our approach and concentrate on exploring the nonlinearities with a net while using linear regression for modeling the linear dependencies.

4.2.4   *Residual Error Net*

The idea is to train a network only on the nonlinear features and add the outputs to the linear model. We solve for the linear model (fit on the training set) and use a new target: old target - output of linear regression (equal to the residual error). On the residuals we train a net with 54 hidden units. The normalized mean square error (E_{NMS}) on the residuals does not become smaller than 0.984 on the training data (i.e., in-sample!), even after 400 epochs of training. As a E_{NMS} of 1 corresponds to predicting the mean, this result shows that learning the residuals is very hard. Out-of-sample the E_{NMS} is higher (0.99), leading to a final correlation coefficient of 0.61 (between the target and the sum of the net and the linear regression).

In addition, to force the net into a nonlinear range, we initialize the weights about 10 to 100 times bigger than usual. The tanh transfer function of the hidden units is almost 'saturated' to ± 1 (after normalization). The only difference we observe is that the net needs now about two epochs of learning to get to the position in weight space where nets with smaller weights are usually after one epoch. After that they behave similarly and produce the same results.

4.3 Classification

As we cannot improve the results of the linear regression in the regression task, we reformulate the problem to a classification task. We want to predict whether a student passes or fails in the medical exam. Our target until now was the (normalized) score in this exam, therefore, the pass/fail rule leads to a minimum score required to pass.

4.3.1   *Linear Classifier*

For this problem the lowest baseline is 81% correct decisions, because this is the a priori probability of a student to pass. Therefore, when one 'predicts' always 'pass' one makes 81% correct decisions. Applying the threshold of the minimum required score to the output of the linear regression model gives 82% correct decisions (out-of-sample). However, this linear classifier is of greater value than the simple 'always predict pass' classifier, because the mutual information between the linear classifier and the target is non-zero, whereas the mutual information between the 'always predict pass' classifier and the target is zero. So, the linear classifier contains information about the actual distribution of the target, though one may not be able to extract this information (adapted from a problem in [2]). Plotting the 'hit-rate' (p(y='p'|t='p') = model decides pass for target pass) versus the 'false-alarm rate' (p(y='p'|t='f') = model decides pass for target fail) for different values of the threshold (minimum score required to decide pass) gives the Receiver Operating Characteristic (ROC). In our context, these curves can be used to evaluate different models: A model with a higher hit-rate than another one for the same false-alarm rate has a better 'decidability' than the second model, i.e., it can distinguish the pass/fail cases better than the second model. For example our 'always predict pass' model has a hit rate of one (which is desired) but unfortunately also a false-alarm rate of one (which is the worst possible). More details about ROCs can be found in [2].

For the linear model, the question arises whether the metric 'percentage correct decisions' and 'correlation coefficient' are equivalent in some way. Showing this is not too hard, assuming a normal distribution for the output of the linear model y (standard deviation 0.6, mean 0) and the target t (standard deviation 1, mean 0, correlation between the t and y is 0.6, see figure 4 for a histogram of the data). Then two possibilities exist for making an error for a decision based on the linear model:

· the student passed the exam (t large enough), but y is too small (the linear model decided fail)

· the student failed the exam (t too small), but y is too big (the linear model decided pass)

Integrating over these two areas leads to a (error) probability of 17%, i.e., the probability for a right decision is 83%, which fits nicely with the above results.

4.3.2   *Bayes Classifier*

Another approach for a classification problem is to apply Bayes decision theory. It requires to assume a specific distribution of the classes fail/pass in the 10 dimensional input space. We assume two normal distributions, calculate their means and covariance matrices and with these the discriminant function, which determines the most probable class for a given pattern. The discriminant function is based on the probabilities of the classes given a pattern. The Bayes classifier makes about 83% correct decisions (out-of-sample), which is a little bit better than the linear model.

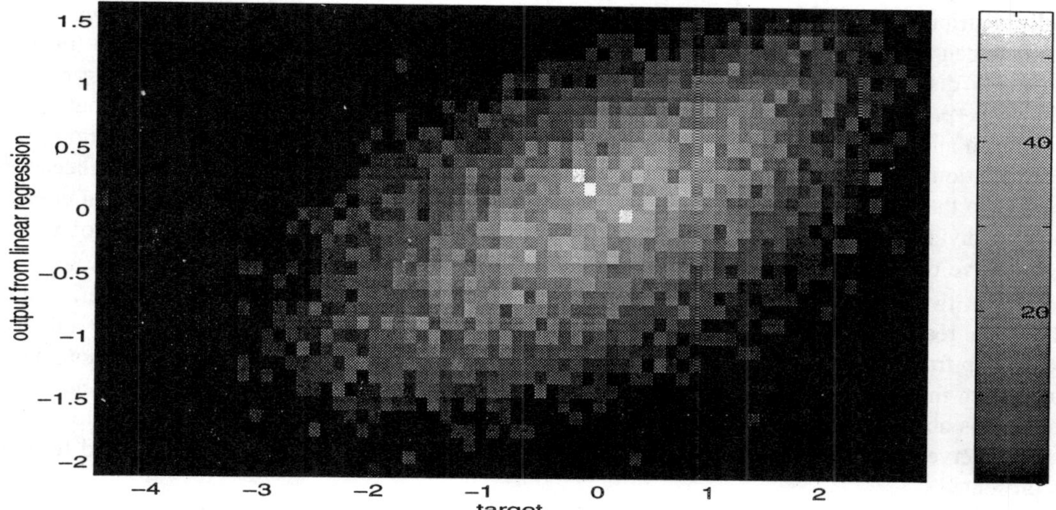

Figure 4 Histogram of the target and the model output. Gray scales correspond to number of points.

4.3.3 Boosting

Because one has to assume a specific distribution for the Bayes classifier, there is hope that other methods (for which no such specific assumptions are necessary) might outperform the Bayes classifier. Net N1 of the boosting network decides 82% correctly (these figures, as do all the following, relate to the test set, however, the ones for the training data are about the same). From the data it is presented it decides for 94% pass. N2 is trained on data, on which N1 made 50% incorrect decisions (and these decisions are 88% incorrect, because a student who failed was classified as passed). This means that N2 is trained on data with higher a priori probability for failing (46%) than N1. So, it decides only for 55% pass on the test data with 81% a priori probability for pass. This leads to about 57% agreement between N1 and N2, mostly (93%) on students who passed. On the agreement set of data 92% of the decisions are right, which looks very good. Still, in this data set the a priori probability for pass is 90%. On the disagreement data set N3 classifies 73% right. However, the a priori probability for pass is 72%.

As we have shown, none of the nets make a significantly better prediction than a prediction based on the a priori probabilities. Thus, the overall percentage for correct decision does not exceed 83%.

To summarize we can explain the observed behavior, by stating that N1 decides more often for pass, N2 more often for fail, and N3 gets the hard cases, which it cannot solve any better than other models (such as the Bayes classifier or just N1).

4.3.4 Soft classifiers

Implemented as above, the Bayes classifier gives a hard decision based on whether the probability of one class given the (input) pattern is higher than the probability of the other class given the pattern. But we can also calculate the probability of a class given the pattern, which leads to a soft classifier. We can then use the relative entropy of the soft Bayes classifier as baseline for evaluating the other approaches.

5   Discussion

Considering normally distributed random variables for the inputs and outputs, a data driven model can only find linear dependencies between the inputs and outputs. We will not provide a general proof for this, but one for one dimension: Any normally distributed random variable x, can be transformed into any other normally distributed random variable y by $y=\alpha x+\beta$. The parameter α adjusts the variance and β the mean. As any normal distribution is fully specified by its mean and variance, a linear transformation can always transform one normal distribution into any other normal distribution. A linear transformation is also the only possible transformation to do this, because applying a function f(x) to the random variable x leads to a new random variable y, whose density function equals the density function of x divided by the absolute value of the derivative of f(x). So, if the density functions of x and y are normal, the derivative of f(x) must be constant and hence f(x) linear.

In the studied case all but two of the input and output variables are almost normally distributed. Considering the above argument, this is the reason why linear regression gives similar results to the nonlinear methods: Only a linear function is required to map from normal distributed inputs to normal distributed outputs. As all the applied nonlinear methods do not outperform the linear ones and the correlation between the output of the (nonlinear) neural network and the linear regression is about one, i.e., the neural network is not making use of its possible nonlinear features, we conclude that the observed distortions from a normal distribution in the variables cannot be modeled by the nonlinear methods presented.

Nonlinear modeling can be performed relatively easily using flexible neural networks. But to really understand how good the achieved results are, evaluating the model and comparing them to simple baselines is absolutely necessary. We presented some possible baselines and applied them to our case.

In summary, neither for the regression nor for the classification task could any of the applied nonlinear methods outperform the simple linear regression. We could not find any significant nonlinear dependencies in the given data. Given this and the fact that at least two years elapse between the input observation (the aptitude test and the final grade of school) and the university exam, the target, the results of the linear regression are limited by the noise (including not enough relevant inputs) in the system, rather than by the limitations of the method (linearity, no interactive dependencies between inputs). Similar results were found by LeBaron and Weigend in [5] on data from the New York Stock Exchange.

Acknowledgments
We would like to thank Günter Trost and his team from the *Institut für Test- und Begabungsforschung der Studienstiftung des deutschten Volkes* for the data and Jens Timmer for discussion.

References

[1]   Thomas M. Cover, Joy A. Thomas, *Elements of Information Theory* (Wiley 1991)

[2]   C. Douglas Creelman, Neil A. Macmillan, *Detection Theory: A User's Guide* (Cambridge University Press 1991)

[3]   H. Drucker, C. Cortes, L. D. Jackel, Y. LeCun, V. Vapnik, *Boosting and Other Machine Learning Algorithms* in Machine Learning: Proceedings of the Eleventh International Conference (ML '94), 1994, pages 53-61

[4]   R. G. Gallager, *Information Theory and Reliable Communication* (Wiley 1968)

[5]   Blake LeBaron, Andreas S. Weigend, *Evaluating Neural Network Predictors by Bootstrapping* in Proceedings of International Conference on Neural Information Processing (ICONIP '94), 1994, pages 1207-1212

[6]   P. McCullagh and J.A. Nelder, *Generalized Linear Models* (Chapman and Hall 1989)

What is the "True Price"? –
State Space Models for High Frequency Financial Data

John Moody and Lizhong Wu
Oregon Graduate Institute, Computer Science Dept., Portland, OR 97291-1000, USA
Email: moody@cse.ogi.edu and lwu@cse.ogi.edu

Abstract—

In our analysis of tick-by-tick interbank foreign exchange (FX) data, we have found statistically-significant structures in the price series on various time scales. These structures include negative autocorrelations in successive tick-by-tick returns and positive autocorrelations (trends) on longer time scales. To account for the observed structures, we propose state space models for financial time series in which the observed price is a noisy version of an unobserved, less-noisy "true price" process.

The "true prices" in our models are stochastic processes with short-term, long-term, or multi-scale memory structures. The processes we consider include random walks, random trends, and fractional Brownian motions. For fractional Brownian motion processes, we represent the multi-scale correlational structures using self-similar wavelet decompositions (Wornell & Oppenheim 1992). We estimate the state space model parameters using the Kalman filter and EM algorithms.

Since both the observational noise and the changes in the true price series have non-gaussian distributions, the Kalman filter and EM algorithms are not able to completely separate the observational noise from the true price components. To improve this separation, we perform a neural-network-based independent component analysis (ICA) using algorithms developed for the blind separation of signals.

Statistical analysis of our true price models supports our assertion that the estimated true prices are significantly different from the observed prices, and that significant non-random structures exist in the FX markets. Sonification of the observed price and "true price" series supports this finding by revealing obvious perceptual differences between the signals. We believe that our proposed "true price" models may enable us to discover new arbitrage opportunities and to construct better forecasting and trading models.

1   Introduction

The motivation of this study comes from our analysis of tick-by-tick, interbank foreign exchange rate data, (Moody & Wu, (1994),(1995*b*),(1995*a*),(1996)). This set of data consists of non-binding quotations from market makers. In this work, we have identified two properties of the correlational structure of tick-by-tick FX data:

- Negative correlations in successive tick-by-tick price changes. See the left panel of Figure 1.
- Positive autocorrelations on longer time scales. See the right panel of Figure 1.

This second effect is not necessarily easy to measure, since the strong tick-by-tick anticorrelations can mask it.

The strong anticorrelation at lag 1 in the tick-by-tick returns is believed by financial economists to be caused by market microstructure effects, particularly the inventory effect (Lyons (1993),O'Hara (1995)). Regardless of its cause, we will argue that it can be explained empirically as an effect due to additive observational noise in the indicative price quotes.

To reliably detect the presence of long term memory structures in financial time series when short term autocorrelations are present, we proposed a new unbiased rescaled range statistic, R/S^*, that eliminates the contaminating effects of autocorrelations on time scale q. The right panel of Figure 1 shows our R/S^* analysis of FX prices (Moody & Wu 1996). As explained in the figure caption, the apparent price behavior on time scales up to 100 ticks changes completely as the effects of tick-by-tick negative autocorrelations are removed. The apparent behavior of the tick-by-tick DEM/USD series shifts from mean-reverting to mean-averting. From this experiment, we can see that the spuriously observed mean reversion in the original price series is actually due to short-term negative autocorrelations, rather than to intrinsic dependencies in the price movements, and that the underlying behavior of the series on longer time scales is actually trending.

Our goal is to estimate the underlying, unobservable, prices by removing the noise in the recorded quotations. The outline of this paper is as follows. Section 2 formalizes and defines models for the given problem. We describe three models which we will study and compare in this paper. These three models are: the steady model, the linear growth model, and the fractional Brownian motion model. The first two models assume that the underlying prices are independent or short-term dependent, while the fractional Brownian motion model assumes that the underlying prices may have long-term memory. We briefly describe model estimation for the first two models in Section 2 and focus on estimating fractional Brownian motion in Section 3. We first review several modeling techniques for fractional Brownian motions and then describe wavelet decomposition methods for estimating fractional Brownian motions. Empirical results are presented in Section 4, where we first compare the "true prices" obtained based on different models studied in this paper, and then show the long term correlation structure revealed by our "true

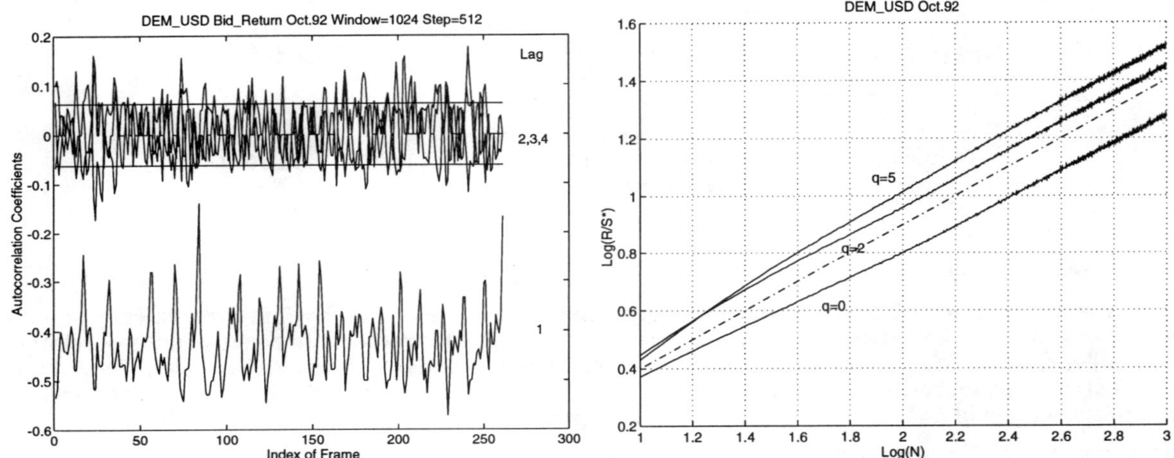

Figure 1: Short-term and long-term correlation structures for DEM/USD during October 1992. The left panel is autocorrelation coefficients $\{1,2,3,4\}$ versus time frame. Each time frame contains 1024 ticks and successive frames overlap by 512 ticks. The right panel is the $[R/S^*](N)$ using lag parameters $q = \{0,2,5\}$. $[R/S^*](N)$ (Moody & Wu 1996) is an unbiased rescaled range (R/S) analysis that considers the effect of the short-term covariances (with $q > 0$). When $q = 0$, $[R/S^*](N) = [R/S](N)$. The figure shows that while the raw price series suggest that FX prices are mean-reverting (R/S curve with $q = 0$), the underlying true prices in fact exhibit trending behavior. The dashed line corresponds to random-walks.

price" models. We conclude in Section 5.

2   State Space Models

State space or "true price" models assume that the recorded price quotations can be described by

$$q(t) = p(t) + \varepsilon(t) , \tag{1}$$

where $p(t)$ is the underlying "true price" and $\varepsilon(t)$ is zero mean random noise. Our task is thus to estimate $p(t)$ assuming some model, given the observed series $q(t)$.[1]

In this paper, we study and compare the following three types of models for the underlying price $p(t)$:

1. Steady model (Random Walk + Noise):
   This model assumes that the underlying prices follow a random-walk process, i.e

   $$p(t) = p(t-1) + \delta(t) , \tag{2}$$

   where $\delta(t)$ is a process noise. Assuming that both the observation noise ($\varepsilon(t)$ in (1)) and the process noise are white, the autocovariances of the observed returns $r_q(t) = q(t) - q(t-1)$ are

   $$E[r_q^2(t)] = 2\sigma_\varepsilon^2 + \sigma_\delta^2 \tag{3}$$
   $$E[r_q(t)r_q(t-1)] = -\sigma_\varepsilon^2 \tag{4}$$
   $$E[r_q(t)r_q(t-\tau)] = 0 , \text{ for } \tau \geq 2 . \tag{5}$$

   It is straightforward to estimate σ_ε^2 and σ_δ^2 from measurements of the autocovariances. The state $p(t)$ can be estimated via the Kalman filter.

   Figure 2 plots the **Signal-to-Noise Ratio** of the model, defined as $SNR = \sigma_\delta^2/\sigma_\varepsilon^2$, for DEM/USD in September 1995. Its nonstationarity requires that our model should be adaptive through time. The observed SNR is remarkable for two reasons: (1) it is usually much less than one, and (2) it varies significantly in magnitude, suggesting that there are periods with significant price movements (high SNR) separated by periods of almost no price movement (low SNR).

2. Linear growth model (Random Trend + Random Walk + Noise)
   This model assumes that the underlying prices follow:

   $$p(t) = p(t-1) + \beta(t-1) + \delta_1(t) \tag{6}$$
   $$\beta(t) = \beta(t-1) + \delta_2(t) . \tag{7}$$

   With the assumption that the process and observation noises are white, we can solve this model using the Kalman filter.

---

[1]Bolland & Connor (1996) have used state space models to identify triangle arbitrage opportunities in groups of currencies.

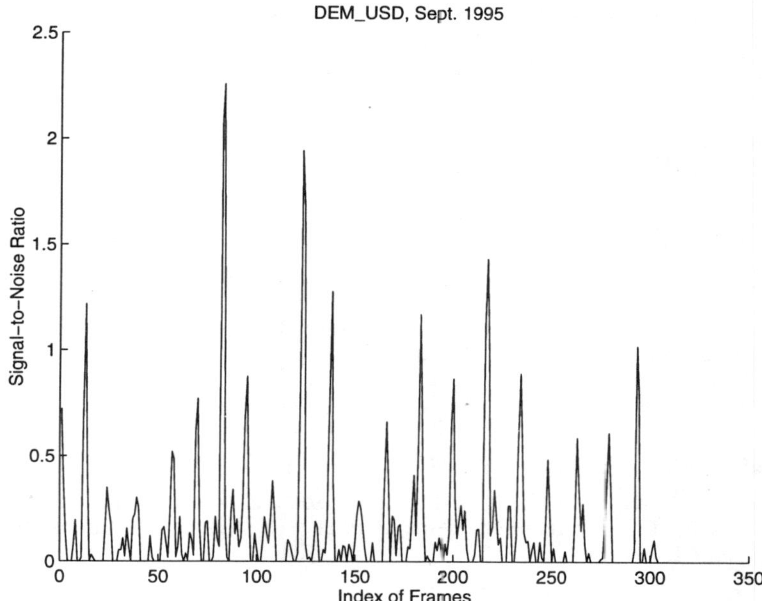

Figure 2: SNR in the steady model for DEM/USD in September 1995. Each frame consists of 1024 ticks and the frames overlap 512 ticks.

3. Fractional Brownian Motion (FBM) model

Here, the underlying price series is assumed to follow fractional Brownian motion. Fractional Brownian motion is a generalization of the usual Brownian motion or random-walk. It was introduced to model processes that have long memory or $1/f$-type spectral behaviors (Beran (1994)), and have a statistical self-similarity property (Feder (1988)). Since Mandelbrot et al. first found the presence of long-memory components in asset returns, see, for example, Mandelbrot (1971), there have been many empirical reports to support this finding (Granger (1980),Peters (1989),Diebold & Rudebusch (1989)). For FBMs, the dependence between distant observations, though small, is by no means negligible. Compared to short memory series such as ARMA processes, the dependences of long-term persistent processes decay hyperbolically instead of exponentially. Conventional approaches like ARMA models are therefore inadequate to capture the correlational structures embedded in long memory series.

In the next section, we will study fractional Brownian motion modeling with wavelet representations.

3 Estimating Fractional Brownian Motion with Wavelet Decompositions

There have been many models developed for fractional Brownian motion processes. Some well-known and recently developed models include:

- filtered white noise, (Mandelbrot & Van Ness (1968),Feder (1988));

- aggregation of short-memory models, (Granger (1980));

- fractional difference models, (Granger & Joyeux (1980),Hosking (1981));

- driving white noise through an infinite cascade of pole-zero sections (Keshner (1982));

- orthonormal wavelet basis expansions with uncorrelated random coefficients (Flandrin (1989),Mallet (1989),Wornell (1990),Flandrin (1992),Tewfik & Kim (1992),Vergassola & Frisch (1991),Wornell & Oppenheim (1992)).

To systematically compare these approaches is another study topic. However, the latter approach, wavelets, has certain advantages for estimating state space models. Bjorn (1995) has also used wavelets for financial time series analysis, but not in a state space context.

3.1 Estimating Wavelet Decompositions via the EM Algorithm

The wavelet transform decomposes a signal into self-similar wavelets which are derived from one elementary waveform by means of shifts and dilations. This is naturally reminiscent of the self-similar property of fractional Brownian motions, in which any portion of a given process can be viewed, in a statistical sense, as a scaled version of a larger or smaller sample of the same process. The above correspondence sets up a bridge between the wavelet transform and fractional Brownian motions. In fact, the multi-resolution analysis with wavelet decompositions is particularly well suited to analyzing the underlying statistical property of fractional Brownian motions when observational noise is present.

Taking the wavelet transform of (1), (see, for example, Daubechies (1988),Mallet (1989)), we get

$$Q_n^m = P_n^m + \varepsilon_n^m \text{ , for } m \in \mathcal{M} \text{ and } n \in \mathcal{N}(m) \text{ ,} \tag{8}$$

with m representing the scale level and n for the time index of the components. Under the Gaussian assumption, P_n^m can be estimated by (see (Flandrin (1992),Wornell & Oppenheim (1992))):

$$\hat{P}_n^m = \mathbf{E}[P_n^m | Q_n^m] = S(m, \theta) Q_n^m \text{ ,} \tag{9}$$

where

$$S(m, \theta) = \frac{\sigma^2 \beta^{-m}}{\sigma^2 \beta^{-m} + \sigma_\varepsilon^2} \tag{10}$$

is a wavelet analog of the Wiener filter that serves as a smoothing function. Denoting the wavelet basis functions as $\psi_n^m(t)$, this yields the following estimate of the "true price"

$$\hat{p}(t) = \sum_{m,n} \hat{P}_n^m \psi_n^m(t) = \sum_{m,n} S(m, \theta) Q_n^m \psi_n^m(t) \text{ .} \tag{11}$$

The model parameters $\theta = (\beta, \sigma^2, \sigma_\varepsilon^2)$ can be estimated using the EM algorithm.

Note that the factor $S(m, \theta)$ has a thresholding or smoothing role: at coarser scales (small m) where the signal predominates, the coefficients Q_n^m are retained, while at finer scales (large m) where noise predominates, the coefficients Q_n^m are discarded.

In Figure 3, we visualize (11) for a set of DEM/USD tick-by-tick prices. The smoothing factor $S(m, \theta)$ decays from 1 to 0 as the scale level m goes from coarse to fine. At coarser scales, the signals are mostly retained, while at finer scales, the signals are mostly discarded.

3.2　Independent Component Analysis

Since both the observational noise and the changes in the true price series have non-gaussian distributions, the Kalman filter and EM algorithms are not able to completely separate the observational noise from the true price components. To improve this separation, we perform a neural-network-based independent component analysis (ICA) using algorithms developed for the blind separation of signals (Bell & Sejnowski 1995, Amari, Cichocki & Yang 1996).

ICA finds a separation of the signals with reduced statistical dependence at not only second order (cross-correlations), but at higher orders as well (eg. fourth order cross-cumulants). Our ICA is performed by using the true price and observational noise components estimated via the Kalman filter or EM algorithms as reference inputs to the blind separation algorithm.

4　Empirical Results and Discussions

Figure 4 compares a segment of "true prices" to the observed prices. We see that the "true prices" are much smoother and less noisy.

4.1　Comparisons between models

We have estimated three "true prices" based on different models. The question that arises is: how do these different estimated prices differ and relate? To answer this, we did pair-by-pair homogeneous χ^2 testings for the distributions of the estimated returns for the different models. As shown in Figure 5, our analysis accepts the hypothesis that the returns come from different populations. Thus, all "true price" return series are significantly different from the observed price return, and the choice of "true price" model among the three models studied yields significantly different results.

4.2　Autocorrelation Analysis

Figure 6 depicts the autocorrelation functions of the changes in the "true price" and the noise components, and compares them to the original returns. The true price model is estimated under the FBM assumptions, and the autocorrelation analysis is performed after further separating the signals using ICA.

We compute the short-run autocorrelations for the lags up to 50 for windows of length 1024 ticks. Figure 6 shows their means and standard deviations for September 1995. From the figure, we can see that both the noise component changes and the original returns show very similar autocorrelation functions, which are dominated by their significantly negative, first-order autocorrelations. The mean values for the other orders are basically equal to zero. The autocorrelations of the "true price" component show positive correlations except at first-order.

We can conclude from the above autocorrelation analysis that

1. Changes in the "true prices" exhibit slight, but significant trends on tick-by-tick time-scales.

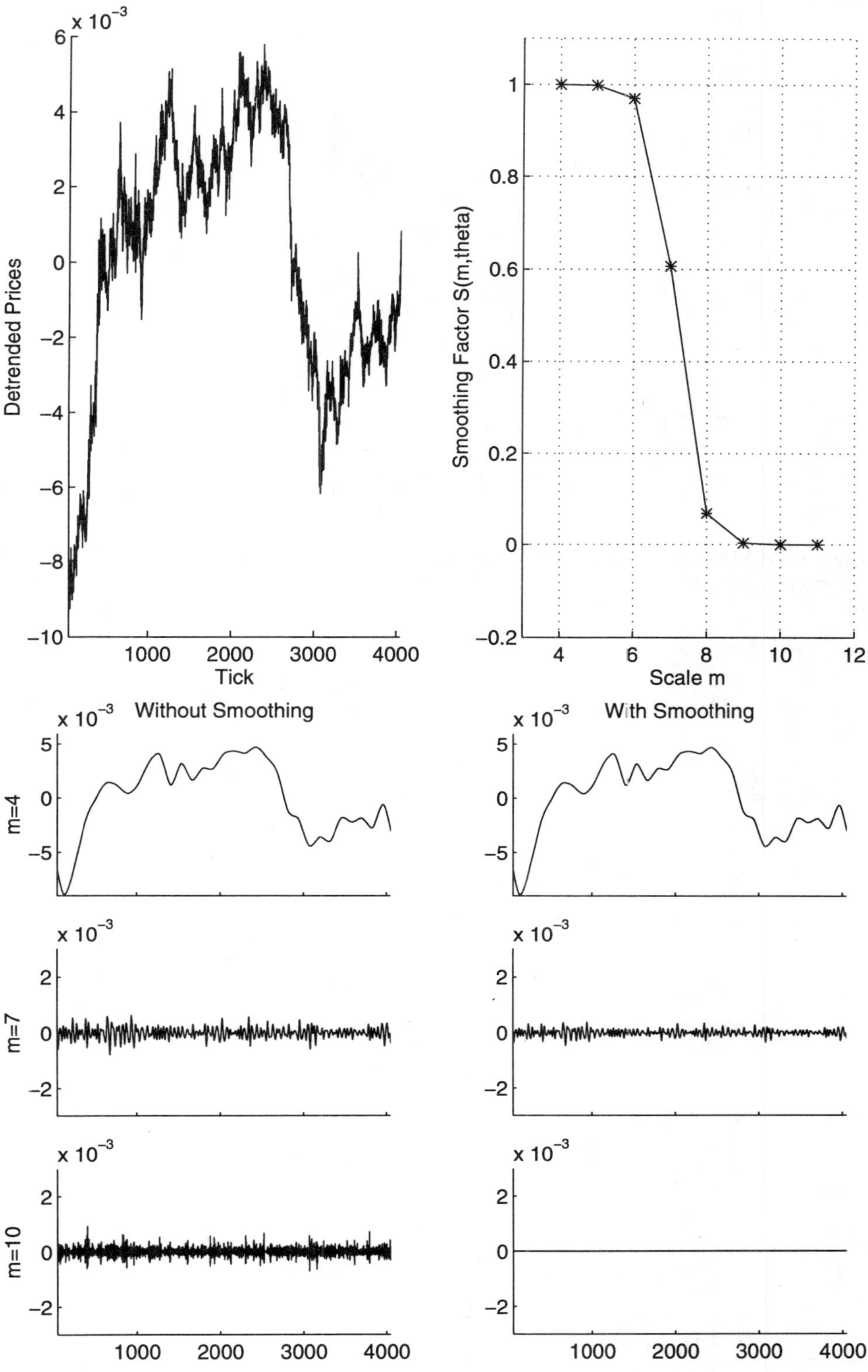

Figure 3: Visualizing (11) for a set of DEM/USD prices after being detrended as shown in the upper-left panel. The smoothing function $S(m, \theta)$ is plotted in the upper-right panel. Lower panels compare the original and smoothed reconstructed signals at scales of 4, 7 and 10. The signals are mostly retained at coarser scales (small m), while at finer scales (large m), the signals are mostly discarded.

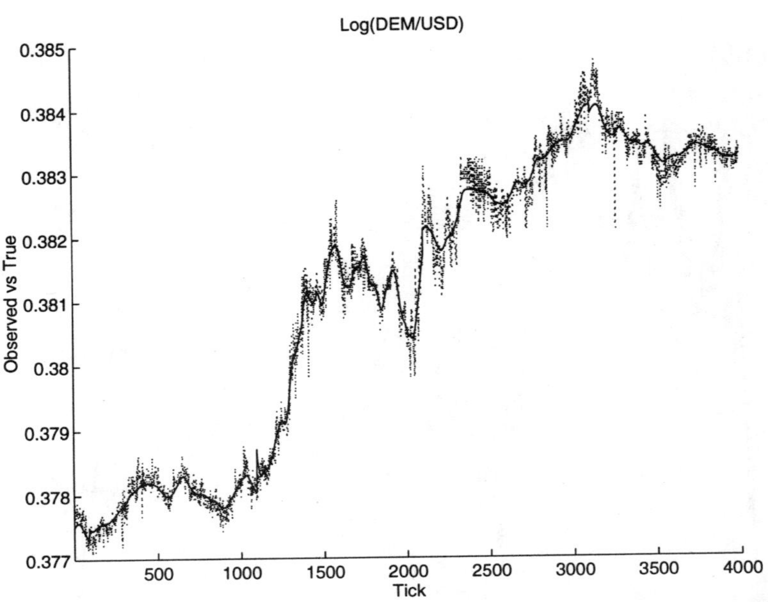

Figure 4: Observed DEM/USD (dotted curve) and the "true prices" estimate under the model of Fractional Brownian motion assumption (solid curve).

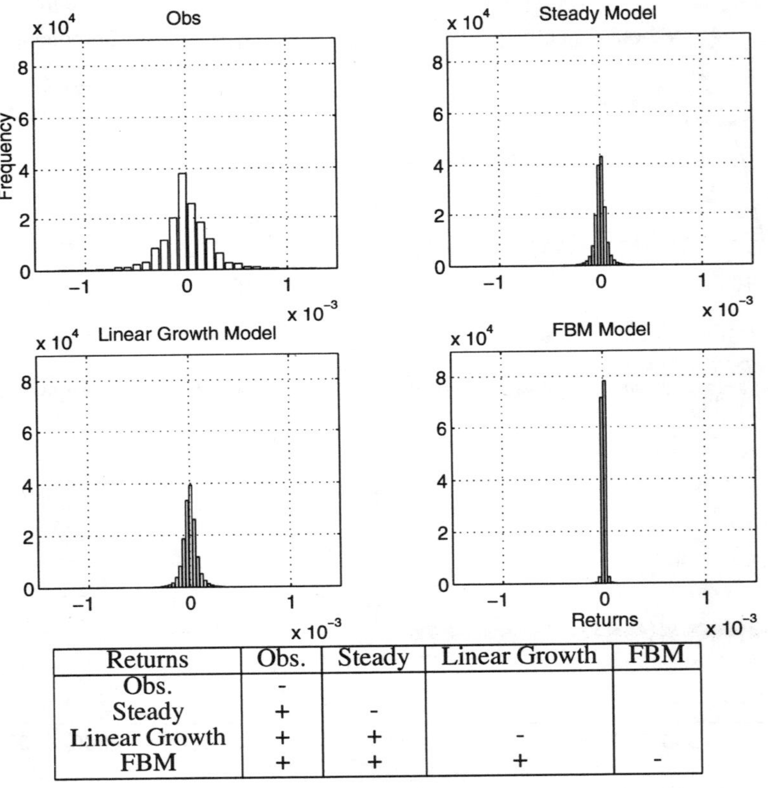

Returns	Obs.	Steady	Linear Growth	FBM
Obs.	-			
Steady	+	-		
Linear Growth	+	+	-	
FBM	+	+	+	-

Figure 5: Comparison of histograms and pair-by-pair homogeneous χ^2 testings for observed returns and denoised and smoothed "true price" returns for three state space models. "-" indicates that the hypothesis that the pairs of returns come from different populations is rejected, and "+" indicates that the hypothesis is accepted. The significance level is 99%. The data are DEM/USD price quotes for Sept. 1995.

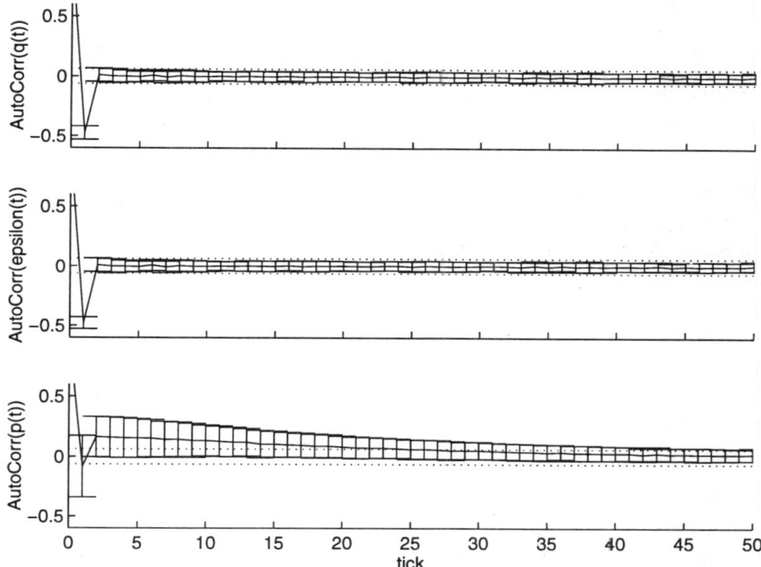

Figure 6: Comparison of autocorrelation functions of the changes in the original observed prices (the upper panel), the observational noise component (the middle panel) and the "true price" component (the lower panel) for the FBM model. DEM/USD data for September 1995 is divided into 293 sub-sets of 1024 tick windows with overlaps of 512 ticks. The autocorrelation results presented here are the means and standard deviations for the 293 windows. The horizontal dotted lines represent the 95% significance band for a single 1024 tick window. The 95% significance bands for the full month are smaller by a factor of $\sqrt{147} = 12.1$, where 147 is the number of non-overlapping windows. The mean "true price" autocorrelation coefficients for the full month are thus significantly different from zero for lags 2 through 50. This indicates the existence of trends in the true price (lower panel). However, these trends are masked in the observed price returns by the additive noise (upper panel).

2. The autocorrelation function of original returns reflects only the anticorrelation of price changes at lag 1 (believed by economists to be due to the inventory effect). It further confirms that the existence of the strong, short-term anticorrelations will foil a standard autocorrelation analysis on longer time scales. Subsequently, we can see the importance of "true price" modeling.

4.3   Sonification of True Prices

The statistical differences between the observed price series, estimated true price series, and white noise can be easily perceived by playing the price changes through a sound generator. The results are quite striking. In particular, the true prices for the FX markets exhibit periods of relative quiet, occasional waves of activity, and intermittent impulse noise (presumably due to news).

5   Concluding Remarks

We have proposed using state space models to analyze high frequency financial data. These models decompose the observed prices into unobserved, underlying "true prices" plus observational noise. We have presented three such true price models, including random walks, random trends, and fractional Brownian motions. The random walk and random trend models are estimated using Kalman filters, while wavelet decompositions and the EM algorithm are used to estimate the FBM models.

These models are able to explain observed correlation structure in the DEM/USD exchange rates. This includes anticorrelations in successive observed price changes and positive correlations (trends) on longer time scales.

Our statistical modeling of high frequency intra-day FX price series has demonstrated that signals do in fact exist in noisy FX data and that the conventional random-walk models of efficient market theory do not explain the high frequency structure that is present in the data. We believe that our proposed "true price" models will enable us discover new arbitrage opportunities (Bolland & Connor 1996) and to construct better forecasting and trading models.

References

Amari, S., Cichocki, A. & Yang, H. (1996), A new learning algorithm for blind signal separation, *in* D. Touretzky, M. Mozer & M. Hasselmo, eds, 'Advances in Neural Information Processing Systems 8', MIT Press: Cambridge, MA.

Bell, A. & Sejnowski, T. (1995), 'An information-maximization approach to blind separation and blind deconvolution', *Neural Computation* **7**(6), 1129–1159.

Beran, J. (1994), *Statistics for Long-Memory Processes*, New York: Chapman and Hall.

Bjorn, V. (1995), Multiresolution methods for financial time series prediction, *in* 'Conference on Computational Intelligence for Financial Engineering', IEEE Press, Piscataway, NJ.

Bolland, P. & Connor, J. (1996), Identification of fx arbitrage opportunities with a non-linear multivariate kalman filter, *in* A. Refenes, Y. Abu-Mostafa, J. Moody & A. Weigend, eds, '**Neural Networks in the Capital Markets**, Proceedings of the Third International Conference (London, October 1995)', World Scientific, London.

Daubechies, I. (1988), 'Orthonormal bases of compactly supported wavelets', *Commun. Pure Appl. Math.* **41**, 909–996.

Diebold, F. X. & Rudebusch, G. D. (1989), 'Long memory and persistence in aggregate output', *Journal of Monetary Economics* **24**, 189–209.

Feder, J. (1988), *Fractals*, Plenum Press, New York.

Flandrin, P. (1989), 'On the spectrum of fractional brownian motions', *IEEE Transactions on Information Theory* **35**, 197–199.

Flandrin, P. (1992), 'Wavelet analysis and synthesis of fractional brownian motions', *IEEE Transactions on Information Theory* **38**(2), 910–917.

Granger, C. (1980), 'Long memory relationships and the aggregation of dynamic models', *Journal of Econometrics* **14**, 227–38.

Granger, C. & Joyeux, R. (1980), 'An introduction to long-memory time series models and fractional differencing', *Journal of Time Series Analysis* **1**, 15–29.

Hosking, J. (1981), 'Fractional differencing', *Biometrika* **68**, 165–76.

Keshner, M. (1982), '1/f noise', *Proceedings IEEE* **70**, 212–218.

Lyons, R. (1993), Tests of microstructural hypotheses in the foreign exchange market, Working Paper Series 4471, National Bureau of Economic Research, INC.

Mallet, S. (1989), 'A theory for multiresolution signal decomposition: The wavelet representation', *IEEE Transactions on Pattern Analysis and Machine Intelligence* **11**(7), 674–693.

Mandelbrot, B. (1971), 'When can price be arbitraged efficiently? a limit to the validity of hte random walk and martinggale models', *Review of Economics and Statistics* **53**, 225–236.

Mandelbrot, B. & Van Ness, J. (1968), 'Fractional Brownian motion, fractional noise, and applications', *SIAM Review* **10**.

Moody, J. & Wu, L. (1994), Statistical analysis and forecasting of high frequency foreign exchange rates, *in* 'International workshop on Neural Networks in the Capital Markets', Pasadena, California.

Moody, J. & Wu, L. (1995*a*), Price behavior and Hurst exponents of tick-by-tick interbank foreign exchange rates, *in* 'Conference on Computational Intelligence for Financial Engineering', New York city.

Moody, J. & Wu, L. (1995*b*), Statistical analysis and forecasting of high frequency foreign exchange rates, *in* 'First international conference on High Frequency data in Finance', Zurich, Switzerland.

Moody, J. & Wu, L. (1996), Improved estimates for the rescaled range and hurst exponents, *in* A. Refenes, Y. Abu-Mostafa, J. Moody & A. Weigend, eds, '**Neural Networks in the Capital Markets**, Proceedings of the Third International Conference (London, October 1995)', World Scientific, London.

O'Hara, M. (1995), *Market Microstructure Theory*, Blackwell Business.

Peters, E. (1989), 'Fractal structure in the capital markets', *Financial Analysts Journal* pp. 32–37.

Tewfik, A. & Kim, M. (1992), 'Correlation structure of the discrete wavelet coefficients of fractional brownian motions', *IEEE Transactions on Information Theory* **38**(2), 904–909.

Vergassola, M. & Frisch, U. (1991), 'Wavelet transforms of self-similar processes', *Physica D* **54**, 58.

Wornell, G. (1990), 'A karhunene-loeve-like expansion for 1/f processes via wavelets', *IEEE Transactions on Information Theory* **36**, 859–861.

Wornell, G. & Oppenheim, A. (1992), 'Estimation of fractal signals from noisy measurements using wavelets', *IEEE Transactions on Signal Processing* **40**(3), 611–623.

Experiments in Bond Rating with Probabilistic Neural Networks

Alvin J. Surkan†, Alexei N. Skurikhin ‡

†Computer Science Department/University of Nebraska
Lincoln, NE 68588-0115, USA
‡Mathematics Department/Institute of Physics & Power Engineering
249020 Obninsk, RUSSIA

Abstract— A probabilistic neural network or PNN model was constructed and trained to optimize a classifier that performs bond rating. This classifier was designed to simulate the rating levels published by a major publisher of bond ratings. For these experiments several classifier networks were trained with 1663 patterns, each having the values of 13 financial variables. A well established 21-level rating scale was regrouped into 17 classes that were more equally populated. Four variants of the PNN defined by combinations of constraints on prior probabilities and variance associated with the classes were trained and compared. The experiments demonstrated that the variant of the PNN that had equal prior probabilities for the classes and one common value for the variance in that class was significantly superior. It gave an accuracy of almost 90% in classifying the training patterns and 55% for 1480 test patterns that were set aside and not used in building the classifier.

1   Introduction

For capital markets a valuable service is provided by publishers of financial data with groups of experts who assign ratings to bond issues of corporations. Such a rating service is labor intensive because it requires data collection, compilation, verification, and evaluation as well as analysis by experts who are specialists in distinct market sectors. The annual open publication of corporate financial data and ratings makes it possible to assemble data bases comprised of financial ratios paired with their professionally assigned bond ratings. Typically, the latter are expressed on a variety of scales that are meaningful to other bond rating organizations and investment banks. For this study a scale with 18 rating levels labeled by integers in the interval [2 to 19] was used. No samples had label 3.

The public domain availability of these data and a growing need for rapid, reproducible predictions of bond ratings make the construction of computer-implemented models especially relevant for exploring more intelligent methods for extracting some of the knowledge in data bases that is already used by experts who assign bond ratings. One class of such models based on the trained neural network paradigm should emulate the expert's rating process well enough to shed significant light on mechanisms for objectively using financial ratios to obtain reliable and improved bond ratings.

2   The Bond Rating Problem

Commercial publications distribute the basic data for calculating financial ratios. The ratios are defined and normalized by financial specialists for the purpose of helping experts in rating bond issues of various corporations before they borrow capital. Typically, correlation exists in the ratings assigned to bond issues and they may be sustained for periods that exceed 5 years. It is expected that for prediction purposes these ratios will carry some meaningful information that is contained in records that track the financial ratios of corporations for as long as they have been rated. Since neural networks have been applied to problems related to bond rating with success (see Surkan et al references [4-9], it is increasingly appropriate to see how larger financial data bases with larger numbers of variables are able to support the training of other variants of neural networks.

To experiment with predictive neural network models of the bond rating process, data sets were obtained for nearly 700 corporations spanning the years 1990 to 1994, as a basis for predicting bond ratings assigned by a recognized bond rating company for each year up to 1995. For these experiments there were a total of 3143 data patterns in 13 variables and financial ratios. The patterns are distributed in rating categories as shown in the statistics of Table 1. For the purpose of these initial experiments, the set of bond rating categories was partitioned to be adequately populated. The data base of patterns was split roughly in half for the purpose of developing and testing a probabilistic neural network or PNN model that was designed to predict bond ratings.

Table 1. Descriptive Statistics for Financial Data Bases Used for Rating Bonds

SUMMARY STATISTICS DESCRIBING DATA-SET					
Index of the Class	Number level Code	Letter Finance Rating	Number in each Class	Number of Training Patterns	Number of Test Patterns
1	2	AAA	65	35	30
2	4	AA+	26	16	10
3	5	AA	114	64	50
4	6	AA-	121	61	60
5	7	A+	193	103	90
6	8	A	310	160	150
7	9	A-	213	113	100
8	10	BBB+	216	116	100
9	11	BBB	302	152	150
10	12	BBB-	219	119	100
11	13	BB+	157	87	70
12	14	BB	288	148	140
13	15	BB-	329	169	160
14	16	B+	394	204	190
15	17	B	117	67	50
16	18	B-	52	32	20
17	19	(*)	27	17	10
Total pattern Count			3143	1663	1480
(*) Includes ratings of CCC+, CCC, CCC- or D					

Table 2. Results for Different Parameter Definitions with Traiing Data

PERCENT ACCURATE CORRECT CLASSIFICATION FOR VARIOUS METHODS OF PNN DESIGN AFTER TRAINING				
Bond Rating	Method used in Probabilistic Neural Network			
code	ep-ss	ep-sv	nep-sv	ep-sc
2	100	100	100	100
4	100	100	100	100
5	96.87	100	100	100
6	93.44	100	100	99
7	92.33	99	99	95.14
8	75	93.1	96.87	98.75
9	77.87	90.2	87.61	81.41
10	77.58	89.65	89.65	81.03
11	73.02	82.23	87.5	89.47
12	73.94	88.23	86.55	82.35
13	65.51	82.75	75.86	59.77
14	54.72	70.27	81.08	81.08
15	40.82	57.39	97.63	95.85
16	47.05	65.68	99.01	96.56
17	85.07	89.55	82.08	95.52
18	100	100	59.37	59.37
19	100	100	29.41	11.76
Averages	79.59	88.70	86.56	83.94

3 Legend with Labels Used to Identify the Variants of the Methods

"ep-ss" equal prior probabilities and the same σ for all variables and all classes.
"ep-sv" equal prior probabilities and separate σ for each variable.
"nep-sv" not equal prior probabilities is the number of samples in each class and different σ for each variable.
"ep-sc" equal prior probabilities and different σ for each variable and each class.

4 Probabilistic Neural Networks and Application

The probabilistic neural network (PNN) described by Specht [3] has its origin in the ideas of Bayesian classification (see Mood and Graybill) [1] which uses classical estimators of a probability density function (PDF). Mathematically, the problem to be solved with the PNN is the classification of input vectors into one of several classes in a Bayesian-optimal manner. The Bayes optimal decision rule states that an input vector $\mathbf{x}$ is to be classified as a member of class i if

$$\mathbf{h}_i\, c_i\, \mathbf{f}_i(x) \;>\; \mathbf{h}_j\, c_j\, \mathbf{f}_j(x) \tag{1}$$

where: $\mathbf{h}_i$ is the prior probability of an unknown sample being drawn from class i and
$\quad\quad\;\; c_i$ is the cost associated with mis-classifying a sample from class i
$\quad\quad\;\; \mathbf{f}_i$ is weight is a Gaussian function centered about each pattern at x_i

From the above equation it is seen that the probability density function must be determined first. The PNN uses Parzen's method for estimating the PDF [1]. For this PNN, the function $\mathbf{f}_i$ is the weight function defined below and used to estimate the PDF or probability density function.

$$\mathbf{f}(x) = \frac{1}{(2\pi)^{P/2}\sigma^P m} \sum_{i=1}^{m} e^{-\frac{|x - x_i|^2}{2\sigma^2}} \tag{2}$$

where: m is total number of training patterns;
$\quad\quad\;\;$ p is the dimension of the input vector;
$\quad\quad\;\;$ s is a smoothing parameter giving the standard deviation of a Gaussian distribution.

The structure of the PNN is shown in Figure 1. Following the input layer, the PNN has two hidden layers and a single output layer. The input pattern layer has one neuron for each pattern. Each input neuron computes a distance between the input pattern and the training pattern represented by that neuron. This distance then provides the weights for the neuron's activation function. The summation layer has one neuron for each class. A layer following the summation neurons collects the activations of pattern layer neurons from the members of the class that corresponds with each summation neuron. The final activation of the ith summation neuron provides directly an estimate of the PDF at the ith population. The output neuron is a threshold unit that decides which of its inputs receives the largest signal.

Figure 1. Schematic of a Probabilistic Neural Network Showing the Names of the Layers

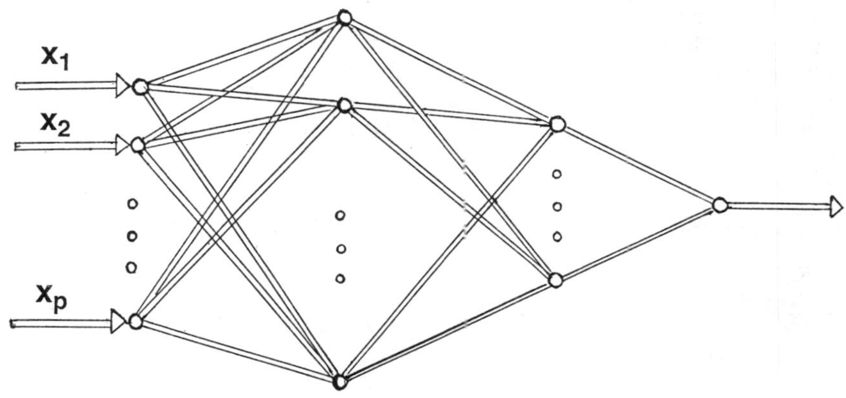

5   Parameters Defining the PNN Architecture

Finding a good value of the variance σ is critical in the performance of the PNN. In these experiments σ was defined in three ways. The first gave a single value of σ parameter to all the variables for all the classes and makes the assumption of equal prior probabilities. The second approach used separate σ for each variable to suppress the effects of variance of unimportant variables. Also, in these experiments two methods are used for specifying and comparing the effects of prior probabilities.

These methods differ as to how prior probabilities are incorporated. The prior probabilities are either set equal for all classes or they are set in proportion to the number of training patterns in each class. In combination with these two methods one can employ different σs for each variable. Under the assumption of equal prior probabilities one may use a different σ for each class. To calculate the σ's, a gradient-based method is used. The values of σ used in implementing the search ranged from 0.0001 to 15.

6   Preprocessing of the Raw Data

For these experiments, the data patterns were partitioned into 17 classes (see Table 1) with some grouping of poorly populated rating classes. Before using data, individual components of multivariate sample vectors were standardized to a Z-score by subtracting the means from the raw values and dividing by their standard deviations. This normalization equalizes the contribution of each variable to remove the effects of offset and scale.

As a rule, normal patterns (non-outlier) were slightly concentrated in the training set (i.e., the patterns which can be grouped closely relative to each other and are not outliers). However, several outliers may also be intentionally inserted in each class for training. Because some outliers where shifted out of the training set, the density of outliers in the test set was enhanced in comparison to the training set. This introduces a bias toward more difficulty in classifying the patterns in the test set.

7   Results of Simulation Experiments

Significantly different sets of results were obtained using the four methods described earlier for construction of the PNN. Results of the simulation experiments are summarized in Tables 2-6. Table 2 gives the percent correctly classified in the training data set using the four methods. Tables 3-6 are confusion matrices indicating classification results grouped by class. For a perfect prediction of the class memberships, only the diagonal elements are non-zero while the off-diagonal elements are all zero. Experimentally, it was found that the greatest accuracy is obtained by the method with equal prior probabilities and different σ's for each variable.

8   Discussion of Results

The first PNN approach we designate (ep-ss) had equal prior probabilities and a single value of σ was attached to all variables leading to the first improvement in the performance of a PNN. This can be expected to be most successful when the PNN is presented only with patterns with variables that have similar variances. Experimentally, it is concluded that it is not the case for this problem data. We have no information as to which are the most important variables. Also, it is possible that their influences are masked by large variations in less important variables. In the second approach designated (ep-sv), the variables again assume equal prior probabilities and there are distinct or different values of the s for each of the classes. This combination permits small σs to be assigned to the less important variables so as to suppress or eliminate their effects relative to the more important variables. The maximum improvement in classification accuracy indicates that this approach is advantageous. A natural extension of the second approach (nep-ds) uses a different σ for each prior probability (proportional to the number of sample patterns in each class) and has different σs for each of the classes. This method which gives the highest accuracy, nearly 89% on the training set, introduces the hidden danger to many parameters leading to overfitting.

Table 3. Confusion matrix for "ep-ss" method

cls	2	4	5	6	7	8	9	10	11	12	13	14	15	16	17	18	19	Percent Correct
2	25	2	2	-	-	-	1	-	-	-	-	-	-	-	-	-	-	90
4	2	5	3	-	-	-	-	-	-	-	-	-	-	-	-	-	-	100
5	10	-	21	5	6	2	-	-	2	1	3	-	-	-	-	-	-	52
6	4	7	4	23	6	4	1	4	2	2	-	-	3	-	-	-	-	55
7	5	2	9	17	27	4	10	4	5	4	1	-	2	-	-	-	-	53.33
8	6	-	6	22	17	25	10	26	16	2	5	6	5	-	2	-	2	43.66
9	-	2	-	9	9	6	12	31	12	3	2	1	6	-	3	-	4	49
10	5	-	1	2	7	6	9	26	14	2	9	2	5	1	1	6	4	49
11	1	-	1	11	3	10	8	35	15	12	8	7	4	1	10	2	22	41.33
12	-	1	-	-	-	1	5	30	10	8	12	2	9	4	5	-	13	30
13	-	-	-	1	1	1	3	6	6	3	14	1	1	3	15	-	15	25.71
14	1	-	-	2	1	-	1	10	1	3	12	14	11	13	26	1	44	26.42
15	1	-	-	-	4	-	2	4	5	7	11	13	9	14	33	4	53	22.5
16	3	-	-	-	-	1	-	5	4	6	6	16	14	12	55	11	57	42.63
17	2	-	-	2	-	-	-	1	-	1	-	1	1	6	20	2	14	56
18	2	-	-	-	-	-	-	-	-	1	-	2	1	-	3	7	4	70
19	-	-	-	-	-	-	-	-	-	1	-	-	-	-	2	-	7	70

Average Percentage Predicted Correct in the Asssigned Classs or one of two Nearest Classes — 51.03

Table 4. Confusion matrix for "ep-sv" method.

cls	2	4	5	6	7	8	9	10	11	12	13	14	15	16	17	18	19	Percent Correct
2	28	2	-	-	-	-	-	-	-	-	-	-	-	-	-	-	-	100
4	2	6	2	-	-	-	-	-	-	-	-	-	-	-	-	-	-	100
5	12	-	21	4	3	1	-	-	2	4	3	-	-	-	-	-	-	50
6	2	3	3	24	9	8	1	2	1	1	-	1	3	1	-	1	-	60
7	4	1	8	7	29	5	15	3	12	3	-	-	3	-	-	-	-	45.55
8	16	-	1	12	17	37	15	19	19	3	4	3	3	-	1	-	-	46
9	-	3	1	4	7	12	25	16	14	4	2	4	5	2	1	-	-	53
10	5	-	1	5	5	9	21	14	16	6	7	4	3	2	-	2	-	51
11	1	-	-	13	7	9	12	27	19	11	16	8	5	-	8	3	11	38
12	5	-	-	-	1	3	6	21	10	14	14	9	3	-	4	-	10	38
13	-	-	-	2	1	-	4	8	6	2	15	6	5	2	13	-	6	32.85
14	1	-	-	2	-	1	1	4	5	5	6	20	23	11	37	3	21	35
15	1	-	-	-	2	-	1	8	3	5	8	27	19	18	36	6	26	40
16	4	-	-	-	-	-	2	2	5	5	3	17	25	27	62	13	25	60
17	2	-	-	1	-	-	-	-	1	1	-	2	5	5	17	7	9	58
18	2	-	-	-	-	-	-	-	-	1	-	2	-	1	4	5	5	70
19	-	-	-	-	-	-	-	-	-	-	-	-	1	1	3	-	5	50

Average Percentage Predicted Correct in the Asssigned Classs or one of two Nearest Classes — 54.55

Table 5. Confusion matrix for "nep-sv" method.

cls	2	4	5	6	7	8	9	10	11	12	13	14	15	16	17	18	19	Percent Correct
2	11	2	1	-	-	-	-	-	-	-	-	-	-	-	16	-	-	43.33
4	2	6	2	-	-	-	-	-	-	-	-	-	-	-	-	-	-	100
5	2	-	21	4	3	2	-	-	2	4	2	-	-	10	-	-	-	50
6	3	3	3	23	8	8	3	1	3	3	-	-	1	3	1	-	-	56.66
7	1	1	4	8	27	13	11	3	12	3	-	-	3	4	-	-	-	53.33
8	-	-	2	8	20	44	11	17	20	4	5	3	4	12	-	-	-	50
9	-	5	1	1	8	18	19	14	14	-	5	8	3	-	-	-	-	51
10	-	-	-	3	5	15	17	11	20	6	3	3	8	7	-	2	-	48
11	-	-	1	8	7	13	4	26	36	8	7	11	14	12	-	3	-	46.66
12	-	1	-	-	-	4	9	19	21	8	6	6	9	16	1	-	-	35
13	-	-	-	1	-	1	4	6	12	6	3	7	15	14	1	-	-	22.85
14	-	-	-	-	-	2	-	-	7	-	-	108	12	19	-	-	-	85.71
15	-	-	-	-	2	-	1	6	7	5	2	23	36	70	5	3	-	80.62
16	-	-	-	-	-	1	-	1	7	7	2	19	55	87	8	3	-	78.94
17	-	-	-	-	-	-	-	1	1	-	-	4	10	26	6	1	1	66
18	-	-	-	-	-	-	-	-	-	1	-	3	4	10	-	2	-	10
19	-	-	-	-	-	-	-	-	-	-	-	1	2	5	-	-	2	20

Average Percentage Predicted Correct in the Asssigned Classs or one of two Nearest Classes — 52.82

Table 6. Confusion matrix for "ep-sc" method.

cls	2	4	5	6	7	8	9	10	11	12	13	14	15	16	17	18	19	Percent Correct
2	13	2	1	-	-	13	-	1	-	-	-	-	-	-	-	-	-	
4	2	5	3	-	-	-	-	-	-	-	-	-	-	-	-	-	-	100
5	5	-	24	4	2	6	-	-	2	2	4	-	1	-	-	-	-	56
6	4	7	3	20	7	6	2	2	3	1	-	-	5	-	-	-	-	50
7	3	2	9	11	22	16	11	4	6	3	-	-	3	-	-	-	-	54.44
8	-	-	5	14	15	51	12	14	19	3	4	9	2	2	-	-	-	52
9	-	1	-	2	8	22	12	13	26	2	1	4	7	2	-	-	-	47
10	-	-	-	2	6	20	7	11	35	2	1	5	4	3	-	3	1	53
11	-	-	1	8	2	17	5	18	45	3	5	26	5	13	1	1	-	44
12	-	1	-	1	-	4	4	16	33	7	4	12	6	12	-	-	-	44
13	-	-	-	1	1	2	2	6	21	3	-	8	4	22	-	-	-	15.71
14	-	-	-	2	1	1	-	4	14	2	2	29	20	56	5	2	2	36.42
15	-	-	-	-	3	2	1	2	13	2	2	27	18	80	8	2	-	78.12
16	-	-	-	-	-	3	-	2	9	6	2	29	21	106	5	7	-	69.47
17	-	-	-	1	-	2	-	-	2	1	1	2	4	30	6	-	1	72
18	-	-	-	-	-	2	-	-	-	1	-	2	1	11	1	2	-	15
19	-	-	-	-	-	-	-	-	1	-	1	-	6	-	-	2		20

Average Percentage Predicted Correct in the Asssigned Classs or one of two Nearest Classes — 47.48

Finally, the second worst classification accuracy of 84% was obtained with the (ep-sc) method with equal prior probabilities and different classes for each variable. There are strong arguments for the classes having significantly different sigmas (variances) and, therefore, weights as a result of the importance of scaling introduced naturally by data collection and definition of the variable values. The third approach (ep-ss) and (epds) with equal prior probabilities and either same or different σs obtained results that were inferior (only 83% accurate) to the others. We conclude that the conditions necessary for its successful application were not satisfied.

9 Conclusions

Considering the high complexity of the decision making by cooperative teams of human professionals that we are trying to simulate a complex process with a neural network and that there is a significant amount of context sensitivity in financial data, the accuracy of prediction obtained by the PNN for the test data set is surprisingly good. Additional improvements in accuracy can be expected to be obtainable using other methods that are not gradient-based. Although the model's accuracy in classifying the training patterns was nearly 90 %, this is not considered any more significant than it is for other traditional model fitting processes. In the context of any form of blind model fitting there may be a danger of constructing and identifying a model with too many parameters which may become too finely tuned to the training data to exhibit good quality generalization. An alternative approach to the problem of bond rating with computers might be to use a combination of stochasticastic search like genetic algorithms, followed by a gradient-based search which in the final stages will optimize the values of the variance parameters.

10 Directions for future Research

An important focus for further research will be the interpretation and explanation of the classification results obtained by the PNN. Since the PNN is intrinsically a classifier which is based on Bayes theory, it is expected to provide insight which will lead to clearer explanations of the network's actions as a rating tool. The PNN directly provides confidence levels for each result and this is may be particularly useful to people willing to consider relying on neural network-based solutions to this complex problem. Also, since the real-world problem data contains some outliers, the PNN is especially attractive because it tends to eliminate the effects of the outliers. The results of our preliminary experiments indicate that continuation of this research is likely to be encouraging. Also, more comprehensive experimentation may suggest possible refinements for further improvement of the accuracy of prediction.

11 Acknowledgments

Although all of these data used for these experiments are available in the public domain and could be compiled and derived directly from the open literature, the task of preparing it would be a prohibitively time-consuming effort. For this research, we appreciate the cooperation of the Standard and Poor Inc., New York for providing computer files with high quality financial and bond rating data.

References

[1] Mood, A.M., and Graybill, F.A. (1962). Introduction to the theory of statistics. New York: MacMillan.

[2] Parzen, E., (1962) " On Estimation of a Probability Density Function and Mode", Annals of Mathematical Statistics, 33:1065-1076, 1962.

[3] Specht, D.F., (1990)"Probabilistic Neural Networks", Neural Networks, Volume 3, pp.109-118, 1990.

[4] Surkan, A.J. and J. Clay Singleton)"Neural Networks as Bond Rating Tools" HICSS92 25th Hawaii International Conference on Systems Science, Volume 4, pp 499-503, January 7-10, 1992, Koloa, Hawaii.

[5] Surkan, A.J. and X.Ying. (1991) Training Neural Networks to Derive Explicit Bond Rating Formulas" paper No. 11 at IJCNN'91 International Joint Conference on Neural Networks, November 18-21, 1991, Singapore. see abstract IJCNN'91: Volume 2, pp. 903, July 8-12, 1991. Seattle , WA

[6] Surkan, A.J. and J. Clay Singleton (1990) "Neural Network Performance in Emulations of Professional Bond Rating Judgements", Proceedings of the INNC International Neural Networks Conference, Volume 1, page 394, July 3-9, 1990, Paris, France.

[7] Surkan, A.J. and J. Clay Singleton (1990) "Neural Networks for Bond Rating Improved by Multiple Hidden Layers", Proceedings of the IJCNN International Joint Conference on Neural Networks, Volume II, pp 157-162, June 25, 1990, San Diego, CA.

[8] Surkan, A.J. and J. Clay Singleton, (1990) "Modeling the Judgement of Bond Rating Agencies", Midwest Finance Association Annual Meeting , March 28-31, 1990, Chicago, IL.

[9] Surkan, A.J. and J. Clay Singleton) in"Neural Networks in Bond Rating" invited chapter 1n 1995 book titled: <u>Neural Networks in the Capital Markets</u>, edited by A-Paul Refense, London Business School, London England. Chapter 20, pages 301-307, published by John Wiley & Son's

Application of Rival Penalized Competitive Learning on Capital Market Prediction : Adaptive RPCL-CLP and RPCL-ART

Wai Man Leung[1], Yiu Ming Cheung[1] and Helen Z.H. Lai[2]

[1]Department of Computer Science and Engineering,
[2]Department of Finance,
The Chinese University of Hong Kong

Abstract—**This article compares the performance of** *Adaptive RPCL-CLP [Cheung, Lai and Xu, 1995]* **with that of** *RPCL-ART [Leung, Cheung, Lai and Xu, 1995]* **on financial prediction. They are evaluated in terms of prediction accuracy as well as profit gains under two simple trading systems. Computer experiments show how Adaptive RPCL-CLP out-performs RPCL-ART and some traditional methods such as MA and Random Walk Models.**

1 Introduction

Recently we have proposed two prediction models by using *Rival Penalized Competitive Learning (RPCL)* [1] - *Adaptive RPCL-CLP* [2] and *RPCL-ART* [3]. As a modification of *RPCL-CLP* [4], Adaptive RPCL-CLP automatically initializes the number of cluster nodes and determine the criterion of new node formation. It implements unsupervized and supervized learning in training and testing phase respectively. Upon prediction, the model parameters are adjusted in response to prediction errors which acts as teaching signals.

RPCL-ART incorporates the RPCL mechanism into the F2 competition, where both the winner and the rival nodes (the second winning F2 node) that pass the vigilance test are updated at Long Term Memory (LTM) in ART model [5,6,7]. It adaptively adjusts the coefficients of Memory Normalized Patterns (MNPs) [5] to tune to the input during the testing phase. As a result, RPCL-ART reduces the memory storage and time consumption required by its predecessor Hybrid ARTTSP [5].

To evaluate the power of these models, we derive two simple trading systems for foreign exchanges. The trading activities are regulated by three signals : 'buy', 'sell' and 'do nothing'. We apply these systems on the conversion rates of U.S. Dollar to Deutsche Mark (U.S.D.-D.M.).

This paper is organized as follows. Section 2 and 3 describe RPCL-ART and Adaptive RPCL-CLP models respectively. Section 4 introduces two simple trading systems for currency exchanges. The results of computer experiments are presented in Section 5. Finally, we draw some conclusions in the last section.

2 RPCL-ART Model

An input pattern P(t) of size d is presented to the F0 field (Fig.1). A special data point called *Input Associative Predictor (IAP)* is attached to P(t) which is classified and normalized as *Memory Normalized Pattern (MNP)*. The IAP is normalized as *Memory Normalized Associative Predictor (MNAP)*. MNP and MNAP are both stored in the recognized category of F2. Denote n_i as the number of MNPs in category C_i, the bottom-up input U_j from F1 to the j-th F2 node is given by

$$U_j = \begin{cases} -1, & \text{if } j-\text{th F2 node is uncommitted,} \\ \left(1 - n_j / \sum_i n_i\right) \times \left(|I \wedge z_j| / (b + |z_j|)\right), & \text{otherwise.} \end{cases} \tag{1}$$

where z_j is the LTM of the j-th F2 node, I is a MNP and $b > 0$. For U_k of the k-th F2 node passing the test, let

$$u_k = \begin{cases} 1, & \text{if } k = c \text{ such that } U_k = max_j(U_j), \\ -1, & \text{if } k = r \text{ such that } U_k = max_{j \neq c}(U_j), \\ 0, & \text{otherwise.} \end{cases} \tag{2}$$

where $0 \leq \gamma_c$, $\gamma_r \leq 1$ are the learning rates for the winner and rival nodes respectively. As regards the recognized category C_J, we update the LTM z_J by

$$z_J{}^{(new)} = z_J{}^{(old)} + \Delta z_J \tag{3}$$

where

$$\Delta z_J = \begin{cases} \gamma_c \, (I \wedge z_J{}^{(old)} - z_J{}^{(old)}), & \text{if } u_J = 1, \\ -\gamma_r \, (I \wedge z_J{}^{(old)} - z_J{}^{(old)}), & \text{if } u_J = -1, \\ 0, & \text{otherwise.} \end{cases} \tag{4}$$

The vigilance parameter $\rho \in [0,1]$ (Fig.1) is the criterion for category formation - the larger the value is, the more categories would be formed and vice versa. At the end of the training phase, the MNP coefficients $\mathbf{B_J}$ of C_J are determined by the Least Square Regression on the MNPs and MNAPs in that category. Thereafter, all MNPs are removed to reduce memory storage. In the testing phase, the coefficient $\mathbf{B_J}$ is updated adaptively. The input pattern and the prediction from the *Denormalizing Subsystem* (as given in [5,6]) are fed into the trading system for trading decision.

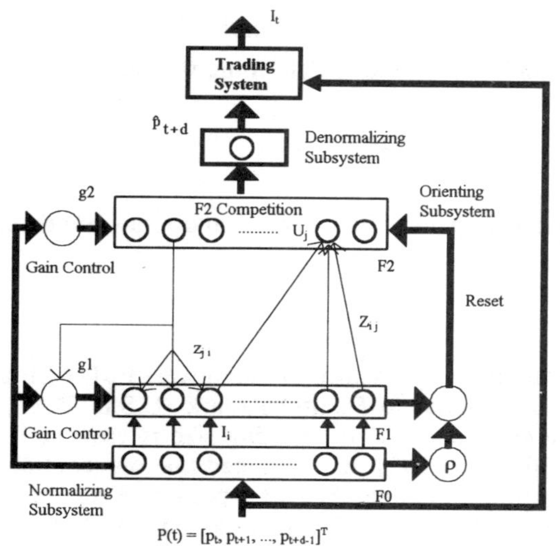

Fig. 1 RPCL-ART architecture with input pattern P(t) and output trading signal in testing phase (A modification of Fuzzy ART). Symbols and notations are given in [5,6].

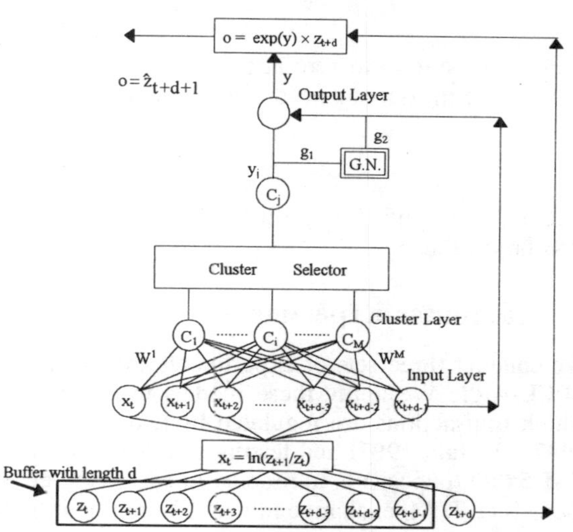

Fig. 2 Architecture of Adaptive RPCL-CLP, where X(t) = [x_t, x_{t+1}, ..., x_{t+d-2}, x_{t+d-1}]^T is a transformed input vector.

3 Adaptive RPCL-CLP Model

The Adaptive RPCL-CLP model [2] is a modified version of the early RPCL-CLP [4], whose architecture consists of three layers: Input Layer, Cluster Layer and Output Layer. To avoid the effects of some common factors included in the series, it is attached with a data pre-processing and post-processing schemes by transforming a given series z_1, z_2, ..., z_{N+1}, to x_1, x_2, ... x_N by $x_t = ln(z_{t+1}/z_t)$ called *Returns* in financial terminology. In Fig.2, we denote Z(t) = [z_t, z_{t+1}, ..., z_{t+d-1}, z_{t+d}]^T, X(t) = [x_t, x_{t+1}, ..., x_{t+d-2}, x_{t+d-1}]^T, where X(t) $\in$ $\Re^d$, $1 \leq t \leq$ N-d. A buffer with length d stores the last d input data points. These d points with the coming data point z_{t+d} constitute a vector Z(t), which is pre-processed to become X(t) before feeding into the Input Layer. The Cluster Layer is built up by the Incremental Clustering and RPCL algorithm [4] where each cluster node C_i is associated with a centroid W^i and a linear predictor. These nodes divide the inputs $\{X(t)\}_1^{N-d}$ into a number of groups. During the testing phase, the coming data point z_{t+d} is combined with those in the buffer to form the vector Z(t), which is transformed to the input vector X(t). The Cluster Selector will select a node C_j from the Cluster Layer such that the distance between X(t) and its centroid is minimum, then the associated linear predictor will predict a value y_j which is combined with x_{t+d-1} (the output of the Random Walk Model which is a good predictor in the efficient market) by the Gating Network [8] as y — the prediction of x_{t+d}. Then y is post-processed to $\hat{z}_{t+d+1}$, the prediction of z_{t+d+1}. For detailed algorithms, please refer to the paper [2].

4 Trading System

Two simple trading systems are derived to regulate transactions for foreign exchanges in testing phase. Given a testing series $\mathbf{Z} \equiv$ [z_1, z_2, ..., z_n]^T of size n, these systems would generate an trading signal I_t: -1, 0 or 1 meaning 'sell', 'do nothing' or 'buy' respectively. For $1 \leq s \leq t \leq n$ we define diff = $z_{t+1} - z_t$ and $q_t = z_s$ such that we just buy a contract at time s. $\hat{z}_t$ is the prediction of z_t.

4.1 System I

Given predefined negative constant α and positive constant β, the trading signal I_t is determined by

$$I_t = \begin{cases} 1, & \text{if } (\hat{z}_{t+1} - z_t)/q_t \leq \alpha \text{ and do not hold a constract at time } t, \\ -1, & \text{if } (\hat{z}_{t+1} - z_t)/q_t \geq \beta \text{ and is holding a constract at time } t, \\ 0, & \text{otherwise.} \end{cases} \tag{5}$$

4.2 System II

Given current information and the prediction, the trading signal I_t and profit gains are determined by

$$I_t = \begin{cases} -1, & \text{if } \hat{z}_{t+1} - z_t > 0, \\ 0, & \text{if } \hat{z}_{t+1} - z_t = 0, \\ 1, & \text{otherwise.} \end{cases} \qquad (6)$$

After we have done buying / selling transaction according to the indicator I_t, we update the Gains:

$$Gains^{(new)} = Gains^{(old)} + \begin{cases} -\text{diff}, & \text{if we have done "buying transaction"}, \\ \text{diff}, & \text{if we have done "selling transaction"}. \end{cases} \qquad (7)$$

Gains will be reset to zero after the current transaction is balanced. We need to determine whether we need to balance the transaction according to the Indicator $I_t{}'$ below:

$$I_t{}' = \begin{cases} 2, & \text{if } |\hat{z}_{t+1} - z_t| > r \times Gains \text{ or } Gains > \lambda, \\ 0, & \text{otherwise.} \end{cases} \qquad (8)$$

where $I_t{}' = 2$ stands for 'cut loss', $I_t{}' = 0$ for 'do nothing', r is a risk factor with $0 \le r \le 1$ and λ is a pre-defined threshold value.

5   Computer Experiments

We conduct three sets of experiments to compare and evaluate the performance of Adaptive RPCL-CLP and RPCL-ART. We apply these models to exchange rates of U.S. Dollar to Deutsche Mark (U.S.D.-D.M.) in which transactions are regulated by two trading systems, *System I* and *II*. The training size is 1679 (1 Dec., 1987 - 29 Jul., 1993) and testing size is 99 (2 Aug., 1993 - 30 Nov., 1993). It is assumed that one contract of US\$ 5,000 (deposit) is transacted in each trial, i.e. the principal is US\$ 5,000. We set 1 point = 0.0001 unit in the U.S.D.-D.M. exchange rate and 1 point gain is equivalent to profit of HK\$ 50 (assume US\$ 1 = HK\$ 7.7).

Experiment 1 and 2 evaluate RPCL-ART and Adaptive RPCL-CLP respectively. Experiment 3 compares the performance of MA(5), MA(10) and Random Walk Models. Trading System I and II are applied to these results. Finally, we summarize our experimental results so as to make a clear comparison.

In the following graphs (Fig.3-8), the vertical axis represents the exchange rates and the horizontal axis denotes the time with five days per interval. The solid and dashed lines are the observation and prediction respectively. N denotes the total number of categories formed. $\rho 1$ and $\rho 2$ are the vigilance parameters of RPCL-ART for training and testing phases respectively. We set $\rho 1 > \rho 2$ so that all the testing patterns could be matched to the categories built in the training phase. acc. is the percentage of prediction with absolute error less than or equal to 0.005. The parameters α and β are set to be -0.0025 and 0.0075 respectively for Trading System I. The profit rate is calculated as follows:

$$Prof.\ R. = \frac{Profit}{Principal} \times 100\% = \frac{Point\ Gains \times HK\$\ 50}{Principal \times HK\$\ 7.7} \times 100\% \qquad (9)$$

5.1   Experiment 1 : Evaluation of RPCL-ART

Experiment 1 compares the performance of RPCL-ART in *Log Return* and *Normal Scale*. As regards Normal Scale Prediction, the training and testing data are original exchange rates z_t without transformation. For Log Return Scale, the input data x_t at time t are pre-processed as $x_t = ln(z_{t+1}/z_t)$. The purpose is to take into account the returns as well as absolute rates.

We fixed an input size of 3 and apply Trading System I and II to the prediction results in 75 and 99 testing days. The results are listed in Table 2 to 5. The smallest r.m.s.e. (root-mean-squared-error) of Log Return and Normal Scale are 0.011583 (Fig.4) and 0.011210 respectively. We obtain the highest point gains (Point) of 1,457 and profit rate (Prof. R.) of 189.22% in Log Return Scale using System II for 99 testing days (Table 5).

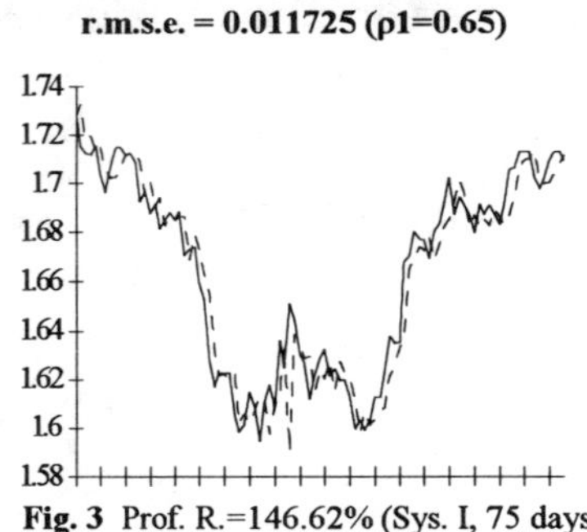

RPCL-ART: Normal Scale
r.m.s.e. = 0.011725 ($\rho 1$=0.65)

Fig. 3 Prof. R.=146.62% (Sys. I, 75 days)

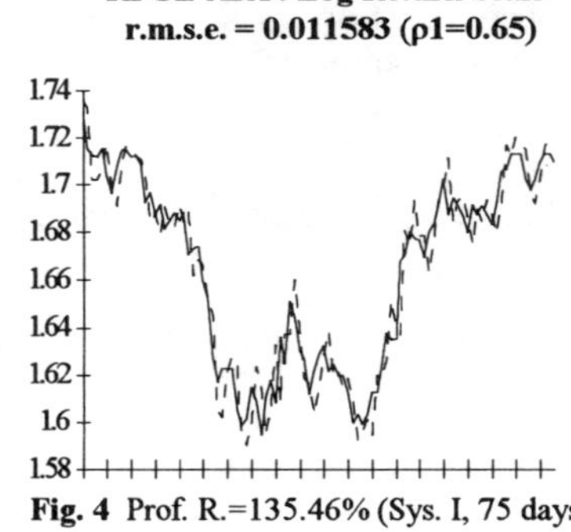

RPCL-ART: Log Return Scale
r.m.s.e. = 0.011583 ($\rho 1$=0.65)

Fig. 4 Prof. R.=135.46% (Sys. I, 75 days)

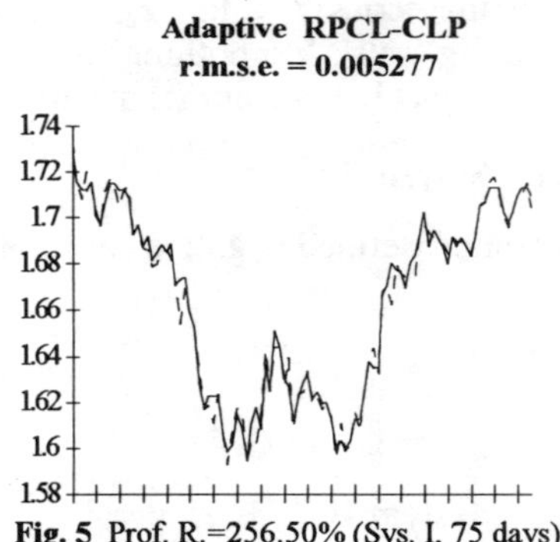

Adaptive RPCL-CLP
r.m.s.e. = 0.005277

Fig. 5 Prof. R.=256.50% (Sys. I, 75 days)

5.1.1   Prediction Accuracy

$\rho 1$	$\rho 2$	Log Return Scale			Normal Scale		
		r.m.s.e.	N	acc.	r.m.s.e.	N	acc.
0.55	0.50	0.011900	15	29.29%	0.011210	21	33.33%
0.65	0.60	0.011583	16	27.27%	0.011725	11	34.34%
0.75	0.70	0.012347	21	37.37%	0.011289	21	27.27%
0.85	0.80	0.011916	31	27.27%	0.011308	33	32.32%

Table 1   Prediction Accuracy of RPCL-ART in Log Return and Normal Scale.

5.1.2   Trading System I : 75 Testing Days

$\rho 1$	$\rho 2$	Log Return Scale			Normal Scale		
		Point	Profit	Prof. R.	Point	Profit	Prof. R.
0.55	0.50	673	USD 4,370	87.40%	979	USD 6,357	127.14%
0.65	0.60	1,043	USD 6,773	135.46%	1,129	USD 7,331	146.62%
0.75	0.70	246	USD 1,597	31.94%	1,169	USD 7,591	151.82%
0.85	0.80	353	USD 2,292	45.84%	1,133	USD 7,357	147.14%
Average		**579**	**USD 3,758**	**75.16%**	**1,103**	**USD 7,159**	**143.18%**

Table 2   RPCL-ART: Profit Gains under Trading System I for 75 testing days.

5.1.3   Trading System I : 99 Testing Days

$\rho 1$	$\rho 2$	Log Return Scale			Normal Scale		
		Point	Profit	Prof. R.	Point	Profit	Prof. R.
0.55	0.50	673	USD 4,370	87.40%	162	USD 1,052	21.04%
0.65	0.60	1,043	USD 6,773	135.46%	364	USD 2,364	47.28%
0.75	0.70	246	USD 1,597	31.94%	1,169	USD 7,591	151.82%
0.85	0.80	353	USD 2,292	45.84%	99	USD 643	12.86%
Average		**579**	**USD 3,758**	**75.16%**	**449**	**USD 2,913**	**58.26%**

Table 3   RPCL-ART: Profit Gains under Trading System I for 99 testing days.

5.1.4   Trading System II : 75 Testing Days

$\rho 1$	$\rho 2$	Log Return Scale			Normal Scale		
		Point	Profit	Prof. R.	Point	Profit	Prof. R.
0.55	0.50	510	USD 3,312	66.24%	986	USD 6,403	128.06%
0.65	0.60	526	USD 3,416	68.32%	1,098	USD 7,130	142.60%
0.75	0.70	210	USD 1,364	27.28%	1,023	USD 6,643	132.86%
0.85	0.80	272	USD 1,766	35.32%	721	USD 4,682	93.64%
Average		**380**	**USD 2,465**	**49.30%**	**957**	**USD 6,214**	**124.28%**

Table 4   RPCL-ART: Profit Gains under Trading System II for 75 testing days.

5.1.5   Trading System II : 99 Testing Days

$\rho 1$	$\rho 2$	Log Return Scale			Normal Scale		
		Point	Profit	Prof. R.	Point	Profit	Prof. R.
0.55	0.50	1,441	USD 9,357	187.14%	551	USD 3,578	71.56%
0.65	0.60	1,457	USD 9,461	189.22%	508	USD 3,299	65.98%
0.75	0.70	1,097	USD 7,123	142.46%	917	USD 5,955	119.10%
0.85	0.80	1,314	USD 8,532	170.64%	983	USD 6,383	127.66%
Average		**1,327**	**USD 8,618**	**172.36%**	**740**	**USD 4,804**	**96.08%**

Table 5   RPCL-ART: Profit Gains under Trading System II for 99 testing days.

5.2   Experiment 2 : Evaluation of Adaptive RPCL-ART

Experiment 2 evaluates the power of Adaptive RPCL-CLP by Trading System I and II in 75 and 99 testing days. The input size is set to 3. The r.m.s.e. is as small as 0.005277 (Fig.5, Table 6) which is far better than that of RPCL-ART. The highest profit rate is 325.98%, using Trading System II in 99 testing days. The accuracy (acc.) is 73.74%, which is twice as much as its counterpart, RPCL-ART.

5.2.1   Prediction Accuracy

r.m.s.e.	N	acc.
0.005277	120	73.74%

Table 6   Prediction Accuracy of Adaptive RPCL-CLP.

5.2.2   Profit Gains

Period	Trading System I			Trading System II		
	Point	**Profit**	**Prof. R.**	**Point**	**Profit**	**Prof. R.**
75 Days	1,975	USD 12,825	256.50%	1,891	USD 12,279	245.58%
99 Days	1,769	USD 11,487	229.74%	2,510	USD 16,299	325.98%

Table 7 Adaptive RPCL-CLP: Profit Gains under Trading System I and II for 75 and 99 testing days.

5.3   Experiment 3 : Evaluation of MA and Random Walk Models

In this experiment we compare the performance of Moving Average and Random Walk Models. We apply MA(5) and MA(10) which are commonly used in financial prediction. The Random Walk Model is

$$\hat{z}_{t+1} = z_t + a_t, \tag{10}$$

where a_t is the white noise with mean zero and variance 0.0001. The smallest r.m.s.e. is 0.013583 obtained by Random Walk Model which yields only 17.92% using Trading System I in 75 testing days. The highest profit rate (70.26%) is obtained by MA(5) using Trading System I.

5.3.1   Prediction Accuracy

Prediction Model	r.m.s.e.	acc.
Moving Average (5)	0.014403	26.26%
Moving Average (10)	0.020277	25.25%
Random Walk	0.013583	30.30%

Table 8 Prediction Accuracy of MA(5), MA(10) and Random Walk Models.

5.3.2   Trading System I

Prediction Model	75 Testing Days			99 Testing Days		
	Point	**Profit**	**Prof. R.**	**Point**	**Profit**	**Prof. R.**
Moving Average (5)	541	USD 3,513	70.26%	541	USD 3,513	70.26%
Moving Average (10)	321	USD 2,084	41.68%	321	USD 2,084	41.68%
Random Walk	138	USD 896	17.92%	59	USD 383	7.66%

Table 9 MA and Random Walk Models: Profit Gains under Trading System I for 75 and 99 testing days.

5.3.3   Trading System II

Prediction Model	75 Testing Days			99 Testing Days		
	Point	**Profit**	**Prof. R.**	**Point**	**Profit**	**Prof. R.**
Moving Average (5)	-740	USD -4,805	-96.10%	-309	USD -2,006	-40.12%
Moving Average (10)	-584	USD -3,792	-75.84%	-1,025	USD -6,656	-133.12%
Random Walk	146	USD 948	18.96%	-13	USD -84	-1.68%

Table 10 MA and Random Walk Models: Profit Gains under Trading System II for 75 and 99 testing days.

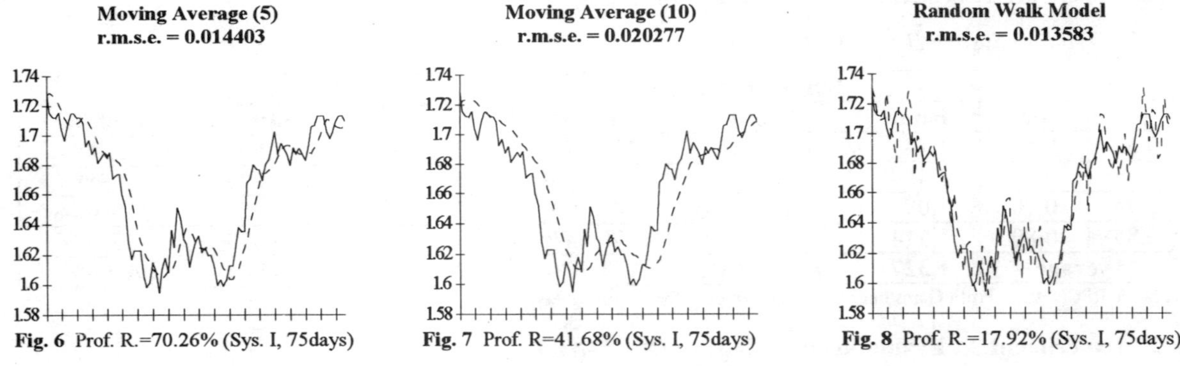

Fig. 6 Prof. R.=70.26% (Sys. I, 75days)   **Fig. 7** Prof. R=41.68% (Sys. I, 75days)   **Fig. 8** Prof. R.=17.92% (Sys. I, 75days)

5.4   Experiment Summary : Summary of Prediction Accuracy and Profits Gain

This sub-section summarizes the prediction accuracy and profit rates of all models we study. As regards RPCL-ART model, we display the best performance in the corresponding items (Table 11). Comparing the Normal Scale Prediction, there is no significant reduction of r.m.s.e. using Log Return Scale (Fig.3, 4 and Table 1). However, Log Return Scale yields a greater profit in long term investment (Table 3 and 5). In Log Return Scale, we obtain average profits of US$ 3,758 and US$ 8,618 (99 testing days) using Trading System I and II respectively, which are higher than that in Normal Scale.

As results show (Table 11 and 12), Adaptive RPCL-CLP is better than RPCL-ART in both prediction accuracy and profit gains. However, RPCL-ART forms fewer categories than Adaptive RPCL-CLP. In the worst case, RPCL-ART form only 33 categories which are much fewer than that of its counterpart (Table 1 and 6). For Adaptive RPCL-CLP, the performance of Trading System II seems to be better than System I in long term investment (Table 7). It is discovered that MA models are even worse than Random Walk Model in term of prediction accuracy (Table 11). MA and Random Walk Models obtain negative profit gains under Trading System II (Table 12). To sum up, Adaptive RPCL-CLP is much better than the other models. Nevertheless, the performance of the trading systems vary from cases to cases.

5.4.1   Prediction Accuracy

Model	r.m.s.e.	N	acc.
RPCL-ART	0.011210	21	33.33%
Adaptive RPCL-CLP	0.005277	120	73.74%
MA(5)	0.014403	-	26.26%
MA(10)	0.020277	-	25.25%
Random Walk	0.013583	-	30.30%

Table 11 Prediction Accuracy of all models.

5.4.2   Profit Gains

Model	Trad. Sys. I		Trad. Sys. II	
	75 Days	99 Days	75 Days	99 Days
RPCL-ART	151.82%	151.82%	142.60%	189.22%
Adaptive RPCL-CLP	256.50%	229.74%	245.58%	325.98%
MA(5)	70.26%	70.26%	-96.10%	-40.12%
MA(10)	41.68%	41.68%	-75.84%	-133.12%
Random Walk	17.92%	7.66%	18.96%	-1.68%

Table 12 All models: Profit Rates under Trading System I an II for 75 and 99 testing days.

6   Conclusion

This paper compares the performance of RPCL-ART, Adaptive RPCL-CLP, MA and Random Walk Models. Two simple trading systems are applied to the exchange rate of U.S.D. to D.M. It is noticed that for RPCL-ART, using Log Return Scale do not improve the accuracy. However, the Log Return Scale results in a higher profit rate in long term investment (99 testing days). Trading System I and II have different performance under various prediction models. Adaptive RPCL-CLP seems to be superior to RPCL-ART in term of prediction accuracy and profit gains. Nevertheless, RPCL-ART forms fewer categories than Adaptive RPCL-CLP. In conclusion, as experiment results show, Adaptive RPCL-CLP has better performance than the other models concerned in this paper.

References

[1] L. Xu, A. Krzyzak and E. Oja, "Rival Penalized Competitive Learning for Clustering Analysis, RBF Net, and Curve Detection," *IEEE Transactions on Neural Networks*, vol. 4, pp. 636-649, 1993.

[2] Y.M. Cheung, Z.H. Lai and L. Xu, "Adaptive Rival Penalized Competitive Learning and Combined Linear Predictor with Application to Financial Investment," *to appear on Proc. of Conference on Computational Intelligence for Financial Engineering (CIFEr)*, 1996.

[3] W.M. Leung, Y.M. Cheung, Z.H. Lai and L. Xu, "Rival Penalized Competitive Learning Enforced ART Model For Stock and Foreign Exchange Prediction," *submitted to World Congress on Neural Networks (WCNN'96)*, 1996.

[4] Y.M. Cheung, W.M. Leung and L. Xu, "A RPCL-CLP Architecture for Financial Time Series Forecasting," *Proc. of IEEE International Conference on Neural Networks (ICNN'95)*, 1995, pp. 829-832.

[5] Y.M. Cheung, W.M. Leung and L. Xu, "Hybrid ARTTSP and Mixture of Multi-Models for Foreign Exchange Rate Prediction," *Proc. of International Conference on Neural Information Processing (ICONIP'95)*, 1995, vol. 1, pp. 429-432.

[6] W.M. Leung, Y.M. Cheung and L. Xu, "Fuzzy ARTTSP: Application of Adaptive Resonance Theory on Non-Stationary Financial Time Series Prediction," *Proc. of International Conference on Neural Information Processing (ICONIP'95)*, 1995, vol. 1, pp. 449-452.

[7] G.A. Carpenter, S. Grossberg, and D.B. Rosen, "Fuzzy ART: Fast Stable Learning and Categorization of Analog Patterns by an Adaptive Resonance System," *Neural Networks*, vol. 4, pp. 759-771, 1991.

[8] L. Xu, M.I. Jordan and G.E. Hinton, "A Modified Gating Network for the Mixtures of Experts Architecture," *Proc. of World Congress on Neural Networks (WCNN'94)*, 1994, vol. 2, pp. 405-410.

Portfolio Selection with Self-Organizing Maps

Ching-Feng Lee†, Wen-Pin Tai‡

† Graduate Institute of Business Administration,
National Taiwan University, Taipei, Taiwan
Email: d1701014@ccsun1.cc.ntu.edu.tw
‡ Dept. Computer Science and Information Engineering,
National Taiwan University, Taipei, Taiwan
Email: d1506008@csie.ntu.edu.tw

Abstract— **A portfolio selection system based on the neural network approach is proposed in this work. We apply the self-organizing feature maps to the portfolio selection problem. The feature maps are utilized to approximate the investing surface for feasible portfolios. By these maps, the relationships among historical data in the investment can be explored. Based on these results, a multi-channel investment analysis system is constructed. We test this system on the stocks of 280 firms in the market. The simulation results have verified the performance of this system.**

1   Introduction

Portfolio management is important for investors to reduce the risk through investment diversification in commodities, securities, and stocks. Investors determine the optimal portfolios based on the information from the statistics. Consider the problem of selecting assets to match fixed liabilities. Investors, for example, the banks, choose the proportions to be invested with a fixed amount of money in order to achieve a desired outturns. Let the efficient portfolios be the investment proportions for high returns, low variances, and low investing prices. Many efforts have been expended to solve the efficient portfolio problem and the choice of optimal portfolios for investors (see, for example, [1][2]). However, most of them discuss the portfolio selection problem from the one-period viewpoint. Investors usually consider their investment strategies for several periods ahead. By these methods, the solutions can be obtained for each individual period separately.

In this study, a long-term portfolio selection system based on the neural network approach is proposed. It employs the self-organizing feature maps [3][4] to learn the efficient frontier of portfolios from the historical data. The feature maps are utilized to approximate the investing surface for feasible portfolios in the return-price-variance space and to offer a representation of the region of efficient portfolios for investment. Testing of the system on the stocks of 280 firms in Taiwan from 1993 through 1995 is carried out. This system has provided an effective framework for portfolio management.

2   System Structure

In this system, the portfolio models with the self-organizing feature maps are applied to the technical assistance to the asset allocation decisions for investors. Figure 1 shows the architecture of the portfolio selection system. Independent parallel investment analyses of different sets of input data are followed by the global asset allocation module. In each channel of investment analyses, data of the selected assets with the similar stochastic behaviors or with the same underlying affecting factors are processed. Different self-organizing maps which are trained to learn the features from the historical data are employed to solve the partial portfolio selection problem. Considering the size of optimal portfolios, we devise this multi-channel structure. This structure also improves the performance of the system.

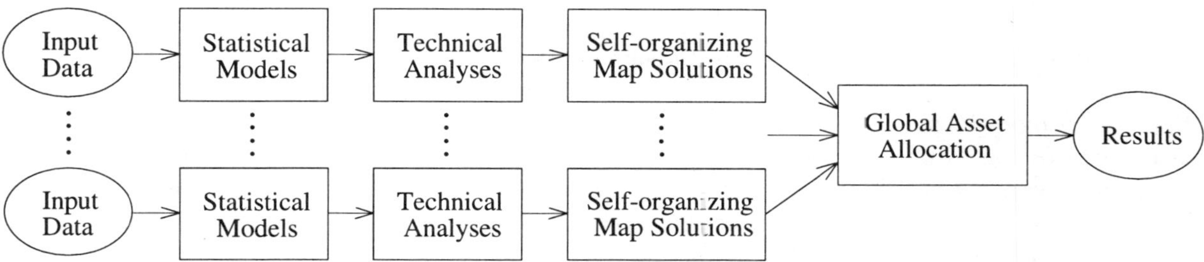

Figure 1: System architecture for portfolio management.

For the investment analysis of each set of input data, such as the time series of market prices, sequential modules based on the financial approach and the neural network approach are applied. The statistical models are used to estimate the short-term statistical values. Technical analyses (see, for example, [5]) mainly forecast the price movements from the available information for investment management. With the topographic representation of feasible portfolios on the self-organizing maps, the range for efficient management and the optimal solutions can be obtained.

In the hierarchical structure, the global asset allocation module determines the optimal portfolios of different sets of assets based on the results of investment analyses. The results of the system offer the proportions of investment diversification for investors.

The self-organizing feature maps are employed in this system to learn from historical data of investment. These maps are trained by the unsupervised competitive neural model. Many recent works have applied the neural network models to the problems of financial data analysis, modeling, and forecasting [6][7][8]. Neural networks are powerful approaches to model the non-linear processes, such as the financial processes. In this system, we make use of the neural network approach to project the multi-dimensional data onto a less-dimensional space, to explore the relationships among the input patterns, to approximate the investment function for feasible portfolios, and to provide assistance to the investment decision-making.

3 Learning Model

3.1 Training Data

Consider that there are n assets, subscripted by $i = 1, 2, \ldots, n$, selected in one set for investment analyses. Investors select assets and determine the portfolios to match fixed liability. Let the liability be subscripted by $n+1$. The expected returns are denoted by the vector $\mathbf{e} = (e_1, e_2, \ldots, e_n, e_{n+1})$ and the prices per unit of selected assets by the vector $\mathbf{p} = (p_1, p_2, \ldots, p_n, 0)$. The proportions to be invested are determined by the vector $\mathbf{x} = (x_1, x_2, \ldots, x_n, -1)$, where $x_i \geq 0$. The optimal solutions for $\mathbf{x}$ can be obtained by the portfolio selection system with the self-organizing maps.

The self-organizing maps are trained to learn the investment from past data. The data of the selected assets are collected for many periods. For each period, investment proportions for high returns, low variances, and low investing prices are concerned. Denote the investing vector by $\mathbf{z} = (E, P, V)$, where E, P, and V are the expected return, the total cost of assets, and the variance, respectively. For the portfolio $\mathbf{x}$, the values of E, P, and V can be calculated by

$$E = \mathbf{x} \cdot \mathbf{e}^t,$$

$$P = \mathbf{x} \cdot \mathbf{p}^t, \quad \text{and}$$

$$V = \frac{1}{m-1} \sum_{j=1}^{m} \left(\mathbf{x} \cdot \mathbf{r}^t - \mathbf{x} \cdot \mathbf{e}^t \right)^2, \tag{1}$$

where $\mathbf{r}$ is the vector of returns data and m is the number of data in one period.

For the long-term portfolio management, we apply the self-organizing model to learn the relationships among historical data in the return-price-variance space. The region for feasible portfolios in the return-price-variance space can be described by a quadratic surface in the three-dimensional space [9][10]. In this system, the two-dimensional feature maps are employed. The investing vectors for the past periods are collected as the training data. All input data are unlabeled for training the feature maps. The two-dimensional feature maps will be adapted to obtain the ordering relationships among the data to offer a representation of the region of efficient portfolios.

3.2   The Self-Organizing Feature Map

The self-organization neural model, biologically motivated by the cortex adaptation of brain, is a competitive learning model which transforms the input stimuli to the weights on the feature map. The unsupervised adaptation of the weight vectors associated with their neurons preserves approximately the distribution and topological relationships of the input on the feature map. The features formed on the map are topologically quantized representation, where the relationships among input data can be effectively explored. This kind of mapping allows the self-organization model to be widely applied in various domains, for example, speech recognition, robotics, and optimization problems.

Let the set of input data in the training process be Z, where $Z \subseteq R^3$. The self-organization model employs a set of neurons, generally arranged in a two-dimensional network, to process the samples from Z. Let the weight vector set be $W \subseteq R^3$. By iterative adaptation, the self-organizing map is developed to transform the input space to the two-dimensional network space. For each evolution step, an input $\mathbf{z} \in Z$ is selected randomly. The similarity matching to the input $\mathbf{z}$ is determined by the rule

$$\|\mathbf{w}_c - \mathbf{z}\| = \min_j \|\mathbf{w}_j - \mathbf{z}\|, \quad \mathbf{w}_j \in W, \tag{2}$$

where the vector $\mathbf{w}_c$ denotes the weight vector of the winning neuron c for the corresponding input vector $\mathbf{z}$.

The similarity matching is followed by the adaptation of the weight vectors. The weight vectors of all neurons in the map are updated with different values, according to the following equation

$$\Delta \mathbf{w}_j = \alpha H(D(c,j))(\mathbf{z} - \mathbf{w}_j), \tag{3}$$

where the parameter $\alpha \in [0, 1)$ is the adaptation rate, and H is the neighborhood function which is monotonously decreasing with the distance metric D in the map coordinate. The parameters in α and H influence the training results on the feature map. For good ordering results of the feature map, these values are experimentally determined during the training process.

4   The Optimal Portfolios

4.1   Interpolated Investing Vectors

The construction of the data representation by the self-organizing feature maps provides the investors the reference data for their investment. With the topographic representation of feasible portfolios on the maps, the range for efficient management and the optimal solutions can be obtained. However, the representation by the feature maps is the quantized approximation of the input space. In this representation, the weight vectors can be regarded as the sample vectors according to the input distribution. Conversion from these discrete sample vectors to the continuous investing surface is necessary for the portfolio selection problem.

Considering the similarity relationships among the input data, we apply the techniques of weighted interpolation in terms of the weight vectors to approximate this conversion. Let the desired investment which is determined with a feature map has the map coordinate $\mathbf{y}$, $\mathbf{y} \in R^2$. Denote the map coordinate of neuron j by $\mathbf{y}_j$. The vector $\mathbf{y}$ may vary continuous in R^2. For the vector $\mathbf{y}$, the mapped investing vector $\mathbf{w}(\mathbf{y})$, $\mathbf{w}(\mathbf{y}) \in R^3$, can be interpolated in terms of the weight vectors by

$$\mathbf{w}(\mathbf{y}) = \sum_{\mathbf{w}_j \in W} \beta_j \mathbf{w}_j, \tag{4}$$

where β_j is the similarity measure between $\mathbf{y}$ and $\mathbf{y}_j$ on the feature maps. A reasonable choice for β_j is

$$\beta_j \equiv \frac{\exp\left(-4\|\mathbf{y} - \mathbf{y}_j\|^2\right)}{\sum_{\mathbf{w}_j \in W} \exp\left(-4\|\mathbf{y} - \mathbf{y}_j\|^2\right)}. \tag{5}$$

Figure 2 illustrates an example for the interpolation of the investing vector $\mathbf{w}(\mathbf{y})$ by the weight vectors.

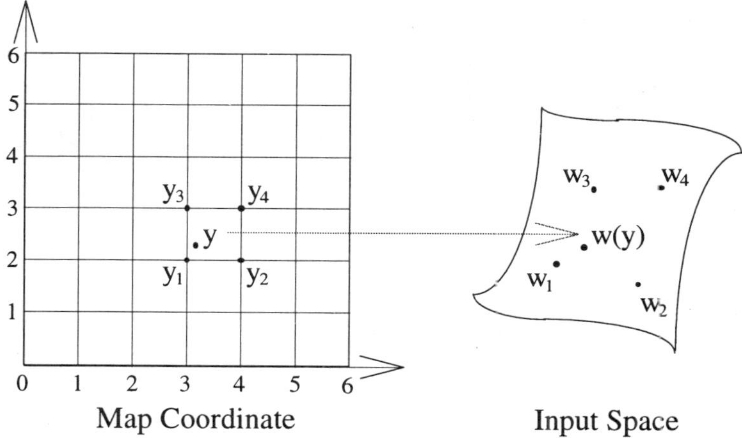

Figure 2: Weighted interpolation to approximate the conversion from the discrete weight vectors $\mathbf{w}_j$, $j = 1 \ldots 4$, to the continuous investing vectors $\mathbf{w}(\mathbf{y})$.

4.2   The Solutions Based on the Maps

After the desired investing vector $\mathbf{w}(\mathbf{y})$ is generated by interpolation using the trained feature maps, the optimal portfolio solutions can be determined by minimizing the variance subject to the constraints of E and P [10]. Solutions for the partial portfolio selection problems in the independent investment analyses are then obtained. All results are integrated and managed in the global asset allocation module. Finally, the system returns the optimal proportions of investment diversification for investors.

5   Testing on the Stocks

To test the portfolio selection system, we use a database containing stocks of 280 firms in Taiwan from January 1993 through December 1995. Weekly investment decision-making is considered, i.e., there are about 150 periods used for the tests. In each independent investment analyses, there are $25 \sim 30$ selected stocks to be diversified. Ten channels structure are constructed in this system.

In each channel of investment analysis, a two-dimensional feature map with 20×20 neurons is trained to learn the past investment. After the map has been trained, the efficient frontier of portfolios which are preferred by the investors can be explicitly visualized by the self-organizing maps. Optimal portfolio solutions based on the feature maps are then obtained.

Figure 3 (a) and (b) illustrate the training results of a self-organizing feature map for one set of 30 selected stocks. The trained weight vectors are plotted in the return-price-variance space, as shown in Figure 3 (a). Figure 3 (b) shows the efficient frontier of portfolios indicated by the self-organizing feature map. All the simulations are carried out on the PCs.

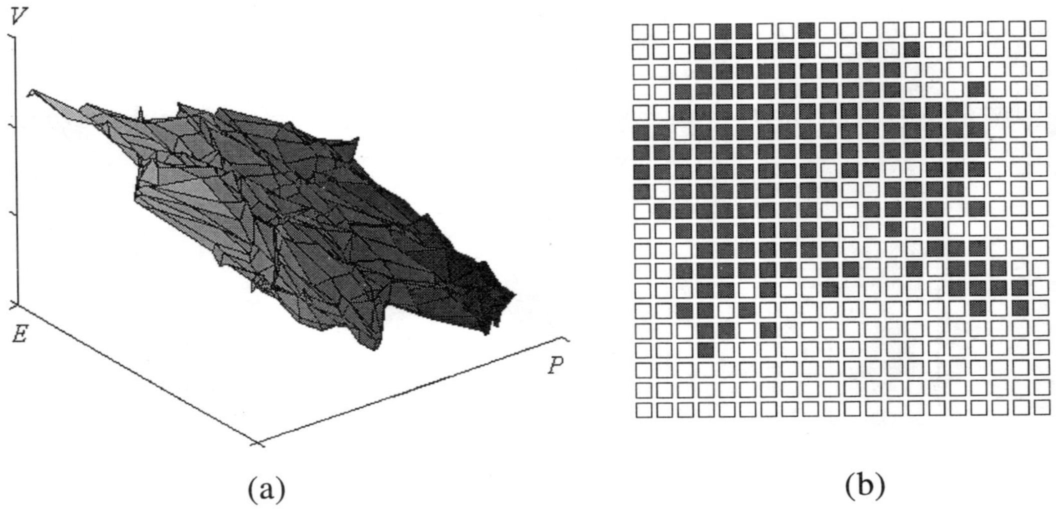

(a)   (b)

Figure 3: The training results of the self-organizing feature map for the investment analysis.

6   Discussion

6.1   Size of the Portfolios

In this proposed system, independent parallel investment analyses (see Figure 1) are devised to deal with the portfolio selection problems of different sets of assets. Data of the selected assets in each set have the similar stochastic behaviors. Optimal portfolios of the variety of assets will be determined in each investment analysis. Consider a set of n selected assets. As the value of n is increased, the risks for investment are reduced. However, the underlying factors which affect the behaviors of the selected assets are too complicated to be analyzed for large n. In addition, the larger the value of n, the higher transaction costs the investors have. Appropriate n value will lead to the better efficient portfolios.

The variance tends to be reduced rapidly with n increased from 1 and reaches the saturation value when n has the value between $10 \sim 15$ (see Chap. 7 in [11]). Each time the value of n is increased, the risk is reduced by a smaller amount. Investors do not need to select vast numbers of assets for diversification.

From the results of our testing on the stock market, the efficient portfolio investment can be obtained when around 25 stocks are included in each set of selected assets. The extra risk reduction with more than 35 stocks will be countervailed by the transaction costs. The size of the portfolios in the investment analyses of the multi-channel system is chosen as this value.

6.2 The Boundary Effect on the Feature Maps

The developed self-organizing feature maps which reflect the relationships among the past data provide the system a means to solve the optimal portfolios. In the system, the desired investing vectors can be obtained by interpolations in terms of the weight vectors. The training results on the feature maps by the self-organization will influence the solutions.

From the training results on the maps, some kind of boundary effects can be observed (see Sect 4.2 in [3]). The training borders on the maps cause the contraction of the distribution of weight vectors. The distribution of the training vectors can not be reflected accurately on the boundary areas. This effect may cause incomplete information of the past data to be preserved on the feature maps. However, we can observe that the portfolios on the boundary area have higher variances for efficient investment, as shown in the Figure 3. In most cases, too high variance is not preferred. Although the boundary effect exists on the feature maps, investors can determine their optimal efficient portfolios with the aid of this system.

References

[1] H. Levy and M. Sarnat, *Portfolio and Investment Selection: Theory and Practice*, Prentice Hall, Englewood Cliffs, 1984.

[2] R. Vince, *Portfolio Management Formulas: Mathematical Trading Methods for the Futures, Options, and Stock Markets*, Wiley, New York, 1990.

[3] T. Kohonen, "Self-organizing formation of topologically correct feature maps," *Biol. Cybern.*, vol. 43, pp. 59-69, 1982

[4] T. Kohonen, *Self-Organizing Maps.* Springer Series in Information Sciences, vol. 30, Berlin, 1995.

[5] J.J. Murphy, *Technical analysis of the futures market*, Prentice-Hall, New York, 1986.

[6] R.R. Trippi and E. Turban, *Neural Networks in Finance and Investing : Using Artificial Intelligence to Improve Real-world Performance*, Probus Pub., Chicago, 1993.

[7] D.E. Baestaens and W.M. Van den Bergh, *Neural Network Solutions for Trading in Financial Markets*, Pitman Pub., London, 1994.

[8] A.-P. Refenes, *Neural Networks in the Capital Markets*, Wiley, Chichester, 1995.

[9] A.J. Wise, "A Theoretical analysis of the matching of assets to liabilities," *J. Inst. Actuaries*, vol. 111, pp. 375-444, 1984.

[10] A.D. Wilkie, "Portfolio selection in the presence of fixed liabilities: a comment on the matching of assets to liabilities," *J. Inst. Actuaries*, vol. 112, pp. 229-278, 1985.

[11] J. Rutterford, *Introduction to Stock Exchange Investment*, Macmillan, London, 1985.

"Clearning" Neural Networks with Continuity Constraint for Prediction of Noisy Time Series

Benyang Tang, William Hsieh, and Fred Tangang

Dept. of Earth and Ocean Sciences, University of British Columbia
Vancouver, Canada, V6T 1Z4
`tang@ocgy.ubc.ca`

Abstract —Neural networks with "clearning" and continuity constraints are described. When a "clearning" neural network is trained, not only the weights, but also the input to the network are adjusted, to minimize a cost function consisting of three terms: The first term measures the difference between the network output and the data (the output constraint), the second term measures the difference between the network input and the data (the input constraint), and the third term measures the difference between the network output and the network input of the next step (the continuity constraint). Both the in-sample and out-sample tests on the Mackey-Glass time series show that the new network gives better performance than a traditional neural network when there is noise in the time series.

1   Introduction to "Clearning"

Normally, when a neural network is trained, only the network weights are adjusted to minimize a cost function which measures only the difference between the network output and the data. Input data are fed directly into the neural network without modification, implying an assumption that the input data are error free. However, in many applications involving noisy data, this assumption does not hold.

Here we use a simple curve fitting to illustrate the problem. Let $\tilde{x}^t$ and $\tilde{y}^t$ ($t=1,...,T$) be the observations of two variables. We want to use a neural network to find a functional relationship $y^t = f(x^t, \mathbf{w})$ between the two variables, where $\mathbf{w}$ are the adjustable weights.

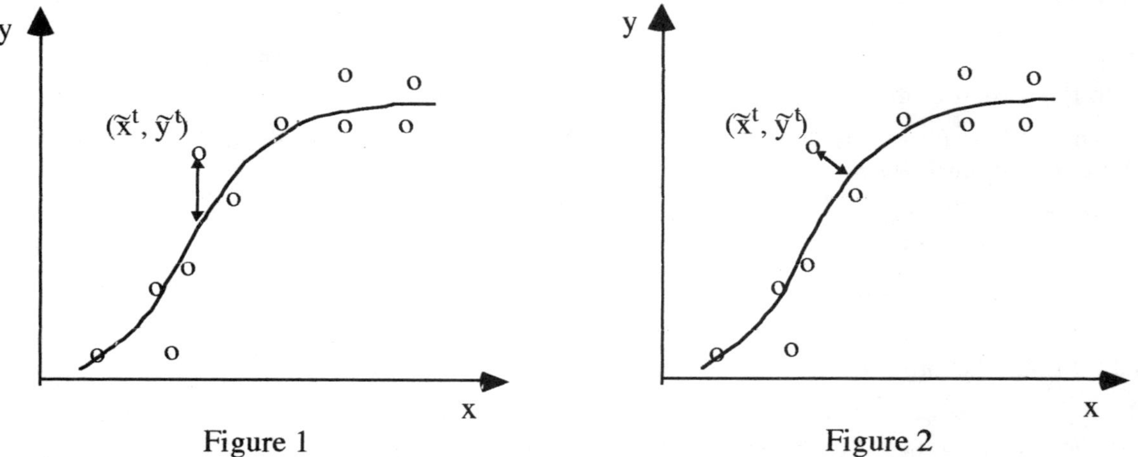

Figure 1   Figure 2

The backpropagation of a traditional neural network minimizes the following cost function,

$$J = \frac{1}{2}\sum_t \left(f(\tilde{x}^t, \mathbf{w}) - \tilde{y}^t \right)^2 , \tag{1}$$

which is the summed squares of the distance between a data point and the curve in the **vertical** direction, as indicated by the arrow line in Fig. 1. We minimize the difference between the data and the model in y direction only and do nothing in the x direction, i.e., we trust the measurement $\tilde{x}^t$ completely. If $\tilde{x}^t$ are measured very accurately, such as the case of $\tilde{x}^t$ being the time, this will not be a problem. However, in most cases, both $\tilde{x}^t$ and $\tilde{y}^t$ are subject to measurement errors. Especially for time series prediction, $\tilde{x}^t$ and $\tilde{y}^t$ are the measurements of the same variable, only at lagged times, and so should be trusted to the same degree.

For simplicity, let us now assume that both $\tilde{x}^t$ and $\tilde{y}^t$ are subject to errors of the same variance. The idea of equal trust to both $\tilde{x}^t$ and $\tilde{y}^t$ leads to a cost function

$$J = \frac{1}{2}\sum_t \left(f(x^t, \mathbf{w}) - \tilde{y}^t \right)^2 + \frac{1}{2}\sum_t (x^t - \tilde{x}^t)^2. \tag{2}$$

The minimization of the above J is the minimization of the summed squares of the distance between the data point $(\tilde{x}^t, \tilde{y}^t)$ and the curve in the direction perpendicular to the tangent of the curve, as indicated by the arrow line in Fig. 2.

The minimization of the cost function (2) is achieved by adjusting not only the weights $\mathbf{w}$, but also the model input x^t. This is similar to initialization through adjoint data assimilation in meteorology and oceanography; there the initial condition is adjusted so that the model trajectory best fits the data.

There is a price to pay for minimizing (2): There are more parameters to be adjusted ($\mathbf{w}$ and x^t), and the minimization process is usually more complicated and needs more computer resources. However, this new form of least squares through (2) has at least two advantages: 1) The curve is better fitted, because a data point affects the closest segment of the curve. The old form of least squares through (1) affects the segment of curve to its vertical direction; this can lead to bias when $\tilde{x}^t$ is subject to error, as can be shown for the case of fitting a straight line. 2) In the course of model fitting, we not only get a model $y^t = f(x^t, \mathbf{w})$, but also the model input x^t, which are generally less noisy than the observed input $\tilde{x}^t$.

We have assumed above that $\tilde{x}^t$ and $\tilde{y}^t$ have errors of the same variance. A more general form of (2) should be

$$J = \frac{\eta}{2}\sum_t \left(f(x^t, \mathbf{w}) - \tilde{y}^t \right)^2 + \frac{\kappa}{2}\sum_t (x^t - \tilde{x}^t)^2, \tag{3}$$

where $\eta = 1/\omega_{e_y}^2$, and $\kappa = 1/\omega_{e_x}^2$, with $\omega_{e_y}^2$ and $\omega_{e_x}^2$ being the variances of errors in $\tilde{y}^t$ and $\tilde{x}^t$, respectively.

The cost function (3) was first proposed by Weigend et al [1]. There the process of minimizing (3) was termed "clearning", after the words "learning" and "cleaning", meaning that the neural network learns from the data and cleans the data at the same time.

2 Continuity Constraint

Let $\tilde{d}^t$ ($t=1,...,T$) be an observed time series. A neural network $y^t = f(\mathbf{x}^t, \mathbf{w})$ is to be found to predict the time series at a lead time ℓ. A "clearning" form of cost function is

$$J = \frac{\eta}{2}\sum_t \left(y^t - \tilde{d}^{t+\ell} \right)^2 + \frac{\kappa}{2}\sum_t (x^t - \tilde{d}^t)^2. \tag{4}$$

Note that the network input $\mathbf{x}^t = [x^t, x^{t-\tau}, x^{t-2\tau}, x^{t-(d-1)\tau}]$ is the time-lagged vectors of x^t ($t=1,...,T$).

If we want to use the trained neural network to make a prediction of lead times longer than ℓ, we can apply the neural network repeatedly, feeding the neural network output as the input of the next stepping. For this purpose, we add a third term to the cost function (4) to ensure the continuity of x^t and y^t,

$$J = \frac{\eta}{2}\sum_t \left(y^t - \tilde{d}^{t+\ell} \right)^2 + \frac{\kappa}{2}\sum_t (x^t - \tilde{d}^t)^2 + \frac{\gamma}{2}\sum_t (x^{t+\ell} - y^t)^2. \tag{5}$$

Note that the third term is not identical to zero. Both $x^{t+\ell}$ and y^t are forced to be close to the very same data $\tilde{d}^{t+\ell}$ by the second and first terms, respectively. However, the quantity $\mathrm{abs}(x^{t+\ell} - y^t)$ can be as big as the sum of $\mathrm{abs}(y^t - \tilde{d}^{t+\ell})$ and $\mathrm{abs}(x^{t+\ell} - \tilde{d}^{t+\ell})$, if $x^{t+\ell}$ and y^t happen to be at the opposite sides of $\tilde{d}^{t+\ell}$. This is not good if the trained network is used for repeated feeding forward. So the third term is there to force $x^{t+\ell}$ to be close to y^t.

The cost function (5) has three terms. We call the first term as output constraint, the second as input constraint, and the third as continuity constraint.

3   Test on the Mackey-Glass Time Series

The Mackey-Glass time series was generated by the delay differential equation [2]

$$\frac{d}{dt}x(t) = a\,\frac{x(t-\tau)}{1+x^{10}(t-\tau)} - b\,x(t) \tag{6}$$

with a=0.2, b=0.1 and τ=17. The time series has been used as a standard benchmark [3] [4]. Noise of normal distribution with a standard deviation of 0.2 was added to the time series. The original Mackey-Glass time series has a standard deviation of 0.226.

The inputs of neural networks are x(t), x(t–1), ..., x(t–24), and the target is x(t+1). The hidden layer has 50 units. The data from t=100 to t=600 were used for training for 500 epochs.

The lead time of the neural network is 1. Predictions of longer lead times up to 84 were made by iteration, feeding the output of the neural network as the input of the next stepping. During the training, the error of the multiple-step prediction against the training data was monitored. This multiple-step error fluctuated during the training, although the one-step error measured by the first term of the cost function (5) decreased monotonously. The final trained network was picked at the epoch where the error of the 84-step prediction is the lowest. It was found that this 84-step in-sample error is a good indication of the out-sample test error.

Before the training started, the weights of the network were initialized randomly. Different initializations (with different seeds for random number generation) usually led to different networks, with slightly different multiple-step prediction errors. In each of the model described bellow, three trainings with different initializations were made, and only the result of best one among the three is given.

The performance of a neural network depends on the parameters η, κ, and γ in the cost function (5). The parameters η=1 and κ=γ=0 corresponds to the traditional neural network. A series of experiments with different η, κ, and γ were performed. Table 1 shows the relative RMS error of the in-sample prediction against the Mackey-Glass time series without noise. Note that this noiseless time series was not available during the training.

	η	κ	γ	0-step error	18-step error	36-step error	54-step error	72-step error	84-step error
A	1	0	0	0.89	0.40	0.42	0.58	0.58	0.46
B	1	1	1	0.63	0.54	0.64	0.71	0.71	0.58
C	1	1	0	0.88	0.69	0.72	0.80	0.88	0.81
D	1	0	1	0.67	0.78	0.94	1.03	1.08	1.19
E	0	1	1	0.50	0.40	0.37	0.44	0.44	0.41
F	1	2	2	0.58	0.45	0.52	0.63	0.63	0.51
G	0	1	2	0.51	0.41	0.36	0.44	0.47	0.50
H	0	2	1	0.51	0.42	0.36	0.43	0.45	0.43

Table 1. In-sample prediction errors.

It is obvious that Model E (with η=0, κ=γ=1) is better than the others. To make sure that the better prediction of Model E is not due to a lucky random initialization, Models A and E were both retrained ten more times, each with different initializations. It was found that the best of the ten trainings of Model E is still much better than the best of the ten trainings of Model A.

Out-sample tests with data within t=[700, 1200] were made. For the out-sample test of the "clearning" models, the following procedure was used: The weights, which were obtained during the model training, were fixed, and the same backpropagation procedure was used to adjust the 50 input points immediately before the initial time of the prediction. This is the training for the input, and there were 500 those trainings, one for the prediction of each data time in the test data. The input trainings were short, each usually requiring less than 30 epochs. A prediction starts from the network output obtained during the input training, instead from the noisy data. Table 2 shows the relative RMS error of the out-sample prediction against the noiseless Mackey-Glass time series for Models A and E.

	η	κ	γ	0-step error	18-step error	36-step error	54-step error	72-step error	84-step error
A	1	0	0	0.92	0.53	0.54	0.55	0.77	0.66
E	0	1	1	0.52	0.51	0.52	0.54	0.63	0.60

Table 2. Out-sample prediction errors.

It can be seen that the "clearning" Model E is better than the traditional Model A in the out-sample test, especially for the 72-step and 84-step predictions. The difference in the 18-, 36-, and 54-step predictions are only marginal.

Note that in both the in-sample and out-sample tests, Model A has fairly large errors in the initial condition when compared with the noiseless Mackey-Glass data. This is because Model A takes the noisy raw data as the initial condition. In contrast, the "clearning" models used the adjusted data as the initial condition, which were closer to the noiseless Mackey-Glass data, even though the noiseless data were not used in the training.

4   Discussions

Both the in-sample and out-sample tests on the noisy Mackey-Glass data indicate that the "clearning" model is better than the traditional model. This result is significant since in most time series applications noises are present in the data. The "clearning" network requires more programming effort and some fine tuning of the parameters η, κ, and γ. The gain in prediction skill may depend on the noise level of the data. For the noiseless Mackey-Glass time series, the traditional network gave slightly better performance than the "clearning" network. The edge of the "clearning" network showed up when the noise level reached to a standard deviation of 0.1.

The tests of the new method was only done on the Mackey-Glass time series. A more definite conclusion still requires careful tests on more data sets. Comparing two methods is not an easy task as it seems to be. The parameters that have to be considered are numerous: weight initializations, the stopping point in the training, the selection of the input, the network structure, the parameters η, κ and γ in the cost function, etc.

Intuitively, one would guess that η and κ should be chosen to be inversely proportional to the error variances in the target data and input data, respectively, as in (3). It is surprising to see that the best models turned out to be those without the first term in the cost function (5) (Models E, G and H). It remains to be seen whether this is also true for other data. At present time we are still seeking explanation.

In the beginning of this study, the inputs were chosen to be $x(t)$, $x(t-6)$, $x(t-12)$, $x(t-18)$, and the target to be $x(t+6)$, following [4]. Thus the trained models had a lead time of 6. It was found later that the inputs and target described in Section 3 produced much better models, both for the traditional networks and the "clearning" networks. A close inspection revealed that more inputs at the consecutive times help smooth out the noise in the predictions.

The "clearning" model has been applied to the forecasting of the climatic condition of the tropical Pacific Ocean. The seasonal forecasts are issued quarterly in NOAA's Experimental Long-Lead Forecast Bulletin, and monthly in our web page: http://www.ocgy.ubc.ca/clim.pred/NINO3.html

References

[1]   A.S. Weigend *et al.*, "Clearning," *Neural Networks in Financial Engineering*, P., Y. Abu-Mostafa, J. E. Moody, and A. S. Weigend (Eds.), London, October 1995, in press.

[2]   M.C. Mackey and L. Glass, "Oscillation and chaos in physiological control system," Science, Vol. 197, pp. 287, 1977.

[3]   J.D Farmer, and J.J. Sidorowich, "Predicting chaotic time series," *Phys. Rev. Lett.*, Vol. 59, pp. 845-848, 1987.

[4]   E. Hartman and J.D. Keeler, "Predicting the future: advantages of semilocal units," *Neural Computation*, Vol. 3, pp566-578, 1991.

Improving Long Term Time Series Prediction
Using a Modified Influence Function

Li. H. Chen and Poy B. Tan
School of Electrical and Electronic Engineering
Nanyang Technological University, Nanyang Avenue,
Singapore 639798, Republic of Singapore.
Phone : +65-799-1207   Fax : +65-791-2687
E-mail : elhchen@ntuix.ntu.ac.sg, ea1814168@ntuvax.ntu.ac.sg

Abstract - An outlier is defined as one associated with a large error between actual and target output of a system. To ensure robustness against outliers during neural network training for time series prediction, the concept of influence function is investigated. A new influence function : Mean Log Squared Error (MLSE) is applied and the weight updating mechanism modified accordingly. To demonstrate the virtue of this setup, a MLP network with its input layer tap-delayed is trained to perform iterated forecasting on a complex chaotic time series. Preliminary results show reliable long term predictions.

1. INTRODUCTION

Conventional neural network models usually employ Mean Squared Error (MSE) cost function as the error metric. This results in a Least Mean Square (LMS) updating strategy. Liano [1] argued that under moderately noisy environments, outliers in the training set can disrupt effective learning and consequently contribute to poor generalization. This is especially so for conventional supervised learning methodologies such as LMS algorithm. For optimum LMS performance, the underlying assumptions requiring normality and independence of the training data or requiring normal or Gaussian error distribution must be satisified [1].

However, in many real world tasks such as time series prediction, outliers are commonplace in the training set. Time series data often contain outliers possibly arising from noisy surroundings or from its intrinsic dynamics, thus violating those essential hypotheses. There are many instances of outliers' occurrence in time series e.g. outliers appear as readings taken on weekends or public holidays in Electric Load Forecasting [2], observations near reinsertion phase in a far-infrared Laser laboratory experiment [3]. In these cases, using LMS strategy in neural networks to perform weight adaptation will definitely be counter-productive.

To overcome the above drawback, the notion of influence function from the field of statistics [1], [4] is applied to time series problems. We propose to replace the MSE metric with Mean Log Squared Error (MLSE) for networks with time delays. This function has a desirable attribute such that big residual errors emerging from outliers will not amplify its weightage with respect to other error signals. This point will be elucidated more in Section 2 when we provide a brief overview on influence functions. Correlation between learning efficiency and influence functions will also be hypothesized. In Section 3, we describe the basic network architecture for robust time series prediction and its incorporation of the new influence function. Simulations are carried out to illustrate and exemplify the concept of the modified influence function in time series. The results obtained are also compared alongside some of other existing neural network methods. Finally a conclusion is given in Section 4.

2. INFLUENCE FUNCTION CONCEPTS

The goal of gradient descent during training is to minimize the objective function E. It can be expressed as :

$$E = \frac{1}{N \times M} \sum_{p=1}^{N} \sum_{k=1}^{M} \rho(r_k^p) \tag{1}$$

where $r_k^p = t_k^p - \hat{y}_k^p$ represents the residual error between target t_k^p and network output $\hat{y}_k^p$ for the kth output unit in the pth training pattern, M is the number of visible output units, N is the total number of training examples, $\rho(\cdot)$ is symmetrical about r_k^p. Without loss of generality, we shall consider the case of M = 1, resulting in summation over k to be dropped from Eq. (1). This corresponds to a uni-variate time series. We shall also refer to r_1^p simply as r^p and so on for t and $\hat{y}$.

To understand how the choice of influence function affect training efficiency, we must look at the gradient descent equation :

$$\Delta \widetilde{w} = -\eta \frac{\partial E}{\partial \widetilde{w}} = -\frac{\eta}{N} \sum_{p=1}^{N} \frac{\partial \rho(r^p)}{\partial r^p} \frac{\partial r^p}{\partial \widetilde{w}} = -\frac{\eta}{N} \sum_{p=1}^{N} \frac{\partial \rho(r^p)}{\partial r^p} \frac{\partial r^p}{\partial \hat{y}^p} \frac{\partial \hat{y}^p}{\partial \widetilde{w}} \tag{2}$$

In the field of robust statistics, influence function can be denoted as:

$$\Phi(r^p) = \frac{\partial \rho(r^p)}{\partial r^p} \tag{3}$$

It can be interpreted from Eq. (2) that gradient descent is a weighted sum of N error signals originated from the deviations between N network estimators $\hat{y}^p$ and their targets t^p. The form of the influence function plays an important part as it moderates the N error gradients. In the context of time series predictions, $\hat{y}^p$ can be interpreted as $\hat{y}(p)$, i.e. the network estimate at time step p. Hence, the summation is over the most recent N observations from the training set.

An outlier is defined generally as one associated with a large residual error between $\hat{y}^p$ and t^p. The huge magnitude of error in an outlier would normally arouse suspicion that this particular pattern might not actually belong to the underlying dynamics. However, in most of the time, they are valid data contaminated by noise or genuine data as a manifestation of critical phase changes or transitions. For MSE metric,

$$\rho(r^p) = \tfrac{1}{2}(r^p)^2 \Rightarrow \Phi(r^p) = r^p \tag{4}$$

Thus $\Phi(r^p)$ is linearly proportional to r^p. If the pth pattern is an outlier, its weightage will be relatively much larger compared to the other (N-1) patterns. Consequently, the error-correction signals contributed by the other (N-1) patterns are masked out. This phenomenon effectively eradicates the influence of the remaining (N-1) data during learning. (See Eq. (2)).

To circumvent this situation, we aim to suppress the influence at large r^p. A particularly suitable influence function for implementation under neural network framework was studied in [1]. It was known as Mean Log Squared Error (MLSE).

$$\rho(r^p) = \log(1 + \tfrac{1}{2}(r^p)^2) \Rightarrow \Phi(r^p) = \frac{r^p}{1 + \tfrac{1}{2}(r^p)^2} \tag{5}$$

Unlike MSE, it does not amplify the residual error caused by outliers. Symmetricity and continuity properties of MSE are retained. Moreover, it behaves almost identical to MSE for small r^p values. The corresponding updating strategy can be derived from Eq. (2), Eq. (3) and Eq. (5) and called Least Mean Log Square (LMLS).

3. SIMULATIONS

To verify the helpfulness in using LMLS over LMS, we conduct experiments on a time series prediction problem. A Multi-Layered Perceptron (MLP) with delayed taps on the input layer only was used [5]. Linear activation function is used on the output layer. This further underlines the importance of picking a suitable influence function based on the arguments regarding outliers as the errors are unbounded. Figure 1 depicts the basic architecture used.

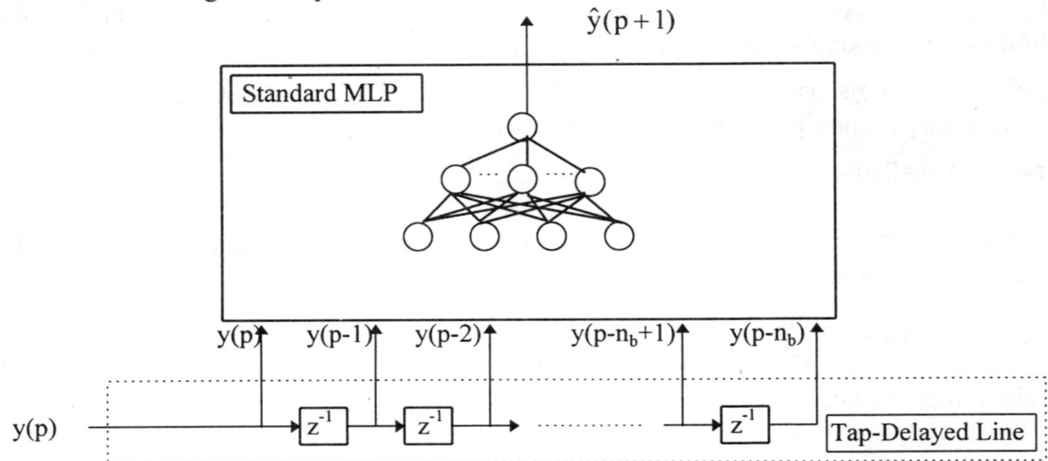

Figure 1 : MLP with Tap-Delayed Line on Input Layer

The task selected is a well known problem in time series prediction (see Fig2). It originated from a chaotic intensity pulsation of a far-infrared laser in a laboratory experiment. Given the first 1000 discrete points of the time series, we attempted to predict the next 400 continuations. Two outliers are evident at around $t \approx 180$ and $t \approx 600$. The onset of these two points signify beginning of reinsertion periods and are crucial information for learning. Readers can refer to [3] for details.

To provide a baseline for comparison, an on-line version of Backpropagation using LMS algorithm with the same MLP tap-delayed structure (MLP-LMS) was also used to train the same task. We also compare our results against that of Wan's Temporal Backpropagation algorithm using FIR synapses (TB-FIR) arranged in feedforward, layered manner [6]. Another set of results was obtained by using a promising structure called Local Recurrent Global Feedforward (LRGF) network proposed by Back [7]. Table 1 summarizes the results obtained. All simulations were performed until maximum epoch was reached or training error fell below a pre-selected tolerance. Fig.3 to Fig.6 shows the prediction performance of the four approaches respectively.

	MLP-LMLS	MLP-LMS	TB-FIR	LRGF
Architecture	1-20-1	1-20-1	1-12-12-1	1-15-1
Delay Taps	30:0 (M)[+]	30:0 (M)[+]	25:5:5 (M)[+]	25:15(M), 5:0(A)[+]
Total Weight Parameters	641	641	1105	721
Training Epochs Performed	30000	14150	30000	30000
Prediction NMSE[*] for 100 time-steps	0.8394	1.3424	0.0551	1.2228
Prediction NMSE[*] for 400 time-steps	1.6074	3.5103	2.8004	2.8568

Table 1 : Results for Time Series Prediction Task

Notes:-

+ : (M) denotes the Moving Average (MA) filter order, (A) denotes the AutoRegressive filter order.

* : $\text{NMSE} = \dfrac{1}{\sigma^2 N} \sum_{p=1}^{N} (t^p - \hat{y}^p)^2$, where σ^2 is the variance of the true continuation $t(k)$ over N time steps

Figure 2 : Training and Testing Set

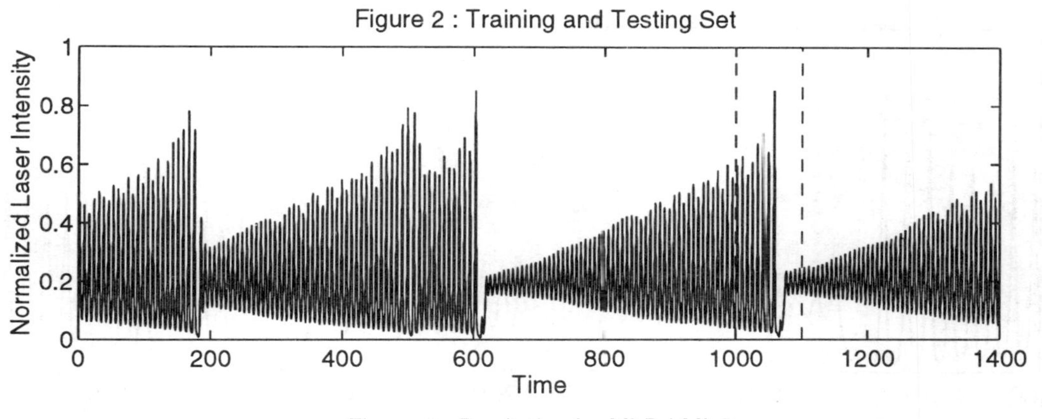

Figure 3 : Prediction by MLP-LMLS

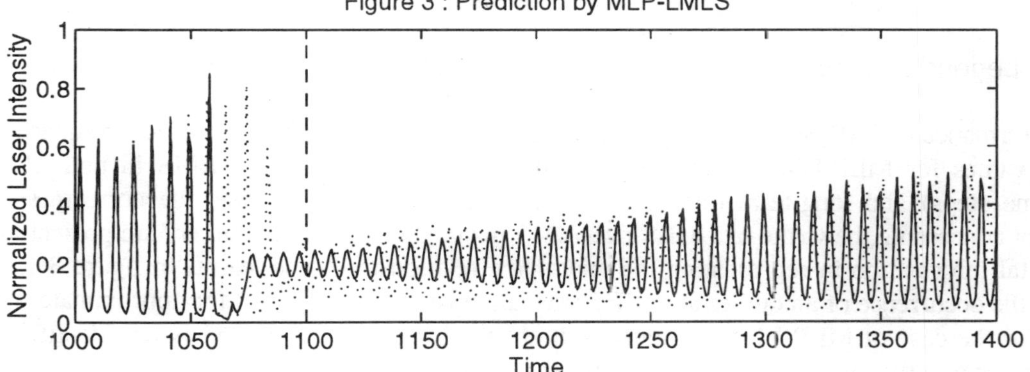

Figure 4 : Prediction by MLP-LMS

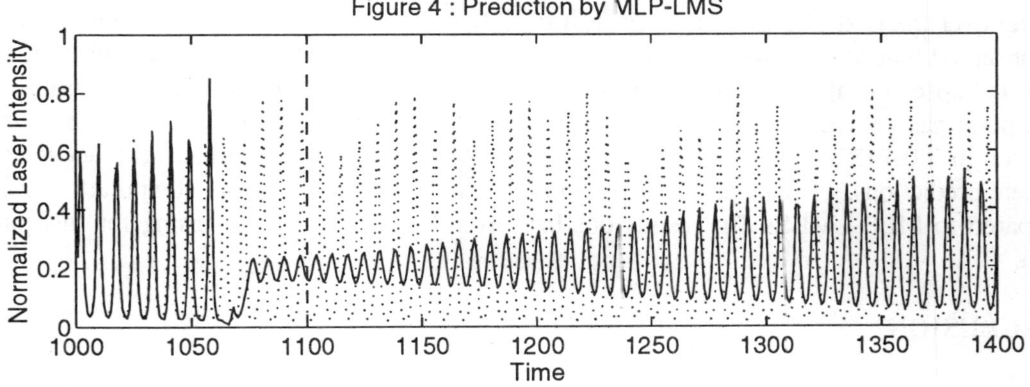

Figure 5 : Prediction by LRGF

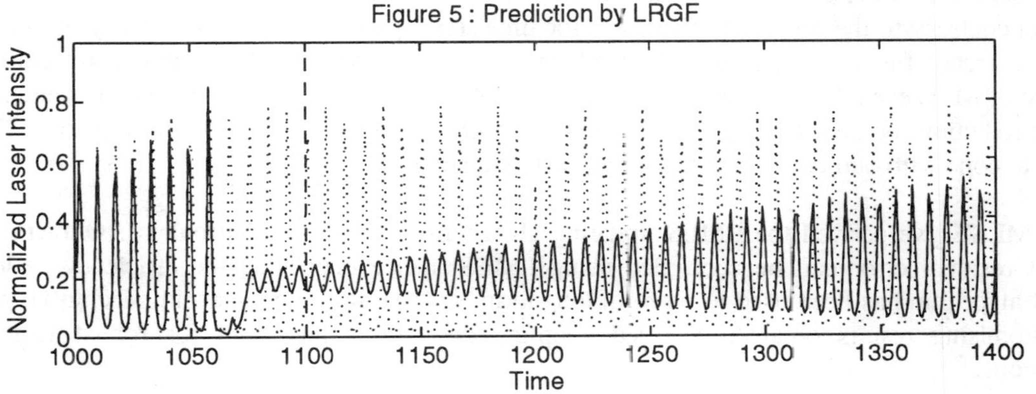

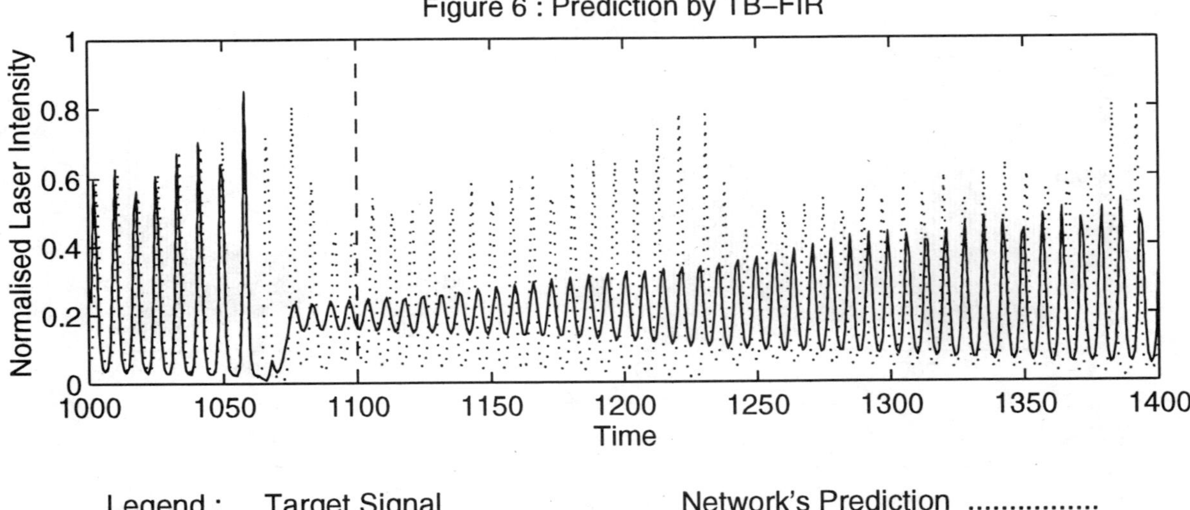

The performance of LMLS using the MLP architecture obviously surpasses its LMS counterpart. The NMSE values for MLP-LMLS shows significant improvement over MLP-LMS in both short-term (100 time steps) and long-term (400 time steps) forecasting. This verifies the correctness of our argument concerning the virtue of LMLS over LMS in situations whereby outliers are present and they carry vital information in representing the underlying relationship to be learnt. In figure 3 for MLP-LMLS, the occurrence of an outlier at t=1065 was anticipated albeit delayed for approximately 25 time steps. For the case of MLP-LMS in figure 4, it shows that outlier at t=1065 is not identified, hence failing to capture the overall pulsating waveform in the long run.

Although TB-FIR yields far superior performance for short-term prediction, its performance degrades drastically over the next 300 time steps as seen from figure 6. Comparing figure 3 against figure 6, it can be observed that MLP-LMLS still manages to reliably reproduce the amplitude pulsation after the intensity collapse. On the other hand, TB-FIR fails to reconstruct the general waveform after the collapse point has passed. In this case, an occurrence of the outlier at the point of collapse introduced gross error in TB-FIR's prediction since it used the MSE metric. This affects the accuracy of its subsequent predictions. TB-FIR also requires more memory and perform more computations per epoch as compared to MLP-LMLS. The results obtained from LRGF are not promising for this particular problem.

4. CONCLUSION

In this paper, we have discussed the use of an alternative Objective Function E: Mean Log Squared Error in contrary to the normal MSE metric for time series prediction. A simple analysis through the use of influence function suggests that MLSE is more robust when tackling outliers in training data. The use of MSE eventually results in erratical gradient computations, hence impeding learning. In time series prediction, outliers can be omni-present and they may represent critical information. Thus the ability to cope with outliers is essential in this task domain.

Using MLSE, we derived the LMLS updating algorithm for time series problems. Outliers causing deviant residual error can be controlled using LMLS, hence improving the efficiency of learning. LMLS algorithm has been used to perform long-term forecasting in a real-world benchmark problem. The promising results obtained justified adopting the LMLS algorithm for robust and reliable prediction.

REFERENCES

[1] K. Liano, "A Robust Approach to Supervised Learning in Neural Network", in Proceedings of IEEE ICNN, Vol. 1, pp 513-516, IEEE Press, 1994.

[2] D. C. Park, M. A. El-Sharkawi, R. J. Marks II, L. E. Atlas, M. J. Damborg, "Electric Load Forecasting Using An Artificial Neural Network", IEEE Transactions on Power Systems, pp. 442-449, Vol. 6, No. 2, May 1991, IEEE Press.

[3] A. S. Weigend, N. A. Gershenfeld, "Time Series Prediction : Forecasting the Future and Understanding the Past", pp. 1-70, Addison-Wesley, 1993.

[4] P. J. Huber, "Robust Statistics", John Wiley & Sons, New York, 1981.

[5] J. L. Hudson, M. Kube, R. A. Adomaitis, I. G. Kevrekidis, A. S. Lapedes, R. M. Farber, "Nonlinear Signal Processing and System Identification : Applications to Time Series from Electrochemical Reactions", Chemical Engineering Science, pp 2075-2081, Vol. 45, No. 8, 1990.

[6] E. A. Wan, "Time Series Prediction by Using a Connectionist Network with Internal Delay Lines", in Times Series Prediction : Forecasting the Future and Understanding the Past, Eds. A. S. Weigend, N. A. Gershenfeld, pp 195-217, Addison-Wesley, 1993,

[7] A. D. Back, "New Techniques for Nonlinear System Identification: A Rapproachment Between Neural Networks and Linear Systems", Ph.D. Thesis, University of Queensland, Australia, 1992.

Study on Flood/Drought predicting through Neuron Network Method Composed of Time—Series Continuation and Related External Variables[1]

Jin Long[1)]   Lou Ying[2)]

[1)] Jiangsu Meteorological Institute, Bei—ji—guo, No. 2 Nanjing 210008, China
[2)] Jiangsu Institute of Climate Application, Nanjing 210009, China

Abstract

The paper concerns a flood/drought prediction model involving the continuation of time series of a predictand and physical factors influening its change as well. Attempt was made to construct a model by the neuron network scheme for the nonlinear mapping relation based on multi—input and single output. The model is found of steadily higher predictive accuracy by testing the output from one and multiple stepwise predictions against observations and comparing the results to those from a traditional statistical model.

Keywords   flood/drought prediction, mixed model, nonlinear mapping, neuron network

I. INTRODUCTION

China suffers monsoon climate—related disasters, especially flood/drought that occur frequently. Therefore, medium—and long—term predictions of wetness/dryness are subject of interest for their the prevention and reduction in agriculture. It is common practice, however, that rainfall or its departure is used as a predictand in current research and operationally[1]. Attempt is made to construct a model with a predictand based on soil humidity as a comprehensive indicator of water regime of crops with the aim to fighting floods/droughts and management of water resources.

II. PRINCIPLES BEHIND THE MIXED MODEL

2.1 Structure of the Model for Predicting Floods/Droughts

At present, statistical technique remains dominant in operational forecasting the wetness/drynees on a long—and a medium—range basis in a meteorological context. Two methods in widespread used are multivariate analysis and time series analysis. The common model based on regression in multivariate analysis has the form

$$Y = \beta_0 + \beta_1 x_1 + \beta_2 x_2 + \cdots\cdots \beta_m x_m \tag{1}$$

where Y is the predictand, x_i the previous—period predictor, β_j the regression coefficient, with $i = j = 1, 2, \cdots\cdots, m$ and ε white noise. Another kind of time series analysis has focus on the predictand itself with reference to "time domain". The common form of the autoregression model AR(P) is given by

$$y_t = B_1 y_{t-1} + B_2 y_{t-2} + \cdots\cdots B_p y_{t-p} + \varepsilon_t \tag{2}$$

where y_t is the predictand's series, B_i the model's coefficient and ε_t white noise. Model (1) is based on the idea that the future state comes from changes in previous—period pertinent factors whilst model (2) relates the future state to previous condition of the very predictand. In fact, for generalized series analysis the 1D time series has its future value dependent on the past through a recurrent relation, namely

$$Y_t = F(Y_{t-1}, Y_{t-2}, \cdots\cdots Y_{t-p}) \tag{3}$$

Likewise, generalized regression analysis can be expressed as

$$Y_t = F(X_1, X_2, \cdots\cdots X_m) \tag{4}$$

---

① This study is Supported by the Proving Natural Science Foundation of Jiangsu

Models (1) and (2) are now in widespread use for flood/drought prediction. However, analysis of medium—/long—term weather process associated with these calamities shows that since the affecting factors are many and combined in a complicated fashion, no fully deterministic equation can give quantitative description and prediction, and the model may not be good enough to depend only on pertinent external factors and determine their occurrence in advance, which may be parasitic utterly on the previous state. It is hence believed that flood/drought prediction may be given by a mixed model involving the previous regime and external variables which most likely is not necessarily linear. If noise contained in the new type of model presented is assumed to be inherent in the original series, then we have a model of generalized matrix form

$$Y_t = \Phi(X_i, Y_{t-1}, Y_{t-2}, \cdots\cdots Y_{t-p}) \tag{5}$$

where X_i, Y_{t-1}, Y_{t-2}, $\cdots\cdots$, Y_{t-p} are all culumn vectors. Denote Φ to be nonlinear mapping from input to output. We shall now deal with the problems as to how to approximate (5) and its possibility to forecast these disasters.

2. 2 Model Establishment and Nonlinear Mapping Realization

Ref.[2]. indicated that flood/drought affect crops through the content of soil humidity (SH). Study of 1D SH series shows that SH at an instant, t, is substantially influenced by the previous regime at $t-1$, $t-2$, etc. And the physical process is understandable, meaning that greater SH at $t-1$ $t-2$, $\cdots\cdots$ will produce stronger evaporation, other conditions being equal, resulting in more water lost, and v. v. Besides, analysis by the SH balance equation reveals that previous rainfall will directly affect subsequent SH; change in sunshine strength has effect, too, by altering the evaporation deoeted by the thermal terms. It is clear from the arguments that change in SH essential to crop growth bears a relation to some meteorological elements as well as the previous SH, a fact that agrees with our considerations in making the mixed model (5) and serves as the basis. The next task is now to make (5) have the function of nonlinear mapping Φ.

The 1980s saw the achievements in the research into information processing in human brain based on neurological progress and the science of computers, and numerous artificial neuron network technology for processing large—scale nonlinear parallel distributed message has since achieved considerable advances in many fields of learning[3,4]. And the feedforward, or BP, network[5], though having some limitations, is still in wide use, representing a kind of nonlinear mapping from multiple input to single output or a set of output, and, in particular, the mapping is realized without the knowledge of the internal structure of the study system but such a structure can be obtained through the teacher's learning/training done of observed sample for simulation with the aid of the BP technique, which provides a theoretically sound basis for preparing the mixed—type model.

III. FLOOD/DROUGHT PREDICTION WITH VERIFICTAION

3. 1 Model Establishment for Prediction

The flood/drought prediction model based on (5) is a 3—layer BP network, one layer being for input and the other for output with the hidden one in between. Nodes of the neighboring layers are joined by a connection weighing coefficient and Sigmiod function serves as the node function. The BP—offered training of a fed matrix is actually an iteration for the revision of the coefficient and threshold value, a step for minimizing the squared error of the sample, viz.,

$$e = 0.5 \sum_{t=1i}^{T} \sum_{i=1}^{P} (z_i - d_i)^2 \tag{6}$$

where z_i denotes the output from the i—th unit in the output layer, d_i the expected output of the unit and T the volume of a sample set. (6) is for nonlinear optimization and solved usually through gradient descent. For detatils of the BP's training algorithm and flow chart of calculation the reader is referred to Ref.[6].

The decade SH is taken as the predictand for (5) in the context of SH averaged over $0-50$ cm soil for January 1992 to March 1995 (total of 117 decades) from Xuzhou Agromteorological Station, Jiangsu with the subsequent data used for test. Continuation is made of the 1D time series scalar to construct part of the date for preparing model (5). The observed SH 1D sequence has the form

$$Y(t_1),\ Y(t_2)\cdots\cdots Y(t_n) \tag{7}$$

which is then extended into a multi—dimensional series by means of the time lag coefficient τ. We thus get

$$\begin{cases} Y(t_1),\ Y(t_2)\cdots\cdots Y(t_n) \\ Y(t_1+\tau),\ Y(t_2+\tau)\cdots\cdots Y(t_n+\tau) \\ \cdots\cdots \\ Y(t_1+k\tau),\ Y(t_2+k\tau)\cdots\cdots Y(t_n+k\tau) \end{cases} \tag{8}$$

the last of which is taken as the column vector on the lhs. of (5), the others as those on its rhs. In establishing the model the 1D SH data is extended into 6D series, leading to the fed matrix—form sample size $N=112$. Further, following the considerations in Subsec. 2. 2, the mid February 1992—mid March 1995 decade mean rainfall and sunshine duration ($N=112$, one decade ahead of the SH data) from the Station are taken as another two column vectors on the rhs of (5). Thus we have a BP—type learning matrix with x_1, x_2, y_{t-5}, y_{t-4}, $\cdots\cdots$, y_{t-1} as input and y_t as expected output.

To meet the conditions of Sigmiod function, the constructed learning matrix after it has been normalized is put on the input points of the BP network (7 input nodes and 1 output node). After adjusting the model the last two decade (early to mid April 1995) of the sample size are predicted for SH with the analysis indicating that, with the learning (momentum) factor taken as 0. 7 (0. 9), the number of hidden nodes as 9 and convergence error of 0. 003, the forecasting error is kept steadily small. On this basis, further experiments were made with these parmeter's values.

3. 2 Analysis of Predictions

To objectively investigate the predictive ability of the established model, 20 decade SH predictions were prepared for spring to summer 1995 with the model and parameter values, followed by comparison to observations. Error analysis from one—step prediction (one decade in advance)in Table 1 shows the effectiveness to be satisfactory. For the 20 forecasts, the maximum (minimum) relative error (RE) is 26. 4%(0. 5%), with the mean of 8. 03%. If the relative error (prediction/observation)$<$10% is taken as a criterion of successful forecast, the accuracy reaches 70% and for the corresponding climatic predictions (only the mean given), the probability of prediction failure amounts to 70%. By use of the expression for residual sum of squares

$$SSE=\sum_{j=1}^{m}(y_j-\hat{y}_j)^2 \tag{9}$$

further calculation can be made of

$$C_1=\frac{SSE_1-SSE_2}{SSE_1} \tag{10}$$

to find out the difference in accuracy between the climatic and Model (5) predictions. In (10) SEE_1 and SEE_2 are the residual sum of squares for 20 climatic forecasts and 20 Model (5) predictions, respectively to that

$$C_1=\frac{438.\ 50-104.\ 74}{438.\ 50}=76.\ 1\% \tag{11}$$

which indicates that the accuracy of Model (5) results is 76. 1% higher than that of its counterparts.

For the experimental predictions with tests, the 20 decade—to—decade forecasts were constructed in the identical conditions of the model structure, input, output, number of hidden nodes and convergence error (which are similar to those for operational forecasting) resulting in applicability of all the forecasts as suggested in Table 1 as regards the error variation. To make further examination of the prognostic model, we made predictions at 2 and 3 decades in advance (or two— and three—stepwise), respectively, for the 20 forecasts (see the corresponding parts of Table 1). Error analyses show that their accuracy is equally desirable and the mean relative error (MRE) is 9. 1% (9. 4%) for the two—(three—) stepwise predictions, very close to the one—stepwise result, a fact that offers basis for prepar

Table 1. Forecast Verification of The Neuron Network Scheme

ON	Abs.	one—step		two—step		three—step	
		Pred.	RE	Pred.	RE	Pred.	RE
1	19.74	19.37	.019	18.98	.039	19.04	.36
2	18.62	19.76	—.061	19.63	—.054	19.58	—.052
3	15.42	19.49	—.264	19.53	—.267	19.38	—.257
4	16.00	16.61	—.038	16.91	—.057	16.85	—.053
5	15.98	16.10	—.008	16.26	—.018	16.27	—.018
6	14.98	14.89	.006	14.48	.034	14.30	.045
7	16.62	13.66	.178	13.76	.172	14.32	.139
8	16.64	16.19	.027	15.78	.052	15.76	.053
9	15.70	15.82	—.008	15.69	.000	15.42	.018
10	19.84	16.30	.179	16.24	.181	16.06	.190
11	16.02	18.51	—.155	19.32	—.206	19.12	—.194
12	20.82	19.45	.066	18.43	.115	17.33	.168
13	20.62	22.40	—.086	22.75	—.103	22.92	—.112
14	25.72	19.68	.235	18.87	.266	21.35	.170
15	26.50	27.91	—.053	27.58	—.041	27.91	—.053
16	29.62	27.56	.070	27.72	.064	24.77	.164
17	27.54	27.68	—.005	27.56	—.001	27.72	—.007
18	26.36	25.86	.019	25.80	.021	25.32	.040
19	26.20	24.54	.063	24.73	.056	24.73	.056
20	21.50	24.29	—.130	23.13	—.076	22.73	—.057
MRE			.083		.091		.094

the next decade ($N=113$). To objectively compare, forecasts and tests were done in a similar way to that in Ref. [7]. That is, after a forecast is constructed for the subsequent decade by the newly—formed prognostic equation, observations for this decade is put into the sample set to build up another subsequent decade and so on, leading to 20 equations, which were used for the period in spring—summer 1 9 9 5, with the accuracy shown in Table 2. Error analyses indicate the steady variation in the complex correlation coefficient (R) of these prognostic equations because of a long sample length for the regression formulae. Test of the regressions shows higher significance level. Inspection of Tables 1 and 2 as regards the corresponding errors reveals the considerable advantage of ANN—yielded accuracy over the regression—given accuracy (relative error of 8.3% versus 9.7%). Also, it is found that for all the experimental forecasts the accuracy for the predicted maxima and minima is a lot higher. Thus, our experiment provides a new way to raise accuracy, a hard nut to crack for traditional statistical forecasting.

Table 2. Forecast Verification of the Regression Method

ON.	Abs.	Pred.	RE	R	n
1	19.74	20.12	—.019	.8284	110
2	18.62	20.17	—.083	.8287	111
3	15.42	19.19	—.245	.8288	112
4	16.00	16.74	—.046	.8279	113
5	15.98	16.67	—.043	.8310	114
6	14.98	16.33	—.090	.8339	115
7	16.62	15.95	.041	.8374	116
8	16.64	17.16	—.031	.8394	117
9	15.70	17.22	—.097	.8413	118
10	19.84	16.85	.151	.8434	119
11	16.02	19.53	—.219	.8408	120
12	20.82	17.15	.176	.8397	121
13	20.62	20.54	.004	.8358	122
14	25.72	20.49	.203	.8358	123
15	26.50	24.61	.071	.8303	124
16	29.62	25.79	.129	.8320	125
17	27.54	28.78	—.045	.8346	126
18	26.36	28.09	—.065	.8377	127
19	26.20	26.26	—.002	.8391	128
20	21.50	25.16	—.170	.8411	129
MRE			.097		

ing better consensus forecasts.

In addition, since the presented model of mixed type is an attempt and so is the realization of nonlinear mapping from input to output with the aid of the BP network, to examine if the calculation scheme is superior to the traditional one becomes an important aspect in verifying the quality of the developed model. For this reason, for the input matrix of the BP network, the expected output is taken as a predictand and the other 7 columns as predictors to establish a prognostic model regressively, leading to the first equation

$$\hat{y}_t = 0.123 - 0.0413x_1 - 0.0111x_2 - 0.0373x_3 - 0.0996x_4 - 0.1479x_5 - 0.1237x_6 - 0.6817x_7 \qquad (12)$$

with $N=112$ and the complex correlation coefficient of 0.8284. On this basis the prediction is done for

To compare the accuracy from the two methods we use (10) to caculate

$$C_2 = \frac{SEE_3 - SSE_2}{SSE_3} = \frac{120.88 - 104.74}{120.88} = 13.3\% \qquad (13)$$

where SSE_3 denotes the residual sum of squares for the regression scheme. Results show that the accuracy given by the developed model is 13.3% higher than that from the regression forecasts due mainly to the fact that the study system is not definitely a linear entity. Considered in the mixed model are not just the evolution of the system itself but the role of external physical processes as well and these integrated effects are revealed through nonlinear mapping, which is able to better describe the substantial relation inside than the linear technique. With the mixed model a SH was made for the decades of October 1995(sowing period for winter wheat), indicating the moisture appropriate for the operation, with the mean relative error of 3. 8% (versus 8. 3% for the regression), a forecast that furnished farmers with a basis of decision—making for irrigation. As such, the mixed model is superior and reliable in contrast to the traditional technique.

IV. CONCLUDING REMARKS

Because of the length of continuous SH measurements, no calculation was performed of the chaos indices (e. g. , incidence dimension and Lyapunov exponent) in disigning the prognostic model so that no study was made of the dimension of its "attractive system" to have fuller arguments in defining the dimension for model establishment. Evidently, a high—quality model depends substantially on of all factors related to the predictand's future state are considered. For this reason, rainfall and insolation duration are included in model (5). Will the forecast accuracy be improved if other contributing meteorological factors, dynamic and thermal, are involved? This is a problem that remains to be investigated.

REFERENCES

1. Zhou Jiabin, Huang Jiayou, Status of Forecasting Methods of Drought and Flood, The Climate Research of Drought and Flood, 1990, china Meteorological Press, PP. 134—142.
2. Jin Long, Luo Ying, Study of a Computation Method for Drought Index and Its Application, Journal of Nanjing Institute of Meteorology, 1992, 15(4), PP. 584—590.
3. K. Y. Lee, Y. T. Cha and J. H. Park, Short—term Load Forecasting Using and Artificial Neural Networks, IEEE Transactions on Power System, 1992, 7(1), PP. 124—132.
4. Y. Y. Yin, X. M. Xu, Applying Neural Networks Technolgy for Multiobjective Land Use Planning, Journal of Environmental Managmemt, 1991, 32, PP. 349—356.
5. S. P. Zhang, H. Watanable and R. Yamada, Prediction of Daily Water Demands by Neural Networks, International Conference on Stochastic and Statistical methods in Hydrololgy and Environmental Engineering, Ontario, Canada, 1993, PP. 217—227.
6. Jin Long, Luo Ying, A Important Method to Defend and Relieve the Damage of Agrometerological Drought, Journal of Nanjing University, SICCND, 1996, PP. 149—155.
7. Michaels, P. J. , R. B. Gerzoff, Statistical Relations Between Summer Thunderstorm Patterns and Continented Midtropospheric Heights, 1984, Mon. Wea. Rev. , 112(2), PP. 778—789.

Non-Linear Time Series Prediction Using an Optimum Neural Network Architecture

Li Lin, and Jarl-Thure Eriksson

Tampere University of Technology

P. O. Box 692, FIN 33101 TAMPERE, Finland

Abstract

An optimal neural network architecture for the modeling and prediction of non-linear time series is presented. The optimum three-layer neural network structure is determined by using a canonical decomposition technique and a cross validation principle. It ensures that the network structure is sufficiently complex to characterize the time series under consideration and also provides the best matched to the observed data. By comparing the predicting performance of the neural network with that of a conventional method for both simulated and real process data, we found that the neural network method achieved much better prediction results than the corresponding AR model.

1 Introduction

Predicting is one of the basic purposes of scientific modeling. The main problem of time series prediction is the identification of the model and the estimation of its parameters.

There are many procedures of predicting the future behaviours of particular series from the information of its present and past. Linear models, such as the autoregressive (AR), the moving average (MA), and the autoregressive/moving average (ARMA), have had some success [1]. However, their prediction power is limited due to their inability to model the evolutionary dynamics of the process.

During the last few years, some neural network methods have been directly introduced for time series prediction and the topic of network architecture specification has received great interest [2] [3] [4]. Building a neural network model involves two distinct tasks: determining the network structure and estimating the weight factors. The former is equivalent to establishing the system order whilst the later is similar to parameter estimation in system identification. Thus how to decide an appropriate network architecture purely from series data is a key issue. The optimal and minimum networks reduce the risk of overfitting and have better generalization properties. Given a fixed structure of multilayer networks, the parameters are usually modified by the stochastic gradient descent method which eventually minimizes a loss function [5].

In this paper, a method based on a canonical decomposition technique [6] and cross validation principle has been used to determine the optimal network architecture for given observed data. It provides a systematic procedure for determining the topology of the multilayer network during the learning process. By prediction experiments based on both simulated and real process data, it is shown that neural networks are capable of making better predictions on non-linear time series data than AR models.

2 Prediction with Multilayer Network

The multilayer neural network has three distinctive characteristics:

1. The nonlinearity of each hidden neuron model in the network makes the input-output relation of the network highly nonlinear.

2. One or more layers of hidden neurons enable the network to learn complex tasks by extracting progressively more meaningful features from the training data.

3. The network exhibits a high degree of connectivity.

It is through the combination of these characteristics together with the ability to learn from experience through training that multilayer network derives its higher computing power. The interconnecting weights between neurons play the role of storing the information or the relationship between input and output. Most of the knowledge representation is done in the nonlinear hidden layers. The complex mathematical interactions between neurons can provide a better model of a certain process.

Time series prediction involves processing of patterns that evolve over time. In neural network prediction temporal information of the series data is spatially brought to the network by a time-lagged vector:

$$\hat{x}_t = f(x_1, x_2, \ldots, x_{t-1}, \underline{w})$$

where $\hat{x}_t$ is the approximation at time t of the value x_t and $\underline{w}$ is a matrix of network weights (including biases). The weights are trained to minimize the cost function:

$$min \sum_t \left(x_t - \hat{x}_t \right)^2$$

From references [8] and [9] we know that a multilayer network with a single or two hidden layers is sufficient to compute a uniform approximation to a given training set represented by the set of input data $x_1,\ldots,x_p$ and a desired output $f(x_1,\ldots,x_p)$. That means the network could be a universal approximator. Because the neurons in a single hidden layer network tend to interact with each other globally, it is difficult to improve the approximation in a complex situation. In practice a two hidden layer network is easier to handle. With two hidden layers the approximation process may become more manageable i.e., local features and global features are extracted in the first and second hidden layer respectively.

The multilayer network used in this study is shown in Fig. 1. The number of input nodes is p, the numbers of nodes in the first and second hidden layer are q and r respectively. A single output node represents one-step ahead value of the time series. A *tanth* function is used for the activation function of hidden layer neurons. The output neuron uses a pure linear function. For the prediction problem, if the output neuron utilizes a nonlinear sigmoid function the outputs of the network are limited to a small range. By using linear functions in the output neuron the network can take wide range values. This selection also coincides with the universal approximation theory [10]

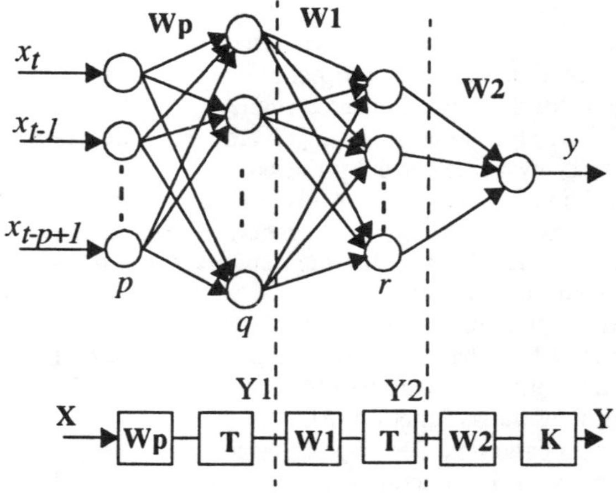

Figure 1. Multilayer neural network

3 Modeling Procedure

3.1 Model Selection

The selection of model is a crucial task for non-linear time series prediction. The training and generalization performances of the neural network are sensitive to the architecture. In practice the design of a multilayer network is more of an art than a science, because many of the numerous features involved in the design are indeed the results of one's own personal experience. There is no definite methodology for determining the architecture for a particular mapping application. Although there has been some reports on the selection procedure of multilayer networks [7] [11], they were just for single hidden layer networks or they did not consider specific characteristics of the time series being modeled. In general, the more neurons in the network, the better it can fit the data, however too many neurons can lead to overfitting. This is because a large number of adjustable parameters will have a strong tendency to learn too many specific input-output relations, with the result that unintended information in the process are stored in the synaptic weights, hence performing poor for unseen data. Too many parameters also imply a greater possibility of error in estimating these parameters. Hence it is important to find the simplest optimal structure, which is less likely to learn the noise in the training data, and thus generalize better results to new data.

There are several criterions for balancing the over-fitting and under-fitting characteristic of the model [12] [13]. The general form of such criterion function is $C(T,O_n)$. Here T is any statistic measures of the performance of the model on the training data, and O_n is a complexity measure of the model. But these criterions rely heavily on the linearity of the model and on the assumption about the error distribution. To get acceptable nonlinear time series prediction, we have to develop a new method of model selection.

3.2 The Combined Method

In this paper we combine the *cross-validation* principle with the *canonical decomposition* technique in order to determine the architecture of a three-layer network. The combined method ensures that the architecture and the specific time series have the best match to each other that resulting in getting minimum prediction error on new data.

A multilayer network can be represented in form of a block diagram consisting of three affine transformations, W_p, W_1, W_2, and a diagonal nonlinear operator T with identical sigmoidal elements and linear operator K as shown in fig.1. Each layer of the network is regarded as a composition of an affine transformation with a nonlinear or linear mapping:

$$Y_1 = T_p(X) = T\,W_p(X)$$
$$Y_2 = T_1(Y_1) = T\,W_1(Y_1)$$
$$Y = T_2(Y_2) = K\,W_2(Y_2)$$

The input training data space X_d is an L-dimensional space in which the input data sequence x_j $(1 < j < p)$ lies. The target data space Y_d is an L-dimensional space within which the target data sequence y_k $(1 < k < K)$ lies. According to [6] and [7], we have the following result.

Theorem: Let X_d and Y_d be any finite data spaces corresponding to the finite dimensional compact manifolds, and let f be any continuous function that maps X_d to Y_d. Within the three-layer feed forward neural network, there exists a *unique* approximated canonical decomposition of f, which is also the *optimal best* approximation to f, iff the number of neurons in each hidden layer matches the dimension of the subspace of the canonical decomposition of f.

This gives the sufficient and necessary condition for the existence of a canonical decomposition approximation to any continuous function by a neural network. That is the first hidden space Y_1 and second space Y_2 must be the maximum subspaces of X_d and Y_d respectively for f made bijective. The dimensions of the maximal subspaces of the input and output spaces are determined by checking the independence of the outputs of each hidden layer according to the following definition.

Definition: Suppose S is an n-dimensional vector space and $a_1, a_2, \dots, a_r$ are vectors of S. Then, given an $n \times r$ matrix $A = |\,a_1\,a_2\dots a_r\,|$, the group of vectors $a_1, a_2, \dots, a_r$ is said to be δ *linearly independent* iff the determinant of $A^T A$ satisfies

$$\det(A^T A) > \delta$$

where δ is an arbitrary small positive real number.

The three-layer neural network as a canonical decomposition approximation decomposes a complex nonlinear function into three simple nonlinear or linear mappings between affine spaces. The hidden layers link the real observed data to the parameters of the underlying structure of the time series.

The motivation of cross-validation is to validate the model on a data set different from the one used for training or parameter estimation. It is a two-step procedure ensuring structural risk-minimization.

Thus in practice the network structure selection procedure can be realized as follows:

> 1) Select training data set of length L_1+L_2;
> 2) Set criterion δ;
> 3) For $p = p_{min}$ to p_{max},
>> For $q = q_{min}$ to q_{max},
>>> For $r = r_{min}$ to r_{max},
>>>> *Initialize the unknown weights and*
>>>> *train the network with data L_1;*
>>>> *Check performance measure $det_1(q, r)$ and $det_2(q, r)$;*

$$If\ det_1 < \delta\ \ break;$$
$$If\ det_2 < \delta\ \ break;$$

        Next r

     Next q

4) Calculate the prediction error $E(p, q, r)$ with data L_2;

   Next p

5) Find the minimum $E(p, q, r)$.

4 Experiments

The above procedure has been tested with as well simulated as real process data. In both cases, the faster BP algorithm was used for the training.

4.1 Simulated data

The simulated time series has been generated from

$$x(t+1) = 1 - 1.4x^2(t) + 0.3x(t-1)$$

The series is noise-free. In the learning phase p varied from 3 to 12 and q and r from 2 to 10. Training data length L_1 is 120 and L_2 is 80. δ is 0.7. Now we are able to get the prediction error E as a function of p, q, and r. The optimal values for p, q, and r are 3, 5, and 2. The corresponding prediction error E is 0.011.

To compare the predictive ability of the neural network model with a standard statistical model the same time series data are fitted to a 3rd order AR-model. The prediction error is 0.55.

The results of the trained neural network and AR model for predicting 60 new vales of $x(t)$ are shown in Figs. 2 and 3. It can be seen that the predicted values of the neural network are quite closed to actual values and clearly better than the values of the AR-model.

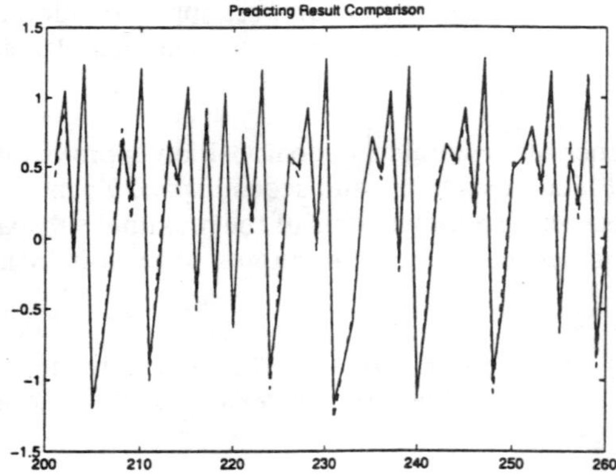

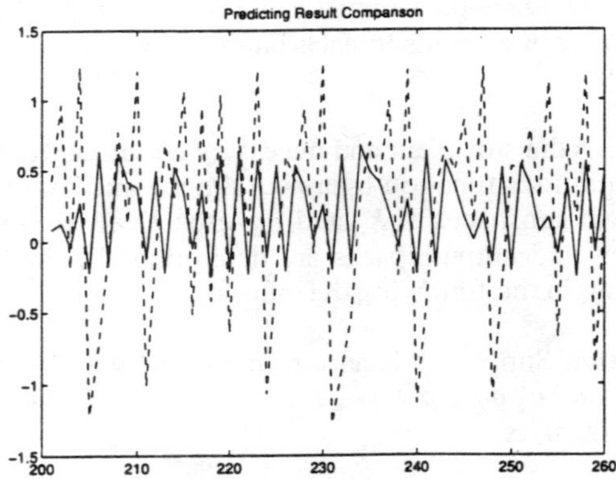

Figure 2. Neural network predictions (solid line) and actual values (dashed line)

Figure 3. AR model predictions (solid line) and actual values (dashed line)

4.2 Real Process Data

The real process data is a wind speed time series acquasited from *MATILDA* wind plant located on the southern coast of Finland.

The wind speed series has highly dynamical nonlinear characteristics. An accurate short-term wind speed prediction is crucial to the whole wind energy conversion system. It has attracted a lot of researchers to do prediction work. In the last few years many approaches have been proposed to solve this problem by neural networks [14] [15]. However the choices of the network structure were achieved more or less by trial and, according to the authors' opinions, hence can not assure the best architecture.

The same data length as in *4.1* is used for training the network. δ is 0.9. The optimal values for p, q, and r are 5, 9 and 5 respectively. The prediction error is 0.13. The 5th order AR model's prediction error is 0.85. The prediction results are shown in Figs. 4 and 5. Again they show that the neural network was capable of capturing the underlying dynamics of non-linear time series much underlying dynamics of non-linear time series much bette than the linear mode than the linear model.

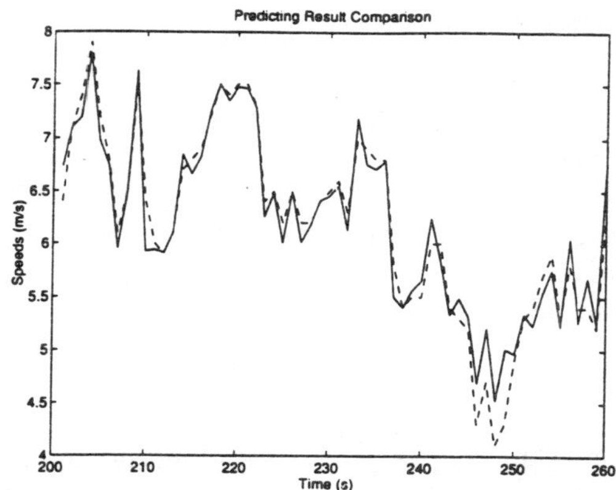

Figure 4. Neural network predictions (solid line)
and actual values (dashed line)

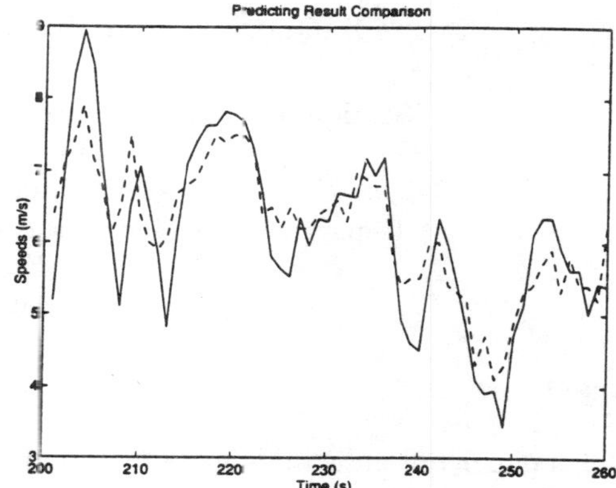

Figure 5. AR model predictions (solid line)
and actual values (dashed line)

5 Conclusions

A method based on optimal neural network architecture for predicting non-linear time series has been presented. The technique relies upon the fact that the number of neurons in each hidden layer is related to the complexity of the input data and upon the characteristics of the non-linear mapping from input to output. By applying the cross validation principle it ensures the best match between the training data and network structure. So a systematic procedure of determining a three-layer neural network architecture is achieved. Experimental results show that the proposed neural network method has significantly higher predicting ability than the linear model.

References

[1]G.E.P. Box and G.M. Jeenkins, Time Series Analysis, Forecasting and Control, Holden-Day, 1970.
[2] A.S. Weigend, B.A. Huberman and D.R. Rumelhart, "Predicting the future: a connectionist approach," International Journal of Neural Systems Vol. 1, No. 3, 1990, pp.193-209.
[3] W.R. Foster, F. Collopy and L.H. Ungar, "Neural network forecasting of short, noisy time series," Computers Chem. Eng., Vol. 16, No. 4, 1992, pp.293-297.
[4] J. Perttula, J. T. Eriksson and Li Lin, "A comparation study of nonlinear prediction techniques," Proc. of NOLTA'95, Las Vegas, U.S.A., pp. 825-828.
[5] D. Rumelhart, G.E. Hilton and R.J. Williams, "Learning internal representations by error propagation," Parallel Distributed Processing: Explorations in the Microstructure of Cognition, D.R. Rumelhart, J.L. McClelland, and the PDP Research Group, (Eds.), ch. 8, The MIT Press, 1986, pp.318-362.
[6] Zhenni Wang, et al, " Multilayer feedforward neural networks: a canonical form approximation of nonlinearity," Int. J. Control, 1992, Vol. 56, No. 3, pp. 655-672.
[7] Zhenni Wang, et al, "A procedure for determining the topology of multilayer feedforward neural networks," Neural Networks, Vol. 7, No. 2, 1994, pp. 291-300.
[8] G. Cybenko, " Approximations by superpositions of a sigmoidal function," Mathematics of control, signals, and systems, Vol. 2, 1989, pp. 303-314.
[9] K. Hornik, et al., "Multilayered feedforward neural networks are universal approximations," Neural networks, Vol. 2, 1990, pp. 359-366.
[10] S. Haykin, "Neural network: a comprehensive Foundation," 1994, Ch. 6.
[11] M. Lehtokangas, et al., "Neural network optimization tool based on predictive MDL principle for time series prediction," Proc. of 1993 IEEE Conf. on Tolls with AI, pp. 338-342.
[12] H. Akaike, "A new look at the statistical model identification," IEEE Trans. Autom. Control, Vol. AC-19, No. 6, Dec. 1974, pp. 716-723.
[13] E.J. Hannan and B.G. Quinn, "The determination of the order an auto-regression," J.R.Statistic. Soc. Ser., B41, 1979, pp. 190-195.
[14] J. F. Farley and P. D. Varhol, "Neural Nets for Predicting Behavior." Byte vol. 19, 1994, pp. 187-190.
[15] J.O.G. Tande and et al., "A 10 sec. forecast of wind turbine output with neural networks," Proc. of European community wind energy conf. 1993, pp.774-777.

Modeling for Nonlinear Time Series Based on Dynamic Neural Network and Inverse System

Z.X. Qin* [†]   H.Y. Zhang[†]   C.W. Chan[‡]   K.C. Cheung [‡]

†Section 301 , Beijing University of Aeronautics and Astronautics
Beijing 100083, P.R.China
email: buaa301@mimi.cnc.ac.cn
‡ Department of Mechanical Engineering, University of Hong Kong
Hong Kong Pokfulam road
email: mechan@hkucc.hku.hk

Abstract

This paper presents a modeling method for a class of nonlinear time series based on dynamic neural network (DNN) and inverse system. The proposed method is applied to model the stochastic process of drift error of inertial component. The simulations validate the modeling scheme.

1. Introduction

Time series represents a large kind of stochastic process. The modeling for time series is necessary and important in many fields such as control engineering, economics and society problem. For example, in high precision inertial navigation system the modeling and identification of the stochastic error model of inertial component is a key technique, since the accuracy of the stochastic error model directly affects the accuracy of navigation system. Other examples such as stock price and population prediction are usually dealt with using time series models. Generally, the AR, MA or ARMA model are adopted in these fields. However, in practical applications, lots of stochastic processes are nonlinear. In this case, ARMA models will be not very efficient and result in a large model error or the order of model will be very high. So nonlinear time series model should be considered. Unfortunately the function type of most nonlinear processes cannot be predetermined, selecting an appropriate fitting function will be significant and difficult.

The advent of neural network brought about new ways in nonlinear problems. It is well known that neural network has the advantage of performance improvement through learning using parallel and distributed processing, which can approximate any nonlinear functions with various complexity and have the potential to deal with many problems that cannot be handled by traditional linear analytical approaches[1,2,3].

In this paper, the modeling method for nonlinear stochastic process based on dynamic neural network and inverse system is discussed.

2. Dynamic neural network

Multiple layer neural network is capable of approximating any nonlinear function[4] with arbitrary accuracy. Therefore a DNN (consisted of a neural network and a delay element as shown in Fig. 1) can be used to model a nonlinear dynamic system (NDS).

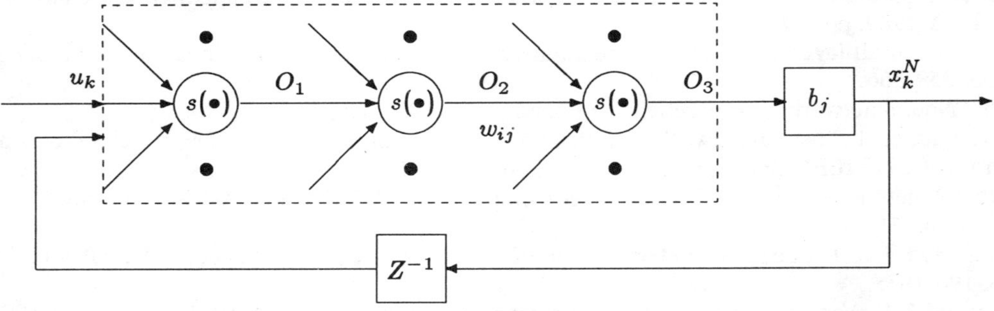

Fig. 1   Dynamic neural network system

---

* The author is currently with Department of Mechanical Engineering, University of Hong Kong

DNN in Fig.1 can be described as

$$X_{k+1}^N = \phi^N(X_k^N, u_k) \tag{1}$$

Assuming that the following nonlinear system is to be modeled [3]

$$X_{k+1} = \phi(X_k, u_k) \tag{2}$$

Suppose the measurement equation of system (2) is known and an input-output sample set is given as $\{u_k, x_k\}$, it is possible to find a DNN (1) to approximate nonlinear dynamic system (2) by selecting an appropriate network and a learning algorithm.

Let the input vectors of each layer of BP neural network be I_1, I_2, I_3 respectively; the output vectors of each layer be O_1, O_2, O_3 respectively; the weight matrices of each layer be W_1, W_2, W_3; the number of neurons in input layer, hidden layer and output layer be n, m and l respectively. The neuron nonlinear function $f()$ is the hyperbolic tangent function

$$f(\alpha) = \frac{e^\alpha - e^{-\alpha}}{e^\alpha + e^{-\alpha}}, \quad f'(\alpha) = (1 + f(\alpha))(1 - f(\alpha)) \tag{3}$$

Let $F(I) = [f(i_1) \cdots f(i_n)]^T$. Hence the input and output of each layer of BP neural network are
$$I_1 = X, O_1 = F(I_1); \quad I_2 = W_2^T O_1, O_2 = F(I_2); \quad I_3 = W_3^T O_2, O_3 = F(I_3)$$

Commonly, the Error Back Propagation algorithm is used for DNN learning. The sample set is composed of input-output data of NDS. Define learning error (or objective function) as

$$E = \frac{1}{2}\sum_{k=1}^{P}(x_k - x_k^N)^2 \tag{4}$$

Where the learning error is a generalized distance between the output of NDS and that of DNN. In general, the weighting matrices are adjusted according to the negative direction of the error gradient. $\Delta W = -\eta \bigtriangledown E, \eta$ is learning step size , $\bigtriangledown E$ is the gradient of E.

In recent years, genetic algorithm (GA)[5,6] is widely studied and used in neural network learning and optimization. GA has many good characteristics and can almost be applied to any optimization field if fitness function (or objective function) is available, and does not require gradient or other auxiliary information about the problem and can be used in parallel manner easily. In this paper 3-layer BP neural network and the Incremental Zooming GA[6] are adopted.

3. Inverse system of time series model

A system Σ with input $u(t)$, output $y(t)$ and state $x(t)$ can described as below

$$y(t) = \theta[x(t_0), u(t)] \quad \text{or} \quad y = \theta u \tag{5}$$

The inverse system of system Σ can be define as Π: $u_d = \hat{\theta} y_d$ with initial condition $x_d(t_0)$ (determined by x_0), which satisfies following equation

$$\theta \hat{\theta} y_d = \theta u_d = y_d \tag{6}$$

System Π_α: $u_d = \hat{\theta}_\alpha \phi$, let $\phi = y_d^{(\alpha)}(t)$, if the following equation is satisfied

$$\theta \hat{\theta}_\alpha \phi = \theta \hat{\theta}_\alpha (D^\alpha y_d) = y_d \qquad (D \triangleq d/dt, D^\alpha \triangleq d^\alpha/(dt)^\alpha) \tag{7}$$

is called α − order integration inverse system of Σ.

It is known that a pseudo-linear system is composed of Σ and Π_α. The pseudo-linear system is called $\hat{\theta}_\alpha \theta$ which satisfies the following equation and is shown in Fig.2

$$D^\alpha y = \phi \tag{8}$$

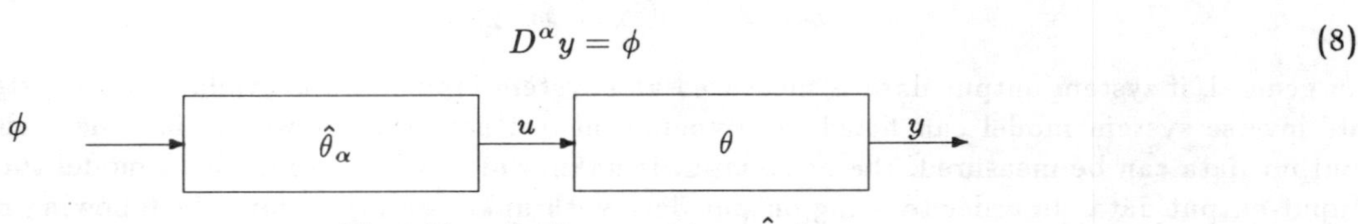

Fig.2 Pseudo-linear system $\hat{\theta}_\alpha \theta$

In the same manner, inverse systems for other types of systems such as discrete system, distributed parameter system and time series model can also be defined.

Pseudo-linear system is very useful and important in modern nonlinear control system. The important reason is that the design of controller for pseudo-linear system can be done the same as linear system. Therefore, if a nonlinear system can be transformed into pseudo-linear system, the controller can be designed more easily.

In this paper, the characteristics of pseudo-linear system will be applied to model time series process. Considering a discrete nonlinear system or nonlinear time series as shown below:

$$\Phi: \quad y_{k+n} = f\big(y_{k+n-1}, y_{k+n-2}, \cdots, y_k, u_{k+m}, u_{k+m-1}, \cdots, u_k\big) \tag{9}$$

If u_{n+m} can be solved from the above equation analytically, the inverse system can be expressed as below

$$\Phi_{n-m}: \quad u_{k+m} = f^{-1}\big(y_{k+n}, y_{k+n-1}, y_{k+n-2}, \cdots, y_k, u_{k+m-1}, \cdots, u_k\big) \tag{10}$$

In time series model y_k is system output and u_k will be noise.

4. Modeling method for nonlinear time series model via DNN and inverse system

In the last part the inverse system for nonlinear time series model is described. In many cases the system model is unknown, so its inverse system can not be known. Sometimes, even if the mathematical model is known the inverse system model can not be solved analytically.

It is feasible to use neural network to model a system and its inverse system, whether the system model is known or unknown. If the input and output data of the system are available it is possible to fit the system and its inverse using neural network.

Consider the following nonlinear AR model

$$x_k = f\big(x_{k-1}, x_{k-2}, \cdots, x_{k-n}\big) + v_k \tag{11}$$

where x_k is system output, v_k is normal noise with mean 0 and variance σ, namely, $v \sim N(0, \sigma)$. Obviously, the inverse system of system (11) can be written as

$$v_k = x_k - f\big(x_{k-1}, x_{k-2}, \cdots, x_{k-n}\big) \tag{12}$$

System (11) and its inverse system can be described using the following diagrams.

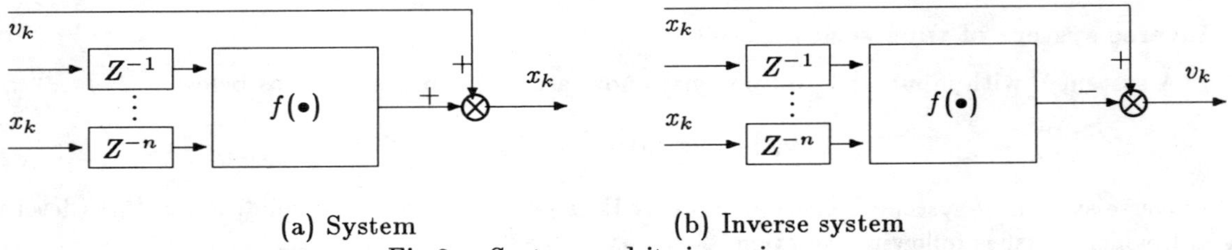

(a) System   (b) Inverse system

Fig.3   System and its inversion

It is clear that if system model (11) is known, its inverse system model can be obtained easily and can be formulated as equation (12). When the system model (11) is unknown, however, the system output data $\{x_k\}$ is available, the system model and its inverse system model can be fitted using dynamic neural network as shown in Fig.1. The proximate model of nonlinear AR model based on dynamic neural network can be expressed as

$$\hat{x}_k = g\big(\hat{x}_{k-1}, \hat{x}_{k-2}, \cdots, \hat{x}_{k-n}\big) + \hat{v}_k \tag{13}$$

Thus the inverse system model is

$$\hat{v}_k = \hat{x}_k - g\big(\hat{x}_{k-1}, \hat{x}_{k-2}, \cdots, \hat{x}_{k-n}\big) \tag{14}$$

In general, if system output data is measured and system input data is available, the system model and its inverse system model can fitted via dynamic neural network. However, in time series model only output data can be measured, the noise input is unknown. It will be difficult to model the system using input-output data. In order to using output data with unknown input data the following reasons will be considered

(a) Although noise input is unknown, in one measurement process the input noise data is certain. The input noise data can be treated as a sample of a Guassian stochastic process and the standard normal distribution conditions, namely, $N(0,\sigma)$ will be satisfied.

(b) Consider system (11) and its inverse system (12), if one of the systems (11) and (12) is known, the other can be solved easily. On the other hand, the output of pseudo-linear system consisted of (11) and (12) as shown in Fig. 4 is linearly dependent upon its input. Therefore, a dynamic neural network system (13) and (14) can be used to fit system (11),(12). The system as shown in Fig.4 is a approximation of the pseudo-linear system shown in Fig.2 based on neural network.

$$x_k \longrightarrow \boxed{\text{eq. (14)}} \xrightarrow{\hat{v}_k} \boxed{\text{eq. (13)}} \xrightarrow{\hat{x}_k}$$

Fig.4 Pseudo-linear system based on neural network

In order to using neural network to fit the nonlinear AR model, and using former consideration and assumption, the following objective function will be adopted.
(a) learning error

$$J = \sum_{k=1}^{P}(x_k - \hat{x}_k)^2 \longrightarrow 0 \tag{15}$$

(b) $\hat{v}_k$ is normal and $\sigma \neq 0$. This will mainly use two objects: mean value

$$\mu = \frac{1}{P}\sum_{k=1}^{P}\hat{v}_k \tag{16}$$

and correlated function

$$r(i) = \frac{1}{N-i}\sum_{k=1}^{P}\hat{v}_k\hat{v}_{k-i} \quad i = 0, 1, \cdots \tag{17}$$

Obviously, it is difficult to train neural network using BP algorithm adopting the above targets, however, GA[5,6] give the chance to train the neural network with complex or multiple objective function like the above.

Also, the proposed method can be applied to the following complicated system — nonlinear ARMA model

$$x_k = g(x_{k-1}, x_{k-2}, \cdots, x_{k-n}, v_k, v_{k-1}, \cdots, v_{k-m}) \tag{18}$$

In this paper nonlinear AR model will be used to model drift error of inertial component and validate the proposed method.

5. Application

As we known before, a gyro drift can be dealt with using time series with a trend item and a stochastic process item as follows

$$\begin{cases} y_k = f(k) + x_k \\ \\ x_k = g(x_{k-1}, x_{k-2}, \cdots, x_{k-n}) + v_k \end{cases} \tag{19}$$

where y_k is gyro drift, $f(k)$ is trend item related with time , temperature or other factors, x_k is stochastic process. Generally, the trend item $f(k)$ should be removed from y_k, then x_k can be handled. When a dynamic neural network is used to fit y_k, $f(k)$ and x_k can be dealt with together. Equation (19) can be rewritten as

$$y_k = h(k, y_{k-1}, y_{k-2}, \cdots, y_{k-n}) + v_k \tag{20}$$

This model will be easily handled using the method in section 4. In this paper y_k is shown in Fig.4 (a). The output of inverse system based on neural network is shown in Fig.4(b). The modeling error is shown is Fig.4(c). (d) is correlated function of the output of inverse system i.e. the noise.

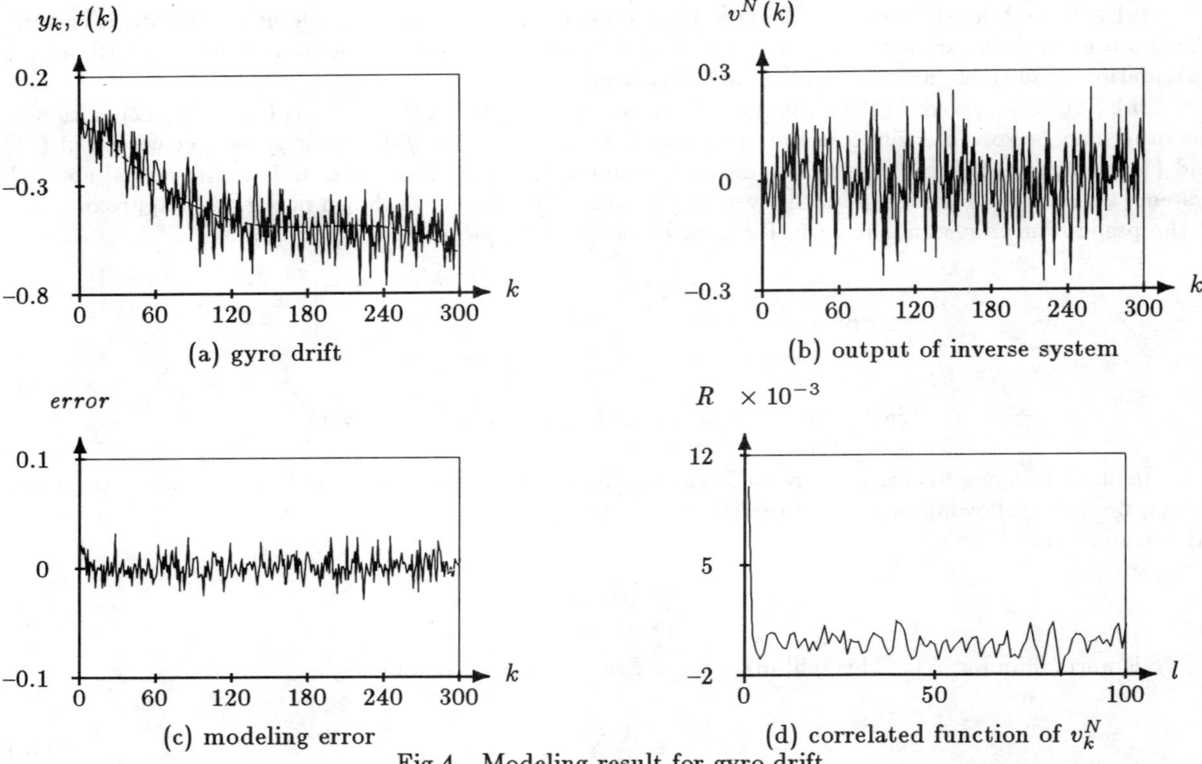

Fig.4   Modeling result for gyro drift

6. Conclusion

A modeling method for time series is presented in this paper based on dynamic neural network and inverse system. The proposed method is applied to model inertial component drift error and nonlinear autoregressive time series is modeled. The proposed method can also be applied to other fields such as population and stock predication.

References

[1]   K.S Narendra and K. Parthasarathy. Identification and Control of Dynamic Systems Using Neural Networks. *IEEE Trans. Neural Networks,* Vol.1, No.1, March 1990.

[2]   K.S. Narendra and S. Mukhopadhyay. Intelligent Control Using Neural Networks.*IEEE Control Systems.* Apr. 1992.

[3]   Z.X.Qin, H.Y.Zhang. Modelling method for Nonlinear Stochastic Dynamic System Based on Neural Network and Extended Kalman Filter. *Proc. of IEEE International Conference on Industrial Technology,* 5-9, December 1994, Guangzhou, China.

[4]   R.H. Nielsen. Theory of the Back-Propagation Neural Network. *Proc. IEEE Int. Conf. Neural Networks,* 1989.

[5]   Vittorio Maniezzo. Genetic Evolution of Topology and Weight Distribution of Neural Networks. *IEEE Trans. on Neural Networks,* Vol.5, No.1, Jan. 1994.

[6]   Z.X. Qin et al. A Incremental Zooming Genetic Algorithm and Its Application to Constraint Optimization. *Proceeding of International Conference on Modelling, Simulation and Optimization.* Gold Coast, Australia, May 6-9, 1996

A Neuro-Evolutionary Framework
for Fuzzy Soft-Constraint Optimisation:
an FX/Futures Trading Portfolio Application

Poomjai Nacaskul (pn2@doc.ic.ac.uk)[†][‡]
† Department of Computing, Imperial College of Science, Technology & Medicine
180 Queen's Gate, London SW7 2BZ, UK
‡ Quantitative Research and Trading, Chase Manhattan Bank, London

Abstract— This paper proposes a fuzzy soft-constraint formulation of a multi-criteria optimisation of an actively-managed FX/Futures trading portfolio. A primary *optimising* objective function is supplemented by secondary *goal-satisfaction* objectives and by *soft-bounds* on the portfolio weights. These supplementary criteria are modelled as *fuzzy soft-constraint relations* with hyperbolic membership characteristics and enforced via a penalty-reward scheme. The optimising criterion and the penalty-rewards combine into a fuzzy multi-criteria performance evaluation function, $\mathcal{P}(\ )$, to be maximised over the solution space $\{x\}$.

Because $\mathcal{P}(x)$ involves algebraic operations and hyperbolic set-partitionings, it can be implemented on a *mapping* Neural Network (NN) architecture. A genetic/evolutionary programming algorithm then maximises this NN-encoded $\mathcal{P}(x)$ over $\{x\}$. We cite practical and modelling benefits of this Neuro-Evolutionary methodology. Finally we propose that a *learning* NN forms a basis for future work in case-based induction of the decision maker's implicit fuzzy utility function.

Keywords: fuzzy goal programming, soft-constraint relation, prediction-trading model, portfolio optimisation, multi-criteria decision model, mapping Neural Network architecture, genetic/evolutionary programming, fuzzy neuro-evolutionary hybrid system, fuzzy utility theory

1   Introduction

A Mathematical Programming (MP) framework for constrained optimisation analysis generally refers to the process of performing a criteria-driven search over a reduced decision space, whereby the problem's objective function directs the search path and its constraint relations define the boundaries of the feasible region. In practice, there is often a degree of imprecision and/or flexibility with regard to the constraint specifications. A fuzzy set [1, 7] framework can address both the numerical *imprecision* of the coefficients in the mathematical expressions as well as the decisional *flexibility* concerning the satisfaction of each constraint relation. This latter feature enables us to better capture our optimisation/decision model.

The use of soft-constraint relations facilitates modelling system objectives which are best represented as statements of goal-satisfactions as well as system constraints which can be relaxed, i.e. at some incurred penalties. In particular, this work is motivated by a decision environment where a primary optimising objective function is supplemented by secondary goal-satisfaction objectives and by soft-bounds on the decision variables.

We propose to model these supplementary criteria as **fuzzy soft-constraint relations** [5] with hyperbolic membership characteristics [4]. Moreover, the fuzzy soft-constraint relations, in turn, are enforced via **fuzzy penalty-reward functions**, linear in the membership values themselves. Finally, in a Multi-Criteria Decision Model (MCDM) environment, the fuzzy penalty-reward functions combine together with the optimising criterion, resulting in a **fuzzy multi-criteria performance evaluation function**, $\mathcal{P}(\ )$, defined over the (vector) solution space $\{x\}$. Hence $\mathcal{P}(x)$ simultaneously reflects how well a particular solution x optimises the primary objective function as well as how much it satisfies, or fails to satisfy, the various soft-constraints specified by the problem.

Our general strategy is to construct $\mathcal{P}(x)$ for a particular problem by examining its optimisation/decision model and its soft-constraint modelling requirements, then maximise this non-linear function, subject only to the problem's remaining 'hard'-constraints, as summarised by $x \in \mathcal{F}$. It is hoped that the proposed fuzzy soft-constraint formulation—with shared commonalities with Fuzzy Mathematical Programming (FMP) [15, 7], Goal Programming (GP) [3] and Fuzzy Goal Programming (FGP) [8, 14]—achieves the soft-constraint modelling realism of fuzzy logic along with the multi-criteria modelling practicality of goal-*satisficing* decision models, and, moreover, that it affords the optimisation/decision model a greater degree of modelling flexibility, allowing optimising criteria to exist alongside goal-aspirations, hard-bounds alongside soft-bounds, and crisp definitions with fuzzy entities, etc.

In term of model implementation, because $\mathcal{P}(x)$ is mathematically equivalent to performing a series of algebraic operations and sigmoidal set-partitionings, i.e. the functionalities of a Feed-Forward Neural Network (NN)[13, 9], any readily available Object-Oriented implementation of NN function classes [11] can be tailored to *encode* this *solution-performance mapping* $\mathcal{P}(x)$. The NN-encoded parameters can be divided into two groups: those pertaining to the problem itself (i.e. the coefficients of the objective function and the constraint relations), and those pertaining to the fuzzification/MCDM/optimisation model (i.e. the sigmoidal temperature parameters which control the shapes of the hyperbolic membership functions, the maximum penalty/reward points, etc.). Let us refer to the latter collectively as the **fuzzy utility parameters**. Here, as with MCDM in general, a decision maker is distinguished by his/her set of fuzzy utility parameters. In theory, a learning NN, *partially encoded* with the problem data only, can be trained to 'self-parameterise' the fuzzy utility parameters, i.e. based on how a particular decision maker ranks or rates different solutions to the same problem. These parameters can then be extracted from a trained NN. Such a modelling exercise brings to the fore, two of the cornerstones in a neural information processing system: a neural architecture's ability to implement a non-linear mapping, and a neuro-model's ability to perform experiential learning and induce an implicit mapping model. We propose such a NN/connectionist framework as a basis for future work in adaptive, **case-based induction** of the decision maker's *implicit* fuzzy utility function.

In term of solution methodology, we opt to solve the non-linear maximisation problem $\{\max \mathcal{P}(x) \mid x \in \mathcal{F}\}$ via a genetic/evolutionary programming algorithm. The use of a non-MP approach is motivated by practical considerations as much as by a view toward generalising the modelling/optimisation framework to encompass applications for which $\mathcal{P}(x)$ is not necessarily a mathematical expression. For example, x may correspond to a set of numbers parametrising an action/decision model whose $\mathcal{P}(x)$ can only be *evaluated* against a data set.

The paper is organised as follows: Section 2 examines a particular multi-criteria FX/Futures trading portfolio optimisation problem, for which Section 3 derives a fuzzy soft-constraint formulation. Section 4 describes the neuro-evolutionary methodology for encoding and solving the formulated discrete optimisation problem and proposes how to generalise the hybrid fuzzy neuro-evolutionary framework for optimisation analysis Section 5 examines an example portfolio solution, and we conclude the discussion.

2   FX/Futures Trading Portfolio Model at Chase Manhattan Bank

The Quantitative Research and Trading (QRT) group at Chase Manhattan Bank, London, has developed a daily prediction and trading model (PTM) for a number of liquid foreign exchange rates in the spot market as well as for interest-rate and equity-index futures. Suppose that QRT has chosen to model-trade n FX spots/Futures contracts, i.e. take positions according to n PTMs, each of which may be reading a 'Long,' 'Square,' or 'Short' signal at a given time. The portfolio optimisation problem is to determine the set of portfolio weights $\{\omega_i \geq 0, \quad i = 1, \ldots, n, \quad \sum_i \omega_i = 1\}$ each ω_i of which, when multiplied to some fixed notional, gives the size of the 'Long' or 'Short' position to be taken or maintained in the ith underlying spot/contract *when* the corresponding i^{th} PTM does generate a 'Long' or 'Short' signal. This clearly forces a break with the 'invest-and-hold' definition of the portfolio weights, as per the traditional *asset* allocation problem. In essence, what is being allocated is the proprietary account's *exposure* to the performance of each PTM in predicting price movements and generating appropriate trading signals. For this and other considerations, this 'portfolio of models' is not being optimised in the classical Markowitz [10] risk-return framework. Moreover, because FX/Futures transaction orders are carried out in (US\$-denominated) lot sizes, each portfolio weight is discretised to a multiple of some percentage unit (e.g. 5%) corresponding to an appropriate minimum transaction order size. Formally, $\omega_i \in \mathcal{D}_{\langle N \rangle} = \{0/N, 1/N, 2/N, \ldots, N/N\}, \quad i = 1, \ldots, n, \ N \geq n$ (e.g. N = 20).

Our portfolio model is based principally on maximising the weighted sum of the individual PTM risk-adjusted returns.[1] This maximising criterion is *supplemented* by three goal-satisfaction criteria, namely that the weighted sums of the relative-return, Sharpe-ratio and the probability-of-ruin measures should be above (or below) their respective thresholds. The rationale is that while the supplementary criteria are crucial in capturing the profitability of the trading *portfolio* and the money management viability of the portfolio *trading*, they are not as information-rich, nor as directly applicable to portfolio models in general, as the risk-adjusted-return measure.[2] Furthermore, we include lower and upper soft-bound *exposure* limits on each weight variable to ensure intra-portfolio diversification. Let x be a vector of n portfolio allocation weights. The n-PTM portfolio optimisation model is stated thus:

$$
\begin{aligned}
\max \quad & c^t x \\
\text{s.t.} \quad & Ax \gtrsim b \\
& \underline{L} \lesssim x \lesssim \underline{U} \\
& x \in \mathcal{W} = \{x \in \mathcal{D}_{\langle N \rangle}^n \mid \|x\|_1 = 1\},
\end{aligned}
\tag{1}
$$

---

[1] The correlations of returns (analogous to the off-diagonal elements in the Markowitz variance-covariance matrix) are negligible—a correlation filter having been applied in the portfolio selection process in order to ensure diversification—and no longer enters into the analysis. In contrast, the Markowitz approach places a closer scrutiny on the off-diagonal elements, whence its concept of portfolio risk differs markedly from a collection of individual return risks. In particular, it seeks to exploit the possibility of portfolio risk reduction via optimal diversification, which, once again, is more meaningful within the 'portfolio of investments' context. Here a unified risk management framework bridging the underlying-price-volatility and model-trading-return concepts of risk is needed and warrants further investigations.

[2] The relative-return does not include a risk measure. The Sharpe-ratio uses the underlying price movement volatility in place of the PTM volatility of returns. The probability-of-ruin criterion echos the belief in a deliberate integration between investment and money management strategies[6].

where $c = \begin{bmatrix} \text{RAR}_1 \\ \vdots \\ \text{RAR}_n \end{bmatrix}$, $A = \begin{bmatrix} \text{RR}_1 \dots \text{RR}_n \\ \text{SR}_1 \dots \text{SR}_n \\ -\text{PR}_1 \dots -\text{PR}_n \end{bmatrix}$, and $b = \begin{bmatrix} \text{RR}_{thresh} \\ \text{SR}_{thresh} \\ -\text{PR}_{thresh} \end{bmatrix}$, with RAR_j, RR_j, SR_j,

and PR_j, $j = 1, \dots, n$, denoting, respectively, the jth PTMs' individual risk-adjusted-return, relative-return, Sharpe-ratio and probability-of-ruin measures, while the subscript *thresh* denotes setting the performance goal thresholds, i.e. the goal-aspiration levels that the solution portfolio is to achieve. The lower and upper bounds are uniformly applied: $[L_j, U_j] = [L, U]$, $j = 1, \dots, n$.

3 Fuzzy Soft-Constraint Optimisation/Decision Model

First, we introduce some notations:
- Sigmoidal Transfer Function:

$$\wp(y) = \wp^{[\theta, \tau]}(y) \overset{\text{def}}{=} \frac{1}{1 + e^{-(y-\theta)/\tau}} \equiv \frac{\tanh((y-\theta)/2\tau) + 1}{2} \in (0,1), \quad y \in \Re, \tag{2}$$

where $\tau > 0$ is the *shape* (temperature) parameter controlling the steepness of this monotone function, and θ is the *threshold* parameter. Note $\wp(\theta) = 0.5$, $\wp'(\theta) = 1/4\tau$.

- Linear Re-Scaling Function:

$$\zeta(y) = \zeta_{[a,b]}^{[c,d]}(y) \overset{\text{def}}{=} c + \frac{(d-c)}{(b-a)}(y-a), \quad y \in [a,b] \Longrightarrow \zeta(y) \in [c,d] \tag{3}$$

3.1 Fuzzy Set Membership Function

Let us focus initially on a fuzzy soft-constraint relation $\{A_i.x \gtrsim b_i\}$, for which we define a slack 'function', $s_i(x) \overset{\text{def}}{=} A_i.x - b_i$. Consider a hyperbolic fuzzy set membership function:

$$\mu_i(x) = \mu_{\{A_i.x \underset{\sim}{\gtrsim} b_i\}}(x) \overset{\text{def}}{=} \wp^{[\theta_i, \tau_i]}(s_i(x)) \in (0,1), \quad \tau_i > 0 \tag{4}$$

This particular form of $\mu_i(x)$ exhibits several desirable features from the optimisation/decision modelling point of view. First and foremost, $\mu_i(x)$ serves as a set-partition function, defining the boundary between the constraint-satisfying subspace $\{x \mid A_i.x \geq b_i\}$ and its complement; solutions in the former are to be rewarded, those in the latter to be penalised. On the other hand, as a *robust* fuzzy set function, $\mu_i(x)$ 'blurs' this constraint-satisfied/constraint-violated set boundary. That is, because it is *functionally smooth*, $\mu_i(x)$ makes for a relatively gradual transition from $0 < \mu_i(x) < 0.5$ for negative $s_i(x)$, to $\mu_i(x) = 0.5$ at $s_i(x) = 0$ and onto $0.5 < \mu_i(x) < 1$ for positive $s_i(x)$, saturating to unity as $s_i(x) \gg 0$ and diminishing to zero as $s_i(x) \ll 0$. Moreover, $\mu_i(x)$ is also explicitly parameterised by θ_i which locates the set-partition boundary, i.e. where $\mu_i(x) = 0.5$, and by τ_i which controls the 'sharpness' of the set-partitioning. They are the fuzzy parameters of our optimisation model. This hyperbolic membership function can also be said summarily to exhibit a decreasing **coefficient of membership satiation** [4], $m(x)$, defined as the second derivative of the membership function,

$$m(x) = \mu''(x), \tag{5}$$

which is positive for x with negative slack ($s_i(x) < 0$) and negative for x with positive slack ($s_i(x) > 0$).

3.2 Fuzzy Penalty-Reward Function

Here we derive a fuzzy penalty-reward function, denoted $\Phi_i(x)$, which assigns some negative point (penalty) to a solution identified with the fuzzy "$\{A_i.x \geq b_i\}$-violating" concept and some positive point (reward) to one identified with "$\{A_i.x \geq b_i\}$-satisfying". Each $\Phi_i(x)$ is to be in direct proportionality, not with the slack measure, $s_i(x)$, but with the membership function value $\mu_i(x)$ itself, whence a linear re-scaling of $\mu_i(x)$. Let $[P_i(x) \leq 0, R_i(x) > 0]$ denote the maximum penalty and the minimum reward points, i.e. assigned to solutions with $\mu_i(x)$ approaching zero and one respectively. The fuzzy penalty-reward function is symbolically represented $\Phi(\ ) = (\zeta \circ \wp)(\ )$, and is given by:

$$\Phi_i(x) = \zeta_{[0,1]}^{[P_i, R_i]}\left(\mu_{\{A_i.x \underset{\sim}{\gtrsim} b_i\}}(x)\right) \in (P_i, R_i), \quad i = 1, \dots, m, \tag{6}$$

where θ_i now locates the boundary where a solution is neither penalised nor rewarded ($\Phi_i(x)$ exactly equals zero). The fuzzy penalty-reward functions enforcing the soft-bound limits on the portfolio weights are similarly constructed, except that the two-sided bound on each variable requires two sigmoidal functions, two sets of fuzzification parameters, and is a scalar function of the individual elements $x_1, \dots, x_j, \dots, x_n$:

$$\begin{aligned}
\Psi_j(x_j) &= \Psi_j^L(x_j) + \Psi_j^U(x_j), \\
\Psi_j^L(x_j) &= \zeta_{[0,1]}^{[P_j^L \leq 0, R_j^L > 0]}\left(\mu_{\{x_j \underset{\sim}{\gtrsim} L_j\}}(x_j)\right), \\
\Psi_j^U(x_j) &= \zeta_{[0,1]}^{[P_j^U \leq 0, R_j^U > 0]}\left(\mu_{\{x_j \underset{\sim}{\lesssim} U_j\}}(x_j)\right), \quad L_j < U_j, \quad j = 1, \dots, n
\end{aligned} \tag{7}$$

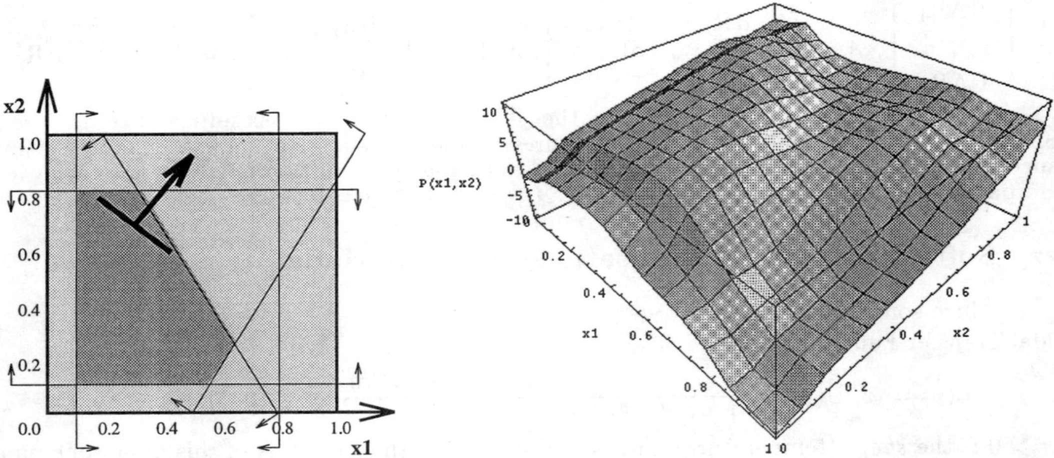

Figure 1: *Fuzzy Soft-Constraint Optm. Prob.*   Figure 2: *Fuzzy Performance Evaluation Function*

3.3   Fuzzy Multi-Criteria Performance Function & Optimisation Problem

For the portfolio problem, the optimising objective function is *optionally*[3] re-scaled as:

$$\Lambda(x) = \zeta_{[c_{min}, c_{max}]}^{[0, O_{max} > 0]}(c^t x),$$
(8)

where $c_{min} = \min_{j=1,\ldots,n}\{c_j\}$ and $c_{max} = \max_{j=1,\ldots,n}\{c_j\}$ are determined, respectively, by solving $\{\min c^t x \mid x \in \mathcal{W}\}$ and $\{\max c^t x \mid x \in \mathcal{W}\}$ [4]. Let O_{max} and the P's and the R's be our MCDM parameters, reflecting the relative importance among each of the $(1 + m + n)$ criteria. Together with the fuzzy parameters (the τ's and the θ's) already defined, they constitute the *fuzzy utility parameters* of our optimisation/decision model. The fuzzy *multi-criteria* performance evaluation function, $\mathcal{P}(x)$, is simply the summation of a (re-scaled) objective function and the fuzzy penalty-rewards. Ultimately, we formalise the following *discrete non-linear optimisation problem:*[4]

$$\max \quad \mathcal{P}(x) = \Lambda(x) + \sum_{i=1}^{m} \Phi_i(x) + \sum_{j=1}^{n} \Psi_j(x_j)$$

$$\text{s.t.} \quad x \in \mathcal{W}$$
(9)

As an illustration, a hypothetical two-variable problem is depicted graphically in fig. 1. It resembles a Linear Programming (LP) problem, except that while the light-shaded area represents the 'true' feasible region, the $[0, 1]^2$ square, the darker-shaded 'pentagon' represents the sub-region bounded by the soft-constraints. The thick arrow represents the objective coefficient vector. For some given set of fuzzy utility parameters, $\mathcal{P}(x_1, x_2)$ yields an evaluation surface such as the one depicted in fig. 2. Notice the rectangular depression corresponding the the fuzzy penalty-reward functions enforcing the $[0.05, 0.80]$ soft-bounds on both variables as well as the 5-sided 'plateau' directly above the said soft-constrained sub-region, whose 'plane' can be seen to tilt upward in the direction corresponding to the linear improvement in the objective function. The remaining task (optimisation) is to locate the highest point of this surface over $[0, 1]^2$.

4   Neuro-Evolutionary Methodology & Extensions

4.1   Mapping NN Architecture & Genetic/Evolutionary Optimisation

Consider a feed-forward neural architecture depicted in fig. 3. The first set of connections forms a dot product $c^t x$ for a given input (solution) vector x, and this value is then re-scaled according to eqn. 8.

---

[3] Because the optimising objective may grow, in this case, linearly in x, without bound, while the maximum penalty points are finite, the problem is bounded only by the remaining 'hard' constraints. In this case, $\mathcal{F} = \mathcal{W}$ suffices, but in general, the optimising objective function is to be normalised [14].

[4] Our fuzzy soft-constraint formulation retains a formal equivalence with the FGP model. To wit, let there be no penalty assignment (maximum penalty points of zero), define $\{w_0 \equiv O_{max}, \; w_i \equiv R_i, \; i = 1, \ldots, m, \text{ and } w_{m+j} \equiv R_j^L + R_j^U, \; j = 1, \ldots, n \mid \sum_{l=0}^{m+n} w_l = 1\}$, and artificially introduce a piecewise-linear membership function [1, 4] on the objective function: $\mu_0(x) \stackrel{\text{def}}{=} max\{0, min\{1, \zeta_{[c_{min}, c_{max}]}^{[0,1]}(c^t x)\}\}$. Clearly, $\mathcal{P}(x) = \sum_{l=0}^{m+n} w_l \mu_l(x)$ is a weighted additive fuzzy achievement function, as per FGP formulation [14]. In other word, FGP derives $\mathcal{P}(x)$ directly from the fuzzy membership functions defined on both the goal-satisficing *as well as* on the optimising objectives. Our handling the fuzzy soft-constraints through a penalty-reward scheme, however, affords more precise as well as intuitive control of the fuzzy-constraint set-partitioning. Moreover, with penalty assignments it is relatively straightforward to benchmark the fuzzy soft-constraint reformulation against the hard-bound version, which can be thought of as maximising $\mathcal{P}(x)$ with very large penalty assignments and the sigmoidal shape parameters approaching zero.

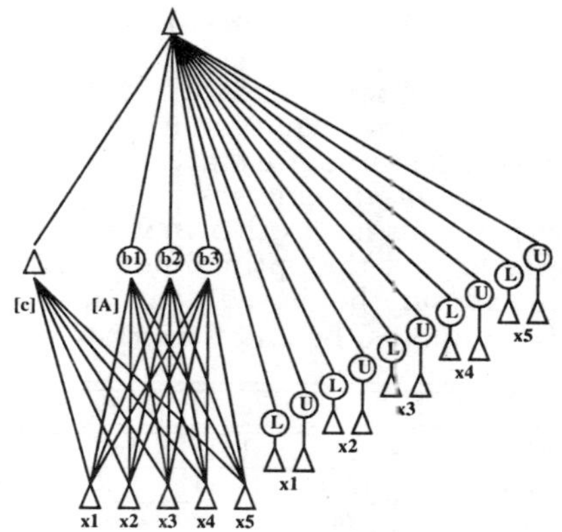

Figure 3: *Neural Architecture Encoding Fuzzy Performance Function*

The 3-by-5 weight matrix implements the Ax multiplication, yielding the inputs to the three hidden-layer neurons fuzzifying the goal-satisfaction soft-constraints. Each portfolio weight variable is also input to a pair of input-layer neurons whose sigmoidal non-linearities fuzzify the soft-bound exposure limits. The connections to the output nodes linearly re-scales the neurons' outputs (fuzzy membership values) into penalty/reward assignments. For a given set of **NN**-encoded fuzzy utility parameters, the NN-mapped output, **NN**(x), is *functionally* equivalent to the performance evaluation function $\mathcal{P}(x)$.

It remains for a genetic/evolutionary optimisation engine is to search over $\mathcal{W}$ to maximise the NN-encoded $\mathcal{P}(x)$, whence the latter constitutes the algorithm's *fitness evaluation function*. To stress the practical benefits over a MP approach, we note how a *structural* constraint such as the discretisation of the portfolio weight space $\mathcal{D}^n_{(N)}$ can be implemented simply and elegantly by designing a genotype-phenotype mapping which *only* generates solutions from $\mathcal{W}$. In contrast, one only has to imagine an equivalent branch-and-bound formulation over the n-dimensional Cartesian grid.

Note that the portfolio optimisation problem considered here is intrinsically linear; the non-linearities in $\mathcal{P}(x)$ are due to fuzzification. As such, it lends itself neatly to a 'standard' feed-forward NN architecture. Nonetheless, it is a straight-forward matter to generalise our neural representation of $\mathcal{P}(x)$ to problems containing non-linear expressions, e.g. a Quadratic Programming (QP) formulation of a fund manager's Markowitz portfolio. For higher-order functionalities, we refer to a Functional Link Net (FLN) architecture [13], which has similarly well-defined mapping and learning behaviours.

So far, we have only partially utilised the neural information processing capability, namely a neural architecture's ability to implement a non-linear mapping. Next, we explore the more definitive part of neural information processing, namely a neuro-model's ability to perform *experiential* learning and *induce* an implicit mapping model.

4.2   Learning NN & Inducing an Implicit Fuzzy Utility Function

The above mathematical/conceptual equivalence between the *mathematical* $\mathcal{P}(x)$ and the *neural* $\mathcal{P}(x)$ is very little more than a programming convenience. Operating strictly in recall mode, the encoded-NN is employed solely for its *mapping* functionality. Now we propose to exploit its *learning* functionality. Suppose a decision maker is asked, in a MCDM setting, to rank and/or rate p solutions on basis of how well each solution x^k, $k = 1, \ldots, p$, optimises the primary objective function as well as how much it satisfies, or fails to satisfy, the various soft-constraints specified by the problem.[5] Clearly, we now have p examples, or patterns, each consisting of an 'input' solution vector x^k and the corresponding 'output' numerical evaluation, $\mathcal{P}^k \in [0, 1]$. Let us denote this *training* set by $\mathcal{L} = \{(x^1, \mathcal{P}^1), \ldots, (x^k, \mathcal{P}^k), \ldots, (x^p, \mathcal{P}^p)\}$.

Suppose that we specify a particular feed-forward NN *architecture* to satisfy the functional requirements necessary for implementing $\mathcal{P}(x)$, but then only *partially encode* the NN parameters, i.e. only those which pertain to the problem data themselves. Then let the NN learn, in an $\mathcal{L}$-supervised manner, allowing only adjustments to those NN parameters which correspond to the fuzzy utility parameters. As usual, the NN training process corresponds to the following mapping error minimisation:

$$\min \left[\frac{1}{p} \sum_{k=1}^{p} \left| \mathcal{P}^k - \mathcal{P}(x^k) \right|^d \right]^{1/d}, \ d = 1, 2 \tag{10}$$

This constitutes an example/case-based induction of the decision maker's implicit fuzzy utility parameters, which are then extracted from a *trained* NN. It is hoped that future work exploring this possibility will tie in with the body of theoretical and practical researches on fuzzy utility theory. [2, 16, 12].

---

[5] To maintain compatibility with FGP proper, further stipulate that such a ranking/rating is bounded to within $[0, 1]$.

5   Example Futures Trading Portfolio Solutions

We present an example portfolio of six PTMs, designated [a], ..., [f], three of which model-trade government bond futures while the others model-trade equity market index futures. Table 1 lists the portfolio data, i.e. the past RAR, RR, SR and PR performance statistics recorded for each PTM. From inspection, it is clear that a sort of *dominance relationship* emerges among them. That is, [b] not only achieves the highest RAR figure, but also outperforms most other PTM's with respect to the three supplementary performance criteria. So one expects to find the optimal portfolio assignment to be essentially driven by the need to satisfy the minimum exposure bounds, L, and the desire to assign as much weighting as possible to [b].[6] In contrast, [d] is dominated by all other PTMs w.r.t. every criterion.

Table 1: *Futures Trading Portfolio Data*						
Prediction-Trading Model	[a]	[b]	[c]	[d]	[e]	[f]
Risk-Adjusted Return (RAR)	12.00	17.54	5.25	1.88	10.45	7.74
Relative Return (RR)	128.4	123.9	188.4	65.4	88.8	104.8
Sharpe Ratio (SR)	1.558	2.095	0.997	0.197	1.333	0.920
Probability of Ruin (PR)	0.083	0.096	0.518	0.835	0.367	0.384

Next, we specify the supplementary performance goal thresholds, i.e. the b_i's (or the 'right-hand-side' values), as well as the soft-bound exposure limits, i.e. the interval $[L, U]$. While it is possible to specify b_i's in an *a priori* manner, we choose instead to determine each b_i as a function of the 'left-hand-side' numbers $(A_{i,[a]}, \ldots, A_{i,[f]})$. We consider two methods of calculations: 'straight-average', $b_i = (A_{i,[a]} + \ldots + A_{i,[f]})/6$, and '$\alpha$-weighting', $b_i = \alpha A_{i.}^{best} + (1 - \alpha)A_{i.}^{worst}$, $0 < \alpha < 1$. We specify $\alpha = 0.75$. In this particular data set, the '75%-weighted' numbers are higher, and therefore make for tougher goal-satisfaction thresholds, than the 'straight-average' numbers, e.g. $0.75 * 188.4 + 0.25 * 65.4 = 158 > (128.4 + 123.9 + 188.4 + 65.4 + 88.8 + 104.8)/6 = 117$. With regard to the upper and lower soft-bound exposure limits, we try two different intervals: $[L, U] = [5\%, 80\%], [10\%, 60\%]$. Thus altogether we have a total of four problem variations.

For each of the four problems considered, we further specify four sets of fuzzy utility parameters. For simplicity and uniformity, we let $\{\Phi_i(x) \in [-1, 1], i = 1, \ldots, m = 3; \Psi_j(x_j) \in [-1, 1], j = 1, \ldots, n = 6\}$. In other word, each supplementary criterion and each soft-bound exposure limit is worth a maximum of -1 penalty point and $+1$ reward. With regard to o_{max} which signifies the relative importance between the primary optimising criterion (RAR) and the $m + n$ soft-constraints ($m = 3$ secondary performance criteria and $n = 6$ soft-bound exposure limits), we specify $o_{max} = k(m + n)$, $k = 1, 2$.[7] Furthermore, we also specify 'high' and 'low' values for the τ's. The higher the value, the 'more fuzzy' the distinction or set-partitioning between soft-constraint satisfaction and violation, while the lower the τ value, the sharper, more 'hard-constraint' like, the fuzzy soft-constraint relation becomes.

The four problem variations (1,2,3,4) together with the four combinations of the fuzzy utility parameters (i,ii,iii,iv) yield a total of sixteen different cases of the optimisation problem $\{\max \mathcal{P}(x) \mid x \in \mathcal{W}\}$, which are solved respectively using a genetic/evolutionary algorithm. The results are listed in Table 2.

Table 2: *Fuzzy Soft-Constraint Optimisation Problems, Model Parameters, and Solutions*										
Prob.	Problem Specifications		Fuzzy Utility Parameters		Portfolio Solution Weights (in %)					
(Vers.)	b_i	$[L, U]$	τ Value	o_{max}	[a]	[b]	[c]	[d]	[e]	[f]
1(i)	$(A_{i,[a]} + \ldots + A_{i,[f]})/6$	[5%, 80%]	'high'	$2(m + n)$	5	75	5	5	5	5
1(ii)				$(m + n)$	10	65	10	5	5	5
1(iii)			'low'	$2(m + n)$	5	75	5	5	5	5
1(iv)				$(m + n)$	5	75	5	5	5	5
2(i)		[10%, 60%]	'high'	$2(m + n)$	15	55	10	0	10	10
2(ii)				$(m + n)$	15	40	15	10	10	10
2(iii)			'low'	$2(m + n)$	10	50	10	10	10	10
2(iv)				$(m + n)$	10	50	10	10	10	10
3(i)	$0.75 A_{i.}^{best} + 0.25 A_{i.}^{worst}$	[5%, 80%]	'high'	$2(m + n)$	5	75	5	5	5	5
3(ii)				$(m + n)$	5	75	5	5	5	5
3(iii)			'low'	$2(m + n)$	5	75	5	5	5	5
3(iv)				$(m + n)$	5	75	5	5	5	5
4(i)		[10%, 60%]	'high'	$2(m + n)$	15	55	10	0	10	10
4(ii)				$(m + n)$	15	55	10	0	10	10
4(iii)			'low'	$2(m + n)$	10	60	10	0	10	10
4(iv)				$(m + n)$	10	60	10	0	10	10

---

[6] This is due to the fact that the four performance criteria are, to an extent, correlated measures (a PTM which is doing well w.r.t. one is likely to do well w.r.t the others) and to the fact that [b] performed exceptionally well during the trading period evaluated, bearing in mind that the performance multi-criteria pertained to *individual* PTMs.

[7] In terms of interpretation, $k = 1$ implies a multi-criteria trade-off profile where a *hypothetical* solution which achieves c_{max}, but which also earns the maximum total of $-(m + n)$ penalty points for violating all the soft-constraints, is worth exactly zero. On the other hand, $k = 2$ states that such a solution would be worth as much as *another* hypothetical solution which earns the maximum total of $+(m + n)$ reward points, but only manages c_{min} for the primary optimising criterion.

Let us observe some of the patterns which emerge among the sixteen solutions, their differences having been magnified here by the relatively 'crude' discretisation (in steps of 5%). On the whole, one sees that all solutions weight heavily toward [b], as is anticipated. This is more pronounced in problems 1 and 3, where a 'wider' interval of soft-bound exposure limit ([5%, 80%] vs. [10%, 60%]) was specified. To a lesser extent, this is also noticeable when comparing solutions to problems with $b_i = 0.75 A_i^{best} + 0.25 A_i^{worst}$ (problems 3 and 4) and those with $b_i = (A_{i,[a]} + \ldots + A_{i,[f]})/6$ (problems 1 and 2), where the former, all else being equal, are more demanding w.r.t. the supplementary performance criteria and therefore exhibit greater bias toward [b], which, once again, tends to dominate. Only w.r.t. the RR criterion is [b] outperformed by both [a] and [c], and this explains the difference between case 1(i) and case 1(ii), the latter giving less bias toward the primary optimising criterion (RAR). Meanwhile, [d] is so comprehensively outperformed by all other PTMs that it is only ever included in the portfolio to satisfy the lower soft-bound exposure limit. But as a tighter [10%, 60%] limit reigns in $x_{[b]}$, the algorithm is 'willing' to suffer penalty (for violating $x_{[d]} > 0.10$) in order to 'free up' additional assignable weight for the better PTM(s). Moreover, note how high τ values tend to push the weight variables 'inward', because the fuzzy boundaries are less sharp and the variables have to move 'deeper' inside the bounds to converge to higher reward points. On the other hand, higher τ values also mean that a given extent of soft-bound violation is less penalised, and therefore more likely to be tolerated (see 2(i) vs. 2(iii)). Lastly, notice how [a] is generally favoured over [c], the former outperforming the latter w.r.t. all but the RR criterion.

We find it more useful to enumerate the varying combinations of problem/model parameters in this way, rather than to try to enumerate the decision model *a priori* to the optimisation analysis, as per traditional utility theory/MCDM framework, as this provides insights into the interactions among the modelled multi-criteria. It would also be possible to examine in greater details each portfolio solution's constituent achievement/reward/penalty points, as these numbers are stored by our optimisation algorithm as well.

6   Conclusions

We introduce a fuzzy set framework within the context of portfolio theory. While our particular portfolio model does not resemble a Markowitz formulation, the latter can be captured via a non-linear extension of our framework. We introduce the explicit penalty-reward concepts to Fuzzy Goal Programming, while retaining a formal equivalence. In term of solution methodology, we forgo Mathematical Programming in favour of a general search strategy based on a genetic/evolutionary programming algorithm, citing practical and modelling benefits. The fuzzy soft-constraint optimisation/decision model is illustrated on a portfolio of daily trading models on equity-index futures contracts. The patterns of weight assignments which emerge are consistent with the problem data and the variously specified fuzzy utility parameters. Finally, we propose Artificial Neural Network, firstly, as a mapping representation to implement the fuzzy multi-criteria performance evaluation function, and, secondly, as a learning machine which in theory is capable of performing a case-based induction of a decision maker's implicit fuzzy utility function. We put forward this fuzzy, multi-criteria optimisation/decision model together with the neuro-evolutionary methodology as a flexible, analytical framework for managing a portfolio of FX/Futures trading models in particular, and for engaging soft-constraint optimisation problems in general.

References

[1] R. E. Bellman and L. A. Zadeh. Decision making in a fuzzy environment. *Management Science*, 17(2):B141–164, 1970.

[2] A. Billot. An existence theorem for fuzzy utility-functions—a new elementary proof. *Fuzzy Sets and Systems*, 74(2):271–276, 1995.

[3] V. Chankong and Y. Haimes. *Multiobjective Decision Making: Theory and Methodology*. North-Holland, NY, 1983.

[4] A. K. Dhingra, S. S. Rao, and V. Kumar. Nonlinear membership functions in multiobjective fuzzy optimisation of mechanical and structural systems. *AIAA Journal*, 30(1):251–260, January 1992.

[5] D. Dubois and H. Prade. Systems of linear fuzzy constraints. *Fuzzy Sets and Systems*, 3:37–48, 1980.

[6] C. Dunis and M. Feeny, editors. *Exchange Rate Forecasting*. Woodhead-Faulkner, 1989.

[7] R. Fullér and H.-J. Zimmermann. Fuzzy reasoning for solving fuzzy mathematical programming problems. *Fuzzy Sets and Systems*, 60:121–133, 1993.

[8] E. L. Hannan. On fuzzy goal programming. *Decision Sciences*, 12:522–531, 1981.

[9] R. Hecht-Nielsen. *Neurocomputing*. Addison-Wesley, Reading, MA, 1990.

[10] H. M. Markowitz. Portfolio selection. *Journal of Finance*, 7:77–91, March 1952.

[11] T. Masters. *Practical Neural Network Recipes in C++*. Academic Press, 1993.

[12] I Nishizaki and F. Seo. Interactive support for fuzzy trade-off evaluation in group decision-making. *Fuzzy Sets and Systems*, 68(3):309–325, 1994.

[13] Y.-H. Pao. *Adaptive Pattern Recognition and Neural Networks*. Addison-Wesley, 1989.

[14] S. S. Rao, K. Sundararaju, B. G. Prakash, and C. Balakrishna. Fuzzy goal programming approach for structural optimisation. *AIAA Journal*, 30(5):1425–1432, May 1992.

[15] H. Tanaka, T. Okuda, and K. Asai. On fuzzy mathematical programming. *Journal of Cybernetics*, 3:37–46, 1974.

[16] M. Yoneda, S. Fukami, and M. Grabisch. Interactive determination of utility function represented as a fuzzy integral. *Information Sciences*, 71(1-2):43–64, 1993.

Foreign Exchange Rates Forecasting with Neural Networks

Jingtao Yao, Hean-Lee Poh, Teo Jašić
Department of Information Systems and Computer Science
National University of Singapore
Singapore 119260
E-mail : yaojt@iscs.nus.sg

Abstract— In this paper, a neural network based foreign exchange rates forecasting method is discussed. Neural networks with time series and technical indicators as inputs are built to capture the underlying "rules" of the movement in currency exchange rates. Before using historical data to train the neural networks, the traditional R/S analysis is used to test the "efficiency" of each market. The study shows that without the use of extensive market data or knowledge, useful prediction can be made and significant paper profit can be achieved with simple technical indicators.

1 Introduction

Since 1973, with the abandonment of the fixed foreign exchange rates and the implementation of the floating exchange rate system by industrialized countries, researchers have been striving for an explanation of the movement of exchange rates. Thus, many kinds of forecasting methods are developed by thousands of researches and experts. Technical and fundamental analysis are among the major forecasting methods which are popularly used in the financial area. Foreign exchange rates are affected by many highly correlated factors. These factors could be economic, political and even psychological factors. The interaction of these factors is in a very complex fashion. Therefore, to forecast the change of foreign exchange rates is generally very difficult. Neural networks are an emerging and challenging computational technology and they offer a new avenue to explore the dynamics of a variety of financial applications. Actually, they are simulated networks with interconnected 'neurons' which try to mimic the function of the brain's central nervous system. Neural networks have been shown to have great potential for financial forecasting. Examples using neural networks in currency applications include Refenes[3], Weigend[4], and Zhang[8]. Feed-forward backpropagation networks are the most commonly used networks and meant for the widest variety of applications.

In this paper, the research results on using neural networks to forecast the exchange rates between the US dollar and five other major currencies, Japanese Yen (JPY), Deutsch Mark (DEM), British Pound(GBP), Swiss Franc(CHF) and Australian Dollar(AUD) are presented. This study shows that without the use of extensive market data or knowledge, useful prediction can be made and significant paper profit can be achieved with simple technical indicators.

2 Foreign Exchange Rate Forecasting

From the very beginning, Forex was determined by the balance of payments. The balance of payments was merely a way of listing receipts and payments in international transactions for a country. The balance was determined mainly by the import and export of goods. Therefor it was not difficult to predict Forex at that time. Later on, interest rates and other demand-supply factors had become more relevant to each currency. Increased Forex trading, and hence speculation due to liquidity and bonds, had also contributed to the difficulty of forecasting Forex.

The application of forecasting method includes two basic steps: analyze data series and select the forecasting method that best fits the data series. To maximize profits from the liquidity market, more and more 'best' forecasting techniques are used by traders. Nowadays, traders no longer rely on a single technique to provide information about the future of the markets but rather use a variety of techniques to obtain multiple signals. Neural networks are often trained by using both technical and fundamental indicators to produce trading signals. To improve the profit gain and to decrease risk is the most important motivations for developing the neural networks. Neural networks can make contributions to the maximization of returns, while reducing costs, and limiting risks. In this paper, a mixed technical method which takes not only the delayed time series data as inputs but also the technical indicators is illustrated. The work discussed in this paper would represent a violation of the *efficient market hypothesis*. The inclusion of fundamental factors will be studied in a different paper.

Variable	Mean	Std. Dev.	Variance	Max(*)
AUD/USD	0.7424	0.0605	0.003642	2.6616
CHF/USD	1.6203	0.3828	0.1466	3.3503
DEM/USD	1.9450	0.4770	0.2263	3.081
GBP/USD	1.6025	0.1978	0.03938	2.7220
JPY/USD	152.240	42.2177	1782.4335	2.6187

Table 1: Data Statistics of Weekly Foreign Exchange Rates: * Maximum value for normalized data - zero mean and unit variance

3   Data Set Construction and Efficient Testing

Historical data are divided into three portions: training, validation and testing sets. The training set contains two thirds of the collected data, while the validation and the testing sets contain two fifteenths and three fifteenths respectively. The division is based on the experience of the authors which can be considered as a rule of thumb. A model is considered good if the error of out-of-sample testing is the lowest compared with the other models. If the trained model is the best one for validation and also the best one for testing, one can assume that it is a good model for future forecasting. The data sets of five currencies studied in this paper comprise 2910 daily rates for a sampling period of between 18 May 1984 and 7 July 1995. The data are chosen and segregated in time order. In other words, the data of the earlier period are used for training, the data of the later period are used for validation, and the data of the latest time period are used for testing. The statistics summary of the weekly data used in this study are shown in Table 1.

In this paper, the weekly closing prices are used as the prediction target of our experiment. They refer to each Friday's closing prices in the Singapore market. In the event of Friday being a holiday, the most recently available closing price for the currency was used. The data set for each currency in this study consist of 510 weekly data. It is segregated as training set: 18 May 1984 to 12 July 1991, validation set: 19 Nov 1991 - 29 Oct 1993 and testing set: 5 Nov 1993 - 7 July 1995.

In a real situation, there is no closing price for Forex. Forex trading takes place 24 hours a day over the world. The 24 hour data should be used in order to capture the underlying rules of the movement in Forex rates. The more data you use the more rules you can get. In this research, the weekly data are used assuming that they have enough information to capture the "rules". Due to the volatility of the currency movement, a different frequency of data maybe needed than the weekly data. The data could be sampled according to the market character, e.g. bullish, bearish, or trading, etc. In other words, when the market is volatile, we sample more data for training, and vice versa. Nonlinear or volatility time scale[7] will be taken into consideration in our further research.

3.1   Testing the Efficient Market Hypothesis

The most famous, widely tested and little believed hypothesis are *Random Walk Hypothesis* and *Efficient Market Hypothesis*[5]. The *Random Walk hypothesis* states that the market prices wander in a purely random and unpredictable way. The *efficient market hypothesis* states that the markets fully reflect all of the available information and prices are adjusted fully and immediately once new information become available. In the actual market, some people do react to information immediately after they have received the information while other people wait for the confirmation of information. The waiting people do not react until a trend is clearly established.

H. E. Hurst, who was a hydrologist, found that most natural phenomena, including river discharge, temperatures, rainfall, and sunspots, follow a *biased random walk* which is a trend with noise. The Hurst Exponent H [1] is a measure of the bias in fractional Brownian motion. The method could be used in economic and financial market time series to see whether these series are also biased random walks which indicates the possibility of forecasting.

The rescaled range analysis (R/S analysis) [1] is able to distinguish a random series from a fractal series, irrespective of the distribution of the underlying series (Gaussian or non-Gaussian). It can be used to detect the long-memory effect in the foreign exchange rate time series over a time period. R captures the maximum and minimum cumulative deviations of the observations x_t of the time series from its mean

Exchange	Hurst Exponent	Correlation
AUD/USD	0.532681	0.046347
CHF/USD	0.553941	0.077645
DEM/USD	0.554672	0.078737
GBP/USD	0.544408	0.063497
JPY/USD	0.540706	0.058053

Table 2: Hurst exponent and Correlation for the experimented five currencies

(μ), and it is a function of time (the number of observations N):

$$R_N = \max_{1 \le t \le N}[x_{t,N}] - \min_{1 \le t \le N}[x_{t,N}] \tag{1}$$

where $x_{t,N}$ is the cumulative deviation over N periods. The R/S ratio of R and the standard deviation S of the original time series can be estimated by the following empirical law: $R/S = N^H$ when observed for various N values. H describes the probability that two consecutive events are likely to occur. The type of series described by $H = 0$ is random, consisting of uncorrelated events. A value of H different from 0.50 denotes the observations that are not independent. When $0 < H < 0.5$, the system is an antipersistent or ergodic series with frequent reversals and high volatility. For the case $(0.5 < H < 1.0)$, H describes a persistent or trend-reinforcing series which is characterized by long memory effects. However, even in the case that the Hurst process describes a biased random walk, the bias can change abruptly either in direction or magnitude. Therefore, only the average cycle length of observed data can be estimated.

As shown in Table 2 , The value of Hurst Exponent for the logarithmic returns of daily exchange rates data is higher than 0.5 for all the observed time series. The highest value is 0.554 for the exchange rate of CHF/USD which denotes a long-memory effect in time series. Hence, there exist possibilities for conducting time series forecasting in the studied data sets.

4   Resulst of Weekly Exchange Rates Forecasting

Time series forecasting is perhaps the most exciting application of neural networks. The objective is to discover the underlying "structure" of the mechanism generating the data, i.e., to discover the relationship between present, past and future observations. In this paper, a purely time delayed time series and a simple technical indicators based time series method are experimented.

4.1   Measurement of Neural Networks

A usual measure to evaluate and compare the predictive power of the model is the Normalized Mean Squared Error (NMSE)[2][6]. Additional evaluation measures include the calculation of correct matching number of the actual and predicted values, x_t and $\hat{x}_t$ respectively, in the testing set with respect to the sign and directional change (expressed in percentages). Directional change statistic is the average of a_k where $a_k = 1$ if $(x_{t+1} - x_t)(\hat{x}_{t+1} - x_t) > 0$, and $a_k = 0$ otherwise. These statistics are desirable because the NMSE measure prediction only in terms of levels. Hence, the quality of the forecast can be measured by the correctness of gradient predictions (D_{stat}) or simply by the return one can expect if one starts with either the USD or the currency in consideration.

To simulate the real profit, a paper profit is used in this study. Assume that a certain amount of seed money is used in this program. The seed money is used to buy a certain amount of another currency when the prediction shows a rise in that currency. At the end the of testing period, the currency should be converted to the original currency of the seed money using the exact direct or cross rate of that day. The results obtained are shown in Table 3 and Table 4. The paper profit is calculated as follows:

$$Return = \left(\frac{money2}{money1}\right)^{\frac{52}{nw}} - 1 \tag{2}$$

where money1 = Seed money on first the testing day; money2 = Money after trading on last the testing day; nw= No. of weeks in testing period.

4.2   Forecasts Using Purely Time Delayed Time Series and Indicators

The purely time delayed forecast method is one of the simplest technical analysis methods. The real targets of the previous periods are used as inputs to the neural network to forecast the next period

Exchange	Model	Test. NMSE (R^2)	Gradient	$Ret1_{US}$
AUD/USD	5-3-1	0.0543 (0.9456)	55.00 %	1.09 %
CHF/USD	5-3-1	0.1100 (0.8900)	56.00 %	8.40%
DEM/USD	6-3-1	0.3153 (0.6847)	51.00 %	4.36 %
GBP/USD	6-3-1	0.1555 (0.8445)	54.74 %	2.30 %
JPY/USD	5-3-1	0.1146 (0.8853)	53.40 %	3.00 %

Table 3: The Testing Results for Neural Network Models (Delay Method) for Weekly Foreign Exchange Data

Exchange	Model	Test. NME	Gradient	$Ret1_{US}$	$Ret1$	$Ret2_{US}$	$Ret2$
AUD/USD	5-3-1	0.035105	73.86 %	8.82%	12.19%	12.43 %	15.90 %
AUD/USD	6-4-1	0.032362	76.14 %	8.97%	12.34%	12.67 %	16.16 %
CHF/USD	5-3-1	0.068819	65.91 %	28.49%	9.99%	22.49 %	4.85 %
CHF/USD	6-4-1	0.065962	64.77 %	32.36%	13.31%	21.64 %	4.15 %
DEM/USD	5-3-1	0.063462	61.36 %	22.86%	8.86%	15.20 %	2.07 %
DEM/USD	6-4-1	0.061730	64.77 %	27.84%	13.27%	18.00 %	4.55 %
GBP/USD	5-3-1	0.061370	73.86 %	7.22%	2.87%	14.78 %	10.13 %
GBP/USD	6-4-1	0.053650	72.73 %	10.62%	6.13%	16.48 %	11.76 %
JPY/USD	5-4-1	1.966195	46.59 %	19.71%	3.47%	0.00 %	-13.57 %
JPY/USD	6-4-1	1.242099	46.59 %	23.42%	6.67%	0.00 %	-13.57 %

Table 4: The Testing Results for Neural Network Models using indicators for Weekly Foreign Exchange Data. *Ret*1: Return using the *Stategy 1*; *Ret*2: Return using the *Stategy 1*; Ret_{US} denotes the seed money is in USD.

exchange rate. In our experiment, five to eight weeks of time delayed data are used. Some of the measurements of the forecasting results are shown in Table 3.

This method sometimes leads to prediction that seems to generate a time-delayed time series of the original time series. With the inclusion of some popular indicators used by traders, it might help to remove some of the time delay characteristics of the prediction.

The father of Dow-Jones, Charles Dow, divided the trend into three different levels, namely the primary trend, the secondary trend, and the minor trend. The advantage of moving average is that it tends to smooth out some of their irregularities that exist between market days. Moving averages are used as inputs to the neural network. MA5, MA10, MA20, MA60, and MA120 are used as the inputs to neural networks. They refer to moving averages for one week, two weeks, one month, one quarter and half a year respectively. One of the diagrams showing the predicted (out) and the actual (tar) time series for the period of Nov 1993 - July 1995 (out of sample) is shown in Figures 1 AUD/USD.

Further, the forecasts for each of the currencies were repeated, but with a hybrid of indicators and one time delay term. The configuration of the neural network is 6-4-1. For example, for Australian Dollar, the results showed that the hit rate of 6-4-1 was slightly higher than that of the pure indicator forecasting method with a configuration of 5-3-1. The hit rate of the former is 76.14% and that of the latter is

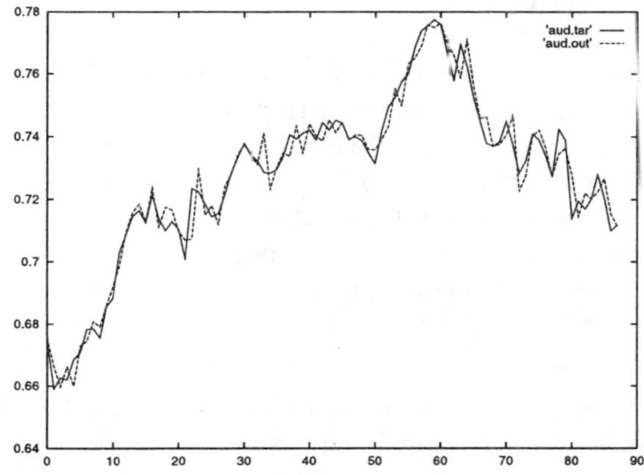

Figure 1: Prediction of the Weekly AUD/USD Nov 1993 - July 1995 (Indicators Method)

73.86%. In general, the addition of an additional term of time delay does not contribute much to the improvement of the hit rate. So, we can safely conclude that hit rates of approximately 70% can be achieved consistently for AUD, GBP, and somewhat lower for CHF and DEM.

Also, from the graphs, one can conclude that the forecasts for the first twenty weeks of the pure testing period look "impressive". This means that, the neural network needs to be retrained, probably every twenty weeks (or half a year) with the latest data to increase the chance of achieving a better forecast. Notice that, in actual application, only validation data sets would be required together with the training data sets.

4.3   Limitations

The data are chosen and segregated in time order in the experiment, This method may have some *recency problems*. Neural networks were only trained using data up till the end of October 1993. In forecasting the Forex after November 1993, the neural network is 'forced' to use knowledge up till 1993 only.

A very small NMSE does not necessarily imply good generalization. The sum of the NMSE of the three parts of data (training, validation and testing) must be kept small, not just the training NMSE alone. Sometimes having small NMSEs for testing and validation is more important than having small NMSE for training.

After experimenting with the choice of data, a very good testing result may not predict well. On the other hand, a model which is trained with randomly chosen data may predict well even with average testing results. Further, better testing results are demonstrated in the period near the end of the training sets. This is a result of the 'recency' problem.

4.4   Trading Strategies

Trading is an art. As there is no perfect forecasting technique, trading profit is ensured only by a good trading strategy taking "full" advantage of a good forecasting method. There are two kinds of trading strategies used in this study. One uses the difference between predictions, and another uses the difference between the predicted and the actual levels to trade.

Strategy 1:

$$\text{if}(\hat{x}_{t+1} - \hat{x}_t) > 0 \text{ then } buy \text{ else } sell \tag{3}$$

Strategy 2:

$$\text{if}(\hat{x}_{t+1} - x_t) > 0 \text{ then } buy \text{ else } sell \tag{4}$$

In actual trading, practitioners may choose one of the strategies. A conservative trading strategy would require a trader to act only when both strategies recommend the same actions.

In this paper, 1% of transaction cost was included in the calculation. The transaction cost of a big fund trading, and thus affecting the market rates was not taken into consideration To be more realistic, a specific amount of transaction cost has to be included in the calculation. If the output of neural network is given in percentage of changes, we can use positive or negative output to show that the currency is going up or down.

5   Comparison with ARIMA

The Box-Jenkins methodology, or *Autoregressive Integrated Moving Average*(ARIMA) Model, provides a systematic procedure for the analysis of time series that was sufficiently general to handle virtually all empirically observed time series data patterns. To compare the forecasting results of the neural networks, a number of ARIMA models were built. Table 5 is the results of ARIMA models with different trading strategies. The entire data set was used as fitting data for the ARIMA models. In other words, the data forecast by ARIMA were already used in the fitting stage of ARIMA model building. hence, the ARIMA models should deliver worse out-of-sample forecasting returns than the ARIMA results indicated in Table 5. Focusing on the gradients, the ARIMA methods can achive about 50% of correctness while up to 73% of correctness can be achieved using neural network models.

From practitioners' point of view, returns are more important than gradient. With reference to Table 5 and 4, the differences between ARIMA models and neural network models are significant. The best return using *Strategy 1* regardless the devaluation and strategies for ARIMA models is only 6.94%, while for neural network models is 28.49%.

Model	Gradient	$Ret1_{US}$	$Ret2_{US}$
AUD101	52.27 %	1.43 %	1.36 %
AUD202	54.32 %	1.53 %	1.21 %
CHF101	38.64 %	6.94 %	-1.42 %
CHF202	55.86 %	5.43 %	0.64 %
DEM101	43.18 %	3.48 %	3.49 %
DEM202	44.62 %	3.48 %	3.22 %
GBP101	53.41 %	2.24 %	3.67 %
GBP202	51.77 %	2.63 %	1.32 %
JPY101	44.32 %	-1.47 %	-0.52 %
JPY202	44.32 %	-0.78 %	0.02 %

Table 5: The Result of Using ARIMA (AUD101 stands for the ARIMA result of AUD using ARIMA(1,0,1) model and the same rules are applied to other currencies)

6   Conclusion and Further Research

In using neural networks to perform technical forecasting, better results are obtained for Australian Dollar, Swiss Franc, and British Pound and perhaps Swiss Francs and Deutsch Mark. The results for Japanese Yen are the worst in terms of using *strategy 2*. The reason could be that the market for Yen is bigger and more efficient than the market for other currencies. So the traders of the Yen market may depend more on technical analysis and they may act quickly after the signs appear. Hence, technical analysis may not be a good tool for forecasting the trends of Yen. This is similar to our forecasting result using ARIMA models.

The hit rate may be a better standard for determining the quality of the forecast. After all, the return depends a lot on the trading strategies and how the forecasting information are being used for trading advantages. However, the level of hit rates and paper profits also depend on the period of forecast. Hence, constant upgrading of the neural networks is necessary. For the practitioners, the levels of exchange rate and trend can be used depending on their expectation of return and risk. In addition to the above-mentioned two strategies, even more different trading strategies may be used by them. To benefit more practitioners, risk based trading strategies will be taken into consideration in future research. The behavior of each markets will also be studied.

7   Acknowledgments

We thank Mary Aviani, Swee-Yuan Tay and Yili Li for invaluable discussions and helpful comments.

References

[1] Hurst, H. E., "Long Term Storage of Reservoirs", *Transactions of the American Society of Civil Engineers* , 116, 1951

[2] Levin, R. I., *Statistics for management* Prentice Hall, 1994

[3] Refenes, A.N., "Managing exchange rate prediction strategies with neural networks" *Techniques and Applications of Neural Networks*, Liverpool, UK, Sept. 1992

[4] Weigend, A.S. "Generalization by weight-elimination applied to currency exchange rate prediction" *IEEE International Joint Conference on Neural Networks*, Singapore, Nov. 1991

[5] Peters, E. E., *Chaos and Order in the Capital markets: A New View of Cycles, Prices, and Market Volatility*, John Wiley & Sons Inc. 1991

[6] Yao, Jingtao, Poh, H.L., "Equity Forecasting: a Case Study on the KLSE Index" *NNCM'95(3rd International Conference On Neural Networks in the Capital Markets)*, 1995, London.

[7] Zhou, B., "Estimating the Variance Parameter From Noisy High Frequency Financial Data," *MIT Sloan School Working Paper*, No. 3739, 1995.

[8] Zhang, Xiru, "Non-linear predictive models for intra-day foreign exchange trading", *International Journal of Intelligent Systems in Accounting, Finance and Management*, Dec. 1994

OPTION PRICING WITH NEURAL NETWORKS

Ming Liu

Department of Systems Engineering and Engineering Management

Chinese University of Hong Kong, Shatin, N.T., Hong Kong, Email: ming@econ.duke.edu

Abstract— **In this paper, we take the stand that it is the assumption of geometric Brownian motion which causes the empirical biases of Black-Sholes formula and propose a nonparametric Neural Networks procedure to discover the complex law of motion of the stock price. With the knowledge of the law of motion of the stock price, we show that significant improvement could be achieved in terms of option pricing.**

1   Neural Network Latent Factor Filter— A nonparametric procedure

Geometric Brownian motion assumption on stock price has been challanged by many empirical studies, a notable example is Lo and Mackinlay (1988). The Black-Scholes (B-S) formula which hinges crucially on this assumption has also been shown demonstrating systematic biases as in a lot of empirical researches (see Rubinstein (1994) and Hull and White (1988) and their references). In this paper, we take the stand that it is the assumption of geometric Brownian motion which causes the empirical biases of B-S formula and propose a nonparamatric Neural Networks procedure to discover the law of motion of the stock price. With the knowledge of the estimated law of motion of the stock price, we show that significant improvement could be achieved in terms of option pricing.

If we believe that the economic system is Markovian, the stock price could then be thought endogenously determined as a function of the state variable which belongs to today's inforamation set $\mathcal{F}_t$. If we use x_t to denote the latent state vector, we could express the price as $f(x_t)$. In this paper, instead of imposing certain functional form on f, we acknowledge our ignorance of this highly nonlinear function and use Neural Networks to estimate it. To be more precise, we assume a single latent factor model with the fundamental factor x as Brownian motion, we then estimate the price function f which we assume is smooth enough and filter out x from the stock price using some nonparametric Neural Network procedure which we termed as Neural Net Latent Factor Filter(NNLFF). For a more careful treatment of this approach, see Liu (1996).

Neural Network Latent Factor Filter utilizes a Neural Network function with certain parameters to approximate the function f. As a nonparametric approach, Neural Network is flexible enough to approximate well any possible function. As shown by Gallant and White (1991) Neural Networks function not only approximates the function itself well but also approximates the first order derivative of the function well. In our context the first derivative of the function f is simply the conditional volatility, Neural Networks could thus approximate well both the price series and the conditional risk. In what follows, we first go over the rudimentals of neural networks and then present the idea of NNLFF. In section 2, we go over how we evaluate the options in the current context. In section 3, we give our empirical results. The fourth section concludes.

1.1   Neural Networks

The basic concept in a Neural Network is the neuron. A neuron receives inputs from each of a set of other units provide inputs $x = (x_1, x_2, \cdots, x_j)$ and output $y = \phi(\sum_{i=1}^{j} a_i x_i + c)$. The mapping $\phi(.)$ is called the *activation* mapping and a_i is called *connection weights* and c is called *bias*. In this paper, a very simple single hidden layer neural network which consists of k hidden neurons and 1 output neuron is used. For each of the k hidden neurons, the activation function (logistic squasher) $G(u) = \frac{exp(u)}{1+exp(u)}$ is used, and the input will be the one dimensional factor x. On top of this hidden layer, we have an output neuron which has the activation mapping as the identity mapping, and the output of the k hidden neurons as its input. In all, as illustrated in figure 1, we use a neural network mapping as follows,

$$f_N(x) = \sum_{j=1}^{k} a_j G(b_j x + c_j); \quad \text{where} \quad G(u) = \frac{e^u}{1 + e^u}. \tag{1}$$

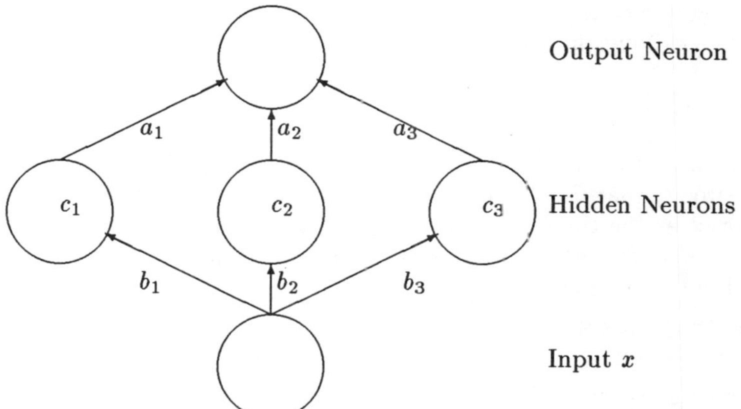

Figure 1: The Neural Networks

1.2 Neural Network Latent Factor Filter

Denote the neural networks approximation as $f_N(\theta, x_t)$, where θ denotes the vector of parameters. If we know the sample path of the underlying factor x, an easy way to estimate the value of θ is to do a nonlinear regression minimizing the distance between the true values and the approximated values as in Gallant and White (1991). It is unfortunate in this case that the sample path of the underlying factor is latent and has to be infered from the price changes. And we impose two equations to make the whole estimation doable,

$$p_t = f_N(\theta, x_t) + \eta_t \text{ with } \eta_t \sim N(0, \sigma_\eta^2) , \tag{2}$$

$$\Delta p_t = f_{Nx}(\theta, x_t)\varepsilon_t + \frac{1}{2}f_{Nxx}(\theta, x_t)\sigma_\varepsilon^2 \text{ where } x_t \equiv \sum_{i=1}^{t-1}\varepsilon_i, \tag{3}$$

where f_{Nx} and f_{Nxx} are the first and second derivatives of function f respectively. We could easily see what the first equation tries to do is to match the level of the price with the artificial neural network model. And instead of minimizing the L^2 distance as in Gallant and White (1991), we impose a probability structure on the error as a normal random variable with σ_η^2. The second equation can be seen as a discrete version of the Ito's Lemma and plays the role of stochastic filter for the sample path of x. As we have discussed in section 1, x is assumed to be Brownian motion. Its increments ε_t has a law as $N(0, \sigma_\varepsilon^2)$, where σ_ε^2 could be thought as the time slipped by across consecutive observations according to the clock of x. We call the above model as the Neural Network Latent Factor Filter.

1.3 Training Rules

Given a neural network model, we need to specify the *learning rule*, a recurcise algorithm in which the weights are modified as the data are processed. The whole process of learning is also called the *training* of neural networks, or in other words, the nonlinear estimation of the weights.

The maximum likelihood principle is used to estimate the NNLFF. It specifies a training rule as follows[1],

$$\hat{\theta} = \text{argmax}_\theta L(\theta; \{p_t\}_{t=1}^T)$$

$$L(\theta; \{p_t\}_{t=1}^T) = -\sum_{t=1}^T (y_t - f_N(\theta, x_t))^2 - \frac{T\log\sigma_\eta^2}{2}$$

$$x_t = \sum_{i=1}^{t-1} \frac{y_t - y_{t-1} - \frac{c_\varepsilon^2 f_{Nxx}(\theta, x_t)}{2}}{\sigma_\varepsilon f_{Nx}(\vartheta, x_t)}.$$

NNLFF gives us both the functional form of the f and also gives us the estimated fundamental factor, both of them are major concerns of empirical finance and could be quite meaningful. We can certainly

---

[1] This learning rule could be seen equivalent to the nonlinear least square estimation method as in Gallant and White (1991) and its consistency could be proved likewise.

extend the above procedure even further by using multi-dimensional neural nets to track down the major economic factors driving the stock market.

2   Option pricing

A call option on a stock gives the buyer the right to buy the stock at a prespecified price (striking price) at the time of maturity. A put option on a stock gives the buyer the right to sell the stock at the prespecified price at the time of maturity. When the possibility of early exercising is allowed, the option will be called American, otherwise, it will be called European. In this paper, only the evaluation of the European call options is studied.

In the work of Black and Scholes (1973), the assumption of geometric Brownian motion has been used to derive a closed form solution for the option price. As mentioned in the opening remark, this assumption has been challenged from different fronts empirically. Different kinds of modifications have been seen in the literature. Among all, the approach of Geske (1979) may be the one closest to us, where option is thought as option on option. Compared with Geske (1979) who uses parametric approach, NNLFF as a nonparametric procedure implies great flexibility and avoids the problem of misspecification of the usual parametric approach.

Given the stock price which can be expressed as function of the fundamental factor, $f(x)$ (or its approximation $f_N(x)$), and suppose the economy is complete, easily then the idea of Black-Scholes can be extended to this occasion. We can find the hedging position which offsets the risk induced by holding the stock. Assume the riskfree interest rate as constant r and denote the option price as $w(x,t)$, it can be easily seen one stock in long position and $\frac{f_1}{w_1}$ option in short position will provide perfect hedging against any risk in the system. And the stochastic differential equation for the value of options can be written as

$$\frac{1}{2}f_{11}\sigma_\varepsilon^2 w_1 - \frac{f_1}{2}w_{11} - f_1 w_2 = rfw_1 - rf_1w. \tag{4}$$

Instead of solving the above SDE, in this paper we adopt the framework of equivalent martingale as elaborated in Harrison and Pliska (1981) and use Monte Carlo integration to derive the option price. First we define the accumulation factor, $B(t) = \exp(\int_0^t rds)$, corresponding to the price of a money market account. Since

$$df = f_1 dx + \frac{1}{2}f_{11}\sigma_\varepsilon^2 dt, \tag{5}$$

if we define $z = \frac{f}{B}$, we will have

$$d\log z = \frac{f_1}{f}dx + (\frac{f_{11}\sigma_\varepsilon^2}{2f} - r)dt - \frac{f_1^2}{2f^2}dt. \tag{6}$$

$d\log z$ could be seen as the excess return of the stock price, and from equation (4) we can define the market price of the risk as

$$\gamma = \frac{2rf - \sigma_\varepsilon^2 f_{11}}{2f_1}. \tag{7}$$

Knowing the market price of the risk, we could easily do a change of measure on the original system and transform the original probability space into a risk-neutral space using the Girsanov theorem. And we could evaluate the price of any kind of contingent claim under this risk-neutral measure and then map it back into the original space and get the market price .

Denote the original probability space as $(\Omega, \mathcal{F}, Q)$, with certain technical conditions we could define $\tilde{Q}$ according to the Radon-Nykdom derivative, $\frac{d\tilde{Q}}{dQ} = \exp(\int_0^T \gamma dx - \frac{1}{2}\int_0^T \gamma^2 dt)$. Under this new probability space $(\Omega, \mathcal{F}, \tilde{Q})$, the prices of any contingent claims become martingales. For European call option which has an endpoint value as $h = \max(f(x(T)) - S, 0)$, where S is the striking price, its price w will be

$$w(t) = B(t)E_t(B(T)^{-1}\exp(\int_t^T \gamma dx - \frac{1}{2}\int_t^T \gamma^2 dt)h), \tag{8}$$

the expectation is derived using the following relationship, $E_t^{\tilde{Q}}(X) = E_t^Q(X\frac{d\tilde{Q}}{dQ})$.

Model	a_1	a_2	a_3	b_2	b_3	c_1	c_2	c_3	σ_ϵ
NNLFF($k = 3$)	5.1d-4	1.5d4	-6.3d3	-3.4d-4	8.9d-4	-2.6	-1.4	-2.4d-1	1.00
NNLFF($k = 2$)	-1.4d2	4.4d2		-4.8d-2		-1.8	-1.8		1.02

Table 1: The estimated Neural Networks

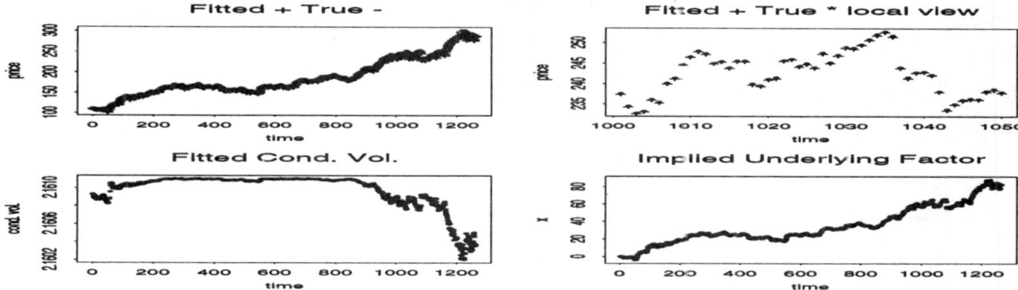

Figure 2: NNLFF $k = 3$ fitting

3 Empirical Result

In summary, what we will show in this section is to first filter the whole time series using the NNLFF approach, which provides a measure of the conditional risk exhibited in the past data series. Then this risk measure is used to evaluate the option values using the Monte Carlo simulation.

3.1 The training of the Neural Network

The data set we use is the S&P 500 daily series, from June 1st 1982 to June 1st 1987, a total of 1265 observations. Although longer time series is available, we use time series of this length. Because we believe any longer term time series may not offer more in terms of capturing the risk involved in the near future, rather it is very likely that the risk will be exaggerated by long term regime switchings which are not relevant since here we only concern about the short term option. We also want to note that the price on June 1st 1987 is 289.83 and we are calculating the option price at a time of pre-crash period.

Out of many possibilities (see Liu (1996)), we end up picking a three units logistic squasher neural networks. The parameters of this neural networks function will be $\{a_1, a_2, a_3, b_1, b_2, b_3, c_1, c_2, c_3\}$, where b_1 is normalized to be -1 and x is normalized as starting from point 0. The two other parameters we use are $\sigma_\eta^2, \sigma_\varepsilon^2$, the measurement error of the stock price and the internal clock of the Brownain motion. We will use the SIMPLEX method to do the maximization which is implemented as in NMSIMP of GQOPT.

Table 1 gives us the estimated values of the coefficients. We note the estimated σ_η (not reported) is very small, which means the neural networks match the data quite well and very little of the variability has been resorted to the measurement error. It means also there is very little error to use the second equation as the filter to filter out the underlying Brownian motion. From the upperright panel of Figure 2, we may see that there is positive correlation between consecutive measurement error.

Since we set our goal as tracking down both the underlying fundamental factor and the functional form of f, we should appraise our estimation along these two dimensions. In Figure 2, we draw the picture of the fitted stock price and the estimated conditional volatility and the underlying factor with NNLFF. And as we can see, most of the dynamics of the price series is captured by the dynamics of the underlying factor and the conditional volatility is relatively constant. In Figure 3, we show the neural net function with domain as $[-90, 10]$. As we can see, the function f is quite linear except in the case of Neuron # 1, which contains a jump, but since the magnitude of Neuron # 1 is quite small, the jump has very little effect on the level of the price. The derivative of the function could be seen from Figure 4. Notice the derivative function seems increasing and convex. Also interestingly, despite the level of Neuron # 2 and Neuron # 3 looks linear, it is convex and concave respectively, this could be seen clearly from their derivatives. The point where the conditional volatility begins to drop roughly corresponds to a point in time around Feb. 10th, 1986. From the picture, NNLFF suggests that prior to Feb, 10th, 1986, the conditional volatility

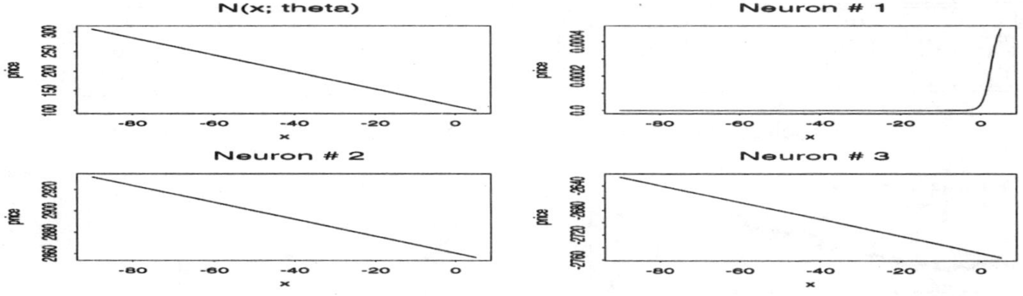

Figure 3: NNLFF $k = 3$ function

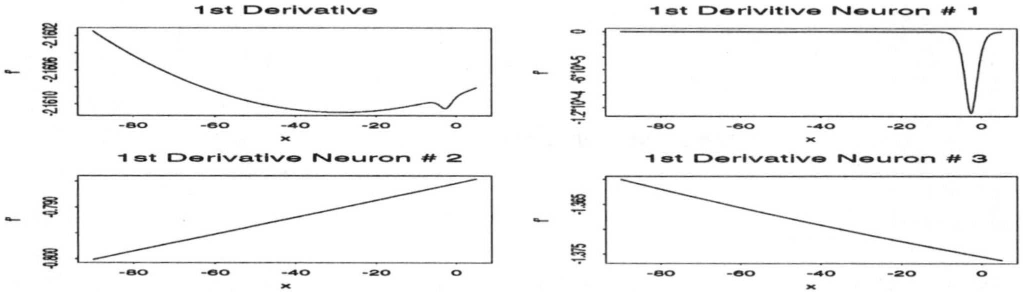

Figure 4: NNLFF $k = 3$ derivative

f_{Nx} is quite constant, and after that date or so, we could see a sharp decrease in the conditional risk. It is worth commenting that this date corresponds well with the timing of the drop of oil price and the resolution of the oil crisis.

3.2   Option pricing with NNLFF

The option values we compute are the prices of the S & P 500 index call options traded on CBOE (Chicago Board Options Exchange) on June 1st, 1987. We focus ourselves on the easiest among all, the one month options. We focus on the one month options since in this case the options are the closest to the European option and we do not need to worry about paying dividends. Another advantage of the near term options is that we do not need to take into account the variability of interest rate. These options will mature on July 18th, and we have a maturity of 33 days (working days). We use the 3 month treasury bill rate on June 1st as the constant discount rate, which is an annual rate of 4.83 per cent. In the calculation, a day is divided into 20 time intervals as an attempt to simulate the continuous sample path implied by the continuous diffusion process. So we have a total of 20*33=660 periods in our simulation. The expectation in equation (8) is computed in a Monte Carlo way as an average of 5000 samples.

In Table 2, we show the forecasts of option prices(we do not report the table for put option, interested reader may see Liu (1996)). In the first row, we give out the striking price, the second row we list the market price of the corresponding option, the third row we show the Black-Scholes option price calculated in the standard way, the fourth row we have the forecasts of option prices with the NNLFF approach ($k = 3$). From Hull and White (1987), when there is a positive correlation between conditional volatility and level, the Black-Scholes formula tends to overprice those deep-in-the money options and this is exactly

Striking	215	220	225	260	270	275	280	285	290	295	300	305	310	315
Market	75.53	70.25	65.12	30.75	20.50	15.25	11.50	7.75	4.75	2.87	1.44	0.75	0.31	0.06
B-S	76.14	71.17	66.20	31.50	21.95	17.49	13.38	9.78	6.81	4.51	2.82	1.67	0.93	0.51
NNLFF	74.45	69.52	64.51	29.97	20.07	15.47	11.16	7.70	4.77	2.77	1.40	0.69	0.24	0.07

Table 2: Comparison of forecasts of call option prices

Norm	B-S^c	NNLFF^c	B-S^p	NNLFF^p
l^1	18.63	4.54	3.36	2.90
l^2	29.09	3.05	1.29	1.50
l^∞	2.24	1.08	0.70	0.88

Table 3: Comparison of option pricing methods

we see in the table.

In Table 3 we use different standards to compare the different pricing methods. The standards we use include l^1, l^2 and l^∞ norm difference between the forecasted value of option price and the market price for all options on the market with different stike price. We evaluate the performance of our procedures in both the case of call option and put option, which is denoted with superscript c and p respectively. And as we could see from Table 3, NNLFF certainly is the best. And for 14 different striking prices, the l^2 norm of the difference between the forecasted value and the market value is only a tenth of that of the Black-Scholes.

4   conclusion

With a very simple functional form, Neural Networks function has the property of approximating well arbitrary functions. For smooth functions, it can virtually match both the derivative of a function and the function itself. In this study, we propose NNLFF to filter both the level and conditional volatility of the stock price. Because of the nonparametric nature of this approach, it could capture better the dynamics especially uncertainty structure of the stock market. And when this approach is used to price options, it can give us better forecasts.

In this paper indeed we find the neural networks approach gives us significantly improved forecasted option values than the Black-Scholes formula when compared with the observed market price. Also interestingly, we find that the law of motion of stock price may be better captured by a linear Brownian motion instead of a geometric Brownian motion locally at least for the years between 1982 to 1987. As a final note, only the forecasting performance of near-maturity options at a particular day is considered in this paper and obviously further empirical study for options with longer maturity is required.

References

[1] Black, F. and M.J. Scholes (1973): "The Pricing of Options and Corporate Liabilities",*Journal of Political Economy*, 81, 637-654.

[2] Cheng, B. and D.M. Titterington (1994): "Neural Networks: A Review from a Statistics Perspective," *Statistical Science*, 9, 2-54.

[3] Geske, R. (1979): "The Valuation of Compound Options," *Journal of Financial Economics*, 7, 63-81.

[4] Gallant, A.R. and H. White (1991): "On Learning the Derivatives of an Unknown Mapping with Multilayer Feedforward Networks," *Neural Networks*, 5, 129-138.

[5] Harrison, J.M. and S. Pliska (1981): "Martingales and Stochastic Integrals in the Theory of Continuous Trading," *Stochastic Processes and Their Applications*, 11, 215-260.

[6] Hull, J. and A. White (1987): "The Pricing of Options on Assets with Stochastic Volatilities," *Journal of Finance*, 42, 281-300.

[7] Liu, M. (1996): "Option Pricing with Neural Networks," *M.S. thesis*, Duke University.

[8] Lo, A. and C. Mackinlay (1988): "Stock Market Prices Do not Follow Random Walks: Evidence from a Simple Specification Test," *Review of Financial Studies*, 1, 41-66.

[9] Rubinstein, M. (1994): "Implied Binomial Trees," *Journal of Finance*, 64, 771-818.

A Genetic-Based Approach for the Derivation of Trading Strategies on the German Stock Market

Andreas Frick‡, Ralf Herrmann†, Martin Kreidler‡, Alexander Narr‡, Detlef Seese‡

† Institute for Decision Theory and Management Science/Department of Economic Sciences
University of Karlsruhe/Germany
E-mail: herrmann@etu.wiwi.uni-karlsruhe.de

‡ Institute for Applied Computer Science and Formal Description Methods/Department of Economic Sciences
University of Karlsruhe/Germany
E-mail: {afr|mkr|ana|seese}@aifb.uni-karlsruhe.de

Abstract— **We investigate price-based heuristic trading rules for buying and selling shares. This is accomplished by transforming time series of share prices from the *Frankfurt Stock Exchange* (FSE) using Point & Figure (P&F) Chart Analysis. This yields formations which are evaluated and transformed into a binary example set. For the above evaluation we used two different methods: First, by comparing the returns of any considered trading strategy with the corresponding riskless interest rate and the average stock market return, second by using its riskadjusted expected return as a benchmark instead of the average stock market return. The latter is calculated using the *Capital Asset Pricing Model* (CAPM).**

The binary example data is iteratively processed by a genetic-based machine learning system. The rules obtained by the classification process classify with an average correctness of about 60 %.

1   Introduction

In the last few years, Genetic Algorithms proved to be a useful tool for computing approximative solutions of hard problems (especially problems for which no general efficient solution is known or those which are provably hard, e.g. **NP**-hard problems). One such hard problem is forecasting in stock markets. By forecasting, we mean finding *rules*[1] that tell an investor when to buy a particular share and when to sell it. On the one hand, the considered buy and sell rules result from the actual return of the stocks and the movement of the stock market in the past, on the other hand they result from the expected return of the stocks and the expected return of the whole stock market in the future.

The main objective of this paper is to show a way, how such rules can automatically be extracted from given capital market data (i.e. share prices) and how afterwards new rules can be found from those by applying a variant of Goldberg's *Simple Classifier System* [8], which regularly generates new rules from the given ones with a Genetic Algorithm and classifies the obtained rules according to their separation quality. "Good" rules survive with a high probability, while "bad" rules are likely to be substituted by new ones generated from the former.

Acknowledgement. We are grateful for the helpful comments and suggestions of Hermann Göppl and David Robbins Griswold.

2   Genetic-Based Machine Learning

One of the most challenging topics in the Artificial Intelligence research area is Machine Learning. The aim is to construct new or to improve already acquired knowledge by using input information. The most active area [13] has been Symbolic Empirical Learning, which means to create or modify general symbolic descriptions, whose structure is a-priori unknown. Such symbolic descriptions frequently have to be developed from a set of given concept examples [12, 13], because in many practical domains it is very easy to come up with such a set but quite difficult to describe the concepts.

Holland [11] introduced the idea to use Genetic Algorithms to improve rules already given or generated newly from scratch. His approach to such a classifier system, well-known as "Michigan Approach", works by manipulating a set (or a population) of rules. If the aim is to improve a given set of rules, then the initial rule population equals the given rule set, otherwise an initial rule set is created at random. Now this population of rules is tested against the set of examples by Supervised Learning. Rules that classify wrongly are punished and rules that classify correctly are rewarded, so that each rule gets a fitness value according to its classification correctness. Most implemented systems have more complicated mechanisms to distribute the reward and they also transfer reward from the bad to the good rules. It is also possible to extend this mechanism by enabling reward transfer along calling queues such that a system can learn multistep tasks. The rules are regularly processed by a Genetic Algorithm in order to remove the bad rules and improve the good ones, i.e. the rules are selected by a probability according to their fitness and recombined by the two "genetic" operations Crossover and Mutation. The main idea is to improve the already good rules by enforcing an interchange of rule components and by trying out new, untested rule

---

[1] We notify that the term "rule" is used in two different meanings in Technical Chart Analysis and Machine Learning.

elements. Bad rules have little chance to survive and to get incorporated into the next generation's rule set.

One problem for using a classifier system is to transform the given example data in a format the system can process. On the one hand, information must not be lost; on the other hand, the representations of the given examples and the system input is completely different. Furthermore, a classifier system has many parameters that influence the behavior of the system in a way that is sometimes not well understood.

In our approach we use a system based on the ANSI-C-version [9] of the *Simple Classifier System* (SCS) proposed by Goldberg [8], which is slightly modified and improved to enhance its stability [6].

3   The Point & Figure Technique

The essential problem an investor on a stock market is confronted with, is the exact timing of his transactions — when to buy and when to sell shares, — presumably the deciding factor of success or failure. The P&F technique is a heuristic method to support his decision making by giving buy and sell signals. This kind of Chart Analysis restricts to just one aspect of market activity – price change and its reversals. Time factors[2] or volume data is not taken into consideration. A P&F Chart therefore has no horizontal time scale and looks like a series of vertical X's and O's, placed into columns from left to right. Each "X" and "O" fills a box which represents the minimum relative price movement with significance for the analysis. Figure 1 illustrates the procedure. The boxes are visualized by dashed lines. Due to its

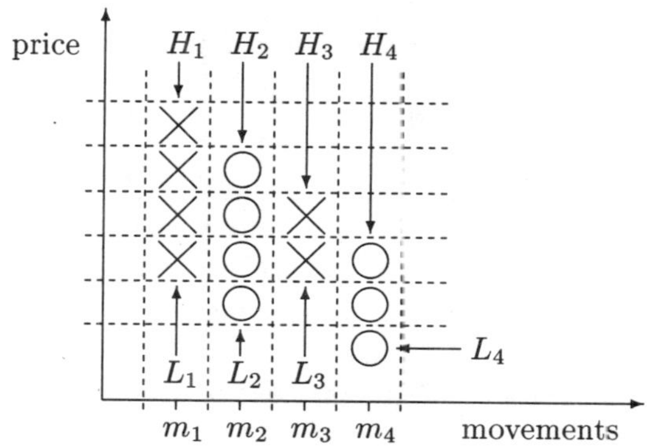

Figure 1: Point & Figure Chart

heuristic character, there exist different procedures for creating such charts (e.g. [2, 3, 10, 14, 17, 18]). We used the following one in our work: "X" signs in the column stand for an increase, while "O" signs stand for decreasing share prices. Such price movements are entered continuously into the chart. Whenever a reversal in the price movement occurs, the sign representing the new price movement is written into a new column. Therefore, each column only consists of one kind of sign. For the practical application of this method two decisions have to be made a-priori: First we have to decide which box size is appropriate and second we have to define the reversal criterion. The box size is influenced by the time frame and the volatility of the observed market. In our study we follow a suggestion of Welcker [18] for german stocks (standard conversion). Values for his approximation can be found below:

share price	price change / box
10 - 14	0.2
14 - 29	0.5
29 - 60	1
60 - 100	2

share price	price change / box
100 - 140	·2
140 - 290	5
290 - 600	10
600 - 1000	20

This approximation is the result of a compromise between simplicity of construction and correctness of logarithmic scale. In addition, we implemented the exact method (modified conversion). Depending on the reversal criterion used, 1-, 3- and 5-point Reversal Charts are distinguishable. For example, a 3-point reversal occurs if the price moves three times the price change represented by a box in the opposite direction of the current price trend. If such a reversal occurs, we have to shift one column to the right in the chart beginning to put "O" signs one box below (with a new tendency downwards) or "X" signs one box above (with a new tendency upwards) the current position in the corresponding direction until the appropriate price level is reached.

Based on this chart, the P&F Analysis tries to identify buy and sell signals, e.g. penetrations of support/resistance lines.

---

[2]I.e. by looking at P&F charts one cannot decide how long a price trend takes.

4   The Conversion of the Stock Market Data

For the efficient application of the SCS, it was necessary to convert the P&F Charts and trading rules into an appropriate binary representation. We accomplished this within two steps, which are explained below:

1. During the first step the stock prices are converted into the P&F Charts. Each price movement m_i (each column in the P&F Chart) is represented by its highest (H_i) and its lowest (L_i) value. An illustration is given in Figure 1. Hence, we get the following formation representation of the P&F Charts:

$$\boxed{\begin{array}{c} \{0|1\} \, , \, H_1 \, , \, H_2 \, , \, H_3 \, , \ldots \\ L_1 \, , \, L_2 \, , \, L_3 \, , \ldots \end{array}}$$

The first entry specifys the direction of the first movement in the chart. "0" stands for a downward and "1" for an upward move. The other entries contain the highs and lows of the following price movements. Because after an upward movement always follows a downward movement and vice versa, it is sufficient to define the direction of the first movement to determine the direction of all movements in the chart (see Figure 1).

2. In the second step the buy and sell rules are generated. To formalize the P&F Chart Technique, it was necessary to transform the representation of step 1 into a new form. The trading rules of the P&F Technique are mainly based on comparisons of highs and lows of the different price movements of the considered formation. A typical example of such a trading rule is: Buy a share if the top of the following "up" is higher than the preceding "up" and the bottom of the following "down" is higher than the preceding "down". Thus, the data was transformed into the following format:

$$\boxed{\begin{array}{c} \{0|1\} \, , \, \frac{H_2}{H_1} \, , \, \frac{H_3}{H_1} \, , \, \frac{H_4}{H_1} \, , \, \frac{H_3}{H_2} \, , \, \frac{H_4}{H_2} \, , \, \frac{H_4}{H_3} \\[1em] \frac{L_2}{L_1} \, , \, \frac{L_3}{L_1} \, , \, \frac{L_4}{L_1} \, , \, \frac{L_3}{L_2} \, , \, \frac{L_4}{L_2} \, , \, \frac{L_4}{L_3} \end{array}}$$

The comparisons of the tops and those of the bottoms of the considered movements are conducted by calculating the quotients $\frac{H_i}{H_j}$ and $\frac{L_i}{L_j}$ with $i \neq j$. These quotients describe the price pattern for our classification system completely. If the top of movement $(i+1)$ is higher than the top of movement i, then $H_{i+1} > H_i$ and thus, $\frac{H_{i+1}}{H_i} > 1$. Analogously for the lows. The sketched trading rule above is formalized in the following manner (using the notions of propositional logic calculus with its standard semantics):

$$\left[\left(\tfrac{L_3}{L_1} > 1\right) \wedge \left(\tfrac{H_4}{H_2} > 1\right) \right] \; \rightarrow \; \text{Buy}$$

A similar sell rule for example is

$$\left[\left(\tfrac{L_4}{L_2} < 1\right) \wedge \left(\tfrac{H_3}{H_1} < 1\right) \right] \; \rightarrow \; \text{Sell}$$

By this kind of representation it is also possible to express resistance and support lines. Note that up to now we have only got formation patterns, but no decision signals (i.e. buy or sell).

5   Evaluation and Classification

Now the above obtained patterns have to provided with a trading decision. We do this in the following way: According to a given time interval (30 days, 90 days, 6 months, 1 year), beginning for each example at the last price of the considered price formation, the return of the recommended trading decision for the considered time interval is looked up in the database in order to decide whether the formation was a gainful buy or sell signal. This is accomplished by comparing the return of the particular trading strategy with the riskless interest rate and either the market return or the expected riskadjusted return for the considered time interval.

The expected riskadjusted return is calculated using the *Capital Asset Pricing Model* (CAPM) [16]. The CAPM postulates the following relation beween risk and return of a risky asset:

$$E(r_i) \; = \; r_f + (E(r_M) - r_f) * \frac{COV(r_i, r_M)}{VAR(r_M)} \; = \; r_f + (E(r_M) - r_f) * \beta_i$$

Hereby $E(r_i)$ is the expected return of asset i, r_f denotes the riskless interest rate, $E(r_M)$ is the expected return of the market portfolio, $VAR(r_M)$ the variance of the market return and $COV(r_i, r_M)$ is the covariance between the returns on the risky asset i and the market portfolio M. $(E(r_m) - r_f)$ is the riskpremium paid for the risk of asset i measured by β_i. We treat the resulting trading strategies as a risky asset that is valuable using the CAPM. The graduation of the formations into buy and sell signals is now quite straightforward: If the return of a share is higher than the corresponding market return resp. its expected riskadjusted return and it is higher than the riskless rate then it is a buy signal. Otherwise it is a sell signal.

Now we have obtained trading decision examples that can be treated by the learning environment for rule generation (SCS). First the whole set is splitted into a training set and a test set. The classifier generates rules from the training set by Supervised Learning and writes them to a file. The rule set then is tested against the set of test examples and the correctness of the rule set is calculated.

6   Results

We implemented our conversion system in ANSI-C on a Sparc station and ran it with input data of the Frankfurt Stock Exchange from the time interval between January 11, 1989 and May 30, 1994. Our sample contains all 30 stocks of the Deutscher Aktienindex (DAX). The riskless interest rates used in our study are Frankfurt Interbank Offer Rate (FIBOR). To calculate the market return, the DAX was used as a proxy.

Since from 3- and 5-point Reversal Charts only very few example data could be extracted, we implemented a modified first step of the conversion that does not work with boxwise P&F Chart Analysis, but takes a percentage as an input which is the minimal percentage that triggers a trend reversal of a share. The modified conversion can be looked at as a kind of continuous version of charts, while the 1-, 3- and 5-point Reversal Charts are discrete. We noticed that the modified conversion was the better means for our purposes.

Using the SCS, we tried to find signals for gainful buy and sell strategies on the stock market. We ran the SCS for 100,000 generations with the standard and the modified conversion. The main problem then was to tune in the parameters both of the conversion and of the SCS in such a way that the SCS converged. Not only, as stated above, the minimal value for a trend reversal is a critical parameter, but also the number of movements per rule. The more moves are ordered to a rule, the less training examples can be found for that particular rule. Furthermore, too few rules can be found, if too much movements are collected within a rule. It is a natural conjecture, that too much movements per rule made the formations too complex. Our tests confirmed this, since then the SCS could not generate a rule set with sufficient quality any more.

A further problem, that is also discussed in [2] was, that existing patterns lose their validity after a certain time. In our terms, this means that rules, which initially classified very good, become worse in the course of time, while initially relatively bad rules get better. This corresponds with the fact that the stock market participants "learn" in the meantime. Thus, it seems to be in agreement with the weak form efficiency of Fama [4, 5] and hence it is generally questionable, if the SCS can find rules to beat the market within the long term.

Our tests achieved an average correctness of classified formations of up to 60 %. Figure 2 shows two of our results. Both outputs were calculated by using three movements per rule, comparison after 90 days with the corresponding riskless interest rate and the market return. The diagram on the left is based upon the whole DAX sample and 1 Point Reversal Chart (Welcker approximation), the one on the right-hand side is calculated with a single stock and the modified conversion with 2 percent reversal criterion. The x axis gives the number of generations, the y axis denotes the percentage of correctly classified examples. The curve on the left converges on a lower percentage level (about 56 %) than that on the right; this is due to the approximation suggested by Welcker (on average, the modified conversion gave slightly better results).

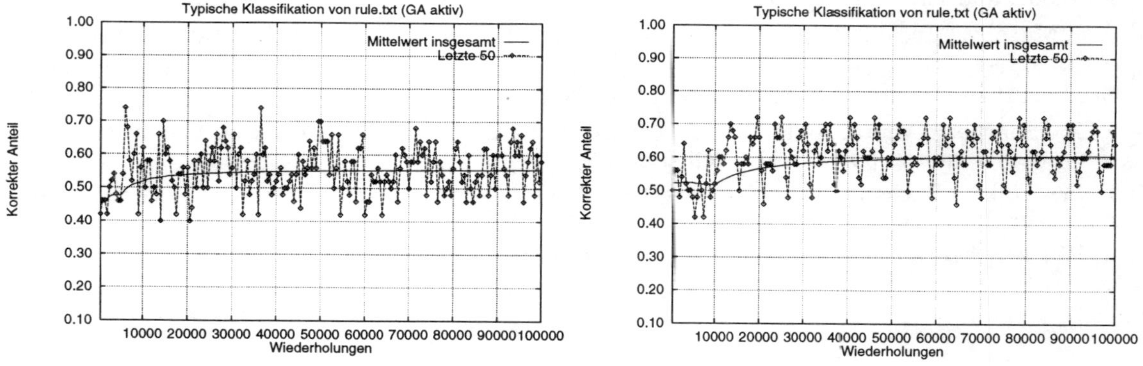

Figure 2: Two SCS outputs

7   Summary and Ongoing Work

The results obtained until now do not allow to reject the weak-form efficiency of the German Stock Market. We suppose that rules which enable an investor to outperform the market, even if there are some, can not exist unchangedly for a long time. Up to now we were not able to find such reliable buy and sell signals with our classifying system. Anyway, we were able to find an efficient way to convert stock market data automatically as inputs for the SCS.

There are two directions of ongoing work. First, modifications of the system (e.g. implementing the Pitt's Approach) and second the application of the system on capital market data: The implementation of variable formation length and the incorporation of the box size into the classification process offers new interesting fields of research. The application of the system should allow to examine if there exist price formations at the stock markets to give reliable buy and sell signals and if it is possible to construct an adaptive system based on Genetic Algorithms which is able to generate new trading strategies to beat the market with. Especially the use of intraday data is a new interesting field of application.

References

[1] F. Allen and R. Karjalainen, "Using Genetic Algorithms To Find Technical Trading Rules", *Technical Report*, Wharton School of the University of Pennsylvania, Rodney L. White Center for Financial Research, May 20, 1995.

[2] R. J. Bauer Jr., "Genetic Algorithms and Investment Strategies", *J. Wiley & Sons, Inc.*, New York, 1994.

[3] W. F. Eng, "The Technical Analysis of Stocks, Options & Futures - Advanced Trading Systems and Techniques", *Probus Publishing*, Chicago, Ill., 1988.

[4] E. G. Fama, "Efficient Capital Markets: A Review of Theory and Empirical Work", Journal of Finance, May 1970, pp. 383-417.

[5] E. G. Fama, "Foundations of Finance", Basic Books, New York, 1976.

[6] A. Frick, "Erweiterungen des Goldbergschen Simple Classifier System" Diplomarbeit, Institut AIFB, Universität Karlsruhe, 1995.

[7] H. Göppl, T. Lüdecke and R. Herrmann, "Deutsche Finanzdatenbank-DFDB: Datenbank-Handbuch Teil 1", *Institut ETU*, Universität Karlsruhe, 1994.

[8] G. Goldberg, "Genetic Algorithms in Search, Optimization and Machine Learning", *Addison-Wesley*, 1989.

[9] Jörg Heitkötter. "SCS-C: A C-Language Implementation of a Simple Classifier System", Reference Manual, Universität Dortmund, 1994.

[10] H. Hockmann, "Prognose von Aktienkursen durch Point and Figure–Analysen", *Gabler Verlag*, Wiesbaden, 1979.

[11] J. H. Holland, and J. S. Reitmann, "Cognitive Systems based on Adaptive Algorithms", In *Pattern-Directed Inference Systems* D. A. Waterman and F. Hayes-Roth eds. Academic Press, New York, NY, 1978.

[12] P. Langley, "On Machine Learning" *Journal of Machine Learning*, Vol. 1, No. 1, pp. 5-10, 1986.

[13] R. Michalski and Y. Kodratoff, "Research in Machine Learning: Recent Progress, Classification of Methods, and Future Directions" vol. 3. *Morgan Kaufmann*, Los Altos, CA, 1990.

[14] J. J. Murphy, "Technische Analyse der Terminmärkte" *Verlag Hoppenstedt & Co.*, Darmstadt, 1991.

[15] A. Narr, "Anwendung des Simple Classifier Systems (SCS) auf die Deutsche Finanzdatenbank", Studienarbeit, Institut AIFB, Universität Karlsruhe, 1996.

[16] W. F. Sharpe, "Capital Asset Prices: A Theory of Market Equilibrium Under Conditions of Risk", *Journal of Finance*, pp. 425-442, Sep. 1964.

[17] F. W. Tölke, "Exchange Rate Analysis with Point & Figure Charts", *Peter Lang Verlag*, Frankfurt am Main, 1992.

[18] J. Welcker, "Technische Aktienanalyse", *Verlag Moderne Industrie*, Zürich, 1991.

An improved time series prediction by applying the layer-by-layer learning method to FIR neural networks

Hee-yeal Yu and S. Y. Bang
Dept. of Computer Science & Engineering
Pohang University of Science and Tehcnology
Pohang, Korea

Abstract— The FIR neural network model was proposed for time series prediction and gave good results. However the learning algorithm used for the FIR network is a kind of the gradient descent method and hence inherits all well-known problems of the method. Recently a new learning algorithm called the optimization layer by layer was proposed for the regular multilayer perceptron network and showed a great improvement in the learning time as well as the performance of the network.
In this paper we develop a new learning algorithm for the FIR neural network model by applying the idea of the optimization layer by layer to the model. The results of the experiment using two popular time series prediction problems show that the new algorithm is far better in the learning time and more accurate in the prediction performance than the original learning algorithm.

1   FIR network structure

The target network to which we apply the OLL learning algorithm is a *two-layer* FIR network as depicted in Fig. 1. The extension of our algorithm to a FIR network with more than two layers is rather straightforward and we explain our algorithm using this basic network. But it should be noted that a *two-layer* FIR network is capable of approximating. For a detail description of a FIR network, please refer to Wan [4]. In the input layer of the network x_0^0 is the bias and $x_1^0, \cdots, x_M^0$ are the input pattern.

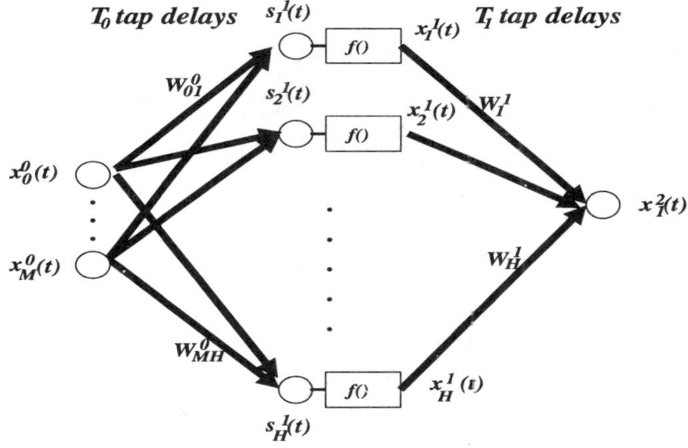

Figure 1: a *two-layer* FIR network

The weight between two neurons is a FIR synapse. The activation function of a hidden neuron is a sigmoidal function of the form $f(x) = 1/(1 + \exp^{-x})$, while that of an output neuron is $f(x) = x$. Let the time delay at the hidden layer and that at the output layer be T_0 and T_1, respectively. Then the activation value of the output neuron $x_1^2(t)$ at time t is as follows:

$$x_1^2(t) = \sum_{h=1}^{H} \mathbf{w}_h^1 \cdot \mathbf{x}_h^1(t) = \sum_{h=1}^{H} \left(w_h^1(0)x_h^1(t) + \cdots + w_h^1(T_1)x_h^1(t - T_1) \right)$$

$$= \sum_{h=1}^{H} \left(w_h^1(0)f\left(\sum_{m=0}^{M} \mathbf{w}_{hm}^0 \cdot \mathbf{x}_m^0(t) \right) + \cdots + w_h^1(T_1)f\left(\sum_{m=0}^{M} \mathbf{w}_{hm}^0 \cdot \mathbf{x}_m^0(t - T_1) \right) \right),$$

where

$$x_h^1(t) = f\left(\sum_{m=0}^{M} \mathbf{w}_{hm}^0 \cdot \mathbf{x}_m^0(t)\right) = f\left(\sum_{m=0}^{M} w_{hm}^0(0)x_m^0(t) + \cdots + w_{hm}^0(T_0)x_m^0(t-T_0)\right).$$

Now we apply the idea of the optimization layer by layer to a FIR network. Please refer to Ergezinger et al [2] for the explanation of the idea. The modifications required for the original idea to be applied to the FIR network come from the unique structure of the FIR network. In the following we will describe a brief derivation of the new learning algorithm. Before getting in the detail let us define the cost function of the FIR network for the training data $\{\mathbf{x}_i^0(t), d(t)\}_{t=1}^{T}$ by

$$E(\mathbf{W}^1, \mathbf{W}^0) = \sum_{t=1}^{T} e(t) = \sum_{t=1}^{T} \frac{1}{2}\left(d(t) - x_1^2(t)\right)^2, \tag{1}$$

where $\mathbf{W}^1 = \{\mathbf{w}_1^1, \cdots, \mathbf{w}_H^1\}$, $\mathbf{W}^0 = \{\cdots, \mathbf{w}_{io}^0, \cdots, \mathbf{w}_{iM}^0, \cdots\}$. In other words we are going to update the FIR synapses $\mathbf{w}_{im}^0$'s of the hidden layer and the FIR synapses $\mathbf{w}_h^1$'s of the output layer in such a way that the above cost function decreases.(Note that a FIR synapse of the hidden layer and that of the output layer are expressed by $\mathbf{w}_{hm}^0$ and $\mathbf{w}_h^1$, respectively, rather than $\mathbf{w}_{hm}^1$ and $\mathbf{w}_h^2$. In this respect we follow the superscript notations in Wan [4].)

2   Optimization of the output layer

The structure of the output layer of the FIR network is similar to ADALINE or an affine combiner as shown in Fig. 1. The goal of the optimization is to find those $\mathbf{w}_i^1$'s that minimize the cost function $E(\mathbf{W}^1) = \sum_{t=1}^{T} \frac{1}{2}\left(d(t) - \sum_{i=1}^{H} \mathbf{w}_i^1 \cdot \mathbf{x}_i^1(t)\right)^2$. Therefore we have to find the value of each $\mathbf{w}_h^1$ which makes the derivative of $E(\mathbf{W}^1)$ with respect to $\mathbf{w}_h^1$ equal to $\mathbf{0}$ as shown in Equation 2.

$$\frac{\partial E}{\partial \mathbf{w}_h^1} = \sum_{t=1}^{T}\left(d(t) - \sum_{i=1}^{H} \mathbf{w}_i^1 \cdot \mathbf{x}_i^1(t)\right)\mathbf{x}_h^1(t) = \mathbf{0}. \tag{2}$$

When we consider all the FIR synapses $\mathbf{w}_h^1$'s of the output layer, we obtain the following linear equations:

$$\sum_{t=1}^{T}\begin{bmatrix}\mathbf{x}_1^1(t)\\ \vdots \\ \mathbf{x}_H^1(t)\end{bmatrix}\begin{bmatrix}\mathbf{x}_1^1(t)^T & \cdots & \mathbf{x}_H^1(t)^T\end{bmatrix}\begin{bmatrix}\mathbf{w}_1^1\\ \vdots \\ \mathbf{w}_H^1\end{bmatrix} = \sum_{t=1}^{T}\begin{bmatrix}d(t)\mathbf{x}_1^1(t)\\ \vdots \\ d(t)\mathbf{x}_H^1(t)\end{bmatrix}. \tag{3}$$

Therefore the solution of these linear equations is the optimal FIR synapses which minimize the cost function.

3   Optimization of the hidden layer

Let the current FIR synapses between the input neuron m and the hidden neuron h be $\mathbf{w}_{hm}^0$, and its new FIR synapses $\mathbf{w}_{new,hm}^0$ be represented as $\mathbf{w}_{new,hm}^0 = \mathbf{w}_{hm}^0 + \Delta\mathbf{w}_{hm}^0$, then the corresponding input to a hidden neuron with those new FIR synapses becomes

$$s_{new,h}^1(t) = \sum_{m=0}^{M} \mathbf{w}_{new,hm}^0 \cdot \mathbf{x}_m^0(t) = \sum_{m=0}^{M} \mathbf{w}_{hm}^0 \cdot \mathbf{x}_m^0(t) + \sum_{m=0}^{M} \Delta\mathbf{w}_{hm}^0 \cdot \mathbf{x}_m^0(t) = s_h^1(t) + \Delta s_h^1(t).$$

The value of the sigmoidal function $f(s_{new,h}^1(t))$ can be expressed by using the first two terms and the remainder R of its Taylor series expansion as follows:

$$f(s_{new,h}^1(t)) = f(s_h^1(t) + \Delta s_h^1(t)) = f(s_h^1(t)) + \frac{\partial f(s_h^1(t))}{\partial s_h^1(t)}\Delta s_h^1(t) + R.$$

Therefore

$$x_{new,h}^1(t) \cong f(s_h^1(t)) + \frac{\partial f(s_h^1(t))}{\partial s_h^1(t)}\Delta s_h^1(t). \tag{4}$$

In turn the output of the network is as follows:

$$x^2_{new,1}(t) = \sum_{h=1}^{H} \mathbf{w}_h^1 \cdot \mathbf{x}_{new,h}^1(t) = \sum_{h=1}^{H} \left(\mathbf{w}_h^1 \cdot \mathbf{x}_h^1(t) + \mathbf{w}_h^1 \cdot \left[f'(s_h^1(t))\Delta s_h^1(t) \quad \cdots \quad f'(s_h^1(t-T_1))\Delta s_h^1(t-T_1) \right]^T \right)$$

$$= x_1^2(t) + \Delta x_1^2(t) = x_1^2(t) + \sum_{h=1}^{H} \mathbf{w}_{lin,h}^1 \cdot \Delta \mathbf{s}_h^1(t). \tag{5}$$

Here $\mathbf{w}_{lin,h}^1(t)$ denotes $\left[f'(s_h^1(t))w_h^1(0) \quad \cdots \quad f'(s_h^1(t-T_1))w_h^1(T_1) \right]^T$. The error due to the FIR synapse change which reflects the linearization of the activation function is $E_{lin} = \sum_{t=1}^{T} \frac{1}{2}(e(t) - \Delta x_1^2(t))^2$ instead of $E = \sum_{t=1}^{T} \frac{1}{2}(d(t) - x_1^2(t))^2 = \sum_{t=1}^{T} \frac{1}{2}e(t)^2$. If we can assume that $\Delta s_h^1(t)$ is small enough and hence the third term of its Taylor series expansion $\epsilon_h(t) \equiv \frac{1}{2}f''(s_h^1(t))(\Delta s_h^1(t))^2$ is small enough, we may use the above cost function E_{lin}. But since in general we have to take care of the third or higher order terms of the expansion, we have to consider the following additional cost function:

$$E_{pen} = \frac{1}{H(T_1+1)} \sum_{t=1}^{T} \sum_{j=1}^{H} \left(|w_j^1(0)\epsilon_j(t)| + \cdots + |w_j^1(T_1)\epsilon_j(t-T_1)| \right). \tag{6}$$

Therefore the total cost function may become minimal with those FIR synapse values which make the derivatives of the two cost functions, E_{lin} and E_{pen}, **0** at the same time:

$$\frac{\partial E_{lin}}{\partial \Delta \mathbf{w}_{hm}^0} + \mu \frac{\partial E_{pen}}{\partial \Delta \mathbf{w}_{hm}^0} = \mathbf{0} \tag{7}$$

If they do not make the cost function minimal, we try to find a new set of FIR synapse values after adjusting the weighting factor μ. The value of μ is usually increased by a small amount each time.

Without any derivation process because of the space limit, we just give the results of these two derivatives. $\frac{\partial E_{lin}}{\partial \Delta \mathbf{w}_{hm}^0}$ becomes

$$\sum_{j=1}^{H} \sum_{i=0}^{M} \left[\sum_t \mathbf{w}_{lin,j}^1(t) \cdot \mathbf{x}_i^0(t) \quad \cdots \quad \sum_t \mathbf{w}_{lin,j}^1(t) \cdot \mathbf{x}_i^0(t-T_0) \right]^T \cdot \Delta \mathbf{w}_{ji}^0 \times \begin{bmatrix} \sum_t \mathbf{w}_{lin,h}^1(t) \cdot \mathbf{x}_m^0(t) \\ \vdots \\ \sum_t \mathbf{w}_{lin,h}^1(t) \cdot \mathbf{x}_m^0(t-T_0) \end{bmatrix}$$

$$- \begin{bmatrix} \sum_t e(t) \times \mathbf{w}_{lin,h}^1(t) \cdot \mathbf{x}_m^0(t) \\ \vdots \\ \sum_t e(t) \times \mathbf{w}_{lin,h}^1(t) \cdot \mathbf{x}_m^0(t-T_0) \end{bmatrix}. \tag{8}$$

On the other hand $\frac{\partial E_{pen}}{\partial \Delta \mathbf{w}_{hm}^0}$ becomes

$$\frac{1}{H(T_1+1)} \sum_{i=0}^{M} \sum_t \left[\begin{matrix} \sum_{d=0}^{T_1} |w_h^1(d)f''(s_h^1(t-d))|\mathbf{x}_m^0(t)[d]\mathbf{x}_i^0(t)[d] & \cdots \\ \vdots \\ \sum_{d=0}^{T_1} |w_h^1(d)f''(s_h^1(t-d))|\mathbf{x}_m^0(t-T_0)[d]\mathbf{x}_i^0(t-T_0)[d] & \cdots \\ \sum_{d=0}^{T_1} |w_h^1(d)f''(s_h^1(t-d))|\mathbf{x}_m^0(t)[d]\mathbf{x}_i^0(t-T_0)[d] \\ \vdots \\ \sum_{d=0}^{T_1} |w_h^1(d)f''(s_h^1(t-d))|\mathbf{x}_m^0(t-T_0)[d]\mathbf{x}_i^0(t-T_0)[d] \end{matrix} \right] \Delta \mathbf{w}_{hi}^0. \tag{9}$$

Now let $\mathbf{a}_{hm,ji}[k]$, $\mathbf{A}_{hm,ji}$ and $\mathbf{b}_{hm}$ be defined as

$$\mathbf{a}_{hm,ji}[k] \equiv \left[\sum_{t=1}^{T} \mathbf{w}_{lin,h}^1 \cdot \mathbf{x}_m^0(t-k) \times \mathbf{w}_{lin,j}^1(t) \cdot \mathbf{x}_i^0(t) \quad \cdots \quad \sum_t \mathbf{w}_{lin,h}^1 \cdot \mathbf{x}_m^0(t-k) \times \mathbf{w}_{lin,j}^1(t) \cdot \mathbf{x}_i^0(t-T_0) \right]^T$$

$$\mathbf{A}_{hm,ji} \equiv \begin{bmatrix} \mathbf{a}_{hm,ji}[0]^T \\ \vdots \\ \mathbf{a}_{hm,ji}[T_0]^T \end{bmatrix} \quad \mathbf{b}_{hm} \equiv \left[\sum_{t=1}^{T} \mathbf{w}_{lin,h}^1(t) \cdot \mathbf{x}_m^0(t) \times e(t) \quad \cdots \quad \sum_t \mathbf{w}_{lin,h}^1(t) \cdot \mathbf{x}_m^0(t-T_0) \times e(t) \right]^T.$$

and $\mathbf{C}_{hm,i}$ be the matrix in Equation 9, then the FIR synapse $\Delta\mathbf{w}^0_{hm}$ which minimizes the two cost functions, E_{lin} and E_{pen} satisfies the followings:

$$\mathbf{b}_{hm} = \sum_{i=0}^{M}\sum_{j=1}^{H} \mathbf{A}_{hm,ji}\Delta\mathbf{w}^0_{ji} + \frac{\mu}{H(T_1+1)}\sum_{i=o}^{M}\mathbf{C}_{hm,i}\Delta\mathbf{w}^0_{hi} \tag{10}$$

$$\mathbf{B}_{hm,ji} \equiv \begin{cases} \mathbf{A}_{hm,ji} & \text{for } j \neq h \\ \mathbf{A}_{hm,ji} + \frac{\mu}{H(T_1+1)}\mathbf{C}_{hm,i} & \text{for } j = h \end{cases} \tag{11}$$

$$\sum_{i=0}^{M}\sum_{j=1}^{H} \mathbf{B}_{hm,ji}\Delta\mathbf{w}^0_{ji} = \mathbf{b}_{hm}. \tag{12}$$

4   Outline of the entire learning algorithm

We have seen how to update the FIR synapses of the output layer and those of hidden layer separately. The outline of our new learning algorithm for a FIR network can be stated as follows:

```
proc FIR-OLL
        NN := FIR Neural Network to be learned with initial FIR synapse(W¹, W⁰);
        μ := initial value;
        do            /* Minimize the cost function by layer by layer*/
            output_layer_learn();
            hidden_layer_learn();
        until NN's cost function E < target value or μ > 1
end-proc
proc output_layer_learn() /* update the FIR synapses of the output layer per 2*/
        calculate E_old by Equation 1
        find W¹* by Equation 3
        calculate E_new using W¹* by Equation 1
        if E_old > E_new
            W¹ := W¹*
end-proc
prod hidden_layer_learn() /* update the FIR synapses of the hidden layer per 3 */
        calculate E_old by Equation 1
        do            /* repeat the process if necessary */
            find ΔW⁰* by Equation 11
            calculate E_new using W⁰ + ΔW⁰* by Equation 1
            if E_old > E_new
                W⁰ := W⁰ + ΔW⁰*
                break
            else
                increase μ by 1.1 times /* put a more weight on E_pen */
        until μ > 1
end-proc
```

At the initial point we set the parameters $\mathbf{W}^1, \mathbf{W}^0$ to random numbers near 0 and usually μ to 10^{-4}.

5   Performance evaluation

In order to evaluate the performance of the proposed learning algorithm for a FIR network we used the following two dynamical systems. One is the Lorenz equation of three dimensional time series [3] and the other the Mackey-Glass equation of one dimensional time series [1]. Both are popular problems to evaluate time series predictors [2]. A predictor is supposed to always predict the value at the next one time in the time series. The following normalized mean squared error was used as a performance measure:

$$NMSE = \frac{1}{\sigma^2 N} \sum_{t=1}^{N} \left(x(t) - \hat{x}(t) \right)^2 \ . \tag{13}$$

For each dynamic system we performed two kinds of experiments. The first is to compare the performance of the MLP network with the optimization layer by layer(MLP-OLL) learning algorithm proposed by Ergezinger *et al.* and that of the FIR network with the optimization layer by layer(FIR-OLL) learning algorithm proposed here. This experiment was performed in order to find which network model is more suitable for time series prediction since both use the same principle of learning algorithm. The second is to compare the performances of FIR-OLL proposed here and the stochastic error backpropagation(FIR-BP) learning algorithm for the FIR network. This experiment was performed in order to find which learning method is better for the FIR network. By using the results of these two kinds of evaluations, we obtained a conclusion that FIR-OLL was best among the algorithms compared. Because of the space limit we present only two graphs here.

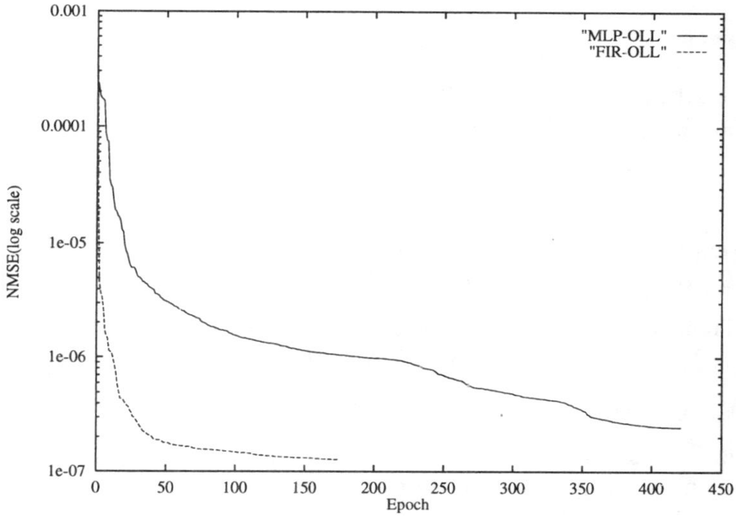

Figure 2: Learning curves by MLP-OLL and FIR-OLL to Lorenz equation

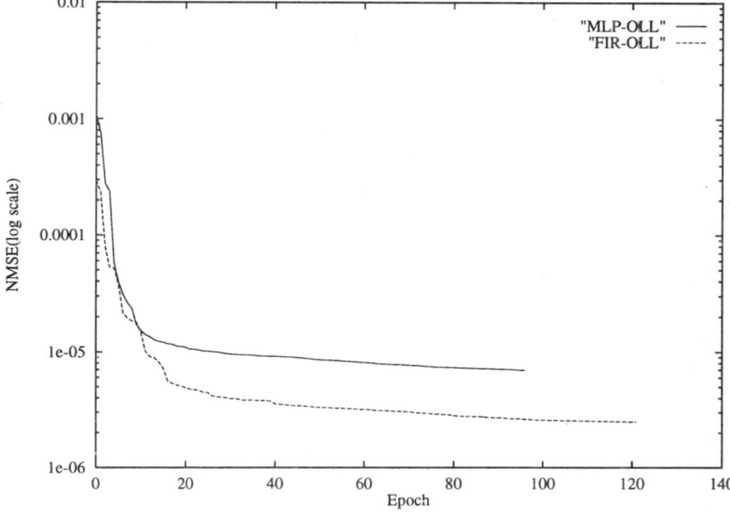

Figure 3: Learning curves by MLP-OLL and FIR-OLL to Mackey-Glass equation

6   Conclusion

The new learning algorithm uses the same principle as the optimization layer by layer learning algorithm which was proposed for the regular multilayer perceptron network and gave a much better result than various improved BP algorithms.

The new learning algorithm for the FIR network has the same properties as the original layer by layer learning algorithm. Under the layer by layer learning algorithm we linearize non-linear neurons and update the weights to the values which make the cost function equal to **0** layer by layer. Furthermore we update the weights of a layer all at once using the entire training data rather than once for each training data. These processes make it possible to learn much faster and not to be caught by a local minimum.

We performed experiments to evaluate the performance of the proposed algorithm using the two time series problems, Lorenz equation and Mackey-Glass equation, which are frequently used for such an evaluation. According to the experimental results the FIR network performed better than the regular multilayer perceptron network when the same optimization layer by layer principle was used. Furthermore the new algorithm performed better than the existing BP algorithm when they were applied to a FIR network. In case of the latter experiment the improvements were about 100 to 1000 times in terms of the learning speed and about 100 times in terms of the prediction accuracy.

Acknowledgements

This study was supported in part by Korea Telecom under contract 95-55, by a grant 92-21-00-05 from Korea Science Foundation and by SERI under contract 94-32.

References

[1] Day, S. D. & Davenport, M. R. (1991). Continuous-time temporal back-propagation with adaptable time delays. *IEEE Trans. on Neural Networks.*

[2] Ergezinger, S. & Thomsen, E. (1995). An Accelerated Learning Algorithm for Multilayer perceptrons: Optimization Layer by Layer. *IEEE Trans. on Neural Networks*, **6**.

[3] Lorenz, E. N. (1963). Deteministic nonperiodict flow. *J. Atmos. Sci.*, **20**, 130.

[4] Wan, E. A. (1993). Time Series Prediction by Using a Connectionist Network with Internal Delay Lines. Weigend, A. S. & Gershenfeld, N. A. (Eds.), *Time Series Prediction: Forecasting the Future and Understanding the Past*. Addison-Wesley.

Canonical Momenta Indicators of Financial Markets and Neocortical EEG

Lester Ingber
Lester Ingber Research
P.O. Box 857, McLean, Virginia 22101, U.S.A.
ingber@ingber.com, ingber@alumni.caltech.edu

Abstract—A paradigm of statistical mechanics of financial markets (SMFM) is fit to multivariate financial markets using Adaptive Simulated Annealing (ASA), a global optimization algorithm, to perform maximum likelihood fits of Lagrangians defined by path integrals of multivariate conditional probabilities. Canonical momenta are thereby derived and used as technical indicators in a recursive ASA optimization process to tune trading rules. These trading rules are then used on out-of-sample data, to demonstrate that they can profit from the SMFM model, to illustrate that these markets are likely not efficient. This methodology can be extended to other systems, e.g., electroencephalography. This approach to complex systems emphasizes the utility of blending an intuitive and powerful mathematical-physics formalism to generate indicators which are used by AI-type rule-based models of management.

1. Introduction

Over a decade ago, the author published a paper suggesting the use of newly developed methods of multivariate nonlinear nonequilibrium calculus to approach a statistical mechanics of financial markets (SMFM) [1]. These methods were applied to interest-rate term-structure systems [2,3]. Still, for some time, the standard accepted paradigm of financial markets has been rooted in equilibrium processes [4]. There is a current effort by many to examine nonlinear and nonequilibrium processes in these markets [5], and this paper reinforces this point of view. Another paper gives some earlier 1991 results using this approach [6].

There are several issues that are clarified here, by presenting calculations of a specific trading model: (A) It is demonstrated how multivariate markets might be formulated in a nonequilibrium paradigm. (B) It is demonstrated that numerical methods of global optimization can be used to fit such SMFM models to data. (C) A variational principle possessed by SMFM permits derivation of technical indicators, such as canonical momenta, that can be used to describe deviations from most likely evolving states of the multivariate system. (D) These technical indicators can be embedded in realistic trading scenarios, to test whether they can profit from nonequilibrium in markets.

Section 2 outlines the formalism used to develop the nonlinear nonequilibrium SMFM model. Section 3 describes application of SMFM to SP500 cash and future data, using Adaptive Simulated Annealing (ASA) [7] to fit the short-time conditional probabilities developed in Section 2, and to establish trading rules by recursively optimizing with ASA, using optimized technical indicators developed from SMFM. These calculations were briefly mentioned in another ASA paper [8]. Section 4 describes similar applications, now in progress, to correlating customized electroencephalographic (EEG) momenta indicators to physiological and behavioral states of humans. Section 5 is a brief conclusion.

2. SMFM Model

2.1. Random walk model

The use of Brownian motion as a model for financial systems is generally attributed to Bachelier [9], though he incorrectly intuited that the noise scaled linearly instead of as the square root relative to the random log-price variable. Einstein is generally credited with using the correct mathematical description in a larger physical context of statistical systems. However, several studies imply that changing prices of many markets do not follow a random walk, that they may have long-term dependences in price correlations, and that they may not be efficient in quickly arbitraging new information [10-12]. A random walk for returns, rate of change of prices over prices, is described by a Langevin equation with simple additive noise η, typically representing the continual random influx of information into the market.

$$\dot{\Gamma} = -\gamma_1 + \gamma_2 \eta \ ,$$

$$\dot{\Gamma} = d\Gamma/dt \ ,$$

$$< \eta(t) >_\eta = 0 \ , \ < \eta(t), \eta(t') >_\eta = \delta(t - t') \ , \tag{1}$$

where γ_1 and γ_2 are constants, and Γ is the logarithm of (scaled) price. Price, although the most dramatic observable, may not be the only appropriate dependent variable or order parameter for the system of markets [13]. This possibility has also been called the "semistrong form of the efficient market hypothesis" [10].

It is necessary to explore the possibilities that a given market evolves in nonequilibrium, e.g., evolving irreversibly, as well as nonlinearly, e.g., $\gamma_{1,2}$ may be functions of Γ. Irreversibility, e.g., causality [14] and nonlinearity [15], have been suggested as processes necessary to take into account in order to understand markets, but modern methods of statistical mechanics now provide a more explicit paradigm to consistently include these processes in *bona fide* probability distributions. Reservations have been expressed about these earlier models at the time of their presentation [16].

Developments in nonlinear nonequilibrium statistical mechanics in the late 1970's and their application to a variety of testable physical phenomena illustrate the importance of properly treating nonlinearities and nonequilibrium in systems where simpler analyses prototypical of linear equilibrium Brownian motion do not suffice [17].

2.2. Statistical mechanics of large systems

Aggregation problems in nonlinear nonequilibrium systems, e.g., as defines a market composed of many traders [1], typically are "solved" (accommodated) by having new entities/languages developed at these disparate scales in order to efficiently pass information back and forth [18,19]. This is quite different from the nature of quasi-equilibrium quasi-linear systems, where thermodynamic or cybernetic approaches are possible. These approaches typically fail for nonequilibrium nonlinear systems.

These new methods of nonlinear statistical mechanics only recently have been applied to complex large-scale physical problems, demonstrating that observed data can be described by the use of these algebraic functional forms. Success was gained for large-scale systems in neuroscience, in a series of papers on statistical mechanics of neocortical interactions [20-30], and in nuclear physics [31-33]. This methodology has been used for problems in combat analyses [19,34-37]. These methods have been suggested for financial markets [1], applied to a term structure model of interest rates [2,3], and to optimization of trading [6].

2.3. Statistical development

When other order parameters in addition to price are included to study markets, Eq. (1) is accordingly generalized to a set of Langevin equations.

$$\dot{M}^G = f^G + \hat{g}^G_j \eta^j \; , \; (G = 1, \cdots, \Lambda) \; , \; (j = 1, \cdots, N) \; ,$$

$$\dot{M}^G = dM^G/d\Theta \; ,$$

$$< \eta^j(\Theta) >_\eta = 0 \; , \; < \eta^j(\Theta), \eta^{j'}(\Theta') >_\eta = \delta^{jj'} \delta(\Theta - \Theta') \; , \tag{2}$$

where f^G and $\hat{g}^G_j$ are generally nonlinear functions of mesoscopic order parameters M^G, j is a microscopic index indicating the source of fluctuations, and $N \geq \Lambda$. The Einstein convention of summing over repeated indices is used. Vertical bars on an index, e.g., |j|, imply no sum is to be taken on repeated indices. Θ is used here to emphasize that the most appropriate time scale for trading may not be real time t.

Via a somewhat lengthy, albeit instructive calculation, outlined in several other papers [1,3,25], involving an intermediate derivation of a corresponding Fokker-Planck or Schrödinger-type equation for the conditional probability distribution $P[M(\Theta)|M(\Theta_0)]$, the Langevin rate Eq. (2) is developed into the probability distribution for M^G at long-time macroscopic time event $\Theta = (u+1)\theta + \Theta_0$, in terms of a Stratonovich path-integral over mesoscopic Gaussian conditional probabilities [38-40]. Here, macroscopic variables are defined as the long-time limit of the evolving mesoscopic system. The corresponding Schrödinger-type equation is [39,41]

$$\partial P/\partial \Theta = \frac{1}{2}(g^{GG'}P)_{,GG'} - (g^G P)_{,G} + V \; ,$$

$$g^{GG'} = k_T \delta^{jk} \hat{g}^G_j \hat{g}^{G'}_k \; , \; g^G = f^G + \frac{1}{2} \delta^{jk} \hat{g}^{G'}_j \hat{g}^G_{k,G'} \; ,$$

$$[\cdots]_{,G} = \partial[\cdots]/\partial M^G \; . \tag{3}$$

This is properly referred to as a Fokker-Planck equation when $V \equiv 0$. Note that although the partial differential Eq. (3) contains equivalent information regarding M^G as in the stochastic differential Eq. (2), all references to j have been properly averaged over. I.e., $\hat{g}^G_j$ in Eq. (2) is an entity with parameters in both microscopic and mesoscopic spaces, but M is a purely mesoscopic variable, and this is more clearly reflected in Eq. (3).

The path integral representation is given in terms of the Lagrangian L.

$$P[M_\Theta|M_{\Theta_0}]dM(\Theta) = \int \cdots \int DM \exp(-S)\delta[M(\Theta_0) = M_0]\delta[M(\Theta) = M_\Theta] \; ,$$

$$S = k_T^{-1} \min \int_{\Theta_0}^{\Theta} d\Theta' L \; ,$$

$$DM = \lim_{u \to \infty} \prod_{\rho=1}^{u+1} g^{1/2} \prod_G (2\pi\theta)^{-1/2} dM_\rho^G \,,$$

$$L(\dot{M}^G, M^G, \Theta) = \frac{1}{2}(\dot{M}^G - h^G) g_{GG'}(\dot{M}^{G'} - h^{G'}) + \frac{1}{2} h^G_{;G} + R/6 - V \,,$$

$$h^G = g^G - \frac{1}{2} g^{-1/2}(g^{1/2} g^{GG'})_{,G'} \,,$$

$$g_{GG'} = (g^{GG'})^{-1} \,, \quad g = \det(g_{GG'}) \,,$$

$$h^G_{;G} = h^G_{,G} + \Gamma^F_{GF} h^G = g^{-1/2}(g^{1/2} h^G)_{,G} \,,$$

$$\Gamma^F_{JK} \equiv g^{LF}[JK, L] = g^{LF}(g_{JL,K} + g_{KL,J} - g_{JK,L}) \,,$$

$$R = g^{JL} R_{JL} = g^{JL} g^{JK} R_{FJKL} \,,$$

$$R_{FJKL} = \frac{1}{2}(g_{FK,JL} - g_{JK,FL} - g_{FL,JK} + g_{JL,FK}) + g_{MN}(\Gamma^M_{FK} \Gamma^N_{JL} - \Gamma^M_{FL} \Gamma^N_{JK}) \,. \tag{4}$$

Mesoscopic variables have been defined as M^G in the Langevin and Fokker-Planck representations, in terms of their development from the microscopic system labeled by j. The Riemannian curvature term R arises from nonlinear $g_{GG'}$, which is a bona fide metric of this parameter space [39].

2.4. Algebraic complexity yields simple intuitive results

It must be emphasized that the output need not be confined to complex algebraic forms or tables of numbers. Because L possesses a variational principle, sets of contour graphs, at different long-time epochs of the path-integral of P over its variables at all intermediate times, give a visually intuitive and accurate decision-aid to view the dynamic evolution of the scenario. For example, this Lagrangian approach permits a quantitative assessment of concepts usually only loosely defined.

$$\text{``Momentum''} = \Pi^G = \frac{\partial L}{\partial(\partial M^G/\partial\Theta)} \,,$$

$$\text{``Mass''} g_{GG'} = \frac{\partial^2 L}{\partial(\partial M^G/\partial\Theta)\partial(\partial M^{G'}/\partial\Theta)} \,,$$

$$\text{``Force''} = \frac{\partial L}{\partial M^G} \,,$$

$$\text{``}F = ma\text{''}: \quad \delta L = 0 = \frac{\partial L}{\partial M^G} - \frac{\partial}{\partial\Theta} \frac{\partial L}{\partial(\partial M^G/\partial\Theta)} \,, \tag{5}$$

where M^G are the variables and L is the Lagrangian. These physical entities provide another form of intuitive, but quantitatively precise, presentation of these analyses. For example, daily newspapers use this terminology to discuss the movement of security prices. Here, we will use the canonical momenta as indicators to develop trading rules.

2.5. Fitting parameters

The short-time path-integral Lagrangian of a Λ-dimensional system can be developed into a scalar "dynamic cost function," C, in terms of parameters, e.g., generically represented as $C(\bar{\alpha})$,

$$C(\bar{\alpha}) = L\Delta\Theta + \frac{\Lambda}{2} \ln(2\pi\Delta\Theta) - \frac{1}{2} \ln g \,, \tag{6}$$

which can be used with the ASA algorithm [7], originally called Very Fast Simulated Reannealing (VFSR) [42], to find the (statistically) best fit of parameters. The cost function for a given system is obtained by the product of P's over all data epochs, i.e., a sum of C's is obtained. Then, since we essentially are performing a maximum likelihood fit, the cost functions obtained from somewhat different theories or data can provide a relative statistical measure of their likelihood, e.g., $P_{12} \sim \exp(C_2 - C_1)$.

If there are competing mathematical forms, then it is advantageous to utilize the path-integral to calculate the long-time evolution of P [19,35]. Experience has demonstrated that the long-time correlations derived from theory, measured against the observed data, is a viable and expedient way of rejecting models not in accord with observed evidence.

2.6. Numerical methodology

ASA [42] fits short-time probability distributions to observed data, using a maximum likelihood technique on the Lagrangian. This algorithm has been developed to fit observed data to a theoretical cost function over a D-dimensional parameter space [42], adapting for varying sensitivities of parameters during the fit.

Simulated annealing (SA) was developed in 1983 to deal with highly nonlinear problems [43], as an extension of a Monte-Carlo importance-sampling technique developed in 1953 for chemical physics problems. It helps to visualize the problems presented by such complex systems as a geographical terrain. For example, consider a mountain range, with two "parameters," e.g., along the North–South and East–West directions. We wish to find the lowest valley in this terrain. SA approaches this problem similar to using a bouncing ball that can bounce over mountains from valley to valley. We start at a high "temperature," where the temperature is an SA parameter that mimics the effect of a fast moving particle in a hot object like a hot molten metal, thereby permitting the ball to make very high bounces and being able to bounce over any mountain to access any valley, given enough bounces. As the temperature is made relatively colder, the ball cannot bounce so high, and it also can settle to become trapped in relatively smaller ranges of valleys.

We imagine that our mountain range is aptly described by a "cost function." We define probability distributions of the two directional parameters, called generating distributions since they generate possible valleys or states we are to explore. We define another distribution, called the acceptance distribution, which depends on the difference of cost functions of the present generated valley we are to explore and the last saved lowest valley. The acceptance distribution decides probabilistically whether to stay in a new lower valley or to bounce out of it. All the generating and acceptance distributions depend on temperatures.

In 1984 [44], it was established that SA possessed a proof that, by carefully controlling the rates of cooling of temperatures, it could statistically find the best minimum, e.g., the lowest valley of our example above. This was good news for people trying to solve hard problems which could not be solved by other algorithms. The bad news was that the guarantee was only good if they were willing to run SA forever. In 1987, a method of fast annealing (FA) was developed [45], which permitted lowering the temperature exponentially faster, thereby statistically guaranteeing that the minimum could be found in some finite time. However, that time still could be quite long. Shortly thereafter, in 1987 the author developed Very Fast Simulated Reannealing (VFSR) [42], now called Adaptive Simulated Annealing (ASA), which is exponentially faster than FA. It is used world-wide across many disciplines [8], and the feedback of many users regularly scrutinizing the source code ensures the soundness of the code as it becomes more flexible and powerful [46].

ASA has been applied to many problems by many people in many disciplines [8,46,47]. The code is available via anonymous ftp from ftp.ingber.com, which also can be accessed via the world-wide web (WWW) as http://www.ingber.com/.

3. Fitting SMFM to SP500

3.1. Data processing

For the purposes of this paper, it suffices to consider a two-variable problem, SP500 prices of futures, p^1, and cash, p^2. (Note that in a previous paper [6], these two variables were inadvertently incorrectly reversed.) Data included 251 points of 1989 and 252 points of 1990 daily closing data. Time between data was taken as real time t, e.g., a weekend added two days to the time between data of a Monday and a previous Friday.

It was decided that relative data should be more important to the dynamics of the SMFM model than absolute data, and an arbitrary form was developed to preprocess data used in the fits,

$$M^i(t) = p^i(t + \Delta t)/p^i(t) , \tag{7}$$

where $i = \{1, 2\} = \{\text{futures, cash}\}$, and Δt was the time between neighboring data points, and $t + \Delta t$ is the current trading time. The ratio served to served to suppress strong drifts in the absolute data.

3.2. ASA fits of SMFM to data

Two source of noise were assumed, so that the equations of this SMFM model are

$$\frac{dM^G}{dt} = \sum_{G'=1}^{2} f^G_{G'} M^{G'} + \sum_{i=1}^{2} \hat{g}^G_i \eta^i , \ G = \{1,2\} . \tag{8}$$

The 8 parameters, $\{f^G_{G'}, \hat{g}^G_i\}$ were all taken to be constants.

As discussed previously, the path-integral representation was used to define an effective cost function. Minimization of the cost function was performed using ASA. Some experimentation with the fitting process led to a scheme whereby after sufficient importance-sampling, the optimization was shunted over to a quasi-local code, the

Broyden-Fletcher-Goldfarb-Shanno (BFGS) algorithm [48], to add another decimal of precision. If ASA was shunted over too quickly to BFGS, then poor fits were obtained, i.e., the fit stopped in a higher local minimum.

Using 1989 data, the parameters $f_{G'}^G$ were constrained to lie between -1.0 and 1.0. The parameters $\hat{g}_i^G$ were constrained to lie between 0 and 1.0. The values of the parameters, obtained by this fitting process were: $f_1^1 = 0.0686821$, $f_2^1 = -0.068713$, $\hat{g}_1^1 = 0.000122309$, $\hat{g}_2^1 = 0.000224755$, $f_1^2 = 0.645019$, $f_2^2 = -0.645172$, $\hat{g}_1^2 = 0.00209127$, $\hat{g}_2^2 = 0.00122221$.

3.3. ASA fits of trading rules

A simple model of trading was developed. Two time-weighted moving averages, of wide and narrow windows, a_w and a_n were defined for each of the two momenta variables. During each new epoch of a_w, always using the fits of the SMFM model described in the previous section as a zeroth order estimate, the parameters $\{f_{G'}^G, \hat{g}^G\}$ were refit using data within each epoch. Averaged canonical momenta, i.e., using Eq. (5), were calculated for each new set of a_w and a_n windows. Fluctuation parameters $\Delta\Pi_w^G$ and $\Delta\Pi_n^G$, were defined, such that any change in trading position required that there was some reasonable information outside of these fluctuations that could be used as criteria for trading decisions. No trading was performed for the first few days of the year until the momenta could be calculated. Commissions of $70 were paid every time a new trade of 100 units was taken. Thus, there were 6 trading parameters used in this example, $\{a_w, a_n, \Delta\Pi_w^G, \Delta\Pi_n^G\}$.

The order of choices made for daily trading are as follows. A 0 represents no positions are open and no trading is performed until enough data is gathered, e.g., to calculate momenta. A 1 represents entering a long position, whether from a waiting or a short position, or a current long position was maintained. This was performed if the both wide-window and narrow-window averaged momenta of both cash and futures prices were both greater than their $\Delta\Pi_w^G$ and $\Delta\Pi_n^G$ fluctuation parameters. A -1 represents entering a short position, whether from a waiting or a long position, or a current short position was maintained. This was performed if the both wide-window and narrow-window averaged momenta of both cash and futures prices were both less than their $\Delta\Pi_w^G$ and $\Delta\Pi_n^G$ fluctuation parameters.

3.4. In-sample ASA fits of trading rules

For the data of 1989, recursive optimization was performed. The trading parameters were optimized in an outer shell, using the negative of the net yearly profit/loss as a cost function. This could have been weighted by something like the absolute value of maximum loss to help minimize risk, but this was not done here. The inner shell of optimization fine-tuning of the SMFM model was performed daily over the current a_w epoch.

At first, ASA and shunting over to BFGS was used for each shell, but it was realized that good results could be obtained using ASA and BFGS on the outer shell, and just BFGS on the inner shell (always using the ASA and BFGS derived zeroth order SMFM parameters as described above). Thus, recursive optimization was performed to establish the required goodness-of-fit, and more efficient local optimization was used only in those instances where it could replicate the global optimization. This is expected to be quite system dependent.

The trading-rule parameters were constrained to lie within the following ranges: a_w integers between 15 and 25, a_n integers between 3 and 14, $\Delta\Pi_w^G$ and $\Delta\Pi_n^G$ between 0 and 200. The trading parameters fit by this procedure were: $a_w = 18$, $a_n = 11$, $\Delta\Pi_w^1 = 30.3474$, $\Delta\Pi_w^2 = 98.0307$, $\Delta\Pi_n^1 = 11.2855$, $\Delta\Pi_n^2 = 54.8492$.

The summary of results was: cumulative profit = $54170, number of profitable long positions = 11, number of profitable short positions = 8, number of losing long positions = 5, number of losing short positions = 6, maximum profit of any given trade = $11005, maximum loss of any trade = $-$2545, maximum accumulated profit during year = $54170, maximum loss sustained during year = $0.

3.5. Out-of-sample SMFM trading

The trading process described above was applied to the 1990 out-of-sample SP500 data. Note that 1990 was a "bear" market, while 1989 was a "bull" market. Thus, these two years had quite different overall contexts, and this was believed to provide a stronger test of this methodology than picking two years with similar contexts.

The inner shell of optimization was performed as described above for 1990 as well. The summary of results was: cumulative profit = $28300, number of profitable long positions = 10, number of profitable short positions = 6, number of losing long positions = 6, number of losing short positions = 10, maximum profit of any given trade = $6780, maximum loss of any trade = $-$2450, maximum accumulated profit during year = $29965, maximum loss sustained during year = $-$5945. Tables of results are available as file markets96_momenta_tbl.txt.Z in http://www.ingber.com/MISC.DIR/ and ftp.ingber.com/MISC.DIR.

Only one variable, the futures SP500, was actually traded, albeit the code can accommodate trading on multiple markets. There is more leverage and liquidity in actually trading the futures market. The multivariable coupling to the cash market entered in three important ways: (1) The SMFM fits were to the coupled system, requiring a global optimization of all parameters in both markets to define the time evolution of the futures market. (2) The canonical momenta for the futures market is in terms of the partial derivative of the full Lagrangian; the dependency on the cash market enters both as a function of the relative value of the off-diagonal to diagonal terms in the metric, as well as a contribution to the drifts and diffusions from this market. (3) The canonical momenta of both markets were used as technical indicators for trading the futures market.

3.6. Reversing data sets

The same procedures described above were repeated, but using the 1990 SP500 data set for training and the 1989 data set for testing.

For the training phase, using 1990 data, the parameters $f_{G'}^G$ were constrained to lie between -1.0 and 1.0. The parameters $\hat{g}_i^G$ were constrained to lie between 0 and 1.0. The values of the parameters, obtained by this fitting process were: $f_1^1 = 0.0685466$, $f_2^1 = -0.068571$, $\hat{g}_1^1 = 7.52368 \ 10^{-6}$, $\hat{g}_2^1 = 0.000274467$, $f_1^2 = 0.642585$, $f_2^2 = -0.642732$, $\hat{g}_1^2 = 9.30768 \ 10^{-5}$, $\hat{g}_2^2 = 0.00265532$. Note that these values are quite close to those obtained above when fitting the 1989 data.

The trading-rule parameters were constrained to lie within the following ranges: a_w integers between 15 and 25, a_n integers between 3 and 14, $\Delta\Pi_w^G$ and $\Delta\Pi_n^G$ between 0 and 200. The trading parameters fit by this procedure were: $a_w = 11$, $a_n = 8$, $\Delta\Pi_w^1 = 23.2324$, $\Delta\Pi_w^2 = 135.212$, $\Delta\Pi_n^1 = 169.512$, $\Delta\Pi_n^2 = 9.50857$,

The summary of results was: cumulative profit = \$42405, number of profitable long positions = 11, number of profitable short positions = 8, number of losing long positions = 7, number of losing short positions = 6, maximum profit of any given trade = \$8280, maximum loss of any trade = −\$1895, maximum accumulated profit during year = \$47605, maximum loss sustained during year = −\$2915.

For the testing phase, the summary of results was: cumulative profit = \$35790, number of profitable long positions = 10, number of profitable short positions = 6, number of losing long positions = 6, number of losing short positions = 3, maximum profit of any given trade = \$9780, maximum loss of any trade = −\$4270, maximum accumulated profit during year = \$35790, maximum loss sustained during year = \$0. Tables of results are available as file markets96_momenta_tbl.txt.Z in http://www.ingber.com/MISC.DIR/ and ftp.ingber.com/MISC.DIR.

4. Extrapolations to EEG

4.1. Customized Momenta Indicators of EEG

These techniques are quite generic, and can be applied to a model of statistical mechanics of neocortical interactions (SMNI) which has utilized similar mathematical and numerical algorithms [20-23,25,26,29,30,49]. In this approach, the SMNI model is fit to EEG data, e.g., as previously performed [25]. This develops a zeroth order guess for SMNI parameters for a given subject's training data. Next, ASA is used recursively to seek parameterized predictor rules, e.g., modeled according to guidelines used by clinicians. The parameterized predictor rules form an outer ASA shell, while regularly fine-tuning the SMNI inner-shell parameters within a moving window (one of the outer-shell parameters). The outer-shell cost function is defined as some measure of successful predictions of upcoming EEG events.

In the testing phase, the outer-shell parameters fit in the training phase are used in out-of-sample data. Again, the process of regularly fine-tuning the inner-shell of SMNI parameters is used in this phase.

If these SMNI techniques can find patterns of such such upcoming activity some time before the trained eye of the clinician, then the costs of time and pain in preparation for surgery can be reduced. This project will determine inter-electrode and intra-electrode activities prior to spike activity to determine likely electrode circuitries highly correlated to the onset of seizures. This can only do better than simple averaging or filtering of such activity, as typically used as input to determine dipole locations of activity prior to the onset of seizures.

If a subset of electrode circuitries are determined to be highly correlated to the onset of seizures, then their associated regions of activity can be used as a first approximate of underlying dipole sources of brain activity affecting seizures. This first approximate may be better than using a spherical head model to deduce such a first guess. Such first approximates can then be used for more realistic dipole source modeling, including the actual shape of the brain surface to determine likely localized areas of diseased tissue.

These momenta indicators should be considered as supplemental to other clinical indicators. This is how they are being used in financial trading systems.

5. Conclusion

A complete sample scenario has been presented: (a) developing a multivariate nonlinear nonequilibrium model of financial markets; (b) fitting the model to data using methods of ASA global optimization; (c) deriving technical indicators to express dynamics about most likely states; (d) optimizing trading rules using these technical indicators; (e) trading on out-of-sample data to determine if steps (a)–(d) are at least sufficient to profit by the knowledge gained of these financial markets, i.e., these markets are not efficient.

Just based the models and representative calculations presented here, no comparisons can yet be made of any relative superiority of these techniques over other models of markets and other sets of trading rules. Rather, this exercise should be viewed as an explicit demonstration (1) that financial markets can be modeled as nonlinear nonequilibrium systems, and (2) that financial markets are not efficient and that they can be properly fit and profitably traded on real data.

Canonical momenta may offer an intuitive yet detailed coordinate system of some complex systems, which can be used as reasonable indicators of new and/or strong trends of behavior, upon which reasonable decisions and actions can be based. A description has been given of a project in progress, using this same methodology to customize canonical momenta indicators of EEG to human behavioral and physiological states [50].

References

[1] L. Ingber, "Statistical mechanics of nonlinear nonequilibrium financial markets," *Math. Modelling* **5** (6), pp. 343-361, 1984.

[2] L. Ingber, "Statistical mechanical aids to calculating term structure models," *Phys. Rev. A* **42** (12), pp. 7057-7064, 1990.

[3] L. Ingber, M.F. Wehner, G.M. Jabbour, and T.M. Barnhill, "Application of statistical mechanics methodology to term-structure bond-pricing models," *Mathl. Comput. Modelling* **15** (11), pp. 77-98, 1991.

[4] R.C. Merton, *Continuous-Time Finance*, Blackwell, Cambridge, MA, (1992).

[5] W. Brock, J. Lakonishok, and B. LeBaron, "Simple technical trading rules and the stochastic properties of stock returns," *J. Finance* **47** (5), pp. 1731-1763, 1992.

[6] L. Ingber, "Statistical mechanics of nonlinear nonequilibrium financial markets: Applications to optimized trading," *Mathl. Computer Modelling* , pp. (to be published), 1996.

[7] L. Ingber, "Adaptive Simulated Annealing (ASA)," [http://www.ingber.com/ASA-shar, ASA-shar.Z, ASA.tar.Z, ASA.tar.gz, ASA.zip], Lester Ingber Research, McLean, VA, 1993.

[8] L. Ingber, "Simulated annealing: Practice versus theory," *Mathl. Comput. Modelling* **18** (11), pp. 29-57, 1993.

[9] L. Bachelier, "Théorie de la Spéculation," *Annales de l'Ecole Normale Supérieure* **3**, 1900.

[10] M. C. Jensen, "Some anomalous evidence regarding market efficiency, an editorial introduction," *J. Finan. Econ.* **6**, pp. 95-101, 1978.

[11] B. B. Mandelbrot, "When can price be arbitraged efficiently? A limit to the validity of the random walk and martingale models," *Rev. Econ. Statist.* **53**, pp. 225-236, 1971.

[12] S. J. Taylor, "Tests of the random walk hypothesis against a price-trend hypothesis," *J. Finan. Quant. Anal.* **17**, pp. 37-61, 1982.

[13] P. Brown, A. W. Kleidon, and T. A. Marsh, "New evidence on the nature of size-related anomalies in stock prices," *J. Fin. Econ.* **12**, pp. 33-56, 1983.

[14] C. W. J. Granger, "Investigating causal relations by econometric models and cross-spectral methods," *Econometrica* **37**, pp. 424-438, 1969.

[15] P. K. Clark, "A subordinated stochastic process model with finite variance for speculative prices," *Econometrica* **41**, pp. 135-155, 1973.

[16] B. B. Mandelbrot, "Comments on: 'A subordinated stochastic process model with finite variance for speculative prices,' by Peter K. Clark," *Econometrica* **41**, pp. 157-159, 1973.

[17] H. Haken, *Synergetics*, Springer, New York, (1983).

[18] L. Ingber, "Mesoscales in neocortex and in command, control and communications (C^3) systems," in *Systems with Learning and Memory Abilities: Proceedings, University of Paris 15-19 June 1987*, (Edited by J. Delacour and J.C.S. Levy), pp. 387-409, Elsevier, Amsterdam, 1988.

[19] L. Ingber, "Mathematical comparison of JANUS(T) simulation to National Training Center," in *The Science of Command and Control: Part II, Coping With Complexity*, (Edited by S.E. Johnson and A.H. Levis), pp. 165-176, AFCEA International, Washington, DC, 1989.

[20] L. Ingber, "Statistical mechanics of neocortical interactions. Dynamics of synaptic modification," *Phys. Rev. A* **28**, pp. 395-416, 1983.

[21] L. Ingber, "Statistical mechanics of neocortical interactions. Derivation of short-term-memory capacity," *Phys. Rev. A* **29**, pp. 3346-3358, 1984.

[22] L. Ingber, "Statistical mechanics of neocortical interactions. EEG dispersion relations," *IEEE Trans. Biomed. Eng.* **32**, pp. 91-94, 1985.

[23] L. Ingber, "Statistical mechanics of neocortical interactions: Stability and duration of the 7±2 rule of short-term-memory capacity," *Phys. Rev. A* **31**, pp. 1183-1186, 1985.

[24] L. Ingber and P.L. Nunez, "Multiple scales of statistical physics of neocortex: Application to electroencephalography," *Mathl. Comput. Modelling* **13** (7), pp. 83-95, 1990.

[25] L. Ingber, "Statistical mechanics of neocortical interactions: A scaling paradigm applied to electroencephalography," *Phys. Rev. A* **44** (6), pp. 4017-4060, 1991.

[26] L. Ingber, "Generic mesoscopic neural networks based on statistical mechanics of neocortical interactions," *Phys. Rev. A* **45** (4), pp. R2183-R2186, 1992.

[27] L. Ingber, "Statistical mechanics of neocortical interactions: Path-integral evolution of short-term memory," *Phys. Rev. E* **49** (5B), pp. 4652-4664, 1994.

[28] L. Ingber and P.L. Nunez, "Statistical mechanics of neocortical interactions: High resolution path-integral calculation of short-term memory," *Phys. Rev. E* **51** (5), pp. 5074-5083, 1995.

[29] L. Ingber, "Statistical mechanics of multiple scales of neocortical interactions," in *Neocortical Dynamics and Human EEG Rhythms*, (Edited by P.L. Nunez), pp. 628-681, Oxford University Press, New York, NY, 1995.

[30] L. Ingber, "Statistical mechanics of neocortical interactions: Multiple scales of EEG," *Electroencephal. clin. Neurophysiol.* , pp. (to be published), 1996.

[31] L. Ingber, "Riemannian corrections to velocity-dependent nuclear forces," *Phys. Rev. C* **28**, pp. 2536-2539, 1983.

[32] L. Ingber, "Path-integral Riemannian contributions to nuclear Schrödinger equation," *Phys. Rev. D* **29**, pp. 1171-1174, 1984.

[33] L. Ingber, "Riemannian contributions to short-ranged velocity-dependent nucleon-nucleon interactions," *Phys. Rev. D* **33**, pp. 3781-3784, 1986.

[34] L. Ingber, "Mathematical comparison of computer models to exercise data," in *1989 JDL C^2 Symposium: National Defense University, Washington, DC, 27-29 June 1989*, pp. 169-192, SAIC, McLean, VA, 1989.

[35] L. Ingber, H. Fujio, and M.F. Wehner, "Mathematical comparison of combat computer models to exercise data," *Mathl. Comput. Modelling* **15** (1), pp. 65-90, 1991.

[36] L. Ingber and D.D. Sworder, "Statistical mechanics of combat with human factors," *Mathl. Comput. Modelling* **15** (11), pp. 99-127, 1991.

[37] L. Ingber, "Statistical mechanics of combat and extensions," in *Toward a Science of Command, Control, and Communications*, (Edited by C. Jones), pp. 117-149, American Institute of Aeronautics and Astronautics, Washington, D.C., 1993.

[38] K.S. Cheng, "Quantization of a general dynamical system by Feynman's path integration formulation," *J. Math. Phys.* **13**, pp. 1723-1726, 1972.

[39] R. Graham, "Path-integral methods on nonequilibrium thermodynamics and statistics," in *Stochastic Processes in Nonequilibrium Systems*, (Edited by L. Garrido, P. Seglar and P.J. Shepherd), pp. 82-138, Springer, New York, NY, 1978.

[40] F. Langouche, D. Roekaerts, and E. Tirapegui, "Short derivation of Feynman Lagrangian for general diffusion process," *J. Phys. A* **113**, pp. 449-452, 1980.

[41] F. Langouche, D. Roekaerts, and E. Tirapegui, "Discretization problems of functional integrals in phase space," *Phys. Rev. D* **20**, pp. 419-432, 1979.

[42] L. Ingber, "Very fast simulated re-annealing," *Mathl. Comput. Modelling* **12** (8), pp. 967-973, 1989.

[43] S. Kirkpatrick, C.D. Gelatt, Jr., and M.P. Vecchi, "Optimization by simulated annealing," *Science* **220** (4598), pp. 671-680, 1983.

[44] S. Geman and D. Geman, "Stochastic relaxation, Gibbs distribution and the Bayesian restoration in images," *IEEE Trans. Patt. Anal. Mac. Int.* **6** (6), pp. 721-741, 1984.

[45] H. Szu and R. Hartley, "Fast simulated annealing," *Phys. Lett. A* **122** (3-4), pp. 157-162, 1987.

[46] L. Ingber, "Adaptive simulated annealing (ASA): Lessons learned," *Control and Cybernetics* **25** (1), pp. (to be published), 1996.

[47] M. Wofsey, "Technology: Shortcut tests validity of complicated formulas," *The Wall Street Journal* **222** (60), pp. B1, 1993.

[48] D.F. Shanno and K.H. Phua, "Minimization of unconstrained multivariate functions," *ACM Trans. Mathl. Software* **2**, pp. 87-94, 1976.

[49] L. Ingber, "Statistical mechanics of neocortical interactions. I. Basic formulation," *Physica D* **5**, pp. 83-107, 1982.

[50] L. Ingber, "Canonical momenta indicators of neocortical EEG," in *Physics Computing 96 (PC96)*, PC96, Krakow, Poland, 1996.

Financial Engineering
and
Time Series Forecasting

(Poster Presentation)

A Case Study for Hong Kong Weather Forecasting

James Liu and Loretta Wong

Department of Computing
Hong Kong Polytechnic University
Hung Hom, Kowloon, Hong Kong
csnkliu@comp.polyu.edu.hk

Abstract

Traditional weather forecasting relies on a number of atmospheric prediction methods which could involve the use of certain model assumptions, statistics, and complex approximation schemes. This is for simulating the meteorological behaviour, and the system dynamic developments to give prediction to various types of synoptic flow, pressure systems and some weather events. It often needs to process and assimilate very large amounts of data from several sources plus intuitive perception to make a routine forecast. This paper presents a preliminary study of using artificial neural networks to help process the meteorological data so as to learn the relevant characteristics for forecasting the rainfall in Hong Kong. The simulation illustrates the capabilities of the networks for the analysis and representation of data. It shows that the approach has produced reasonable accurate weather forecast, paving the way to enhance and improve the qualitative analysis of our meteorological systems in the region.

Keywords: *Artificial neural network, machine learning, weather forecast*

1   Introduction

Meteorologists and forecasters have been using numerical models for studying weather systems and various meteorological phenomenon (e.g. McGregor et al [6], 1993; Smith [11], 1994). The forecasting based on such classical approaches requires the modeling of fluid and thermal dynamic systems and its behavior. The simulation requires long series of computation to approximate the physics and dynamic transition states using complex difference equations, integration schemes and computational algorithms. It requires substantial computer resources yet it often gives not so accurate prediction due to model constraints such as the adoption of incomplete boundary conditions, model assumptions and numerical instabilities (Liu [5], 1987).

On the other hand, weather stations such as the Royal Observatory Hong Kong adopts a number of atmospheric prediction methods to give prediction to various types of synoptic flow, pressure systems and some weather events. Most of these methods are based on the empirical approach involving the process and assimilation of very large amounts of data from several sources plus intuitive perception to make a routine forecast. In this paper, we present a preliminary study of employing machine learning techniques to automate the knowledge acquisition process and learn the behavior of our weather system. We shall focus on using the backprogration network for predicting the occurrence of rain/no-rain in the rainy season in Hong Kong over a period of 24 hours. As a supplement, we shall investigate the performance of using two other different classification networks - radial basis function network and learning vector quantization for our forecasting purpose.

2   Artificial Neural Networks

A classical application of artificial neural network to weather forecasting was applied by Widrow and Smith [13] (1963) to predict the occurrence of rainfall on the following day on the basis of fluctuations in the barometric pressure in the two preceding days. The percentage of successful predictions was comparable to that achieved by the official weather prediction agency, which employed a large set of parameters for weather forecasting (Karayiannis and Venetsanopoulos [4], 1993).

The popular backpropagation network (**BPN**) adopted in this study was the one using momentum algorithm. For comparison purpose, two other classification networks were used for predicting the rainfall. The first one was the radial basis function network (**RBFN**) which is a two-layer feedforward network whose output nodes form a linear combination of the basis functions computed by the hidden layer nodes. Each unit in the hidden layer of the network has its own centroid, and for each input vector $X = (x_1, x_2, x_3 \ldots x_n)$, it computes the distance (usually Euclidean distance) between X and its centroid. The training of this network is done by finding the centroids, widths and the weights connecting the hidden nodes and the output nodes.

Another one was a two-layer fully-connected classification network called learning vector quantization (**LVQ**). It contains a Kohonen layer which learns and performs the classification. The basis of any LVQ classification scheme is that prototypes in the Kohonen layer are learned from the training set. These prototypes are representative of the training vectors and, once learned, classification of an unseen data vector is made by assigning the class of the closest prototype.

Details about the contruct of these networks can be obtained from Widrow et al [14] (1994).

3   Data Collection

Meteorological data for the period from 1984 to 1992 were supplied by the Hong Kong Royal Observatory. These were observations taken at Royal Observatory Headquarters and King's Park. Since we were interested in data for the rainy season here, we therefore concentrated in extracting the May-October data each year during the said period for our experiments.

3.1   Data Preparation

Major elements that were considered as input parameters in this study included: air temperature, air pressure, wind direction and speed, humidity, amount of rainfall, cloud amount and sunshine. In additions, we also incorporated other factors such as what month of the season, measurements of some physical processes like evaporation and potential evapotranspiration contributing to the water content in the atmosphere. Three sets of data were created with the following characteristics:

Data Set A

Data collected at 2400 hours, their daily means, maximum and minimums were included. Nonlinear transformation were applied to some input variables to provide a normally distributed inputs. The data set was used in experiments for the prediction of the occurrence of rain/no-rain.

Data Set B

5-day means of some elements were added in this data set. They were: air pressure, maximum and minimum of air temperature, dew point, daily rainfall, prevailing wind direction, and wind speed.

The data for some variables taken at a time frame different from 2400 hours were also included. For example, the atmospheric pressure at 0000 hour was added. In additions, variables such as vapor pressure, relative humidity, minimum grass temperature, soil temperature, duration of bright sunshine and global solar radiation were deleted from this data set (suggested by Dr Cheng from Royal Observatory Hong Kong).

Note that no transformation was applied to all input variables in this set. The data were used in the prediction of rainfall levels.

Data Set C

Data taken every 4 hours for some input variables (e.g. atmospheric pressure, dew point) were added to Data Set B. They were used for rainfall depth prediction.

3.2   Data Preprocessing

There were 1656 cases extracted from the selected periods with a total of 32 missing values found. Those missing values were filled by taking the average of the month of the corresponding variable for three years. Since full metric units have been adopted by Royal Observatory in 1986 [7], data of some elements reported in 1984 and 1985 had to be converted to the metric units (e.g. the unit of wind speed recorded in knots was converted to meters per second).

The distribution of the input parameters were examined and some of the parameters were transformed by nonlinear functions to make them more normal as it is easier to train the neural network if data is normally distributed (Chung and Kumar [1], 1993). The normality of the transformed data was determined by its skewness coefficient, kurtosis coefficient and distribution (Stein [12], 1993). 75% of the total cases was then selected randomly as for the training set and the rest was used as for the testing set.

3.3   Output Representation

For the prediction of the occurrence of rainfall during a period of 24 hours beginning at the start of the day (0000 hour), days with zero amount of rainfall was defined to be no rain and the rest was defined to be rain. Table 1 shows the category of rainfall specified for the prediction of rainfall level the following day.

Category(mm)	Nil	Trace	Light	Moderate	Heavy
Range in depth	$0 \leq d < 0.05$	$0.05 \leq d < 0.1$	$0.1 \leq d < 4.9$	$4.9 \leq d < 25.0$	$d > 25.0$

Table 1: Rainfall categories

4 Experimental Results

A neural network toolkit, known as NeuralWorks Professional II/Plus1[1] version 5 running on SUN SPARC workstation was used for the study. The input units in the neural network represented data values of various measurements such as temperature, atmospheric pressure, dew point. A total of 49 input units and 2 output units were used. The daily mean, its maximum and minimum as well as data taken at 2400 hours of the previous day were used to predict the occurrence of rain in the following day, beginning at midnight. The weather categories of rain and no-rain were coded as binary values (i.e. 0 or 1). One hidden-layer neural networks were used throughout the experiments as it was shown that one hidden-layer can form an arbitrarily close approximation to any nonlinear mapping (Schizas et al [10], 1989).

4.1 Rain/No-rain Prediction

It is necessary to select and optimize the architecture of some networks, the parameters of the training algorithm, and the representation of the training set, which possibly require much time-consuming experiments by the model designer, as there is no rules of thumb available to assist the task. As for the BPN, various trial runs were done by increasing the number of hidden nodes in step of 10 from 0 to 150 while for that of RBFN, the number of hidden nodes were increased in step of 25 from 25 to 125.

The number of prototypes in the Kohonen layer used in LVQ was determined by a percentage on the number of records in the training file. The number of prototypes was therefore adjusted by increasing the percentage from 1% to 15%.

The architecture of neural network was represented by (**I-H-O**) where "I" was the number of input units, "H" was the number of hidden nodes and "O" was the number of output units. The classification rate on the testing data consisting of 416 cases was monitored every 5 learning cycles during training. Tables 2- 4 show the optimal performance for various architecture for BPN, RBFN and LVQ respectively. As shown in Table 2, the optimal performance for BPN varies from 0.69 to 0.71. The best architecture was (49-100-2) attained after 5 learning cycles and it gave the optimal performance of 0.71.

Network	Optimal Performance	Obtained at Learning Cycle
49-0-2	0.70	180
49-10-2	0.70	60
49-20-2	0.71	55
49-30-2	0.71	120
49-40-2	0.70	200
49-50-2	0.70	30
49-60-2	0.71	10
49-70-2	0.70	30
49-80-2	0.69	40
49-90-2	0.70	130
49-100-2	0.71	5
49-110-2	0.71	150
49-120-2	0.69	45
49-130-2	0.70	40
49-140-2	0.71	105
49-150-2	0.70	85

Table 2: Optimal performance for BPN

For RBFN, the first 50 learning cycles was the unsupervised learning phase. Although the optimal performance of various architecture were similar, (49-50-2) was a better network for its steady performance after a large number of learning cycles.

The best architecture for LVQ was the one with 12 prototypes in the Kohonen layer (49-12-2), its peak performance was 0.7 at learning cycle 50 and it gave an overall better performance than other architecture. Table 4 shows that the optimal performance varies from 0.63 to 0.7.

Table 5 gives a general comparison of three different paradigms. It shows that there was no significant difference in the generalization performance of various network architectures. However, RBFN and LVQ are more efficient (in terms of number of operations) than BPN.

---

[1]Neural network simulator by NeuralWare, Inc,Pittsburgh, PA 15276-9910, USA.

Network	Optimal Performance	Obtained at Learning Cycle
49-25-2	0.71	105
49-50-2	0.71	90
49-75-2	0.70	65
49-100-2	0.70	130
49-125-2	0.70	165

Table 3: Optimal performance for RBFN

Network	Optimal Performance	Obtained at Learning Cycle
49-12-2	0.70	50
49-24-2	0.67	10
49-37-2	0.68	15
49-49-2	0.68	60
49-62-2	0.68	50
49-74-2	0.65	10
49-86-2	0.66	20
49-99-2	0.65	10
49-111-2	0.66	10
49-124-2	0.63	25
49-186-2	0.65	30

Table 4: Optimal performance for LVQ

4.2 Rainfall Depth Prediction

Numerous attempts had been tried to use BPN to predict the depth of the rainfall. Initial simulations considered events in which the rainfall depth for the next 24 hours was at least 0.1 mm and it was in either of three categories, i.e. light, moderate and heavy as defined in Table 1. Figure 1 shows the performance of all the architectures during training. In general, the performance became steady after 450 learning circles. The best performance was found to be 0.59 using the (49-30-3) architecture.

Further attempts have been made to improve the prediction by considering all categories of rainfall, and incorporating mean data that represented the trend on some selected input variables taken at different time frame. The optimal performance, nevertheless, has only reached to that between 0.45 and 0.46 as shown in Table 6.

4.3 Validation

Forecast on the occurrence of rain in the next 24 hours made by the Observatory for the period from May to October, 1994 [9] was used. An estimation on the correct prediction of rain/no-rain was calculated. The forecast made by the Observatory was considered to be correct when it predicted that there would be no rain for the next 24 hours and the actual amount of rainfall was nil. The accuracy rate was found to be about 0.78. Although it was slightly better than that performed by the neural network, it seems that the latter approach is capable of extracting necessary information from historical surface data of limited input variables. It is likely that the performance of the neural network may improve if it can interpolate data from other weather stations and at different atmospheric levels.

5　Conclusion and further work

This study shows that the neural networks of the three paradigms - BPN, RBFN and LVQ, are capable of extracting necessary information from historical data. Results indicate that their performance are comparable and they attained reasonable performance on the prediction of the occurrence of rain/no-rain in the next 24 hours. The peak performance was about 0.71 and results showed that there was no significant difference in the optimal performance with respect to different architectures. However, RBFN

Algothrim	Network	Performance	Training Cycles
BPN	49-20-2	0.71	55
	49-30-2	0.71	120
	49-60-2	0.71	10
RBFN	49-25-2	0.71	105
	49-50-2	0.71	90
LVQ	49-12-2	0.70	50

Table 5: Performance comparison of BPN, RBFN and LVQ

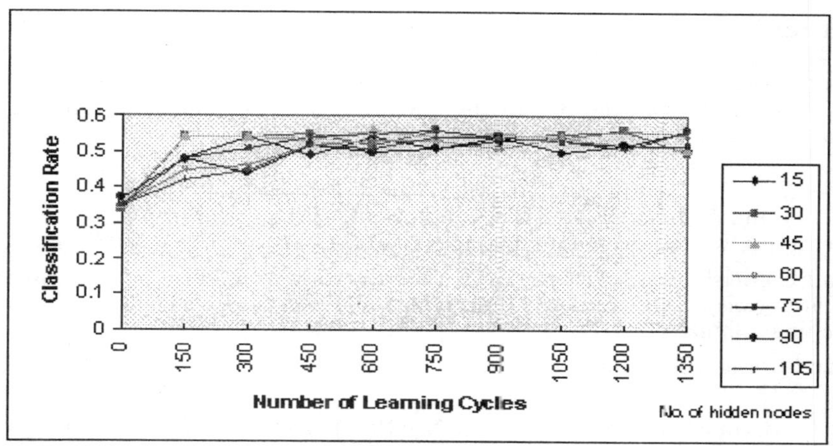

Figure 1: Generalization performance re Rainfall Depth Prediction

Network	Optimal Performance	Obtained at Learning Cycle
49-15-5	0.45	1101
49-30-5	0.45	911
49-45-5	0.46	736
49-60-5	0.45	611
49-75-5	0.46	1085
49-90-2	0.46	924
49-105-2	0.45	600

Table 6: Optimal generalization performance

and LVQ are more efficient than BPN due to less number of learning operations during the training process.

An attempt to improve the accuracy for predicting the depth of rainfall was not that satisfactory. The performance on the prediction of rainfall depth within 3 categories was 0.59 and the average performance on the prediction of rainfall depth within 5 categories was about 0.45. The inclusion of data taken at a frequent interval did not improve the performance. Possible reasons for the poor performance on the prediction of the rainfall depth are:

1. The rainfall is a random event and the cause for the occurrence of rainfall is very complex. Even under the same weather condition, it may be possible that it will rain at this moment but it will not at the other moment. Therefore it is difficult for the neural network to extract all necessary features for the that purpose.

2. The number of explanatory variables used for the inputs may not be sufficient to capture the necessary features for the prediction over a 24hour period since any significant change of weather condition may take place during then.

3. Forecasting experts require information of synoptic situations for their study before they make a prediction of the future distribution of the weather elements over a particular area. Such information is required in forecasting since local area is not a closed system and its weather is affected by surrounding area. However, for simplicity and data unavailability, this information was not included in the study.

The performance of BPN depends heavily on the values of the learning rate and the momentum and there is no design methodology on choosing the values for these parameters. So, a learning algorithm to be used in BPN without the need of setting these parameters should be sought if this paradigm is to be used in further study.

Future work should be to improve the accuracy on the prediction of the mean depth of rainfall in the next 24 hours. Time series of meteorological data, terrain factors, etc. shall be incorporated and the generalization capability of different classification networks should be investigated further. On the other hand, some ideas of variable generation and variable reduction to facilitate discovery of new forecasting heuristics (e.g. Dai and Ciesielski [2], 1993), and the use of scme self-error-correction algorithms and rule improvement algorithms should be investigated. This hybrid development is in support of other weather forecasting such as temperature changes, sever thunder storm, lightening, etc. and will be the subject of future research.

Acknowledgement

This research is under the continue support from RGC grant 0354063A3610. The authors also gratefully acknowledge Dr C. M. Cheng from the Royal Observatory Hong Kong for his invaluable advice.

References

[1] Chung, C. Y. C. and Kumar, V. R. (1993), Knowledge Acquisition using a Neural Network for a Weather Forecasting Knowledge-based System. *Neural Computing and Applications*, pp. 215-223.

[2] Dai, H. H. and Ciesielski, V. B. (1993), An Knowledge Based Successive Constrained Discovery Algorithm for Large Noisy Data Bases. *In Proceedings of Third International Conference for Computer Scientists*, Beijing, China.

[3] Hush, D. R. and Horne, Bill. (1993), Progress in Supervised Neural Networks. *IEEE Signal Processing Magazine*, pp. 8-39.

[4] Karayiannis, N. B. and Venetsanopoulos, A. N. (1993), *Artificial Neural Networks Learning Algorithms, Performance Evaluation, and Applications*, Kluwer Academic Publishers, USA.

[5] Liu, N. K. (1987), Computational Aspects of a Fine-mesh Sea Breeze Model. *M Phil Dissertation*, Department of Mathematics, Murdoch University, Western Australia.

[6] McGregor, J. L., Walsh, K. J. and Katzfey, J. J. (1993), Climate simulations for Tasmania. *In Fourth International Conference on Southern Hemisphere Meteorology and Oceanography:* preprints. Hobart, pp. 514-515. Boston, Mass: American Meteorological Society.

[7] Royal Observatory, Hong Kong (1984-1986), *Surface Observations in Hong Kong*, The Government Printer, HK.

[8] Royal Observatory, Hong Kong (1987-1992), *Surface Observations in Hong Kong*, The Government Printer, HK.

[9] Royal Observatory, Hong Kong (1994), *The Facts*. The Government Printer, HK.

[10] Schizas, C. N., Michaelides, S., Pattichis, C. S. and Livesay, R. R. (1989), Artificial Neural Networks in Forecasting Minimum Temperature. *In Proceedings of the 1st IEE International Conference on Artificial Neural Networks*, pp. 112-114.

[11] Smith, I. N. (1994), A GCM simulation of global climate trends : 1950-1988. *Journal of Climate*, 7(5), pp. 732-744.

[12] Stein, R. (1993), Selecting Data for Neural Networks. *AI Expert*, pp. 42-47.

[13] Widrow, B. and Smith, F. W. (1963), Pattern-Recognizing Control Systems. *In Proceedings of Computer and Informations Sciences Symposium*, Spartan Books, Washington, DC, USA.

[14] Widrow, B., Rumelhart, D. and Lehr, M. (1994), Neural Networks: Applications in Industry, Business and Science. *Communications of the ACM*, 37(3), pp. 93-105.

An alternative choice of output in neural network for the generation of trading signals in a financial market

Lam King Chung*, Lam Kin†

* Department of Statistics, The University of Hong Kong,
Hong Kong

† Department of Statistics, The University of Hong Kong,
Hong Kong
and
Department of Finance & Decision Sciences, Business School,
The Hong Kong Baptist University,
Hong Kong

Abstract

Applying neural network to make trading decision is a topic that has received much attention in recent years. In most cases, neural networks are trained to forecast the price change in a fixed time horizon and then trading signals are generated based on these forecasts. However, the trading recommendation may depend on the choice of horizon and optimal horizon may vary over time. Thus, this method may miss valuable trading opportunities because of the unsuitable horizon. Alternatively, neural networks, which are trained to generate the trading signal directly, are also reported. Here the target trading signal used for training can incorporate nearly all the trading opportunities but a lot of expertise is demanded to obtain these target trading signals. Here, we propose another kind of output, called largest change. This choice of output is tried out in the Hang Seng Index Futures contract trading, it is found that the largest change output outperforms the fixed horizon output.

1. Introduction

This paper considers a simple but important aspect in applying a neural network to generate trading signals in the financial market. This basic problem has been investigated in numerous researches in the literature. To mention a few, we can cite Mehta (1994), Refenes et. el. (1993), and Moody and Utans (1992), etc. Although this problem can be very simply stated, there are a large variety of ways to handle it, such as using different network structures, using different inputs and using different outputs. In this paper, we will focus on the selection of the input and output variables.

More complicated practical problems can in fact be solved by the basic problem we consider here. For example, in the asset allocation application considered by Zapranis and Refenes (1994), they forecast the profitability of all the stocks from the past market information, which is similar to the basic problem considered here. The only difference is that instead of having one asset, a portfolio of stocks has to be constructed. Thus, a thorough investigation on the basic problem is worthwhile before we go on for the more complex problems.

2. Outputs Selection

There are many ways of using neural networks to generate trading signals. The most common is to generate the trading signal via fixed time period forecasting. Neural networks are trained to forecast the k-step-ahead prices and trading signals will be generated with the forecasted prices. At time t, the output considered in the network is x_{t+k}, the k-step-ahead price. Denote the forecasted price by $\hat{x}_{t+k}$. The trading signal at time t can be generated by the following rules

$$\begin{cases} \text{long if } \hat{x}_{t+k} > x_t \\ \text{short if } \hat{x}_{t+k} < x_t \end{cases} \quad \text{...} \quad (1)$$

Such an approach has been widely used in the literature, see for example, Mehta (1994), Bjorn (1994) and Hsu et. el. (1993).

The choice of k is a trade-off between two factors. For a larger k which corresponds to a longer forecasting time period, the magnitude of market price change will probably be larger and it is more likely to develop a profitable trading opportunity. However, when the forecasting time period is too long, the accuracy of the forecast will decrease. Thus, the trading performance could be better for a smaller value of k. As a result, there exists an optimal value of k to balance between these two factors, which can be found by trial and error. In particular, for the daily Heng Seng Index Futures series which are considered in this paper, a forecasting horizon of 10 days works well.

There are some variations on the above method. Firstly, more than one forecasts can be made which correspond to different fixed time periods. This can help to trace out the path of the prices in more details. However, it is not clear how a trading rule can be constructed from such multi-periods forecasts. Second, some summary statistics reflecting the whole dynamics of the price changes can be forecasted rather than only forecasting the price change at a fixed point of time. One example can be found in Kimoto and Asakawa (1990) who forecast the monthly prices averages in next month. As the moving average captures the information from a series of prices rather than only one, this enhances the performance of the trading signal generated.

On the other hand, it is possible to generate trading signals directly. That is to let the neural network do all the work and train the network to generate the trading signal directly from the inputs. Some of the applications using this type of outputs are Chauvin (1994), Binks and Allinson (1991), Bergerson and Wunsch II (1991), Margarita (1991) and Zaremba (1990). What we need here is a set of target trading signals for the training of the neural network. In most cases, these target trading signals are expert generated, as in Bergerson and Wunsch (1991), or it can come from price patterns recognized by technical chartists or form patterns library, as in Binks and Allinson (1991).

This paper proposes an alternative in choosing an output to generate trading signals. One weakness in the fixed horizon approach is that the price movements within the fixed period of time has not been taken into consideration. Thus, if the network forecasts a higher price k days later, the recommended trading signal would be a buy. However, the market may go down a lot first before it rebounds to recover in a period of k days. We propose to forego the fixed horizon approach and consider a variable horizon as follows. The new approach will consider all the price movement after the time where the forecast is done

Let t be the time epoch at which a forecast has to be made. If the price goes down after time t, there should be a time, say t+r, at which the price first recovers its original value x_t. We now consider the investment horizon from t to t+r and train the network to forecast how low the price goes before it recovers. More specifically, we let

$$L = \min_{t \le i \le t+r} x_i - x_t \quad \text{...} \quad (2)$$

and L is chosen to be the output of the neural network in this case. If the price goes up immediately after time t, we consider the horizon until t+r, at which the price first drop below its original value x_t. In this case, the output is chosen to be

$$L = \max_{t \le i \le t+r} x_i - x_t \quad \text{...} \quad (3)$$

Here $L = x_{t+k}$, called largest change, is used as the neural network output and note that our forecasting horizon, k, is a variable not having a fixed value.

There is a technical point in defining the output L mentioned above. Notice that L is not well defined if after a drop (rise) in price, the price never rebounds (goes back) to its original value. We propose to solve this problem operationally by putting a upper limit on the variable horizon k. We can restrict r to be not larger than 30, say specifically if r is larger than 30, then (2) is replaced by

$$L = \min_{t \le i \le t+30} x_i - x_t \quad \text{...} \quad (4)$$

and (3) is replaced by

$$L = \max_{t \le i \le t+30} x_i - x_t \quad \text{...} \quad (5)$$

Figure 1 illustrates how L is defined. In part (a) and (c), r≤30 and in the figures (b) and (d), r>30.

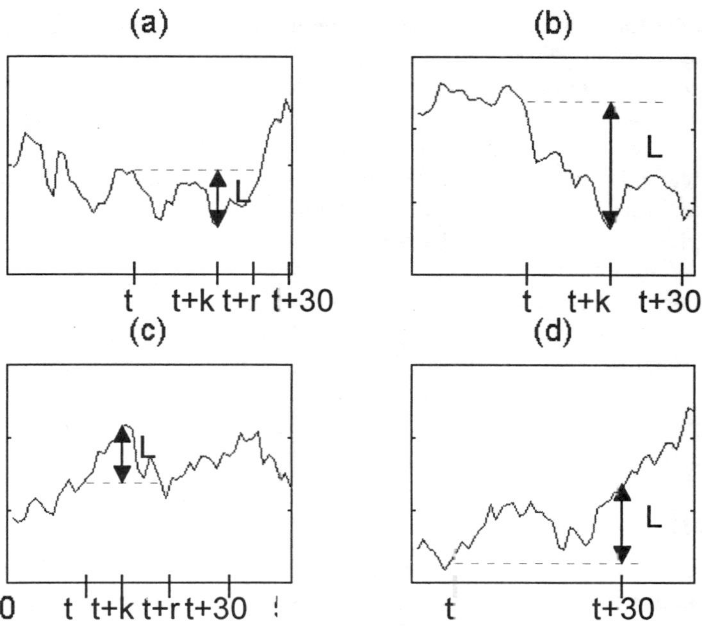

Figure 1

Trading signals can easily be generated with the forecasted L value. Obviously a trade is profitable if its profit is larger than the associated trading cost. Let T be the trading cost associated with a transaction. As a result, it costs 2T if we take a long (short) position and cover it later. Thus, the trading decision can be given as follows.

(i) If the current position is neutral, the trading decision is

$$\begin{cases} \text{long if } L > 2T \\ \text{short if } L < -2T \\ \text{neutral otherwise} \end{cases} \quad\text{...} \quad (6)$$

(ii) If the current position is long, the trading decision is

$$\begin{cases} \text{short if } L > 2T \\ \text{long otherwise} \end{cases} \quad\text{...} \quad (7)$$

(iii) If the current position is short, the trading decision is

$$\begin{cases} \text{long if } L < 2T \\ \text{short otherwise} \end{cases} \quad\text{...} \quad (8)$$

Note that no neutral position will be taken except at the start. With (6), (7) and (8), we can generate the trading signals from the forecasted L values. In this paper L is used as an output in the neural network to generate trading signals for the Hang Seng Index Futures market. The performance is found to be satisfactory and it is found that this variable horizon approach in fact outperforms the fixed horizon approach

3. Inputs Selection

In order to use a neural network to generate the forecasted price change which leads to a trading signal in a particular point of time, we need to input the market information available at that particular point of time. One of the easily available and useful information is the historical prices itself. The application we consider here is constrained to the use of historical prices only. The rationale of using the historical prices have been well discussed in the area of technical trading. In brief, when there is new market information, some but not all the traders realize it and carry out trading. These transactions will be reflected in the prices which can be used technically to forecast future price movements.

The most direct way to use the price information is to treat it as inputs. As we want to include all the useful market information at time t, not only the price at the forecasting time, x_t, will be used but also the price trend before the forecasting, i.e. x_{t-1}, ..., will be used. Some examples can be found in Mehta (1994) and Binks and Allinson (1991).

However, this may not be an effective way to incorporate the information in the market as each input can only reflect the price at one particular point of time. In fact, some statistics can be constructed to summarize the prices across a whole period. The knowledge in technical analysis is useful here also. The technical indicators are found to be useful in revealing the market situations, such as moving average indicator, relative strength indicator, moving average convergent and divergent indicator, etc. Some examples can be found in Chauvin (1994), Hsu et. el. (1993), Weigend, et. el. (1992) and Bergerson and Wunsch II (1991).

In this paper, we compare two sets of inputs. The first set consists of price changes from time t-i to time t, where i takes on a variety of values. The second set consists of the differences of the moving averages at time t-i and the price at t-I, where can also take on variety of values. Empirical results obtained in this paper suggest that the use of the second set of inputs outperforms that of the first set in the particular application of the Hang Seng Index Futures market.

4. Empirical Results

The empirical work is carried out on generating trading decision of the Hang Seng index Futures. This market is highly active and the futures contracts are heavily traded. Thus, it is very suitable to be used to evaluate the performance of the neural networks. The data set used is the daily closing prices of the Hang Seng Index Futures from 1, Jan, 1987 to 31, Dec, 1994. The first 3/4 of the data set is used for the training of the neural network and the last 1/4 of the data set is used for the evaluation of the neural network performance.

The neural network used are multilayer perceptron network with one hidden layer having 5 units, hyperbolic tangent transfer function, sum of square error function and regulation training. Here we only use a very simple network, multilayer perceptron network. The reason is that, in Chen et. el. (1995), this simple network is shown to be a universal approximator and can approximate any arbitrary function. Thus, it is justifiable to use this simple network structure. We use hyperbolic tangent transfer function because it can incorporate both the positive and negative outputs. Also, it is found that a network with hyperbolic tangent transfer function can be trained faster than one with sigmoidal transfer function. The reason for using regulation training is that it is found to be very effective on the short and noisy data set by Weigend et. el. (1992). Our data set is short and noisy so the regulation training is very suitable.

Under the above setting, we simulate the trading of the Hang Seng Index Futures contract using trading signals generated by neural networks with various choice of inputs and outputs and compare their performance. All inputs or output used are in the form of relative changes in order to keep maintain the same scaling in our training set and testing set. Note that the data span a period of 8 years. Thus, normalization is necessary. In the first two simulated trading, we try a simple output, the price change in a fixed horizon of 10 days, with two different choice of inputs. We perform simulated trading 1 and 2 as follows.

Simulated trading 1) Inputs: $(x_t-x_{t-1})/x_t$, $(x_t-x_{t-2})/x_t$, $(x_t-x_{t-3})/x_t$, $(x_t-x_{t-10})/x_t$, $(x_t-x_{t-20})/x_t$, $(x_t-x_{t-30})/x_t$.
Output: $(x_t-x_{t+10})/x_t$.

Simulated trading 2) Inputs: $(m_t-x_t)/x_t$, $(m_{t-1}-x_{t-1})/x_{t-1}$, $(m_{t-2}-x_{t-2})/x_{t-2}$, $(m_{t-10}-x_{t-10})/x_{t-10}$, $(m_{t-20}-x_{t-20})/x_{t-20}$, $(m_{t-30}-x_{t-30})/x_{t-30}$ where m_t is the 20 days moving average at day t.
Output: $(x_t-x_{t+10})/x_t$.

Then, we use the moving averages as inputs and with two different choice of inputs. Then, simulated trading 3 and 4 are carried out.

Simulated trading 3) Inputs: $(x_t-x_{t-1})/x_t$, $(x_t-x_{t-2})/x_t$, $(x_t-x_{t-3})/x_t$, $(x_t-x_{t-10})/x_t$, $(x_t-x_{t-20})/x_t$, $(x_t-x_{t-30})/x_t$.
Output: $(x_t-x_{t+k})/x_t$ where t+k is the time with the largest change.

Simulated trading 4) Inputs: $(m_t-x_t)/x_t$, $(m_{t-1}-x_{t-1})/x_{t-1}$, $(m_{t-2}-x_{t-2})/x_{t-2}$, $(m_{t-10}-x_{t-10})/x_{t-10}$, $(m_{t-20}-x_{t-20})/x_{t-20}$, $(m_{t-30}-x_{t-30})/x_{t-30}$.
Output: $(x_t-x_{t+k})/x_t$ where t+k is the time with the largest change.

The result of three simulated trading are summarized in table 1. It is found that moving averages inputs outperforms that of simple inputs and the largest change output performs better than the traditional method of fixed horizon output.

Simulation	1		2		3		4	
Data Set	Train	Test	Train	Test	Train	Test	Train	Test
Profit in %	126.48	13.34	68.56	18.77	333.25	31.95	344.41	45.83
SD on Trades	2.06	1.99	2.07	1.99	2.05	1.99	2.05	1.99
SD on Starts	21.74	6.5	10.97	11.58	12.28	7.82	14.28	15.87
Profit in Points	4808.5	787	2484	1341.7	11264	2614	10957	3978
SD on Trades	72.4	189.2	72.48	189.5	71.7	188.8	71.75	188.6
SD on Starts	1039	658	371.9	1320	386.8	731.9	913	1788
Buys	22	8	30	11	28	9	37	15
Sells	22	8	29	11	28	9	38	15
Days in Market	1602	533	1602	533	1595	530	1595	530

Table 1

The performance measurement used in table 1 is the percentage return totaled over all the trades and a transaction cost of 0.2% for each change in position is incorporated here. In each training of a neural network, 10 random starts are tried. In the first row of table 1, the total (over all trades in each start) percentage profit is averaged over all random starts. The standard deviation (over all trades in each start) of percentage profit is averaged over all random starts and is given in row 2. The standard deviation of the total profit over various random starts is given in row 3. In row 4, the performance measure is the total trading profit in terms of index points. Two respective standard deviation in terms of index points are presented in row 5 and row 6.

References

A.D.Zapranis and A.N.Refenes (1994), 'Neural Networks in Tactical Asset Allocation: towards a Methodology for Hypothesis Testing and Confidence Intervals', Proceedings of Neural Networks in the Capital Markets .

A.N.Refenes,M.Azema-Barac,L.Chan and S.A.Karoussos (1993), 'Currency Exchange Rate Prediction and Neural Netwrk Design Strategies', Neural Computing and Application, 1, P. 46-58.

Andreas S. Weigend, Bernardo A. Huberman and David E. Rumelhart (1992), 'Predicting Sunspots and Exchange Rates with Connectionist Networks', Nonlinear Modeling an dForecasting, SFI Studies in the sciences of complexity 7, 7, P. 395-432.

David L.Binks and Nigel M.Allinson (1991), 'Financial Data Recongoition and Prediction Using Neural Networks', Artificial Neural Networks 1, 1, P. 1709-1712.

Jonh Moody and Joachim Utans (1992), 'Principled Architecture Selection for Neural Networks: Application to Corporate Bond Rating Prediction', Advance in Neural Information Processing System 4, 4, P. 683-690.

Kari Bergerson and Donald C. Wunsch II (1991), 'A Commodity Trading Model based on a Neural Network-Expert Systme Hybrid', IJCNN 91, 1, P. 289-293.

Mahendra Mehta (1994), 'Trading in foreign Exchange market using Kalman filter and Neural Network', Proceedings of Neural Networks in the Capital Markets .

Sergio Margarita (1991), 'Neural Network, Genetic Algorithms and Stock Trading', Artificial Neural Networks 1, 1, P. 1763-1766.

Takashi Kimoto and Kazuo Asakawa (1990), 'Stock Market Prediction System with Modular Neural Networks', IJCNN 90, 1, P. 1-6.

Thomas Zaremba (1990), 'Ch.12 Case Study Ill: Technology in Search of a Buck', Neural Network PC Tools , P. 251-283.

Tianping Chen, Hong Chen and Ruey Wen Liu (1995), 'Approximation Capability in C(R) by Multilayer Feedforward Networks and Related Problems', IEEE Transaction on Neural Networks, 6, P. 25-30.

Vance Bjorn (1994), 'Optimal Multiresulotion Decompostion of Financial Time Series', Proceedings of Neural Networks in the Capital Markets .

W.Hsu, L.S.Hsu and M.F.Tenorio (1993), 'Parameter Significance Estimation and Financial Prediction', Neural Computing and Application, 1, P. 280-286.

Yves Chauvin (1994), 'Trading Decision Learning: From Theory to Personal Traders', Proceedings of Neural Networks in the Capital Markets .

Time Series Prediction
with Hierarchical Radial Basis Function

T. Fröhlinghaus and K.Y. Szeto

Dept. of Physics
The Hong Kong Telecom Institute of Information Technology,
The Hong Kong University of Science and Technology,
Clear Water Bay, Kowloon, Hong Kong.
Email: PHSZETO@USTHK.UST.HK

Abstract— **Time series prediction using neural network with variable embedding dimensions and layers are implemented with the Hierarchical Radial Basis Function (HRBF) network. The forecasting task is divided into a data clustering step, characterized by the layer depth parameter N_l, and a function approximation step, characterized by the embedding dimension D_v of the time series. By generating a collection of HRBF-networks with different N_l and D_v, we use a density measure on their output values to select the best prediction. Tests on the Mackey-Glass series confirm that this method outperforms those which assume fixed network parameters.**

1 Introduction

Many research works on forecasting are based on neural networks [1], which are general purpose tools for applications in pattern recognition. As training set for the prediction task, we consider a series $(x_i)_{i=1,...,N_p}$ of N_p equidistant measurements $x_i = x(t_i)$, which are samples from an observable $x(t)$ for $t_i = t_0 + i\,\Delta t$ with delay time Δt. The future development one wants to predict are the unknown values $(x_i)_{i>N_p}$ of the time series. This extrapolation problem can be expressed as an interpolation task of finding the relation between overlapping delay vectors $s_i = (x_i, \ldots, x_{i+D_v-1})$ and their subsequent points $p_i = x_{i+D_v}$. In other words, we want to create an approximation function $\mathcal{F}(s)$ with $\mathcal{F}(s_i) \approx p_i$. In this paper, we use Hierarchical Radial Basis Function networks [2] which allow an adjustment between accuracy inside and generalization outside the example set.

When trained to model the relation between some input and output quantities, a neural network will adapt itself according to the incoming data. In doing so its neurons are arranged in a way that depend on the density distribution of these input data, while the proper functionality is fitted to the output values. Closed techniques like back-propagation [3] try to solve both problems simultaneously, thereby entailing a slow learning procedure with the risk of running into local minima. For this reason Moody and Darken [4] proposed the idea of *hybrid networks*, where this optimization process is split up into *unsupervised localization* of neurons and *supervised approximation* of the data.

2 Hierarchical Network Architecture

The first step of our approach is the decomposition of the input space into disjoint clusters, each of them attached to a single neuron as its representative. HRBF-networks perform this kind of classification iteratively: beginning with the whole example set as root element, successive bisection of its arising subclusters yields a binary tree of neurons. Each layer of such a tree forms its own decomposition of the phase space, thereby having a granularity that grows with increasing layer depth. The center z_α of such a cluster α is the mean of its including points s_i, while the width σ_α is computed as the average distance to the centers of neighbouring clusters. The activation function of the corresponding neuron has a Gaussian form,

$$R_\alpha(s) = \exp\left(-(s - z_\alpha)^2/\sigma_\alpha^2\right) \tag{1}$$

which is normalized through

$$P_\alpha(s) = R_\alpha(s)/\sum_{\tilde{\alpha}} R_{\tilde{\alpha}}(s) \tag{2}$$

according to all other clusters $\tilde{\alpha}$ of the same layer. This gives us a radial basis function with isotropic extension.

Since a HRBF-network disconnects phase space structuring from function approximation, we first have to determine the centers z_α and widths σ_α of all clusters. Decompositions of phase space are usually performed by *vector quantization* techniques, which distribute a small set of *code book vectors* evenly over a phase space attractor, thereby yielding suitable cluster centers. Several procedures like *K-means clustering* [5], *maximum-entropy clustering* [6] or the *neural-gas algorithm* [7] use different kinds of stochastic gradient descent to minimize the distortion error

$$E = \int_s p_d(s) \left(s - z_{\alpha(s)} \right)^2 d^d s, \qquad (3)$$

with $\alpha(s)$ denoting the cluster nearest to s. These methods are very slow due to the large number of iterations needed for convergence. For this reason we replace the static algorithm by a fast dynamical one, which is a variant of the *isodata procedure* [8] and works on every bisection step as follows:

1: divide α arbitrary into equal sized subsets λ, ρ.
2: compute their mass centers z_λ, z_ρ.
3: compute distances $\|s - z_\lambda\|$, $\|s - z_\rho\|$ for all s.
4: if s is closer to the other subcluster: change its attachment and update mass centers.
5: iterate step 2, 3, and 4 until convergence.

3 Function Approximation

The next step of our approach is to give a good approximation to the training data with a suitable linear combination of single layers RBFs. An example of this method can be found in the work of Moody and Darken [4], where the gradient descent technique was used. We follow the improvement by Stokbro et al. [9], who combine the activation functions with local linear fits:

$$\mathcal{F}(s) = \sum_\alpha (a_\alpha + b_\alpha s) \, P_\alpha(s). \qquad (4)$$

Up to now we utilized only a single layer of a binary cluster tree for our interpolation task, thus considering just the leafs without any superior structure. In extending our method to a *multi-scale-approach,* we will incorporate the information of all upper layers, thereby constructing a hierarchy of approximations. At first the uppermost node is used to compute a very rough estimate $\mathcal{F}_1(s)$ which is simply a linear interpolation determined by choosing suitable weight parameters a_α, b_α to minimize their mean square error

$$E = \frac{1}{2} \sum_i (\mathcal{F}(s_i) - p_i)^2. \qquad (5)$$

The resulting errors $p_i^{(1)} = p_i - \mathcal{F}_1(s_i)$ will be approximated on the second layer with a function $\mathcal{F}_2(s)$ which represents finer details. While repeating this stepwise refinement on the following layers, a sequence of interpolation functions is created, each of them approximating the residual error of the preceeding layer and thus representing more detailed structures. Finally, the entire function is the sum of all the single layer approximations:

$$\mathcal{F}(s) = \sum_{i=1}^{N_l} \mathcal{F}_i(s). \qquad (6)$$

The free parameters of our HRBF-network are the embedding dimension D_v of the input space and the layer depth N_l of the cluster tree. On every prediction step, a collection of HRBF-networks with distinct parameters yields a whole set of potential results. They are the bases for determining an accurate prediction by some general density measure. Neworks with different combinations of these parameters are created and a statistics of their predictions are taken. When several predictions based on distinct information capacity and varying accuracy are known, simple density measures can suggest a good selection and thus the best matching network parameters. For our heuristic approach we consider all output values as one closed point set. We propose the following robust algorithm to find a confident value within a region of high density of the predicted values:

1: collect predictions to one point set $\{y_i\}_{i=1,\ldots,N}$ and sort them in ascending order
2: define observation window $[y_\lambda, y_\rho]$ with $\lambda = 1, \rho = N$.
3: compute distance measure $\bar{y} = 2 \sqrt[(\rho - \lambda)]{\prod_{i=\lambda}^{\rho-1} (y_{i+1} - y_i)}$.
4: compute density measure $w(y) = \sum_{i=1}^N \exp\left(-\frac{(y-y_i)^2}{\bar{y}^2}\right)$ for y_λ, y_ρ.
5: shrink window by excluding its border lower density.
6: iterate step 3 to 4 for remaining set until $\lambda = \rho$.
7: choose residual prediction y_λ as output.

4   Experiments on the Mackey Glass Equation

A common benchmark for the comparison of the performance of our HRBF network to various forecasting methods is the Mackey-Glass equation,

$$\dot{x}(t) = \frac{a\,x(t-\tau)}{1 + x(t-\tau)^c} - b\,x(t) \tag{7}$$

which has been developed to model the production of blood cells[10]. For parameters $a = 0.2$, $b = 0.1$, $c = 10$ and $\tau = 17$, this delay differential equation has the whole interval $[t_0 - \tau, t_0]$ as its initial condition and produce chaotic behavior when sampled with the delay time $\Delta t = 6$. Since it has no analytical solution, conversion into a difference equation requires special numerical techniques. We follow Wulff's approach [11]. We take 500 consecutive values of the resulting time series as training data to test if this small set is sufficient for an accurate representation of the dynamics. The value of training set size is N_p, which ranges from 500 to 100000 in our experiments.

To compare our variable-dimension and variable-clustering approach with fixed-parameter techniques, we computed predictions based on the following four strategies:

(a) N_l, D_v, N_p **fixed:** Exhaustive tests on the given example data proved that $D_v = 4$ and $N_l = 6$ lead to the most accurate predictions when using just one HRBF-network with constant layer depth.

(b) N_l, D_v **variable,** N_p **fixed:** Each of the three attractors for $D_v = 3, \ldots, 5$ is fitted with its clusterings on layer depth $N_l = 1, \ldots, 8$, thus having 24 output candidates for a single one-step-prediction.

(c) N_l, N_p **variable,** D_v **fixed:** In addition to the original 500-point training data, three of its overlapping subsections were exploited, each of them containing 400 values. Altogether four networks with eight layers are obtained, which generate every time 32 possible predictions.

(d) N_l, D_v, N_p **variable:** Finally, all four data sets form a foundation for the creation of 16 distinct HRBF-networks with dimensions D_v ranging from 3 to 6. The range of N_l is again from 1 to 8. This ensemble produces 128 output values on every prediction step.

To demonstrate how the prediction errors of these approaches grow with time, 1 000 different starting sequences including their known following values have been utilized as test sets. For each initial condition and each strategy, the absolute differences between the true and the predicted series were calculated. Since arithmetic means are very sensitive to single exceptions values, we used the geometrical means of these series of differences as a more evident measure. Fig.1 shows the results of the Mackey-Glass series using these four strategies. The oscillations have their smallest amplitudes just before overfitting occurs, so the interesting candidates for the predicted value should be characterized through a high point density around them. Obviously, all *multi-network-strategies* outperform the one with constant parameters. As $D_v = 4$ is clearly the best choice for a fixed dimension, its variation causes only a small gain in accuracy. The utilization of additional subsets from the training data promises better results, because one gets further information about the dimension-specific oscillation of the underlying approximation process. So for the Mackey-Glass data a single fine grain oscillation as in (c) performes better then the various coarse grain ones in (b), even though other time series may suggest a different conclusion. Nevertheless, we get the most accurate predictions when combining both ideas and exploiting several detailed oscillations, as it has been done for strategy (d).

To compare with various works on the Mackey-Glass series [4, 7, 12, 13], we list in Table.1 several algorithms and network architectures together with their performance measures. While direct approximations always use a time delay $\Delta = 85$ for this task, the iterated ones perform 14 prediction steps each with $\Delta t = 6$ and thus obtain a delay of $\Delta = 84$.

5   Conclusion

In conclusion, we have introduced a method to examine the predicted values using HRBF-networks. The advantages of HRBF-networks lie in their multi-scale approximation based on several clusterings with distinct granularity, and their structuring of the optimization process within a single layer. By allowing an adjustment between accuracy and smoothness, they can find a good generalization of the given example data. While many researchers try to find exactly one optimal representation for a time series in a single phase space, we believe that the use of several networks as a platform for further analysis produces better results, as proven in our analysis of the Mackey-Glass series.

We acknowledge the support of a grant through the Hong Kong Telecom Institute of Information Technology.

References

[1] A. S. Weigend and N. A. Gershenfeld, editors. *Time Series Prediction: Forecasting the Future and Understanding the Past*, volume XV of *Santa Fe Institute Studies in the Sciences of Complexity*. Addison-Wesley, 1993.

[2] T. Fröhlinghaus, A. Weichert, and P. Ruján. "Hierarchical neural networks for time series analysis and control," *Network*, 5(1):101–116, 1994.

[3] A. Lapedes and R. Farber. "Nonlinear signal processing using neural networks," Technical Report LA-UR-87-2662, Los Alamos National Laboratory, Los Alamos, NM, 1987.

[4] J. Moody and C. Darken. "Fast learning in networks of locally tuned processing units," *Neural Computation*, 1(2):281–294, 1989.

[5] S. P. Lloyd. "Least squares quantization in pcm," *IEEE Transactions on Information Theory*, IT-28:2, 1982.

[6] K. Rose, F. Gurewitz, and G. Fox. "Statistical mechanics and phase transitions in clustering," *Phys. Rev. Lett.*, 65(8):945–948, 1990.

[7] T. M. Martinetz, S. G. Berkovich, and K. J. Schulten. " Neural-gas network for vector quantization and its application to time-series prediction," *IEEE Transactions on Neural Networks*, 4(4):558–569, 1993.

[8] R. O. Duda and P. E. Hart. *Pattern Classification and Scene Analysis.* New York: Wiley, 1973.

[9] K. Stokbro, D. K. Umberger, and J. A. Hertz. " Exploiting neurons with localized receptive fields to learn chaos," *Complex Systems*, 4(4):603–622, 1990.

[10] M. C. Mackey and L. Glass. " Oscillations and chaos in physiological control systems," *Science*, 197:287–289, 1977.

[11] N. H. Wulff. " Learning dynamics with recurrent networks," Master's thesis, Nils Bohr Institute and NORDITA, Blegdamsvej 17, 2100 Copenhagen Ø, Denmark, 1992.

[12] R. S. Crowder. " Predicting the mackey-glass timeseries with cascade-correlation learning," In *Proceedings of the Connectionist Models Summer School*, pages 117–123, 1990.

[13] J. Platt. " A resource-allocating network for function interpolation," *Neural Computation*, 3(2):213–225, 1990.

Prediction technique	Error
6th-order Polynomial	0.32
Cascade-Correlation	0.32
RBF-Network	0.15
Neural-Gas Network	0.07
Resource Allocating Network (RAN)	0.066
Hashing B-spline	0.05
Back-Propagation	0.05
HRBF-Network, strategy (a)	0.034
HRBF-Network, strategy (b)	0.028
HRBF-Network, strategy (c)	0.012
HRBF-Network, strategy (d)	0.009

Table 1: Normalized RMS-errors for 500 examples.

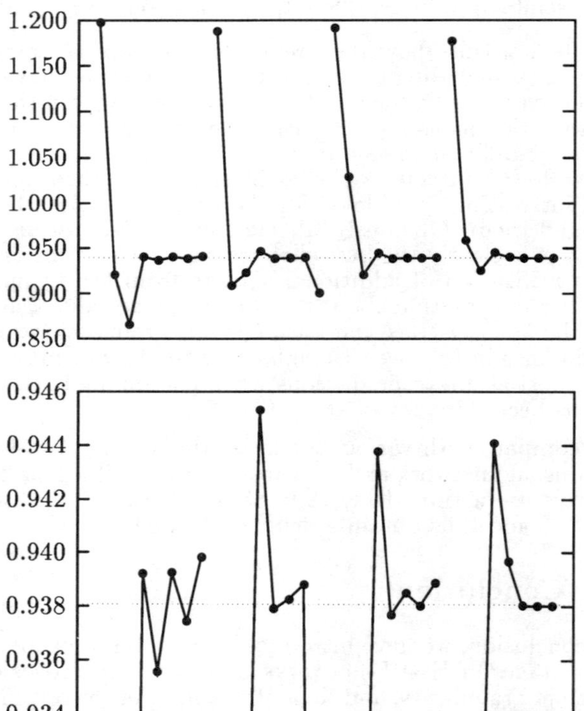

Figure 1: Oscillations for a one-step-prediction of the Mackey-Glass series. The four curves correspond from left to right $D_v = 3, \ldots, 6$, each with 8 points: $N_l = 1, \ldots, 8$. The lower graph magnifies the interval around the real value.

Evolutionary Computing

(Oral Presentation)

A Genetic Approach to Video Indexing

C. L. Chow, Antonio Si, Rynson W.H. Lau, and H. V. Leong

Department of Computing
The Hong Kong Polytechnic University
Hunghom, Hong Kong
{csclchow, csasi, cswhlau, cshleong}@comp.polyu.edu.hk

Abstract

Technological advances in the past decade had rendered integrating video data within applications possible. However, video data will only become an effective part of everyday computing when we can manage them with similar database management facilities that we currently use on literal data. In this paper, we introduce an indexing technique which complements raw video data with a logical content index. The content index is established by applying a genetic algorithm to extract the keywords which best describe the content of an video stream, from the subtitle of an input video stream. This index provides a high level semantic description to the video data, allowing users to manipulate the video data in a way similar to conventional database management systems.

1   Introduction

One major problem to efficiently incorporate multi-media data in computing applications is the time-consuming process of identifying and retrieving the appropriate images, video or audio segments with respect to some user requirements. Currently, there is a great demand and has been an enthusiastic research interest in developing multi-media retrieval systems which function in a way analogous to conventional database management systems for literal data.

Since data of different media have their own characteristics, it is unlikely that a general purpose multi-media retrieval system could be developed to handle all kinds of media data. Our research, currently, focuses on video data. Existing approaches to video management can be roughly divided into two categories. One is the structured modeling approach [11, 13], which divides the input video stream into atomic shots. Another is the stratification approach [1] in which the video stream is divided into overlapping segments (chunks), with each segment representing only a single event. The goal of these approaches is to allow each video segment to be easily described. To identify appropriate video segments, it is important that the semantic objects and their attributes appearing in the video segments must be indexed. Existing image analysis and video segmentation [12, 15] techniques are not sufficient to identify the semantic objects and their attributes due to the *semantic mismatch* between what users perceive and what are used to characterize the video data; video data are usually characterized according to their low level syntactic features such as color, texture, motion vector and so forth while users usually perceive video data in a much higher level context. To bridge this semantic gap, approaches which require users to manually provide textual information to describe the semantic objects and their contextual information have been proposed [1, 6, 13].

In this paper, we describe the design of a video retrieval system for a special kind of video data, the documentary video. It uses the keyword-based approach to meaningfully describe the content of each video segment. However, unlike previous approaches which require users to identify appropriate keywords for each video segment manually, our approach is based on a genetic algorithm [5] which extracts the keywords automatically from the subtitle of the video stream. The implementation of the genetic algorithm and some preliminary results will also be illustrated.

The remainder of this paper is organized as follows. Section 2 is dedicated to a brief survey on existing techniques for video indexing. In Section 3, we briefly describe the video indexing system that we are developing, followed by a detailed description of our genetic approach to video indexing. In Section 4, we present some preliminary results from some simple experiments on our content index. Section 5 offers a brief concluding remark and some highlights to future work.

2   Related Work

Existing work on video retrieval has been focused almost entirely on video segmentation techniques which partition a video stream into a collection of video segments, each containing a sequence of video frames. The idea is to allow segments of video to be indexed independently; this allows each video segment to be retrieved and manipulated.

Chua and Ruan [4] propose a video retrieval and sequencing system, which supports the entire process of video information management: segmenting, indexing, retrieving, and sequencing of video data. In the system, each video shot is logged using text descriptions, audio dialogues, and cinematic attributes. A two-layered, concept-based model is used as the basis for accurately retrieving relevant video shots based on free-text queries, issued by users.

Chang et al. [2] propose a generic video database, composed of six modules. An object annotation module provides users with a friendly interface to mark the start and the end frame of a video object and to build annotations of each video segment. A content acquisition/retrieval module provides image/video processing routines in order to support content-based retrieval. A video management module has the capability to compress video data from video sources and decompress it for playing. A video indexing module provides the annotation and other information for good indices to speed up retrieval of the desired video objects. A query processing module provides the way to query video objects using a variety of query methods and interfaces. However, unlike conventional SQL queries, queries specified against a video database are usually imprecise; video databases are required to evaluate properties of the data specified in a query. Finally, an interactive browsing module provides user friendly interfaces to browse the video segments.

Tonomura et al. [13, 14] propose a video processing method that analyzes a video stream and automatically segments it into shots. Each shot is indexed using the extracted features, such as camera work information and representative colors. Lee and Kao [8] develop a mechanism for indexing video data based on the concept of objects and object motion with interactive annotation. A motion representation for the track of a moving object is presented. The access methods of video queries are introduced and a prototype of video indexing system is implemented.

The major contribution in our work is a novel technique based on the genetic algorithm, in selecting keywords at multiple resolutions for efficient retrieval of image segments at different scales, by suitably adjusting the parameters. We also illustrate how this is applied in a video indexing system.

3 Overview of the Genetic Approach to Video Indexing

A high level architecture of the video indexing system [7] that we are developing is shown in Figure 1. The segmentation module partitions the input video stream into a collection of segments based on existing segmentation techniques [12, 15]. Meanwhile, the keyword identification module extracts keywords from the video stream and identifies those that best describe the content of each segment. The index generation module employs a genetic algorithm to establish a content index based on the keywords of each segment. The content index allows the query processing module to identify candidate segments that match a keyword-based user query. In the rest of this paper, we focus on the index generation module and show how a genetic algorithm can be used to generate the required content indexing structure for query processing. The method we adopt can be divided into two steps: subtitle parsing and index generation, as will be further explained in the subsequent sections.

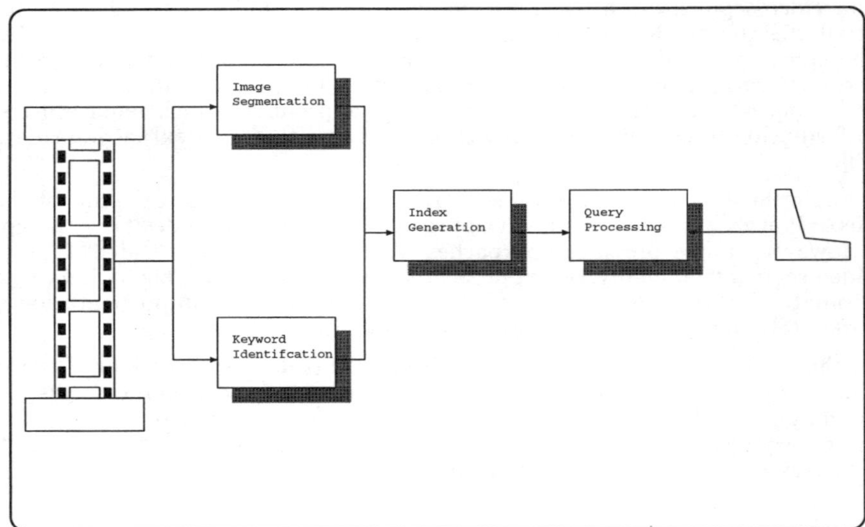

Figure 1: Architecture of the video indexing system

3.1 Subtitle Parsing

To extract keywords for the indexing module, each word extracted from the subtitle of the video stream is first checked against a dictionary containing closed-class words [9], which include pronouns, prepositions, conjunctions, and interjections. All closed-class words are removed from consideration since they do not carry any semantic information about the video stream. In contrast, open-class words, which are usually meaning-bearing, such as nouns, verbs, adjectives, and adverbs are potential keywords for the segments and are passed to the indexing module. Each open-class word is further transformed to its lemma form [9], i.e., singular form for nouns and infinitive form for verbs, with the aid of a dictionary and some simple transformation rules.

To identify the keywords, statistical analysis techniques employed in traditional document retrieval systems [9, 10] are also adopted here. In brief, a histogram representing the occurrence frequencies of each distinct word is established. Each word will be qualified as a potential keyword if its occurrence frequency is within the interval $\mu - \alpha\sigma$ and $\mu + \beta\sigma$, where μ and σ are the mean and standard deviation of the occurrence frequencies. The input parameters α and β are to be tuned. In general, owing to the skewed distribution of the words, the value of α is small while the value of β is larger. When the occurrence frequency of a word is above a certain threshold λ (where $\lambda \geq \mu + \beta\sigma$), it can be regarded as a closed-class word and will be inserted to the dictionary for future references. Consequently, a set of keywords $A = \{a_1, a_2, ..., a_n\}$ is generated.

3.2 Index Generation

For each segment, S_i, a set of keywords $K_i \subseteq A$ will be assigned. Each word extracted from the subtitle of segment S_i will belong to K_i if it belongs to A. In effect, the keywords for each segment constitute a layer of content index to the segments. For each pair of segments S_i and S_j, a fitness value, $f(K_i, K_j)$ is computed as the Jaccard's score [3, 5], which is a common measure of association in information retrieval.

$$f(K_i, K_j) = \frac{|K_i \bigcap K_j|}{|K_i \bigcup K_j|}$$

Alternatively, one can incorporate the weight of each keyword in computing the Jaccard's score. The weight of the keywords could be determined by their relative occurrence frequencies with respect to the whole subtitle of the movie. This alternative approach, however, is not considered in this paper and is left for future work.

All segments whose fitness values are greater than a threshold, ϵ, are grouped into a collection. A new parent segment is created for each collection, modeling a supersegment-subsegment relationship. Note that a segment can have multiple supersegments if it belongs to multiple collections. For each newly created segment, a genetic algorithm [3] is employed to identify a set of best descriptive keywords from the keywords associated with its subsegments. A second level of content index is therefore created. The fitness values between any two segments in the second level can thus be computed. Another higher level of segments and their corresponding keywords can be created recursively, until all the fitness values between any two segments within a particular level fall below ϵ, or only one segment remains in that level. This generates a multi-layer index to the original video segments.

3.3 Keywords Generation

We denote the ith segment at level l by $S_{l.i}$ and the keywords of $S_{l.i}$ by $K_{l.i}$. Therefore, the original set of segments for the video stream can be denoted by $S_{1.1}, S_{1.2}, ..., S_{1.n}$ where n is the total number of segments. With the genetic algorithm to generate keywords for a segment, $S_{l.k}$, which contains m subsegments $S_{l-1.1}, S_{l-1.2}, ..., S_{l-1.m}$, with keywords $K_{l-1.1}, K_{l-1.2}, ..., K_{l-1.m}$, five steps are required: reference set generation, reproduction, crossover, mutation, and iteration. These steps are carried out as follows:

1. *Reference set generation*: Every genetic algorithm requires a fixed set of reference keywords. We generate the reference set $R_{l.k}$ of $S_{l.k}$ by the union of all the keywords of its subsegments. Each subsegment $S_{l-1.i}$ will be associated with a binary vector of length $|R_{l.k}|$ with respect to $R_{l.k}$, indicating the presence or absence of each distinct keyword in $K_{l-1.i}$.

2. *Reproduction*: A new set of m subsegments will be selected from the original set of subsegments of $S_{l.k}$, contributing to the generation of keywords for $S_{l.k}$. Each subsegment, $S_{l-1.i}$, will have a probability p_i of being selected which is proportional to its fitness value with respect to the reference set, i.e., $f(K_{l-1.i}, R_{l.k})$; therefore, a subsegment might be selected a multiple number of times if its probability value is high while a subsegment with low probability value might not be selected at all. The result of this step will be a new set of subsegments $\{S'_{l-1.1}, S'_{l-1.2}, ..., S'_{l-1.m}\}$, and their associated keywords, possibly with duplicates.

3. *Crossover*: For each subsegment $S'_{l-1.i}$, a random number r between 0 and 1 is generated. If $r < p_C$, $S'_{l-1.i}$ will be selected for performing the crossover operation. Here, p_C indicates the *probability of crossover*. The binary vector of the two subsegments selected for crossover will be mated randomly as in [3]. The result from this step will be another new set of subsegments $\{S''_{l-1.1}, S''_{l-1.2}, ..., S''_{l-1.m''}\}$, and the corresponding keyword sets. If the weight for each keyword could be determined, the crossover point could be biased towards those keywords with a lower weights rather than performing in a random manner. This enhanced version would allow the important keywords to remain within the keywords

vector while dropping out those unimportant ones. Again, this enhanced version will be addressed in the future.

4. *Mutation*: For each subsegment $S''_{l-1.i}$, another random number r between 0 and 1 is generated for every entry of its binary vector. If $r < p_M$, the entry is flip-flopped, simulating a mutation process. Here, p_M indicates the *probability of mutation*. The results from this step will be yet another new set of subsegments $\{S'''_{l-1.1}, S'''_{l-1.2}, ..., S'''_{l-1.m'''}\}$. Once again, the mutation process could be biased towards the unimportant keywords if the weights of the keywords are determined.

5. *Iteration*: The average fitness value between the keywords of each new subsegment and the keywords in $R_{l.k}$ is computed. Steps 2 to 4 are repeated until the average fitness values across several subsequent iterations remain relatively constant. The union of the keywords for the most currently generated subsegments will be assigned to segment $S_{l.k}$.

3.4   Query Processing

The rationale behind a multi-layer indexing structure is that the keywords of a segment at a particular level represent a global description of the content captured by its subsegments; this allows a user query to be evaluated in a "hill-climbing" manner. Each user query is composed of a set of keywords, Q, denoting the user's perception on the video segment(s) s/he would like to retrieve. The identified video segments which are relevant to the query will be presented to the user and could then be incorporated into any user applications such as video editing and hypertext document processing.

For a content index with t levels, to evaluate a user query, Q, the keywords specified in Q is first compared against the keywords of each segment, $S_{t.k}$, within the top level of the content index using the Jaccard fitness equation, i.e., $f(Q, K_{t.k})$. If the fitness value is higher than a relevance threshold, ω, $S_{t.k}$ is considered to be relevant to the query. Since $S_{t.k}$ indicates a high level description to its subsegments, all video segments belonging to the hierarchy rooted at $S_{t.k}$ will be relevant to the query. To confine the number of segments to be retrieved, the query could be further compared to the subsegments of $S_{t.k}$. Again, the Jaccard fitness equation is used to determine if a subsegment of $S_{t.k}$, $S_{t-1.i}$, is relevant to Q. Again, all video segments belong to the hierarchy rooted at $S_{t-1.i}$ will be considered to be relevant to the query if the fitness value between Q and $S_{t-1.i}$ is greater than ω. By recursively comparing Q with subsegments of $S_{t-1.i}$, we could further confine the number of segments to be retrieved. The number of levels that need to be compared with Q will depend on the number of segments that need to be retrieved. On one hand, the more levels the query will be compared, the more precise will be the retrieved segments, but the fewer number of segments will be recalled; on the other hand, the fewer levels the query is compared, the more segments will be recalled, but the less precise the retrieved segments will be.

One problem with such a keyword-based query evaluation method is that users have to be aware of the keywords used to index the top level segments of the content index. We resolve this issue by allowing the threshold value, ω, to be dynamically adjusted according to the level of the segments against which the query is compared. A higher value of ω will require a better matching between the keywords provided in the query and the keywords of a segment. We can therefore set the threshold value to a low value when the query is evaluated against the top level index in case the two sets of keywords might not match well. Only when the fitness value surpasses the threshold may the query be propagated down to the next level. Meanwhile, since the second level segments are more specific, the threshold must be increased to dictate a stronger degree of matching, in order for the query to be successful. This will continue recursively and the threshold will increase as the query is being propagated down the indexing structure. The performance of such a query processing technique under various threshold adjustment schemes will be reported in a future paper.

4   Experimental Results

We have implemented the genetic algorithm using different threshold values for supersegment generation. Since the video segmentation and keywords generation modules are still in their implementation stage, in order to test for the flexibility and feasibility of our approach in creating the content index, we decide to experiment our index generation scheme by using an article to simulate the subtitle of a documentary video. Since our focus here is not on segmentation, we, therefore, break the article into different segments manually. The article contains about 1800 words and is on the topic of planetary science spacecraft. We discover that the set of keywords extracted by the algorithm is very close to what a human being will likely extract.

As a first step, the set of keywords are generated for the segments in the first level, by employing the statistical filtering method. We have set the parameters $\alpha = 0.2$ and $\beta = 5$. Then the Jaccard's score for every pair of level 1 segments is calculated and those segments whose fitness values are greater than a threshold, ϵ, are grouped into a supersegment. In our experiment, we have used different values for the Jaccard's threshold, ϵ, to investigate the behavior of the algorithm. The probabilities p_C and p_M used in the genetic algorithm are 0.1 and 0.001 respectively. Note that the value of p_M should be small since large value of p_M will likely cause the population to evolve continually without converging. Table 1 summarizes the findings of our experiments with different values of the Jaccard's threshold ϵ.

Threshold value ϵ	$\epsilon = 0.2$	$\epsilon = 0.18$	$\epsilon = 0.16$	$\epsilon = 0.14$
Total number of levels	2	3	3	4
Level 1 - Number of segments {number of keywords in each segment}	15 {2, 18, 15, 17 22, 33, 30, 8, 9, 30, 33, 45, 49, 26, 30}	15 {2, 18, 15, 17, 22, 44, 30, 8, 9, 30, 33, 45, 49, 26, 30}	15 {2, 18, 15, 17, 22, 44, 30, 8, 9, 30, 33, 45, 49, 26, 30}	15 {2, 18, 15, 17, 22, 44, 30, 8, 9, 30, 33, 45, 49, 26, 30}
Level 2 - Number of segments {number of keywords in each segment}	3 {21, 52, 39}	4 {17, 48, 60, 36}	6 {18, 18, 42, 76, 40, 58}	8 {41, 20, 42, 74, 33, 43, 57, 64}
Level 3 - Number of segments {number of keywords in each segment}	0 {}	1 {28}	2 {29, 100}	3 {117, 31, 135}
Level 4 - Number of segments {number of keywords in each segment}	0 {}	0 {}	0 {}	1 {132}

Table 1: Experimental results

For example, with $\epsilon = 0.18$, three levels of segments are produced, and the sole top level segment contains 18 keywords, which are:

{closeup, cloud, craft, crater, entire, fact, find, fly, giant, image, make, mariner, mars, martian, november, orbit, planet, previously, reach, red, return, sister, space, system, take, think, two, venus}.

Since the top level keywords survive the genetic algorithm, they are of a high quality and can be used to represent the article. These top level keywords are then used to process against queries submitted by users. We can also observe from the table that the higher the Jaccard's threshold ϵ is, the fewer the number of levels and the number of segments within each level are formed. Furthermore, each segment contains much fewer keywords as ϵ increases. We also notice from our experiments that the algorithm seems to coverage faster with a larger ϵ.

5 Conclusion

In this paper, we have described the importance of a high level content index as a tool for searching appropriate video segments that are relevant to some user queries. We propose a multi-layer indexing structure which allows user queries to be evaluated in a hill-climbing manner. The index is generated incrementally such that upper level indices are generated by recursively applying a genetic algorithm to the lower level indices. Preliminary results are also delineated to indicate that the genetic algorithm is feasible and the generated index structure is reasonable.

We are currently conducting extensive experiments to further validate our ideas and results. In particular, we are testing our index generation scheme against real documentary videos. Furthermore, to validate the usefulness of the content index, it must be tested against real user queries. In this respect, traditional precision and recall metrics from document retrieval system [10] can be fruitfully employed here.

Acknowledgements

This research is supported in part by the University Central Research Grant numbers 340/115 and 350/571.

References

[1] T. G. Auguierre-Smith and N. C. Pincever. Parsing Movies in Context. In *Proceedings of USENIX*, pages 157–168, 1991.

[2] C. W. Chang, K. F. Lin, and S. Y. Lee. The Characteristics of Digital Video and Considerations of Designing Video Databases. In *Proceedings of ACM International Conference on Information and Knowledge Management*, pages 370–377, 1995.

[3] H. Chen. A Machine Learning Approach to Document Retrieval: An Overview and an Experiment. In 27th *Hawaii International Conference on System Sciences*, pages 631–640, 1994.

[4] T. S. Chua and L. Q. Ruan. A Video Retrieval and Sequencing System. *ACM Transactions on Information Systems*, 13(4):373–407, 1995.

[5] D. E. Goldberg. *Genetic Algorithms in Search, Optimization, and Machine Learning*. Addison-Wesley, 1989.

[6] B. J. Hann, P. Kahn, V. A. Riley, J. H. Coombs, and N. K. Meyrowitz. IRIS Hypermedia Services. *Communications of ACM*, 35(1):36–51, 1992.

[7] R.W.H. Lau, H. V. Leong, and A. Si. A Semantic Movie Indexing Scheme. In *Proceedings of International Symposium on Digital Libraries*, pages 242–249, 1995.

[8] S. Y. Lee and H. M. Kao. Video Indexing - An Approach based on Moving Object and Track. *Storage and Retrieval for Image and Video Databases, SPIE*, 1908:25–36, 1993.

[9] Y. Maarek, D. Berry, and G. Kaiser. An information retrieval approach for automatically constructing software libraries. *IEEE Transactions on Software Engineering*, 1991.

[10] S. Robertson, C. Rijsbergen, and M. Porter. *Probabilistic models of indexing and searching*, pages 35–56. Butterworths, 1981.

[11] B. Rubin and G. Davenport. Structured Content Modeling for Cinematic Information. *SIGCHI Bulletin*, 21(2):78–79, 1989.

[12] S. Smoliar and H. Zhang. Content-Based Video Indexing and Retrieval. *IEEE Multimedia*, 1(2):62–72, 1994.

[13] Y. Tonomura. Video Handling Based on Structured Information for Hypermedia Systems. In *Proceedings of the International Conference on Multimedia Information Systems*, pages 333–344, 1991.

[14] Y. Tonomura, A. Akutsu, Y. Taniguchi, and G. Suzuki. Structured Video Computing. *IEEE Multimedia*, 1(3):34–43, 1994.

[15] H. Zhang, C. Low, and S. Smoliar. Video Parsing and Browsing Using Compressed Data. *Multimedia Tools and Applications*, 1(1):89–111, 1995.

Feature Selection in Automatic Signature Verification Based on Genetic Algorithms

George S.K. Fung   *James N.K. Liu*   *Rynson W.H. Lau*

Department of Computing
The Hong Kong Polytechnic University
Hung Hom, Hong Kong
`{csskfung, csnkliu, cswhlau}@comp.polyu.edu.hk`

Abstract

Signature is one of the most recognized means for personal identification. There is a pressing need to have an automatic signature verification system. Most of the existing work, feature set that has been regarded as significant to signature verification was defined by those researchers based on their own experience. Nevertheless, there were no solid procedures specified for identifying these important features. In our approach, genetic algorithms (GAs) has been adopted to select the smallest subset of features for which its error rate is within the feasible region. Although the solution achieved would not be optimal, it would be near optimal and can be found within a reasonable computational time. From our experimental results, we have discovered three important behaviors of the system: the presence of some features creates confusion to the classifier for the verification process, there may not exist an "unique" key feature set for the system to attain results within some feasible error, GAs is a promising approach to solve the feature selection problem in signature verification system.

1   Introduction

Personal identification techniques can be categorized into four different types: something remembered (e.g. passwords, PINs), something possessed (e.g. magnetic card, key), a physical characteristic (e.g. finger prints, facial appearance) and an action performed (e.g. signature verification). Using signature verification as the mean, there are three distinctive advantages: signature verification has been widely accepted as the primary form of legal attestation, signatures (in dynamic sense) cannot be lost, stolen or given away, and the data collection hardware is available. Basically, the signature verification process can be broken down into five sub-processes: data acquisition, preprocessing, feature extraction and selection, comparison process and performance evaluation [1].

Since computer verification of signatures based solely on the 2D pattern of a signature is likely to be a very complex machine-vision type of procedure, it would be desirable that a simpler, faster and more reliable procedure can be achieved by incorporating with sufficient dynamic data [2]. Therefore, in the data acquisition stage, a digitizing tablet and an instrumented cordless pen are used to collect the dynamic behavior of the signatures. "Features" are a set of transformation of the signature data that are able to expose the differences between genuine signatures and forgeries [3]. Since handwritten signatures are the results of human act, it is subject to intra-personal variations. To achieve a feasible automatic handwritten signature verification system, one of the approaches is to identify the features set that will maximize the inter-personal variations and minimize the intra-personal variations at the same time. For most applications, the parameters, or even personalized parameters approach is used. However, three basic problems haven't been resolved. They include (1) the choice of a criterion for parameter selection, (2) the determination of an optimal number of parameters, and (3) the lack of valuable statistical model of true signatures versus forgeries distribution. These problems could be solved or by-passed by introducing the genetic algorithm based feature selection approach for large scale feature selection [4]. In the comparison process stage, since signatures are represented by vectors in feature space, the comparison process will be straightforward by evaluating the distance between classes. The performance of the system strongly depends on testing conditions and environment. In the validation of the system, three different types of forgeries need to be examined including 'simple', 'random' and 'skilled' forgeries.

2   Feature Selection

In the design of automatic pattern classifiers, one of the most important problems is the feature selection. In feature selection, a small subset is selected from an initially large set of parameters or descriptors (i.e. features) which the classifier is based on and it determines the class of the observed object [5]. Therefore, the dimensionality of the feature space will be reduced by feature selection. As a result, the computational cost of the verification process can be reduced. Basically, there are two versions of feature selection problem which address specific objective and lead to distinct type of optimization [4]: (1) the objective is to find a subset that gives the lowest error rate of a classifier and the problem leads to unconstrainted combinatorial optimization with the error rate as the search criterion, (2) the objective is to find the smallest subset of features for which the error rate is below a given threshold and the problem leads to a constrainted combinatorial optimization task in which the error rate serves as a constraint and the number of features is the primary search criterion.

In this paper, the GA approach was used to achieve the optimization of the feature selection problem. GA works in a manner that resembles the mechanism of natural behavior. It works with a population of individuals, each representing a possible solution to the specific problem, called chromosome. In the application of GA to feature selection, each chromosome represents a subset of features, that is, the presence or absence of kth feature is represented by the kth bit of the chromosome. A fitness score is assigned to each individual according to how good a solution to the problem is. The highly fit individuals are given opportunities to crossover and/or to mutate. A pair of offspring chromosomes is produced by the crossover of two chromosomes which are syntheses of their parents. The process that produces a near identical copy of chromosome with some components of it altered, is called mutation. As the least fit members of the population are less likely to get selected for reproduction, therefore they will become vanished. This optimization process is carried out in cycles called generations. Since the best individuals are selected to produce the new generation, this generation contains a higher proportion of the characteristics possessed by the good members of the previous generation. Since the more fit individuals have better chance to reproduce, the better promising areas of the search space are explored. Therefore, if the GA is well-designed, the population will converge to an optimal, or near optimal, solution to the problem. The book by Goldberg [6] provides full details on the GA.

In this paper, we worked on seeking the smallest subset of features for which the classifier's performance would not deteriorate below a certain specified level. The fitness function has been defined as followings:

$$a = \{\alpha_1,\ldots,\alpha_d\} \tag{1}$$

$$pen(e) = \frac{\exp((e - thres)/m) - 1}{\exp(1) - 1}. \tag{2}$$

$$J(a) = l(a) + pen(err(a)), \tag{3}$$

$$f(a_i) = (1+\varepsilon)\max_{a_j \in \Pi} J(a_j) - J(a_i), \tag{4}$$

where a is the feature selection vector,

         α_i is 0 if the ith feature is excluded from the subset and 1 if it is included in the subset,

         d is the number of original features,

         pen denotes the partial penalty function,

         e denotes the error rate,

         $thres$ denotes the feasibility threshold,

         m denotes the scale factor (i.e. tolerance margin)

         J denotes the total penalty function,

         err denotes the error rate function,

         l denotes the number of included features,

         f denotes the fitness function,

         ε is a small positive constant,

         Π denotes a population $\{a_1,\ldots,a_n\}$ of feature selection vectors.

There are four properties of the penalty function that make it suitable for feature selection purpose. First of all, a small reward is given to the feature subsets for which the error rate is under the feasibility threshold. Also, at the same level, the adaptability of the feature subsets are judged by the error rates associated with them. Moreover, a small penalty, in the range 0 to 1, is given to the feature subsets for which the error rate is ranged between *thres* and *thres+m*. Finally, a high penalty, *pen*, (over 1) is given to the feature subsets with the error rate over *thres+m*, so these subsets could not compete with the subsets that are with one more feature.

3   Experiment and Data Base

Signatures were collected with a CalComp Drawing Board III and a Pressure Cordless Pen. The sampling rate was set to 100 samples per second. There were 32 volunteers involved in the sampling of 320 signatures, that is, 10 signature samples were collected from each volunteer to minimize the biasing effect. Signature samples were signed within a predefined rectangular window to minimize the orientation, rotation and scaling problems. From the data collection program, eight signals in the function of time were collected or computed for each signature sample: the pen tip position along the x and y axes of the tablet, (x, y), the pen tip distance above the drawing surface of the tablet, (z), the tilt angle of the pen against the x and y axes of the tablet, (tx, ty), the pressure exerted on the pen tip, (p), the pen tip velocity along the x and y axes of the tablet, (vx, vy). An example of signature sample is given in Figure 1.

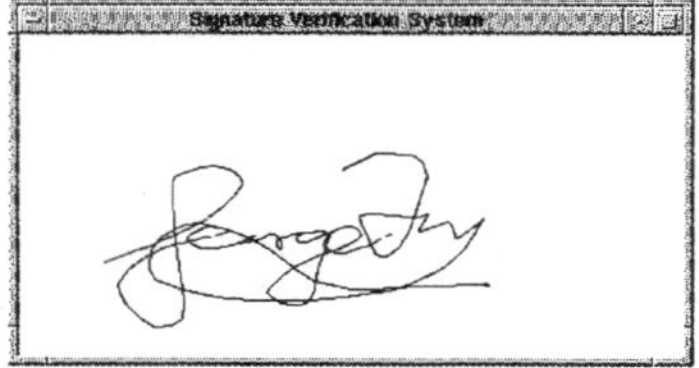
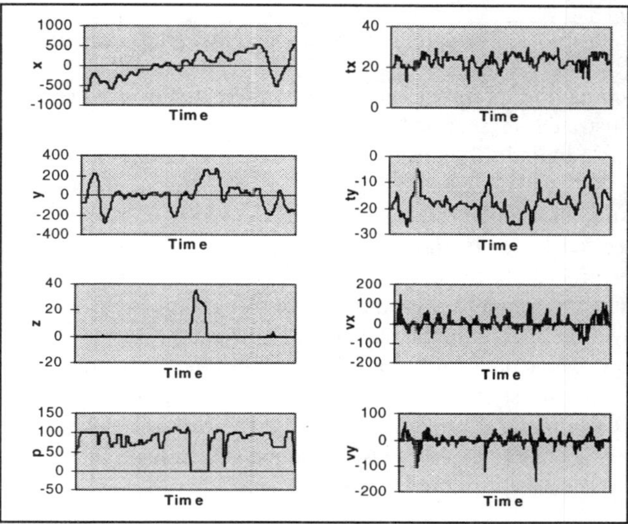

Figure 1. An example of signature sample

Based on the 44 original feature set in [7], we expanded and modified it to the set with 91 features that were extracted from the eight different signals. These 91 features are defined as in Table 1. To solve the position variance of the signature sample, the x and y are shifted by the mean of x and y respectively. Therefore, the means of new x and new y will be meaningless since they will be equal to zero. Also, since all the values of z and p signals are always positive, the features that consider positive and negative signals separately will not be useful. However, we found that the ranges of the values of the 91 features can vary a lot, this will cause the classifier bias to the features with larger ranges. Therefore, to avoid this scaling problem, all the values of the features were scaled to unit standard deviation. As shown in Table 2, the scaled values fall in a small range.

FEATURE NUMBER								FEATURE
X	Y	Z	TX	TY	P	VX	VY	
-	-	21	29	42	55	63	76	mean
1	11	22	30	43	56	64	77	standard deviation
2	12	23	31	44	57	65	78	minimum
3	13	24	32	45	58	66	79	maximum
4	14	-	33	46	-	67	80	average absolute
5	15	-	34	47	-	68	81	average positive
6	16	-	35	48	-	69	82	number of positive samples
7	17	-	36	49	-	70	83	average negative
8	18	-	37	50	-	71	84	number of negative samples
9	19	25	38	51	59	72	85	number of zero-crossing
-	-	26	39	52	60	73	86	maximum - scaled mean
10	20	27	40	53	61	74	87	maximum - minimum
-	-	28	41	54	62	75	88	scaled mean - minimum
89								total time
90								time up / total time
91								time down / total time

Table 1. The 91 Original Features

F	Value	F	Value	F	Value	F	Value	F	Value	F	Value
1	-0.11646	17	0.481721	33	-0.51212	49	0.074269	65	0.136445	81	-0.18433
2	-0.83001	18	0.312946	34	-0.51128	50	-0.07901	66	-0.08078	82	0.50911
3	-0.1353	19	1.260781	35	0.374944	51	-0.36642	67	-0.12044	83	0.195747
4	0.272695	20	-0.1369	36	0.095854	52	-0.41716	68	-0.05054	84	0.353716
5	0.274964	21	-0.88618	37	-0.08594	53	-0.92975	69	0.554939	85	0.27135
6	0.424597	22	-0.44953	38	-0.20067	54	-0.8824	70	0.135644	86	-0.10607
7	-0.27043	23	0.080492	39	-0.18574	55	1.029322	71	0.320967	87	-0.13451
8	0.293589	24	-0.14169	40	-0.29098	56	-0.48706	72	0.246951	88	-0.1362
9	-0.70715	25	1.404353	41	-0.32822	57	0.056888	73	-0.08123	89	0.374471
10	-0.12414	26	-0.02287	42	0.298498	58	-0.19659	74	-0.12458	90	-0.9276
11	-0.12305	27	-0.156	43	-0.52911	59	-0.4767	75	-0.13638	91	0.927603
12	0.127745	28	-0.28816	44	0.942917	60	-1.53121	76	0.125908		
13	-0.13485	29	-0.51041	45	-0.48193	61	-0.19972	77	-0.10596		
14	-0.48585	30	-0.2465	46	0.298265	62	0.979564	78	0.136241		
15	-0.48997	31	0.155961	47	0.298381	63	0.133646	79	-0.10563		
16	0.353821	32	-0.27381	48	0.404307	64	-0.12257	80	-0.20383		

Table 2. The values of the 91 features after scaling to unit standard deviation

After the data acquisition, preprocessing and feature extraction stages, features were to be selected based on the methodology illustrated in section 2. In order to reduce the computation complexity, the nearest neighbor technique [8] was adopted to determine the correct classification rate. Some results are shown in Figure 2. As shown in Figure 2(a), with 7 selected features, we can achieve up to 93% hit rate. Comparing to the performance of the system using all 91 features, we have achieved 88.4% hit rate. As a conclusion, a higher hit rate could be achieved by selecting lesser features. Therefore, some features might confuse and mislead the classifier during the intercrossing process because these features could be noisy or insignificant. From Figure 2, the selected features reached a sub-optimal solution within 300 generations. Therefore, it is feasible to use genetic algorithms for features selection in automatic signature verification system as the solution could be obtained within reasonable period of machine time. In Table 3, the selected feature sets at different feasible error rate settings after 500 generations are shown. We found that, with higher hit rate, the selected features were not able to build up from adding extra features on the lower hit rate feature set. Also, the intersection between these features sets were very small. We believe that there is no unique key features that their inclusion can guarantee higher hit rate. All feature set have to be considered as a whole set.

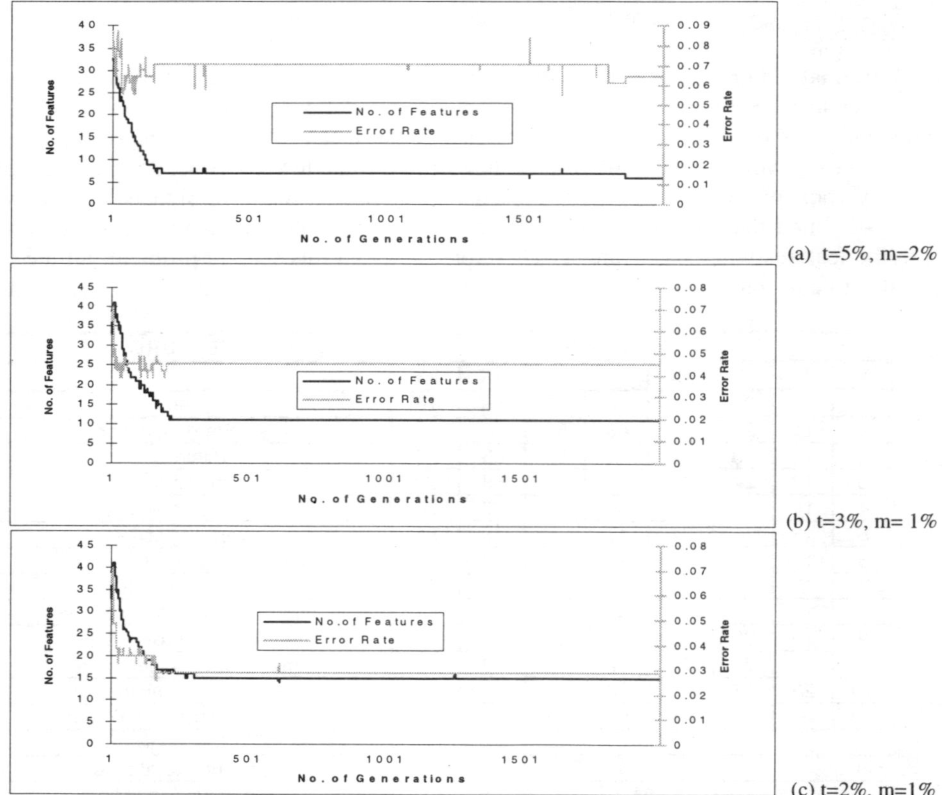

Figure 2. Results showing the performance of the signature verification
system with different feasible error rate settings

Feasible Error Rate Setting	Selected Features Set after 500 generations
t=5%, m=2%	{ 2, 12, 34,47,62,71,72 }
t=3%, m=1%	{ 2, 6, 7, 14, 18, 19, 25, 34, 59, 85,91 }
t=2%, m=1%	{ 2, 6, 10, 12, 15, 16, 19, 24, 25, 34, 47, 60, 71, 77, 84 }

Table 3. Selected Features Set at different settings after 500 generations

4 Conclusion

In this paper, we have applied genetic algorithms to feature selection problem in automatic handwritten signature verification system. Since handwritten signatures are the results of human act, it is subject to intra-personal variations. To develop a feasible automatic handwritten signature verification system, one of the approaches is to identify the features set that will maximize the inter-personal variations and minimize the intra-personal variations at the same time. In this study, our objective was to search for the smallest subset of features for which its error rate should be smaller than a certain threshold using GAs. Therefore, the fitness function has to be defined by the error rate and the number of selected features. Signatures were collected using a digitizing tablet and an instrumented cordless pen. Based on these raw signals, 91 possible features which are believed to be useful for signature verification were computed for each signature samples. To avoid the scaling problem caused by the range variation of different features, all of the feature data was scaled to unit standard deviation. From our experimental results, we have discovered three important behaviors of the system. Firstly, some of the features are not that significant and their presence will induce noise to create confusion and mislead the classifier for the verification process. Secondly, there may not exist an "unique" key feature set to provide sufficient information for the signature verification system to attain results within some feasible error. Thirdly, it appears quite promising to apply GAs to solve the feature selection problem in signature verification system. Currently, we are studying the performance of the system with association to the type II (False Acceptance Rate) error. Also, as we have stated that signature is a human action, our future research direction is to incorporate fuzzy concepts within GAs.

Acknowledgments

This work is supported by University Research Grant #350/491 and is partly supported by the Departmental Grant #351/046.

References

[1] Plamondon, R., and Lorette, G., Automatic Signature Verification and Writer Identification - The State of the Art, *Pattern Recognition*, **22**, 107-131, 1989.

[2] Nelson, W., and Kishon, E., Use of Dynamic Features for Signature Verification, *Proc. IEEE Int. Conf. on Systems, Man, and Cybernetics*, **1**, 201-205, 1991.

[3] Nelson, W., Turin, W., and Hastie, T., Statistical Methods for On-Line Signature Verification, *IJPRAI*, **8**(3), 749-770, 1994.

[4] Sklansky, J., and Siedlecki, W., A Note on Genetic Algorithms for Large-scale Feature Selection, *Pattern Recognition Letters*, **10**, 335-347, 1989.

[5] Sklansky, J., and Siedlecki, W., Large-Scale Feature Selection, *Handbook of Pattern Recognition and Computer Vision* (Eds. Chen, C.H., Pau, L.F., and Wang, P.S.P.),World Scientific Publishing Company, 1993.

[6] Goldberg, D.E., *Genetic Algorithms in Search, Optimization and Machine Learning*. Addison-Wesley, 1989.

[7] Crane, H.D., and Ostrem, J.S., Automatic Signature Verification Using a Three-Axis Force-Sensitive Pen, *IEEE Transactions of Systems, Man and Cybernetics*, **13**(3), 329-337, 1983.

[8] Dasarathy, B.V., *Nearest Neighbor(NN) Norms: NN Pattern Classification Techniques*. IEEE Computer Society Press, 1991.

Gene-Exchange-Based Autonomous Dynamic Load Balancing Model

Toru Ohira†, Ryusuke Sawatari‡, Mario Tokoro†‡
† Sony Computer Science Laboratory
3-14-13 Higashi-gotanda,
Tokyo 141, Japan
(ohira, mario)@csl.sony.co.jp
‡ Department of Computer Science
Keio University,
3-14-1 Hiyoshi, Yokohama 223, Japan
(sawatari, mario)@mt.cs.keio.ac.jp

Abstract— **This paper emphasizes the role of genes as information carriers, encoding properties of individuals in a mutually interacting environment in order to construct a model autonomous load distribution system. The model deals with a system comprised of many mutually connected and communicating computational units. Each unit encodes its dynamically changing load distribution into "gene" packets and exchange them with its immediate neighbors. Based on the local transaction of these genes, each processor decides locally on task transactions, rather than using a central control unit or a global fitness function. We found through simulation experiments that crossover procedures on genes from neighboring units can enhance the autonomous load distribution efficiency. Based on these simulation experiments, we infer and discuss the general characteristics of the emergent behavior of this gene-exchange-based model as well as a direction for implementation on a real computer network.**

1   Introduction

A standard GA emphasizes the adaptation aspect of evolution with a selection mechanism based on a global fitness function [1]. Other aspects of the functions of genes and genetic operations are also important in nature. Genes act as compact carriers of individual information and genetic operations help the spatial spread of information and help to maintain of diversity. The main theme of this paper is to use this latter aspects of genes and genetic operations in trying to construct an emergent adaptive system composed of many simple units, each of which encodes its information onto genes, exchanges genes with its neighboring units, and takes action based on local decision rules rather than referring to a global fitness function.

As a concrete example, we propose a gene-exchange-based dynamic load balancing model and a simulation study applied to a 1-dimensional network. In a dynamic load balancing task, where processes are given to the network one after the other, we would like to have the network better spread its load autonomously without a central control unit (see e.g. [2]). In the model, each computational unit encodes its current load information onto binary genes in a distributed manner with a certain scheme. It then exchanges the genes with its two neighbors to obtain its local load information. When a process arrives at a particular computational unit, the unit decides whether it should process the task or transfer it to either of its two neighbors with lower loads based on the local information read from genes. We have found through simulation that when we further introduce crossovers of genes from neighboring units, the spread of the load over the network is improved. We examine the effect of crossovers with quantitative data from simulation experiments with varying conditions.

Based on these simulation experiments, we infer and discuss the general characteristics of the emergent behavior of this gene-exchange-based model as well as a direction for implementation on a real computer network.

2   Model

In this section, we describe the dynamic load balancing model based on the gene-exchange mechanism.

2.1   Architecture

The model we discuss here is for a one–dimensional ring network of processors (Fig.1). However, the

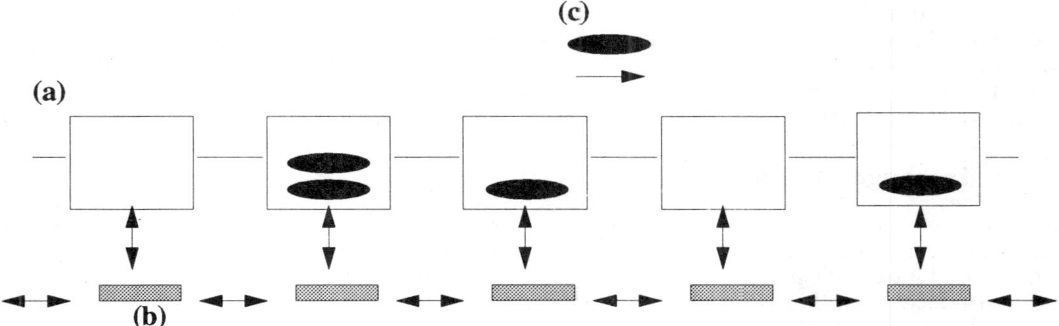

Figure 1: Schematic view of the dynamic load balancing system model with gene-exchange.The elements are (a)processor, (b)gene, and (c)process (task).

model itself is general enough to extend to general network architectures. The aim of the model is the better distribution of tasks, which are introduced to processors in the network one after the other, based solely on local information exchange and local decisions. The network does not possess a central control unit or a global fitness function to evaluate the distribution strategy. Rather, it relies on an emergent behavior based on local actions and decisions based on gene exchanges. We consider the load balancing of two properties in each processor in the network: CPU capability (P_c) and memory capability (P_m). Hence, each processor's state is characterized by these two variables (P_c, P_m). The computational tasks (processes) are given to the network at a fixed time interval τ. During processing, each task is assumed to consume the resources of a processor and decreases its computational capability by (d_c, d_m). Each task is assumed to be processed in time L once a processor starts processing. Hence, the load on the network changes dynamically. The actions of each processor are as follows:

• At each time step, each processor encodes its current load state (P_c, P_m) onto a gene in the manner described in the following sub-section. Then it exchanges copies of the gene with its two neighbors. Each processor creates a new gene based on the crossover and rotation mechanism described below. These process are repeated iteratively.

• When a task is given to a processor either from outside or from one of its two neighbors, it decodes information written onto the genes of neighboring sites. It then computes the following local decision function to choose the best site to move the task.

$$V = w_c G_c d_c + w_m G_m d_m \tag{1}$$

where G_c and G_m are information decoded from genes, and w_c and w_m are parameters to control the decision weighting between memory or CPU. If V is largest for that processor, then the processor starts to process the task itself and its state changes to $(P_c - d_c, P_m - d_m)$. If one of its neighbor has the largest V, it passes the task to its neighbor.

These two actions, gene transactions and task transactions, of each processor is repeated aiming to distribute tasks to more processors in the network without a global evaluation.

2.2   Information Coding onto Genes

The method of coding the processor state is described here. We employ a "distributed representation" of information coding (e.g. [3]). In this representation, bits on the gene collectively carry the information encoded. This is analogous to information representation in neural networks, where the collective activity of neurons in the network encode information, rather than a single neuron representing particular information (see e.g.[4]). We will now describe our "distributed encoding" scheme. We number each bit from the left of the gene 0 through n. Two pieces of information (P_c, P_m) for the processors are encoded. For this we randomly pick P_c numbers from the even integers 0 though n. In the same manner, we pick P_m odd numbers. The set S is defined as the set of $P_c + P_m$ numbers picked from $[0, n]$. The 0th bit on the gene is chosen to be 0 or 1 randomly. The 1st bit is set to be different from the 0th bit, if the number 1 is found in the set S. Otherwise, it is set to be the same as the 0th bit. We repeat this procedure for the entire gene. Namely, if k is in set S, the $k+1$th bit is set to be different from the kth bit. Otherwise, the $k+1$th bit is set to be the same as the kth bit. In Figure 2, we gave the example of $(P_c, P_m) = (2, 4)$, and when $S = (3, 4, 7, 9, 10, 13)$.

Bit #   0 1 2 3   4 5 6 7   8 9 10 11 12 13 14 15 16

| 0 | 0 | 0 | 0 | 1 | 0 | 0 | 0 | 1 | 1 | 0 | 1 | 1 | 1 | 0 | 0 | 0 |

Figure 2: Example of a gene with the proposed encoding scheme.

This encoding scheme is a rather complex scheme to encode two pieces of information. The following points, however, are advantages. First, each bit in this coding carries an equal small amount of information. Hence, information deterioration due to errors in encoding or decoding is kept small. Secondly this uniform bit encoding can take advantage of operations such as crossovers used in genetic algorithms. The third point gives a potential security function. Note that each bit is used and shared by both pieces of information and that there are multiple representation for a single set of information . This fusion of multiple pieces of information over randomly distributed bits could be developed for security purposes.

2.3   Gene Exchange Mechanism

Each processor in the network encodes its current state onto its gene in the manner described in the previous subsection. The simple local gene transaction is to exchange copies of these genes with its two neighbors. Thus, each processor will have three genes including its own from which it can decode information to decide whether it should process a task or pass it to one of its neighbors. We call this gene transaction "no-crossover exchange." By passing the tasks iteratively to processor of more processing power, this exchange method can achieve task distribution. As will be shown in the next section , however, the gene transaction with crossover can improve the load balancing performance. The mechanism of gene exchange with crossover is as follows (Figure 3). After the initial genes are created with the encoding

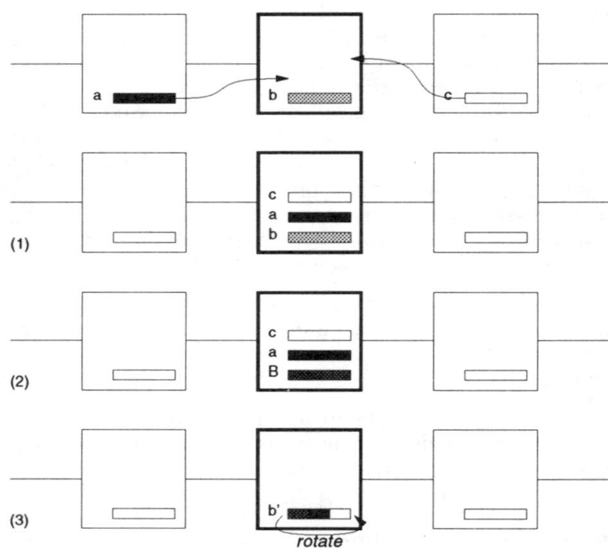

Figure 3: Gene exchange mechanism with crossovers.

method described above, each processor performs a crossover of neighboring genes. For the 1–dimensional network, one third of the gene slices from two genes from neighbors and from its own gene reflecting its current state are needed. Then, the bit position of the created gene is rotated by a random amount. The "crossed gene" constructed in this manner does not reflect directly the (P_c, P_m) of its processors state. Rather, it reflects roughly the "average state" of neighboring processors, which we denote as (G_c, G_m). The iterative procedure of this gene transaction carries the processors' state information spatially. The random rotation procedure is introduced to prevent some part of the gene information simply being passed from one to the other. In this "crossover exchange," a processor bases its decision for a task transaction by comparing the crossed genes, decoding (G_c, G_m) from neighboring processors and evaluating the local decision function V

3   Simulation Results

In this section, we consider how the proposed model described in the previous section performs as a dynamic load balancing model.

The model network contains $N = 80$ processors. For simplicity, we consider that all processors are of equal capability with quantized levels of $0 \leq P_c \leq 180$ and $0 \leq P_m \leq 200$. In order to accommodate these levels, the gene length is set to be 400 bits. We set the basic time step $t = 1$ as the time taken for the processor to update its genes. The tasks has a fixed "lifetime" of L which is introduced from a single point in the network at a fixed frequency with a time interval of τ. The "weight" of each task on the processors' CPU and memory are set to be $d_c = 20$ and $d_m = 20$. The balance between CPU and memory in the local decision function is set to be equal with $w_c = w_m = 0.5$.

With the above parameters set, we compare the two gene exchanged models with and without crossovers. As a measure of model performance, we have first tracked the number of processors in use in the network. The more processors are used, the better the loads are distributed. Examples of simulation results with varying L and τ are shown in Figure 4. (Simulations are repeated 100 times for each parameter set and the average number of busy processors are plotted.) Figure 5 shows the load distribution on the CPU at a sample time. We clearly observe that the crossover exchange model enhances the load balancing

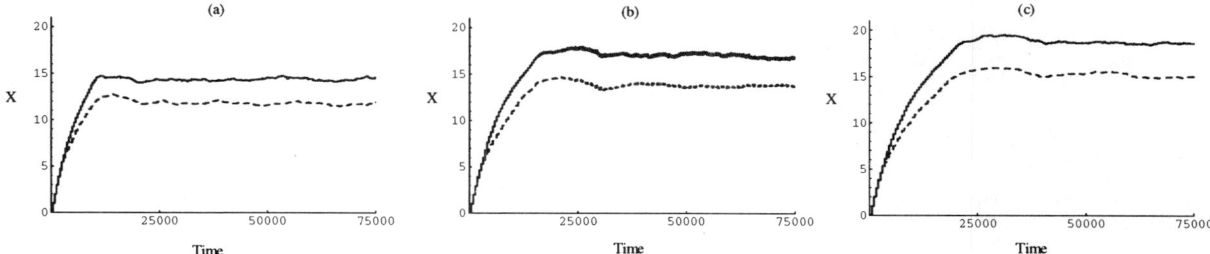

Figure 4: Number of busy processors, X, as a function of time with the crossover model (solid line) and non-crossover model (dashed line). The parameters are (a)$L = 10000$, $\tau = 400$, (b)$L = 15000$, $\tau = 450$, and (c)$L = 20000$, $\tau = 500$.

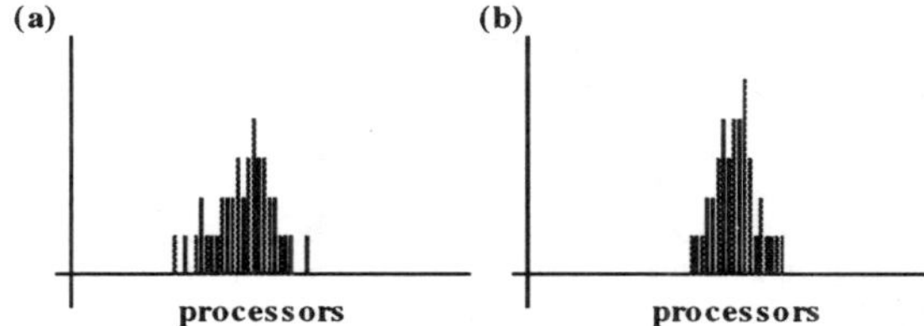

Figure 5: Load distribution on CPU over the network. (a) crossover model (b) non-crossover model. The parameters are $L = 100000$, and $\tau = 2500$. The data is taken at time $t = 150000$.(The load distribution on memory is similar.)

nature of the system. It is generally found as shown in the figures that the crossover procedure is more effective when the "lifetime" of tasks are longer. To gain more insight into the system, we next plotted the average time for a task to "migrate" over the network before it is started to be processed by one of the processors (Figure 6). The figure shows that the tasks in the crossover model require more time

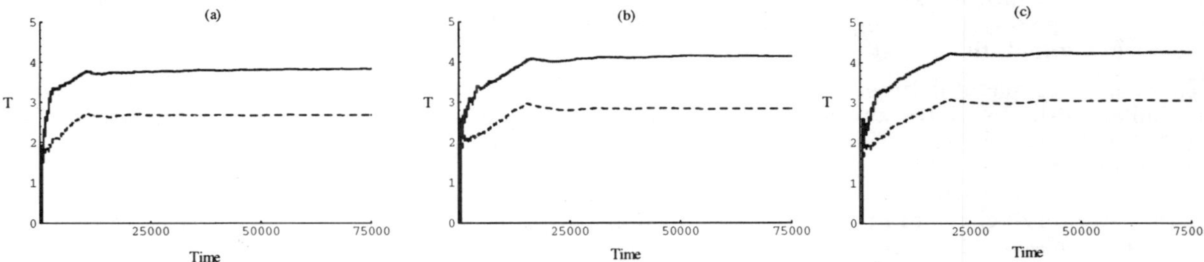

Figure 6: Average migration time of tasks, T, as a function of time with the crossover model (solid line) and non-crossover model (dashed line). The parameters are (a)$L = 10000$, $\tau = 400$, (b)$L = 15000$, $\tau = 450$, and (c)$L = 20000$, $\tau = 500$.

to "migrate" over the network. This reflects a part of the inevitable trade-off for this setup of single point introduction of tasks onto the network: it takes more time to distribute tasks further away from the point of introduction. It should be noted, however, that the increase in migration time with the crossover model as we increase the lifetime of the tasks is not substantial compared to the increase in task distribution.

Next we turn our attention to the effect of errors in gene transaction information between the two models. We simulated the situation as a decoding error. When a processor decodes information from the genes, it reads $(G_c + \alpha_c \eta, G_m + \alpha_m \eta)$. The α_c and α_m are parameters to specify the size of decoding errors, and η is a random variable in $(0, 1)$. We have compared how the average number of busy processor can be affected by this error with and without the crossover model. The simulations are performed with the same set as above with $L = 20000$ and $\tau = 500$. The average number of busy processor is taken as $t = 30000$ and plotted against varying $\alpha = \alpha_c = \alpha_m$. (Figure 7).

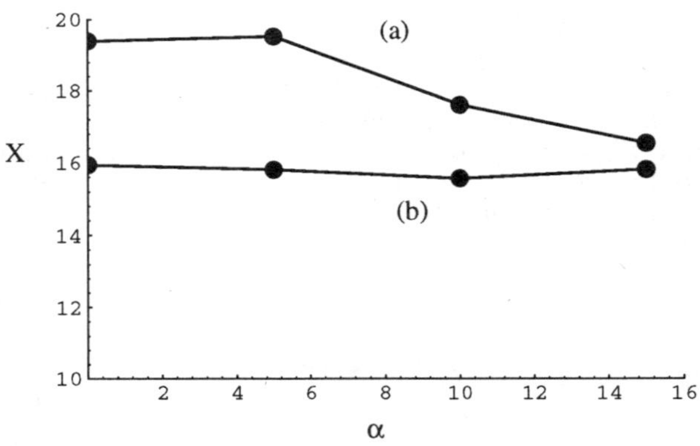

Figure 7: Average number of busy processors, X, as a function of increasing decoding errors, α, with (a) the crossover model, and (b) the non-crossover model.

We see that the increased decoding error gradually destroys the enhanced load balancing capability which comes from using crossovers. The reason is thought to be destruction of local information passing by decoding errors. It should be noted, however, that the model with crossover keeps its advantage in load balancing up to around an error of magnitude up to around 10% of the bits on each gene. We have considered decoding errors in our simulation. The cause of the error, however, can be other factors such as errors during transmission. Though the detailed behavior would be different, we expect from our results here that the model with crossover can tolerate a certain amount of such errors.

Through these simulation results, the model with crossover can be more effective when the transaction time of tasks is not substantial compared to the "lifetime" of the tasks. One effect we infer from the better distribution of the model with crossover is that the "local minima" in the computational capability are "smoothed out" better by the crossover. Also, the crossover model can maintain its effectiveness, thought it diminishes gradually, in the presence of decoding errors. More thorough quantitive analyses and simulations are needed to fully uncover the effect of the role of crossovers in spreading information spatially.

4   Discussion

The proposed model here belong to a class of models aiming at "emergent computation." Related models spans from researches in such areas as distributed artificial intelligence [5, 6] and artificial neural networks, to network computation models [7, 8]. The major challenge in such models are how one can design a local rules or strategies without a global or central evaluation function or unit for the effective collective information behavior to emerge. Our model here is an application of ideas used in GA aiming at an emergent computational system.

There are a couple of discussion points. The first point is that the function of crossover in this context is similar to the simulated annealing scheme for neural networks [9]. Just as stochastic updating of the system enhances the chances of jumping out of the local minimum, the crossovers here introduce the chance of coming out of local minima. The difference is that our model is achieving this through a local information diffusing process, rather than using external noise. The second point is that we have seen more oscillatory behavior in the dynamics of load distribution. We belive that this is related to the delay in the transmission of information due to local crossover. Though it is microscopically intricate, analytical concepts such as "Delayed Random Walks"[10] could be used to describe the macroscopic structure of such behavior. Finally, we are currently looking in the direction of implementation on an actual computer network. The basic design of the model can be transformed rather transparently, and this is under way. Problems may arise from the more asynchronous nature of real multiple computer activities. Analysis of the behavior of real network systems, however, is expected to lead us to more insight into the design of autonomous emergent information processing systems.

References

[1] J. Holland, *Adaptation in Natural and Artificial Systems*. Michigan: University of Michigan Press, 1975.

[2] S. Chowdhury, "The greedy load sharing algorithm," *Journal of Parallel and Distributed Computing*, vol.9, 1990.

[3] T. Ohira, R. Sawatari, and M. Tokoro, "Distributed interaction with Computon" in *Agents Breaking Away*, W. Van de Velde and J. W. Perran (Eds.), Lecture Notes in Artificial Intelligence 1038. Berlin, Springer, 1995

[4] J. Cowan, "Fault and Failure Tolerance," Santa Fe Institute Technical Report 95-10-096, July 1995.

[5] J. Rosenshein and M. Genesereth, "Deals Among Rational Agents," *Proceedings of IJCAI-85*, pp.91-99, 1985.

[6] G. Zlotkin and J. Rosenschein, "Negotiation and Task Sharing Among Autonomous Agents in Co-operative Domains," *Proceedings of IJCAI-89*, pp.912-917, 1989.

[7] B. Huberman, (Ed.) *The Ecology of Computation*, North-Holland, 1988.

[8] M. Tokoro, "Computational Field Model: Toward a new computational model / Methodology for Open Distributed Environment," *Proceedings of Workshop on OS for the 90s and Beyond*, Kaiserslautern, Germany, July, 1991. Also Available as Sony Computer Science Laboratory Technical Report TR-90-006, June, 1990.

[9] S. Kirkpatrick *et al.*, "Optimization by Simulated Annealing," *Science*, vol. 220, pp. 671-680, 1983.

[10] T. Ohira and J. Milton, "Delayed random walks," *Physical Review E*, vol. 52, No. 3, pp. 3277-3281, 1995. Also Available as Sony Computer Science Laboratory Technical Report TR-94-026, November, 1994.

A Soft Computing Approach to the Management of the Chemical Plant Start-up

M. A. Fernandes† ‡, L. A. V. Carvalho† and F. Mora-Camino‡

† COPPE/Systems Eng. and Computing, University Federal of Rio de Janeiro
Ilha do Fundão - Box: 68511
21.945-970 - Rio de Janeiro - Brazil
alfredo@cos.ufrj.br

‡ LAAS/CNRS, University Paul Sabatier
7, Av. Colonel Roche
31.077 - Toulouse Cedex - France
fernande@laas.fr and mora@laas.fr

Keywords: Hybrid Systems, Process Start-up, Hybrid Petri Nets, Genetic Algorithms, Evolutionary Computing.

Abstract—

The synthesis of operational procedures for process industry have been studied in the last years as well by control engineers as by AI researchers. It appears that the two principal difficulties attached to this problem are the choice of an adequate representation for the process and the synthesis of an efficient search method. So, in this communication these two difficulties are coped with. The plant and process representations proposed here use an Hybrid Petri Net formalism so that its continuous and discrete activities are conveniently modeled. Then Genetic Algorithms and Evolutionary Computing techniques can be used to search for an optimal sequence of operations which leads the plant start-up process to completion.

1　Introduction

This problem which consists in finding, given the initial idle state of the plant, a sequence of operations that allows the right process initiation, was first considered as a control problem and presents symbolic features which are compatible with the use of AI tools like Expert Systems or Planning techniques[7, 8]. Two solution approaches for this problem have been developped. The first (and earlier) reduces the problem to the management of connections between subsystems and the start-up problem consists in finding, based on empirical knowledge, a feasible sequence of openning and closing actions on valves[1, 3]. In the second approach the dynamics of the different components of the system and their operational limitations have been taken into account using AI techniques such as inference machine and planning, leading in general to improved solutions[2, 4].

As this problem presents simultaneously discrete and continuous aspects, the adopted representation should be able to express them. So the Hybrid Petri Net[10, 11] formalism has been retained in the proposed approach presented in this communication. Then based on sequences generated with the grammar associated to the corresponding Hybrid Petri Net, the discrete part of the problem uses a Genetic Algorithm which introduces a differenciated crossing-over technique to search for an optimal start-up sequence. The performance of the resulting specialized Genetic Algorithm is compared with the one of a "blind" classical Genetic Algorithm. The continuous part of the problem uses an Evolutionary Computing algorithm[12, 13] which establishes the level of the flow rates represented by the continuous transitions in the Hybrid Petri Net.

2　Hybrid Petri Nets

Earlier approaches for the representation of a process in view of the solution of its start-up problem shown that there was a need for a general formalism able to put together all the relevant available information. In fact, the considered representations were issued using usual data structures supported by programming languages such as Prolog or Lisp. So, the search methods were naturally built accordingly with the structures of these languages. Nevertheless, these representations were unable to take into account and formalize the simultaneous continuous and discrete aspects of the process.

The formalism used here, Hybrid Petri Nets (HPN)[10], seems to be able to integrate the many different informations about the process dynamics and constraints and to provide a sound framework for discrete optimization. Recall that Petri Net(PN)[9, 11] is a graphical and mathematical tool for describing relations between conditions and events in complex discrete dynamical systems. A Petri Net can be seen as a bipartite graph, with a set of n *places* (P) and a set of m *transitions* (T), where P and T are finite and not empty, with $P \cap T = \emptyset$. The places and the transitions are connected by arcs. The arcs which connect places and transitions(both ways) make up two positive integer matrices, $Pre_{n \times m}$

of preconditions and $Pos_{n \times m}$ of poscondinions. A PN is *marked* when every place contains an integer number(positive or zero) of *tokens* or *marks*. A PN marking, M, determines the state of the PN and the state evolution is given by the processing rule $M_i = M_0 + W.S_i$, where M_0 is the initial marking, W is a matrix $|Pos - Pre|$ and S_i is the transitions sequence vector. The transition t_j can be *fired*(or it is enabled) with the M_k marking, if the $M_k(p_i) \geq Pre(p_i, t_j), \forall p_i \in P$.

However this first type of Petri Nets is not sufficient to represent continuous activities. So the Continuous Petri Nets(CPN)[9, 11] have been introduced with this aim. The features of CPN are caracterized by real number tokens and by continuous transitions associated with the notion of *firing quantity* (in this case a transition t_j is fired if $M_k(p_i) > 0, \forall p_i$ connected to t_j). This way, the prior formalism can be enhanced to lead to a global representation of the hybrid dynamics of the process. Other developped Petri Nets variations and extensions related to concepts such as time, stochastic processes and synchronization are not of direct interest here. In this study we considered more particularly *Autonomous Hybrid Petri Nets*(figure 1), where the time factor is not made explicit.

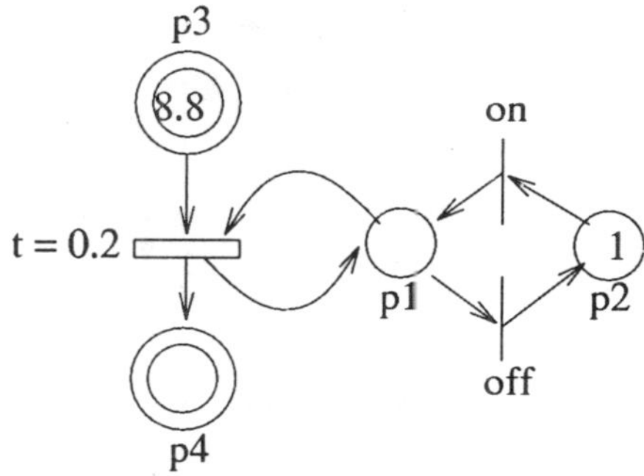

Figure 1: An Hybrid Petri Net

In the example of figure 1, the rectangles represent the continuous transitions, the lines represent discrete ones, double circles represent continuous places and the simple circle represent the discrete ones. The t firing takes out a quantity $0.2.Pre(p_3, t)$ from p_3 and adding $0.2.Pos(p_4, t)$ to p_4. The new marking of p_3 is 8.6 and the new marking of p_4 is 0.2, since $Pre(p_3, t) = Pos(p_4, t) = 1$ depending on the p_1 marking. In the case considered here the machine is down and t is not firable. Note that symbocally t means a production process.

The discrete transitions fire following the rules of the classical PN while in the case of the continuous ones it is necessary to check also the state of the incident either continuous or discrete places. In fact, HPN and PN use fundamentally the same processing rules to fire transitions. However, the firing of a continuous transition t_j, extracts a quantity of firing $x.Pre(p_i, t_j)$ from places p_i and adds $x.Pos(p_k, t_j)$ to places p_k, where p_i and p_k are respectively, input and output places for t_j. An important consistency condition for an HPN is that if p_i is a discrete place and t_j is a continuous transition then $Pre(p_i, t_j) = Pos(p_i, t_j)$.

3 Process Representation with HPN

Consider the plant of figure 2(a). The aim with this plant is to get and maintain determinated temperatures and flowrates at some selected points in the process. The Hybrid Petri Net construction (figure 2(b)) takes into account some aspects related to the process. For exemple, when the process is idle it can be subdivided into four smaller subprocesses related to each heat-exchanger, $HX1$, $HX2$, $HX3$ and $HX4$. In each of these subprocesses the continuous part is identified with activities of flow transference related with steam heating or cooling. So, four continuous transitions are associated with each subprocess: two represent input flow(tc_0 and tc_1), one represents the output flows (tc_8) and one output flow for connection with the next subprocess. The discrete part of each subprocess is related to operations such as check of operational states of equipments (t_1), presence of steam into sources(t_3) and other operational parameters of the equipments(t_5). The positive answers to these verifications are given by t_0, t_2 and t_4. The whole HPN(figure 2(b)) contains 28 discrete places, 8 continuous places, 28 discrete transitions and 12 continuous transitions. The four subprocesses are similar, the transitions t_6, t_{13}, t_{20} and t_{27} represent the termination of each subprocess, respectively.

4 The Proposed Search Method

The search for a solution, i.e., a sequence containing discrete and continuous events that allows the initialization of the plant operation, is divided in two steps, one discrete and one continuous. Both of them are based on genetic optimization[5]: the first one searches for the discrete sequence and the second one determines the threshold quantities firing the continuous transitions.

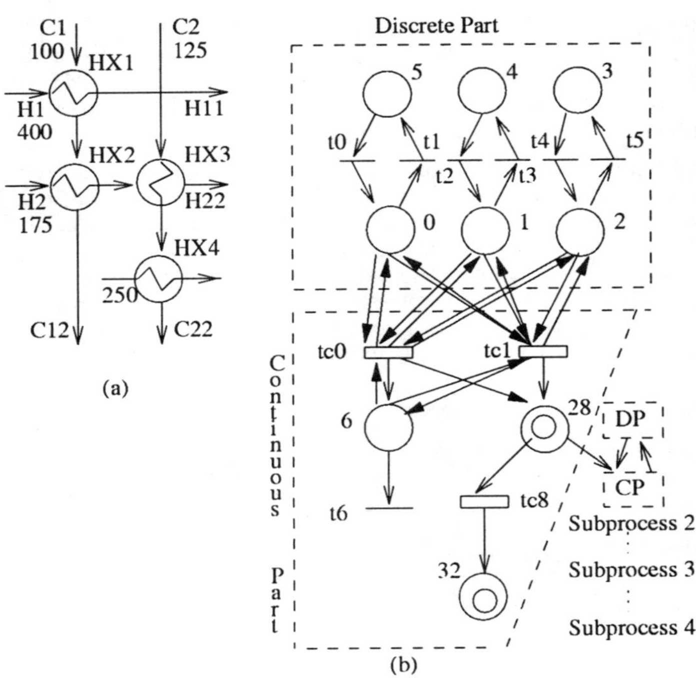

Figure 2: (a)Fragment of a Chemical Plant, (b) HPN associated to plant

4.1 Discrete Optimization Algorithm

In the first algorithm, the initial population is created from the grammar associated with the Petri Net representing the plant taking only into account the discrete transitions.

The number of transitions in each subprocess is given by an integer (N_t) chosen randomly into the range $[0, \lfloor (N - NPr)/NPr \rfloor]$, where NPr is the number of subprocesses. The difference $N - NPr$ is considered since NPr final transitions take part to all sequences. The adaptation function can be chosen as

$$f_{adapt} = \sum_{p_j \in P} \| M_{fs}(p_j) - M_g(p_j) \|^2$$

where, $M_{fs} = M_0 + W.S$ is the final state of the sequence s which is under evaluation. Here S is made up by counting the number of times each transition t appears in the sequence s. M_i and M_g are respectively the initial state and the goal state.

The next generations are created by means of two operators. The first operator selects two sequences, s_1 and s_2, and creates two other sequences, s_1' and s_2', which are made up by the following way: generate new transitions from a selected point into each subsequence of s_1, such as the subsequence length of s_1' is compatible with the subsequence length of s_2. The same procedure is used for s_2'. In fact, we get here a new operator, *crossed-mutation*, where crossing-over and mutation are put together (see the figure 3).

The second operator, reproduction, is a mere copy of the best sequence. The initial states are taken as the number of tokens (0 or 1) in each HPN places given by M_{0i}. M_g is the goal state and s_{f_i} are the final sequences. Some results are displayed in table 1, where G is the number of generations, M is the population size, N is the maximum length of the sequences and P_c is the crossed-mutation probability.

Iinitial State	Final State	G	M	N	P_c	Final Seq.
M_{01}	M_g	45	100	20	0.8	s_{f_1}
M_{02}	M_g	40	100	13	0.8	s_{f_2}
M_{03}	M_g	30	100	10	0.8	s_{f_3}
M_{04}	M_g	20	50	15	0.8	s_{f_4}
M_{05}	M_g	45	100	19	0.75	s_{f_5}

Table 1: Discrete Optimization Performance

where,

M_{01} : 000111011100001110000011100000 $\qquad$ s_{f_1} : $t_2 t_0 t_4 t_6 t_7 t_8 t_7 t_9 t_{11} t_{13} t_{14} t_{18} t_{16} t_{20} t_{21} t_{25} t_{23} t_{27}$

M_{02} : 111000011100000001110111 0000 $\qquad$ s_{f_2} : $t_6 t_9 t_{11} t_7 t_{13} t_{20} t_{21} t_{23} t_{25} t_{27}$

M_{03} : 000111000011100001110000 1110 $\qquad$ s_{f_3} : $t_4 t_0 t_2 t_6 t_{13} t_{20} t_{27}$

M_{04} : 010101010011000010110001 0110 $\qquad$ s_{f_4} : $t_4 t_0 t_6 t_7 t_{13} t_{17} t_{16} t_{18} t_{20} t_{22} t_{25} t_{21} t_{27}$

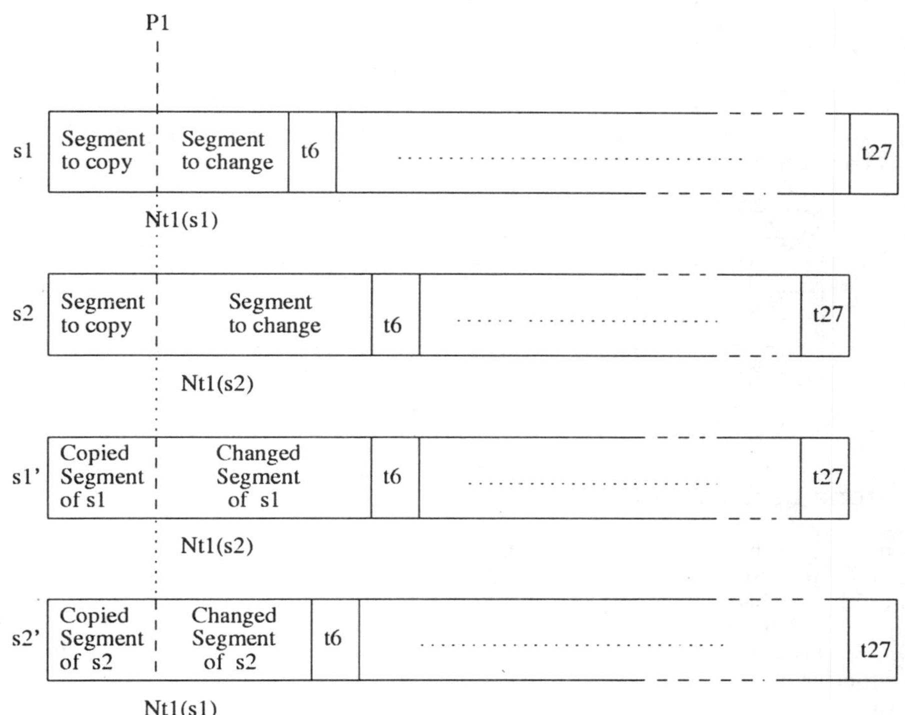

Figure 3: Crossed-Mutation Operator

$$M_{05} : 01010101001100111000010101000 \qquad s_{f_5} : t_0 t_4 t_6 t_{10} t_7 t_9 t_{13} t_{16} t_{18} t_{14} t_{20} t_{21} t_{25} t_{26} t_{25} t_{27}$$

and M_g : 11100000001110000111000001110.

In the classical Genetic Algorithm, the initial population is randomly created by means of the HPN discrete transitions. The crossing-over and mutation operators are classical but they discriminate the different subsequences in each sequence of transitions. The reproduction is also the copy of the best sequence. The resulting performance is shown in table 2, where M_{0i} and M_g have been already defined and where P_m is the mutation probability.

Initial State	Final State	G	M	N	P_c	P_m	Final Seq.
M_{01}	M_g	65	140	20	0.8	0.01	s_{f_1}
M_{02}	M_g	65	140	18	0.75	0.01	s_{f_2}
M_{03}	M_g	65	140	16	0.7	0.01	s_{f_3}
M_{04}	M_g	65	140	16	0.8	0.01	s_{f_4}
M_{05}	M_g	65	140	17	0.75	0.01	s_{f_5}

Table 2: Performance with Standard GA

whit,

$$s_{f_1} : t_4 t_0 t_2 t_6 t_9 t_7 t_{11} t_{13} t_{16} t_{18} t_{14} t_{18} t_{20} t_{21} t_{23} t_{25} t_{27}$$
$$s_{f_2} : t_3 t_2 t_6 t_{11} t_9 t_{13} t_{20} t_{25} t_{21} t_{23} t_{27}$$
$$s_{f_3} : t_4 t_2 t_0 t_6 t_{13} t_{17} t_{16} t_{20} t_{22} t_{21} t_{26} t_{25} t_{27}$$
$$s_{f_4} : t_4 t_0 t_6 t_{13} t_{18} t_{20} t_{25} t_{27}$$
$$s_{f_5} : t_0 t_4 t_6 t_7 t_{13} t_{14} t_{18} t_{19} t_{16} t_{18} t_{20} t_{21} t_{25} t_{21} t_{27}$$

4.2 Continuous Optimization Algorithm

The second algorithm copes with the continuous aspect of the problem. It is based on Evolutionary Computing techniques as introduced by Fogel[13]. The proposed algorithm manipulates the sequence of real numbers and takes into account a penalty term in the adaptation function to cope with constraints about temperatures and flowrates. The initial population is randomly generated as a set of real number sequences, where the sequence length is the number of the continuous transitions. New generations are created by the mutation and reproduction operators. Each individual generates another by adding a zero mean Gaussian random variable to each sequence component associated to the individual. If any component exceeds a constrained range it is reset to the violated limit. Then each sequence is faced with 10 others, the 40 best sequences are selected and make up the next generation. The initial conditions are represented in figure 2(a) by the initial temperatures. The considered constraints can be $285 \leq T_{H11} \leq 320$, $T_{C22} \geq 150$ and $F_{C12} = 5000 \pm 500$. The adaptation function in this case is given by

$$f_{adapt2} = \sum \|Var_{goal} - Var_{res}\|^2 + F_{penalty}$$

where, Var_{goal} and Var_{res} are the goal and current values of the variables considered in the constraints. This algorithm has been run 20 times and the resulting performance is shown in table 3.

Steam	Goal State		Achieved Performance	
	Flowrate	Temperature	Flowrate	Temperature
H_{11}	20000	300	19961.82	309.87
H_{22}	60000	250	60416.19	247.56
C_{12}	5000	250	4971.18	181.84
C_{22}	80000	175	80669.33	173.05

Table 3: Continuous Optimization Performance

5 Conclusions and Perspectives

In this communication it has been shown that planning techniques, Petri Nets representation and Genetic Algorithms can be put together to solve the start-up problem of systems of high complexity such as chemical plants. It has been observed that Petri Net representation can be made compatible with GA search techniques resulting in a new crossing-over operator which leads to improved results in relation to the application of classical Genetic Algorithm. So, we get a new perspective to use Petri Nets and GA to synthetise supervision layers for hybrid dynamical systems.

References

[1] O'Shima, E., "Safety Supervision of Valve Operations", *Journal of Chemical Engineering of Japan*, Vol. 11, No. 5, pp. 390-395, 1978.

[2] Fusillo, R. H. and Powers, G. J., "A Synthesis Method for Chemical Plant Operating Procedures", *Computer Chemical Engineering*, Vol. 11, No. 4, pp. 369-382, 1987.

[3] Foulkes, N. R., Walton, M. J., Andow, P. K. and Galluzzo M., "Computer-Aided Synthesis of Complex Pump and Valve Operations", *Computer Chemical Engineering*, Vol. 12, No. 9/10, pp. 1035-1044.

[4] Tomita, S., Hwang, K. O'Shima, E. and McGreavy, C., "Automatic Synthesizer of Operating Procedures for Chemical Plant by Use of Fragmentary Knowledge", *Journal of Chemical Engineering of Japan*, Vol. 22, No. 4, pp. 364-372, 1989.

[5] Goldberg, D. E., *Genetic Algorithms in Search, Optimization, and Machine Learning*, Addison-Wesley Company, 1989.

[6] Grefenstette, J. J., "Optimization of Control Parameters for Genetic Algorithms", *IEEE Transacitons on Systems, Man and Cybernetics*, Vol. 16, No. 1, pp. 122-128, 1986.

[7] Astrom, K. J., Anton, J. J. and Arzén, K. E., "Expert Control", *Automatica*, Vol. 22, No. 3, pp. 277-286, 1986.

[8] Astrom, K. J., "Intelligent Control", *ECC 91 European Control Conference*, Grenoble, Jul/1991.

[9] Murata, T., "Petri Nets: Properties, Analysis and Applications", *Proceedings of the IEEE*, Vol. 77, No. 4, Abril/1989.

[10] Le Bail, J., Alla, H. and David R., "Hybrid Petri Nets", *European Control Conference 91*, pp. 1472-1477, Grenoble, Jul/1991.

[11] David, R., "Modeling of Dynamic Systems by Petri Nets", *European Control Conference 91*, pp. 136-147, Grenoble, Jul/1991.

[12] Homaifar, A., Qi, C. Q. and Lai, S. H., "Constrained Optimization Via Genetic Algorithms", *Simulation*, pp. 242-254, April/1994.

[13] Fogel, D. B., "A Comparison of Evolutionary Programming and Genetic Algorithms on Selected Constrained Optimization Problems", *Simulation*, pp. 397-404, June/1995.

A Real-Time Evolutionary Algorithm for In-Situ Ellipsometer Data Analysis

Percy P.C. Yip*, Yoh-Han Pao*, Steven R. LeClair**, and Kurt G. Eyink**

*AI WARE, Inc, Cleveland, OH 44106, U.S.A.
**U.S. Air Force Wright Laboratories, WPAFB, Dayton, OH 45433, U.S.A.

Abstract. Ellipsometry is a widely used technique for determining the optical properties of a surface. Recently reports on the studies of the use of ellipsometry for in-situ analysis and control of growing films are increasing because powerful computers can now be easily obtained at reasonable price. For in-situ ellipsometer data analysis, solutions of inversion of Fresnel equations must be obtained in real-time. Attempts on usage of optimization techniques and neural-net computing have been reported for the inversion task, but results are far from satisfactory. In this paper, we propose the use of GESA for in-situ ellipsometer data analysis, and report on the results with simulated data and experimental data. Results show that GESA provides satisfactory solutions in real-time.

1 Introduction

Ellipsometry [1] is a widely used technique for determining optical properties of a surface from measurements of the change in polarization state of reflecting light. Recently, reports on the studies of the use of ellipsometry for in-situ analysis and control of growing films are increasing due to its non-destructive characteristic, and a need for increasing yield of fabrication processes [2-3]. When a beam of circularly polarized light with wavelength λ is reflected from the surface of a material with a complex refractive index, the reflected beam is observed to be elliptically polarized. This is because the in-plane and out-of-plane components of the incident beam are reflected with different reflectance and an additional phase shift is introduced between the two components. The experimental situation is illustrated schematically in Figure 1.

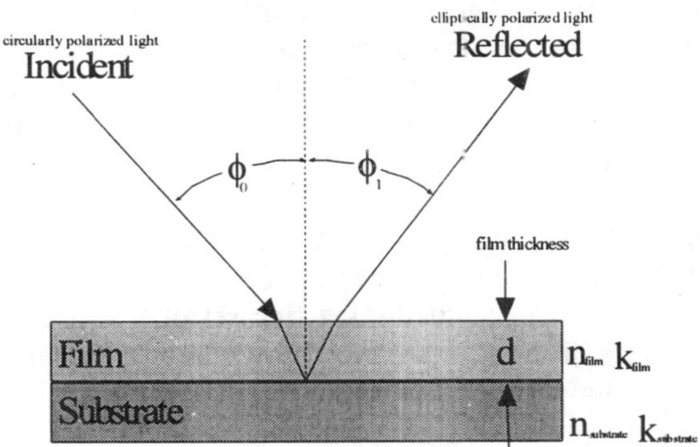

$$\Psi = f_1(n_{substrate}, k_{substrate}, n_{film}, k_{film}, d, \phi_0, \lambda)$$

$$\delta = f_2(n_{substrate}, k_{substrate}, n_{film}, k_{film}, d, \phi_0, \lambda)$$

where $n_{substrate}, k_{substrate}, \phi_0$ and λ are known in any one experiment.

Figure 1. Illustration of reflection from a composite structure consisting of a thin film and a substrate

At any growth stage, the state of the reflected light is completely characterized and measured in terms of two parameters Ψ and δ. In addition, given values of the refractive indices and of the film thickness, we can also calculate values of Ψ and δ with a set of transcendental equations. However the inverse process is of greater importance in in-situ monitoring. Namely, given values of Ψ and δ (usually several sets of Ψ and δ), we want to invert the set of transcendental equations to estimate values of refractive indices and film thickness. A complex refractive index of a material is characterized by two values, namely n and k. There are two major problems relating to the inversion process: (1) these transcendental equations are not invertible; (2) measured Ψ and δ are usually noisy (we will denote the measured data as Ψm and δm), and so are different from the theoretical ones. A number of attempts have been proposed to solve these problems [4-5]. They include iterative optimization and neural-net computing. Iterative optimization techniques are found to be inadequate because they are too sensitive to the chosen initial points. Neural networks have been proposed to augment iterative optimization methods to find good initial points, but results reported are not very satisfactory.

Evolutionary Algorithms and Genetic Algorithms are powerful optimization techniques derived from simulating evolutionary processes [6-10]. These population-based search techniques are capable of locating global minimum given enough time. However, these techniques are not suitable for a sequential machine to tackle real-time problems because of slow convergence. In this paper, we demonstrate that fast convergence rate can be achieved with a mechanism of regionally guided search [11]. Guided Evolutionary Simulated Annealing (GESA) [11] is one such technique that was motivated by combining genetic algorithms and simulated annealing [12] in order to speed up the convergence rate. We report on the use of GESA for in-situ ellipsometer data interpretation. In Section 2, we describe the GESA approach, and how GESA can be applied for in-situ ellipsometer data interpretation. Results of applying GESA approach to both simulated data and experimental data are given in Section 3, and we conclude our discussion with Section 4.

2 GESA Approach for Ellipsometer Data Analysis

GESA is a population-based search approach. It differs from other similar approaches in that regions with good performance are rewarded with more search focus. A basic version of GESA can be described as follows: the algorithm starts with N solution candidates, called parents. Each parent will generate a number of children, say M children. Each child will be evaluated based on a stochastic manner, and is classified as good or bad. The fitness value of each family is defined as the number of good children in that family. A good child in each family is selected as the parent of that family for the next generation. The performance index for each family depends on the number of good children in the family. In the next generation, the number of children that will be generated in a family depends on the performance index of the family. When a child is generated from its parent, it is regionally close to the parent. Hence the performance index of a family provides performance index of a region. More detailed information on GESA can be found in [13,14].

Before demonstrating how to apply GESA to ellipsometer data interpretation, we have to introduce the concept of pseudo-substrate. Several sets of Ψm(t) and δm(t) are measured in succession, which corresponds to having grown several layers of the film in succession. Conceptually, the first set of Ψm and δm is regarded as relating to a pseudo-substrate, and successive layers of the film are then grown in that pseudo-substrate. With that concept in mind, we can formulate the task as an optimization task as follow:

To find ns(t), ks(t), nfilm(t), kfilm(t), d(t) such that

$$\left\{ \frac{1}{P} \sum_{k=0}^{P-1} \left\{ [\, \psi_m(t-k) - \psi(t-k) \,]^2 + [\, \delta_m(t-k) - \delta(t-k)]^2 \right\} \right\}^{\frac{1}{2}}$$

where ns(t), ks(t) are the optical properties of the pseudo-substrate,
nfilm(t), kfilm(t) are the optical properties of the film,
and d(t) is the thickness between two successive layers.

3 Results

In our current implementation, seven points were used to reduce the noise effect, and the optimal values of ns, ks, nfilm, kfilm, and d were found. We simulated the process and generated noiseless data using nfilm = 4.5, kfilm = 0.5 and d = 6.0. Figure 2 shows the trajectory of the simulated data, and an instance of 7 points is given in Figure 3. The results are summarized in Table 1. We put the objective value (i.e. root mean square error) in the table so that we know how well the interpretation is. The mean values of the results are almost the same as the actual values of the corresponding parameters. We have not obtained the exact results all the times because of the time constraint that we imposed on the search. We restricted to get a solution within 10 seconds in a Pentium 90MHz machine. To see if the algorithm is robust against measurement noise, we have tested with a set of data pairs. The data set was obtained with careful control so that the film was believed to be fairly homogenous. Figure 4 shows the trajectory of the experimental data. Figure 5 shows an instance of 7 points. From Figure 5, we can see that it is very noisy. Error would be introduced and propagated if the first point were used to determine the pseudo-substrate. It explains why we propose not to use the first point to determine the pseudo-substrate. We summarize our results in Table 2. After the growth, we measured the optical properties of the film ex-situ, and the results were found to be very close to the mean values of the results in Table 2. It should be noted that we have not put the values of ns and ks in the tables because they are conceptual entities, and they cannot be verified.

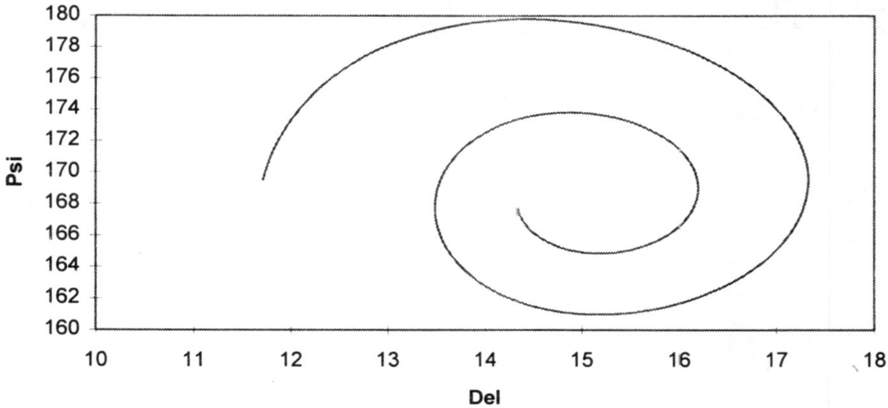

Figure 2. A trajectory of the theoretical (simulated) data

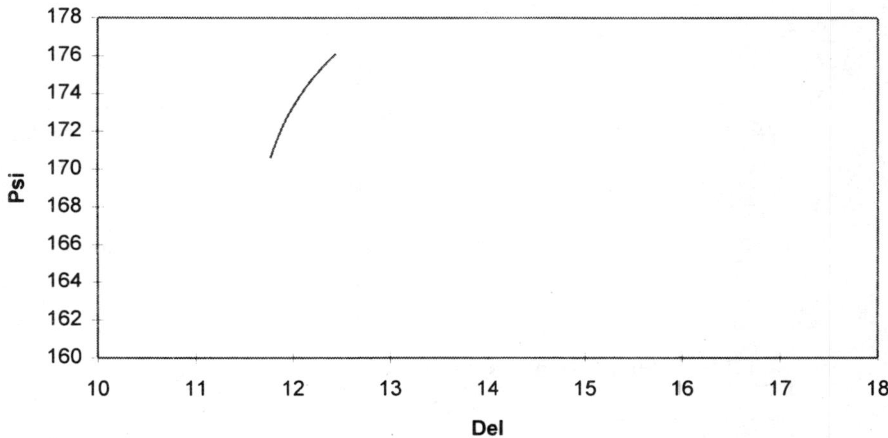

Figure 3. An instance of seven simulated points for interpretation

Table 1. Summary of results using simulated data

	nfilm	kfilm	d	RMS
mean	4.5022007	0.502624	5.9930703	0.0001052
std.dev.	0.0037308	0.0071852	0.1058193	0.0002221

Del/Psi Trajectory for the Experimental Data

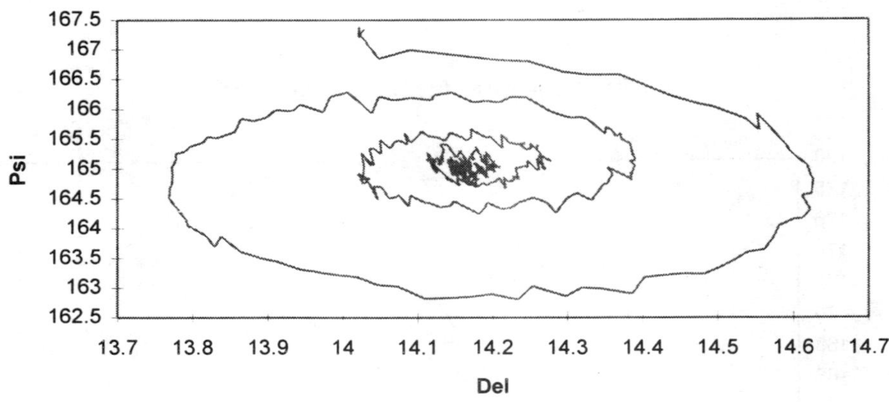

Figure 4. A trajectory of the experimental data

The first 7 points in the Del/Psi Trajectory

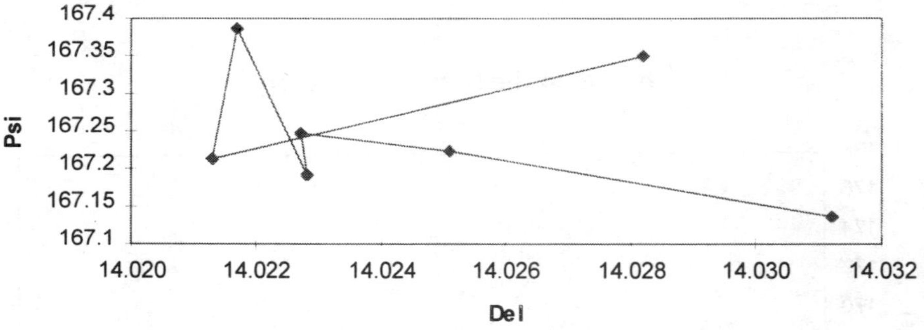

Figure 5. An instance of seven experimental points for interpretation

Table 2. Summary of results using the experimental data

	nfilm	kfilm	d	RMS
mean	4.4084714	0.587772	5.9939573	0.0047036
std. dev.	0.0148243	0.0174793	0.2808951	0.0031416

4 Conclusion

We have proposed the use of a novel evolutionary algorithm, GESA, for real-time ellipsometer data interpretation. It is possible to obtain good results in a reasonable short time because of its regionally guided search property. We have demonstrated our approach with both simulated data and experimental data. Our proposed approach is found to be robust against measurement noise. With our proposed approach, we can estimate both optical properties of the film and the thickness simultaneously.

The current approach will be integrated with other equipment for monitoring and controlling the growth of thin films in a MBE process, and further results will be reported in the future.

Acknowledgment

The authors would like to thank Dr. Boris Igelnik for suggesting other optimization approaches, and Mr. Zhuo Meng for implementing those approaches so that we can compare our results with all those approaches.

References

[1] H. G. Tompkins, *A Users' Guide to Ellipsometry*. San Diego: Academic Press, Inc., 1993.

[2] R. W. Collins, "Automatic rotating element ellipsometers: calibration, operation, and real-time applications," *Review of Scientific Instruments*, vol. 61, pp. 2029-2062, 1990.

[3] J. Woollam et al., "In situ and ex situ ellipsometric characterization for semiconductor technology," *SPIE*, vol. 1678, pp. 246-253, 1992.

[4] F. K. Urban III and M. F. Tabet, "Real time, in-situ ellipsometry solutions using artificial neural network preprocessing," *Thin Solid Films*, vol. 245, pp. 161-173, 1994.

[5] J. C. Comfort, and F. K. Urban III, "Numerical techniques useful in the practice of ellipsometry," *Thin Solid Films*, vol. 270, pp. 78-84, 1995.

[6] L. J. Fogel, A.J. Owens and M. J. Walsh, *Artificial Intelligence through Simulated Evolution*. New York: John Wiley, 1966.

[7] J. H. Holland, *Adaptation in Natural and Artificial Systems*. Ann Arbor: University of Michigan Press, 1975.

[8] D. E. Goldberg, *Genetic Algorithms in Search, Optimization & Machine Learning*. Addison-Wesley, 1989.

[9] H.-P. Schwefel, *Numerical Optimization of Computer Models*, Chichester: John Wiley, 1981.

[10] D. B. Fogel, *System Identification through Simulated Evolution: A Machine Learning Approach to Modeling*, Ginn Press, 1991.

[11] P. C. Yip, *The Role of Regional Guidance in Optimization: The Guided Evolutionary Simulated Annealing Approach*, Ph.D. Dissertation, Case Western Reserve University, 1993.

[12] S. Kirkpatrick, C. D. Gelatt, Jr., M. P. Vecchi, "Optimization by simulated annealing," *Science*, vol. 220, pp.671-680, May, 1983.

[13] P.P.C. Yip and Y.H. Pao, "A guided evolutionary simulated annealing approach to the quadratic assignment problem," *IEEE Transactions on Systems, Man, and Cybernetics*, vol. 24, no. 9, pp. 1383-1387, Sept.,1994.

[14] P.P.C. Yip and Y.H. Pao, "Combinatorial optimization with use of guided evolutionary simulated annealing," *IEEE Transactions on Neural networks*, vol. 6, no. 2, pp. 290-295, March, 1995.

The Self-encoding Genetic Algorithm

Xuejun Wang, Xizhi Shi, Zheng Lu

IVSNR, Shanghai Jiao Tong University
1954 Hua Shan Road
Shanghai, 200030
China
E-mail: xzshi@sjtu.edu.cn

Abstract

This thesis proposed the self-encoding genetic algorithm, which are adapted to those problems defined in a continuous real space. The algorithm adopts a certain floating-point encoding strategy, evolves and searches a continuous space on the basis of parameters themselves, is coincident with the natural evolution and adapted to the current calculation tools such as personal computers. Both the crossover operator and the mutation operator of the algorithm are simple, and the data storage of it is convenient so that it is able to deal with more complicated problems. Comparing with real value genetic algorithms, the algorithm maintains those important characteristics of basic genetic algorithms.

1   Introduction

The weights' optimization of neural networks is a nonlinear search problem. However, the classical BP algorithm is Gradient-descent in itself. As a result, local minimums are always pitfalls when training neural networks by BP algorithm. Recently, since the genetic algorithms have worked out some nonlinear optimization problems, the genetic reinforcement learning of neural networks becomes popular. However, these attempts have largely met with modest results.

The definition space of NN weights is continuous real value space generally, while basic genetic algorithms proposed by Professor Holland are based on discrete space. Therefore, it is often necessary to discretize the continuous space of NN weights, or decide a encoding strategy, before genetic reinforcement learning.

Both popular encoding strategies at present are real value encoding strategy and binary encoding strategy. The encoding unit of the real value encoding strategy is real number, and the scope of encoding unit changed from vocabulary $\{0,1\}$ to continuous real value space. All genetic algorithms adopting the real value encoding strategy can be called real value genetic algorithms, or floating genetic algorithms. In essence, these algorithms only use genetic algorithms in the optimization of weights combination, while the optimization of a weight itself is realized by other search algorithms such as simulated annealing. The binary encoding strategy adopts the fixed-point binary encoding strategy the precision of which is fixed. All genetic algorithms adopting binary encoding strategy can be called binary genetic algorithms. After encoding, binary genetic algorithms becomes pure basic genetic algorithms. However, the application results of real value genetic algorithms are often more better, although application results of both are not satisfying.

---

* This thesis is supported by the Dept. of Information Science, NSF of China, and the grant number is 69572025

2   Standpoints

Despite the better application results, real value genetic algorithms are far away from basic genetic algorithms. If there is only one weight, the so-called real value genetic algorithms is actually simulated annealing or other algorithms.

As to the present binary genetic algorithms, there are three important false conceptions: fixed-point binary number, the precondition of given definite search space, the necessity of laborious code string storage and calculation.

When we want to solve a discrete problem, fixed-point binary numbers are undoubtedly suitable. However, to represent real numbers, fixed-point binary numbers, the precision of which is finite, have been replaced by floating-point numbers, the effective-figure of which is finite, in many fields, including most of computer fields. Somehow, all current binary genetic algorithms proposed persist in adopting fixed-point binary numbers to represent real numbers and calculating in a computer which uses floating-point numbers mechanically. It would be marvelous if these miscellanies performed perfectly. For example, we and the computer seldom care about the accurate value of a real number x whose level is 10^{10} is $x+1$ or $x+0.1$. Six or seven effective-figures are often enough. According to the standard of IEEE, a float number in current personal computers have 23 binary effective-figures, about six or seven decimal effective-figures. However, if a current binary genetic algorithm whose precision is fixed wants to search in a space $\left[0,10^{10}\right]$, it has to always pay a lot of attention to the differences between $x, x+1$ and $x+0.1$ while the computer ignores them when the level of x is 10^{10} and the effective-figures may be not enough when the level of x is 10^{-1} and the difference between x and $x+0.1$ is very important.

Another false conception of binary genetic algorithms is the precondition of given definite search space. It is incredible that an evolving species "know" its evolution scope. The evolution scope should be limited naturally by the environment and natural selection. The precondition was added to the basic genetic algorithms in order to conveniently solve discrete problem. Somehow, binary genetic algorithms mechanically inherit it again.

The last false conception of binary genetic algorithms is the necessity of laborious code string storage and calculation. Both beginning and ending of NN learning are only relevant with real number, and the encoding strategy matches a real number with a code segment one by one. As a result, it is possible to change the calculating procedure from

$$\begin{array}{c} real \quad number \\ parameter \quad series \end{array} \xrightarrow{} \begin{array}{c} code \quad series \\ basic \quad genetic \quad algorithms \end{array} \xrightarrow{} \begin{array}{c} real \quad number \\ parameter \quad series \end{array}$$

to

$$\begin{array}{c} real \quad number \\ parameter \quad series \end{array} \xrightarrow{a \; certain \; genetic \; algotithm} \begin{array}{c} real \quad number \\ parameter \quad series \end{array}$$

The change makes the laborious code string storage and calculation unnecessary.

Starting from these standpoints, we proposed the self-encoding genetic algorithm.

3   The self-encoding genetic algorithm

The binary encoding strategy is based on the indefinite geometrical series

$$\frac{1}{2^1}, \frac{1}{2^2}, \cdots, \frac{1}{2^n}, \cdots,$$

the sum of which is

$$S = \lim_{n \to \infty} S_n = \frac{0.5 - 0.5^{(n+1)}}{1 - 0.5} = 1.$$

Assuming it is in the continuous real space $[a, a + l]$, the weight w can be represent with

$$w = a + x_1 * \frac{l}{2^1} + x_2 * \frac{l}{2^2} + \cdots + x_n * \frac{l}{2^n} + \cdots, \quad x_i \in \{0,1\} \quad i = 1,2,\cdots,n,\cdots.$$

Keeping the fore N terms, we get

$$w' = a + x_1 * \frac{l}{2^1} + x_2 * \frac{l}{2^2} + \cdots + x_N * \frac{l}{2^N}, \quad x_i \in \{0,1\} \quad i = 1,2,\cdots,N.$$

As long as the N is large enough, w' can approximate w according to any given precision. Therefore, given a definite precision, or given a definite N, w can be represented by code string $(x_1 x_2 \cdots x_N)$. This is the binary encoding strategy.

Canceling the precondition of the given definite space and encoding with the weight w itself, we get

$$w = \frac{w}{2^1} + \frac{w}{2^2} + \cdots + \frac{w}{2^n} + \cdots$$

and

$$w' = \frac{w}{2^1} + \frac{w}{2^2} + \cdots + \frac{w}{2^N}.$$

As long as the N is large enough, w' can approximate w according to any given precision. Therefore, given a definite effective-figures number, or given a definite N, w can be represented by code string $(1_1 1_2 \cdots 1_N)$.

This is the self-encoding strategy, the encoding strategy of the self-encoding genetic algorithm. There are two important differences between the two strategy. First, a code string coming from self-encoding strategy is composed from the vocabulary $\{1\}$ instead of $\{0,1\}$. Second, any gene of a code string coming from binary encoding strategy represents a non-negative value, $x_i * \dfrac{l}{2^i}$ because l is positive, while the value of a gene of a code string coming from self-encoding strategy, $x_i * \dfrac{w}{2^i}$, may be negative. Both differences heavily affected the mutation operator.

The crossover operator of self-encoding genetic algorithm is composed of two divisions: the crossover of part weights series between two individuals and the crossover of part codes in counter-weights between two individuals.

Assuming the two individuals which will crossover each other are

$$\left(u_1 v_1 w_1 x_1 y_1 z_1\right) \text{ and } \left(u_2 v_2 w_2 x_2 y_2 z_2\right).$$

The crossover of part weights series is direct and straightforward. Assuming the crossover point is between w and x, the crossover changes both individuals to

$$\left(u_1 v_1 w_1 x_2 y_2 z_2\right) \text{ and } \left(u_2 v_2 w_2 x_1 y_1 z_1\right).$$

The crossover of part codes in counter-weights between two individuals can be calculated directly. Assuming counterweights w_1 and w_2, the code strings of which are $\left(1_1^1 1_2^1 \cdots 1_N^1\right)$ and $\left(1_1^2 1_2^2 \cdots 1_N^2\right)$ respectively, will exchange the fore k ($k = 1,2,\cdots,N$) codes, the crossover changes both individuals to

$$\left(u_1 v_1 w_1' x_2 y_2 z_2\right) \text{ and } \left(u_2 v_2 w_2' x_1 y_1 z_1\right).$$

the code strings of w_1' and w_2' are

$$\left(1_1^1 1_2^1 \cdots 1_k^1 1_{k+1}^2 1_{k+2}^2 \cdots 1_N^2\right)$$

and

$$\left(1_1^2 1_2^2 \cdots 1_k^2 1_{k+1}^1 1_{k+2}^1 \cdots 1_N^1\right).$$

That is

$$w_1' = \frac{w_1}{2^1} + \frac{w_1}{2^2} + \cdots + \frac{w_1}{2^k} + \frac{w_2}{2^{k+1}} + \frac{w_2}{2^{k+2}} + \cdots + \frac{w_2}{2^N}$$

and

$$w_2' = \frac{w_2}{2^1} + \frac{w_2}{2^2} + \cdots + \frac{w_2}{2^k} + \frac{w_1}{2^{k+1}} + \frac{w_1}{2^{k+2}} + \cdots + \frac{w_1}{2^N}.$$

Since

$$\frac{1}{2^1} + \frac{1}{2^2} + \cdots + \frac{1}{2^k} = \frac{\frac{1}{2^1} - \frac{1}{2^k} * \frac{1}{2}}{1 - \frac{1}{2}} = 1 - \frac{1}{2^k},$$

both w_1' and w_2' can be directly calculated respectively according to following formulae

$$w_1' = w_1 * \left(1 - \frac{1}{2^k}\right) + w_2 * \frac{1}{2^k}$$

and

$$w_2' = w_2 * \left(1 - \frac{1}{2^k}\right) + w_1 * \frac{1}{2^k}.$$

The mutation operator of the self-encoding genetic algorithm appears heavily different from binary genetic algorithms mainly because the two important differences in encoding strategies. The mutation operator of binary genetic algorithms is just to change a code from 1 to 0 or vice versa while self-encoding genetic algorithm adopts the basic conception of changing a code from 1 to 0 or 2. If the No. k ($k = 1, 2, \cdots, N$) code of weight w mutates, the code string will change from

$$\left(1_1 1_2 \cdots 1_{k-1} 1_k 1_{k+1} 1_{k+2} \cdots 1_N\right)$$

to

$$\left(1_1 1_2 \cdots 1_{k-1} 0_k 1_{k+1} 1_{k+2} \cdots 1_N\right)$$

or

$$\left(1_1 1_2 \cdots 1_{k-1} 2_k 1_{k+1} 1_{k+2} \cdots 1_N\right),$$

which can be directly calculated according to

$$w' = w - \frac{w}{2^k} = w * \left(1 - \frac{1}{2^k}\right)$$

or

$$w' = w + \frac{w}{2^k} = w * \left(1 + \frac{1}{2^k}\right).$$

However, there are still three important lapses. First, since

$$\left| w * \left(1 - \frac{1}{2^k}\right)\left(1 + \frac{1}{2^k}\right) \right| = \left| w * \left(1 - \frac{1}{2^{2k}}\right) \right| < |w|,$$

we can conclude that the mutation have a trend to make $|w|$ smaller, which maybe influence the trend toward optimum solutions. Second, in order to be suitable for diversified problems, the scope which the weight w could reach through one mutation should be adjustable. Third, in order to search the continuous real space from negative to positive, the mutation must be revised.

At last, we get the mutation operator, to multiply w by factors $\left(1 + 2^k\right)$ or $\frac{1}{\left(1 + 2^k\right)}$,

$k = M, M - 1, \cdots, 1, 0, -1, -2, \cdots, -N$ when the search space is totally positive space or negative space, and to multiply w by factors $\left(1 + 2^k\right)$, $\dfrac{1}{\left(1 + 2^k\right)}$, $-\left(1 + 2^k\right)$ or $-\dfrac{1}{\left(1 + 2^k\right)}$, $k = M, M - 1, \cdots, 1, 0, -1, -2, \cdots, -N$ when the search space is from negative to positive.

Zero included in the search space is considered as a tiny space. That is, any weights located in the tiny space should be transformed into zero; the multiplication of the weight whose value is zero and a factor should be transformed into that of the border value of the tiny space and the factor. If it was required for the algorithm to search in a given space, the only change would be those crossovers and mutations which make weights beyond the given space should be gotten rid of.

The self-encoding genetic algorithm has three important characteristics:

1. The algorithm evolves and searches the space on the basis of parameters themselves adopting a floating-point encoding strategy, which is coincident with the natural evolution and adapted to the current calculating tools such as personal computers.

2. Both the crossover operator and the mutation operator of the algorithm are simple, and the data storage of it is convenient so that it is able to deal with more complicated problems.

3. Comparing with real value genetic algorithms, the algorithm maintains those important characteristics of basic genetic algorithms.

4. The algorithm has an characteristic of accumulation search. That is, if the result of present evolution search, A_{max}, isn't satisfying, an evaluation that there isn't any more excellent result in the space $\left[\dfrac{1}{1 + 2^M} A_{max}, \left(1 + 2^M\right) A_{max}\right]$ can be still made. The evaluation is rather conservative because if there were any escalating part of a more excellent result in the space and the part is not overly smaller than A_{max}, the algorithm is still able to find the more excellent result along the escalating part.

4   Example

The inverted pendulum problem is a classic control problem that involves both pole-balancing and cart-centering. This is a well studied control problem which represents an inherently unstable mechanical system of a cart and a pole constrained to move within a vertical plane. At any point in time, the available state information includes the angle of the pole, θ, and the angular velocity of the pole, $\dot{\theta}$, as well as the position of the cart, ρ, and the velocity of the cart, $\dot{\rho}$. The cart is placed on a track of finite length. Using θ, $\dot{\theta}$, ρ and $\dot{\rho}$ as inputs, the output of the neural network is an action to be applied to the cart: either full-push left or full-push right. One of these two actions occurs at each time step [3].

$$\ddot{\theta}_t = \frac{mg*\sin\theta_t - \cos\theta_t*\left[F_t + m_p l\dot{\theta}^2*\sin\theta_t\right]}{(4/3)ml - m_p l*\cos^2\theta_t},$$

$$\ddot{\rho}_t = \frac{F_t + m_p l*\left[\dot{\theta}_t^2*\sin\theta_t - \ddot{\theta}_t*\cos\theta_t\right]}{m}.$$

The system can be simulated by numerically approximating the equations of motion using Euler's method with a time step of $\tau = 0.02$ and discrete time equations of the form $\theta(t + 1) = \theta(t) + \tau\dot{\theta}(t)$. The sampling rate of the system's state variables was the same as the rate of application of the control force (50 Hz).

A network with five input units (four state variables and a constant bias input), five hidden units and one output unit is used to control the inverted pendulum. The network is fully connected between the input layer and the hidden layer; the input layer is also fully and directly connected to the output unit. All five hidden units also feed into the output unit. Each string of the population is concatenated by the 35 weights of the network. The only monitor or "critic" is an accumulator which determines how long a particular neural network is able to avoid failure; this length of time is a direct measure of fitness. A failure signal is generated when the cart crashes into one end of the track, the velocity of the cart is beyond the permitted, or the angle of the pole is beyond a particular angle Θ. With the angle Θ increasing, the problem becomes more nonlinear, and the training using real number genetic algorithm becomes more difficult.

Adopting $M = 10$, $N = 23$, population in a generation $P = 200$, crossover rate $P_c = 0.9$ and mutation rate $P_m = 0.001$ while each weight is considered as a composition of $4*(M + N + 1)$ genes, initializing the population in the space $[-1,1]$, we successfully trained the problem by the self-encoding genetic algorithm. Initializing the pseudo-random series provided by Borland C++ with the integers from 1 to 20, presuming $\Theta = 72°$, taking no account of the accumulation search and variation of M, the algorithm finds a solution above 10000 lasting steps within 1000 generations for 13 times. Though the result is difficult to compare with reference [3] because these experiments are small and not adequate because of the limitation of low speed computer, it does seem that the algorithm is a strong competitor.

References

[1] David E. Goldberg, Genetic Algorithms in Search, Optimization, and Machine Learning, Addison Wesley, 1989.

[2] Zbigniew Michalewicz, Genetic Algorithms + Data Structures = Evolution Programs, Springer Verlag, 1992.

[3] Darrell Whitley, Stephen Dominic and Rajarshi Das, Genetic Reinforcement Learning with Multilayer Neural Networks, in Proceedings of the Fourth International Conference on Genetic Algorithms, 1991, pp. 101-108.

[4] Vittorio Maniezzo, Genetic Evolution of the Topology and Weight Distribution of Neural Networks, IEEE Transactions on Neural Networks, 1994, No. 1, pp. 39-53.

[5] Wirt Atmar, Notes on the Simulation of Evolution, IEEE Transaction on Neural Networks, 1994, No. 1, pp. 130-147.

[6] Percy. P. C. Yip, Yoh-Han Pao, Combinatorial Optimization with Use of Guided Evolutionary Simulated Annealing, IEEE Transaction on Neural Networks, 1995, No. 2, pp. 290-295.

[7] Anderson C. W., Learning to Control an Inverted Pendulum Using Neural Networks, IEEE Control Systems Magazine, 1989, Vol. 9, No. 3, pp. 31-37.

A fusion technique of GA and SA and its application to QAPs

Lae-Jeong Park and Cheol Hoon Park

Department of Electrical Engineering, Korea Advanced Institute of Science and Technology
373-1 Kusong-dong, Yusong-gu, Taejon 305-701, Korea
Tel: 82-42-869-3453 Fax: 82-42-869-3410 E-mail: chpark@expo.kaist.ac.kr

Abstract— **This paper explains a new fusion technique of genetic algorithm(GA) and simulated annealing(SA) and its application to the quadratic assignment problem(QAP). Based on their own search characteristics the proposed technique consists of two stages: the GA stage and the SA stage. The GA identifies promising regions more quickly than the SA by virtue of utilizing multiple solutions. And the SA tries to perform probabilistic fine-tuning wandering around the solution found by the GA. Empirical comparisons of SA, GAs, and the proposed hybrid have been carried out over a well-known NP-complete problem, QAP.**

1   Introduction

Since the early 80s, simulated annealing(SA)[1] and so-called evolutionary algorithms(EAs) such as genetic algorithms(GAs)[2, 3], evolution strategies(ES)[4], and evolutionary programming(EP)[5] have been proposed as general-purpose iterative stochastic search algorithms. They have been widely used as optimization techniques in various NP-complete optimization problems. Although SA and GAs are good candidates for optimization with little a priori information on the problem, they are apparently different in some aspects and thus their performance and scope vary from a problem to another. Moreover, the property of asymptotic convergence to the global minimum is not of practical interest because the finite search space of the optimization problem can be enumerated in the finite time. Practically, we are interested in the finite-time performance of the two algorithms. In this sense for stochastic search algorithms it is of importance to consider how good solutions they can provide in the given computation time, e.g., the ratio of the performance and the amount of computation time. SA generally requires a slow cooling schedule and a high temperature in the beginning to obtain high quality of final solutions. These conditions generally cause SA to take much time to identify promising search regions because of wandering in the beginning of search process. On the other hand, GAs identify promising regions quickly by utilizing multiple solutions but they suffer from premature convergence. Also, GAs are often susceptible to fine tunning within the promising region.

In this paper, we suggest a fusion technique of SA and GA as a step toward developing an effective stochastic search algorithm in terms of the performance as well as the time complexity. It consists of two stages: the GA stage and the SA stage. The GA identifies promising regions more quickly than the SA by virtue of utilizing not a single solution but multiple solutions. The incorporation of knowledge-based techniques into the GA is also helpful in quickly identifying promising regions. And then, the SA tries to perform probabilistic fine-tuning wandering around the vicinity of the best solution found by the GA. Empirical comparisons of SA, GAs, and the proposed hybrid have been carried out over a NP-complete problem: the quadratic assignment problem(QAP). The QAP is chosen because it is difficult to solve and it has a number of real-world interpretations and applications. This paper is organized as follows. Section 2 presents previous works of hybridization of SA and GAs. The description of the QAP is shown in section 3. Section 4 discusses the fusion technique of SA and GA. Empirical experiments on QAP are shown and discussed in section 5. Finally the conclusion is made in section 6.

2   Brief reviews of previous works

Many attempts at hybridization or fusion of SA and GAs have been proposed since the advent of GAs as effective optimization tools. Sirag and Weisser have proposed a thermodynamic genetic operator that incorporates the annealing schedule scheme into GAs[6]. Instead of the probability of accepting the perturbated solutions, the probability of applying a genetic operator is controlled by annealing scheme in this method. Brown *et al.* presented a hybrid, so-called SAGA. Each iteration of the SAGA consists of several generations of GA, followed by SA on each solution in the population[7]. A similar approach, so-called AG algorithm was adopted in a different perspective: SA with population-based transition and short chain length by the genetic operators-based equilibrium control[8]. Most of these works on hybridizing GAs and SA have focused on not development of hybrid algorithms better than the two, but improvement of the performance of GAs. In words, they showed that their hybrids are better than GAs in several optimization problems.

3 The quadratic assignment problem

The QAP formulated first by Koopmans and Beckmann[9] is a well-known classical combinatorial optimization problem. It can be described as follows. We are given a set of n distinct objects to be placed uniquely in n locations. Formally, QAP can be represented by the following two $n \times n$ matrices and a cost function:

$D = \{d_{ij}\}$, the distance between location i and j.
$F = \{f_{hk}\}$, the flow(of products or other quantity) between facilities h and k.

A solution is represented by a permutation π such that an assignment of facility $h = \pi(i)$ to location i, for each $i = 1, ..., n$. The problem is thus to find a permutation π that minimizes the total cost:

$$\min_{\pi}\{\sum_{i=1}^{n}\sum_{j=1}^{n} d_{ij} f_{\pi(i)\,\pi(j)}\} \tag{1}$$

The QAP is a generalization of several other problems including traveling salesman problem(TSP) and matching problem and thus it is NP-complete. It is reported that the QAP is in general tougher than the TSP.

4 A fusion technique of SA and GAs

Although SA and GAs have concrete theoretical backgrounds on global convergence as $t \to \infty$, the important thing is how good solutions they can find in the reasonable amount of time. For stochastic search algorithms, a practical interest is a ratio of the quality of solutions to the computation time, and we call it *performance-to-time ratio*, PTR. The higher PTR is, the more useful a stochastic algorithm is. Our objective is to design a fusion technique of GAs and SA through observations of their own characteristics so as to improve the performance of GAs as well as to reduce the time complexity of SA for obtaining similar performance of SA.

A possible fusion type is to combine both of them serially. That is, SA is executed at the best solution found by some generations of GAs. We call it *Serial Hybrid of GA and SA*, SHGASA. The main motivation is based on the following observation. GAs are good at spanning entire search space, but not well suited for fine tuning. On the other hand, SA initially spans the search space by escaping local minima and turns into a local search, that is, it performs fine-tuning as time goes on. It is appealing to develop a fusion scheme where the SA and GA have distinct roles in the search: a GA tries to identify promising regions and then SA tries to perform fine-tuning, or find a local minimum around a region identified by a GA. It seems to be an useful property for design process of fusion algorithms because we can separate exploration and exploitation in some measure. The SHGASA approach combines advantages inherited by SA and GAs. However the SHGASA has still the following key issues to be solved in order to be a more effective fusion scheme.

- method to ensure reliability of correct identification of the GA.
- method to determine the transition time from the GA stage to the SA stage.
- method to choose adequate initial value of temperature of SA.

4.1 Identification of promising regions by the GA stage

First of all, the GA stage has to ensure that the finial population evolved by the GA identifies a promising region on the search space correctly. The reliability of GA's identification of a correct promising region severely depends on parameters of the GA as well as the nature of the cost function of the given problem. Especially, population size is critical to the performance of a GA among control parameters of the GA. Although the population sizing problem has been discussed both empirically and analytically, it remains an open research topic in the GA community. In order to increase possibility of identifying a promising region, we adopt a fine-grain GA [11] instead of a canonical, panmictic GA. It is reported that the local mating and selection(or competition) of fine-grain GA can improve the performance as well as enhance a chance for finding promising regions by maintaining population diversity better than the panmictic GA. In our fine-grain GA, the population is distributed on a 2-D torus topology, selection and mating are only possible with neighboring individuals (we choose the Moore neighborhood where each individual has eight neighbors).

4.2   Transition from GA to SA

Like any other serial hybrid algorithm it is important to determine when the GA returns its control to SA. Our transition criterion is as follows. By keeping track of change of the best solution found so far, the GA hands control over the SA when the the change rate is lower than a threshold. The threshold is determined by the initial change rate as shown in equation 2.

$$\frac{\sum_{k=i}^{M_1+i} \hat{b_k}}{M_1} \leq \beta \frac{\sum_{k=0}^{M_1} \hat{b_k}}{M_1} \tag{2}$$

where $\hat{b_k} = \min_{M_2 k \leq i \leq M_2(k+1)} b_i$, b_i is the best solution found so far at the i-th iteration, and M_2 is the sampling window.

4.3   Annealing scheme of the SA stage

The geometric annealing scheme is used in the SA stage of the SHGASA because it gives rather shorter convergence rate than others. With the assumption that each chain length L_k at temperature T_k is the same, the chain length L is given by

$$L = N_A \frac{\log \alpha}{\log \frac{T_f}{T_0}} \tag{3}$$

where N_A is the total number of evaluations allowed for the SA stage, cooling rate α, initial and final values of temperature T_0 and T_f. Usually, the initial value of temperature is set to a sufficiently high value, but such strategy cannot be used in the SHGASA approach because high values of T_0 destroy the work done by the GA stage. As a result, more care should be taken to determine T_0. The scheme is to utilize information on landscape within the localized region identified by the GA by randomly sampling solutions around the best solution as shown in the following procedure.

1. Estimate the expected change of the cost function value by randomly generating solutions in the neighborhood of the best found by the GA. $\gamma_1 N$ sampling is tried when N is the problem size and then the mean absolute value of the change, $\hat{C}$ is calculated.
2. The initial value of temperature is set to $\gamma_2 \hat{C}$.

5   Experimental results

We have analyzed the finite-time behavior of GAs, SA, and SHGASA empirically by running algorithms on ten test problems taken from the QAPLIB library [10]. They include problems with numbers of facilities between 12 and 81 (NUG12, NUG15, NUG20, NUG30, SKO42, SKO49, SKO56, SKO64, SKO72, SKO81). Besides SA and SHGASA, two typical versions of GA, $(\mu + \mu)$-GA and elitism-GA are tested so as to cover many variations of evolutionary algorithms. All parameters are determined by trial-and-error or empirical experience of several runs. The parameter values of SA are as follows: the cooling rate α is 0.99, the final value of temperature T_f is 0.5, and three values of T_0(1000, 5000, 10000) are used to check how much the performance of SA depends on T_0. The population size of GAs is chosen approximately according to $7N$. Three sets of crossover rate and mutation rate, (p_c, p_m) are also tested. Note that two GAs have different values of (p_c, p_m), that is, high disruptiveness for $(\mu + \mu)$-GA and low disruptiveness for the elitism-GA. In order to test the PTR of each algorithm, two sets of the total number of evaluation, N_A is given. Also, N_A is determined such that it is proportional to the problem size. The single swap operator is used as the transition for SA and the mutation for GA.

Twenty runs are performed in each experiment and all results are averaged. First, we discuss the results obtained for NUG12 to NUG30 by the two GAs. The elitism-GA is worse than $(\mu + \mu)$-GA and SA because of lack of mechanism that strongly focuses to promising regions. The two GAs with large population size(two times) were tested, but they showed slightly better or similar results. The crossover used in this experimental study, position-based crossover does not seem to be useful for these QAPs. Certainly, the SA is better than the $(\mu + \mu)$-GA in terms of the average of costs of the final best solutions on problems from NUG12 to SKO81. As expected, the SA shows slow convergence rate at the early course of the search, but gives the high-quality solution finally by virtue of enough number of evaluations. Although the GA is worse than the SA in terms of the final best solutions, GA finds good solutions quickly on all test problems. However, further improvement cannot be obtained because of the premature convergence resulting from getting stuck in local minima. The table 1 shows that the best results of SA and the SHGASA on ten benchmark problems. Parameters of the SHGASA are as follows. 3×3 Moore neighborhood, M_1 and M_2 are 10, β is 0.05, γ_1 is 10, and γ_2 is 0.1. The SHGASA gives slightly better final solutions than the SA. Although we cannot say that the SHGASA is better than the SA in the statistical sense, it is certain that the standard deviation of the performance of the SHGASA is smaller than that of the SA. By using of the GA for identifying promising regions, we reduce the time for the SA to identify good regions and thus we can achieve good solutions more rapidly or better solutions than the SA as expected. Regardless of rough setting of control parameters, the SHGASA shows promising results on all ten problems. The convergence rates of SA, the GA, and the SHGASA are shown in figure 1 on SKO72 and SKO81.

6 Conclusion

We have presented a hybrid of SA and GA, so-called the SHGASA based on the search behaviors of SA and GAs. The SHGASA, SA, and GAs have been applied to QAPs with various difference size so as to examine their performance empirically. The canonical GA with elitism were considerably ineffective in even small-size problems, and the $(\mu + \mu)$-GA gave good results. The SA provided better final solutions than GAs though it showed very slow convergence rate initially. GAs do not produce better solutions than the SA using a single-point even when the sufficient number of evaluations is given. The proposed hybrid showed that it can achieve more significant improvement than GAs as well as slighter reduction of time complexity than SA on several QAPs. The present work is far from exhaustive to generally discuss the performance of SA, GAs, and the SHGASA. Many researchers have reported that GAs may not be better than SA, even not comparable to SA as an optimization technique. Similar results of comparisons of SA and GAs on QAPs can be obtained in [12]. The proposed hybrid can be one of hybrids that enable us to obtain good solutions comparable to those of SA. We are trying to enhance the reliability of GA's identification of promising regions.

7 Acknowledgment

This work has supported by Electronics and Telecommunications Research Institute(ETRI) and Korea Science and Engineering Foundation(KOSEF).

References

[1] S. Kirkpatrick, C. D. Gelatt, and M. P. Vecchi, "Optimization by simulated annealing," *Science*, Vol. 220, pp. 671-680, 1983.

[2] J. J. Holland, *Adaptation in natural and artificial systems*, MA: MIT Press, 1991.

[3] D. E. Goldberg, *Genetic algorithms in search, optimization, and machine learning*, Addison-Wesley, 1989.

[4] I. Rechenberg, *Evolutionsstrategie: optimierung technischer systeme nach prinzipien der biologischen evolution*, Stuttgart: Frommann-Holzboog, 1973.

[5] L. J. Fogel, A. J. Owens, and M. J. Walsh, *Artificial intelligence through simulated evolution*, New York: John Wiley, 1966.

[6] D. Sirag and P. Weisser, "Toward a unified thermodynamic genetic operator," *Proc. Int. Conf. Genetic Algorithms*, pp. 116-122, 1987.

[7] D. Brown, C. Huntley, and A. Spillane, "A parallel genetic heuristic for the quadratic assignment problem," *Proc. Int. Conf. Genetic Algorithms*, pp. 406-415, 1989.

[8] F.-T. Lin, C.-Y. Kao and C.-C. Hsu, "Applying the genetic approach to simulated annealing in solving some NP-hard problems," *IEEE Trans. on System, Man, and Cybernetics*, Vol. 23, pp. 1752-1767, 1993.

[9] T. C. Koopmans and M. J. Beckmann, "Assignment problems and the location of economic activities," *Econometrica*, Vol. 25, pp. 53-76, 1957.

[10] R. E. Burkard, "Quadratic assignment problems," *European Journal of Operational Research*, Vol. 15, 1984.

[11] B. Manderick and P. Spiessens, "Fine-grained parallel genetic algorithms," *Proc. Int. Conf. Genetic Algorithms*, pp. 428-433, 1989.

[12] V. Maniezzo and M. Dorigo, "Algodesk: an experimental comparison of eight evolutionary heuristics applied to the quadratic assignment problem," *European J. of Operational Research*, Vol. 81, pp. 188-204, 1995.

Table 1: Empirical results of SA and SHGASA on ten benchmark problems with $N = 12, 15, 20, 30, 42, 49, 56, 64, 72, 81$. ( ) indicates the best known of each problem. $\bar{C}$, σ_C, and C_{best} represent the average cost, standard deviation, and the best of the best solutions over 20 runs, respectively.

Problems	N_A ($\times$ 1000)	SA				SHGASA			
		T_0	$\bar{C}$	σ_C	C_{best}	(p_c, p_m)	$\bar{C}$	σ_C	C_{best}
12 (578)	150	1000	578.4	1.2	578	(0.0,1.0)	579.2	2.9	578
15 (1150)	150	10000	1152.6	4.2	1150	(0.0,1.0)	1151.0	1.0	1150
20 (2570)	225	1000	2583.5	9.7	2570	(0.0,1.0)	2574.4	6.4	2570
30 (6124)	300	1000	6162.8	23.4	6124	(0.0,1.0)	6150.4	18.7	6124
42 (15812)	450	5000	15890.1	40.7	15816	(0.0,1.0)	15871.7	37.5	15816
49 (23386)	525	1000	23487.5	37.9	23412	(0.0,1.0)	23462.3	37.7	23416
56 (34458)	600	1000	34604.5	90.0	34468	(0.0,1.0)	34594.4	65.5	34490
64 (48498)	675	1000	48695.4	109.5	48502	(0.0,1.0)	48661.1	95.4	48522
72 (66256)	750	5000	66567.5	89.4	66422	(0.0,1.0)	66552.6	76.8	66408
81 (90998)	825	5000	91346.5	149.5	91164	(0.0,1.0)	91247.9	141.1	91084

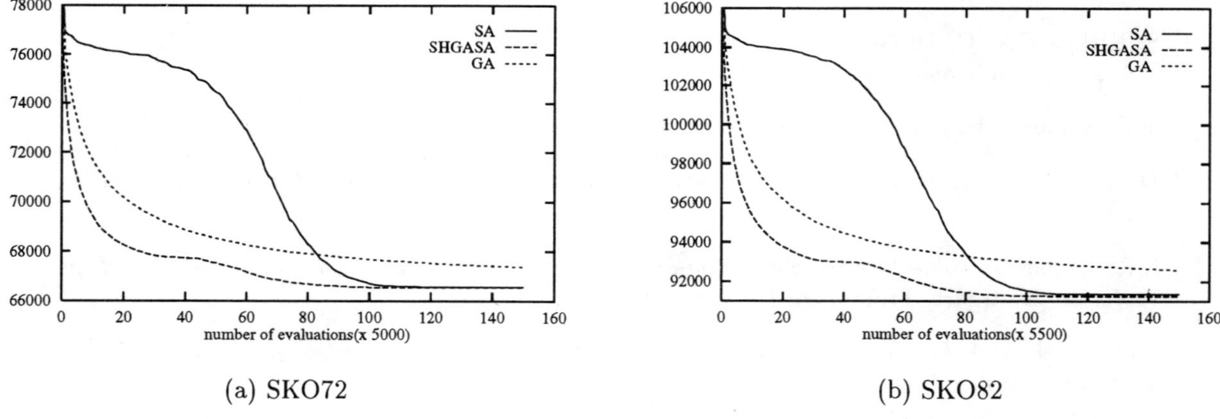

(a) SKO72   (b) SKO82

Figure 1: Convergence of the averages of the best solutions of SA, GA, and SHGASA on two benchmark problems. (a) SKO72, (b) SKO81.

Evolutionary Computing

(Poster Presentation)

An Adaptive Fuzzy Neural Network with Evolutionary Learning Algorithm*

Yao Susu, Wei Chengjian and He Zhenya
Southeast University, Dept. of Radio Engineering
Nanjing 210096, P.R. China

Abstract

An adaptive fuzzy neural network with evolutionary programming is proposed to realise fuzzy implication and reasoning. This network consists of two parts. The premise is the description of fuzzy subspace of inputs and its consequent is realised with wavelet approximation. An improved evolutionary programming is applied to optimize rule bases and consequent parameters. The method of fuzzy modeling using the proposed neural network and evolutionary learning algorithm is presented together with the experimental results of modeling a two dimensional non-linear function.

1 Introduction

A fuzzy inference system using linguistic variables can model human knowledge and reasoning processing without employing precise quantitative analyses, so it is well suited for dealing with ill-defined and uncertain system. Fuzzy identification has now found many applications in control, prediction and inference. Generally, model building by input-output data is characterised by two things; one is a mathematical tool to express a system model and other is the method of identification. A general mathematical tool has been proposed by Takagi and Sugeno in 1985 to build a fuzzy model of a system. Their method is based on a fuzzy partition of input space[1]. In each fuzzy subspace a linear input-output relation is formed by estimating optimum parameters. On the other hand, fuzzy neural networks that are the combination of fuzzy systems and neural networks have been adopted to implement identification of systems [2]. However, transforming human knowledge or experience into the rule base and tuning the membership functions are thought as two difficult problems. Linear input-output relation may not suit for more complex situations. In this paper, we propose an adaptive fuzzy neural network with wavelet approximation. An improved evolutionary programming is applied to optimise rule bases and tune the membership functions so as to minimise the output error.

2 Fuzzy If-Then Rules and Fuzzy Inference System

Assume that the membership function of a fuzzy set is denoted as $\mu(x), \quad x \in X$. Then the fuzzy if-then rules can be expressed as the following form:

$$\text{IF } x \text{ is } \mu \text{ THEN } z$$

where μ can also be replaced by a linguistic value, for example, IF x is small THEN z. In this expression, the premise part is a linguistic label which is associated with an appropriate membership function. The consequent part is described by a linguistic value or a nonfuzzy value. Based on a set of fuzzy if-then rules, a fuzzy inference system can be constructed. Usually, a fuzzy inference system consists of four principal elements:

· fuzzifier which performs a mapping from the observed crisp input degrees of match with linguistic values;

· a fuzzy rule base consists of a number of fuzzy if-then rules;

---

* This work was supported by the Climbing Programming-National Key Project for Fundamental Research in China, Grant NSC 92097

· fuzzy inference unit which performs the inference operations based on fuzzy rules;

· defuzzifier which transforms the fuzzy results of the inference into a crisp output.

Several types of fuzzy reasoning approaches have been developed. Takagi and Sugeno proposed a fuzzy if-then rule reasoning algorithm that is based on a fuzzy partition of input space. The if-then rule can be expressed by the following format:

$$If \ x_1 \ is \ A \ AND \ x_2 \ is \ B \quad THEN$$

$$f = c_1 x_1 + c_2 x_2 + c_3$$

where c_i are called rule consequent parameters. To form fuzzy if-then rules, several types of fuzzy neural network (FNN) structures and learning algorithms have been studied by some authors[3][4]. In the next section, we will describe a FNN with wavelet approximation.

3 Fuzzy Neural Network Architecture

1) Network architecture

According to the process of fuzzy reasoning the fuzzy neural networks can be divided into the premise part and the consequence part. Different configurations of fuzzy networks have been reported in recent literature[5]. The basic idea of the composition method of the fuzzy network is to realise the process of fuzzy reasoning using neural network structure and identify parameters of fuzzy reasoning by the connection weights of a neural network. In this paper, we adopt a five-layer fuzzy neural network (FNN) architecture (Fig. 1). The layer functions are described as follows:

Layer 1: The node function in this layer is written as $\qquad O_i^1 = \mu_{A_i}(x)$

where x is the input value to node i , and A_i the fuzzy set. The membership function $\mu_{A_i}(x)$ is chosen to be bell-shaped function, i.e.,

$$\mu_{A_i} = \frac{1}{1 + \left[\left(\frac{x - c_i}{a_i} \right)^2 \right]^{b_i}}$$

where $\{a_i, b_i, c_i\}$ are referred to as premise parameters.

Layer 2: Every node in this layer multiplies the incoming signal or performs the max operation, i.e.,

$$O_i^i = \mu_{A_i}(x_1) \wedge \mu_{B_i}(x_2)$$

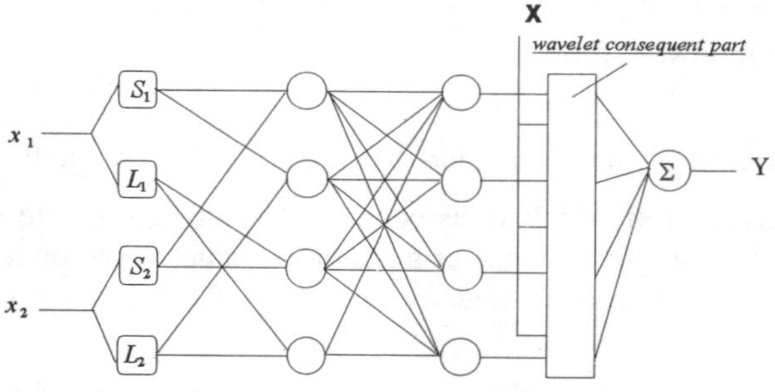

Fig. 1. A simple fuzzy neural network architecture with two input variables

Layer 3: Every node calculates the normalised ratio of the i-th rule's firing strength.

Layer 4: Every node in this layer performs non-linear mapping $O_i^4 = O_i^3 W_i(x_1,\cdots,x_n)$

where, $W_i(x_1,\cdots,x_n)$ denote transformation function that implies the output value when input satisfies the premise. This layer is associated with the consequent part of the inference system.
Layer 5: The output of this layer is the summation of all incoming signals.

2) Wavelet approximation

In the layer 4 of the proposed FNN architecture, a wavelet approximation is used to describe input-output relation instead of a linear equation. The continuous wavelet decomposition allows us to represent any function using a family of functions obtained by dilating and translating a wavelet prototype function $\psi(x)$, which takes the form:

$$\psi_{s,t}(x) = |s|^{-\frac{1}{2}}\psi(\frac{x-t}{s})\tag{1}$$

where s is a dilation factor and t a translation factor. $\psi(x)$ has to be square integrable and satisfy:

$$C_\psi = \int |\xi|^{-1}|\hat{\psi}(\xi)|^2 d\xi < \infty\tag{2}$$

The continuous wavelet decomposition is defined as the inner product of signal and wavelets

$$W_f(s,t) = \langle f, \psi_{s,t} \rangle\tag{3}$$

The function $f(x)$ can then be reconstructed by performing the inverse operation and integrating over the transform space

$$f(x) = \frac{1}{C_\psi}\iint W_f(s,t)\psi_{s,t}\frac{dsdt}{s^2}\tag{4}$$

Hence, wavelet approximation can be represented as the collection of all finite sums of the form [6]

$$f(x) = \sum_{k=1}^{N} W_k \psi(s_k - t_k)\tag{5}$$

4 Evolutionary Learning Algorithm

In order to minimise overall error between the actual output and desired output an evolutionary programming is employed in this work to tune parameter sets. Evolutionary programming (EP)[7] is a class of direct probabilistic search algorithms based on the model of organic evolution, whose main advantage lies in its robustness of search and problem independence. The basic operation of EP is based on a population of individuals which represent points in the search space. Each individual has some fitness values associated with an evolution function. This approach is to explore the search space and to discover better solutions by evolving the individuals over time. The initial populations is selected in accordance with a uniform distribution and is scored with respect to a given objective function. For each generation, the algorithm calculates the fittest value individuals for production. The offspring are reproduced by mutation operation, i.e., each individual is mutated and assigned by a Gaussian random variable with mean zero and an adaptable variance. The best offspring that means it wins in the competition against others is selected to become the parent of the next generation. This procedure continuous until a suitable solution is obtained.
There are two approaches to improve the evolutionary programming. One is the method of creating offspring from their parents and other one is the procedure of selection.
The Guided Evolutionary Simulated Annealing (GESA) search technique belongs to the second category. It generates a set of initial solutions randomly, say N solutions, and each solution is called a parent of a family.

Then it generates a set of new solutions (say M) for each parent, which are called the children of each family. N parents and M*N children compete by using Boltzman machine-like mechanism. The best solution in each family is selected to be the parent of next generation and the better the family, the larger the acceptance number of members of that family. This acceptance number determines the number of children allocated to that family for the next generation. This gives a regional guidance to the stochastic search process of evolutionary programming. This iteration process is the same as that in simulated annealing procedures.

Similar with the competition process of the GESA, we use Cauchy distribution in the evolutionary programming instead of Gaussian distribution, which is described in more details as follows:

Step 1: Set initial temperature t;
Step 2: Randomly select N parents, assigning an error score to every parent;
Step 3: Create offspring by using Cauchy distribution;
Step 4: Find the best child for each parents;
Step 5: Find the parents for the next generation, for each family, the best child serves as the parent for next generation if

$$y_1 < y_2 \ or \ \exp(-(y_1 - y_2)/t) > \rho$$ where y_1 is the error score of the best child, y_2 is the error score of its parent, t is the temperature coefficient, and ρ is a random number uniformly distributed between zero and one;

Step 6: Find the number of children that will be generated from the parents of the next generation. The details of this step are given as follows:

(1). Repeat (2) to (5) for each family, goto (6);
(2). count=0;
(3). Repeat (4) for each child, goto (5);
(4). If the error score of the child is lower than the lowest error score,   the count is increased by 1.

If not, then the count is increased by 1 if $\exp(-(y_1 - y_2)/t) > \rho$ where y_1 is the error score of the child, y_2 is the lowest error score ever found, t is the temperature coefficient, and ρ is a random number uniformly distributed between zero and one;

(5). Acceptance number of the family is equal to the count;
(6). Sum up the acceptance numbers of all the families;
(7). For each family, the number of children generated can be calculated according to the following formula

$$M = \frac{T * A}{S}$$

where M is the number of children that will be generated for that family, T is the total number of points, A is the acceptance number for that family, and S is the sum of the acceptance number.

Step 7: Decrease the temperature coefficient
Step 8: Repeat Step 3 to Step 7 until an acceptable solution has been found.

5 Simulation Results

We consider using the proposed method to model a non-linear equation which is written as follows:

$$f = \frac{\sin(x)}{x} \frac{\sin(y)}{y}$$

The ranges of x and y are $[-10,10] \times [-10,10]$. 121 training data pairs are obtained from the above equation.

Nine rules with three membership functions that are associated with each input variable are contained. The premise parameter set is composed of 18 parameters and consequent parameters are 207. The original data and resulting 2-D surface are shown in Fig. 2. The MSE (mean square error) is 0.002 after 300 epochs. Fig 3 and Fig. 4 illustrate the membership functions before and after training.

6 Conclusion

we have proposed the fuzzy identification principal using wavelet approximation and given a new fuzzy neural network architecture. Since wavelets have shown their excellent performance in nonstationary signal analysis and non-linear function modeling, the identification results of consequent part in fuzzy implication using our method is quite effective, which has been examined by the simulation of 2-D non-linear approximation. By employing evolutionary programming, we can optimise premise parameters and consequent parameters without requiring any gradient information, which may be flexible to chose membership functions with different shapes.

References

[1] T. Takagi and M. Sugeno, "Fuzzy identification of systems and its applications to modeling and control", IEEE Trans. on Systems, Man, and Cybernetics, Vol. SMC-15, No.1, pp.116-132, 1985.

[2] M.Sugeno and T. Takagi, "Multi-dimensional fuzzy reasoning", Fuzzy Sets and Systems, Vol. 9, No.2, 1983.

[3] J.J. Buckley and Y. Hayashi, "Fuzzy neural nets and applications", Fuzzy Systems and AI, 3 pp.11-41, 1992,

[4] L.X. Wang and J.M. Mendel, "Fuzzy basis functions, universal approximation and orthogonal least squares learning", IEEE Trans. Neural Network, 3(5), pp.807-814, 1992.

[5] S. Horikawa, et al, "On fuzzy modeling using fuzzy neural networks with the back-propagation algorithm ", IEEE Trans. Neural Networks, 3(5), pp.801-806, 1992.

[6] Q. Zhang and A. Benveniste, "Wavelet network", IEEE Trans. Neural Network, 3(6), pp.889-898, 1992.

[7] D.B. Fogel, L.J. Fogel and V.W. Porto, Evolving neural networks, Biological Cybernetics, Vol. 63, 1990, pp. 487-493.

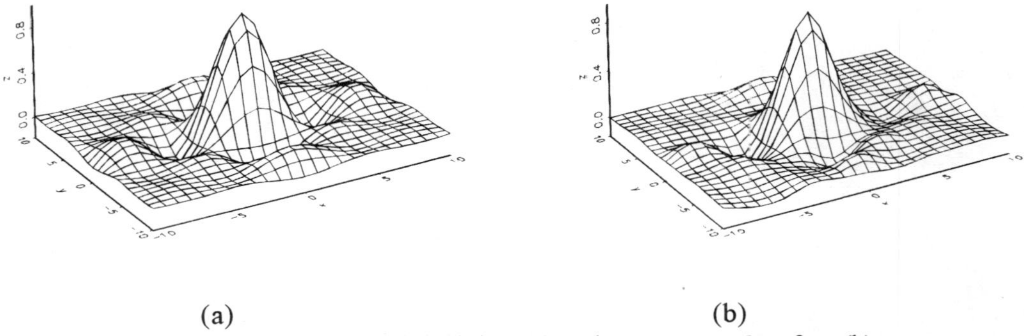

(a)   (b)

Fig. 2. The original data (a) and reconstructed surface (b)

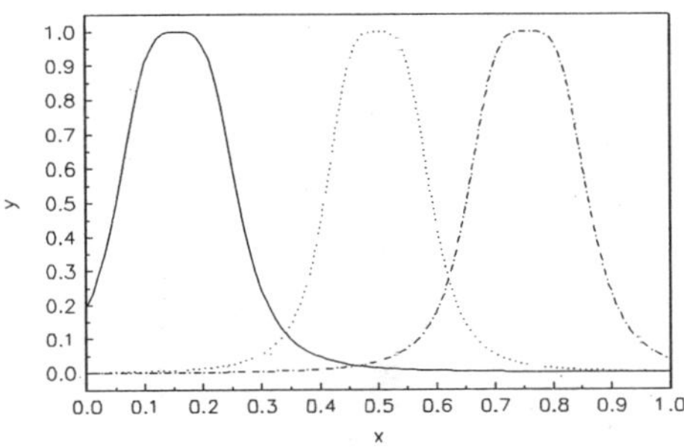

Fig. 3. The initial membership function for both x and y

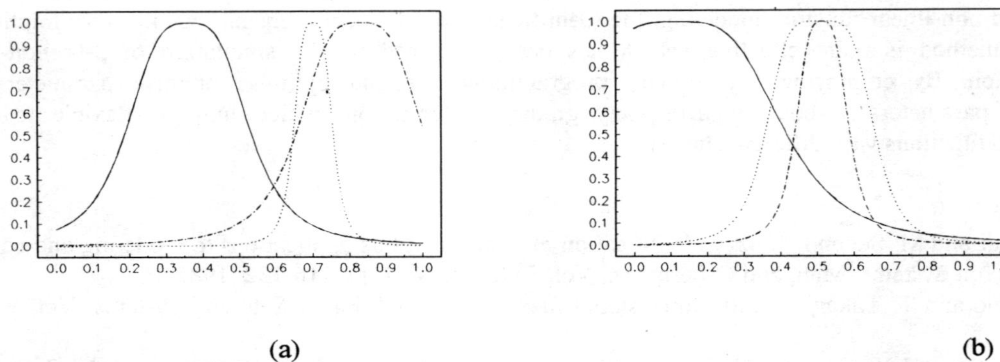

(a)   (b)

Fig. 4 The tuned membership functions for x (a) and y (b)

Neuroscience and Biophysics

(Oral Presentation)

A Two Dimensional Network Model of Nucleus Laminaris Based on a Realistic Neuron Model for sound Location of Barn Owl

Kazunari Kono[a], Yoshiki Kashimori[b], and Takeshi Kambara[a,b]
[a]Department of Information Network Systems
Graduate School of Information Systems
[b]Department of Applied Physics and Chemistry
The University of Electro-Communications,Chofu,Tokyo,182,Japan
e-mail   kono@nerve.pc.uec.ac.jp

Abstract— The brain of barn owl makes sound location by analyzing the interaural differences in arrival time and intensity of sound. The owl can detect the binaural time disparity less than $\frac{1}{100}$ of the neural relaxation time ($1msec$). We represent a network model of nucleus laminaris which detects the time disparity between a tone delivered to right ear and a tone to left ear. We construct a two dimensional single layer network virtually corresponding to multiple Jeffress models arraying parally, when , the linear arrays of neurons corresponding to the Jeffress model are interconnected with each other . If the synaptic connections are made suitably ,the location of firing neurons can indicate a correct magnitude of the time disparity . We compare the results for the network constructed with formal neuron model with the results for the network constructing of realistic neuron model.

1   Introduction

The brain of barn owl makes sound location by analyzing the interaural differences in arrival time and intensity of sound. The binaural time and intensity cues are processed in anatomically separate pathways that start from the cochlear nucleus in both ears. Both the cues are processed along the neuron pathways to the higher sensory brain modality , parallely . The barn owl forms the map for detecting the location of sound in the brain, based on the binaural arrival time and intensity informations. [1]
The nucleus laminaris(NL),the first site of binaural convergence in the pathway ,receives phase informations in the form of phase-locked spike from the nucleus magnocellularis and detects the time disparity between a tone delivered to right ear and that to left one.
The Jeffress model has been presented for the neuronal mechanism in the detection of the time disparity [2]. The anatomical and physiological evidences suggesting that the NL uses neuronal circuits similar to the Jeffress model have been reported. This model contains two important concepts,the first being the principle of delay line and coincidence detection, and the second states that the anatomical location of the firing neuron in an array encodes the magnitude of the time disparity [1].
Despite the widespread acceptance of the Jeffress model , the nature of the delay lines and cellular mechanisms of coincidence detection have not yet been known. Especially,the time disparity is evaluated with accuracies of the order of $10\mu sec$ by the brain of owl. That is , the owl can detect the binaural time disparity less than $\frac{1}{100}$ of the neural relaxation time($1msec$). It is remarkable that such a system constructed by neurons with much less accuracy for coding of the time disparity can achieve such a precise temporal resolution at the behavioral level.
To clarify the neuronal mechanism of the detection of the time disparity in NL, we presented a neural architecture for the coding of the time disparity [3]. The model consists of multilayers of linear arrays of formal neurons,where each linear array corresponds to the Jeffress model.
The interlayer connection consists of on center-off surround connection. The network model sharpens gradually,or step by step a wide firing pattern over quite many neurons in the first layer induced by the input signals from both ears,as the signals propagate from one layer to the next. This model encodes magnitude of the time disparity with the location of firing neurons on the ordered array of one dimensional neurons,where the correct location is found by passing the signals of time disparity through a multilayer network. [3]
However,this model includes two points different from the observed structure of nucleus laminaris(NL) that the neural network of NL is two dimensional[4] and dose not consist of multiple layers .

Therefore, in the present paper,we constructed a model of NL which consists of a two dimensional single layer network of formal neuron model,and investigated the ability of this model for a detection of the time disparity. If the synaptic connections are made suitably ,the location of firing neurons can indicate a correct magnitude of the time disparity .
The model and calculated results are described in section 2. However,the response of this model to the inputs of sound from both ears is not robust. That is , when the inputs have noise with respect to sound period or sound phase , the location of firing neurons induced by such noisy inputs is distributed over a certain broad area of the network. Then,a correct magnitude of the time disparity can not be detected by such a broad neural firing.
We found the reason why the two dimensional model failed to sharpen the neural firing area against noisy

inputs. The origin of such broad firing comes from the firing property of the formal neuron model used as shown in section 2. Therefore , we adopt a more realistic neuron model with correct refractory period and adaptation to a continuing stimulus and construct a two dimensional network model of NL. The model and calculated results are described in section 3.

2   A Two Dimensional Network Based on Formal Neuron Model

We constructed a two dimensional single layer network virtually corresponding to multiple Jeffress models arraying parallely as seen in Fig1. The linear arrays of formal neurons corresponding to the Jeffress model are interconnected with each other.
We investigate here the ability of this model for a detection of the time disparity .

2.1   Description of the model

The two dimensional network model is shown in Fig1.
A liner array of formal neurons along the horizontal axis corresponds to the Jeffress model.

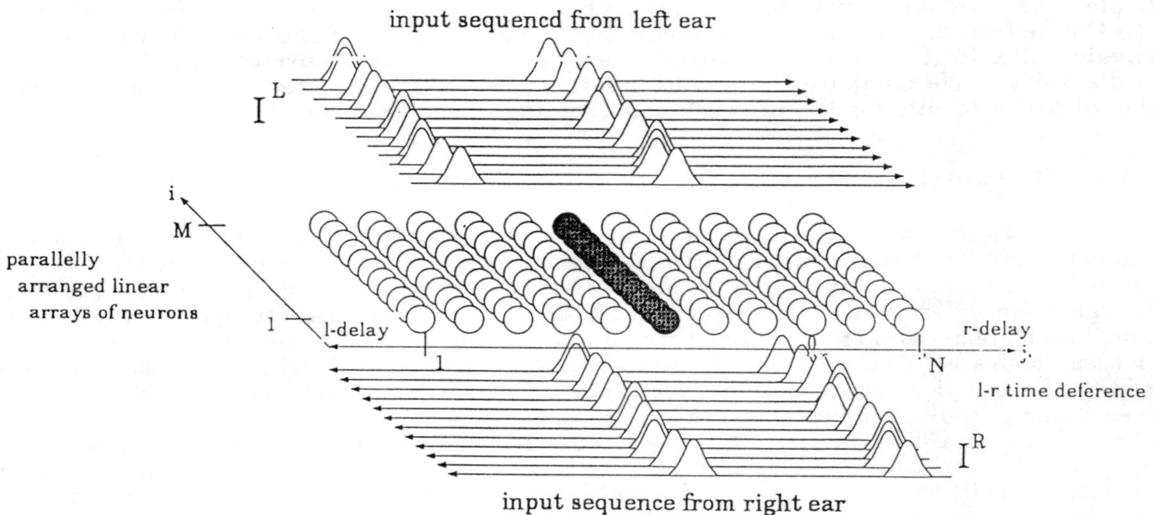

Fig 1 The two dimensional Jeffress model. Each Jeffress line works as a broad coincidence detector. Inputs I^L and I^R are injected to each layer.

The membrane potential(V_{ij}) of a neuron at (i,j)site is calculated by

$$\tau \frac{dV_{ij}}{dt} = -V_{ij} + I_{ij}^L + I_{ij}^R + \sum \gamma_{ij,kl} X_{kl}, \tag{1}$$

$$X_{ij}(t) = \frac{1}{1 + e^{\frac{V_{ij} - th}{\epsilon}}}, \tag{2}$$

$$I_i^L(j,t) = ga(-j + t - dl), \tag{3}$$

$$I_i^R(j,t) = ga(-((N-1) - j) + t - dr), \tag{4}$$

where $\gamma_{ij,kl}$ is a synaptic weight of mutual connection between (i,j)neuron and (k,l)neuron. X_{ij} are output of neuron(i,j), th is a threshold for firing, ε is a constant parameter. The inputs($I_i^L(j,t)$ and $I_i^R(j,t)$) from the left and right ears are presented as the form of phase-locked spike with a Gaussian shape. The Gaussian distribution function represents a duration of input impulse ,

$$ga(t) = \frac{0.1}{\sqrt{2\pi}} e^{\frac{-(0.1t - 5.0)^2}{2}}. \tag{5}$$

Figure 2 shows the form of mutual connection between (i,j)neuron and (k,l)neuron in the network model. The (i,j)neuron has excitable connections from the neurons which code same time disparity in the other Jeffress line, and has inhibitory connections from the neurons which code different time disparity in the same Jeffress line and other Jeffress lines.

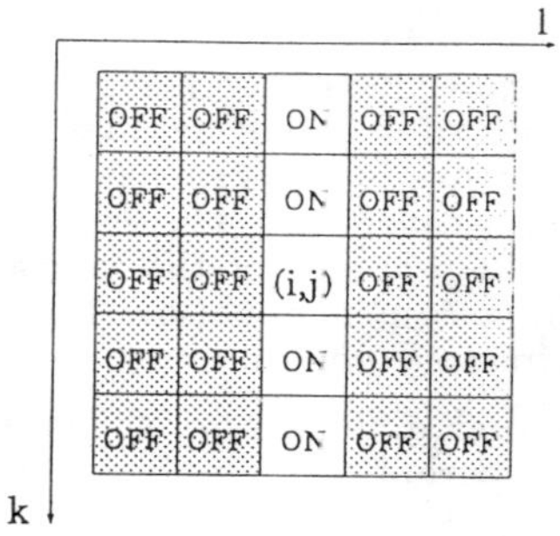

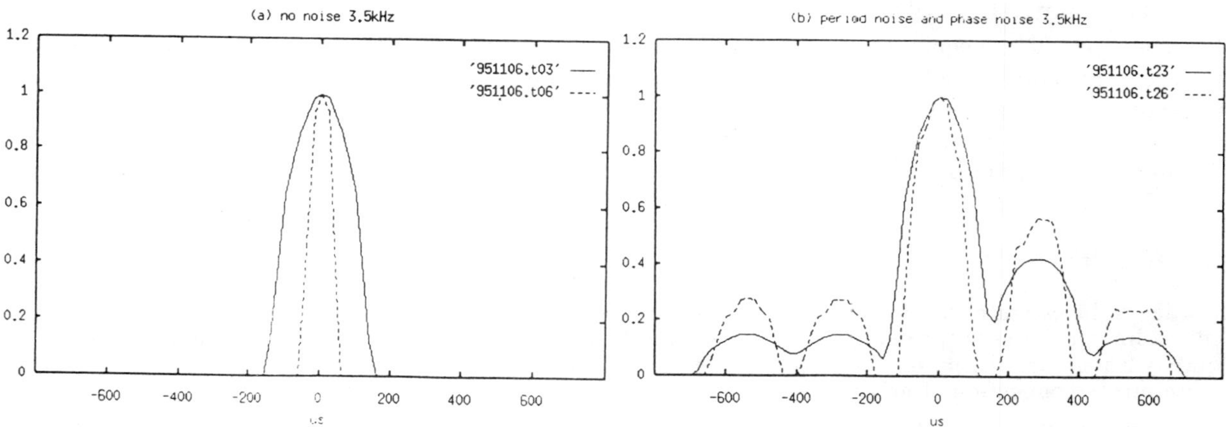

Fig 2 The pattern of mutual connection between the central $(i.j)$neuron and other neurons. ON and OFF mean excitatory and inhibitory connection , respectively.

We consider also the effect of noise on the sharpening mechanism of the firing pattern. Input $I_i^L(j,t)$ and $I_i^R(j,t)$ include two kinds of noise; noise induced by stochastic firing of a neuron and thermal noise induced by a spike transduction on an axon fiber. The former noise deviate from the true time disparity by multiples of the period of the external sound wave . The latter noise have a Gaussian distribution with about $40\mu sec$ standard deviation.

2.2 Results

In order to investigate the sharpening ability of the present model , we calculate the firing pattern of each linear layer in the two dimensional model. Figure 3(a) shows the calculated response pattern of a linear layer for the input signals from both the ears which are put simultaneously into the layers. It is seen in Fig.3(a) that the width of the firing pattern decreases noticeably by the inhibitory connection with neighboring layers and the time disparity is made considerably clear.

We investigate the effect of noise on sharpening mechanism of the firing pattern. Inputs with the two kinds of noise described in section2 are injected to each linear layer in the model. Figure 3(b) shows the calculated response pattern of a linear layer for the noisy inputs. The pattern has some peaks of weak firing strength induced by the noise. Furthermore, the width of firing pattern is not sharpened by the inhibitory connection of neighboring layers. This noise effect comes from the following reasons: Since the center site of the firing pattern in each linear layer is fluctuated by the noise, the inhibitory effect from the neighboring layers dose not act on synchronously and becomes weaker. Thus, the architecture of the two dimensional network model seems not useful for the detection of the time disparity of the inputs with noise.

Fig3 The calculated firing pattern of the system induced by the input signals. Time disparity of the input signal is $0\mu sec$. Input frequency is 3.5kHz. (a)Input from each ears are put simultaneously into the system. (b)Input from each ears include of oscillation period noise and noise of phase. Solid and dashed lines mean the firing pattern of neurons in the system without and with mutual connection of neighboring layer , respectively.

2.3   Concluding remarks

We have shown that the width of the firing pattern for the inputs without noise is sharpened noticeably by inhibitory connection of neighboring layers. However,when the inputs include noise,the network does not sharpen the wide range of the firing pattern. Furthermore, the neurons of the network continue to excite for a long time, because each neuron is excited by excitatory connection each other. These results come from the response property of the formal neuron model: Since the output of the formal neuron model is described by a sigmoid function, the formal neuron model does not have any function ceasing excitation such as refractory period.

In order to overcome such difficulties of the two dimensional model , we must consider a realistic neuron which has a refractory period , an adaptation of threshold value for firing , and an impulsive output. We describe the network model based on a realistic model in section 3.

3   A two dimensional network based on a realistic neuron model

We replaced the formal neuron model with a realistic neuron model to investigate the sharpening ability of the model . Then, the sharpening ability of the model is compared with that of the previous model described in section 2. We use MacGregor model as a realistic neuron model. The MacGregor model have realistic properties such as a refractory period , adaptation of threshold value for firing , and impulsive output .

3.1   Description of the model

The dynamics of the network is given by the following equations ;

$$\tau_E \frac{dE_{ij}}{dt} = -E_{ij} - g_{ij}^K(E_{ij} - E^K) - g_{ij}^{Na}(E_{ij} - E^{Na}) + I_{ij}^L + I_{ij}^R, \tag{6}$$

$$\tau_\theta \frac{d\theta_{ij}}{dt} = -(\theta_{ij} - \theta_0) + C_\theta E, \tag{7}$$

$$\tau_{g^K} \frac{dg_{ij}^K}{dt} = -g_{ij}^K + C_{g^K} * S_{ij}, \tag{8}$$

$$\tau_{g^{Na}} \frac{dg_{ij}^{Na}}{dt} = -g_{ij}^{Na} + \sum \gamma_{ij,kl}, (P_{ij} - E_{ij}) \tag{9}$$

$$S_{ij} = \begin{cases} 0 & E < \theta_{ij} \\ 1 & E \geq \theta_{ij}, \end{cases} \tag{10}$$

$$P_{ij} = E_{ij} + S_{ij} * (50 - E_{ij}). \tag{11}$$

where E_{ij} is membrane potential of a neuron at (i,j) site , θ_{ij} is threshold of (i,j)neuron , θ_0 is the firing threshold for any resting cell , C_θ is a constant parameter between$(0 \sim 1)$, g_{ij}^K is potassium conductance of (i,j)neuron , E^K is equilibrium potential of potassium conductance , C_{g^K} is the rate of the postfiring increase of potassium conductance , g_{ij}^{Na} is sodium conductance of (i,j)neuron , E^{Na} is equilibrium potential of sodium conductance , $\gamma_{ij,kl}$ is a synaptic weight of mutual connection between (i,j) neuron and (k,l)neuron , S_{ij} is spiking variable of (i,j)neuron , P_{ij} is an impulsive output function of (i,j)neuron . The inputs $I_i^L(j,t)$ and $I_i^R(j,t)$ are the same as the inputs of previous model.

3.2   Results

In order to investigate the sharpening ability of the new model , we calculate the firing pattern of each Jeffress line in the network model. Figure 4 shows the calculated firing pattern of a Jeffress line for the inputs without time disparity. It is seen in Fig. 4 that the wide range of the firing pattern is sharpened by inhibitory connection of neighboring lines .

We investigate the effect of noise on the sharpening mechanism of the firing pattern by using the new model. Input includes the same noise as that used in subsection 2.2 . The calculated response pattern of a Jeffress line for the noisy inputs is similar to the pattern shown in Fig 3(b) . The width of the firing pattern is not sharpened noticeably by inhibitory connection with the neighboring line and property of a realistic neuron. This reason mainly comes from the network architecture described in section 2. When the signal lines from a single ear are joined into a single node consisting of MacGregor neurons and the signal lines are distributed from the node to the Jeffress lines in the network model , the degree of coincident detection for the time disparity becomes quite sharp even for the noisy signals. Then , the response pattern becomes quite similar to the pattern shown in Fig .4 . This sharpening for the noisy signals comes from the fact that the signals joined into a node are synchronized with each other and as a result the signals emitting from the node are uniform and noiseless .

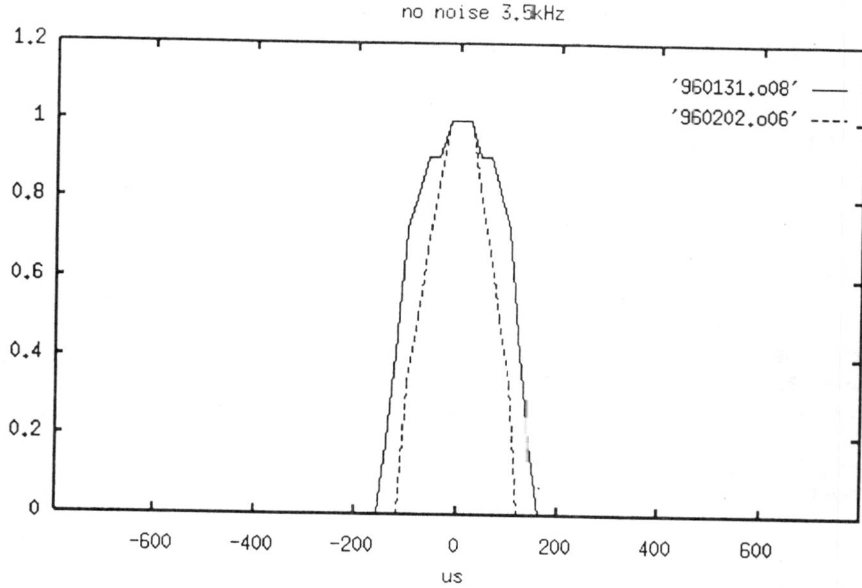

Fig4 The calculated firing pattern for the input signals. Time disparity of input signal is $0\mu sec$. Input frequency is 3.5kHz. The same input signals without noise from each ears are injected simultaneously into the Jeffress lines . Solid and dashed lines mean the firing pattern of neurons in the network without and with mutual connection of neighboring lines , respectively.

3.3   Concluding remarks

We have constructed the two dimensional network based on a realistic neuron model and studied the response properties of the network. Using the new network, the lasting firing of neurons in the previous network model disappears due to the refractory effect of the MacGregor model. The response property of the new network model is more realistic than that of the previous one. The synchronized uniform input signals are absolutely necessary to obtain a sharp coincident detection for the time disparity. The synchronization can not be made by the formal neuron model , but by a more realistic model with proper nonlinear properties. On the other hand , this type of synchronization is not required for the detection of difference in sound intensity between right and left ears . The degree of the detection is increased through the linear superposition of input signals . The result will be described a forthcoming paper.

References

[1] C.E.Carr and M.Konishi,"A circuit for detection of interaural time difference in the brain stem of the barn owl" *J,Neurosci,*vol.10,pp.3227-3246,1990.

[2] L.A.Jeffress,"A place theory of sound localization",*J. Comp. Physiol. Psychol.* vol.41,pp.35-39,1948.

[3] Tamura N.,et al.,"A neural network model of nucleus laminaris for sound location of barn owl"proc of ICONIP'94,seoul,Korea,Vol.1,pp.671-675,1994

[4] Konishi.M ,"Listening with two ears",Scientific American,268,pp.66-73,1993

Spatio-Temporal Representation of Odor Information in Olfactory Bulb

Osamu Hoshino†, Yoshiki Kashimori‡ and Takeshi Kambara†‡
† Department of Information Network Science
Graduate School of Information Systems
‡ Department of Applied Physics and Chemistry
The University of Electro-Communications,Chofu,Tokyo,182,Japan
e-mail: hoshino @ nerve. pc. uec. ac. jp

Abstract

In order to clarify the mechanism of neural information processing along the path from epithelium
to olfactory bulb, we propose a model in which spatial representation of odor information in the
epithelium is transformed into spatio-temporal representation in the olfactory bulb. The spatio-
temporal pattern of neural activities consist of a temporal sequence of spatial firing patterns of a
mitral cell network. Each spatial pattern encodes each constituent ingredient of an odor and the
temporal sequence encodes the order of mixing ratio of the ingredients. By using a realistic neural
network model of olfactory bulb, we show how limit cycle attractors are generated, that is, how odors
are memorized. We clarify also the role of chaotically itinerant state in recognition of known odors
and in response to novel odors.

1   Introduction

Mechanism of information processing in olfactory system has been studied by many scientists in recent
years, and by now several important observed results have been reported. Anatomical structure of olfactory system enables us to estimate how odor information proceeds form receptor neurons to olfactory
cortex. Each odor is composed of multiple chemical ingredients with various mixing ratio. Sensory neurons distributed over the olfactory epithelium may respond selectively to the ingredients. Sensory neurons
respondent to the same kind of odor ingredients innervate a single or a few glomeruli (Mori, 1995). Then,
the odor information classified into ingredients is propagated into middle and deep layers of olfactory bulb
in which the odor information is represented by spatio-temporal patterns of neural activities (Skarda &
Freeman, 1987).

Recent work on the mammalian olfactory system have proved one-to-one correspondence between an
odor receptor type and an olfactory glomerulus (Mori, 1995). Although the sensory neurons expressing
a particular receptor type are widely distributed on the epithelium and intermingled with other type
of sensory neurons, axons of the neurons with an equivalent receptor protein converge to a single or
a few glomeruli. When an odor consisting of various chemical ingredients with various mixing ratio is
received by the epithelium, the sensory neurons relevant to the ingredients are activated with the strength
corresponding to the mixing ratio of ingredients. The spatial pattern of neural firing distributed almost
continuously on the epithelium is integrated into glomeruli in the olfactory bulb. An information of each
ingredient is encoded as variation in the membrane potential of primary dendrites of mitral cells belonging
to a single glomerulus. Thus, odor information is converted from the spatially continuous representation
made on the epithelium to a spatially digitalized representation made by using feature detectable units
or glomeruli.

The odorant-specific information was found (Freeman & Diprisco, 1986; Freeman & Baird, 1987
) to exist in the spatio-temporal variation patterns of the amplitude of oscillation of EEG potential
which was observed over the entire olfactory bulb. Because every neuron in the bulb participates in
the oscillation, whole neurons participate in every response process for odor discrimination. The spatio-
temporal patterns of neural activities, which encode odor information, are dynamically stable, that is,
correspond to dynamical attractors included in the neural network. It has been shown (Freeman &
Diprisco, 1986; Freeman & Baird, 1987; Skarda & Freeman, 1987) that the odorant-specific information
is encoded as dynamical attractors characteristic of odors. The attractors may be produced through
self-organized changes in strength of synaptic connections induced by the odorant stimulation.

In order to understand the mechanism of information processing in olfactory system, one needs to know
what informations included in odorants are encoded by the spatio-temporal patterns of neural activities
and how the system processes the neural activity patterns for odor recognition and memorization.

In the present paper, we propose meaning and role of the dynamical neural activity patterns in information processing in the olfactory bulb, based on the study of dynamical properties of a realistic neural

model of the olfactory bulb. The spatial firing patterns in the bulb induced by an odorant denote what kinds of ingredients the odorant includes. The temporal patterns consist of a temporal sequence of several spatial patterns. Order in the sequence encodes magnitude of mixing ratio of the constituent ingredient relevant to the pattern, that is the larger the ratio for an ingredient is, the more early the spatial pattern relevant to the ingredient appears. Thus, the spatio-temporal patterns of neural activities can induce complete information of an odor.

Freeman and his colleagues have shown that the main components of neural activities in olfactory bulb are chaotic and the chaotic activities relate closely to perception and memorization of odorants (Freeman, 1992; Skarda and Freeman, 1987; Yao and Freeman, 1990). They proposed the functional roles of the chaotic neural activities based on their experimental and theoretical studies. The chaotic state is interpreted as a global chaotic attractor composed of a basal state of chaos and multiple wings (Yao & Freeman, 1990). The recognition of an odorant is induced by the transition from the basal state to a wing or from one wing to another. The central part of the attractor is its basal chaotic activity, and each of the wings is a low-dimensional chaos similar to a limit cycle attractor. In this scheme, when an input odor is recognized, the transition from the basal state to a wing characteristic of relevant odor occurs, and the system comes back to the basal state whenever the input is terminated.

In the present paper, by using a realistic neural network model of olfactory bulb, we show how the limit cycle attractors corresponding to the spatio-temporal patterns relevant to odorant are generated, that is, how odors are memorized. We clarify also the role of chaotically itinerant state in recognition of known odorants and in response to novel odorants, where the chaotically itinerant state means that dynamical state of the neural network itinerates chaotically among multiple limit cycle attractors memorized in the network and corresponds to the global chaotic attractor proposed by Freeman.

2   Model

We show in Figure 1 a neural network model of olfactory system which is separated into several functional blocks such as epithelium, glomerulus, mitral cell, and olfactory cortex. Output of sensory neurons (SN) of the epithelium is projected into glomeruli which interconnect with periglomerular neurons (PG). Each glomerulus include only one mitral cell for simplicity. Outputs of mitral cells are sent to pyramidal cells (PC) of the olfactory cortex via LOT. Mitral cells (M) of the olfactory bulb interconnect with each other either via excitatory or inhibitory synaptic connection, and each of the mitral cells is connected to a granule cell (G) with inhibitory synaptic connection. Although the physiological nature of lateral connections within the mitral cell layer has not been clear yet, full lateral connections between mitral cells are assumed. Then the mitral cell layer corresponds to an associative neural network. Dynamical evolution of membrane potential of mitral cells, periglomerular cells, and granule cells is defined by

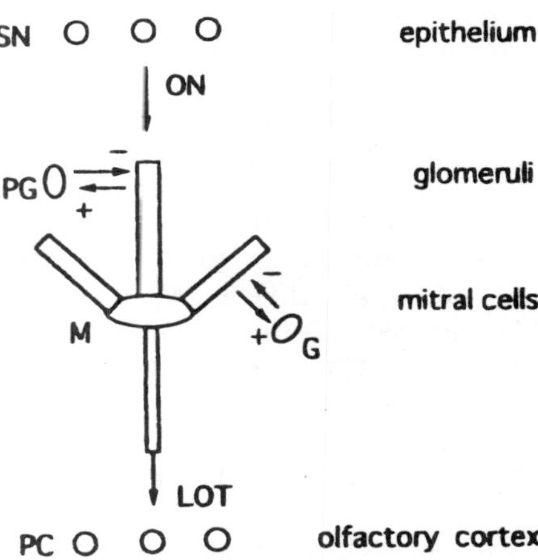

FIGURE 1. Model of a olfactory system. The output of sensory neurons (SN) of epithelium is projected into glomeruli which are interconnected with periglomerular neurons (PG). The outputs of mitral cells are sent to pyramidal cells (PC) of olfactory cortex via LOT. Mitral cells (M) of the olfactory bulb are interconnected with each other either via excitatory or inhibitory synaptic connection, and each of the mitral cells is connected to a granule cell (G) with inhibitory synaptic connection.

$$\tau_{m,i}\frac{du_{m,i}(t)}{dt} = -u_{m,i}(t) + \sum_{j=1}^{N}\sum_{\tau_{ij}=0}^{\tau_{max}} w_{mm,ij}(t,\tau_{ij}) \cdot V_{m,j}(t-\tau_{ij}) + w_{mp} \cdot V_{p,i}(t) + w_{mg} \cdot V_{g,i}(t) + a \cdot I_i(t), \quad (1)$$

$$\tau_{p,i}\frac{du_{p,i}(t)}{dt} = -u_{p,i}(t) - w_{pm} \cdot u_{m,i}(t), \quad (2)$$

$$\tau_{g,i}\frac{du_{g,i}(t)}{dt} = -u_{g,i}(t) + w_{gm} \cdot u_{m,i}(t), \quad (3)$$

where $u_{m,i}, u_{p,i}$ and $u_{g,i}$ are the membrane potentials of ith mitral cell, ith periglomerular cell, and ith granule cell, respectively. $\tau_{m,i}$, $\tau_{p,i}$ and $\tau_{g,i}$ are decay times of the membrane potentials. N is the number of mitral cells, a set of a periglomerular cell and a granule cell is connected to each mitral cell. τ_{ij} is delay time of signal propagation from cell j to i, and τ_{max} is the maximum delay time. These signal delays are omnipresent in the brain (Miller, 1987) and play an important role in stabilization of temporal sequences of firing patterns (Sompolinsky & Kanter, 1986). Signal transport is fast along a thick myelinated axon, taking at most a few milliseconds. However, a considerable portion of the axons takes the form of very fine myelinated fibers or unmyelinated ones. These kinds of axons give rise to longer signal delays in axons, up to 100-200 ms (Lee et al., 1986; Miller, 1987). $w_{mm,ij}$ is strength of the synaptic connection from mitral cell j to mitral cell i. w_{pm}, w_{gm}, w_{mp}, and w_{mg} are strength of the synaptic connection from mitral to periglomerular cell, mitral to granule cell, periglomerular to mitral cell, and granule to mitral cell, respectively. $V_{m,i}$, $V_{p,i}$, $V_{g,i}$ are outputs of ith mitral cell, ith periglomerular cell, and ith granule cell, respectively. I_i is an input stimulus to ith mitral cell modified with the positive constant a. Output activities of the mitral cells, periglomerular cells, and granule cells are defined by

$$Prob[V_{m,i}(t) = 1] = f_m[u_{m,i}(t)], \tag{4}$$

$$V_{p,i}(t) = f_p[u_{p,i}(t)], \tag{5}$$

$$V_{g,i}(t) = f_g[u_{g,i}(t)], \tag{6}$$

$$f_x[y] = \frac{1}{1 + e^{-\eta_x(y-\theta_x)}}, \quad (x = m, p, g) \tag{7}$$

where η_x is the steepness of the sigmoid function f_x, and θ_x is threshold for $x-$kind of cells. Eq.4 means the probability of firing, that is, $V_{m,i}(t) = 1$ in the axons of mitral cell i is given by f_m. f_p and f_g are the output potentials at dendro-dendritic synapses of the periglomerular and granule cells, respectively. In the learning processes for novel input odors, synaptic connections between mitral cells with signal delays are modified according to an Hebbian learning rule (Herz, 1989) defined by

$$\tau_{w,ij} \frac{dw_{mm,ij}(t, \tau_{ij})}{dt} = -w_{mm,ij}(t, \tau_{ij}) + \epsilon_{ij}(\tau_{ij}) \cdot [2V_{m,i}(t) - 1] \cdot V_{m,j}(t - \tau_{ij}), \tag{8}$$

where $\tau_{w,ij}$ is a decay time, and $\epsilon_{ij}(\tau_{ij})$ is proportional to the number of synapses from mitral cells j to i whose signaling delay time is τ_{ij}. Numerical calculations have been performed mainly by a network composed of 36 mitral cells ($N = 36$), and the distribution of delay times is uniform, that is, $\epsilon_{ij} = \epsilon = 1.0$. The network parameter values used are $\tau_{m,i} = \tau_{p,i} = \tau_{g,i} = 20$msec, $\theta_1 = 0.1$, $\theta_2 = 0.9$, $\theta_3 = 0.9$, $\eta_1 = 14.0$, $\eta_1 = 21.0$, and $\eta_3 = 21.0$ in the cases without any specification.

3 Memorization of Novel Odors

Each glomerulus encodes each kind of chemical ingredients of odorant. Therefore, a spatial distribution of glomeruli activated by an odorant denotes what kinds of ingredients are included in the odorant. Strength of input from receptor neurons to each glomerulus denotes what amount of the relevant ingredient is included in the odorant. Hopfield (1995) has shown that odor of input strength can be transformed to temporal order of firing of mitral cells. Thus, an odorant is encoded by a temporal sequence of different spatial patterns, that is, a spatio-temporal pattern of neural activities in the mitral cell layer.

In the present section, we study memorization process of this type of spatio-temporal patterns in the present neural model. A temporal sequence of M orthogonal firing patterns $\{\xi_i^\mu; 1 \leq i \leq N, \mu = 1, 2, \cdots, M\}$ is applied sequentially as input stimuli to the mitral cells, where the duration of application of each pattern is Δ msec. Patterns $\{\xi_i^\mu\}$ are made by giving each ξ_i^μ a value 0 or 1. This spatio-temporal pattern corresponds to one odorant. The pattern ξ_i^1 encodes the strongest ingredients of the odorant, the pattern ξ_i^2 encodes the next strongest ones, and so on. The application of stimuli of patterns is repeated cyclically during T msec, where $T = n\Delta M$. ΔM corresponds to the duration of one inspiration. The Hebbian learning process is carried out for T msec in a self-organizing manner given by Eq.8. Another temporal sequence of M spatial patterns $\{\xi_i^\mu; 1 \leq i \leq N, \mu = M, M+1, \cdots, 2M\}$ is learned as another odorant in the same manner.

Thus totally two spatio-temporal patterns are embedded into the network as memories of two odorants. These patterns correspond to two limit cycle attractors in the network dynamics.

In order to investigate the dynamical behavior of the network, we calculate the measure overlap defined by

$$O_\mu(t) = N^{-1} \sum_{i=1}^{N} \xi_i^\mu \cdot V_{m,i}(t). \qquad (9)$$

If $\{V_{m,i}(t)\} = \{\xi_i^\mu\}$, the network is in the firing state of pattern μ and thus $O_\mu(t) = 1.0$. In general, $O_\mu(t)$ ranges between -1.0 and 1.0, and measures how close the firing state of the network is to the pattern μ. We define an appearance of the state whose overlap with the pattern μ is greater than 0.8 as a practical retrieval of the pattern μ, because the measure overlap of 0.8 is close enough to the pattern μ to distinguish the current state from another pattern. We show in Figure 2 the learning procedure of a novel odor. The temporal sequence of firing patterns $\{\mu = 1, 2, 3\}$ is repeatedly applied to the network as input stimuli, and a self-organized synaptic modification defined by Eq.8 is carried out simultaneously. Note that the sequence with a different order of the same spatial patterns (e.g., $\{\mu = 3, 2, 1\}$) expresses another type of odor. After the learning process has been completed, the two spatio-temporal patterns, that is, two limit cycle attractors, have been memorized as two known odors. Then, state of the network without stimulation itinerates chaotically between the two limit cycle attractors as shown in Figure 3.

Appearance of chaotically itinerant state is sensitive to length of the maximum delay time τ_{max} in Eq.1. If τ_{max} is too long, each limit cycle attractor becomes much more stable and results in disappearance of the chaotically itinerant motion. On the other hand, If τ_{max} is too short, stable point attractors corresponding to spatial patterns $\{\xi_i^\mu\}$, instead of limit cycle attractors, are generated, and thus the network fails to memorize the odor information. The role of chaotic itinerancy in the information processing is described in the next section.

4 Recognition of Odors

We show in Figure 4 response properties of the network induced by several different kinds of odor stimuli, including known and unknown odors.

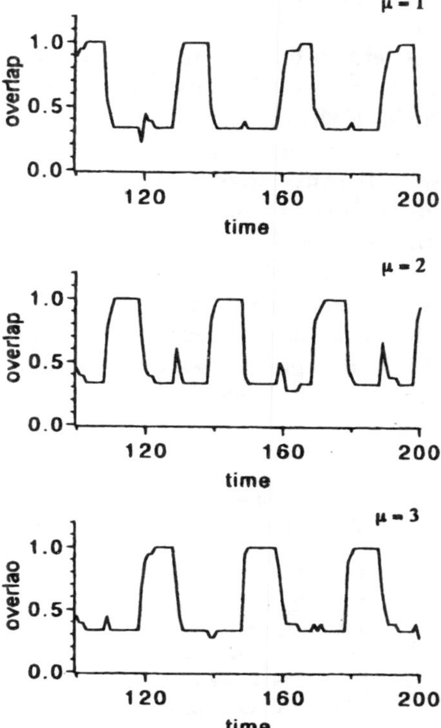

FIGURE 2. Memorization of a novel odor as a temporal sequence of spatial patterns. The overlaps of the current firing pattern of the network with each of the patterns $\{\mu = 1, 2, 3\}$ are shown as a function of time (t) in the first learning process. The temporal sequence of patterns $\mu = 1, 2, 3$, is applied to primary dendrites of mitral cells, and then Hebbian learning is carried out in a self-organising manner according to Eq.(8), where $\Delta = 10$ steps of time (1 step of time is equivalent to 5msec) and $T = 180$ steps of time. $\tau_{m,i} = \tau_{p,i} = \tau_{g,i} = 5msec$, $\tau_{max} = 50msec$, and $\eta_h = 100.0$.

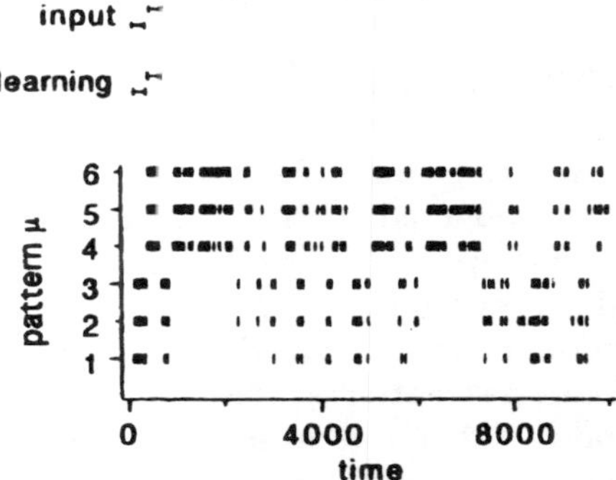

FIGURE 3. Dynamical behavior of the network after the two learning processes. Retrievals of the memorised patterns are indicated by vertical bars during and after the two learning processes. The horizontal bars indicate the period [100:280] of the first learning process for the input pattern sequence $\{\mu = 1, 2, 3\}$ and the period [400:580] of the second process for the input $\{\mu = 4, 5, 6\}$, respectively. We define appearance of the state whose overlap with pattern μ is greater than 0.8 as retrieval of pattern μ. By each learning process, each temporal sequence of novel input patterns is memorised as a limit cycle attractor relevant to a known odor. After the two learning processes have been completed, the state of the network itinerates chaotically between the two limit cycle attractors.

In the state of the chaotically itinerant motion between memorized two limit cycle attractors, a temporal sequence of spatial patterns is applied to the network as an odor stimulus. When the the sequence is equivalent to one of the sequences which have been embedded in the learning process as limit cycle attractors, state of the network is fixed to the relevant limit cycle attractor, as seen in Figure 4(a). After switching off the input, dynamical state of the network reverses to the chaotically itinerant state again, as seen also in Figure 4(a). On the other hand, when the temporal sequence applied is not equivalent to any of the memorized sequences, state of the network keeps itinerating between the two limit cycle attractors. If the stimuli, like the sequence of $\{\mu = 3, 2, 1\}$ or $\{\mu = 6, 5, 4\}$, consist of the same spatial patterns as those for the memorized odors but the temporal sequences are different from the sequences for the memorized odors, then the network keeps in the chaotically itinerant state as seen in Figure 4(b), that is, the network recognized these stimuli as unknown. Even if the stimulus applied is slightly different from the memorized sequences, such that one or two spatial patterns in the sequence $\{\mu = 1, 2, 3\}$ or $\{\mu = 4, 5, 6\}$ are replaced by a slightly different patterns, the the network recognizes the stimulus as known one. Recognition of the network is quite robust.

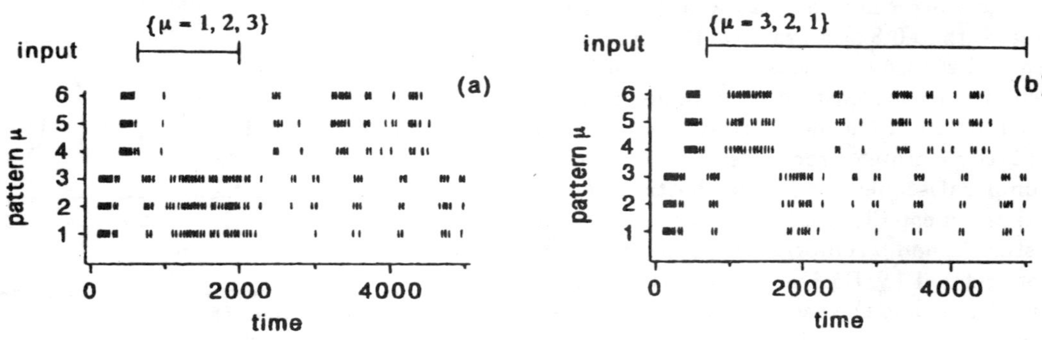

FIGURE 4. Response properties of the network induced by input odors. In the state of chaotically itinerant motion between the two limit cycle attractors, a temporal sequence of spatial patterns is applied to the network during the period, shown by a horizontal bar. (a) When the sequence $\{\mu = 1, 2, 3\}$ corresponding to a known odor is applied, the state of the network has converged on the relevant limit cycle attractor. After switching off the input, the network reverses to the chaotically itinerant state. (b) When a sequence corresponding to a completely unknown odor, $\{\mu = 3, 2, 1\}$, for example, is applied, the state of the network keeps itinerating between the limit cycle attractors.

5 Discussion

Skarda and Freeman (1987) and Tsuda (1992) summarized the functional roles of cortical chaos which have been proposed so far. We investigate how the functional roles may be played in the recognition and memorization of odors, by using the present model of olfactory bulb. (1) A role as a novelty filter: When input is similar to one of the memorized patterns, the network is forced to the attractor of memory nearest to the input. On the other hand, input is novel for the network, that is, quite different from any memorized patterns, the network stays in the chaotically itinerant state. This role was realized in our model. (2) A role as a memory searcher: The chaotically itinerant motion among the memorized patterns is very useful for memory search tasks, because the chaotic transition blocks pinning on spurious attractors in the network and promotes successive retrieval of true attractors relevant to the memorized patterns. In connection with this point, for the chaotically itinerant state and a nonitinerant state, we calculated the minimum intensity of input stimulus with which a memorized patter relevant to the input can be retrieved. The minimum intensity for the former state is much smaller than for the latter state. Therefore, the present result shows that the chaotic itinerancy makes pattern retrievals easier. (3) A role as a catalyst for learning: The chaotically itinerant state may help a learning of new pattern without destruction of old memories. The present model in the chaotically itinerant state can memorize new patterns as partners in the chaotic itinerancy.

A more detailed description about the role of the chaotically itinerant state of neural networks in pattern recognition and memorization has been given elsewhere (Hoshino et al., 1996).

References

Freeman, W.J. (1992). Tutorial on neurobiology: From single neurons to brain chaos. *Int. J. Bifurcation and Chaos*, **2**, 451-482.

Freeman, W.J. & Viana Di Prisco, G. (1986). Correlation of olfactory EEG with behavior: Time series analysis. *Behavioral Neuroscience*, **100**, 753-763.

Freeman, W.J. & Baird, B. (1987). Correlation of olfactory EEG with behavior: Spatial analysis. *Behavioral Neuroscience*, **101**, 393-408.

Herz, A., Sulzer, R., Kühn, R, & van Hemmen, L. (1989). Hebbian learning reconsidered: Representation of static and dynamic object in associative neural nets. *Biol. Cybern.*, **60**, 457-467.

Hopfield, J.J. (1995). Pattern recognition computation using action potential timing for stimulus representation. *Nature*, **376**, 33-36.

Hoshino, O., Kashimori, Y., & Kambara, T (1996). Submitted to *Neural Networks*.

Lee, K.H., Chung, K., Chung, J.M., & Coggeshall, R.E. (1986). Correlation of cell body size, and signal conduction velocity for individually labelled dorsal root ganglion cells in the cat. *J. Comp. Neurol.*, **243**, 335-346.

Miller, R. (1987). Representation of brief temporal patterns, Hebbian synapses, and the left-hemisphere dominance for phoneme recognition. *Psychobiology*, **15**, 241-247.

Mori, R. (1995). Relation of chemical structure to specificity if response in olfactory glomeruli. *Current Opinion in Neurobiology*, **5**, 467-474.

Skarda, C. A. & Freeman, W.J. (1987). How brain make chaos in order to make sense of the world. *Behavioral and brain science*, **10**, 161-195.

Sompolinsky, H. & Kanter, L. (1986). Temporal association in asymmetric neural networks. *Phys. Rev. Lett.*, **67**, 2861-2864.

Tsuda, I (1992). Dynamic link of memory - Chaotic memory map in nonequilibrium neural networks. *Neural Networks*, **5**, 313-326.

Yao, Y., & Freeman, W.J. (1990). Model of biological pattern recognition with partially chaotic dynamics. *Neural Networks*, **3**, 153-170.

Effect of Temporal Pattern of Peripheral Taste Nerve Activity on Self-Organization of Gustatory Neuron Types in Hindbrain

Kazunori Waki†, Yoshiki Kashimori‡, Akira Tsuboi‡ and Takeshi Kambara†‡
† Department of Information Network Science
Graduate School of Information Systems
‡ Department of Applied Physics and Chemistry
The University of Electro-Communications,Chofu,Tokyo,182,Japan
e-mail: waki@nerve.pc.uec.ac.jp

Abstract— The peripheral taste nerves code taste qualities based on spatiotemporal activity patterns across the nerves but the gustatory informations transmitted from the peripheral nerves are processed in hindbrain based on the neuron types which are specifically sensitive to taste qualities. In the present paper, we show how the temporal firing patterns elicited in the peripheral nerve fibers are determined depending on taste qualities and intensities by using a microscopic model of taste receptor cell and peripheral neuron. In order to study how the gustatory neuron types formed in the hindbrain reflect the temporal patterns of peripheral nerve activities, we propose a neural network model of the hindbrain. The synaptic connections in the model can be self-organized under inputs of spatiotemporal firing patterns across the peripheral nerve fibers and the synaptic modification in the model depends straightforwardly on temporal feature of the input signals.

1   Introduction

The recognition of taste qualities and intensities is made through the processes which start from the taste transduction in the receptor cells and end with the information processing in the cerebral cortical gustatory area by way of the integration of peripheral inputs in the peripheral taste nerves. In the present paper, we study neural mechanism of encoding taste qualities and intensities in the pathway from the taste receptor cells to hindbrain.

Because most mammalian taste receptors are broadly responsive across the prototypical taste qualities, the peripheral taste neurons, which innervate directly the receptor cells, code the taste qualities based on the patterns of relative amounts of activity across many neurons[1]. A pattern of neural activity elicited by a taste stimulus is expected to be unique to the quality and intensity of that stimulus, that is, to serve as its neural representation[1].

However, it has been shown [1] that many neurons in the hindbrain have more specific sensitivity for four primary tastes, for example, one neuron is most sensitive to sweet stimuli but the other is most sensitive to sweet stimuli. The hindbrain neurons can be classified into gustatory neuron types on the basis of their maximum sensitivities and the neural response profiles within each type are similar and orderly. Each neuron type staffs an almost independent information channel with sole responsibility for mediating a taste quality fixed to some extent. The gustatory information broadly distributed over the peripheral nerve fibers is converged on neuron types in the hindbrain.

It has been observed that the gustatory neurons in forebrain are systematically more broadly responsive to stimuli representing the four primary taste qualities. Gustatory information encoded by relatively narrowly tuned neuron types in the hindbrain is processed by rather broadly tuned neurons in the forebrain. Activity in hindbrain neurons may more accurately represent gustatory discriminations, whereas that of forebrain neurons may reflect the interactions of taste with other sensory information[1].

In the previous paper [2], in order to know how the broadly sensitive taste cells respond to mixed taste stimuli, we studied the mechanism of taste transduction in the receptor cells by using a realistic model of the multisensitive cells of the rat. The transduction pathways considered are amiloride sensitive Na^+ channels for $NaCl$ and HCl, and $cAMP$ mediating K^+ channels for sucrose. The calculated responses of various multisensitive cells induced by single stimuli of $NaCl$, HCl, or sucrose reproduce experimentally observed responses as well. The response of multisensitive taste cells to mixed taste stimuli is nonlinear. Whether the response of a cell to a binary mixture becomes synergetic or antagonistic can be estimated from the individual responses of the cell to each component of the mixture.

Furthermore , in order to know how the peripheral taste nerves respond to a variety of taste stimuli with variation in the rate of their discharge pattern, we studied the mechanism through which the distribution patterns of the interspike intervals in the nerve are induced by the taste stimuli, by using a microscopic model of peripheral taste neuron and taste receptor cell [3]. The calculated patterns for salty, sour, and sweet stimuli reproduced well the characteristic features of the observed patterns. The temporal patterns of peripheral nerve response depend not only on the taste quality but also on the type of taste receptor cells and the strength of taste stimulation [3].

In the present paper, we are concerned with the information processing in the hindbrain, In order to study what types of gustatory neurons are self-organized under various taste stimulation and how the temporal patterns of peripheral nerve response affect the formation of gustatory neuron types, we make a microscopic model of neural network of the hindbrain. We investigate more detailedly the relations of temporal patterns of peripheral nerve response to taste qualities and intensities by using the previous model [3]. Convey and Erichson [4] showed that a prototypical taste could be identified with at least 70% accuracy, based purely on the temporal patterns. The temporal patterns as well as spatial patterns across taste nerve fibers contribute significantly to discriminability among taste qualities [1,7].

2 Model of Taste Receptive System

The model consists of three main parts, a taste receptor cell, a synaptic connection part, and a peripheral taste neuron. A schematic drawing of the model is given in Fig. 1.

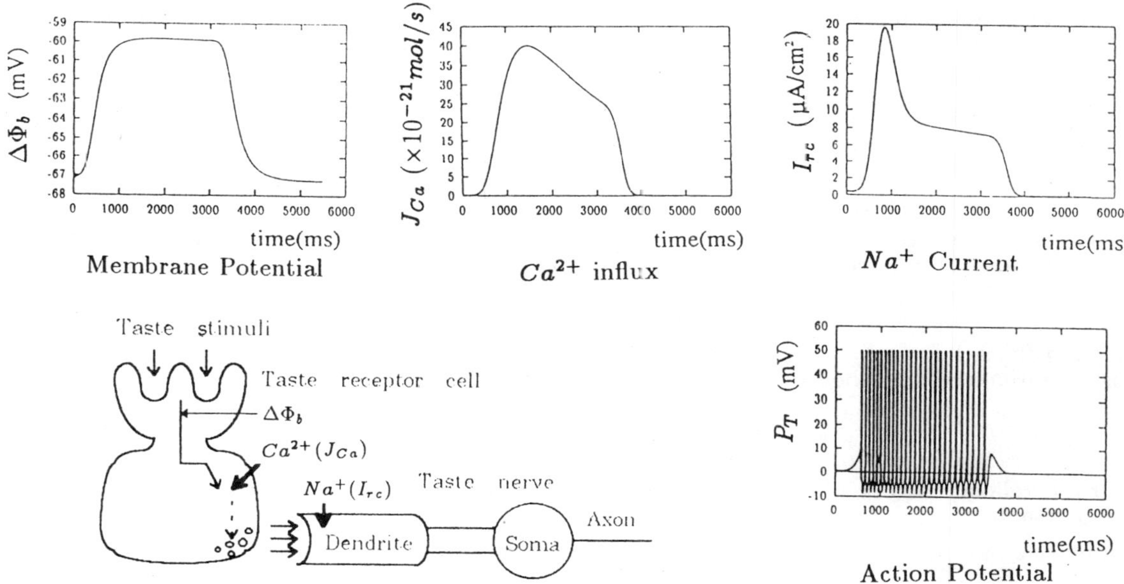

Fig. 1 A schematic drawing of a taste receptor cell and a peripheral taste neuron and their response properties induced by a taste stimulation whose temporal variation is similar to that of membrane potential.

2.1 Taste receptor system and synaptic connection part

The receptor system consists of a taste receptor cell, tight junction, and basement membrane which construct the four kinds of compartment, mucosal bath, intracellular space, interstitial space, and serosal bath. The four compartments are bordered with four kinds of membranes, apical, basolateral, and basement membranes and tight junction. When a taste stimulus is applied in the mucosal bath, the electric potentials across the apical membrane and across the basolateral membrane vary corresponding to the kind and concentration of taste stimulant. We consider here salty, sour, and sweet stimuli. The detailed mathematical description of the taste transduction is given in ref. [2].

Variations $\Delta\Phi_b$ in the potential across the basolateral membrane, which is schematically represented in Fig.1, may transfer into the impulse discharge P_T of peripheral neuron through the synaptic connection. The signal transfer across the synapse is made through the following main five processes: 1. Injection J_{Ca} of Ca^{2+} into the taste receptor cell through the Ca^{2+} channels whose gate is opened by the depolarization of basolateral membrane potential. 2. Activation of the fusion-promoting factor induced by Ca^{2+} binding to the factor. The complex, $fpf^* \cdot Ca^{2+}$, facilitates fusion of vesicles including neurotransmitter molecules. A typical temporal variation of the influx J_{Ca} of Ca^{2+} is shown in Fig. 1. 3. Neurotransmitter release produced by the vesicle fusion. 4. Opening of the Na^+ channels in the postsynaptic terminal of the peripheral neuron. 5. Depolarization of the postsynaptic membrane potential. The depolarization is induced by the inward Na^+ current I_{rc} through the open channels.

The detailed description of these processes was given in ref. [3].

2.2 Peripheral taste neuron

The impulse discharges P_T of the peripheral taste neuron are induced by the inward Na^+ current I_{rc}. We describe the response property of the taste neuron using the point model neuron of MacGregor [5].

$$\tau_{mT}\frac{dV_{T,i}(t)}{dt} = -V_{T,i}(t) + \frac{1}{G_T}\left[G_{N,i}(t)(V_N - V_{T,i}(t)) + G_{K,i}(t)(V_K - V_{T,i}(t)) + I_{rc}(t)\right], \qquad (1)$$

$$V_{T,i}(t) = E_{T,i}(t) - E_{Tr}, \quad V_N = E_N - E_{Tr}, \quad V_K = E_K - E_{Tr}, \qquad (2)$$

where $E_{T,i}(t)$ and E_{Tr} are instantaneus and resting membrane potential, respectively, of the soma of ith taste neuron, $E_{Tr} = (g_K E_K + g_N E_N)/G_T$, $G_T = g_K + g_N$, g_K and g_N are conductivities of K^+ and Na^+ channels, respectively, in the resting state, E_K and E_N are reversal potentials of the K^+ and Na^+ channels, respectively, $G_{K,i}(t)$ and $G_{N,i}(t)$ are time varying components of K^+ and Na^+ channel conductances, respectively, $I_{rc}(t)$ is the inward Na^+ current induced by taste stimulus, and τ_{mT} is relaxation time of the membrane potential.

The time varying conductances $G_{N,i}(t)$ and $G_{K,i}(t)$ are determined through the membrane potertial $V_{T,i}(t)$ as

$$G_{N,i}(t) = g_N\left[\exp\left(\frac{V_{T,i}(t)}{V_{nl}}\right) - 1\right], \qquad (3)$$

$$\tau_{GK}\frac{dG_{K,i}(t)}{dt} = -G_{k,i}(t) + b \cdot S_{T,i}(t), \qquad (4)$$

where V_{nl} is the rate constant of nonlinear voltage dependence, τ_{GK} is relaxation time of K^+ channel conductance, b is the rate constant, and $S_{T,i}(t)$ is spiking index given by

$$S_{T,i}(t) = H(V_{T,i}(t) - T_{T,i}(t)). \qquad (5)$$

Here, $H(x)$ takes 1 for $x \geq 0$ and 0 for $x < 0$, and $T_{T,i}(t)$ is the threshould for spike generation in the ith taste neuron and described by

$$\tau_{th}\frac{dT_{T,i}(t)}{dt} = -(T_{T,i}(t) - T_0) + C \cdot V_{T,i}(t), \qquad (6)$$

where τ_{th} is relaxation time of the threshold, T_0 is the threshold in the resting state, and C is accommodation constant.

The impulsive output potential $P_{T,i}(t)$ of the ith taste neuron is represented by

$$P_{T,i}(t) = V_{T,i}(t) + S_{T,i}(t)(P_0 - V_{T,i}(t)), \qquad (7)$$

where P_0 is the height of impulse above the level of resting potential $E_{T,r}$.

3 Model for Self-Organization of Gustatory Neuron Types in Hindbrain

3.1 Network model of taste receptive syatem and hindbrain

The network model is schematically shown in Fig. 2. Each peripheral taste neuron innervates a single taste receptor cell as shown detailedly in FIg. 1. Each taste neuron is connected with all neurons of the hindbrain by feedforward excitatory synapse. Hindbrain neurons are connected with each other by feedback inhibitory synapse. Connection strength of these synapses is determined in a self-organizing manner according to the Hebbian learning rule under various taste stimulation.

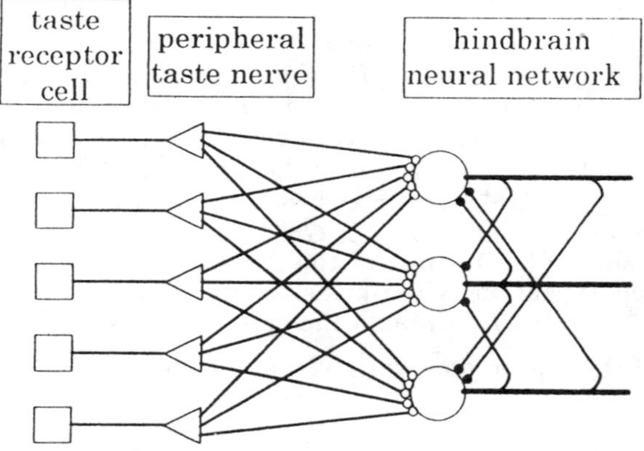

Fig. 2 Network model of taste receptive system and hindbrain. Empty small circles are excitatory synapses and filled small circles are inhibitory synapses.

3.2   Model of neural network of hindbrain

The response proprety of hindbrain is described by using the following dynamical equations for membrane potential $E_{H,i}(t)$ of the soma and axonal output $P_{H,i}(t)$.

$$\tau_{mH}\frac{dV_{H,i}(t)}{dt} = -V_{H,i}(t) + \frac{1}{G_H}\left(G_{N,i}(t)\left(V_N - V_{H,i}(t)\right) + G_{K,i}(t)\left(V_K - V_{H,i}(t)\right) + \sum_{j=1}^{M} I_{j,i}^{E}(t) \right.$$

$$\left. + \sum_{k=1}^{N}{}' I_{k,i}^{I}(t) \right), \tag{8}$$

$$V_{H,i}(t) = E_{H,i}(t) - E_{Hr}, \quad V_N = E_N - E_{Hr}, \quad V_K = E_K - E_{Hr}, \tag{9}$$

where the meanings of τ_{mH}, G_H, $G_{N,i}(t)$, $G_{K,i}(t)$, E_{Hr}, E_N, and E_k are equivalent to those of relevant quantities in Eqs. 1 and 2. The voltage dependent conductances $G_{N,i}(t)$ and $G_{K,i}(t)$ are determined by equations equivalent to Eqs. 3 and 4, respectively. The axonal impulsive potential $P_{H,i}(t)$ is also given by an equation equivalent to Eq. 7.

The input current $I_{j,i}^{E}(t)$ from jth taste neuron is induced by an impulsive stimulation $P_{T,j}(t)$ through an excitatory synaptic connection. It is given by

$$I_{j,i}^{E}(t) = g_{j,i}^{E}(t)\left(V_E - V_{H,i}(t)\right), \tag{10}$$

$$\tau_{GE}\frac{dg_{j,i}^{E}(t)}{dt} = -g_{j,i}^{E}(t) + q_{j,i}P_{T,j}(t), \tag{11}$$

where $g_{j,i}^{E}(t)$ is the instantaneous conductivity of excitatory ion channels, $V_E = E_E - E_{Hr}$, E_E is the reversal potential of the channels, τ_{GE} is the relaxation time of the conductivity, and $q_{j,i}$ is the strength of synaptic connection from jth taste neuron to ith hindbrain neuron and is positive.

The input current $J_{k,i}^{I}(t)$ from kth hindbrain neuron is induced by an impulsive output $P_{H,k}(t)$ through an inhibitory synaptic connection, and is described by

$$I_{k,i}^{I}(t) = g_{k,i}^{I}(t)\left(V_I - V_{H,i}(t)\right), \tag{12}$$

$$\tau_{GI}\frac{dg_{k,i}^{I}(t)}{dt} = -g_{k,i}^{I}(t) + W_{k,i}P_{H,k}(t), \tag{13}$$

where $g_{k,i}^{I}(t)$ is the instantaneous conductivity of inhibitory ion channels, $V_I = E_I - E_{Hr}$, E_I is the reversal potential of the inhibitory channels, τ_{GI} is the relaxation time of the conductivity of the channels, and $W_{k,i}$ is the synaptic strength.

3.3   Modification of synaptic strength

In the self-organizing processes of gustatory neuron types in the hindbrain neural network, synaptic connections between taste neurons and hindbrain neurons and between hindbrain neurons are modified simultaneously according to the Hebbian and anti-Hebbian learning rules, respectively, given by

$$\tau_q \frac{dq_{j,i}(t)}{dt} = -q_{j,i}(t) + \alpha_q S_{H,i}(t)\int_{-\infty}^{t} \exp\left(\frac{x-t}{\beta_q}\right) S_{T,j}(x)\,dx, \tag{14}$$

$$\tau_W \frac{dW_{k,i}(t)}{dt} = -W_{k,i}(t) + \alpha_W S_{H,i}(t)\int_{-\infty}^{t} \exp\left(\frac{x-t}{\beta_W}\right) S_{H,k}(x)\,dx, \tag{15}$$

where τ_q and τ_W are the decay time of excitatory and inhibitory synaptic strength, respectively, α_q and α_w are the rates of strength change, and the effects of past feedforward signal $S_{T,j}(x)$ and past feedback signal $S_{H,k}(x)$ are taken into account such that they decay exponentially with the decay times of β_q and β_W.

4   Results

Firstly we investigate how the patterns of impulse trains induced in the peripheral taste neuron changes depending on quality and intensity of taste stimuli applied to the receptor cell. We calculated the temporal variations of impulse discharges, integrated response pattern and distribution of interspicke intervals for three kinds of taste stimuli, salty, sour, and sweet substances. The results are shown in Fig. 3. The interspike distance distribution changes depending not only on taste quality but also on concentration of taste substance in stimulant solution. We show the calculated dependences on stimulant concentration for the three taste qualities in Table 1.

We considered what is the main factor by which a distribution patern of interspike distances is determined. It has been found from the present study that the direct factor is the rising rate of the depolarization of the basolateral membrane potential induced by taste stimulation: When the depolarization occurs quite

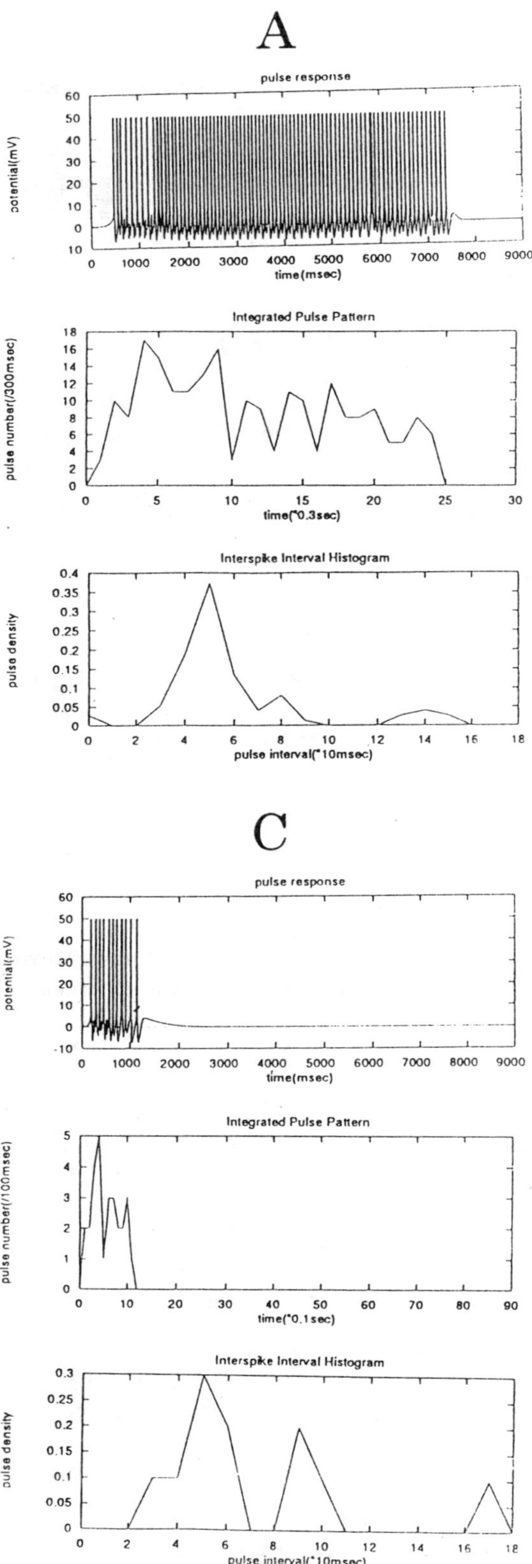

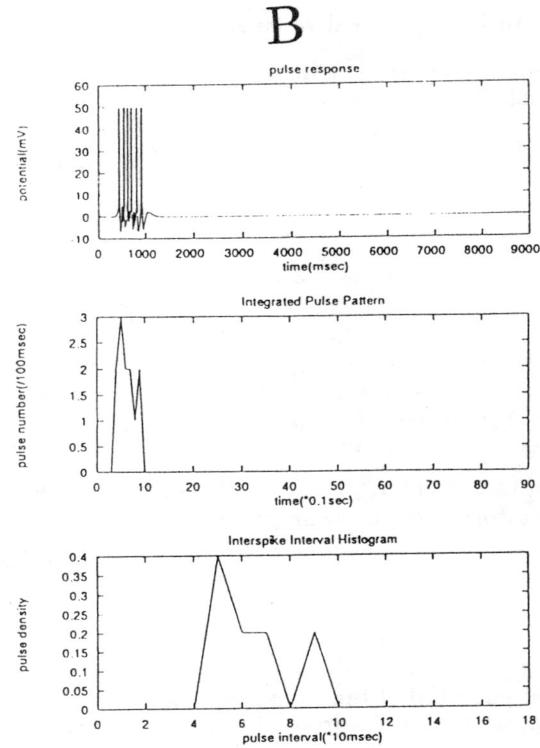

Fig. 3 The calculated response properties of a peripheral taste neuron induced by (A) $120mM\,NaCl$, (B) $9mM\,HCl$, and (C) $300mM$ sucrose. The upper panel shows the temporal variation of impulse discharges, the middle panel shows the impulse number integrated over a certain time duration, and the lower panel shows the distribution of interspike intervals.

Table 1 Dependence of interspike interval pattern on taste quality and intensity.

Taste	Concentration or Sensitivity low ↔ high		
NaCl	Gam	Gam, Bmd	Exp
HCl	Gam, Bmd	Exp	Exp
Sucrose	Bmd	Bmd	Bmd

Gam, Exp, and Bmd mean gamma function type, exponential function type, and bimodal(double peaks) function type, respectively.

rapidly, the distribution pattern becomes exponential; In the case where the depolarization occurs slowly, the pattern becomes gamma; The bimodal pattern appears for a middle rising rate of the depolarization.

When the type of taste cell is fixed, the rising rate increases with increasing the stimulus strength or concentration. Therefore, the distribution pattern of interspike interval tends to become exponential with increasing the stimulus strength. The distribution pattern is apt to become bimodal and change from bimodal to gamma with decreasing the stimulus strength. This tendency of the pattern dependence on the stimulus strength is consistent with the observed tendency.

It is seen in Table 1 that this tendency of the pattern dependence on the stimulus strength holds for $NaCl$ and HCl stimuli. However, the tendency appears not to hold for sugar stimulus. This comes from the feature of the taste transduction mechanism for sugar. The potential depolarization in the receptor cell due to sugar may occur through the blocking of K^+ channels in the basolateral membrane by $cAMP$ molecules which are produced through the signals from the sugar receptive proteins in the apical membrane. This indirect transduction mechanism makes the response of the cell to sugar insensitive compared with the sensitivity to $NaCl$ and HCl. This is the reason why the distribution patterns of the interspike interval tend to become the same pattern(bimodal) for a wide range of strength.

5   Concluding Remarks

It has been shown based on an experimental analysis of the temporal pattern contribution [6] that time-based decisions are about 50% reliable in discriminating statistically among the four primary taste qualities. This implies that temporal patterns may enhance the resolution among stimuli, which is provided mainly by the spatial code based on the across fiber patterns.

So far, only the role of the spatial firing patterns in the taste recognition has been mainly considered. It was also shown by using a laterally inhibitory neural network formed with Hebbian and anti-Hebbian synaptic connections [7] that neuron types specifically sensitive to four primary tastes were self-organized by stimulation of spatial activity patterns across many peripheral nerves with broad sensitivity. However, it is not yet clear what role the temporal patterns play in the organization process of gustatory neuron types in the hindbrain.

In the present paper, we have shown how temporal firing patterns elicited in the peripheral taste nerve fibers are determined depending on taste qualities and intencities. We have proposed also a neural network model of the hindbrain in which the synaptic connections can be self-organized under inputs of spatiotemporal firing patterns across the peripheral nerve fibers and the synaptic modification depends straightforwardly on temporal feature of the inputs.

Using this model, we are going to study how the gustatory neuron types formed in the hindbrain reflect the temporal patterns of peripheral nerve activity induced by taste stimuli with various qualities and intensities. The results will be presented in the conference.

References

[1] T. R. Scott. "Coding in the gustatory system." in Neurobiology of Taste and Smell, T. E. Finger and W. L. Silver (eds.), Wiley, New York, pp. 355-378, 1987.

[2] Y. Kashimori et al., "A study of nonlinear responses of multiple sensitive taste cells to mixed taste stimuli based on a dynamical model of the receptor systems", *Am. J. Physiol.*, 1996 (in press).

[3] A. Tsuboi et al., "What extent can temporal pattern of afferent nerve response code quality of taste stimuli ?", *Proc. Inf. Conf. Neural Information processing*, 94-seoul, pp. 1056-1060, 1994.

[4] E. Convey and R. P. Erickson, "Temporal coding of sensory quality: Evidence from single unit taste responses in the rat NST." *Neurosci. Abstr.*, **5**, p. 401, 1979.

[5] R. J. MacGregor, "Neural and Brain Modeling", *Acad. Press*, San Diego, 1987.

[6] P. M. DiLorezo and J. S. Schwartzbaum, "Coding of gustatory information in the pontine parabrachial neuclei of the rabit: Temporal patterns of neural response." *Brain Res.*, **251**, pp. 245-257, 1982.

[7] H. Barlow and P. Földiak, "Adaptation and Decorrelation in the Cortex." in The Computing Neuron, R. M. Darbin et al. (eds.) Addison-Wesley, Wokingham, pp. 54-72, 1989.

Modeling of Propagation of action potential of Neural Fiber and its Applications

Zhao Si-lan   Li Yan-ping

Department of Biophysics, Beijing Medical University, Beijing, 100083 China

E-mail: xhan @ sun.ihep.ac.cn

Abstract

According to the character of propagation of action potential of neural fiber, the Tripole Model has been used to extract the physiological parameters of somatosensory evoked potenials of legs. This method provides the new indexes to diagnose the injured degree of nerve ending of diabetic patients and improved the practical effect of clinical diagnosis.

Keywords   Tripole model   injured degree of nerve ending

1. Introduction

To obtain the indexes of electric propagation of neural fibers (NF) by somatosensory evoked potential (SEP) from stimulating point to recording point is an effective method to diagnose the disease of that nerve systems. But now in clinical, the doctors only interest the amplitude and latency of SEP waveform for diagnosis. Unfortunately, the important information of the waveform of SEP is thrown away, so the diagnosis by SEP still has some faults. For example, we found 75 patients who suffer from diabetic disease, their courses of disease are from one month to tewnty four years, recording their peripheral SEPs from sural nerve (SN) and posterier tibial nerve (PN), by the routine diagnosis of SEPs, only 35 patients' SEPs indexes are out of the normal ranges, it is not conformed with the experiences of the doctors. These facts show that the routine diagnosis methods of SEP in clinical is not effective to obtain the injured degree of nerve ending for diabetic patients in the early stage of disease. So we think that it is necessary to try to extract some information of wareform of SEP to improve the diagnosis method of SEP in clinical. The Tripole model was used to simulate the propagation process of action potential of nerve fibers. According to the experimental values of SEP, we can get the velocity distribution of the total fibers which was excited by the stimulations, these indexes show more valuable for clinical diagnosis of the disease of nerve systems.

2. The Tripole Model of propagation of action potential of neural fiber (APNF) [1]

(1) The potential change at the recording point after stimulations

When an impulse travels along a myelinated neural fiber, an inward flow of current only can go through from the Ranvier's node, it forms a "sink" at the point of excitation.   The current streams

---

The project supported by National Science Foundation of China and by National education commitee Foundation of China.

in this sink flow from the neighboring inactive areas of the nerve, these areas may be called "sources". As a result of this local circurt, the membrane at the source area is discharged and a new locus of excitation is set up. The transmission of nerve impulse is due to the fact that local circurt at the action area stimulates the neighboring inaction areas.

The nerve is embedded in tissue which is a conducting medium or a volume conductor, in which current flows may pass through. The general form of travelling impulse along the nerve fiber recorded in a volume conductor is triphasic. The triphasic action potential may be recorded by recording electrode as the impluse approaches,arrives and departs [2] (see Fig.1.).

(2) Tripole Model of propagation of APNF

Consider a point current source embedded in a half infinite inhomogenrous medium. We set up a rectangular coordinate system with origin at this point source (Fig.2.). The Y-Z plane runs parallel with the boundary, and the distance between them is h. The X axis goes toward the surface of the medium. The conductivity along Z axis is σ_z , and the other along the directions perpendicular to Z is σ_r (Fig.2.).

According to images method [3], we obtain the potential Φ on point P(X,0,Z) in X-Z plane caused by the point source I and the image source I' is:

$$\Phi = \frac{1}{4\pi\sigma_r}\left(\frac{I}{r_1} + \frac{I'}{r_2}\right) = \frac{1}{4\pi\sigma_r}\left(\frac{I}{\sqrt{KX^2+Z^2}} + \frac{I'}{\sqrt{K(2h-X)^2+Z^2}}\right) \tag{1}$$

where $K=\sigma_z/\sigma_r$, which describes the inhomogeneity of medium [4]. On the boundary, X=h,

$$\Phi(h,0,Z) = \frac{I}{2\pi\sigma_r}\frac{1}{\sqrt{Kh^2+Z^2}} \tag{2}$$

Suppose the point source moves with velocity V along Z axis and the source starts from origin at t=0. At time t, the potential recorded at point P(h,0,L) on the surface is

$$\Phi(t) = \frac{I}{2\pi\sigma_r}\frac{1}{\sqrt{Kh^2+(L-Vt)^2}} \tag{3}$$

Considering the triphasic action potential in a volume conductor, we can simulated the APNF by Tripole Model, two current sources and a sink in between, the three points are all on Z axis, they travel along the nerve fiber. Let this tripole moves along Z axis with velocity V, the strength of the two sources and the sink are $\alpha_1 I$ and $\alpha_2 I$ and -I respectively. The distances between the skin and source points are d_1 and d_2 as fig.3. Let the recording electrode always on the skin surface just above the fiber, so that we may only consider the potential in X-Z plane. Then the potentials recorded at P(h,0,L) is:

$$f(V,t) = \frac{I}{2\pi\sigma_r}\left[\frac{\alpha_1}{\sqrt{(L-Vt-d_1)^2+Kh^2}} - \frac{1}{\sqrt{(L-Vt)^2+Kh^2}} + \frac{\alpha_2}{\sqrt{(L-Vt+d_2)^2+Kh^2}}\right] \tag{4}$$

Using the reference value of σ_z , σ_r ,h [5][6][7], and the description about the amplitude, duration time of APNF [5][7][8], we obtain the APNF from (4) as fig.4.

(3) Parameters of Tripole Model of APNF

According to the reference papers and the experimental conditions we may obtain the parameters σ_r, σ_z, h, I and based on the parameter identification we may get other parameters.

When the posterior tibial nerve (PN) is stimulated at toe and recorded at the middle point between heel and medial malleolus; and when the sural nerve (SN) is stimulated at the back of malleolus, and recorded at the SURA's point, we consider to set the parameters as:

$$h=0.1 \text{ cm} \qquad I=0.8 \text{ } \mu A \qquad \sigma_r=0.05\Omega^{-1}m^{-1} \qquad \sigma_z=1\Omega^{-1}m^{-1}$$
$$d_1=1.75 \text{ cm} \qquad d_2=0.5 \text{ cm} \qquad \alpha_1=0.2 \qquad \alpha_2=0.8$$

By the above parameters, we may simulate the waveform $f(V_j,t)$ of APNF as Fig.4.

3. Compound action potential and its velocity distribution of propagation in nerve trunk

After stimulation, we only can record a compound action potential of nerve trunk. This compound action potential (CAP) of nerve trunk is composed of a large number of APNFs which have different conductive velocities. We suppose that:

a. CAP is constructed by the linear superposition of APNFs;

b. When the nerve trunk are stimulated slightly, only the myelinated fibers are activated synchronously;

c. Nerve fibers can be grouped into classses based on different conductive velocities, where each class may be represented by an known APNF.

Then the CAP recorded at time t after stimulus can be written as following:

$$C(t) = \sum_{j=1}^{M} \beta(V_j) f(V_j, t) \tag{5}$$

Where the nerve fibers are grouped into M classes. In the jth class, the conductive velocity is V_j, the number of action fibers is $\beta(V_j)$, and the waveform of APNF is $f(V_j, t)$.

Based on the recorded CAP data and the known $f(V_j, t)$, the $\beta(V_j)$ in each class can be estimated by identification. We may analyse all the peripheral evoked potentials in this way.

4. The Tripole Model applied to diagnose the injured indexes of nerve ending of diabetic patients

(1) Experimental methods

Schwarzer Electromyograph EGM 2000 is used for stimulation to subjects, averaging and recording of SEPs. Let the bandpass with the range of 0.5-3000Hz. The duration and frequency for electric stimuli are 0.2 ms and 5/s respectively. The intensity is strong enough to make subject just get felling of stimulation.

Every subject is recorded both SEPs of PN and SN. The PN is stimulated at toe by a ring electrode, recorded at the middle point between heel and medial malleolus. The SN is stimulated at the back of malleolus, and recorded at the SURA's point versus a referential electrode keep a distance about 1.5cm-2cm at the same horizontal line.

The recording data of the waveforms of SEPs of PN and SN transmitted into computer.   The data for computation are obtained by extracting the sampling points of the main waveform of   SEP figure and adding some other points on the base line as Fig.5.

(2)Subjects and the results of routine diagnosis

39 normal subjects ageing from 41-48 (22male,17 female).

75 patients suffer from diabetes. The courses of disease are from one month to 24 years (40 male, 35 female).

According to the routine diagnosis only 42% among the 75 patients, their latencys or amplitudes of SEPs of PN or SN are out of the normal range. This is not conformed with the clinical facts.

(3)System identification of SEPs of PN and SN

Every data of all the SEPs of PN and SN is analysed to estimate the $\beta(V_j)$ in (5) by steepest method, the optimal $\beta(V_j)$ which fitted the c(t).........(5) well can be estimated. According to the physiological knowlege, the range of conductive velocities is about 30 m/s to 80 m/s, we try to set every 3 m/s an interval for a group in (5). let we have M groups:

$$N = \sum_{j=1}^{M} \beta(V_j)$$

N is the total member of fibers excited. In the normal subjects, the theoretical waveforms of CAP of estimation fit the experimental data faily well in the major peak, the relative error of every point is within 15% or 20% as Fig.6.

Let X axis is velocity, Y axis is $\beta(V_j)/N$ (contribution), we may obtain a velocity distribution Figure (see Fig.7), and extract some useful new parameters as below for diagnosis.

V_{AV}(m/s):mean velocity of the distribution

V_{max}(m/s):velocity group which has the largest contribution to CAP

W_{max}(%):relative contribution of Vmax to CAP

W_{ran}(%):sum of all relative contribution of the velocity groups which $\beta(V_j)/N>10\%$

$$D_r = \frac{1}{T}\sum_{i=1}^{T} [C(t_i) - \sum_{j=1}^{M} \beta(V_j) f(V_j,t_i)]^2 \qquad \text{:fitting degree with model}$$

With this method, we may get five parameters from SEP of PN as:

PV_{AV} PV_{max} PW_{max} PW_{ran} PD_r

the five parameters get from SEP of SN as

SV_{AV} SV_{max} SW_{max} SW_{ran} SD_r

We also consider that indexes directly given by the measurement from the EMG 2000. Such as latency (L), amplititude (A), average velocity (AV) and intensity of stimulation (I) also include some information of SEP. Let the L, A, AV, I of PN be PL, PA, PAV, PI, the L, A, AV, PI of SN be SL, SA, SAV, SI.

For every subjects, we may get total 18 indexes, it is difficult to apply in clinical directly. So we use stepwise discriminatory method to select 7 main variable from the 18 ones, to divide the normal subjects and the diabetic patients. The discriminant functions are:

F1=0.596SAV+0.015SDr+0.370SW$_{ran}$+0.448SI+0.871SV$_{AV}$+1.047PV+0.508PA-102.389

F2=0.523SAV+0.086SDr+0.295SW$_{ran}$+0.477SI+0.769SV$_{AV}$+0.876PV+0.359PA-92.513

Acoording to these discriminant functions, 78.6% among the diabetic patients have abnormal indexes of SEPs. This result is much better than the routine diagnosis (The patients' courses of disease are short, or they only suffer from slight disease, their ending nerves may not have been injured.).

5. Discussion

(1) Some data of SEPs of diabetic patients can not fit the model well as the normal ones, probably we may change the parameters d_1, d_2, α_1 and α_2 or change model to fit the total data well, then we may go further for clinical diagnosis.

(2) To diagnose the injured degree of ending nerve of diabetic patients more precisely later on, we may select the patients suffer from different degrees of diabetic disease by clinical diagnosis, then use the stepwise discriminant method to correspounding multiple classes, then we may get the precise method for diagnosis, it may be more helpful for clinical applications.

References

[1] Zhao S. L. et al.: Mathematical Model and its Clinical Applications for Evoked Peripheral Potentials, Cybernetics and Systems (90), World Scientific, pp. 489-496, (1990).

[2] Yu J., et al.: Model Study of Evoked Peripheral Potentials, Acta Biophysica Sinnica (in Chinese}, Vol. 6, No. 3, pp. 287-293, (1990).

[3] Brazier, M. A. B.: Electrical Activity of the nervous sysstem, 4th ed., The Williams & Wikins Company, Baltimore, pp. 51-74, (1977).

[4] Jackson, J. D.: Classical Electradynamics, New York, Wiley, pp. 26-97, (1962).

[5] Fleisher, S. M.: Med. Biol. Eng. Comput., 22, pp. 440-447, (1984).

[6] Schoonhoven, R. et al.: IEEE Trans. Biomed. Eng., BME-33, pp.327-334, (1986).

[7] Stegeman, D. F., and J. P. C. De Weerd: Electroencephal. Clin. Neurophsiol., 54, pp. 436-448, (1982).

[8] Stegeman, D. F. et al.: Biol. Cybern., 33, pp. 97-111,(1979).

[9] Gasser, H. S. and H. Grundfest: Amer. J. Physiol., 127, pp. 393-414, (1939).

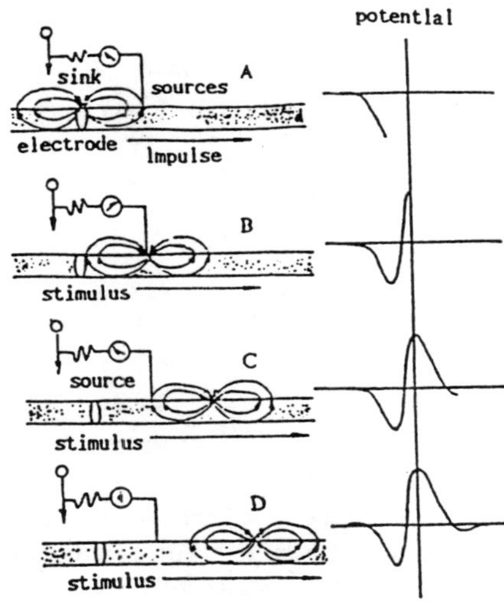

Fig. 1 . Scheme of the conduction of an impulse
along a nerve fiber in volume conductor
(From Brazier[1])

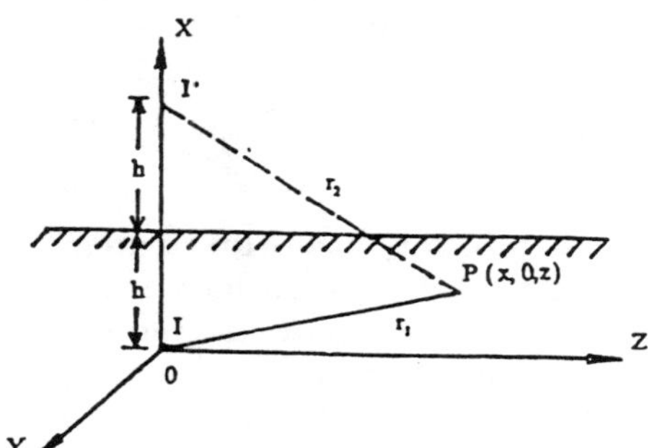

Fig. 2 . The potential produced
by a point source in a half-inf-
inite volume conductor

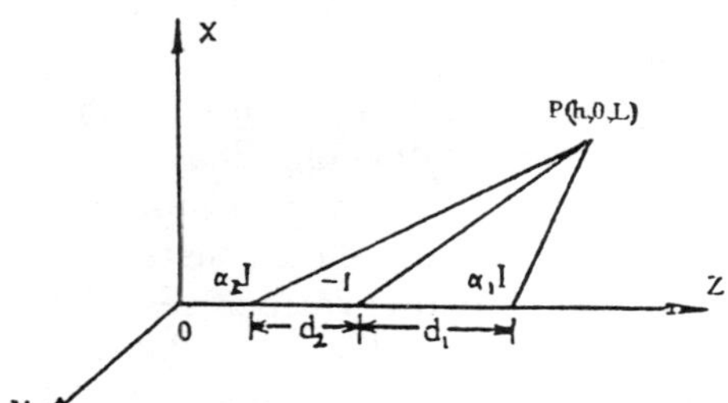

Fig. 3 . Tripole model of SFAP

Fig. 4 Simulated APNF waveform

$h=0.1cm$ $I=0.8\mu A$ $\sigma_r=0.05\Omega^{-1}m^{-1}$ $\sigma_z=1\Omega^{-1}m^{-1}$

$d_1=1.75cm$ $d_2=0.5cm$ $\alpha_1=0.2$ $\alpha_2=0.8$

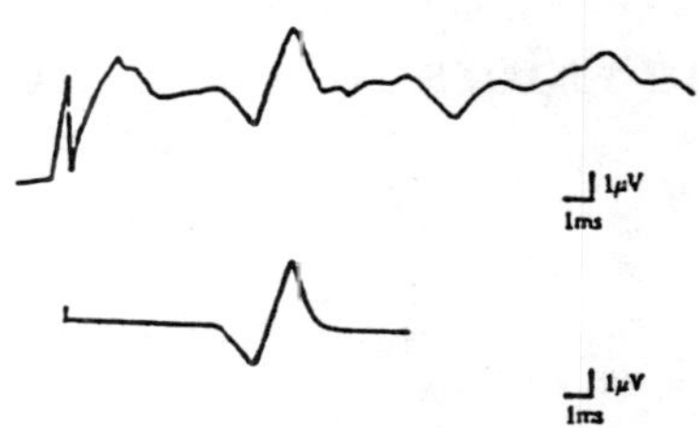

Fig. 5 Extraction of the waveform
Points from the sampled data

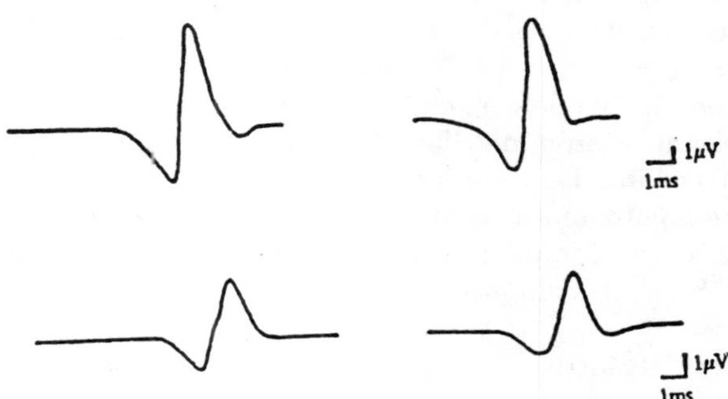

Fig. 6 Comparison of the reconstructed waveforms
(right) with the original ones (left)

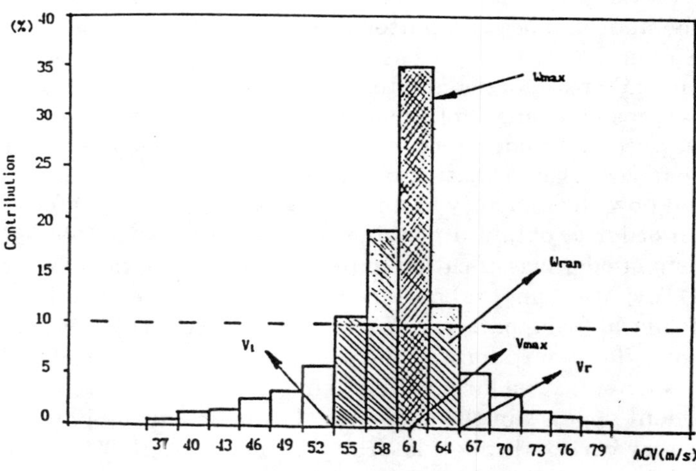

Fig.7 Velocity distribution figure

Hierarchical Classification of Spatio-Temporal Firing Patterns Encoding Odors in a Neural Network Model of Olfactory Cortex

Tetsuya Oyamada † , Osamu Hoshino † ,
Yoshiki Kashimori ‡ and Takeshi Kambara † ‡
† Graduate School of Information Systems
‡ Department of Applied Physics and Chemistry
The University of Electro-Communications,Chofu,Tokyo,182,Japan
e-mail: oyamada@nerve.pc.uec.ac.jp

abstract

We propose a mechanism of odor classification in olfactory cortex based on the following hypothesis. The spatio-temporal patterns in olfactory bulb encode simultaneously both components of odor and their mixing ratio. We constructed a functional model of olfactory cortex which consists of three compartments. When a temporal sequence of spatial patterns, that is, a spatio-temporal pattern, is injected from LOT to the network of olfactory cortex, a neural activity state of each compartment is fixed to each spatial pattern. This means that each compartment recognizes each component of an odor. The classification of an odor is made by using a combination of firing patterns fixed in all the compartments. The fixed pattern in the first compartment corresponds to the strongest component of the odor. The fixed pattern in a compartment corresponds to minor component as the compartment is located farther from the rostral side. This type of classification is a hierarchical classification.

1.Introduction

Population coding - distributed representation - has been considered to be a very powerful strategy adopted by brains for their information processing [1].   In the strategy, usual entities such as letters, words, and smells are represented by correlated activity patterns imposed on an assembly of neurons, where each single neuron may play multiple roles in different kinds of representations[2]. The neuronal activity patterns are dynamically stable, that is, correspond to dynamical attractors in neural networks. It has been shown [3,4,5] that odor-specific information are encoded as dynamical attractors characteristic of odors. The attractors may be produced through self-organized changes in strength of synaptic connections induced by odor stimulation. A key event for the neural process in odor recognition is transition between attractors[5]. However, one does not know clearly what information of odors are encoded by the spatio-temporal patterns of neural activities and how the olfactory system processes the patterns for odor recognition.

In order to obtain a possible solution of these problems, in the present paper, we study mechanism of odor classification in piriform cortex (olfactory cortex) based on the following ideas.

(1) A spatio-temporal pattern of neural activities in olfactory bulb consists of a temporal sequence of spatial firing patterns of a mitral cell network[6]. Each spatial pattern encodes each constituent molecules of an odor and the temporal sequence encodes the magnitude of mixing ratio of the odor components. The larger the mixing ratio is, the more early the spatial pattern relevant to the component appears in the sequence. The neural firing patterns in olfactory bulb are propagated to olfactory cortex through lateral olfactory tract (LOT) as input stimulation. The plausibility of this idea is shown detailedly in ref.[6].

(2) Odor classification in olfactory cortex is made by forming the spatio-temporal patterns propagated through LOT into classes. The classes are defined according to strength of mixing ratio of the odor components. The first class denotes the component with the largest mixing ratio, the second class does the component with the next largest ratio, and so on. The network of olfactory cortex is divided   into compartments corresponding to the classes. An odor component corresponding to each class is recognized in the compartment relevant to the class. The compartments are arranged in an order of strength of mixing ratio from rostral side of olfactory cortex to caudal side. The strongest component is recognized firstly, the next strongest one is recognized secondly, and so on, because the neural activity patterns induced by the input from LOT propagate from the rostral side to the caudal side [7,8]. This means that the stronger, that is , the more important the odor component is, the more rapidly it is recognized.

(3) The recognition of each component in each relevant compartment is made as follows. Many spatial firing patterns corresponding to odor components are memorized in a compartment network. When there is no stimulation, a neural activity of the compartment stays in the chaotically

itinerant state where the compartment shows one of the memorized patterns for a while and the pattern is randomly transfered to the other memorized pattern, that is, the current activity pattern itinerates chaotically among the memorized patterns. When the compartment is stimulated by a spatial firing pattern through LOT, the firing state is fixed to the memorized pattern corresponding to the input. If there is no memorized pattern which is similar to the input pattern, the compartment stays in the chaotically itinerant state.

(4) The classification of an odor in olfactory cortex is made by using a combination of firing pattern fixed in each compartment. This type of classification correspond to a hierarchical classification, because the fixed pattern in the first compartment determines the main characteristics of the odor applied and odor characteristics determined by each compartment becomes minor as the compartment is located at a longer distance from the rostral side.

2. A Neural Network Model of the Olfactory Cortex

2.1. Network structure of the olfactory cortex

The olfactory cortex is constructed with three kinds of network layers in a broad sense[7,8] as shown in Fig.1. The top and bottom layers consist of inter neurons which make inhibitory synaptic connections with pyramidal cells in the middle layer. The pyramidal cells are connected to each other with excitatory synapse, that is, the middle layer corresponds to an excitatory associative network. The spatio-temporal information from LOT propagate from the rostral part of olfactory cortex to the caudal part (See Fig.1).

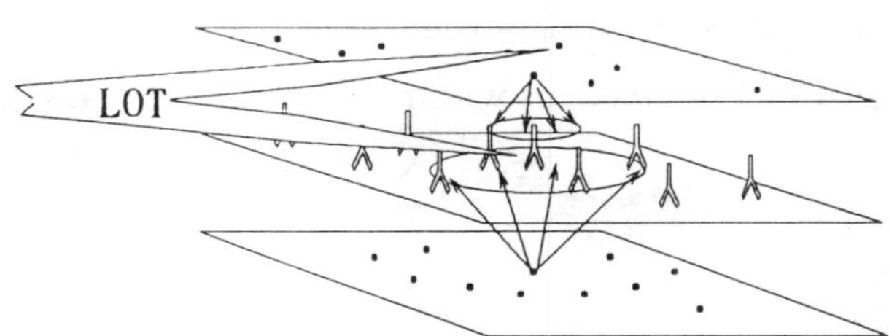

Fig.1. Schematic structure of olfactory cortex.

An effect of spatially and temporally continual flow of signals from the rostral side to the caudal side is essential for dynamical information processing in the olfactory cortex. In order to make this effect tractable, we divide the network of olfactory cortex into several compartments as shown in Fig.2. In a compartment the signals propagate without time delay. When the signals transfer from one compartment to another one, it takes a certain time for the signal propagation. In the present paper, we use a network model consisting of rostral, middle, and caudal ones shown in Fig.2, in order to show, as plainly as possible, a plausibility of our idea about mechanism of dynamical information processing in the olfactory cortex.

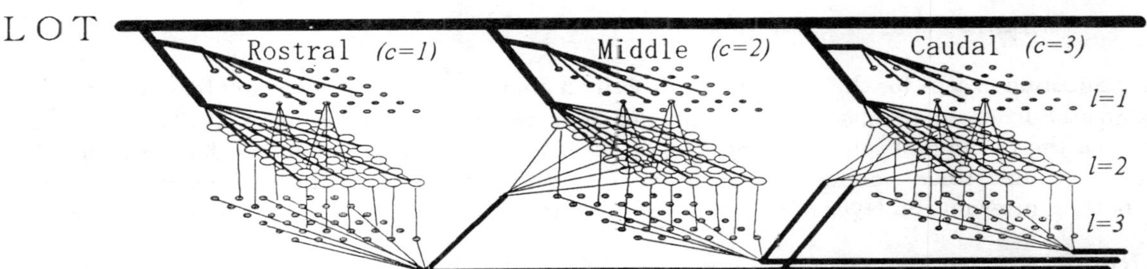

Fig. 2. The compartment model of olfactory cortex.

2.2. Equations for network dynamics

Time evolution of internal state of neurons is given by

$$\frac{du_{c.l.n}(t)}{dt} = \sum_{c'=1}^{C}\sum_{l'=1}^{3}\sum_{n'=0}^{N} w_{c'.l'.n',c.l.n}\, f\big[u_{c'.l'.n'}(t)\big] - \frac{u_{c.l.n}(t)}{\tau_u} + I_{c.l.n}(t) , \qquad (1)$$

$$f\big[u(t)\big] = \begin{cases} 1 & with\ the\ probability\ \ P = \frac{1}{2}\left\{ tanh\left[\frac{u(t)-\theta}{\gamma}\right] + 1\right\} \\[2ex] 0 & with\ the\ probability\ \ (1-P) \end{cases} \qquad (2)$$

$u_{c.a.i}$ is internal state of neuron i in layer l of compartment c. The output function $f[\ ]$ is takes 1 or

0 according to the probability P or $(1\text{-}P)$, and $I(t)$ is an input from LOT. Self organized change of synaptic strength w is given based on Hebbian learning rule as

$$\frac{dw_{c.l.n,c'.l'.n'}(t)}{dt} = h\cdot\int_{t-tw}^{t} f\!\left[u_{c.l.n}(t')\right]\cdot f\!\left[u_{c'.l'.n'}(t')\right]dt' - \frac{w_{c.l.n,c'.l'.n'}(t)}{\tau_w}. \tag{3}$$

2.3 Construction of chaotically itinerant state

The neural activity state of each compartment without stimulation is the state in which the activity pattern itinerates chaotically among memorized spatial firing patterns encoding odor components. We construct the chaotically itinaerant state in each compartment by giving the strength of synaptic connections $w_{c.l.n,c'.l'.n'}$ according to the following equations which include the storage prescription term $(\overset{m}{S},\overset{m}{S})$ and the pattern transition term $(\overset{m}{S},\overset{m+1}{S})$ [9].

(I) intracompartment connections ($c = c'$)

   (I - i) connections within a pyramidal cell layer ($l=l'=2$)

$$w_{c.2.n,c.2.n'} = \frac{1}{\overset{m}{N}_f}\sum_{m=1}^{M}\beta\cdot\overset{m+1}{S}_{c.2.n}\overset{m}{S}_{c.2.n'} \qquad\text{for }\;\overset{m+1}{S}_{c.2.n}=1 \text{ and }\;\overset{m}{S}_{c.2.n'}=0 \tag{4}$$

$$w_{c.l.n,c.2.n'} = \frac{1}{\overset{m}{N}_f}\sum_{m=1}^{M}\alpha\cdot\overset{m}{S}_{c.2.n}\cdot\left(2\cdot\overset{m}{S}_{c.2.n'}-1\right) + \frac{1}{\overset{m}{N}_f}\sum_{m=1}^{M}\beta\cdot\overset{m+1}{S}_{c.2.n}\overset{m}{S}_{,c.2.n'} \qquad\text{otherwise} \tag{5}$$

   (I - ii) connections between the pyramidal cell ($l=2$) and the top interneuron layers ($l=1$)

$$w_{c.2.n,c.l.n} = C_{2.1} \qquad(\text{a positive constant}) \tag{6}$$

$$w_{c.l.n,c.2.n'} = \frac{1}{\overset{m}{N}_f}\sum_{m=1}^{M}\alpha\cdot\overset{m}{S}_{c.2.n}\cdot\left(2\cdot\overset{m}{S}_{c.2.n'}-1\right) \qquad\text{for }\;\overset{m+1}{S}_{c.2.n}=1 \text{ and }\;\overset{m}{S}_{c.2.n'}=0 \tag{7}$$

   (I - iii) connections from pyramidal cell layer ($l=2$) to the bottom interneuron layer ($l'=3$)

$$w_{c.2.n,c.3.n} = C_{2.3} \qquad(\text{a positive constant}) \tag{8}$$

(II) intercompartment connections ($c < c'$)

$$w_{c.3.n,c'.2.n} = C_{c.3,c'.2} \qquad(\text{negative constant}) \tag{9}$$

All connection except for the connections described above are zero. The parameters α and β relate to stabilization of embedded patterns and their destabilization, respectively. The connections between the pyramidal cell layer and the top interneuron layers mean a feed forward inhibition. The intercompartment connections occur only from the pyramidal cell layer of one compartment to the bottom interneuron layer of the adjacent compartment on the caudal side as shown in FIg.2.

3. Results

3-1. Chaotically itinerant state

In order to generate a chaotically itinerant state in the three compartments, we adopt three, four, and five kinds of firing patterns for the rostral, middle and caudal compartments, respectively, which are shown in Fig.3, The current firing pattern in each compartment itinerates chaotically among the memorized patterns as seen in Fig.3, where the current network state is represented by using its Hamming distance from each memorized pattern. When the Hamming distance from m-th pattern is less than $4\sim5$ (this means 97.5% of matching) , a small black point is drawn on the m-th row at the time step.

3.2. Recognition of a spatial pattern in each compartment

When an input $I_{c.l.n}$ corresponding to a spatial pattern is applied to a compartment in a chaotically itinerant state, the firing state of the compartment becomes a memorized pattern relevant to the input in the case where the input pattern is very similar to one of the memorized patterns as shown schematically in Fig.4. On the other hand, in the case where the input pattern is not similar to any memorized patterns, the firing state stays in the chaotically itinerant state. Even in the former case, the firing state returns to the chaotically itinerant state, when the input is switched off. However, when the synaptic strength w are continually changed according to Eq.(3) during the application of input, the firing state stays in the memorized pattern relevant to the input even after switching the input off and stopping the synaptic change as shown in Fig.3. We consider this process as a recognition of input pattern.

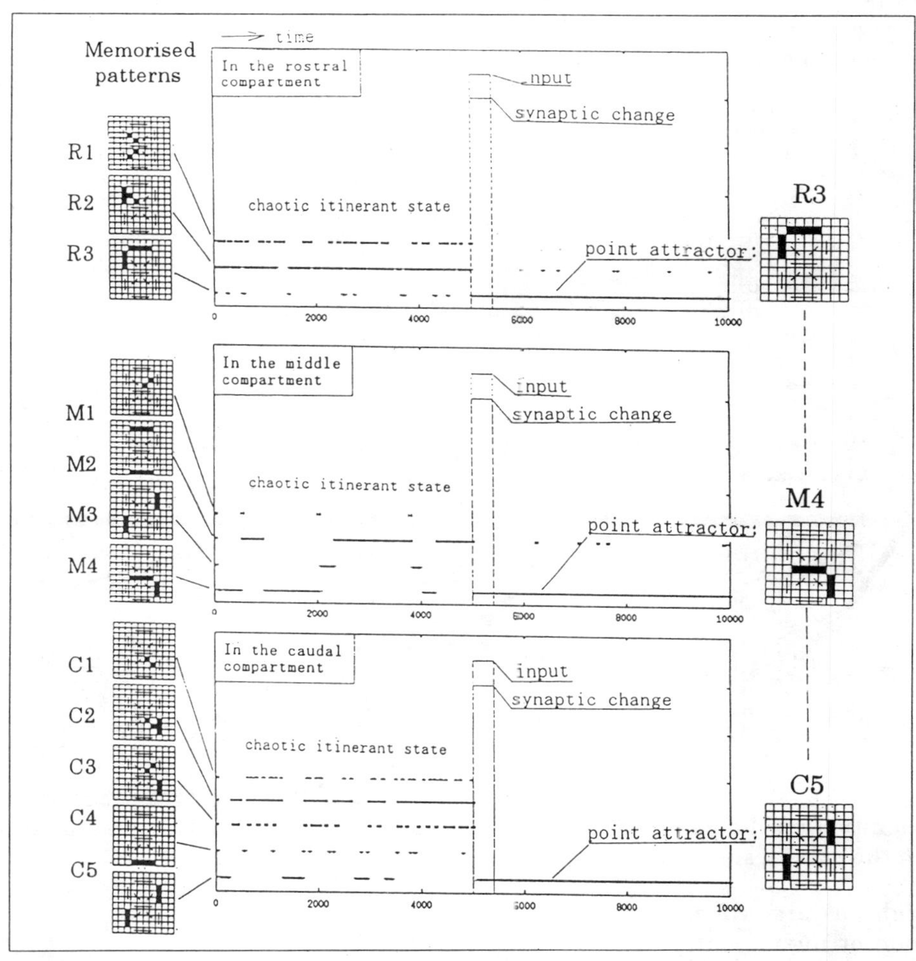

Fig.3

Recognition process for an input with the spatio-temporal pattern (R3→M4→C5→　R3→.....). When the spatio-temporal pattern is applied to the network from LOT, the firing state is fixed to the corresponding to the pattern in each compartment after some synaptic changes. Then the temporal pattern is classified by the combination of the three fixed patterns.

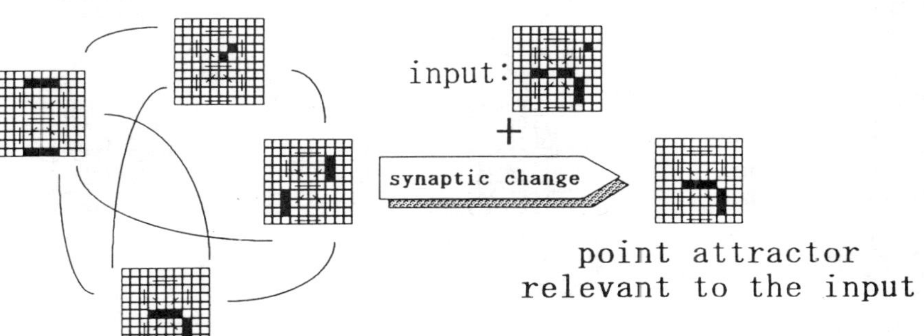

Fig.4. Recognition process for a spatial pattern.

3-3. Recognition of spatio-temporal pattern.

Odor stimulation is applied to olfactory cortex through LOT as spatio-temporal pattern (See Fig.5). When a temporal sequence of spatial patterns is given to the network consisting of the compartments, the rostral compartment recognizes the first spatial pattern of the sequence as mentioned in subsection 3-2. If the 1st spatial pattern is fixed in the rostral compartment, the 1st pattern could not appear in the middle and caudal compartments by effect of inhibition from the rostral compartment. That is , the rostral compartment apply the inhibition corresponding to the fixing pattern to the middle compartment through the bottom interneuron layer. Thus the middle compartment can recognize the 2nd spatial pattern of the sequence and the caudal compartment recognizes the 3rd pattern as shown (Fig .6). The spatio-temporal pattern recognized as a combination of spatial patterns fixed on each compartment.

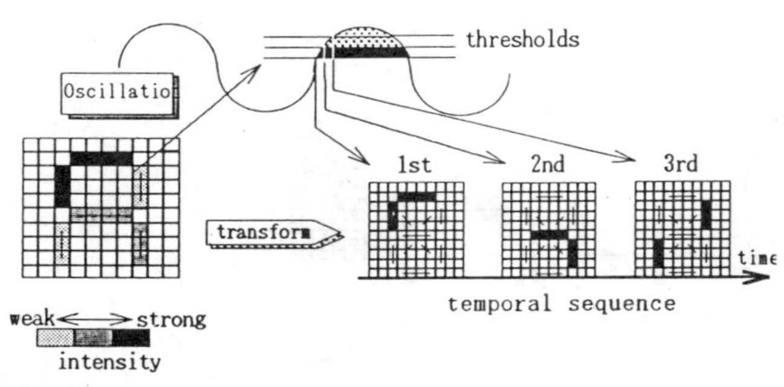

Fig.5. Transformation mechanism.
Odor stimulation is transformed to spatio-temporal pattern in the olfactory bulb based on the Hopfield mechanism[10]. Each spatial pattern codes each constituent components of an odor and the temporal sequence codes the magnitude of mixing ratio of the odor components.

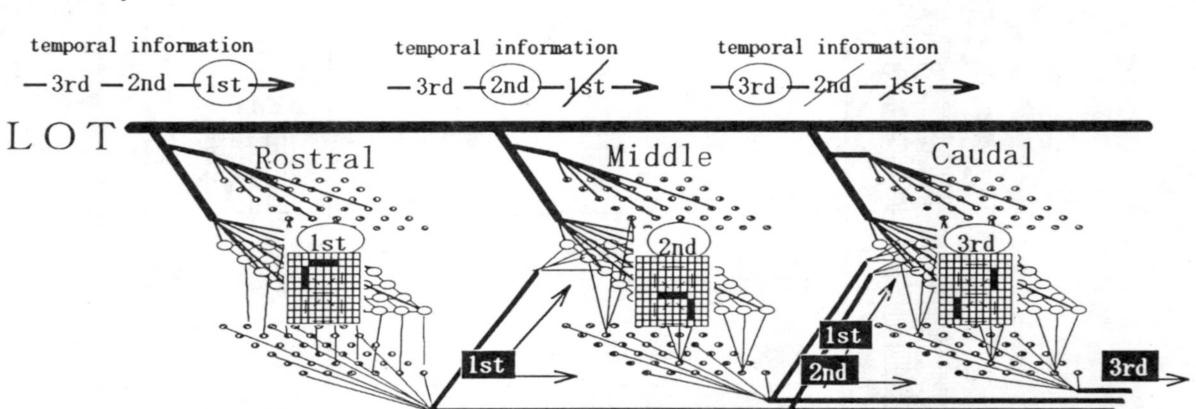

Fig.6 Recognition mechanism of a spatio-temporal pattern along the information propagation from the rostral side to the caudal side.

3-4. Hierarchical classification

The magnitude of mixing ratio of odor components is encoded as temporal sequence. Therefore the first spatial pattern in a sequence corresponds to the main characteristics of odor, that is the broad classification is firstly made in the rostral side. Thus, the spatio-temporal pattern is classified hierarchically in more detail as the pattern propagates from the rostral side to the caudal side.

Quite different odorants are classified only by the rostral side, but classification between similar odorants requires the patterns fixed in the caudal compartment as shown in Fig.7. That is, the classification based on the strength of mixing ratio of each component of an odor is hierarchical.

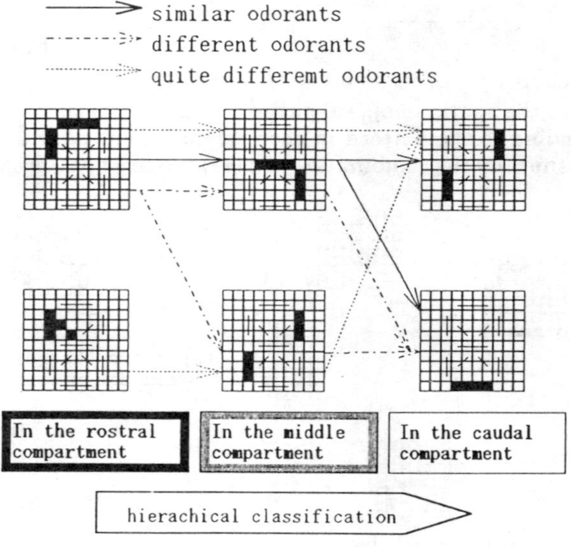

Fig.7 Scheme of hie1rarchical classification.

4 Conclusion

Based on a hypothesis that spatio-temporal pattern in a olfactory system encodes simultaneously both components of odor and their mixing-ratio, we have proposed a mechanism by which the olfactory cortex can classify such spatio-temporal patterns injected from LOT .

The classification of an odor in olfactory cortex is made by using a combination of firing patterns fixed in each compartment. This type of classification corresponds to a hierarchical classification, because the fixed pattern in the first compartment determines the main characteristics of the odor applied and odor characteristics determined by each compartment becomes minor as the compartment is located at a longer distance from the rostral side.

References

[1] E.Vaadia et al. , "Correlated activity of neurons: A neural code for higher brain functions ? " In Neural Cooperativity, J.Kruger (Ed), Springer-Verlag, Berlin, PP.249-279, 1991.

[2] S.Thorpe, " Localized versus distributed respresentations. In the hund book of brain theory and neural networks", M.A.Arbib (Ed.), MIT Press, Cambrige, MA. PP, 549-552, 1995.

[3] W.J.Freeman and G.V.Di Prisco, "Correlation of olfactory EEG with behavior : Apatial analysis." Behavioral Neuroscience, 100, PP. 753-763,1986.

[4] W.J. Freeman and B.Baired, "Correlation of ofactory EEG with behavior : Spatial analysis." Behavioral Neuroscience, 101, PP. 393-408, 1987.

[5] C.A.Skarada and W.J.Freeman, " How brain makes chaos in order to make sense of the world." Behavioral underbrain sceence, 10, PP 161-195, 1987.

[6] O.Hoshino et al., "spatio-temporal representation of odor information in olfactory bulb." Proceedings of Int. Conf. on Neural Information processing '96 Hong kong, 1996.

[7] H.Liljenstrom,"Modeling the dynamics of olfactory cortex using simplified network nits and realistic architecture,"Int.J.Neural Syst,vol.2, PP.1-15,1991.

[8] T.Oyamada et al.., "Transduction of impulse trairs carried by LOT to the spatio-temporal patterns in the neural network modek of the olfactory cortex."Proceedings of Int. Conf.on Information Processings (ICONIP'95) 1, PP 133-136, 1995.

[9] J.J.Hopfield, "Neural networks and physical systems with emergent collective computational abilities." Proc. Nafl. Acad. Sci. USA, 79, PP. 2554-2558, 1982.

[10] J.J. Hopfield, "Pattern recognition computation using action potential timing for stimulus representaion." Nature, 376, PP. 33-36, 1995.

Diagnostic information extraction from automated ECG analysis in anterior myocardial infarction using neural networks

Koji OGURI, Akira IWATA†, Kazunobu Yamauchi‡

† Nagoya Institute of Technology , Nagoya , Japan
‡ Nagoya University Hospital , Nagoya , Japan

Aichi Prefectural University , Nagoya , Japan
Tel +81 52 851 2191   Fax +81 52 852 5829
oguri@center.nitech.ac.jp

Abstract— The diagnostic algorithm in currently available automated ECG analysis mainly uses the "if-then" rule, according to which it is difficult to extract ambiguous medical information from ECG data sufficiently enough to make an accurate diagnosis. There is a large number of patients who are falsely diagnosed as having cardiac diseases by automated ECG analysis, despite of the fact that they do not actually suffer from the diseases. The authors have devised a new differentiation technique by applying neural networks to ECG diagnosis of anterior myocardial infarction, which is high in both sensitivity and specificity. In this study, we evaluated the performance of this neural network system in differentiating cases with anterior myocardial infarction from those without the disease, using patients who had been classified into the category of "abnormal" by automated ECG analysis and were later found on reexamination by cardiologists to be included in the category of "not abnormal." The system correctly differentiated between the two categories with a recognition rate of 91.9%. We also tried to extract information about the anterior myocardial infarction from each lead and the peak values from the ECG, and confirmed that the information extracted from the present system is theoretically correct.

1   Introduction

Automated ECG analysis has recently been widely performed at various medical institutions for ECG diagnosis of cardiac diseases, irrespective of the presence or absence of cardiologists at the institutions. The analysis uses a diagnostic algorithm by which patients with a suspected disease are all classified into the category of abnormal, and considerable emphasis has been placed on the improvement of sensitivity of the equipment in order to avoid any "omission" in initial diagnosis. In current diagnostic procedures, reexaminations are performed by cardiologists to make a definite diagnosis on patients classified as suffering from disease by the automated ECG analysis system. In reality, the position of each lead over the body surface for one patient, may not be identical to that for other patients because of differences in the body type or sex. The automated diagnostic equipment cannot take such individualized factors into account when making a diagnosis. In addition, it is difficult for this system to extract specialized medical information from ECG data. It has been pointed out that the use of conventional, analytic algorithm alone has to the improvement of limitations differentiation. As a matter of fact the cardiologists' decision making has not yet been programmed to a satisfactory extent (Fig.1). For these reasons, there is a large number of patients who are falsely classified into the category of abnormal by automated ECG analysis despite the fact that they do not actually suffer from cardiac diseases. Reexamination of these patients not only has a psychologically bad influence upon them, but also consumes unnecessary time for medical examination by doctors.

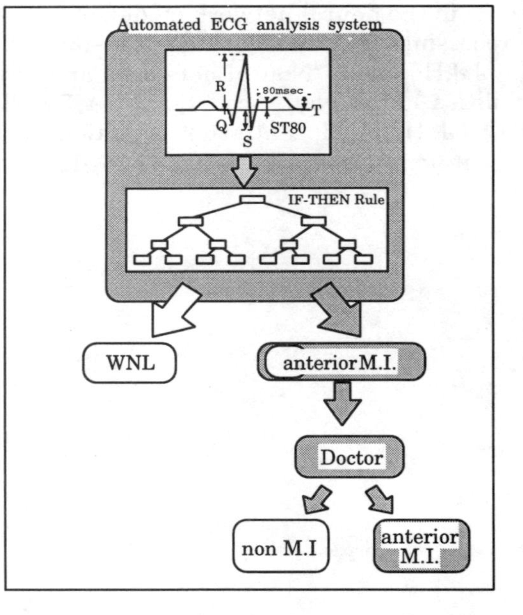

Figure 1: Today's diagnosis flow

Neural networks have been highly evaluated since they are able to process ambiguous information such as medical information [1]. In this study, the performance of a neural network system for differentiation of anterior myocardial infarction was evaluated in patients who had been diagnosed as having the disease by automated ECG analysis. The effectiveness of ECG diagnosis using the neural network system and its capability to extract information were also studied.

2   Data

The subjects of this differentiation study were 132 patients who had been diagnosed as having anterior myocardial infarction on examination with automated ECG diagnostic equipment using standard 12 leads (FCP4301, Fukuda Denshi) and who were reexamined later by cardiologists for the purpose of confirming the diagnosis on the basis of patient history, echocardiography, and myocardial scintigraphy. For 66 out of 132 patients, as shown in Fig.2, anterior myocardial infarction was diagnosed by the automated ECG analysis but the diagnosis was overruled on the second examination. For the remaining 66, the disease was confirmed on the second examination. ECG data were obtained with 8 leads (i.e. V1 - V6, I, and II), at which peak values of Q, R, S, ST80 and T were recorded. A total of 40 different parameters were recorded for each subject. These ECG data were all verified by cardiologists.

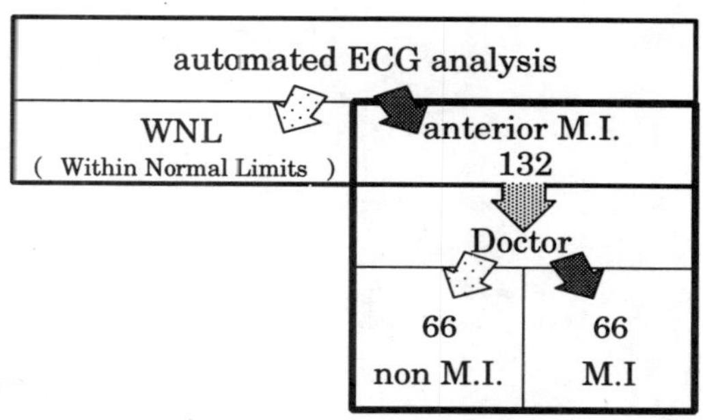

Figure 2: Data

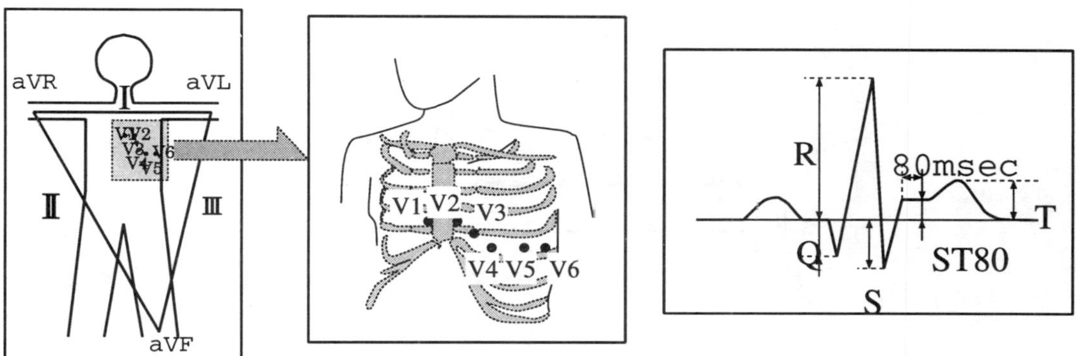

Figure 3: Lead and ECG parameter

3   System

Fig.4 illustrates a conceptual diagram for the system used in this study. The system is a simple 3-component neural network, consisting of an input component, an intermediate component, and an output component. The input component contains 40 parameters, i.e. 5 peak values for each of the 8 leads. The output component is composed of 2 categories, one for myocardial infarction and the other for non-myocardial infarction. The learning rule used was Back Propagation. Pretreatment was conducted through the use of equation (1) described below in order to handle any lack of information regarding input data, any data significantly different from the other data group, or any other problematic data. The number of data for the intermediate component was determined in accordance with the Rule of Thumb.

$$X_n = (x - \alpha_{min})W + 0.1 \qquad (1)$$
$$W = \frac{0.8}{\alpha_{max} - \alpha_{min}}$$

$$
\begin{aligned}
x &: \textit{value before pretreatment} \\
X_n &: \textit{value after pretreatment} \\
\alpha_{max} &: \textit{maximum value of data} \\
\alpha_{min} &: \textit{minimum value of data}
\end{aligned}
$$

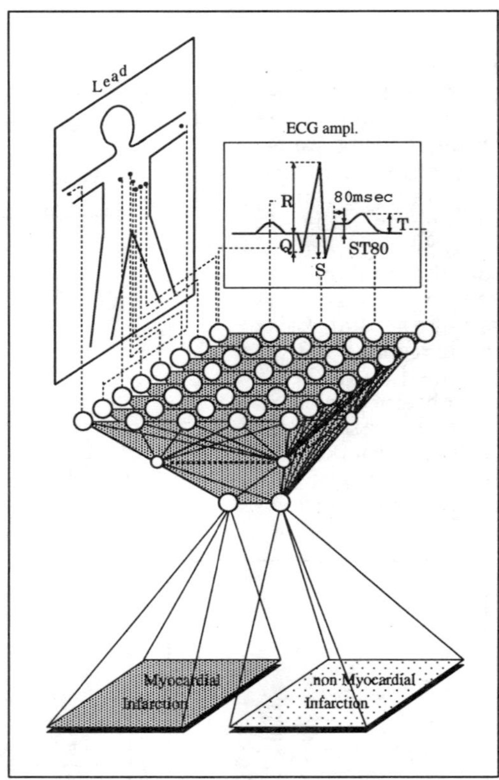

Figure 4: Conceptual diagram for the system

4   Classification Test

4.1   Classification by "Leave One Out"

4.1.1   Methods

For the purpose of evaluating the present system, a classification test by the "Leave One Out" method was performed using the data obtained from the 132 patients. The number of data was 40 for the input component and 2 for the output component, i.e. anterior myocardial infarction or non-anterior myocardial infarction. The number of data for the intermediate component was 11 through 20, i.e. in 10 different ways. The number of iterations was varied from 10, 20, ... 100, 200, ... through 1000 times (i.e. 19 different ways).

4.1.2   Results and discussion

The classification test results obtained by the "Leave One Out" method are shown in Table 1. The highest recognition rate of 96.2% was obtained when the number of data for the intermediate component was 11 and the number of iterations ranged from 500 to 800, and for 400 to 900 iterations when the number of intermediate component was 12. The highest sensitivity of 97.0% was gained when the number of data for the intermediate component was 11, 12, 13, 14, and 16. The highest specificity of 96.45% was achieved when the number of data for the intermediate component was 10, 11, 12, 14, 17, 18, 19, and 20 and the number of iterations exceeded 400.

Table 1: Results of Leave One Out

sens.[%]	spec.[%]	rec.rate[%]
97.0	95.5	96.2

4.2   Classification when training data were segregated from testing data

4.2.1   Methods

For the purpose of evaluating the present system, another classification test was performed through the use of data divided into two categories, i.e. one for training and the other for testing. The network configuration for this test was set as follows since this setting produced one of the most satisfactory results in the "Leave One Out" differentiation test: therefore, the intermediate component was 12 and the number of iterations was 900. The data used were from 33 patients with anterior myocardial infarction and 33 healthy sub jects, who were all randomly selected, and then classified into one of the two categories, i.e. one for training and the other for testing. This procedure was repeated 40 times for the implementation of classfication tests.

4.2.2 Results and discussion

The sensitivity, specificity, and recognition rate of the system were calculated from the obtained test results shown below. A value of 100% was achieved once for sensitivity and 4 times for specificity. The mean value over the 40 trials was 91.9% for recognition rate,90.2% for sensitivity, and 93.3% for specificity. Evaluation of all 40 trials revealed the fact that trials producing higher sensitivity resulted in lower specificity. The trials for which the accuracy of diagnosis was low in this differentiation test included patients who were mis-identified by the "Leave One Out" differentiation test. The presence of complications such as hypertension was confirmed by cardiologists for these patients. On the other hand, the trials showing high accuracy of diagnosis did not include patients with such complications. These findings indicate that differentiation of patients with several diseases is complex and that it is difficult to recognize such patients on the basis of ECG information even when the neural network is utilized.

Table 2: Test results

Try	sens.[%]	spec.[%]	rec. rate[%]
2	93.9	100	97.0
5	97.0	93.9	95.5
10	93.9	93.9	93.9
19	93.9	97.0	95.5
25	81.8	100	90.9
28	84.9	100	92.4
34	97.0	93.9	95.5
35	100	75.8	87.9
36	97.0	93.9	95.5
40	84.9	100	92.4
aver.	90.2	93.3	91.9

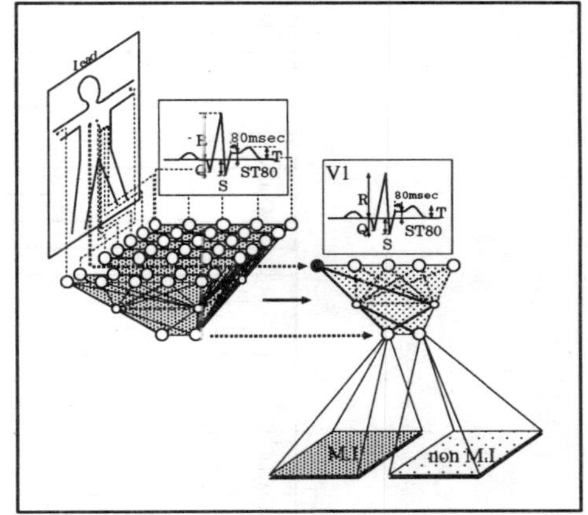

Figure 5: Information extraction test concept

5 Information Extraction Test

5.1 Methods

The authors investigated to what extent theoretical information of cardiac diseases can be extracted from ECG data through the use of the present system. It is generally hard to analyze output results of a neural network system in order to identify the reasons that lead to those results. In this test, network connections to selected input parameters were blocked, and the results obtained were compared with those obtained when such blockage was not performed. Comparing how recognition rate, sensitivity, and specificity changed, the input parameters on which this neural network system focused at the time of classification were identified. For the purpose of evaluating the influence of each lead and its peak values, classication tests were repeated by the following method: an input component in each test was a subset consisting of ECG segments determined by various combinations of the 5 peak values of parameters Q, R, S, ST80, and T. 31 different ways of networking were set up by blocking connections between the intermediate component and the input parameters excluded from the subset concerned. Classification tests were conducted for each lead. The input data used were from 50 patients who were randomly selected among 63 patients with anterior myocardial infarction, and from 50 healthy subjects randomly selected among 63, that is, from 100 in all. The population of 63 patients with the disease did not include those who would be mis-identified even by cardiologists in the differentiation test. The number of data for the intermediate component was determined in accordance with the Rule of Thumb.

5.2 Results and discussion

Table 3 shows the classification test results with the V4 lead, the tests were also conducted with the other leads. Table 3 shows the differentiation test results obtained for each subset with the V4 lead: Each of the horizontal line represents a subset ; 31 combinations V of parameters a subset consisted Q, R, S, ST80, and T are displated ; net connections to missing input parameters were blocked. of ECG segments determined by various combinations of the 5 parameters, i.e. Q, R, S, ST80, and T, for which network connections to the input parameters not included in the subset concerned were blocked. Since the data used were from patients without any complication, the sensitivity achieved was 98% and the specificity was 100%. As the number of data for input parameters decreased, the sensitivity and the recognition rate became lower, although no substantial change was noted in specificity.On the basis of the above-described results, we tried to identify the input parameters on which this neural network system focused and to determine the relevance of the identified parameters to the algorithm used by cardiologists for ECG analysis, in order to evaluate to what extent this system extracts information from ECG data. Fig. 6 shows a map indicating the degree of focus. The degree of focus was calculated by the equation described below.

$$Degree\ of\ focus = 1 - \frac{x_0 - x}{x_0} \tag{2}$$

Where:

x : *Individual recognition rate in the classification concerned*
x_0 : *Recognition rate of the present system*

Table 3: Classification test results with the V_4 lead

Q	R	S	ST80	T	sens. [%]	spec.[%]	rec. rate[%]
Q					42	100	71
	R				60	98	79
		S			8	94	51
			ST80		74	84	79
				T	94	96	95
Q	R				62	98	80
Q		S			42	100	71
Q			ST80		68	98	83
Q				T	92	98	95
	R	S			62	98	80
	R		ST80		86	90	88
	R			T	98	98	98
		S	ST80		72	94	83
		S		T	98	98	98
			ST80	T	92	98	95
Q	R	S			62	98	80
Q	R		ST80		86	92	89
Q	R			T	98	98	98
Q		S	ST80		78	98	88
Q		S		T	98	98	98
Q			ST80	T	96	98	97
	R	S	ST80		84	94	89
	R	S		T	98	100	99
	R		ST80	T	98	98	98
		S	ST80	T	96	98	97
Q	R	S	ST80		86	92	89
Q	R	S		T	98	100	99
Q	R		ST80	T	98	100	99
Q		S	ST80	T	98	98	98
	R	S	ST80	T	98	100	99
Q	R	S	ST80	T	98	100	99

The vertical line of this figure represents the individual leads used in the test, which is regarded as position information, and the horizontal line, different ECG segments determined by various combinations of the 5 parameters peak values. On Fig. 6 , the crossing of position information parameters involved gives the degree of focus. For each input a higher degree of focus is represented by a darker shade. A darker shade of a lead or parameter box indicates that the lead or parameter is given more importance by the system when it diagnoses anterior myocardial infarction. Evaluation of the recognition rate (Fig. 6) reveals that the present system makes recognition by substantially focusing on the V3 and V4 leads

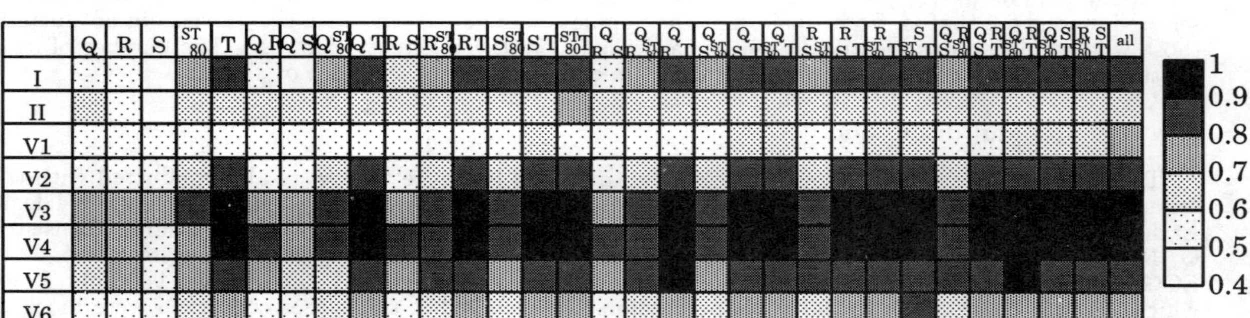

Figure 6: Degree of focus on recognition rate

as well as ST80 and T parameters. These leads and parameters were found to be almost identical to the items that cardiologists focus on when making a diagnosis.

6   Conclusion

As described above, the performance of this neural network system for Recognition of anterior my-ocardial infarction was evaluated in patients who had been diagnosed as having the disease by automated ECG analysis. The overall diagnostic accuracy of the system proved quite high, exceeding 90%. Next, differentiation tests were performed with individual leads through the use of different combinations of parameters, which revealed that the present system focuses on the V3, V4, and V5 leads as well as ST80 and T parameters when it recognizes the disease. These leads and parameters are identical to the items that cardiologists pay special attention to when diagnosing anterior myocardial infarction. The importance of T wave in diagnosing the disease, which is pointed out by cardiologists, is indicated by the present system. This has been noted by B. Heden, et al [2] who performed classification tests us-ing neural networks to diagnose inferior myocardial infarction. M.R.S. Reddy, et al [3] compared the rate of recognition of anterior myocardial infarction achieved by a neural network system with that by cardiologists, and concluded that the diagnostic accuracy by the neural network system was identical to that by cardiologists. However, since the input data selected by Reddy, et al did not include T wave but instead used the amplitude and width of Q, R, and S with V2, V3, and V4 leads, they did not notice the importance of T wave.

The "if-then" rule commonly used in the currently available diagnostic algorithm for automated ECG analysis considers the width of Q wave, ratio of Q wave's peak value to R wave's peak value, and T wave's peak value, all with V2, V3, and V4 leads in order to diagnose anterior myocardial infarction. It is said that cardiologists pay special attention to Q, ST, and T when diagnosing the disease. From the viewpoint of internal medicine, abnormal Q waves, elevation of ST segment, and coronary T waves represent myocardial necrosis, myocardial injuries, and myocardial ischemia, respectively. Depending on the body type or sex of patients, however, the finding of QS wave or poor R wave progression with V1 - V3 leads may not be always associated with myocardial infarction. This is why currently diagnostic systems misclassify cases as suffering from myocardial infarction. Therefore there remains a large difference between the diagnostic accuracy achieved by automated ECG analysis and that by cardiologists. It is therefore considered that the use of the "if-then" rule alone for an ECG diagnosis of myocardial infarction would not provide satisfactory results. On the other hand, the neural network performs non-linear treatment and is excellent in pattern recognition. The differentiation test results obtained with the neural network system used in this study also reveal a high diagnostic accuracy in processing ambiguous information provided by electrocardiography. In light of the above described results and findings, combining neural networks and the algorithm for automated ECG analysis is judged effective in improving the accuracy of automated ECG analysis

References

[1] Giovanni Bortolan,Rosanna Degani,Jos L. Willems, "NEURAL NETWORKS FOR ECG CLASSIFICA-TION,"*Computers In Cardiology* ,pp269~272 , 1990.

[2] B Heden,L Edenbrandt,WK Haisty Jr,O Pahlm, "Neural Networks for ECG Diagnosis of Inferior Myocardial Infarction," *Computers In Cardiology*, pp345~347 , 1993.

[3] M.R.S.Reddy,L.Edenbrandt,J.Svensson, W.K.Haisty,O.Pahlm, "Neural Network versus Electrocardiographer and Conventional Computer Criteria in Diagnosing Anterior Infarct from the ECG," *Computers In Cardiology*, pp667~670 , 1992.

Simulations on Sign Selective Process in Jamming Avoidance Response of Electric Fish *Eigenmannia*

Yoshiki Kashimori and Takeshi Kambara
Department of Applied Physics and Chemistry,
The University of Electro-communications,Chofu,Tokyo,182 Japan
e-mail:kashi@nerve.pc.uec.ac.jp

Abstract— To clarify the neuronal mechanism producing jamming avoidance response (JAR) of electric fish, we present the neural network models of electrosensory lateral line lobe(ELL) and torus semicircularis (TS) in the midbrain of the fish. These models reproduce well the observed functions and reveal the mechanism by which the functions are realized. We also propose the integration mechanism by which the sign of difference(Df) in frequency of electric organ discharge (EOD) between the fish and the neighbor is evaluated. Although the fish has wrong information besides correct information for detection of the sign of Df, the correct information is adopted without fail based on joint computation of amplitude and phase of jamming EOD signal.

1   Introduction

In many sensory systems, it is important problem how information of external stimulus is processed along the pathways from receptors to central nerve systems(CNS) and the result is connected with behavior. This problem has not been yet clear in most sensory system. The exceptions are sound location of barn owl and electrolocation of electric fish. The neural mechanisms of information processing in these behaviors have been clarified based on physiological and ethological experiments. In the present paper,we construct a neural model of the electrosensory system of electric fish and clarify the microscopic mechanism for jamming avoidance response using the model.

The weakly electric fish *Eigenmannia* uses distortions of electric field around its body surface to perceive its environment[1]. The electric field around the body is detected by electroreceptors located on the body surface. When two fishes with similar electric organ discharge (EOD) frequencies meet, each fish is capable of shifting its EOD frequency so as to increase the frequency difference between them. This behavior is called jamming avoidance response (JAR). In order to make JAR, the fish must determine whether its neighbor has a frequency higher or lower than its own. The function of information processing relevant to JAR of *Eigenmannia* is well defined in each neural system along the pathways from receptors to CNS based on the physiological and ethological experiments[1]. The schematic structure of the neural system relevant to JAR is shown in Fig. 1.

Eigenmannia uses two cues for JAR; modulation of EOD amplitude and modulation of EOD phase. In the initial stage, the two modulations of jamming signal are coded by two types of electroreceptors. The informations are conveyed separately to the midbrain, electrosensory lateral line lobe(ELL) and torus semicircularis (TS). Neurons in ELL code the modulations of stimulus amplitude, while neurons in TS code the modulations of stimulus phase. Both the informations about the amplitude and phase modulations are integrated over the an array of electroreceptors on the body surface and converge into deeper laminæ of the torus. Using the information, the fish can discriminate the sign of frequency difference between its own EOD and neighbor's EOD.

Eigenmannia can detect difference in zero-crossing times of EOD down to 1 μsec [2], where the zero-crossing times encode EOD phase. Any neural mechanism realising such a hyperacuity has not been yet known. Furthermore, it has not been clear how the fish integrates the information about amplitude and phase modulations over an array of electroreceptors and determines the sign of frequency difference(Df) based on the integrated result.

In order to clarify the neuronal mechanism producing JAR, we proposed a microscopic model of electroreceptors[3,6] and neural network models of the midbrain, ELL and TS[4,5]. We have clarified the neural mechanism by which the amplitude and phase modulations are encoded by the receptor model and the sign of Df is determined from the integration of the informations encoded. However, the model of TS is too simple to detect the difference of zero-crossing times of the order of 10 μsec. In order to detect such an extremely fine time disparity, a neuron model must have realistic properties such as refractory period and adaptation of threshold value for firing.

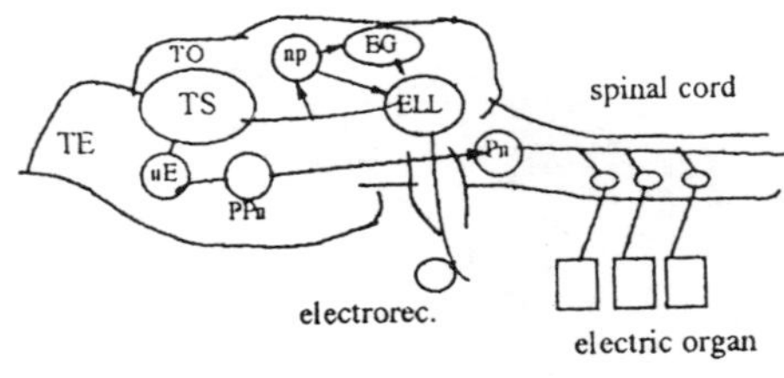

Fig. 1 Sketch of neural structures and pathways involved in JAR of electric fish

In the present study, we use a network model based on MacGregor model which is a simplified version of Hodgkin-Huxley model. The microscopic properties of the neuron and on center-off surround internal connection of the network play an essential role in detection of such a fine time disparity.

We propose also the integration mechanism by which the sign of frequency difference (Df) is discriminated. Although the fish has wrong information besides correct information for detection of sign of Df, the wrong information is omitted through joint computation of the integrated informations about amplitude and phase.

2   A Neural Network Model of Electrosensory Lateral Line Lobe (ELL)

The extensive experimental studies about structure and function of ELL[1] have been made to understand the neural mechanism of the information processing in the ELL. Basilar pyramidal cells(bp) in ELL are excited by an increase in stimulus amplitude. The center-surround organization in the receptive field of cells in ELL has been found. The basilar pyramidal cells have an on center-off surround receptive field as shown in Fig. 2, while the nonbasilar pyramidal cells(nbp) have an off center-on surround field[1].

We present a neural network model of ELL based on its anatomical structure. Figure 2 shows a model of receptor innervation to a bp cell. A bp cell is excited directly by central input from P-afferent nerve and inhibited indirectly by peripheral input via granule cells. The dynamical states of the bp cell and the granule cells are described by the following equations,

$$\tau_{bp}\frac{dV_{bp}}{dt} = -V_{bp} + \sum_{i=1}^{N} w_i^{exc}I_i + \sum_{j=1}^{N'} w_j^{inh} f_j(t - \Delta t), \tag{1}$$

$$\tau_{gr}\frac{dV_{gr}^j}{dt} = -V_{gr}^j + I_j, \tag{2}$$

where V_{bp} and V_{gr}^j are the membrane potentials of the bp cell and of jth granule cell, respectively, τ_{bp} and τ_{gr} are relaxation time constants for the potentials of bp and granule cell, w_i^{exc} and w_j^{inh} are the synaptic strength of excitatory and inhibitory connections, and f is an output of granule cell, which is given by a sigmoid function.

Δt is a delay time for signal propagation over a longer distance from bp to peripheral sites at which the granule cells are. N and N' are the numbers of the central input fibers and the granule cells, I is the input from P-afferent nerve. As the stimulus amplitude is increased, firing rate of the bp cell increases. However, the increase of firing rate is inhibited by the inputs via the granule cells with a time delay. The model of nbp cell for coding a fall of stimulus amplitude has a similar receptor field structure except for the off center-on surround innervation.

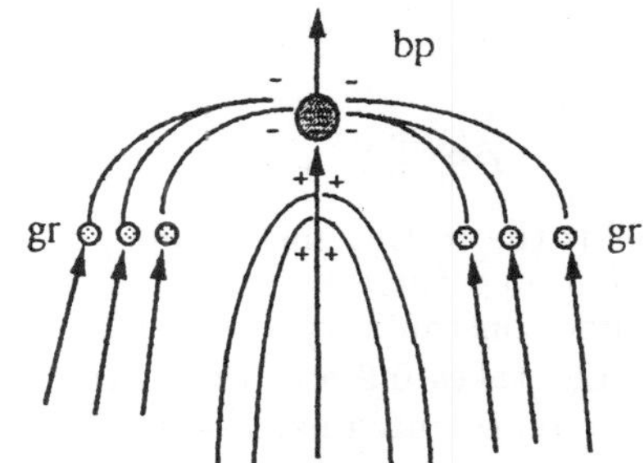

Fig. 2 A model of basilar pyramidal cell system. bp cell is excited by the central inputs (+) and is inhibited by peripheral inputs (-) via granule cell(gr) with a time delay.

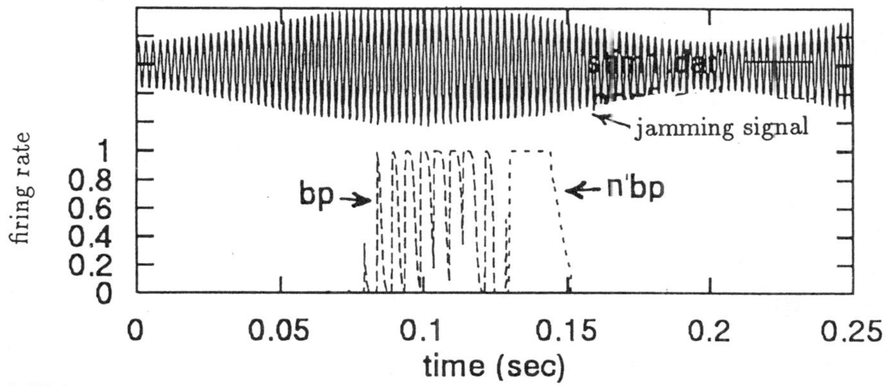

Fig. 3 Firing rates of bp and nbp cells induced by a jamming signal shown on the top. bp and nbp cells code a rise and a fall of stimulus amplitude, respectively, as shown.

Figure 3 shows the firing rates of bp and nbp cells for the input from P-afferent nerves. The bp and nbp cells code a rise and a fall of stimulus amplitude as seen in Fig. 3, respectively.

3 A Neural Network model of Torus Semicircularis (TS)

Small cell(SC) in TS gets information about zero-crossing times of the jamming EOD stimulus received by T-receptors being at two different points on the body surface. Each small cell detects the time disparity between pulse trains transmitted from T-afferent nerves on one point to dendrite of SC and pulse trans from other point to soma of SC[7,8] as shown in Fig. 4. The small cell can detect the time disparity of the order of 10 μsec.

In order to clarify the neural mechanism producing such a hyperacuity of detection in TS, we present neural network model of TS shown in Fig. 4. The linearly array of small cells detects the time difference as *coincidence detector* proposed by Jefferess[9]. In the Jefferess model, only one cell corresponding to relevant time disparity is allowed to fire. Therefore, the line works as a map for the detection of time disparity. However, the firing condition used in the Jefferess model is not applicable to the present situation in which the hyperacuity is realized, because the relaxation time of each neuron is of the order of 1 msec. When the time difference between two input pulses is 10 μsec , about 100 neurons fire almost simultaneously as seen in Fig. 4. Therefore, the Jefferess model can not detect the time disparity less than 1 msec. Our task is that by using small cell model with realistic properties such as relaxation time, refractory period, and adaptation of threshold value for firing, we find a realistic neural architecture to detect such a fine time disparity(- 10 μ sec). We used a modified MacGregor model for a single neuron[10]. The following equations describe kinetics of the membrane potentials, the threshold function, and the potasium conductance for ith small cell:

$$\tau_V \frac{dV_i}{dt} = -(V_i - V_i^0) - g_K^i(V_i - V_K) - (g_s^1 + g_s^2)(V_i - V_{Na}) - \sum_j^{exc} g_s^{ij}(V_i - V_{Na}) - \sum_j^{inh} g_s^{ij}(V_i - V_K), \quad (3)$$

$$\tau_{\theta_i^n} \frac{d\theta_i}{dt} = -(\theta_i - \theta_0) + C_\theta(V_i - V_i^0); \quad (n = 1 \ \ for \ \ d\theta/dt > 0, \ \ n = 2 \ \ for \ \ d\theta/dt < 0) \quad (4)$$

$$\tau_K \frac{dg_K^i}{dt} = -g_K^i + C_K(V_i - V_i^0), \quad (5)$$

$$PS_i = V_i + S(50 - V_i); \qquad S = 1 \ \ for \ \ V_i > \theta_i \ \ S = 0 \ \ otherwise, \quad (6)$$

where, V_i^0 is the resting membrane potential, and takes -65 mV and τ_V takes 1 msec. τ_K takes 5 msec, C_K does 5.0, and the reversal potential, V_K, takes -85 mV, V_{Na} does 57 mV. The threshold θ_i has two kinds of time constants, τ_θ^1 and τ_θ^2 take typically 0.9 msec and 5 msec, respectively. The threshold driving constant, C_θ, takes 0.9 and the resting threshold, θ_0, takes -53 mV. Postsynaptic conductances, g_s^1, g_s^2 and g_s^{ij}, are represented usual alpha functions, takes

$$g_s^X = g_s^X(0)\frac{t - ti}{\tau_s}exp[1 - \frac{t - t_i}{\tau_s}], \quad (X = 1, 2, ij) \quad (7)$$

where t_i is the time when input pulse arrives at ith small cell, and τ_s is the rising time of EPSP.

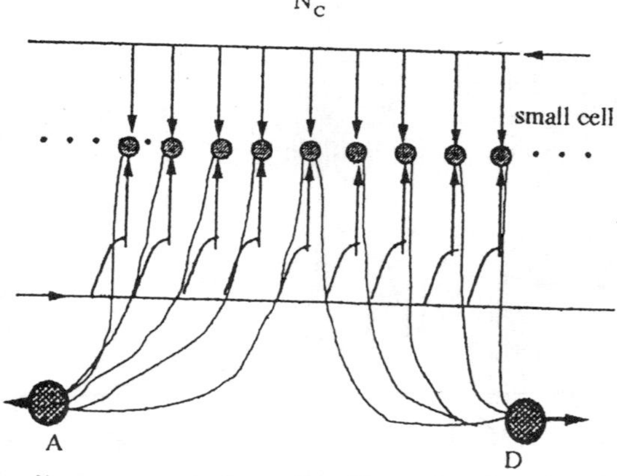

Fig. 4 A model of TS. The linear array of small cells codes the time disparity as coincidence detector in a broad sense. The firing rates of neurons A and D are changed depending on the place of the most actively firing cell.

The strength, w_{iA} and w_{iD} of synaptic connection from ith small cell to the neurons A and D are increased monotonically as the small cell goes away from the central neuron (N_C). The dynamical states of the neurons A and D are given by

$$\tau_Y \frac{dV_Y}{dt} = -V_Y + \sum_{i=} w_{iY}(PS_i - V_i^0) \quad (Y = A, D) \tag{8}$$

$$X_Y = \frac{1}{1 + e^{-(V_Y - V_{th})/\epsilon}}, \tag{9}$$

where, X_Y is the firing rate of neuron Y. The neurons A and D detect the time disparity through variation of their firing rate induced by the spatial variation of synaptic strength as shown below.

Figure 5(a) shows the spatio-temporal pattern of firing rate of small cells in the linear array of the cells, which is induced by input trains from T-receptors. The sites of small cells with the maximum firing rate, which corresponding to the time disparity between the two input pulses, move from the right to the left side in the linear array shown in Fig. 4.

Figure 5(b) shows the firing rate of the neurons A and D. In the region of phase advance, the firing rate of the neuron A is larger than that of neuron D. On the other hand, in the region of phase delay, the firing rate of the neuron D is larger than that of neuron A.

It is seen in the result that the neurons A and D can detect the time disparity or phase disparity in spite of the broad firing pattern in the linear array.

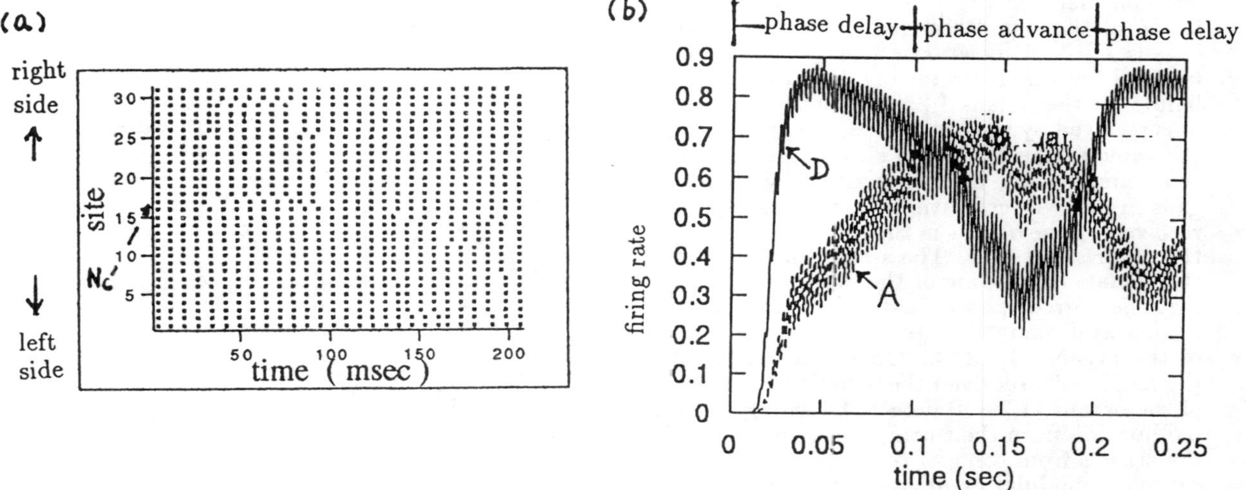

Fig. 5 (a) The spatio-temporal variation of firing rate of small cells in the linear array of the cells. This is a two dimensional projection of three dimentional representation of the variation. (b) The temporal variation of firing rate of the neurons A and D.

4   Joint Computation of Amplitude and Phase Information

We consider here the mechanism of selection of the sign cf difference Df between frequency of the fish's EOD and that of neighbor's EOD. Amplitude and phase informations converge on deeper laminae of the torus where sign selective cells recognize four types of combinations of phase and amplitude modulations to detect the sign of Df. The four types of combinations of amplitude and phase informations coded in ELL and TS are; E(rise in amplitude)-A(phase advance), E-D(phase delay), I(fall in amplitude) -Delay, and I-A. Neurons responding to E-D type and I-A type combinations fire for the stimuli with positive Df, while the neurons responding to E-A type and I-D type fire for the stimuli with negative Df.

The degree of interference of a fish's own EOD field with neighbor's EOD field changes with positions on body surface of the fish as seen in Fig. 6a. Because the interference becomes maximum at the area A and minimum at B, amplitude and phase modulations due to the interference becomes quite noticeable around A but negligible around B. The position on the body surface at which the maximum interference occurs is changed depending on the position of neighboring fish. Therefore, in order to detect the correct sign of Df, it is essentially important to integrate the informations of amplitude and phase modulations over the wide area of body surface.

In order to clarify the integration mechanism by which the correct sign of Df is discriminated, we simulate the sign selective process by using the model in which the receptive organs including P-receptor cells or T-receptor cells are distributed on the body surface, as shown in Fig. 6b. For simplicity, we assume that the fish has a cylindrical form with radius r_0. The position (r, ϕ) of a neighboring fish is taken as $r = 2r_0$ and $\phi = 45°$. Then, the jamming signal received by ith organ is given by

$$S_i(t) = S_1 sin(2\pi f_1 t) + S_2 cos\theta_i sin(2\pi f_2 t + \pi),\qquad(10)$$

where S_1 and f_1 are the amplitude and frequency of the fish's own EOD, respectively, and S_2 and f_2 are those of the neighbor's EOD, respectively. θ_i is angle between the fish'own EOD field and neighbor's EOD field.

We describe here how the correct phase modulation of the jamming signal is computed based on the integration mechanism. Since the fish does not know the amplitude and phase of his own EOD signal, the fish cannot directly how largely the jamming signal received is modulated from his own signal. The fish knows the degree of phase modulation through the work of small cells in TS that the cells compare a zero-crossing time of jamming signal received at one point of the body surface with a zero-crossing time at the other point. We consider the degree of the phase modulation of the signal received by the receptive organs 1,2, ...,9 shown in Fig. 6b. The modulation is noticeable for the organs 3-7, but negligible for the organs 1,2,8,9. That is, the signals received by the organs(1,2,8,9) are almost the same as the fish's own siganl. Each small cell compares the signals received by the organs in its own receptive field with the signals received by the organs in the receptive fields of the other small cells. The small cells received the signals from some of the organs (3-7) detect the correct phase modulation from their comparison maily with the signals from some of the organs (1,2,8,9). On the other hand, the small cells received the signals from some of the organs (1,2,8,9) detect the wrong phase modulation from their comparison maily with the signals from some of the organs (3-7), because the modulation detected is the reverse of the correct one. Thus, some of the small cells indicate the correct information, but some of them inducate the wrong information. However, such wrong informations are excluded by joint computation of amplitude and phase information in sign selective neurons. A sign selective neuron receives the outputs of TS and ELL whose receptive field corresponds to each organ. Thus, sign selective neuron works as a "AND-gating" neuron for both the outputs.

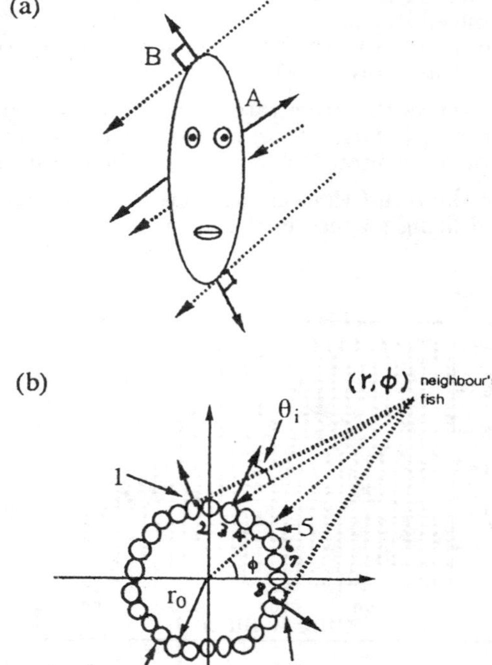

Fig. 6 (a) Electric field around the fish. The solid lines and the dashed lines mean the fish's own EOD field and the neighbor's EOD field, respectively,. (b) A model for the sign selective process. The receptive organs are arrayed on the body surface of the fish.

Since the firing rates of the neurons coding the amplitude information from the organs 1, 2, 8, and 9 are very small, sign selective neurons relevant to these organs do not fire. Therefore, the wrong information is excluded by the AND-gating process. We simulate the joint computation of amplitude and phase information by using the neural network model described in section 2 and 3. Figure 7 shows the firing rates of the four types of sign selective neurons relevant to the organs(1-5).

In the case of Df=+5 Hz, E-D and I-A type neurons fire as shown in Fig. 7, while other types of neurons do not fire. Thus, the fish can discriminate the correct sign of Df. The system are also robust for the stimuli with Gaussian noise. Since the noisy amplitude and phase information are omitted by the integration mechanism of peripheral region, ELL and TS receive information with less jitter. Thus, Gaussian noise does not induce the drastic change of the firing patterns in Fig. 7. Since the fish can detect separately the information of it's own EOD and the neighbor's EOD, it is necessary for the detection of sign of Df to integrate many elementary informations received over the body surface.

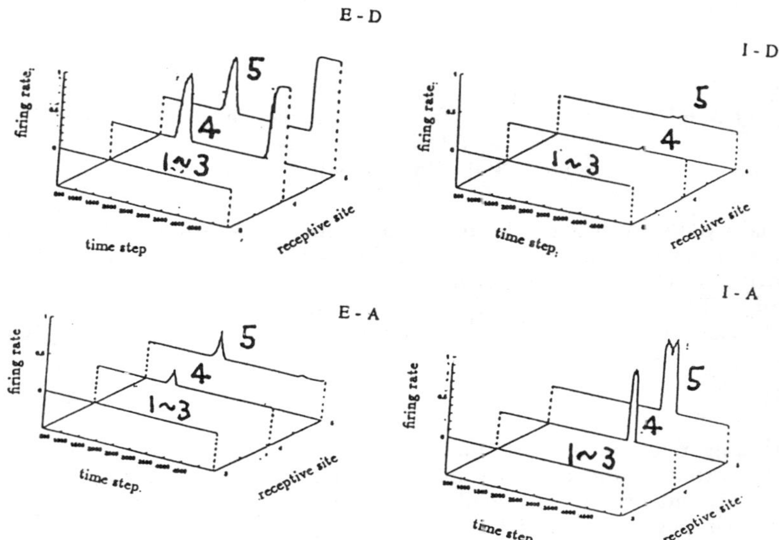

Fig. 7 The firing rates of four types of sign selective neurons whose receptive field corresponds to receptive organs, 1 - 5. In the case of the positive Df(+5 Hz), the neurons coding the correct combinations of amplitude and phase information fire.

5 Conclusion

We have presented the neural network models of ELL and TS. For phase modulation of EOD field whose time disparity is larger than 100 μsec, these network can reproduce well the observed functions. However, the mechanism for detection of small modulations whose disparity is of the order of 10 μsec is not yet clear.

We have proposed the integration mechanism by which the sign of Df is evaluated correctly. In the lower neural system, the information of jamming signal is coded separately in the parallel pathways of amplitude and phase information, while these parallely processed information are integrated in the higher neural system. In the pathway of JAR, only particular neuron does not detect the sign of Df. The fish discriminates the sign of Df by integrating the amplitude and phase information received over the wide range of boby surface. This strategy may guarantee the robustness of sign selection for local lesion of neural circuit and movement of neighboring fish.

References

[1] W. Heiligenberg, *Neural Nets in Electric Fish*. Cambridge:MIT Press, 1991.

[2] M. Kawasaki. *et al.*, "Temporal hyperacuity in single neurons in electric fish " *Nature*, vol. 336, pp 173-176, 1988.

[3] Y. Kashimori *et al.* "A Theretical study of the neural mechanism inducing the jamming avoidance response of electric fish *Eigenmannia* ", *Proc. of 1993 Int. Joint. Conf. on Neural Networks*, Nagoya, Oct, 26-29, 1993, pp. 89-92.

[4] Y. Kashimori *et al.*," A Neural Network Model for Analysis of Amplitude and Phase Modulations in Jamming Avoidance Response in Electric Fish *Eigenmannia* " , *Proc. of ICONIP'94*, Seoul, Korea, Oct 17-20, 1994, pp. 1060-1066.

[5] Y. Kashimori *et al.*, "A Neural Network Model for Detection of Time Disparity in Electric Fish *Eigenmannia* ", *Proc. of ICONIP'95*, Beijin, China, Oct - Nov , 1995, pp.129-132.

[6] Y. Kashimori *et al*, "A Model of P- and T-electroreceptors of Weakly Electric Fish.", Biophys. J., 1996 (in press).

[7] C. Carr *et al.*, "A time comparison circuit in the electric fish midbrain I. Behavior and physiology", *J. Neurosci.*, vol. 6, pp. 107-119, 1986.

[8] C. Carr *et al.*, "A time comparison circuit in the electric fish midbrain II.functional morphorogy" , *J. Neurosci.*, vol. 6 , pp. 1372-1383, 1986.

[9] L. A. Jefferess, " A place theory of sound location", *J. Comp. Physio. Psycho.*, vol. 41, pp. 35-39, 1948.

[10] W. W. Lytton, "Simulations of a phase comparing neuron of the electric fish *Eigenmannia* ", *J. Comp. Physiol, A*, vol. 169,pp.117-125, 1991.

Model explaining subjective contour

Koichi Ikuta, Kunihiko Fukushima
Department of Biophysical Engineering, Faculty of Engineering Science, Osaka University
Toyonaka, Osaka 560. Japan
E-mail: ikuta@bpe.es.osaka-u.ac.jp

Abstract— **There is a psychological phenomenon which is known as the subjective contour. We propose a neural network model which explains this phenomenon. The model is composed of three modules which correspond to the retina and the area of the visual cortex V1, V2, respectively. The model has been simulated on a computer. It is shown that the model behaves as human visual system does when the illusory figure is given.**

1 Introduction

There are many intriguing phenomena in human visual system. The subjective contour is one of the phenomena. When we watch a kind of figure like the Kanizsa figure (Fig. 1), we can see or perceive illusory contours which are not present physically. This illusory contour is called subjective contour, and has been studied mainly in psychological field.

Recently von der Heydt and Peterhans [?]-[?] has reported that there are cells which responds to subjective contour in monkey's visual cortex V2. Several models explaining subjective contour have hitherto been proposed, including the model by Grossberg and Mingolla [?], the model by Finkel and Edelman [?], and our models [?]-[?].

The illusory figure often accompany the other kinds of illusions. In the case of Kanizsa figure, we perceive as though a white triangle is occluding three disks and the inside of the triangle looks brighter than its outside. These phenomena suggests that the subjective contour plays important role for the 3D perception and for the process of grouping and separating the figures from background. In our view, these phenomena appear as the by-product of the visual process which compensates the imperfect retinal image. This paper offers we a model which can present humanlike behavior to the illusory figures.

2 Model

2.1 Outline

The cells composing the model have a non-linear response function:

$$\varphi[x] = \begin{cases} (x - \theta)/(1 + x - \theta) & (x \geq \theta) \\ 0 & (x < \theta), \end{cases} \tag{1}$$

where x indicates the input signal to the cell, and θ is threshold of the cell.

Our model consists of three modules (Fig. 2). The first module corresponds to the retina or the LGN physiologically, and is composed of only one layer (Input Layer). The input layer is the 2D arrangement of cells. Each cell of the layer responds proportionally to the strength of luminance at each location.

The next module corresponds to area V1 of the cortex. The module consists of two blocks where function is detecting local features as simple cells do. One of the block is called ED (Edge Detecting) block, which

Figure 1: **Kanizsa illusion.** We perceive a white triangle covering three black disks.

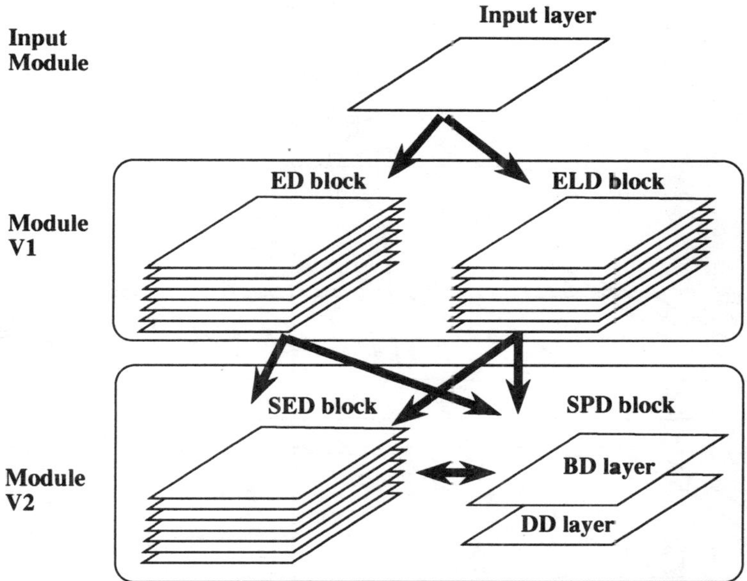

Figure 2: **Outline of the model.**

detects the edge feature in the stimulus pattern. The other block detects the End of Line, we call it ELD (End of Line Detecting) block. Each block consists of the 36 layers, each of which detects ends of lines with specific orientation (preferred orientation). The difference of the preferred orientation between the layers is 10 degree. The size of the layers is the same as the size of input layer, and each layer of these blocks has a retinotopy to the input layer. Fig. 3 illustrates the connections between the blocks and the input layer. Although there are many kinds of simple cells in V1, here we introduce only two blocks for making the model simple.

The third module is composed of layers in which key processing of our model is done. This module corresponds to area V2 of the cortex. The module consists of two blocks which we call SED (Subjective Edge Detecting) block and SPD (Subjective Plane Detecting) block. The SED block detects both subjective and physical contours. The SPD block detects subjective planes which are enclosed by contours, where the contours can be either subjective of physical. In Fig. 1, for example, the white triangle is a subjective plane. The SED block and the SPD block have connections from both the ED and the ELD blocks. Each block has feedback connections within the block. There are also connections between the SED and the SPD blocks. Responses corresponding to subjective contours are generated in the SED block by the feedback connections as time passes. We will describe a detail of these two blocks below.

2.2   SED block

The SED block is composed of a number of layers. The arrangement of the block is the same as that of the ED block. The SED block receives connections from the ED and ELD blocks in one-to-one fashion. This causes the SED block respond to the subjective edge made by end-stopped lines.

In the SED block, each cell has lateral connections to neighboring cells. The distribution of the lateral connections are illustrated in Fig. 4. When one cell of the block is activated, the cell sends excitatory signals to the surrounding cells which are located in the direction of preferred orientation of the layer. These connections make the response diffuse in the direction of the preferred orientation. The activated cell also sends signals to cells of other layers, too. The cell sends excitatory signals in the direction which is an intermediate direction between the preferred orientation of the cell and that of the layer receiving the signals. And the connections become weaker as the distance of the layers become bigger.

Let $E_{V2}^t(\boldsymbol{n}, k)$ be the response of a cell of the SED block at time t, where $(\boldsymbol{n}, k)$ indicates the location of the cell (position $\boldsymbol{n}$ of kth layer) in the block. The response is given by

$$E_{V2}^{t+1}(\boldsymbol{n}, k) = \varphi \left[\sum_{\nu, \kappa} w_{EE}(\boldsymbol{\nu}, \kappa, k) E_{V2}^t(\boldsymbol{n} + \boldsymbol{\nu}, k) + \alpha_1 E_{V1}^t(\boldsymbol{n}, k) + \alpha_2 L_{V1}^t(\boldsymbol{n}, k) - \alpha_3 I^t(\boldsymbol{n}, k) \right], \qquad (2)$$

where E_{V1} and L_{V1} indicate the responses of cells in the ED and the ELD blocks, respectively. w_{EE} is the spatial distribution of the lateral connections in the SED block. The $I^t(\boldsymbol{n}, k)$ indicates the signal of a inhibitory cell which each cell of the SED layer has. In this model, we assume that the activities of the cells of SED block are suppressed by the strong inhibition by the inhibitory in the usual condition. The cells of the SED blocks are not activated unless the SPD block weakens the signals from the inhibitory cells. This disinhibition will be explained later. $\alpha_1, \alpha_2, \alpha_3$ are constants.

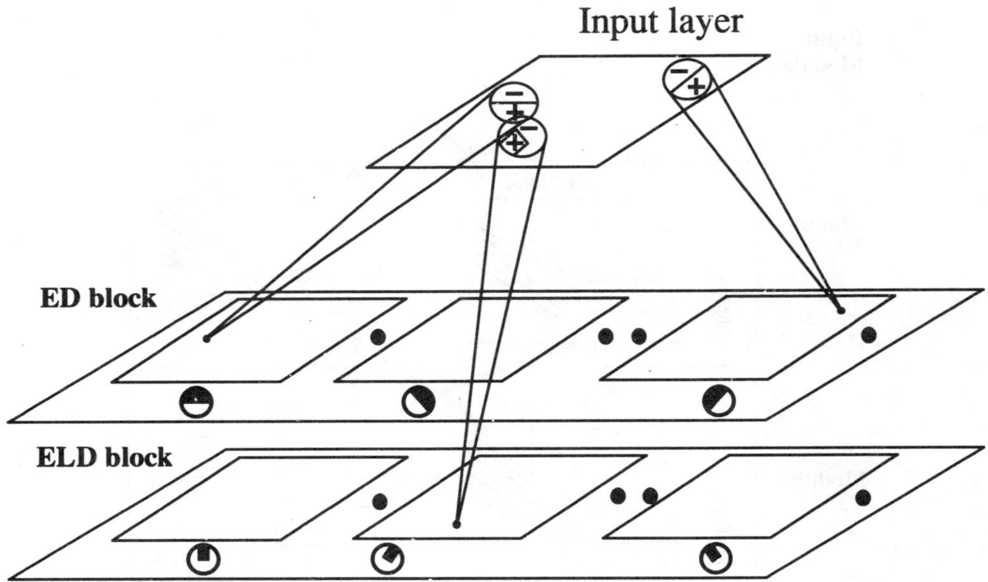

Figure 3: **Connections from input layer to the ED block and the ELD block.** the ED block detects the edge feature, the ELD layer detects the feature of end-stopped line in the stimulus pattern. Each layer keeps retinotopy to the input layer.

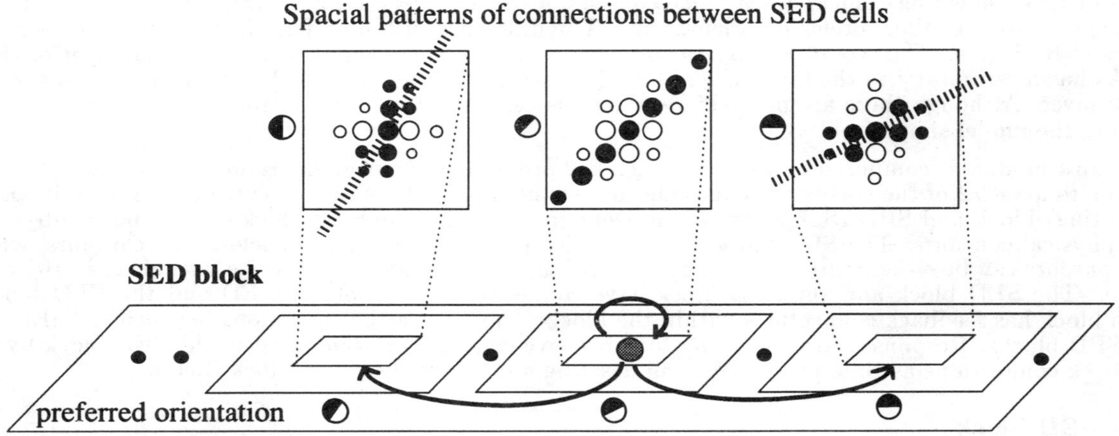

Figure 4: **Lateral Connections of the SED block.** Each cell of the SED block has lateral connections to surrounding cells. The distribution of the connections has one direction which corresponds to the preferred orientation of the layer.

2.3   SPD block

The SPD block is composed of two layers. One of the layers detects bright planes, and the other layer detects dark planes. We call them BD (Brightness Detecting) and DD (Darkness Detecting) layers, respectively.

These layers receive connections from the ED, the ELD block and the SED blocks. Responses corresponding to subjective planes are generated based on the information of edges and end of lines. Fig. 5 illustrates the connections. The process done by the connections are like inverse processing for detecting edges and ends of lines. The process generates responses of the peripheral part of the subjective planes.

These connections are weak, and the responses made by the connections are very weak in the usual condition. However, the strong responses emerge at positions where is inside of the corner made by edges like Fig. **??**.

Both BD and DD layers have internal connections within their own layers. The internal connections, which have positive isotropic distributions, works for interpolating responses which correspond to mid parts of subjective planes. In other words, the connections make the responses corresponding to the inside of the corners of planes diffuse throughout the layers.

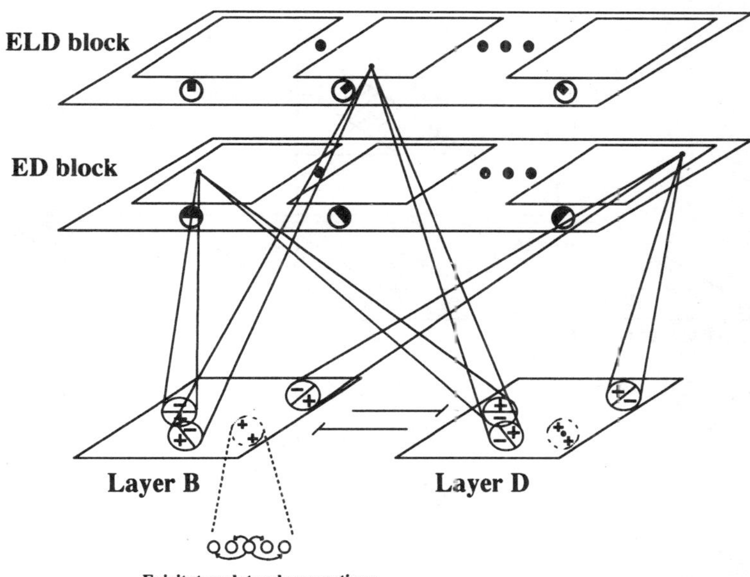

Figure 5: **The connections of the SPD block.** The connections to the PD block are illustrated. The connections from the SED block is the same as the connections from the ED block, it is omitted here.

As illustrated in Fig. 5, the spatial distributions of connections from three blocks (the ED, PD and SED blocks) have negative areas. If there are edges or ends of lines, subjective contours at one position, the diffusing is stopped at the position by inhibitions made by the features. In short, the contours (including subjective contour) work as barrier, and prevent diffusing of the responses out of subjective planes.

Both BD and DD layer has the inhibitory connections to each other layer. It prevents the activation of both layers at the same position.

Let $b^t(\boldsymbol{n})$ and $d^t(\boldsymbol{n})$ be the response of the BD layer and DD layer.

$$
\begin{aligned}
b^{t+1}(\boldsymbol{n}) \;=\; \varphi\Bigg[&\sum_{\nu,\kappa} w_{E_{V_2}B}(\boldsymbol{\nu},\kappa)E_{V2}^t(\boldsymbol{n}+\boldsymbol{\nu},\kappa) + \sum_{\nu,\kappa} w_{E_{V_1}B}(\boldsymbol{\nu},\kappa)L_{V1}^t(\boldsymbol{n}+\boldsymbol{\nu},\kappa) \\
&+ \sum_{\nu,\kappa} w_{L_{V_1}B}(\boldsymbol{\nu},\kappa)L_{V1}^t(\boldsymbol{n}+\boldsymbol{\nu},\kappa) + \sum_{\nu} w_g(\boldsymbol{\nu})b^t(\boldsymbol{n}+\boldsymbol{\nu}) - \alpha_4 d^t(\boldsymbol{n}) \Bigg]
\end{aligned}
\tag{3}
$$

$$
\begin{aligned}
d^{t+1}(\boldsymbol{n}) \;=\; \varphi\Bigg[&\sum_{\nu,\kappa} w_{E_{V_2}D}(\boldsymbol{\nu},\kappa)E_{V2}^t(\boldsymbol{n}+\boldsymbol{\nu},\kappa) + \sum_{\nu,\kappa} w_{E_{V_1}D}(\boldsymbol{\nu},\kappa)E_{V1}^t(\boldsymbol{n}+\boldsymbol{\nu},\kappa) \\
&+ \sum_{\nu,\kappa} w_{L_{V_1}D}(\boldsymbol{\nu},\kappa)L_{V1}^t(\boldsymbol{n}+\boldsymbol{\nu},\kappa) + \sum_{\nu} w_g(\boldsymbol{\nu})d^t(\boldsymbol{n}+\boldsymbol{\nu}) - \alpha_4 b^t(\boldsymbol{n}) \Bigg],
\end{aligned}
\tag{4}
$$

where $w_{E_{V_2}B}$ and w_{EB}, w_{LB} are the connections from the SED, the ED and the ELD blocks to the BD layer, respectively. These connections are illustrated in Fig. 5. $w_{E_{V_2}D}$ and w_{ED}, w_{LD} are the connections to the D layer. w_g is the internal connections for diffusing. α_4 is a constant.

2.4 Interaction between SED block and SPD block

As mentioned before, the SPD block receives connections ($w_{E_{V_2}B}$ and $w_{E_{V_2}D}$) from the SED block. The responses corresponding to the subjective planes are provided by these connections. As shown (2), the cells of the SED block receive signals from inhibitory cells ($I^t(\boldsymbol{n},k)$). This output of the inhibitory cell is controlled by the signals from cells ($b^t(\boldsymbol{n})$ and $d^t(\boldsymbol{n})$) of the SPD block:

$$
I^{t+1}(\boldsymbol{n},k) = \varphi\Bigg[\alpha_5 - \Big\{ \sum_{\nu} w_{BI}(\boldsymbol{\nu},k)b^t(\boldsymbol{n}+\boldsymbol{\nu}) + \sum_{\nu} w_{DI}(\boldsymbol{\nu},k)d^t(\boldsymbol{n}+\boldsymbol{\nu}) \Big\} \Bigg],
\tag{5}
$$

where α_5 is a constant, which is large than the second and the third terms in (5). Large value is set to α_5. We assume that the inhibitory cells have discharges. A cell of the SED block can be activated only

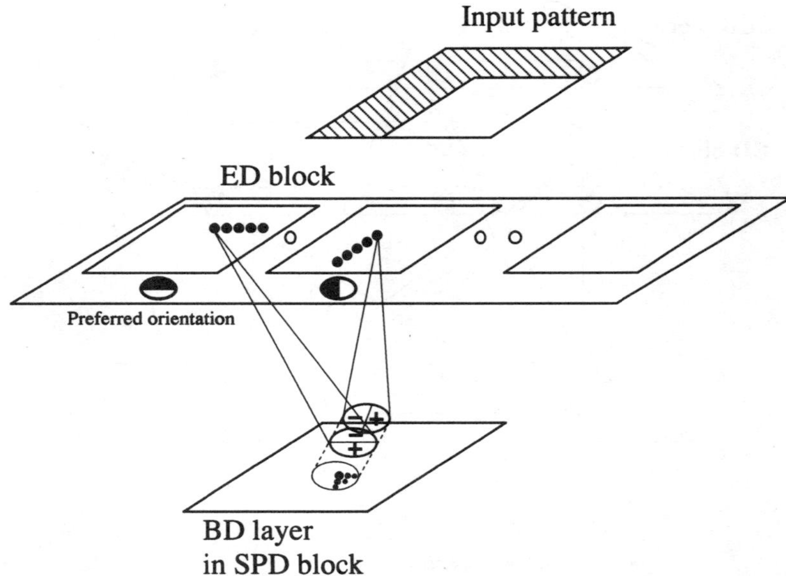

Figure 6: **The response of BD layer to a stimulus pattern.** In the BD layer, cells whose positions correspond to the inside of the corner of stimulus pattern have strong responses, because the cells receive the positive signals from several activated cells of ED block.

when output of the inhibitory cell is inhibited by the signals.

In (6), k indicates the layer's number corresponding to that of the SED block. Connections $w_{BI}(\nu, k)$ and $w_{DI}(\nu, k)$ work as if it extracts the oriented edge of kth layer from the BD and the DD layer. These two connections has opposite contrast to each other, because the property which the cells of the BD and the DD respond to has opposite character (brightness and darkness).

The response of inhibitory cell ($I^t(\boldsymbol{n}, k)$) is suppressed, if an edge pattern whose orientation is similar to the preferred orientation of the kth layer is generated in the SPD block.

In other words, the cells of SPD block disinhibit the cells of SED block which match to the local response pattern of the SPD block.

3   Simulation

We simulated this model with three illusory figures of Kanizsa. The size of each layer of the model is 100×100. In Fig. **??** shows the results of the simulations. First column shows stimulus patterns, and second column shows the patterns that the all layer's response patterns of SED block are added. Third column and forth column shows the response patterns of the BD layer and DD layer of the SPD block. In these three kinds of response patterns, white pixels represent activated state of cells.

In (a), the standard Kanizsa figure is presented as stimulus pattern. The response of the SED block shows a triangle as we perceives when we watch the stimulus pattern. The response pattern of B layer shows the bright triangle plane covering three disks.

The stimulus pattern of (b) is composed of three disks whose combination is not likely to generate a subjective triangle. In the results, there is no response pattern corresponding to subjective contours. The responses of the BD layer diffused throughout the layer. These responses mean that there are three dark objects on the bright background.

The stimulus pattern of (c) contains two end-stopped lines in the location where the smooth subjective contour is likely to be perceived by human eyes. The SED layer shows the response pattern corresponding to the subjective contour as human perceives. The BD layer also show the response pattern corresponding to a fan shape covering three disks. The diffusing of the response is stopped at subjective contours.

No cell of the BD and the DD layer responds the areas which surround the three disks. In the case of (c), the area of stimulus pattern is segmented into three parts (one bright fan, three dark disks, background).

References

[1] Rüdiger von der Heydt and Esther Peterhans: "Mechanisms of contour perception in monkey visual cortex. 1. Lines of pattern discontinuity.", *J. Neurosci.*, **9**(5), 1731-1748 (1989).

Figure 7: **The results of simulations**. The model was simulated with 3 stimulus patterns.

[2] Rüdiger von der Heydt and Esther Peterhans: "Mechanisms of contour perception in monkey visual cortex. 2. Contours bridging gaps.", *J. Neurosci.*, **9**(5). 1749-1763 (1989).

[3] Stephen Grossberg and Ennio Mingolla: "Neural dynamics of perceptual grouping: Textures, boundaries, and emergent segmentations.", *Perception & Psychophysics.*, **38**(2), 141-171 (1985).

[4] Leif H. Finkel and Gerald M. Edelman: "Integration of distributed cortical systems by reentry: A computer simulation of interactive functionally segregated visual areas", *J. Nuerosci.*, **9**, 3188-3208 (1989).

[5] Koichi Ikuta and Kunihiko Fukushima: "A neural network model explaining subjective contour" (in Japanese), IEICE Technical Report., **NC90**-132 (Mar. 1991).

[6] Koichi Ikuta and Kunihiko Fukushima: "A neural network model explaining subjective contour" (in japanese),Annual Conference of Japanese Neural Network Society., P6-12, (Dec. 1991).

[7] Koichi Ikuta and Kunihiko Fukushima: "A neural network model explaining subjective contour" (in Japanese), IEICE Technical Report., **NC91**-109 (Mar. 1992).

[8] Koichi Ikuta and Kunihiko Fukushima: "A neural network model explaining subjective contour", Proceeding of The 2nd International Conference On Fuzzy Logic And Neural Networks., P653-656, (July 1992).

Computer Simulation of Emergence of Group Intelligence in Fish School

Yoshimasa Narita [†], Yoshiki Kashimori [†], Naoyuki Sasaki [‡] and Takeshi Kambara [†]

[†] Department of Applied Physics and Chemistry,
University of Electro-Communicaions,
Chofu, Tokyo, 182, JAPAN
E-mail : PBC02522@niftyserve.or.jp
[‡] Laboratory of Applied Mathematics,
Nippon Dental University,
Fujimi, Chiyoda-ku, Tokyo, 102, JAPAN

Abstract

We have made the computer simulations to clarify the essential mechanism of fish schooling. Though each fish does not know the movement of entire school and there is no reader in the group, they gather and move together in our simulation model. The effect of lateral line of fish was also studied. The frequency of changing direction and the fish density of school decreases when the individuals use only the information of lateral line.

We are trying to clarify a group intelligence of fish school. We assume that group intelligence are abilities emerged when individuals make shoal. One of the most important functions of schooling behavior is to reduce the probability that any given individual will be attacked by predators. In order to clarify what the group intelligence is and how the group intelligence emerges, we study predator-avoidance behaviors of fish school using our fish school model.

1. Introduction

Schooling behavior of fish is a typical example of self-organized grouping in which numerous fish individual perform a unified collective movement. The fish schools are not formed by leaders but by relatively local interactions between fish individuals. A fish group shows a great diversity in schooling behavior depending on its condition. When the group is on a movement the fish swim in highly parallel with each other. While feeding or resting the fish show a nearly random orientation. When the fish are attacked by predators, the fish show several kinds of predator avoidance collective behaviors such as split, cruise, flash expansion and vacuole [1]. The schooling mechanism has been actively investigated experimentally and theoretically [2-4]. The results suggests that mutual attraction and parallel orientation contribute mainly to school formation. It was also shown that the most important senses for schooling are the eyes and the lateral line. However, it is not clear how diverse collective behaviors are organized under various situations, because observation of the behaviors could be made in only several limiting conditions [1-3]. In the present paper, we formulate a model of fish schooling mechanism and make computer simulation to clarify what are the essential mechanism for school organization. Especially, we have interest in emergence of group intelligence in fish school. One of the most important function of fish schooling behavior is to reduce the probability that any given individual will be attacked by a predator. To facilitate this function, individuals within the school engage in a repertoire of group tactics that confer protection upon them. In order to clarify what the group intelligence of fish school is and how the group intelligence is emerged, we study predator-avoidance behaviors of fish school using our fish school model.

2. Basic Observed Results for Fish Schooling

2-1. Interaction between neighboring fish based on visual information

Schooling results from the interaction that an individual controls its movement in relation to neighbors and affects simultaneously on the neighbors [2]. Many workers consider three basic behavior patterns responsible for schooling: avoidance, approach and parallel orientation. A fish adjusts its distance to neighbors based on the information from its eyesight [2,5]. If a neighbor which an individual remarks is too near, the individual will avoid the neighbor. If the neighbor is too far, the individual will approach to the neighbor. The individual will move to the same direction as the neighbor's movement, when the neighbor is within the parallel orientation area. Fig.1 shows ranges of the three reaction areas. Every fish can not see the outside of attraction area and the dead angle area. The dead angle is +30 to -30 degree outside behind the fish. Followings are the numbers of parameters [2,5].

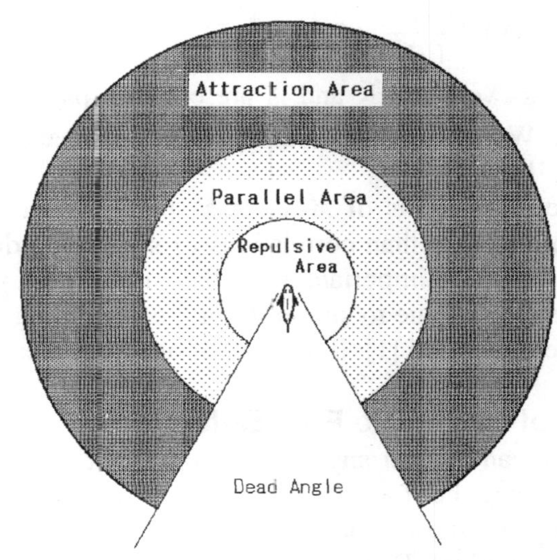

Fig.1   Parameters of interaction

Repulsive area	$0 < Dij \leqq 0.5BL$
Parallel area	$0.5BL < Dij \leqq 2.0BL$
Attraction area	$2.0BL < Dij \leqq 5.0BL$

Where BL is Body Length, Dij is Distance from fish i to j.

2-2. Detection of averaged movement of fish group around a fish based on

Lateral line is a organ through which the fish measures pressure of water. A fish can know roughly the movement of whole school through the lateral line [6]. However, the information of the movement caught is not the moving direction and speed simply averaged over whole but the direction and speed averaged with weight which is inversely proportional to a cube of the distance to each fish. Therefore, the information caught through the lateral line is practically the information made by neighbors only, i.e. almost local information. Following equation is the information from lateral line.

$$\alpha_{Li} = \frac{\sum_j \theta_j \, D_{ij}^{-3}}{\sum_j D_{ij}^{-3}} \qquad (1)$$

Where α_{Li} is directional information from lateral line, θ_j is a direction(heading) of other individual j, D_{ij} is a distance from j to i.

Effects of the information caught through eyes and lateral line on fish motion were studied detailedly by Partridge and Pitcher [3]. The fish whose eyes are masked can follow the school movement, but swim a little more apart from neighbors than does a normal fish. The fish of which lateral line are cut also can follow the school, but swims a little closer to neighbors than does normal fish [6]. Thus, the density of school becomes somewhat high when all fish act only by using vision.

2-3. Swimming speed of individuals

Aoki[2] analyzed the magnitude distribution of swimming speeds of Gnathopogon elongatus elongatus and Trachulus japonics. It was shown that the magnitude distribution for both species is reasonably represented by gamma distribution. The gamma distribution is given by

$$f(v) = \frac{A^K}{\Gamma(K)} e^{-Av} v^{K-1} \tag{2}$$

where v is velocity, K and A are constant parameters, $v \geq 0, K > 0, A > 0, \Gamma(K)$ is a gamma function. We take 4 and 3.3 as the values of K and A, respectively, based on the observations of Aoki [2,5].

Since correlations of swimming speed between fishes in both Gnathopogon and Tracurus school are weaker than correlations of swimming direction, the absolute magnitude of speed of each fish is less important than the movement direction. Apparent uniformity of speed is considered to be due to similarity in the swimming ability of schooling members rather than the adjustment of speed [1]. It does not result from their intentional adjustment of speed.

3. Model for Single Fish Behaviors

A fish can not get any information about the movement of its group as a whole, schooling behavior may be formed based on only the local interaction between neighboring fishes. Therefore, we present here the rules only for behaviors of an individual fish interacting with another individual. Behaviors of a fish group are generated by computer simulation made based on the following basic rules:

1) Time evolution is discretized. One step of time is represented by Δt.
2) Each fish moves in a two-dimensional horizontal plane without boundary.
3) At the beginning of the simulation, the positions and the moving directions of all fishes are given by using an uniform random number, where the positions are within a circle area with a certain radius. The initial value of speed for each fish is generated by a random number with a gamma distribution of eq.2.
4) One fish is picked up randomly from within the fish group at each time step and moved to a new position.
5) The new position after one time step Δt is determined as follows.
   At first, the fish j, to which the relevant fish i attends, is picked up out of the neighbors according to the probability proportional to D_{ij}^{-1}.

The position $\left(x_i(t), y_i(t)\right)$ of i-th fish at time $t + \Delta t$ is calculated as

$$x_i(t + \Delta t) = x_i(t) + v_i(t)\cos\alpha_i(t) \tag{3}$$

$$y_i(t + \Delta t) = y_i(t) + v_i(t)\sin\alpha_i(t) \tag{4}$$

$$\alpha_i(t + \Delta t) = \alpha_i(t) + \beta_{ij}(t) + \sqrt{2}\,\beta_0 R_g \tag{5}$$

Where $\alpha_i(t)$ is a moving direction of i-th fish at time t, $\beta_{ij}(t)$ is a variation in the direction of i-th fish which is determined based on the relative relation to a neighbor j, $\sqrt{2}\,\beta_0 R_g$ means a spontaneous fluctuation of the moving direction, β_0 denotes a the maximum fluctuation, R_g is a gaussian random number between -1 and +1, $v_i(t)$ is the speed of i-th fish at time t. The constant β_0 takes 15 degree based on the observations of Aoki [2]. β_{ij} is determined by the following rules.

When the fish j is in the attractive area shown in fig.1, β_{ij} is the direction from i to j.

When the fish j is in the parallel area, β_{ij} is the same direction of j.

When the fish j is in the repulsive area, β_{ij} is the direction from i to j plus 90 degree or minus 90 degree.

In every case, the value of β_{ij} is adjusted so as to be in the range of -45 to +45.

4. Emergence of Schooling Behaviors

To investigate the condition under which the schooling behaviors are made by individuals using only the information from vision, the effect of three types of adjusting principles was examined. Under the first principle, an individual adjusts its motion only to the nearest anterior fish. Schooling did not emerge in this case, but many unstable groups of fish appeared. Under the second principle, a fish always adjusts to the nearest neighbor within the visible range. The result of simulation was similar to the first case. In the simulation under the third principle, in which every individual adjust to one of neighboring fishes with the frequency inversely proportional to the distance, they gathered and moved together .A snapshot of schooling in the simulation is shown in fig.2. The school sometimes changed its moving direction, where the leading group in the school firstly changes the direction, and then, the others follow the leading group.

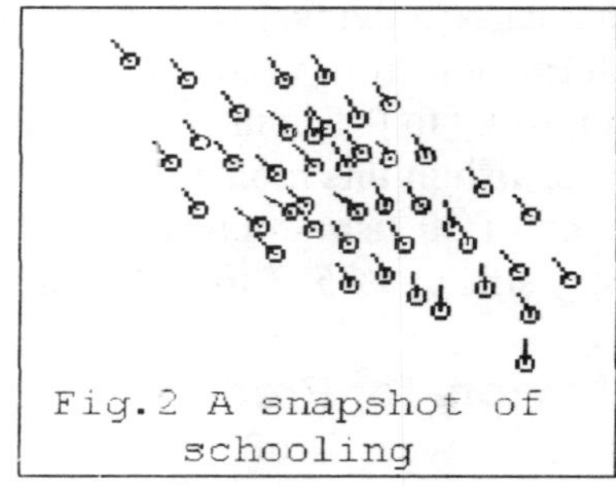

The effect of lateral line on the schooling was also studied by computer simulations. Lateral line has an effect to parallel orientation of fish. When the individuals use the information only from lateral line, the formation of school is long and the density of the school is low in comparison with the school which is made by using only the information from vision. The frequency of changing direction decreases when the individuals use only the information from lateral line.

Fig.3 shows the temporal variations of expanse and polarity of a school starting in a dispersed state. Expanse represents extent of fish group around the center of mass. Polarity means standard deviation from the moving direction averaged over whole school. They gathered first and then all individuals were within a parallel area of someone at the step 29. It is seen from the fluctuation of polarity shown in fig.3 that the school often changed the direction. This fluctuation comes from the time delay required for the fishes tailing the top group to adjust their direction to a new moving direction. This corresponds to the observed latency of response in the experiment of fish school [2].

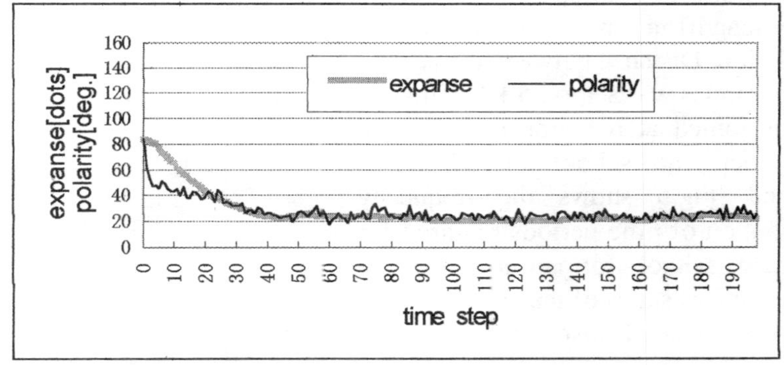

Fig.3 Temporal variations in expanse and polarity of a school

Fig.4 shows the frequency distribution of time periods required for a school formation since the fish group starts from the various initial states determined by the method described in section 3. The simulation has been made 5000 times to obtain the results shown in fig.4. It is defined as a schooling

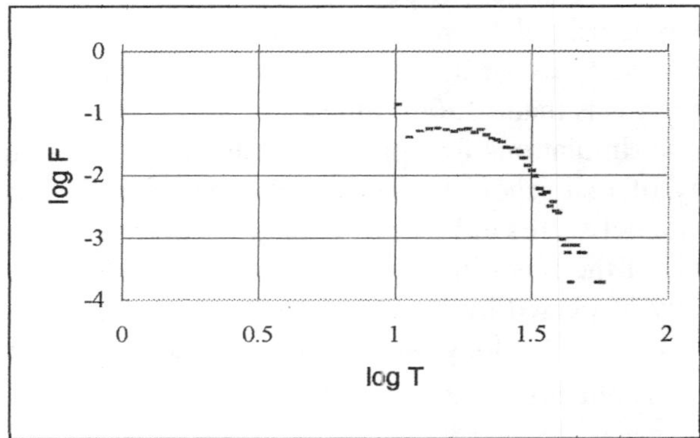

Fig.4 The frequency F of each time period required for a school formation

state that each individual is within a parallel area of someone and there exists only one school. The information from vision and lateral line are adopted for determination of a next direction in the ratio of 0.9 to 0.1 in the case of fig.4, because the vision is much important to approach. The number of fish in this model was 60. Fig.4 shows stability of the model in a dynamic sense. The simulation of 30 fish group was also run 5000 times. In the case of 30 fish model, the peek of frequency sifts to 1.35. This indicates that the attracting force is proportional to density of school.

5. Behaviors for Predator Evasion

Various types of maneuvers have been observed in the anti-predator behaviors of fish school [1]. Some of them are the avoid, herd, vacuole, hourglass, split and flash expansion. Generally, a fish school is reformed quickly after dispersion of school [1]. Using our model, we studied the reforming behavior of a fish school after split and flash expansion occurred.

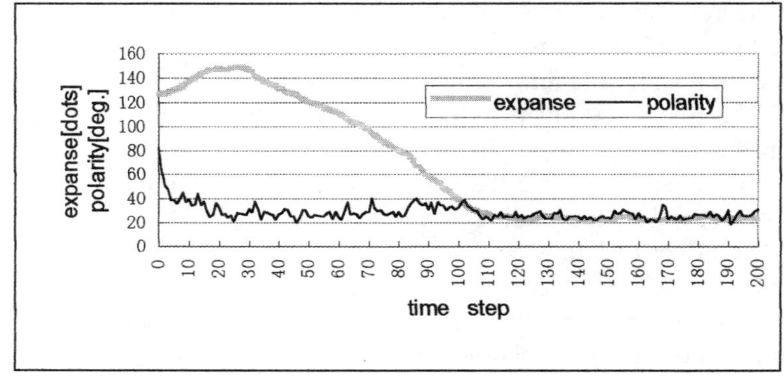

Fig.5 Temporal variations of expanse and polarity in the reforming process after the splitting into two groups

Fig.5 shows the temporal variations of expanse and polarity in the reforming process after the splitting into two groups. These groups of 30 fishes ware put within the two circles with 5 BL (body length) radius at the beginning of simulation. Distance between the centers of two circles was set to 25 BL. The two groups joined at the time step 96 and after that one school of 60 fishes retained. Fig.6 shows the frequency distribution of time periods required for a single school formation since the various initial states of the splitting.

We simulated also the reforming behavior after the flash expansion shown in Fig.7. The frequency distribution of time periods required for a single school formation after the various flash expansions is shown in fig.8, where the simulation was made 15000 times.

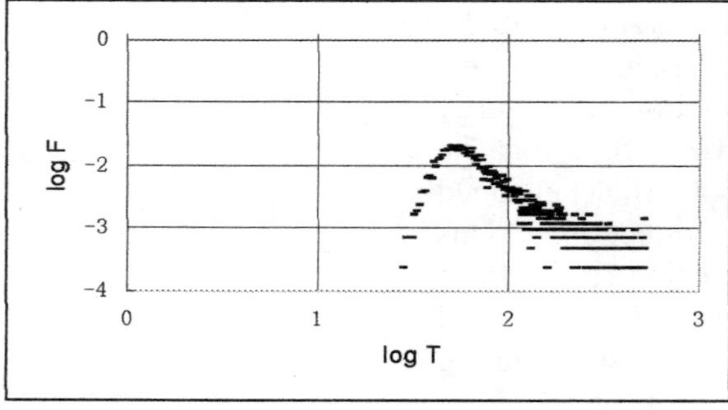

Fig.6   The frequency F of each time period T required for a single school formation. The simulation was made 5000 times.

These simulations for split and flash expansion indicate the stability of fish school in our model. The schooling dynamics of our model seems to be good enough to study the response to predator. If the schooling dynamics is weak, fish of the school are easily dispersed by attack of predators and easily eaten by the predators. As long as a school attacked by predators maintains collective motion, the fishes are not easily eaten.

Fig.7   Flash expansion behavior of a fish group

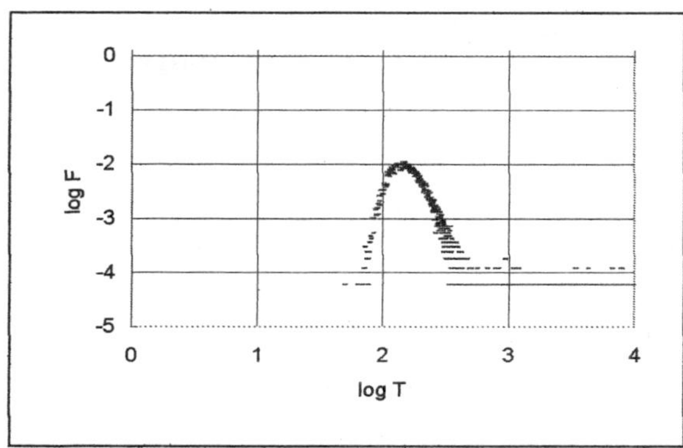

Fig.8
The frequency of each time period T required for a school formation after each flash expansion.
The simulation was made 15000 times.

6. Concluding Remarks

The various simulations have been performed to clarify the essential mechanism of fish schooling in the present paper. This work made a base to study of group intelligence. The mechanism of group intelligence will be examined by a new model made based on the present model. As mentioned before, we assume that group intelligence in fish group is abilities emerged when school is formed.

We are highly interested in group intelligence emerged on the behavior of predator evasion, because group intelligence may be the most clearly exerted to evade attack of predator. In order to clarify what the group intelligence of fish school is and how the group intelligence is emerged, we are going to make a model applicable to the predator-avoidance behaviors of fish and attacking behaviors of predator.

References

[1] T.J.Pitcher and C.J.Wyche, "Predator-avoidance behaviors of sand-eel schools: why schools seldom split" in Predators and play in fishes, D.L.G.Noakes et al.(eds), Dr W.Junk Publishers, The Hague, pp.193-204, 1983

[2] I.Aoki, "An analysis of the schooling behavior of fish: Internal organization and communication process", Bull. Ocean. Res. Inst. Univ. Tokyo, 12, pp.1-65, 1980

[3] B.L.Partridge and T.J.Pitcher, "The sensory basis of fish schools: Relative roles of lateral line and vision", J. Comp. Physiol. A, 135, pp.315-325, 1980

[4] A.Huth and C.Wissel, "The simulation of the movement of fish schools", J. Theor. Biol., 156, pp.365-385, 1992

[5] I.Aoki, "A simulation on the schooling mechanism in fish", Bull. Jap. Soc. Sci. Fish., 48, pp.1081-1088, 1982

[6] B.L.Partridge, "The structure and function of fish schools", Sci. American, 246, pp.90-99, 1982

Neural Networks and Child Language Development:
Towards a *'Conglomerate'* Neural Network Simulation Architecture

Syed Sibte Raza Abidi

School of Computer Sciences
Universiti Sains Malaysia
11800 Penang, MALAYSIA
E-Mail: sraza@cs.usm.my

Abstract

Neural networks provide a basis for studying child language development in that such networks emphasise *learning*. We report a simulation of some key aspects of child language development during infancy. We argue that in order to simulate the uniquely human language learning, it is important to use a 'conglomerate' neural network architecture that integrates the collective strengths of a variety of neural networks in some principled fashion. We present such a 'conglomerate' neural network architecture - ACCLAIM that integrates both supervised and unsupervised learning algorithms, to simulate the learning of *concepts*, *words*, *conceptual* and *semantic relations* and simple *word-order* rules, thus mimicking the production of child-like *one-word* and *two-word* language. The simulations carried out are 'language informed' as realistic child language data has been used for training the neural networks.

1 Introduction

Neural network community is keenly interested in simulating human learning, and indeed language learning provides an interesting framework to build sophisticated information systems of the future. Language is generally learnt in a 'naturalistic' setting; the setting is very noisy and the input to and output from a child does not always obeys a predetermined sequence and order. There is a premium on the child correcting his or her own errors. Furthermore, child language development appears to be evolutionary, dynamic and involves an interaction of multiple tasks such as motor co-ordination, concept development, categorisation, perception, biological growth and social influences. In this regard, neural networks offers mechanisms, such as adaptive learning, generalisation, self-organisation, feature extraction, and pattern-recognition that appear to have direct relevance towards a computational simulation of child language development.

In this paper we present a 'conglomerate' (or 'modular') neural network based information processing model - ACCLAIM (A Connectionist Child LAnguage development and Imitation Model). ACCLAIM is a large-scale model that comprises a variety of neural networks communicating with each other in a systematic manner to simulate aspects of child language development within the age group of 9-24 months. Architecturally, ACCLAIM aims to achieve a degree of psychological plausibility: language development aspects which can be construed to be innate development have been simulated by using unsupervised learning regimes, and environmentally-determined aspects of language development have been simulated by using supervised learning regimes. The combined learning potential of the various neural networks constituting ACCLAIM are exploited to simulate how *concepts* are acquired and lexicalised; how *words* represented as phonemic features are learnt; how *conceptual relations* are learnt and expressed as *one-word utterances*. Furthermore, to mark a transition from one-word to two-word language, we have simulated how children learn *semantic relations* between conceptual categories and also how children learn *word-order* rules. Finally, we demonstrate how all this learnt knowledge is used to produce child-like *one-word utterances* and *two-word sentences*. The simulations performed using ACCLAIM are 'language informed' such that the data used in 'training' the neural networks was derived from the archives compiled by prominent child language researchers.

2 A Psycholinguistic Model of Child Language Development

We believe that a systematic 'language informed' simulation of child language development need to be based on. a psycholinguistic framework derived from prominent child theories and should use realistic child language data.

Our psycholinguistic framework for simulating child language is originally due to the eminent child psychologist and theorist Jean Piaget. The role neural networks can play in simulating high-level cognitive tasks have been suggested by a number of researchers [1], [2], [3], [4], [5], [6].

Consider the following model of child language development: (a) Cognitive development of a child takes place in 'stages' and is made possible through an interaction between two processes - *assimilation* and *accommodation*; (b) The child is involved in an on-going *conceptualisation* process, perceiving the environment in terms of a set semantic features to form new concepts and to recognise known concepts [7]; (c) The child's lexical growth is predicated by the child's ability to analyse phonemic information received from adult language, leading to the storage of words in terms of their phonemic constituents; (d) 'Ostensive' naming of concepts establishes a relationship between the child's concepts and words, such that, words are verbal manifestations of the child's conceptual knowledge; (e) The child's initial *one-word utterances* reflect their awareness about 'conceptual relations', such as *recurrence*, *disappearance* and so on [8]; (f) The transition from one-word to two-word sentences is marked by the child's ability to plan to manipulate the meaning of individual words in terms of 'semantic relations' which they learn and express by structuring underlying conceptual categories [9]; (g) The child learns the underlying word order of the adult language [9]; (h) the child's two-word sentences reflect the child's *intention* to communicate certain semantic relations pertaining to self or events happening in the environment [9].

From the above model of child language development it is clear that the child is an active information processor and his/her language development is seemingly due to a subtle interplay of inborn capacities, psychological makeup and environmental input. Hence, the above-mentioned 'processes' can be further distinguished by demarcating the environmental considerations from what can be regarded as the 'innate' ability of the brain to learn language. Put simply, our conjecture is that aspects of child language development that can be construed to be innate can be simulated by using 'unsupervised learning' algorithms, whereas the environmentally determined aspects of language development can be simulated by using 'supervised learning' algorithms. Hence, since the child appears to employ a variety of learning mechanisms during language development, a plausible approach to simulate language development would be to include in the simulation model all available learning algorithms that have some parallels with the child's overall learning strategy.

3   A Framework For Developing *Conglomerate* Neural Network Architectures

The discussion of the above mentioned psychological processes involved in child language development implies the existence of a variety of neural networks, each simulating a particular process. This brings into relief the need for a 'conglomerate' (or 'modular') neural network architecture: an architecture that integrates in some principled fashion both supervised and unsupervised learning algorithms, thus exploiting the collective strengths of a variety of neural networks to provide a more 'realistic' simulation. Thus, in a 'conglomerate' neural network architecture simulating language development, both the effects of the environment and that of self-learning or 'innate development' can be distinguished; the former can be simulated through supervised learning networks and the latter through unsupervised networks.

Development of conglomerate neural network architectures, in simple terms, requires the 'mixing and matching' of the relative strengths of a variety of neural networks. We propose a framework for developing conglomerate neural network architectures that distinguishes candidate neural networks on the basis of their intrinsic characterstics such as learning mechanisms, input/output representation schemes, environmental considerations and so on [10]. Our framework mainly emphasises (i) psychological and neurobiological distinctions between various neural networks when selecting neural networks to simulate certain tasks; (ii) architectural specifications - determining the number of layers, number of units in a layer, activation update functions and learning parameters; (iii) a plausible connectivity scheme by which various neural networks can efficiently communicate with each other; and (iv) variety of training strategies, including (a) one neural network learning its training data independently; (b) two or more neural networks learning their specified training data simultaneously; and (c) a co-operative training strategy where one or more neural networks transform the training data to a representation scheme that is interpretable by the principal neural network being trained.

Table 1 lists the various neural networks that are used to implement the above mentioned model of child language development, together with a specification of the typical input and output for each process that may be involved in child language development.

Psychological Process	Typical Input	Typical Output	NN Simulating The Process	The NN's Specifications
Development of a *concept memory*	A vector comprising semantic features representing concepts	The storage of children's concepts and their categorisation	*Concept Memory*	**Kohonen Map** IP = 20 Units OP = 121 Units
Development of a *word lexicon*	Phonemic representations of words - Phonemic Feature Vectors	The storage of children's words and their categorisation	*Word Lexicon*	**Kohonen Map** IP = 5 Units OP = 121 Units
Ostensive naming **of concepts**	Concepts (Semantic feature vectors) & words (Phonemic representations)	An association between children's concepts and the corresponding words - the *naming* of concepts.	*Naming Connections Network*	**Hebbian Connections** IP = OP = 121 Units
Learning *conceptual relations*	Conceptual relations, perceptual entities and functional words	An association between a 12 conceptual relations with 25 functional words (one-word utterances).	*Conceptual Relations Network*	**BP Network** IP = 15 units HI = 5 units OP = 25 units
Learning *semantic relations*	Two-word adult collocations and perceptual stimuli represented as conceptual categories.	Leant semantic relations (associative connections) among 12 concept categories.	*Semantic Relations Network*	**Hebbian Connections** IP = 12 units INT = 17 units OP = 12 units
Learning *word-order*	Auditory stimuli (Two-word adult collocations)	Learnt word-order rules based on adult language. Used to produce two-word sentences.	*Word-Order Testing Network*	**BP Network** IP = 12 units HI = 4 units OP = 12 units

Table 1: The various neural networks implementing the above-mentioned model of child language development. The table legend is IP = Input Layer, OP = Output Layer, HI = Hidden Layer, INT = Intermediate Layer

4   Towards the Architecture of ACCLAIM

Language development is a complex activity and it seems improbable to perform a realistic simulation of language development using just a single neural network. We therefore propose a '*conglomerate*' (or 'modular') approach for simulating language development, whereby individual neural networks are configured in a meaningful manner to realise a 'neural network module'. Within a neural network module the individual neural networks retain their identity and merely interact with each other to provide a more powerful and elaborate response. Each neural network module can then be dedicated to simulate a particular aspect of child language development. For instance, a *concept naming module*, synthesising three neural networks - *concept memory*, *word lexicon* and *naming connections network* can simulate the ostensive naming of concepts. Using the individual neural networks (shown in table 1) as building blocks, we have developed four different modules, where each module can simulate a different aspect of child language development (figure 1a). Extending the modularity approach further, the various modules are then synthesised, based on the tenets of our psycholinguistic model, to realise the unified architecture of a 'conglomerate' language development model - ACCLAIM (figure 1b). A systematic interaction amongst all the constituent neural networks of ACCLAIM not only simulates child language development, but also produces child-like *one-word* and *two-word sentences*.

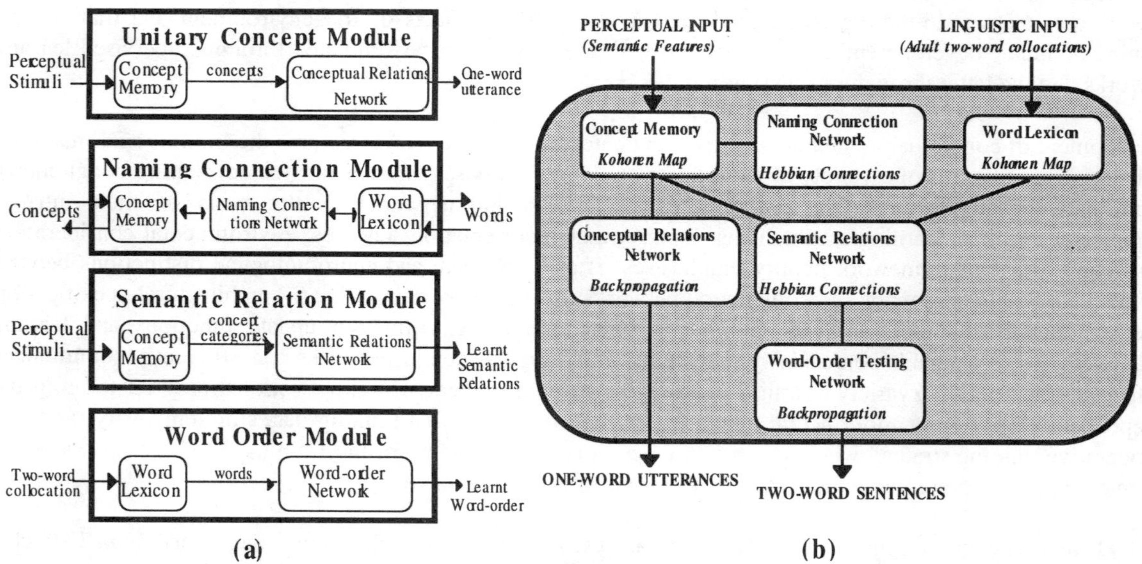

Figure 1: (a) Four neural network modules each comprising more than one neural network and simulating some aspect of child language development; (b) The conglomerate architecture of ACCLAIM

Indeed, a conglomerate approach for developing complex neural network architectures has certain advantages, for instance (i) it allows knowledge learnt by one neural network to be utilised in more than one module, for instance the concepts learnt and stored in the concept memory are used by three different modules - the unitary concept module, concept naming module and the semantic relation module (see figure 1a); (b) within a module one or more neural networks can be used to transform the representation of the training data to a representation that is understood by another neural network for both learning and information retrieval purposes; (c) the results of a simulation incorporating just one module can be used by other modules to perform their respective simulations; and (d) at a deeper level, each module again can be envisaged as an independent neural network model, capable of simulating a psycholinguistic process on its own.

5   A Neural Network Based Simulation of Child Language Development

In ACCLAIM all the simulations were carried out in a 'developmental' manner, starting with no *a priori* information (a randomly connected organisation of processing units) the neural networks were repeatedly presented with a set of 'training patterns' which the networks gradually *learnt* over a period of iterations. This repeated presentation of the training patterns is analogous of the child's increased appreciation of interesting information, and perhaps it is this frequent repitition of information that leads to its assimilation. Table 2 summarises our simulation strategy both at the one-word and two-word stage of language development.

Simulation Task	Learning	Neural Networks Used
One-word language stage		
Concept development, storage and categorisation	Unsupervised	Concept memory
Concept generalisation, neologisms and novel concepts	Unsupervised	Concept memory
Word acquisition, storage and development	Unsupervised	Word lexicon
Learning conceptual relations - production of one-word utterances, generalisation to novel situations	Supervised	Conceptual relations network
Concept lexicalisation - development of naming connections	Unsupervised	Naming connection network
Concept and lexical retrieval	Unsupervised	Concept memory + Naming connection network + Word lexicon
Two-word language stage		
Learning semantic relations and determining the semantic relation between two conceptual categories	Unsupervised	Semantic relation network + Concept memory + Naming connection network + Word lexicon
Learning word-order leading to the production of two-word sentences	Supervised	Word-order testing network + Concept memory + Naming connection network + Word lexicon + Semantic relations network

Table 2: List of simulations carried out, each characterising a key aspect of child language development

Below we briefly describe some of the above-mentioned simulations:
Learning Concepts *(Concept Memory)*: Simulation involved the learning of 42 concepts (taken from Bloom, [8]) represented by a 20-dimensional semantic feature vector, comprising the so-called 'defining features' determining the concept's category and 'individual features' distinguishing the category members. The learnt concept memory exhibited clusters of close concepts or 'concept categories', thus implying an *automatic categorisation* of learnt concepts into categories and sub-categories [11], [12].
Learning Words *(Word Lexicon)*: Simulation involved the learning of 42 words corresponding to the learnt concepts. The words were represented in terms of their phonetic components by a 5-dimensional phonetic feature vector. The learnt word lexicon predicated a discrimination of phonetic information, i.e. the development of the so-called 'similarity neighbourhoods' of similar sounding words [11], [12].
Concept Lexicalisation *(Naming Connection Module)*: Simulation involved the creation of (bi-directional) 'naming connections' between each concept in the concept memory with its corresponding lexical label in the word lexicon. Thus, an activated concept/word would spread its activations acroos the 'learnt' naming connections leading to the retrieval of the corresponding word/concept [11], [12].
Learning Conceptual Relations *(Unitary Concept Module)*: Simulation involved the learning of a mapping between a set of 12 *conceptual relations* and 3 *perceivable entities* (people, objects and events) to a set of 25 *words* [8]. The learnt conceptual relations network accepts a *conceptual relation* as input and as output produces the corresponding *one-word utterance* that best reflects the child's 'intention'. Also, the conceptual relation network can generalise to produce appropriate responses in novel situations.
Learning Semantic Relations *(Semantic Relations Module)*: Simulation involved the development of associative connections between 12 concept categories, implying that certain concept categories are 'semantically related' [9]. Given a concept category its semantic relation with all other categories can be determined by spreading its high activation across the network to other connected concept category units.

Learning Word-order _(Word-Order Module)_: Simulation involved the learning of the inherent word-order in adult language, i.e. learning how to arrange two words to form a sentence. Given two words, the learnt word order testing network would combine two words in the proper order to yield a child-like *two-word sentence*.

6 Input Transformation: Significance of a *Conglomerate* Approach

Our conglomerate approach facilitates a co-operation amongst a number of neural networks for transforming the input stimuli from one representation to another representation. For instance, the input stimuli for the simulation of learning semantic relations is adult language (or simply adult two-word collocations), however what is actually needed for learning semantic relations is the conceptual category information of the two concepts that comprise the adult two-word collocation. This situation calls for the transformation of an adult two-word collocation to the corresponding conceptual category information, in a manner that may have some relevance to the processing of the child. By way of our conglomerate approach, the knowledge acquired by various neural networks can be exploited to transform an input stimuli to the desired representation. For learning semantic relations the *concept memory*, *word lexicon* and the *concept lexicalisation network* are employed according to the following scheme: learning semantic relations begins with the presentation of an adult-two word collocation to the word lexicon, which results in the retrieval of the corresponding two words. The naming connections are then exploited to retrieve the two corresponding concepts. Finally, the category information of the two retrieved concepts, embedded in their semantic feature representations in terms of the defining features, is extracted for the learning of semantic relations. Similarly, word-order learning requires the transformation of an two-word collocation to a semantic relation and this is achieved by an interaction between· the *concept memory*, *word lexicon*, *naming connection* network and *semantic relation network* (see figure 2).

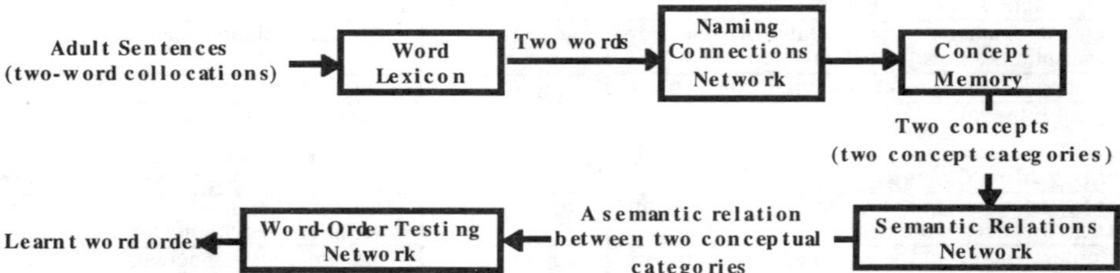

Figure 2: The input transformation procedure for simulating the learning of word-order

Indeed, one could have simulated both the learning of semantic relations and word-order by directly presenting category information to the concerned neural network, however our argument is that such a scheme would not hold much psychological plausibility as compared to our simulation scheme which brings into relief the underlying mechanisms that may be involved in the child's learning of semantic relations and word-order.

7 The Simulation Results: Production of *One-word* and *Two-word Language*

The learnt performance of ACCLAIM is best elicited by demonstrating the ability of ACCLAIM to produce child-like one-word and two-word language (as these two simulations involve an interaction between all the previously 'trained' neural networks) and quantifying the sentences produced against Bloom's [8] data which reports children's utterances with details of the situation in which the utterance was made. Table 3 and 4 present a sample of the one-word and two-word sentences produced by ACCLAIM, respectively.

Simulation of one-word utterances production utilisies the *unitary concept module*. The input stimuli comprising a conceptual relation (representing the underlying 'intention of the child') is presented to the concept memory. In response, the conceptual relations network produces a *one-word utterance* that best represents the child's intention. Simulation of two word sentence production involves an interaction between 5 neural networks, namely the *concept memory, word lexicon, naming connection network, semantic relations network* and the *word-order testing network*. This simulation, involving 3 stages, initiates with the presentation of an input stimuli which comprises two concepts - (1) the child's communicative 'intention', and (ii) a perceptual stimuli: (a) retrieval of two concepts from the concept memory and the corresponding words from the word lexicon; (b) determining the semantic relations between the categories of the two concepts; and (c) evaluation of a word-order hypothesis - determining the correct order in which the two words (corresponding to the concepts) are to be arranged. The two words when combined in the correct order yield a child-like *two-word sentence*.

Real-Life Situation (taken from Bloom)	Child's 1-word Utterance	ACCLAIM's Input Pattern	ACCLAIM's 1-word Utterance
(Mother pointing to chair) What is this?	chair	Pointing + Object (chair)	*obj name (chair)* (output unit 17)
(Allison holding picture to photographer's assistant, off camera) Where's the girl? (Allison turns picture over so she can't see the girl)	girl		
(Allison turning it back to picture side)	n o	Non-existence + People	*no* (output unit 7)
	there	Existence + People	*there* (output unit 5)

Table 3: Sample of the 1-word utterances produced by ACCLAIM compared with those produced by the child -Allison.

Real-Life Situation (taken from Bloom)	Child's 2-word Sentence	Semantic Relation	ACCLAIM's 2-word Sentence
(Mother pointing to chair.) What is this?	that chair	demonstrative + entity (= Object)	*that chair*
(Mother pours herself juice). (Allison picking up empty cup)	more juice	recurrence + object	*more juice*
(Mother pours juice; Allison drinks juice, looks into empty cup. Mother taking cup)	gone juice	negative + object	*gone juice*

Table 4: Sample of the 2-word sentences produced by ACCLAIM compared with those produced by the child -Allison

8 Conclusions

We have attempted a simulation of some aspects of aspects of child language development during the key. developmental periods, c.9-24 months. We have demonstrated how neural networks can be used to both operationalise extant child language corpora and systematise psycholinguistic theories. Furthermore, the results of our simulations indicate a degree of similarity between the learnt behaviours of the neural networks with the kind of behaviours exhibited by children whilst learning language. From a neural network point of view we have demonstrated the efficacy of a conglomerate neural network architecture for simulating high-level cognitive activities. The architecture of ACCLAIM and the resultant processing capabilities achieved, should be an indicator as to how functionally and structurally divergent neural networks when synthesised together in a meaningful manner, i.e. based on a psycholinguistic model, can simulate a high-level cognitive activity such as child language development. We believe that the simulations carried out by ACCLAIM has made a contribution to the on-going research regarding the role of neural networks in simulating human learning.

References

[1] J. McClelland, "PDP: Implications for Cognition and Development", R. Morris (Ed.) Parallel Distributed Processing: *Implications for Psychology and Neurobiology.* Oxford: Clarendon Press, 1989.

[2] W. Bechtel and A. Abrahamsen, *Connectionism and the Mind.* Oxford: Basil Blackwell, 1991.

[3] A. Shawley, A & J. Schopman, J. "Connectionism and the Foundations of Cognitive Science", *Cognitive Systems*, Vol. 2(4), pp. 373-382, 1990.

[4] T. Shultz, "Simulating Stages of Human Cognitive Development with Connectionis Models", L. Birnbaum & G. Collins (Eds.) *Machine Learning: Proc. of the Eighth Intl. Workshop*, San Mateo: Morgan Kaufman, 1991.

[5] D. Levine, *Introduction to Neural and Cognitive Modelling.* Hillsdale: Lawrence Earlbaum Associates, 1991.

[6] M. Seidenberg, "Connectionist Models and Cognitive Theory". *Psychological Science*, Vol. 4, pp. 228-235, 1993

[7] K. Nelson, "Structure and Strategy in Learning to Talk", *Monographs of the Society for Research in Child Development.*, Vol. 38, 1973.

[8] L. Bloom, *One Word at a Time.* Paris: Mouton, 1973.

[9] R. Brown, *A First Language: The Early Stages.* Cambridge, MA: Harvard University Press, 1973.

[10] S.S.R. Abidi, *A Connectionist Simulation: Towards a Model of Child Language Development.* Doctoral Thesis. University of Surrey, Guildford, England, 1994.

[11] S.S.R. Abidi, & K. Ahmad, "Child Language Development: A Connectionist Simulation of the Evolving Concept Memory". M. Aldridge (Ed.) *Child language.* Clevedon: Multilingual Matters Ltd, 1996.

[12] S.S.R. Abidi and K. Ahmad , "Unsupervised Category Learning in a Hybrid Connectionist Architecture", *Proc. of SEARCC '94 computer conference*, Karachi, 1994.

The author acknowledges the support and guidance by Dr. K. Ahmad, Univ. of Surrey, towards this research work.

Neural Control and Robotics

(Oral Presentation)

A neural networks approach for approximate realization of nonlinear H_∞ controller

Xiaofeng Yang, Tielong Shen and Katsutoshi Tamura
Department of Mechanical Engineering, Sophia University
Tokyo, 102 Japan

Abstract— This paper discusses an approximate realization of nonlinear H_∞ state feedback controller based on neural networks. A three-layer neural network is constructed and is trained to satisfy Hamilton-Jacobi inequality, then the state feedback H_∞ controller is designed based on the obtained network approximate solution. It will be shown that the network learning problem can be formulated as a maximum value function optimization problem. A learning algorithm is developed based on nondifferentiable optimization techniques. The efficiency of the proposed method is demonstrated by numerical simulation results.

1　Introduction

It is well-known that the solution of linear H_∞ control problem can be obtained by solving a Riccati inequality [1]. In recent papers, several researchers have extended linear H_∞ control theory to nonlinear systems. The nonlinear H_∞ control problem is solved based on a solution of Hamilton-Jacobi inequality [2, 3]. To apply this theory to nonlinear control problem, a difficulty is that a nonlinear partial differential inequality has to be solved, and this is usually not an easy task. Generally speaking, an analytical solution is not obtainable except for very simple cases. This fact makes the focus turn to find the approximate solution.

It is well-known that a multilayered feedforward neural network can approximate any continuous nonlinear function in arbitrary accuracy on a compact interval with one or more hidden layers [4]. Based on this fact, if a smooth solution of Hamilton-Jacobi inequality exists, we may approximate it by neural networks. In this paper, we construct one of possible forms of the solution by a three-layer network then train it to satisfy Hamilton-Jacobi inequality. It will be shown that the network learning problem for solution of Hamilton-Jacobi inequality can be formulated as a maximum value function optimization problem. The conventional algorithms based on a smooth function is not applicable to this problem since the maximum value function is not differentiable [5]. Hence a learning algorithm based on the nondifferentiable optimization techniques [6] is proposed to ensure successful learning of neural network. After an approximate solution is obtained, then the nonlinear state feedback H_∞ controller can be realized. Numerical simulation compares the efficiency of the nonlinear H_∞ controller based on neural network with the linear H_∞ controller obtained by linearization.

The remainder of this paper is organized as follows. Section 2 gives the problem formulation and then the neural network approximate solution problem, and learning algorithm is described in Section 3. Simulation results and conclusions are described in Section 4 and 5, respectively.

2　Problem Formulation

2.1　Nonlinear state feedback H_∞ control problem

Consider the following affine nonlinear system
$$\dot{x} \;=\; f(x) + g_1(x)d + g_2(x)u \tag{1}$$
$$y \;=\; h(x) \tag{2}$$
where x is a state vector defined on a compact set X including the origin in R^n with control input $u \in R^m$ and disturbance input $d \in R^q$. $y \in R^p$ is the measured variable which is a function of the state x. The mapping $f(x), g_1(x), g_2(x), h(x)$ are smooth (i.e. C^∞) mappings defined in a neighborhood of the origin in R^n with $f(0) = 0, h(0) = 0$.

For this system, we now define the nonlinear state feedback H_∞ control problem as follows.

Nonlinear state feedback H_∞ control problem: Let $\gamma \geq 0$ be given. For given system (1),(2), find a state feedback control law
$$u = \alpha(x) \tag{3}$$
such that the L_2-gain of closed-loop system (from d to $\left[\begin{smallmatrix} y \\ u \end{smallmatrix}\right]$) is less than or equal to γ and the free system (i.e. $d = 0$) is locally asymptotically stable. $\alpha(x)$ is any smooth function with $\alpha(0) = 0$.

To solve this problem, Van der Schaft [2] gives the following theorem.

Theorem :　Let $\gamma > 0$ be given. Suppose the pair of $\{f(x), h(x)\}$ is locally zero-state observable. If there exists a smooth positive definite solution $\Phi(x) > 0$ for $^\forall x \in X$ ($\Phi(0) = 0$) to the Hamilton-Jacobi inequality

$$\frac{\partial \Phi}{\partial x} f + \frac{1}{4}\frac{\partial \Phi}{\partial x}\left(\frac{1}{\gamma^2}g_1 g_1^T - g_2 g_2^T\right)\frac{\partial^T \Phi}{\partial x} + h^T h \leq 0 \tag{4}$$

then the nonlinear state feedback H_∞ control problem is solvable with state feedback

$$u = -\frac{1}{2}g_2^T \frac{\partial^T \Phi}{\partial x} \tag{5}$$

As a direct result of above theorem, for the linearized system of (1),(2) with the form

$$\begin{aligned}\dot{x} &= Ax + B_1 d + B_2 u \tag{6}\\ y &= Cx \tag{7}\end{aligned}$$

where

$$\begin{aligned}A &= f_x(0), \quad B_1 = g_1(0)\\ B_2 &= g_2(0), \quad C = h_x(0)\end{aligned} \tag{8}$$

the following corollary can be easy obtained:

Corollary : Let $\gamma > 0$. Suppose the pair $\{C, A\}$ is detectable. If there exists a positive definite solution $P > 0$ to the Riccati inequality

$$A^T P + PA + P(\frac{1}{\gamma^2}B_1 B_1^T - B_2 B_2^T)P + C^T C < 0 \tag{9}$$

then the closed-loop system (from d to $\left[\begin{smallmatrix}y\\u\end{smallmatrix}\right]$) with the state feedback

$$u = -B_2^T Px \tag{10}$$

has L_2-gain less than or equal to γ and the free system is asymptotically stable.

Hence, the key problem in applying above theorem successfully to any control problem is to find an appropriate function $\Phi(x) > 0$ with $\Phi(0) = 0$ which satisfies the Hamilton-Jacobi inequality. In the following it will be shown that an approximate solution can be obtained by a neural network and then state feedback controller can be realized based on this network.

2.2   Neural network state feedback controller

If a smooth solution $\Phi(x) \geq 0$ for all $x \in X$ exists, it can be written as

$$\Phi(x) = \Theta^T(x)\Theta(x) \tag{11}$$

where $\Theta(x) : X \to R^n$ is a smooth nonlinear function. Hence there exists a neural network which can exactly approximate $\Theta(x)$ on X. Let the network be a three-layer network, then $\Theta(x)$ can be expressed by the network as follows:

$$\Theta(x, W_\Theta, W_\Psi) = W_\Theta \Psi(W_\Psi x) \tag{12}$$

where $W_\Theta \in R^{n \times l}$ and $W_\Psi \in R^{l \times n}$ are interconnection weight matrices, l is the number of hidden neurons. $x = [x_1, x_2, \cdots, x_n]^T$ is the input of network and $\Theta = [\theta_1, \theta_2, \cdots, \theta_n]^T$ is the output. $\Psi(z) : R^n \to R^l$ is the activation function vector of hidden layer with $\Psi(z) = [\psi_1(z_1), \psi_2(z_2), \cdots, \psi_l(z_l)]^T$ and

$$\psi_j(z_j) = \tanh(z_j) = \frac{1 - e^{-2z_j}}{1 + e^{-2z_j}} \quad (j = 1, 2, \cdots, l) \tag{13}$$

Furthermore, the solution $\Phi(x)$ can be constructed by neural network as

$$\begin{aligned}\Phi(x, W_\Theta, W_\Psi) &= \Theta^T(x, W_\Theta, W_\Psi)\Theta(x, W_\Theta, W_\Psi)\\ &= \Psi^T(W_\Psi x)W_\Theta^T W_\Theta \Psi(W_\Psi x)\end{aligned} \tag{14}$$

Using the elementwise notation, neural network (12),(14) can be rewritten as follows and shown in Figure 1.

$$\psi_j = \tanh(\sum_{i=1}^{n} w_{ji}x_i) \quad (i = 1, \cdots, n, \; j = 1, \cdots, l) \tag{15}$$

$$\theta_k = \sum_{j=1}^{l} v_{kj}\psi_j \quad (j = 1, \cdots, l, \; k = 1, \cdots, n) \tag{16}$$

$$\Phi(x, W_\Theta, W_\Psi) = \sum_{k=1}^{n} \theta_k^2 \tag{17}$$

where v_{kj}, w_{ji} are the elements of weight matrices W_Θ and W_Ψ, respectively.

The partial derivative of $\Phi(x, W_\Theta, W_\Psi)$ with respect to x is given by

$$\frac{\partial \Phi(x, W_\Theta, W_\Psi)}{\partial x} = 2\Psi^T(W_\Psi x)W_\Theta^T W_\Theta \Gamma W_\Psi \tag{18}$$

where

$$\Gamma = \mathrm{diag}[\psi_1', \psi_2', \cdots, \psi_l'] \tag{19}$$

with the elements

$$\psi_j' = 1 - \psi_j^2 \quad (j = 1, 2, \cdots, l) \tag{20}$$

thus the neural network state feedback controller is obtained by

$$u = -g_2^T W_\Psi^T \Gamma W_\Theta^T W_\Theta \Psi(W_\Psi x) \tag{21}$$

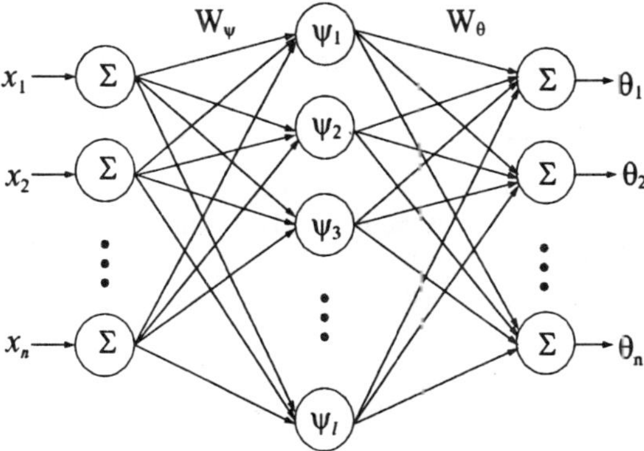

Figure 1: The structure of neural network

Furthermore, consider the Taylor expansion of the activation function of hidden layer of network

$$\tanh(z) = z - \frac{1}{3}z^3 + \frac{2}{15}z^5 - \frac{17}{315}z^7 + \cdots, \quad (|z| < \frac{\pi}{2}) \tag{22}$$

where $\tanh(z) \approx z$ for $|z| \to 0$. Thus, at the origin the linearization of the above controller will become

$$\begin{aligned} u_L &= -g_2^T(0)(W_\Theta W_\Psi)^T (W_\Theta W_\Psi) x \\ &= -B_2^T P x \end{aligned} \tag{23}$$

where

$$P = (W_\Theta W_\Psi)^T W_\Theta W_\Psi \tag{24}$$

is a solution of the corresponding Riccati inequality of the linearized system, so the linear controller is obtained.

3   Neural Network Approximation and Learning Algorithm

3.1   Neural Network Approximation

Define a training data set Δ by

$$\Delta = \{x^s | s = 1, 2, \cdots, N\} \tag{25}$$

which is uniformly distributed in X.

The approximate solution problem is defined as follows:

The approximate solution problem: For a given Δ as training data, Find a weight (W_Θ, W_Ψ) of neural network such that $H(x, W_\Theta, W_\Psi) \leq 0$ is satisfied for all $x \in \Delta$, where

$$\begin{aligned} H(x, W_\Theta, W_\Psi) &= \frac{\partial \Phi(x, W_\Theta, W_\Psi)}{\partial x} f \\ &+ \frac{1}{4} \frac{\partial \Phi(x, W_\Theta, W_\Psi)}{\partial x} \left(\frac{1}{\gamma^2} g_1 g_1^T - g_2 g_2^T \right) \frac{\partial^T \Phi(x, W_\Theta, W_\Psi)}{\partial x} + h^T h \end{aligned} \tag{26}$$

For a given weight (W_Θ, W_Ψ), $H(x, W_\Theta, W_\Psi)$ can be calculated for every $x \in \Delta$ and the maximum value of it can be determined and is given by

$$E(W_\Theta, W_\Psi) = \max_s \{H(x^s, W_\Theta, W_\Psi) | s = 1, 2, \cdots, N\} \tag{27}$$

$E(W_\Theta, W_\Psi)$ is called the maximum value function of H.

Assume that there exists a weight $(\bar{W}_\Theta, \bar{W}_\Psi)$ such that

$$E(\bar{W}_\Theta, \bar{W}_\Psi) \leq 0 \tag{28}$$

Thus

$$\max_s \{H(x^s, \bar{W}_\Theta, \bar{W}_\Psi) | s = 1, 2, \cdots, N\} \leq 0 \tag{29}$$

Hence it follows that

$$H(x^s, \bar{W}_\Theta, \bar{W}_\Psi) \leq 0 \quad {}^\forall x^s \in \Delta \tag{30}$$

By the above analysis, it is clear that the approximate solution problem can be formulated as a maximum value function optimization problem, i.e., finding a weight $(\bar{W}_\Theta, \bar{W}_\Psi)$ of neural network such that $E(\bar{W}_\Theta, \bar{W}_\Psi) \leq 0$ is satisfied. Due to the fact that the maximum value function E is usually not differentiable, the conventional smooth algorithms are no longer applicable to the problem. Thus we developed a learning algorithm based on the nondifferentiable optimization method [5, 7].

3.2 Learning algorithm

For notational convenience, the column extension of matrices W_Θ, W_Ψ is defined by

$$\mathrm{cs}W_\Theta \stackrel{\triangle}{=} [v_{11}\ v_{21}\ \cdots\ v_{n1}\ v_{12}\ v_{22}\ \cdots\ v_{nl}]^T \quad (nl \times 1 \text{ vector}) \tag{31}$$

$$\mathrm{cs}W_\Psi \stackrel{\triangle}{=} [w_{11}\ w_{21}\ \cdots\ w_{l1}\ w_{12}\ w_{22}\ \cdots\ w_{ln}]^T \quad (ln \times 1 \text{ vector}) \tag{32}$$

Since $H(x, W_\Theta, W_\Psi)$ is smooth function of x and W_Θ, W_Ψ, the gradients of $H(x, W_\Theta, W_\Psi)$ with respect to $W_\Theta = \{v_{kj}\}$ and $W_\Psi = \{w_{ji}\}$ can be defined by

$$\frac{\partial H(x, W_\Theta, W_\Psi)}{\partial W_\Theta} \stackrel{\triangle}{=} \frac{\partial H(x, W_\Theta, W_\Psi)}{\partial \mathrm{cs}W_\Theta} \tag{33}$$

$$\frac{\partial H(x, W_\Theta, W_\Psi)}{\partial W_\Psi} \stackrel{\triangle}{=} \frac{\partial H(x, W_\Theta, W_\Psi)}{\partial \mathrm{cs}W_\Psi} \tag{34}$$

Furthermore, the generalized gradient of E at any (W_Θ, W_Ψ) can be expressed as

$$\partial E^\circ(W_\Theta, W_\Psi) = \mathrm{conv}\left\{ \left[\frac{\partial H(x^s, W_\Theta, W_\Psi)}{\partial W_\Theta} \cdot \frac{\partial H(x^s, W_\Theta, W_\Psi)}{\partial W_\Psi} \right]^T \Bigg| s \in S(W_\Theta, W_\Psi) \right\} \tag{35}$$

where conv denotes the convex hull and $S(W_\Theta, W_\Psi)$ is the index set given by

$$S(W_\Theta, W_\Psi) = \{s | E(W_\Theta, W_\Psi) = H(x^s, W_\Theta, W_\Psi)\} \tag{36}$$

The elements of vectors in (33), (34) can be obtained using chain rule differentiation as follows:

$$\frac{\partial H(x, W_\Theta, W_\Psi)}{\partial v_{kj}} = \zeta[kj]f \;+\; \frac{1}{4}\left\{ \zeta[kj]\left(\frac{1}{\gamma^2}g_1 g_1^T - g_2 g_2^T \right) \frac{\partial^T \Phi(x, W_\Theta, W_\Psi)}{\partial x} \right.$$
$$\left. +\; \frac{\partial \Phi(x, W_\Theta, W_\Psi)}{\partial x}\left(\frac{1}{\gamma^2}g_1 g_1^T - g_2 g_2^T \right) \zeta^T[kj] \right\} \tag{37}$$

where $\frac{\partial \Phi(x, W_\Theta, W_\Psi)}{\partial x}$ is given by (18) and $\zeta[kj]$ is a vector defined by

$$\zeta[kj] \stackrel{\triangle}{=} [\zeta_1[kj], \zeta_2[kj], \cdots, \zeta_n[kj]] \tag{38}$$

with the entries

$$\zeta_i[kj] = \frac{\partial^2 \Phi(x, W_\Theta, W_\Psi)}{\partial v_{kj} \partial x_i} = 2\left(\psi_j \sum_{j=1}^{l}(v_{kj}\psi_j' w_{ji}) + \theta_k \psi_j' w_{ji} \right) \; (i = 1, 2, \cdots, n) \tag{39}$$

and

$$\frac{\partial H(x, W_\Theta, W_\Psi)}{\partial w_{ji}} = \xi[ji]f \;+\; \frac{1}{4}\left\{ \xi[ji]\left(\frac{1}{\gamma^2}g_1 g_1^T - g_2 g_2^T \right) \frac{\partial^T \Phi(x, W_\Theta, W_\Psi)}{\partial x} \right.$$
$$\left. +\; \frac{\partial \Phi(x, W_\Theta, W_\Psi)}{\partial x}\left(\frac{1}{\gamma^2}g_1 g_1^T - g_2 g_2^T \right) \xi^T[ji] \right\} \tag{40}$$

where $\xi[ji]$ is a vector defined by

$$\xi[ji] \stackrel{\triangle}{=} [\xi_1[ji], \xi_2[ji], \cdots, \xi_n[ji]] \tag{41}$$

with the entries

$$\xi_q[ji] = \frac{\partial^2 \Phi(x, W_\Theta, W_\Psi)}{\partial w_{ji} \partial x_i} \;=\; 2\sum_{k=1}^{n}(v_{kj}\psi_j' x_q \sum_{j=1}^{l}(v_{kj}\psi_j' w_{ji})$$
$$-2\theta_k v_{kj}\psi_j \psi_j' x_q w_{ji} + \delta_{iq}\theta_k v_{kj}\psi_j') \; (q = 1, 2, \cdots, n) \tag{42}$$

where δ_{iq} is the Kronecker tensor.

Thus depended on the descent method of nondifferentiable optimization, the learning algorithm is given by

$$\begin{bmatrix} \mathrm{cs}W_\Theta^{\mathrm{new}} \\ \mathrm{cs}W_\Psi^{\mathrm{new}} \end{bmatrix} = \begin{bmatrix} \mathrm{cs}W_\Theta^{\mathrm{old}} \\ \mathrm{cs}W_\Psi^{\mathrm{old}} \end{bmatrix} + \eta \begin{bmatrix} D_{W_\Theta} \\ D_{W_\Psi} \end{bmatrix} \tag{43}$$

where $[D_{W_\Theta}\ D_{W_\Psi}]^T$ is the steepest descent direction of $E(W_\Theta, W_\Psi)$ at (W_Θ, W_Ψ) and is expressed as

$$\begin{bmatrix} D_{W_\Theta} \\ D_{W_\Psi} \end{bmatrix} = -\mathrm{Nr}(\partial E^\circ(W_\Theta, W_\Psi)) \tag{44}$$

where $\mathrm{Nr}(\cdot)$ is the element of the convex hull which has the smallest norm and can be solved by Wolfe's algorithm [8].

Finally, the above proposed learning algorithm is summarized as follows:

Step 1: Give a set of training data $\Delta \in X$ and $W_\Theta(0), W_\Psi(0)$ in weight space randomly.

Step 2: Choose the maximum value function E and form the index set $S(W_\Theta, W_\Psi)$. If $E \leq 0$ then stop, otherwise go to the next step.

Step 3: Calculate the gradient using (37) and (40).

Step 4: Use Wolfe's algorithm to solve (44).

Step 5: Adjust the weight using (43), then goto Step 2.

4 Simulation

Consider the H_∞ control problem for the following nonlinear system:

$$\begin{aligned}
\dot{x} &= f(x) + g_1(x)d + g_2(x)u \\
y &= h(x)
\end{aligned}$$

$$f(x) = \begin{bmatrix} 1.2\tanh(x_2) \\ 0 \end{bmatrix} \quad g_1(x) = \begin{bmatrix} 0 \\ \frac{1}{\cos(x_2)} \end{bmatrix}$$

$$g_2(x) = \begin{bmatrix} 0 \\ \frac{1.2}{\cos(x_2)} \end{bmatrix} \quad h(x) = \begin{bmatrix} 1 & 0 \\ 0 & 1 \end{bmatrix} x$$

The linearized system is given by

$$A = \begin{bmatrix} 0 & 1.2 \\ 0 & 0 \end{bmatrix}; \quad B_1 = \begin{bmatrix} 0 \\ 1 \end{bmatrix}; B_2 = \begin{bmatrix} 0 \\ 1.2 \end{bmatrix}; \quad C = \begin{bmatrix} 1 & 0 \\ 0 & 1 \end{bmatrix}$$

Without loss of generality, let $\gamma = 1.5$ and the disturbance $d = 0.5\sin(x_2)$ for this example. A $\mathcal{N}_{2-15-2}$ neural network (2 neuron in input layer, 15 neurons in hidden layer and 2 neuron in output layer), are used to obtain an approximate solution of Hamilton-Jacobi inequality. The initial weights $W_\Theta(0)$, $W_\Psi(0)$ are produced in $[-1\ 1]$ randomly and the training data set $\Delta = \{x^s | s = 1, 2, \cdots, 200\}$, which is uniformly distributed in $[-2\ 2]$, is chosen.

Now, we will compare the obtained neural network nonlinear controller with the linear controller obtained by the linearization as

$$P = \begin{bmatrix} 110.4294 & 123.8937 \\ 123.8937 & 153.9643 \end{bmatrix}$$

Figure 2 shows the initial state response when $x(0) = [0.8\ 0.8]^T$. We can see that the state response in the neural network controller case is slightly better than that in the linear controller case.

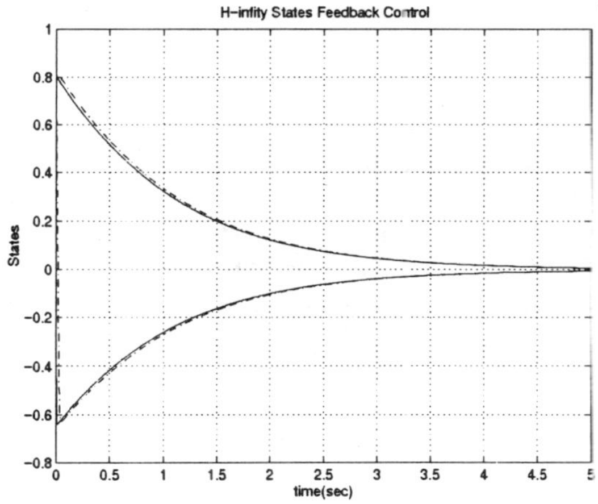

Figure 2: Initial state response; solid-nonlinear, dashdot-linear

If the initial state is not near the origin, the linear H_∞ controller is no longer valid. For this example, we numerically estimated that the stability region in the case of the linear H_∞ controller is about $[-1.58\ 1.58]$

(see Figure 3). In the case of the neural network nonlinear controller, however, the stability region is larger. Figure 4 shows the initial state response when $x(0) = [2\ 2]^T$. We can see that the closed loop system is asymptotically stable.

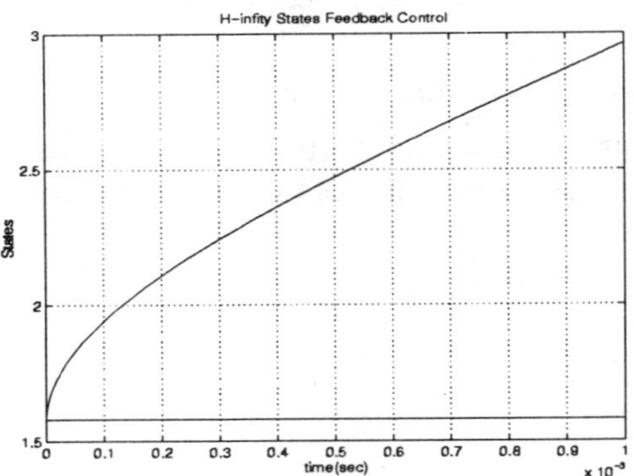

Figure 3: Initial state response for x(0)=[1.58, 1.58] under linear control

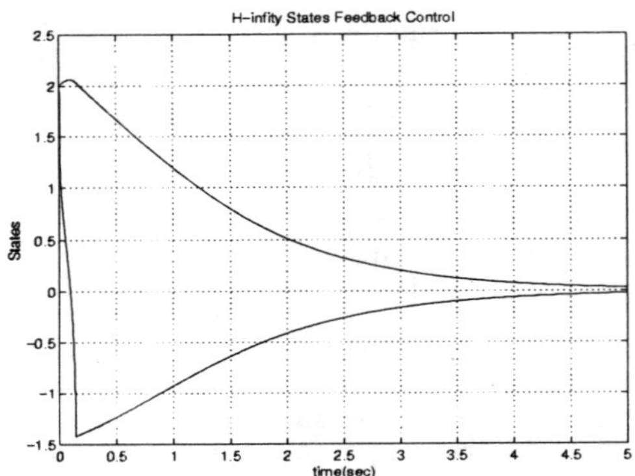

Figure 4: Initial state response for x(0)=[2, 2] under nonlinear control

5   Conclusions

In this paper, the design of nonlinear H_∞ state feedback controller based on neural network is proposed. An approximate solution of Hamilton-Jacobi inequality can be obtained through network learning. An effective learning algorithm based on nondifferentiable optimization techniques to optimize the defined maximum value function is developed. The simulation results demonstrated that better results and larger stability region can be achieved by the nonlinear H_∞ controller based on the neural network.

References

[1] J. C. Doyle *et al.*, "State space solutions to standard H_2 and H_∞ control problems," *IEEE Trans. Automat. Contr.*, vol. 34, pp. 831-846, 1990.

[2] A. J. van der Schaft, "L_2-gain analysis of nonlinear systems and nonlinear state feedback H_∞ control," *IEEE Trans. Automat. Contr.*, vol. 37, pp. 770-784, 1992.

[3] A. Isidori and A. Astofi, "Disturbance attenuation and H_∞ control via measurement feedback in nonlinear systems," *IEEE Trans. Automat. Contr.*, vol. 37, pp. 1283-1293, 1992.

[4] K. Hornik *et al*, "Multilayer feedforward networks are universal approximators," *Neural Networks*, vol. 2, pp. 359-366, 1989.

[5] K. C. Kiwiel, *Methods of descent for nondifferentiable optimization*, Lecture Notes in Mathematics 1133, Springer-Verlag, 1985.

[6] F. H. Clarke, *Optimization and nonsmooth analysis*, Wiley, 1983.

[7] K. Shimizi and E. Aiyoshi, *Mathematical programming* (in Japanese), Tokyo: Syoukoudo Pub. Co., 1984.

[8] P. Wolfe. Finding the nearest point in a polytope, *Mathematical Programming*, vol. 11, pp. 128-149, 1976.

Learning Fine Motion in Robotics:
Experiments with the Hierarchical Extended Kohonen Map

Cristina Versino†, Luca Maria Gambardella†
† IDSIA, Corso Elvezia 36, 6900 Lugano, Switzerland
cristina@idsia.ch, http://www.idsia.ch/~cristina

Abstract— We present a Hierarchical Extended Kohonen Map (HEKM) and a planning system which cooperate to solve the robot path finding problem. The HEKM learns to associate appropriate actions to perceptions under the supervision of the planner. First, we argue for the utility of using the hierarchical version of the KM instead of the "flat" KM: the HEKM provides a natural and economic representation of the robot's perceptual states. Second, we measure the benefits of cooperative learning due to the interaction of neighboring neurons in the HEKM: with cooperation, learning is slowed down in the short run, but the benefits appear later on, resulting in a more satisfactory final performance. Third, we highlight a beneficial side-effect obtained by transferring motion skill from the planner to the HEKM, namely, smoothness of motion.

1 Introduction

The problem of *path finding* has attracted considerable attention by robotics research. This is the problem of moving a robot from a starting position to a goal position avoiding collisions against obstacles in the workspace. Moreover, the robot path should be as *short* and *smooth* as possible. The path is *optimal* if it is the shortest from the starting position to the goal.

Path finders are methods to automatically solve the path finding problem. Traditionally, path finders are either *model-based* or *sensor-based*. While model-based systems address the path finding problem *globally* using a model of the workspace, sensor-based systems consider it *locally*, and rely on robot sensors to avoid obstacles. Both methods have limitations, which are rather complementary. Model-based systems compute optimal free-paths and recover easily from dead-ends, but require a complete description of the robot workspace and are computationally expensive. Sensor-based systems do not need a model of the workspace and require limited computation, but produce sub-optimal paths and may get trapped into dead-ends. In addition, they are difficult to program.

By integrating model-based and sensor-based methods, we can mitigate their respective drawbacks. Thus, in [10] we have described a planner working on an artificial potential field (a model-based system) and a Hierarchical Extended Kohonen Map (a sensor-based system) which cooperate to solve the path finding problem. Along related lines, several authors [7, 4, 5, 6] have proposed to automatically build the sensor-based system as the result of a learning process, where a local planner plays the role of the teacher. All the quoted works present neural networks of *distance-based* units that learn fine motion. Some of them, use self-organizing networks. For example, [4, 6] employed a Self-Organizing Map (SOM) and [5] used a dynamical variant of SOM (DSOM) based on a Growing Neural Gas network [2]. In these works, the preference for SOM-like networks seems to be justified by their *data topology-conserving* character which is supposed to favor in some way the learning of suitable $< perception, action >$ pairs. Surprisingly, none of these works provide experimental evidence for this reasonable, but not obvious, claim.

In this paper we describe a SOM-like neural network which solves path finding problems in cooperation with a planning system. The network learns to associate actions to perceptions under the supervision of the planner. By reporting this experiment we make the following contributions. *First*, we argue for the utility of using a hierarchical version of SOM instead of the basic SOM. *Second*, we measure explicitly the effect of cooperative learning due to the interaction of neighboring neurons. *Third*, we highlight a beneficial side-effect which can be obtained by transferring motion knowledge from the planner to the SOM.

2 A Hierarchical Extended Kohonen Map to learn fine motion

In our experiment the self-organizing network learns $< perception, action >$ pairs produced by the planner [3] while solving instances of the path finding problem. In this experiment we do not consider the problem of recovering from local minima. A *perception* is made of a vector o of readings of 24 obstacle proximity

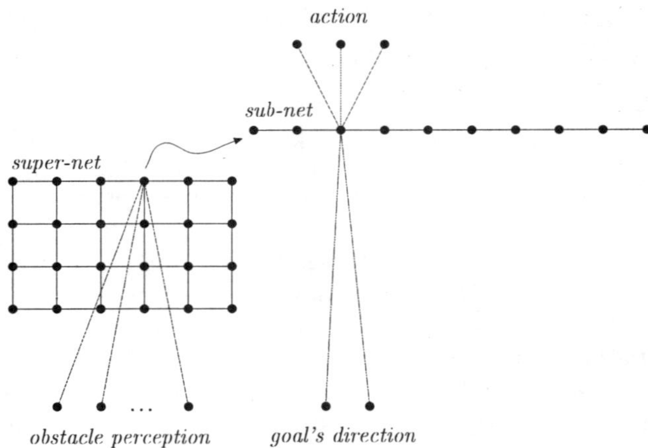

Figure 1: The HEKM network architecture.

sensors, together with the relative goal direction g, a 2 dimensional vector of unitary length. A planner *action a* is a triple representing, an x-translation, a y-translation, and a rotation with respect to the robot's current position and orientation. Both the xy-translations and the rotation take *discrete* values, and can be either positive, negative or null.

The SOM is a Hierarchical Extended Kohonen Map (HEKM) [8]. The map is "hierarchical" because it processes the input perception in sequence (this is explained in more detail later); it is "extended" because it is trained on the output action in a supervised fashion. Essentialy, the network operation is divided into two steps (Figure 1). Given an input perception, the HEKM first determines which is the most similar perception out of the ones experienced sofar (matching step); and second, it triggers the action associated to that perception (triggering step). The perception matching step is carried out in two stages as well. First, o is processed by a KM *super-net*. Second, g is processed by a KM *sub-net* which is associated to the winning neuron in the super-net. Therefore, the overall network architecture is a hierarchical arrangement of subordinated sub-nets: there is a sub-net for each neuron in the super-net. The network action is retrieved as the result of this two-stage competition process.

During training, the proposed $< perception, action >$ pair is learnt by the network through the basic Kohonen's rule. A learning step involves the winner in the super-net, the winner in the corresponding sub-net, and their *neighbors* on the networks as well. To be more specific, o is learnt by the winning neuron in the super-net; g is learnt by modifying the fan-in weight vector of the winning neuron in the sub-net; finally, a is learnt by modifying the fan-out weight vector of the winning neuron in the sub-net. This learning style has been described as a *competitive-cooperative* training rule [8]. It is competitive because neurons compete to respond to input patterns. As a consequence, only that part of the network which is relevant to the current input data undergoes the learning process, and the problem of catastrophic interference is reduced [9]. The rule is also *cooperative* in that the output learnt by the winning neuron is partially associated to the weight vectors of its neighbors to enhance generalization.

For the application to path finding, we have preferred a hierarchical architecture to a "flat" one for three reasons. *First*, it avoids unnecessary repetition of o weights for different g directions, which would be costly in terms of memory requirements. *Second*, it deals naturally with the economic input representation of g as a 2 dimensional vector. A flat network would need either a more distributed codification for g (as in [7]) or a weightning of g (as in [4, 5]) so that during the matching step g does not lose importance with respect to o, whose dimensionality is rather high. *Third*, by processing the input information in two stages, we hope to simplify the adaptation process of the SOM to the perception data distribution.

A portion of the weights of the trained HEKM is depicted in Figure 2. In this experiment, the super-net is a 4×6 grid of neurons, while each sub-net is an array of 10 neurons. The upper drawing shows the super-net weights: they represent prototypical obstacle perceptions. As an example, unit[1] #0 represents the perception of free-space, unit #5 represents the perception of a wall on the right-hand side, unit #7 represents the perception of a wall behind the robot's back. It is possible to observe the *data topology-*

---

[1]Units are numbered from left-to-right and top-to-bottom.

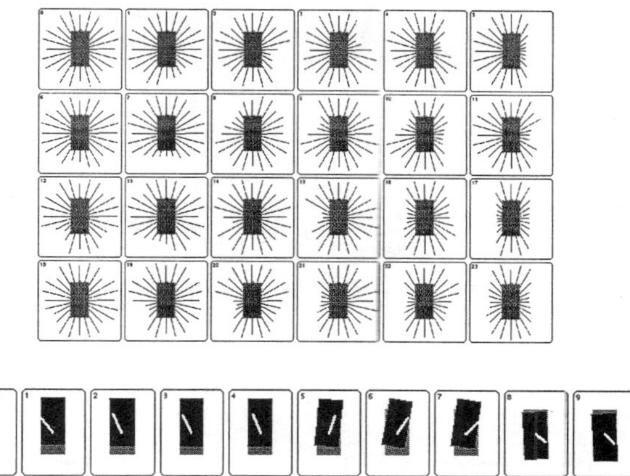

Figure 2: The obstacle perceptions learnt by the super-net (upper drawing). Goal directions and actions learnt by sub-net #17 (lower drawing).

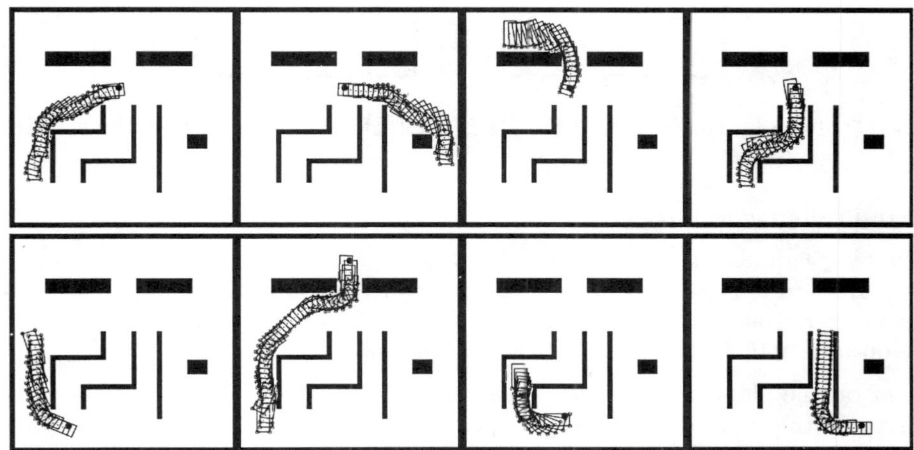

Figure 3: The robot solving the path finding problem with a fixed goal (first row) and with new goal positions (second row).

preserving character of the KM: perception similarity varies in a continuous way on the map. The lower drawing in Figure 2 shows the weights of sub-net #17, which is associated in the super-net to the perception of a narrow corridor. For each neuron, we represent the learnt goal direction (as a white vector) and the learnt action (the gray rectangle is the robot's initial configuration, the black rectangle is the robot's configuration after having performed the action). Again, the data topology-preserving character of the KM can be appreciated in this sub-net.

Figure 3 show some instances of path finding solved by the HEKM in cooperation with the planner. In these trajectories the planner takes control only when the action proposed by the HEKM would lead to a collision. In the first row of the Figure, the goal position (black circle) is fixed and it is the same used to generate the training examples for the HEKM. The second row depicts other trajectories with new goal positions. These runs prove that the motion skill acquired by the HEKM is independent from the chosen goal.

3 Why to use a SOM-like network?

We would like now to discuss the following claim: the data topology-preserving character of the HEKM could favor the learning of fine motion.

This statement can be proved experimentally by performing two separate training sessions. In the first session, the neighborhood parameters (one for the super-net, one for the sub-nets) are set to 0, while in second session they are set to values other than 0 (4 and 5, respectively). In this way, we can study the

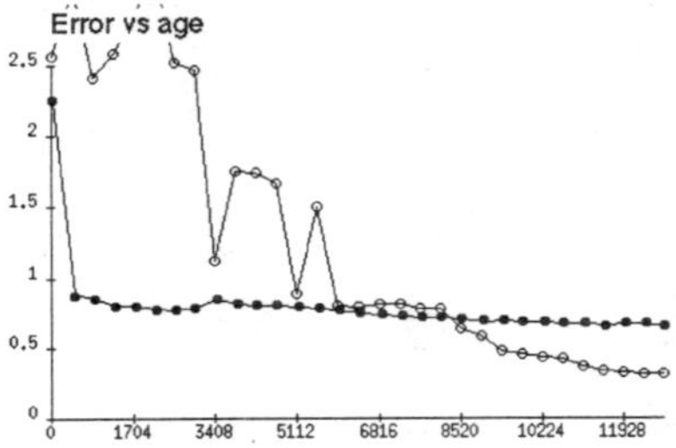
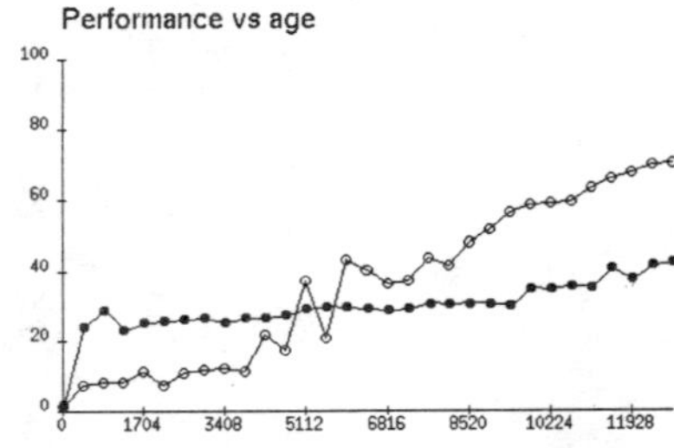

Figure 4: Error (left) and Performance (right) without cooperation (black dots) and with cooperation (white dots).

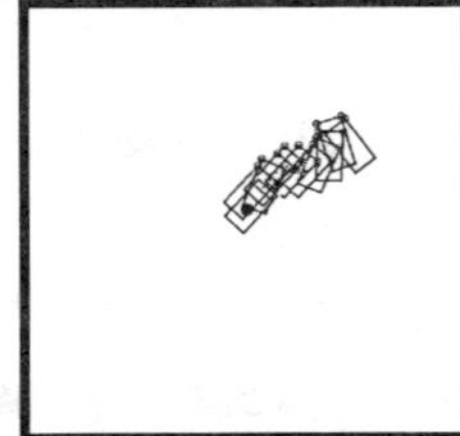
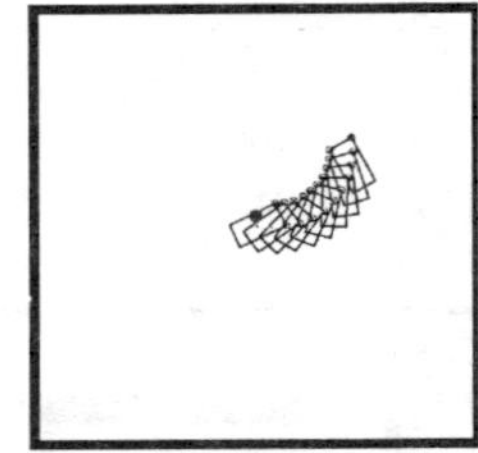

Figure 5: The planner (left) and the HEKM (right) working as stand-alone systems.

effect of cooperation during learning.

To evaluate the two methods, an error criterion and a performance criterion are used. The error measure is the mean squared error between the network output action and the target action proposed by the planner, while the performance criterion is the percentage of optimal actions learnt by the network. By definition, the optimal actions are those proposed by the planner.

Let us comment on the plots of error and performance as a function of the number of training cycles (Figure 4). As far as the error is concerned (left plot), one can see that without cooperation (curve with black dots) a certain error level is reached quite rapidly, but afterwards, no significant improvement is observed. On the contrary, with cooperation (curve with white dots) it takes more time to reach the same error level, but the final error is lower. This type of behavior seems to be typical for cooperating agents, as it reported in [1]. In our experiment, a possible explanation for this could be that, when the cooperation between the neurons is active, it takes more time to find a good "compromise" to satisfy competing learning needs. However, once the compromise is met, the final result gets improved. A corresponding behavior is observed in the performance curves (right plot). With no cooperation a certain performance level is achieved quite rapidly (42%), but after that point no further improvement occurs. With cooperation, the same performance level is obtained later, but the final result is more satisfactory (65%).

4 Planner's path versus HEKM's path

We conclude by highlighting an interesting side-effect which can be obtained by transferring motion knowledge from the planner to the HEKM.

Our planner is a *discrete* system. By "discrete" we refer to the fact that, at each step of the robot trajectory, the planner generates a finite number of neighboring configurations, and chooses, among them, the one which approaches the goal closest while avoiding collisions. The HEKM, on the contrary, tends to produce actions which look like being *continuous*. That is because the action learnt by the network for a given perception is a kind of average action performed by the planner in similar perceptual states. To illustrate this point, we let the planner and the HEKM solve the same path finding problem as *stand-alone* systems (Figure 5). One can immediately appreciate qualitative differences in the two paths. The discrete nature of the planner is evident in the left plot: the robot motion is optimal in terms of path length, but quite abrupt. On the contrary, in the HEKM path (right plot) is smooth but not optimal. This observation can also account for the sub-optimal performance level reached by the HEKM (Figure 4) at the end of training.

5   Conclusions

We have presented a HEKM which learns fine motion under the control of a planner. *First*, we have discussed the utility of using a hierarchical KM instead of the usual "flat" version. The HEKM is more economic in terms of the way memory cells are used. It avoids unnecessary weight repetitions and allows for compact input representations. Clearly, one limitation of the current architecture is the fixed number of neurons and the fixed topology of the network. A growing network could be used instead [5, 2]. *Second*, we have measured the effect of cooperative learning due to the interaction between adjacent neurons. We found that *with cooperation* learning is slowed down in the short run. But the benefits appear later on, resulting in a more satisfactory final performance. Our interpretation is that, at the beginning of learning, neighboring neurons work to meet a compromise to competing needs: this effort becomes rewarding on the long run. *Third*, we have pointed out the complementary nature of the paths generated by the planner and by the HEKM as stand-alone systems. The HEKM produces sub-optimal but smooth solutions, whereas the planner seeks for optimality while sacrificing the continuity of motion. The integration of these two philosophies leads to fruitful results.

Our future work will include the implementation of these ideas on a physical robot.

Acknowledgements

Cristina Versino is supported by the No. 2129-042413.94/1 project of the Fonds National de la Recherche Scientifique, Berne, Suisse. Thanks to Vicente Ruiz de Angulo for his comments on early drafts of this paper. Thanks to *Neuristique* (France) for providing the SN neural network simulator.

References

[1] Clearwater, S.H., Hogg, T., Huberman, B.A. (1992) Cooperative Problem Solving. In Huberman, B.A., Editor, *Computation: The Micro and the Macro View.*, World Scientific.

[2] Fritzke, B. (1995) A Growing Neural Gas Network Learns Topologies. In Tesauro, G., Touretzky, D.S., Leen, T.K., Editors, *Advances in Neural Information Processing Systems 7*, MIT Press, Cambridge MA, pp. 625–632.

[3] Gambardella, L.M., Versino, C. (1994) Learning High-Level Navigation Strategies from Sensor Information and Planner Experience. *Proc. PerAc94, From Perception to Action Conference*, Lausanne, Switzerland, September 7–9, pp. 428–431.

[4] Heikkonen, J., Koikkalainen, P., Oja, E. (1993) Motion Behavior Learning by Self-Organization. *Proc. ICANN93, International Conference on Artificial Neural Networks*, Amsterdam, The Netherlands, September 13–16, pp.262–267.

[5] Heikkonen, J., Millán, J. del R., Cuesta, E. (1995) Incremental Learning from Basic Reflexes in an Autonomous Mobile Robot. *Proc. EANN95, International Conference on Engineering Applications of Neural Networks*, Otaniemi, Espoo, Finland, August 21–23, pp. 119–126.

[6] Knobbe, A.J., Kok, J.N., Overmars, M.H. (1995) Robot Motion Planning in Unknown Environments Using Neural Networks. *Proc. ICANN95, International Conference on Artificial Neural Networks*, Paris, France, October 9–13, pp. 375–380.

[7] Millán, J. del R. (1995) Reinforcement Learning of Goal-Directed Obstacle-Avoiding Reaction Strategies in an Autonomous Mobile Robot. *Robotics and Autonomous Systems*, 15(3), pp. 275–299.

[8] Ritter, H., Martinetz, T., Schulten, K. (1992) *Neural Computation and Self-Organizing Maps. An Introduction*. Addison-Wesley Publishing Comp.

[9] Ruiz de Angulo, V., Torras, C. (1995) On-line Learning with Minimal Degradation in Feedforward Networks. *IEEE Transactions on Neural Networks*, Vol. 6, pp. 657–668.

[10] Versino, C., Gambardella, L.M. (1995) Learning Fine Motion in Robotics by Using Hierarchical Neural Networks. *IDSIA-5-1995 Technical Report.*

A Tree-Structured Neural Network for Real-Time Adaptive Control

Alois P. Heinz

Institut für Informatik, Universität Freiburg
Am Flughafen 17, D-79110 Freiburg, Germany
email: heinz@informatik.uni-freiburg.de

Abstract— A tree-structured neural network (TSNN) is described that meets the special requirements of real-time adaptive modeling and control. It is shown that TSNN are capable of arbitrarily accurate approximation to a given function and its derivatives under certain conditions. The evaluation of a TSNN function and its Jacobian is extremely efficient due to the usage of lazy evaluation, thus reliefing function inversion also. Once a TSNN is constructed or learned from training data, the derived on-line adaptable version is linear in its weight vector; this allows the application of appropriate theories to prove convergence and stability. The real-time adaptation can be implemented very efficiently as a consequence of the lazy evaluation scheme used.

1   Introduction

The demand for intelligent controllers in consumer products as well as in industrial applications is permanently increasing, just as the autonomy and inherent built-in intelligence of these systems increases. Modern controllers have to cope with complex nonlinear and time-varying processes, due to unpredictable changes in the environment or disturbances within the process itself. Increased controller flexibility is also required to compensate for unavailable prior knowledge about the process or to reduce the design costs. Sophisticated controllers therefore need to be self-organizing and able to learn from the environment.

In the following we suppose a control architecture where a predictive model of a plant is maintained based on practical evidence and the control signal is computed from measured values and the desired plant's response using an inverse plant model derived with the help of the Jacobian of the plant model. For details in different neural and fuzzy logic control architectures the reader may refer to [3, 10, 6].

The requirements of real-time adaptive modeling can be divided into representational, learning, and quality issues. The model should be flexible enough to be able to approximate to any given function of practical importance. It should be able to incorporate prior expert knowledge and use a sparse coding scheme and local generalization. The evaluation of the model and its Jacobian as well as on-line adaptation has to be extremely efficient. And it is desirable that the model function is linear in the adjustable variables, because this allows easy convergence and stability analysis [7].

Although it may seem to be very difficult to meet all of the above-mentioned requirements in an easy way we propose a strategy using tree-structured neural networks (TSNN) that appears to work very well in many practical situations: The topology and initial parameters of a TSNN are created and initialized using any available prior knowledge and a representative training data set together with a constructive learning algorithm [5]. During this phase the network's receptive fields are evolved and shaped. In operating mode the topology and certain sensitivity parameters are frozen but the TSNN remains adaptable on a wide range of possible functions. Thus it can be subject to convergence and stability analysis, because of its linear dependence on the remaining adjustable parameters.

In the next section we give a short introduction to tree-structured neural networks, explain some of their characteristic modeling abilities, explain some arithmetic operations that can be applied to them, and we show that TSNN are universal approximators for functions and their derivatives under certain conditions. In section 3 we describe efficient algorithms for the evaluation of a given TSNN function and its Jacobian and for the on-line adaptation. We derive estimates for the algorithm's average case runtimes that are logarithmic in or some root of the network size. A simple example that demonstrates the representational and learning abilities of TSNN is given in section 4. Section 5 contains the conclusions.

2   Modeling Abilities of TSNN

For simplicity and due to limited space the following discussion of TSNN is restricted to real functions of real arguments, but the networks can be extended easily to represent category or vector valued functions of numerical and symbolic arguments also. A (restricted) TSNN T of input dimension n is a labeled binary tree. Each inner node k of T is equipped with a weight vector $\mathbf{w}_k = (w_{k,1} \ldots w_{k,n})^t$, a threshold c_k, and a positive radius R_k. Each leaf L is labeled with a real value v_L. A decision function $d_k : \mathbb{R}^n \to \mathbb{R}$ is associated with each inner node k:

$$d_k(\mathbf{x}) := \sigma\left((\mathbf{w}_k^t \mathbf{x} - c_k)/R_k\right) , \tag{1}$$

where $\sigma : \mathbb{R} \to [0,1]$ is the following sigmoid function:

$$\sigma(x) := \begin{cases} 1/2 + \operatorname{sign}(x)/2 & \text{if } |x| > 1, \text{ and} \\ 1/2 + x\left(1 - |x|/2\right) & \text{else.} \end{cases} \tag{2}$$

The evaluation $v_q(\mathbf{x})$ of a node q of T with respect to a given input vector $\mathbf{x}$ is recursively defined as

$$v_q(\mathbf{x}) := \begin{cases} v_q & \text{if } q \text{ is a leaf, and} \\ v_{q_\ell}(\mathbf{x}) + \left(v_{q_r}(\mathbf{x}) - v_{q_\ell}(\mathbf{x})\right) \times d_k(\mathbf{x}) & \text{else,} \end{cases} \tag{3}$$

where q_ℓ and q_r denote the left and right descendants of q, respectively. It is easy to see that $v_q(\mathbf{x}) \in [\min(v_{q_\ell}(\mathbf{x}), v_{q_r}(\mathbf{x})), \max(v_{q_\ell}(\mathbf{x}), v_{q_r}(\mathbf{x}))]$. The evaluation $v_T(\mathbf{x})$ of the tree T with respect to $\mathbf{x}$ is defined as the evaluation of the root of T,

$$v_T(\mathbf{x}) := v_{\mathrm{root}(T)}(\mathbf{x}) . \tag{4}$$

To come up with a more closed formula for $v_T(\mathbf{x})$ we first define the indicator $I_{k,L}$ to be -1 $(+1)$ if the leaf L belongs to the left (right) sub-tree of inner node k, respectively, and undefined else. The decision contribution $D_{k,L}$ of the pair (k, L) with respect to $\mathbf{x}$ is defined as $D_{k,L}(\mathbf{x}) := I_{k,L}(d_k(\mathbf{x}) - 1/2) + 1/2$. Now, the evaluation of T with respect to $\mathbf{x}$ can be rewritten as

$$v_T(\mathbf{x}) = \sum_{L \in \mathrm{leafs}(T)} v_L \, d_L(\mathbf{x}) , \tag{5}$$

where $d_L(\mathbf{x})$ is defined as

$$d_L(\mathbf{x}) := \prod_{k \in \mathrm{ancestors}(L)} D_{k,L}(\mathbf{x}) . \tag{6}$$

It is easy to realize that

$$\sum_{L \in \mathrm{leafs}(T)} d_L(\mathbf{x}) = 1 \quad \forall \mathbf{x} \in \mathbb{R}^n ; \tag{7}$$

for a proof one can replace all leaf values by 1 and show that then all nodes evaluate to 1. The set $\{d_L\}_{L \in \mathrm{leafs}(T)}$ is a set of kernel functions that form a partition of unity. If all radii of the TSNN are close to zero the resulting function resembles the piece-wise constant functions of the usual decision trees [2, 8]. With positive radii each $d_L(\mathbf{x})$ is an own individually shaped basis function. We'll now consider some arithmetic and representational properties of TSNN functions.

Lemma 1 *The sum of two TSNN functions is a TSNN function.*

Proof: Consider two TSNN T_1 and T_2. Then construct T_{1+2} as follows: Take T_1 and replace each leaf L_1 of T_1 by a copy of T_2 that has all leaf values increased by v_{L_1}. Then

$$v_{T_1}(\mathbf{x}) + v_{T_2}(\mathbf{x}) = \left(\sum_{L_1 \in \mathrm{leafs}(T_1)} v_{L_1} d_{L_1}(\mathbf{x})\right) + \left(\sum_{L_2 \in \mathrm{leafs}(T_2)} v_{L_2} d_{L_2}(\mathbf{x})\right) \tag{8}$$

$$\overset{(7)}{=} \sum_{\substack{L_1 \in \mathrm{leafs}(T_1) \\ L_2 \in \mathrm{leafs}(T_2)}} v_{L_1} d_{L_1}(\mathbf{x}) d_{L_2}(\mathbf{x}) + \sum_{\substack{L_1 \in \mathrm{leafs}(T_1) \\ L_2 \in \mathrm{leafs}(T_2)}} v_{L_2} d_{L_1}(\mathbf{x}) d_{L_2}(\mathbf{x}) \tag{9}$$

$$= \sum_{\substack{L_1 \in \mathrm{leafs}(T_1) \\ L_2 \in \mathrm{leafs}(T_2)}} [v_{L_1} + v_{L_2}] \, d_{L_1}(\mathbf{x}) d_{L_2}(\mathbf{x}) = v_{T_{1+2}}(\mathbf{x}) \tag{10}$$

$\square$

Lemma 2 *The product of two TSNN functions is a TSNN function.*

Proof: For two TSNN T_1 and T_2 construct $T_{1\times 2}$ as follows: Take T_1 and replace each leaf L_1 of T_1 by a copy of T_2 that has all leaf values multiplied by v_{L_1}. Then

$$v_{T_1}(\mathbf{x}) \cdot v_{T_2}(\mathbf{x}) \;=\; \left(\sum_{L_1 \in \text{leafs}(T_1)} v_{L_1} d_{L_1}(\mathbf{x}) \right) \cdot \left(\sum_{L_2 \in \text{leafs}(T_2)} v_{L_2} d_{L_2}(\mathbf{x}) \right) \tag{11}$$

$$=\; \sum_{\substack{L_1 \in \text{leafs}(T_1) \\ L_2 \in \text{leafs}(T_2)}} v_{L_1} v_{L_2} \, d_{L_1}(\mathbf{x}) \, d_{L_2}(\mathbf{x}) \;=\; v_{T_{1\times 2}}(\mathbf{x}) \tag{12}$$

$\square$

Theorem 1 *Any given continuous function $f : K \to \mathbb{R}$, $K \subset \mathbb{R}^n$ and compact, can be uniformly approximated by a sequence of TSNN to within a desired accuracy.*

Proof: The theorem is a direct consequence of the Stone-Weierstrass theorem [4] and follows from Lemmas 1 and 2, if we additionally consider that constants are TSNN functions and that there are TSNN functions that have different values for a given pair of distinct points. $\square$

Theorem 2 *Let $f : K \to \mathbb{R}$, $K \subset \mathbb{R}^n$ and compact, be a given continuous function with continuous derivatives. Then TSNN are capable of simultaneous uniform approximation of f and its derivatives.*

Sketch of proof: A TSNN T can be built that decomposes K according to a n-dimensional grid. Each leaf L of T belongs to a small hyper-rectangle $H_L \subset K$ such that $d_L(\mathbf{x}) = 1$ implies $\mathbf{x} \in H_L$. Then each leaf L of T can be replaced by a TSNN T_L with one inner node and two leafs, whose function approximates to a hyperplane within H_L and has the same value and derivatives than f in the center $\mathbf{x}_{H_L}$ of H_L. Increasing the radii to half the size of the grid width smoothes the TSNN function. Decreasing the grid width leads to better approximation. $\square$

TSNN – as we have seen – can be constructed by expert designers using local decomposition or arithmetic operators like sum and product. A TSNN can also be constructed automatically by a topology enhancing and parameter modifying procedure using a given training set [5]. In this case the height can be restricted to a logarithmic function of the tree size. For efficient parallel evaluation a TSNN can be transformed into a usual feed-forward neural network [1] with three layers [5]. The input vector $\mathbf{x}$ is fed via the input layer to the first hidden layer containing copies of the inner nodes. Their evaluations of $d_k(\mathbf{x})$ are fed to the next layer holding copies of the leafs, who compute the values of $d_L(\mathbf{x})$ and transmit them via v_L-weighted connections to a linear output element. The product operations within the L-elements can be replaced by sums using logarithmic and exponential transformations of the transfer functions in the first and second layer, respectively.

3 Efficient TSNN Evaluation and Adaptation

Efficient evaluation of a modeled function and its Jacobian is extremely important especially in control applications, as already emphasized in the introduction. The basis of the efficient TSNN evaluation is given by (3), (1), and in particular by (2). The fact that $\sigma(x)$ is different from 0 or 1 only in the interval $[-1, 1]$ allows effective lazy evaluation. The evaluation of a given node k makes use of both descendant nodes only if $d_k(\mathbf{x}) \in (0, 1)$.

The evaluation algorithm is given in the upper part of Fig. 1. To derive an upper bound estimate of the average case runtime as a function of the number of tree nodes N we assume that there is a uniform probability p $(0 < p < 1)$ for the event that $d_k(\mathbf{x}) \notin \{0, 1\}$. Then for any given vector a node of height h has to be evaluated with probability $\left(\frac{1+p}{2}\right)^h$. Since this value decreases with increasing h we may assume without loss of generality that the tree has smallest possible height $\lceil \log_2(N+1) - 1 \rceil$. The following can be shown for the average case number of tree nodes $A(N)$ that have to be inspected for the evaluation of the whole tree:

$$A(N) \;\le\; \sum_{h=0}^{\lceil \log_2(N+1)-1 \rceil} 2^h \left(\frac{1+p}{2} \right)^h \;<\; \frac{1}{p}(1+p)^{\log_2(N+1)+1} \tag{13}$$

$$=\; \frac{1+p}{p}(1+p)^{\log_2(N+1)} \;=\; \frac{1+p}{p}(N+1)^{\log_2(1+p)} \tag{14}$$

```
eval := proc (k: node, x: vector): real;
   if leaf (k) then return (v_k) fi;
   d := σ ((w_k^t x − c_k)/R_k);
   if d = 0 then return (eval (k_ℓ, x))
      elif d = 1 then return (eval (k_r, x))
      else return ((1 − d) × eval (k_ℓ, x) + d × eval (k_r, x))
   fi
end;


diffeval := proc (k: node, x: vector): lvector;
   if leaf (k) then return (v_k, 0 $ i = 1..n) fi;
   y := (w_k^t x − c_k)/R_k;
   d := σ (y);
   if d = 0 then return (diffeval (k_ℓ, x))
      elif d = 1 then return (diffeval (k_r, x))
      else L := diffeval (k_ℓ, x);
           R := diffeval (k_r, x);
           return (((1 − d) × L [0] + d × R [0],
                   (1 − d) × L [i] + d × R [i] + (R_[0] − L [0]) × Λ(y) × (w_i/R_k) $ i = 1..n))
   fi
end;
```

Figure 1: The procedure eval evaluates a TSNN function recursively. The procedure diffeval operates in the same fashion but returns a $(n+1)$-dimensional vector with the TSNN function value and all n partial derivatives with respect to the input values. The components of this vector are numbered from 0 to n. The operator $ is used here to denote a sequence. Both algorithms take advantage of lazy evaluation.

$$= \frac{1+p}{p} \sqrt[r]{N+1} \qquad \text{with } r = (\log_2 (1+p))^{-1} \in (1, \infty) \tag{15}$$

Thus, in the average case the runtime is in the order of some root of the tree size. If p is less than about 40%, for example, the average case evaluation runtime is proportional to less than the square root of the number of tree nodes[1]. It is easy to see that $A(N)$ is linear in N if $p = 1$ and logarithmic in N if $p = 0$.

The Jacobian of a real valued function consists of the vector of partial derivatives with respect to each of the input variables. The derivative of a node evaluation $v_q(\mathbf{x})$ with respect to x_i for a leaf is zero and for an inner node given by

$$\frac{\partial v_q(\mathbf{x})}{\partial x_i} = \frac{\partial v_{q_\ell}(\mathbf{x})}{\partial x_i} (1 − d_k(\mathbf{x})) + \frac{\partial v_{q_r}(\mathbf{x})}{\partial x_i} d_k(\mathbf{x}) + (v_{q_r}(\mathbf{x}) − v_{q_\ell}(\mathbf{x})) \Lambda \left(\frac{\mathbf{w}_k^t \mathbf{x} − c_k}{R_k} \right) \frac{w_i}{R_k} \tag{16}$$

where

$$\Lambda(x) := \sigma'(x) = \begin{cases} 0 & \text{if } |x| > 1, \text{ and} \\ 1 − |x| & \text{else.} \end{cases} \tag{17}$$

We should note that, if $d_k(\mathbf{x})$ is zero or one, then $\Lambda(\cdot)$ in (16) is zero and the computation of the derivative requires the inspection of one descendant of q only. In the other case both descendant's evaluations and derivatives are needed. The most efficient way to compute the Jacobian of a TSNN function is therefore a recursive procedure that computes and returns a vector with a node's function value together with all derivatives and makes use of lazy evaluation. The algorithm that can be derived from the pure evaluation algorithm by the methods of algorithmic differentiation [9] is given in the lower part of Fig. 1. Since this algorithm visits the same nodes in the same manner as the pure evaluation algorithm and performs only a constant number of operations per node its average case runtime (15) is of the same order.

As opposed to the tree construction algorithms the on-line adaptation algorithm retrains only the leaf values of a TSNN. A TSNN T has to be adapted if the computed value $v_T(\mathbf{x})$ differs from the observed

---

[1]The probabilities observed in our experiments ranged from about 5% to maximal 40%.

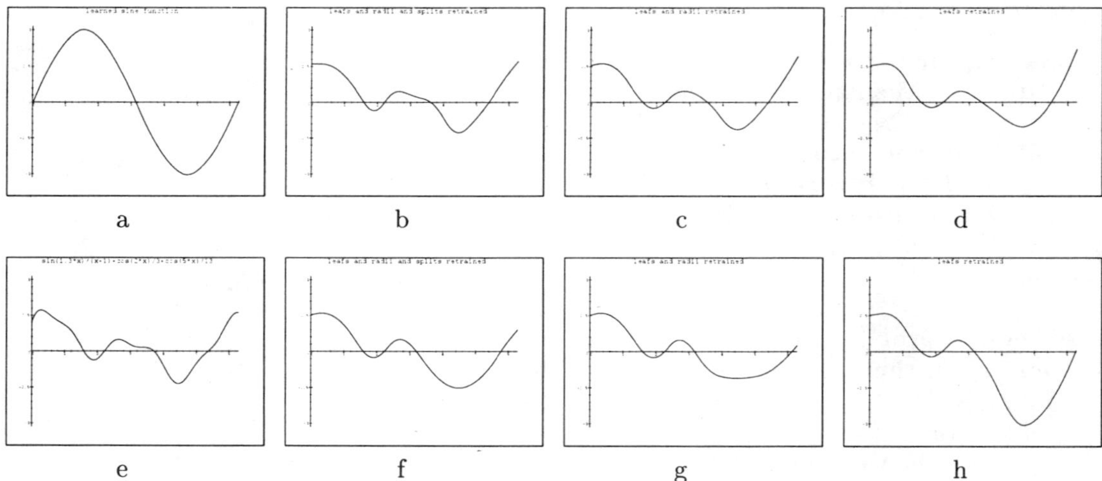

a   b   c   d

e   f   g   h

Figure 2: a: The learned sine function, e: function f, b–d: functions are retrained on the complete input space, f–h: functions are retrained on first half of the interval, b+f: all parameters are retrained, c+g: radii and leaf values are retrained, d+h: only leaf values are retrained.

value $v(\mathbf{x})$. The gradient of the squared error with respect to a given leaf value v_L is

$$\partial E_T(\mathbf{x})/\partial v_L = 2\,(v_T(\mathbf{x}) - v(\mathbf{x}))\,d_L(\mathbf{x})\,. \tag{18}$$

Only leaf nodes that are visited during the evaluation may need some adaptation. The on-line gradient descent adaptation algorithm therefore puts pointers to all leafs visited during the evaluation phase into a list and modifies their values once the error is computed. Since there are fewer leaf nodes than visited nodes, the average case runtime of the on-line adaptation algorithm is of the same order (15) as that of the evaluation algorithm.

4   A Simple TSNN Example

Here we describe a simple experiment we have made to demonstrate the adaptation abilities of TSNN. The construction algorithm was used to build a TSNN from training data that originated from the sine function in the interval $[0, 2\pi]$. A TSNN with 6 inner nodes was constructed, whose function (Fig. 2a) has a maximal aberration from the sine function of less than 0.02. Then this TSNN was retrained with data from the function $f(x) = \sin(1.3x)/(x+1) + \cos(2x)/3 + \cos(5x)/13$ (Fig. 2e) on different conditions. Fig. 2b–d shows the results of adaptation using training data from the total interval $[0, 2\pi]$, whereas Fig. 2f–h depicts the results using data from the first half of the interval only. For Fig. 2b+f all TSNN parameters were readapted, for Fig. 2c+g only radii and leaf values, and for Fig. 2d+h only the leaf values were readapted.

The experiment shows that adaptation is more flexible if all parameters are subject to changes (Fig. 2b). But in this case the TSNN function may be altered to a large extend even in regions where no new data appears (Fig. 2f+g), which is a severe drawback. If only the leaf values are adapted, the TSNN is able to change the function where new information is available but it will remember the once-learned function in regions where no modifications are required (Fig. 2h). Of course, the sensitivity in this case cannot be changed or increased. If oscillation is increased in any region, the on-line adapted TSNN will try to interpolate the new values as good as possible.

5   Conclusions

We have described the architecture of the TSNN network and shown that it is flexible enough to approximate to a given function and its derivatives under certain (practical) conditions. A TSNN can be constructed by an expert designer using application specific knowledge and spatial or functional decomposition with the help of arithmetic operators. Simpler and faster is the automatic construction process from available training data. We have described efficient algorithms for the evaluation of a TSNN function and its Jacobian as well as an on-line adaptation algorithm. The derivated estimates for the average case runtime are less than the order of some root of the network size for all of the algorithms. This efficiency is a direct consequence of the utilized lazy evaluation scheme and makes TSNN especially applicable for real-time adaptive modeling and control tasks.

In the on-line version of a TSNN the network function is linear in the adjustable variables, a very desirable property for models used in control. Each of these parameters controls the amplitude of a individually shaped receptive field in the input space similar to radial basis functions, but in contrast to simple radial basis function networks TSNNs are not afflicted by the curse of dimensionality. During on-line adaptation a TSNN is able to learn a modified functional relation quickly but it will continue to remember the once implemented knowledge in regions where no new evidence is given. This again makes TSNN very suitable for real-time adaptive modeling and control.

References

[1] C. M. Bishop. *Neural Networks for Pattern Recognition.* Oxford University Press, Oxford, 1995.

[2] L. Breiman, J. H. Friedman, R. A. Olshen, and C. J. Stone. *Classification and Regression Trees.* The Wadsworth statistics/probability series. Chapman & Hall, New York, 1984.

[3] M. Brown and C. Harris. *Neurofuzzy Adaptive Modelling and Control.* Systems and Control Engineering. Prentice Hall International, London, UK, 1994.

[4] J. C. Burkill and H. Burkill. *A Second Course in Mathematical Analysis.* Cambridge University Press, Cambridge, England, 1970.

[5] A. P. Heinz. On a class of constructible neural networks. In F. Fogelman-Soulié and P. Gallinari, editors, *ICANN '95, Proceedings of the International Conference on Artificial Neural Networks, Paris, France,* volume 1, pages 563–568, Paris La Défense, France, Oct. 1995. EC2 & Cie.

[6] R. Jager. *Fuzzy Logic in Control.* PhD thesis, Technische Universiteit Delft, Delft, Netherlands, June 1995.

[7] K. S. Narendra and A. M. Annaswamy. *Stable Adaptive Systems.* Prentice Hall, Englewood Cliffs, NJ, 1989.

[8] J. R. Quinlan. *C4.5: Programs for Machine Learning.* Machine Learning. Morgan Kaufmann Publishers, San Mateo, California, 1993.

[9] L. B. Rall. *Automatic Differentiation – Techniques and Applications,* volume 120 of *Lecture Notes in Computer Science.* Springer-Verlag, 1981.

[10] R. Żbikowski, K. J. Hunt, A. Dzieliński, R. Murray-Smith, and P. J. Gawthrop. A review of advances in neural adaptive control systems. Technical Report of the ESPRIT NACT Project TP-1, Glasgow University and Daimler-Benz Research, 1994.

Robust Approximate Pole Assignment via Neuro-Optimization

Daniel Ho†, James Lam‡, Jinhua Xu†, Hei Ka Tam‡
† Department of Mathematics, City University of Hong Kong
Tat Chee Avenue, Hong Kong
‡ Department of Mechanical Engineering, University of Hong Kong
Pokfulam Road, Hong Kong

Abstract

This paper provides a new method for robust approximate pole assignment (RAPA), which is formulated as an unconstrained optimization problem. By exploiting the differentiability of the objective function, the minimization problem is solved via the gradient flow approach, which is ideally suited for neural networks (or analog computer). The architecture of the neural networks is given. Simulation results are used to demonstrate the effectiveness of the proposed method.

1   Introduction

Consider a linear time-invariant multivariable system such that

$$\dot{x} = Ax + Bu \tag{1}$$

where $x \in \mathbb{R}^n$, $u \in \mathbb{R}^m$ represent the state and input vectors respectively, A, B are compatibly dimensioned constant matrices. For simplicity, it is assumed that B is of full column rank. By applying a constant state feedback law

$$u = Kx$$

to (1), $K \in \mathbb{R}^{m \times n}$, the closed-loop system is given by

$$\dot{x} = (A + BK)x$$

Under the assumption that the pair (A, B) is completely controllable, there exists at least one feedback matrix K for a particular choice of desired poles $\lambda_1, \lambda_2, \cdots, \lambda_n$ of the closed-loop system. The existence and construction of such a feedback gain may be characterized as follows (see for example [6]).

Given $\Lambda = \mathrm{diag}(\lambda_1, \lambda_2, \cdots, \lambda_n)$ and T nonsingular, there exists K satisfying

$$(A + BK)T = T\Lambda, \tag{2}$$

if and only if T satisfies

$$U_1^T(AT - T\Lambda) = 0 \tag{3}$$

where

$$B = [U_0 \ U_1] \begin{bmatrix} Z \\ 0 \end{bmatrix}$$

with $U = [U_0 \ U_1]$ orthogonal and Z nonsingular. Furthermore, if K exists then it is given by

$$K = Z^{-1}U_0^T(T\Lambda T^{-1} - A) \tag{4}$$

The matrix T is said to be *admissible* if it satisfies (3). The factorization of matrix B can be obtained from the QR factorization of the matrix B. If $m > 1$, multiple solutions exist and the freedom on K can be used to give the closed-loop system additional robustness property.

The robust pole assignment (RPA) problem was first formulated by Kautsky *et al.* [6] in terms of minimizing some conditioning measures of the closed-loop state matrix. In their work, exact pole assignment, that is to assign desired poles to a fixed set of self-conjugate numbers in the open LHP, was considered. On the other hand, in many applications, the poles assigned are not required to be exactly the same as those specified. This is because the closed-loop system with poles approximately close to the desired ones will possess similar desired behavior [2]. This leads to the idea of robust approximate pole assignment (RAPA) which allows errors in the assignment of poles. The extra freedom on the choice of K are then exploited to further improving the closed-loop robustness against perturbation. For detail discussion of various methods on RPA and RAPA, please refer to [8] for a survey.

The use of neuro-optimization in the RAPA problem in this paper is motivated by recent applications of neural networks for optimization [3] via the gradient flow technique. This technique has been recently applied to solve a number of control engineering related problems [5]. The central idea is to associate the original problem with an initial-value problem of a system of ODEs, in such a way that the solution of the original problem can be given by finding the limiting solution of initial-value problem.

Recently, [4] proposed the gradient flow approach to solve the RPA problem by minimizing the measure $\|T\|_F\|T^{-1}\|_F$ subject to T admissible. The unconstrained minimization problem over a well-defined dense subset on $\mathbb{R}^{m \times n}$ is transformed to a set of ODEs, and then solved by standard numerical routines. Due to the presence of the T^{-1} operation in the differential equations, the formulation of RPA in [4] does not admit natural neural network realization. In this paper, we proposed a method which is an extension of the gradient flow approach of [4] to (i) cover the case of inexact pole assignment, and (ii) formulate the optimization in such a manner that the solution of the ODEs admits a simple neural network realization. Schematic circuit diagrams for such construction are given.

2 Preliminaries and Problem Formulation

There are various ways to measure the conditioning of $A + BK$. Two common measures are the *spectral condition number* given by

$$\kappa_2(T) = \|T\|_2 \, \|T^{-1}\|_2 \tag{5}$$

where T is a nonsingular eigenvector matrix of $A + BK$ and the *Frobenius condition number* given by

$$\kappa_F(T) = \|T\|_F \, \|T^{-1}\|_F \tag{6}$$

and we have

$$1 \le n^{-1}\kappa_F(T) \le \kappa_2(T) \le \kappa_F(T)$$

The condition numbers achieve their respective minima when the eigensystem is perfectly conditioned, that is when T is orthogonal. However, this is not usually attained as T has to satisfy (3). The main advantage of using $\kappa_F(T)$ lies in the differentiability with respect to T. Hence, we will adopt this as a measure of the closed-loop conditioning in this presentation. For any $\alpha \in \mathbb{R}$, $\alpha \ne 0$, $\kappa_F(T) = \kappa_F(\alpha T)$. This implies that $\kappa_F(T)$ has a singular Hessian and the minimization may not converge to a solution. To eliminate the scaling problem, we minimize an alternative measure as in [4, 1] given by

$$\Phi(T) = \|T\|_F^2 + \|T^{-1}\|_F^2 \tag{7}$$

Lam *et al.* [4] showed that any admissible T that minimizes $\Phi(T)$, T also minimizes $\kappa_F(T)$. At the minimum point T^*, we have $\kappa_F(T^*) = \frac{1}{2}\Phi(T^*)$. The RPA problem considered in [4] is to minimize $\Phi(T)$ over all admissible T.

In view of (3) which is to be satisfied only for exactly pole assignment, we consider minimizing $U_1^T(AT - T\Lambda)$ as part of the objective function in the present RAPA problem. Based on the penalty function method, one may consider the objective function

$$\Phi_1(T) := \|T\|_F^2 + \|T^{-1}\|_F^2 + \lambda\|U_1^T(AT - T\Lambda)\|_F^2 \tag{8}$$

where λ is a large positive real number called penalty parameter. Here T is not necessarily admissible and considered as a unconstrained minimization variable. The penalty parameter λ control the accuracy of the approximation of the desired poles. Furthermore, straightforward manipulation gives

$$\frac{1}{2}\frac{\partial \Phi_1}{\partial T} = T - T^{-T}T^{-1}T^{-T} + \lambda A^T U_1 U_1^T(AT - T\Lambda) - \lambda U_1 U_1^T(AT - T\Lambda)\Lambda^T \tag{9}$$

Unfortunately, as in [4] the gradient (9) does not admit a simple neural network realization due to the term T^{-1} which is not instantly available for generating the gradient unless we have an explicit form of T^{-1} in terms of the elements of T. This problem is overcome by approximating T^{-1} by a matrix X. To incorporate this into $\Phi_1(T)$, the term T^{-1} in the $\Phi_1(T)$ in (8) is replaced by X and an additional term $\rho\|TX - I\|_F^2$ is introduced where I is the identity matrix of appropriate dimension and $\rho > 0$ is another penalty parameter. Now, the RAPA problem is formulated as follows:

$$\min_{T,X} \Phi_2(T, X) \equiv \min_{T,X} \left\{ \|T\|_F^2 + \|X\|_F^2 + \lambda\|U_1^T(AT - T\Lambda)\|_F^2 + \rho\|(TX - I)\|_F^2 \right\} \tag{10}$$

3   Optimization with Neural Networks

Using the gradient flow approach, the minimization problem (8) is recast into an associated system of first order differential equations where the limiting solution is sought. With $T = [t_{ij}]$, $X = [x_{ij}]$ the gradient flow associated with (10) is given by

$$\frac{dT}{dt} = -\mu\frac{\partial\Phi_2}{\partial T} \quad ; \quad T(0) = T_0 \tag{11}$$

$$\frac{dX}{dt} = -\mu\frac{\partial\Phi_2}{\partial X} \quad ; \quad X(0) = X_0 \tag{12}$$

where

$$\frac{1}{2}\frac{\partial\Phi_2}{\partial T} = T + \lambda A^T U_1 U_1^T(AT - T\Lambda) - \lambda U_1 U_1^T(AT - T\Lambda)\Lambda^T + \rho(TX - I)X^T \tag{13}$$

$$\frac{1}{2}\frac{\partial\Phi_2}{\partial X} = X + \rho T^T(TX - I) \tag{14}$$

where $\mu > 0$ is some positive constant and T_0 and X_0 are the initial conditions.

Athough there are many standard numerical routines to solve the ODEs (11) and (12), the process of obtaining a solution can be very time consuming. Neural networks offer an alternative efficient way for solution due to its parallel nature. For such computational neural networks, the solution of high order nonlinear matrix differential equations is not a formidable task, but rather a natural one [5].

Apart from the realization point of view that $\Phi_2(T, X)$ is a preferred choice over $\Phi_1(T)$, $\Phi_2(T, X) \in C^1$ is *coercive* (a continuous function $f(\mathbf{v})$ defined for all $\mathbf{v} \in \mathbb{R}^n$ is said to be coercive if $\lim_{\|\mathbf{v}\|\to\infty} f(\mathbf{v}) = +\infty$). This implies that $\Phi_2(T, X)$ has global minimizers which can be found among the critical points of $\Phi_2(T, X)$ [7]. Moreover, $\Phi_2(T, X)$ has compact sublevel sets and thus the solution $(T(t), X(t))$ is defined on $[0, \infty)$ and converges to (T^*, X^*) corresponding to a minimum point of Φ_2 [5]. With $P, Q \in \mathbb{R}^{n\times n}$, define

$$\langle P, Q \rangle := \text{trace}(P^T Q)$$

Then

$$\frac{d\Phi_2}{dt} = \left\langle \frac{\partial\Phi_2}{\partial T}, \frac{dT}{dt} \right\rangle + \left\langle \frac{\partial\Phi_2}{\partial X}, \frac{dX}{dt} \right\rangle = -\mu\left(\left\|\frac{\partial\Phi_2}{\partial T}\right\|_F^2 + \left\|\frac{\partial\Phi_2}{\partial X}\right\|_F^2 \right) \leq 0$$

This guarantees that $\Phi_2(T(t), X(t))$ decreases strictly monotonically in time provided that $(T(0), X(0))$ is not a critical point. The gradient flow (11) and (12) can be implemented directly by the neural networks shown in Figures 1. The outputs of the network are the elements of T and X. The networks consist of integrators, adders and multipliers. For simplicity, we present only the circuits for the output of the elements t_{ij} and x_{ij}.

When the optimal solution, (T^*, X^*), of (10) is obtained, the optimal feedback gain matrix K^* is computed using

$$K^* = Z^{-1}U_0^T(T^*\Lambda X^* - A)$$

However, T^* is not an exact eigenvector matrix of $A + BK^*$. To calculate the Frobenius condition number, we first compute an eigenvector matrix, V_0, of $A + BK^*$. V_0 is unique up to a scaling to its columns. Suppose Λ has distinct eigenvalues. The choice of the eigenvector matrix of $A + BK^*$ should be such that the Frobenius condition number is a minimum. That is, we find $D = \text{diag}(d_1, d_2, \ldots, d_n)$ with $d_i > 0$ to minimize

$$\Theta(D) = \|V_0 D\|_F^2 + \|(V_0 D)^{-1}\|_F^2 \tag{15}$$

It can be established that $\Theta(D)$ is a smooth strictly convex function and the unique globally optimal scaling $D^* = \text{diag}(d_1^*, d_2^*, \ldots, d_n^*)$ has d_i^* given by $d_i^* = \left(\frac{u_i^T u_i}{v_i^T v_i}\right)^{\frac{1}{4}}$ where $V_0 = [v_1, \cdots, v_n]$, $V_0^{-T} = [u_1, \cdots, u_n]$. Finally, $V = V_0 D^*$ is the required eigenvector matrix of $A + BK^*$. For the case of repeated eigenvalues, the scaling for the generalized eigenvectors corresponding to the same Jordan block should be equal.

4 Simulation Results

In this section, we shall simulate the behavior of the neural networks implementation of (11) and (12).

Consider a 2-input-5-state distillation column model [2, 4, 6] given by

$$
A = \begin{bmatrix}
-0.1094 & 0.0628 & 0 & 0 & 0 \\
1.306 & -2.132 & 0.9807 & 0 & 0 \\
0 & 1.595 & -3.149 & 1.547 & 0 \\
0 & 0.0355 & 2.632 & -4.257 & 1.855 \\
0 & 0.00227 & 0 & 0.1636 & -0.1625
\end{bmatrix}, \quad
B = \begin{bmatrix}
0 & 0 \\
0.0638 & 0 \\
0.0838 & -0.1396 \\
0.1004 & -0.2060 \\
0.0063 & -0.0128
\end{bmatrix}
$$

The poles are at -0.077324, -0.014232, -0.89531, -2.8408 and -5.9822. The nominal closed-loop poles are at $-1 \pm 1i$, -0.2, -0.5, -1. The specification is to find a matrix K such that each closed-loop poles have absolute error less than 0.1 from the nominal ones and $\kappa_F(V)$ has to be small.

In the computation, $\mu = 100$ and the penalty parameters λ and ρ in (10) are chosen equal to 3000 to ensure the accuracy of the approximate poles. The closed-loop poles and their respective absolute error (in bracket) are $-0.1850\,(0.0150)$, $-0.4939\,(0.0061)$, $-0.9971\,(0.0029)$, $-1.0323 \pm 0.9944i\,(0.0328)$.

Our neural network method is compared with other published methods in Table 1. The values of $\kappa_2(V)$ and $\kappa_F(V)$ are smaller than those obtained by others. Figure 2(a) gives the variation of objective function $\Phi_2(T(t), X(t))$ over time. The method guarantees that the value objective function decreases monotonically and tends to a minimum, as discussed in Section 3. From Figure 2(c), it is obvious that $\|U_1^T(AT - T\Lambda)\|_F^2$ tends to a very small value. This is necessary to guarantees that the closed-loop poles are close to the exact poles. The variation of $\kappa_F(V)$ is given in Figure 2(d).

Table 1: Comparison of Results

	$\kappa_2(V)$	$\kappa_F(V)$	$\|K\|_2$
Neural Network	32.4	38.1	349.1
Lam & Yan	33.6	39.3	337.4
Byers & Nash	33.1	39.1	354.9
Kautsky *et al.* Method 1	39.4	47.3	311.5

5 Conclusion

In this paper, we have presented a gradient flow approach to robust approximate pole assignment which was formulated as an unconstrained optimization problem. The main advantage of our approach is that it can be implemented by neural networks. Simulation results demonstrated the effectiveness of the proposed method.

References

[1] Byers, R. and S.G. Nash, Approaches to Robust Pole Assignment, *Int. J. Control*, Vol.49, No.1, pp.97-117, 1989.

[2] Chu, E.K., Approximate Pole Assignment, *Int. J. Control*, Vol.58, No.2, pp.471-484, 1993.

[3] Cichocki, A. and R. Unbehauen, *Neural Networks for Optimization and Signal Processing*, John Wiley & Sons, England (1993).

[4] Lam, J. and W.Y. Yan, A Gradient Flow Approach to Robust Pole Assignment Problem, *Int. J. Nonlinear & Robust Control*, Vol.5, pp.175-185, 1995.

[5] Helmke, U. and J.B. Moore, *Optimization and Dynamical Systems*, Springer-Verlag (1994).

[6] Kautsky, J., N.K. Nichols and P. van Dooren, Robust Pole Placement in Linear State Feedback, *Int. J. Control*, Vol.41, No.5, pp.1129-1155, 1985.

[7] Peressini, A.L., F.E. Sullivan and J.J. Uhl, Jr. *The Mathematics of Nonlinear Programming*, New York: Springer-Verlag (1988).

[8] White, B.A., Eigenstructure assignment: a survey, *Proc. Instn. Mech. Engrs.* Vol.209, pp.1-11, 1995

[9] Oh, M., D.W. Gu and S.K. Spurgeon, Robust Pole Assignment in a Specified Region Using Output Feedback, *Optimal Control Applications & Methods*, Vol.14, pp.57-66,1993.

[10] Wilkinson, J.H., *The Algebraic Eigenvalue Problem*, Oxford: Clarendon Press (1965).

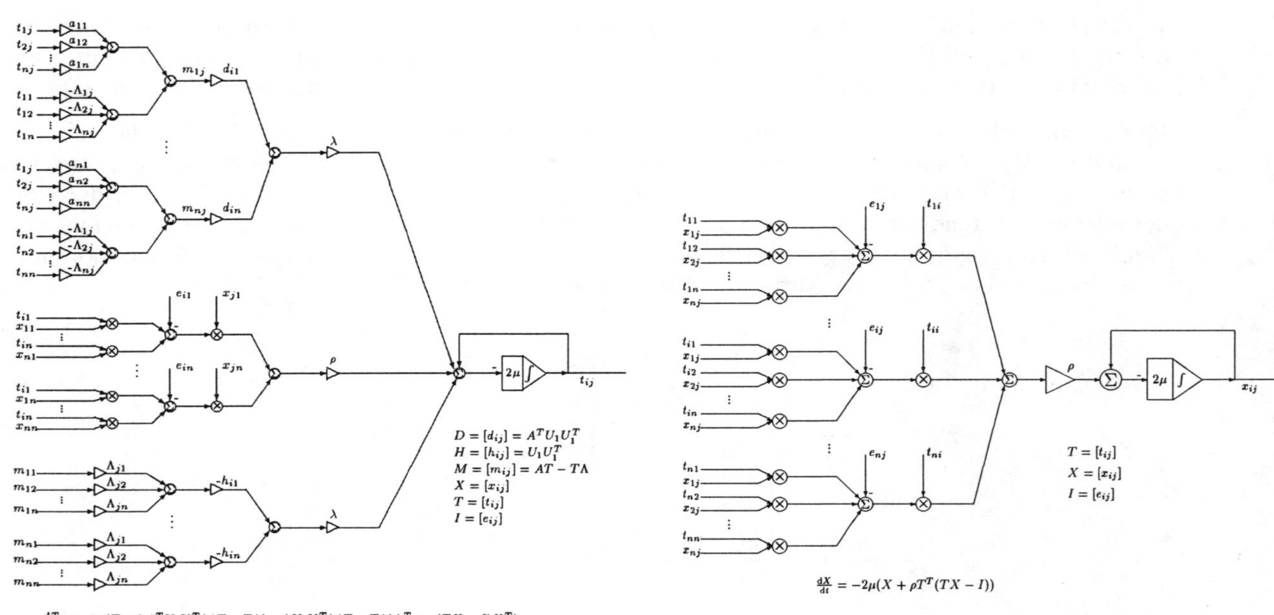

Figure 1: Neural network architecture for the ODE (11) and (12)

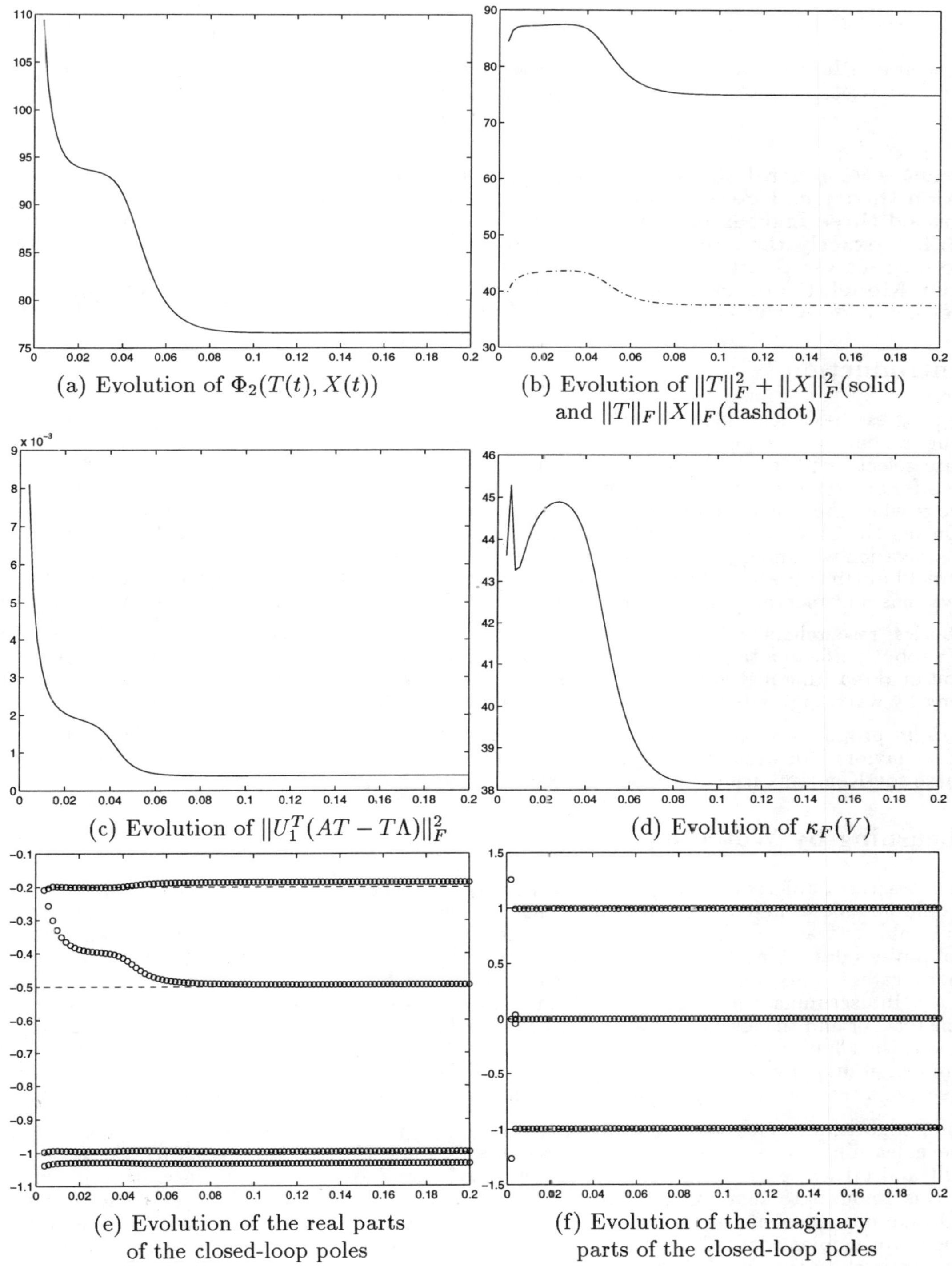

Figure 2: Simulation Result

A Kendama Learning Robot
based on a Dynamic Optimization Principle

Hiroyuki Miyamoto[†], Francesca Gandolfo[‡], Hiroaki Gomi[*], Stefan K. Schaal[♯], Yasuharu Koike[**],

Rieko Osu[†], Eri Nakano[†], Yasuhiro Wada[♯♯], Mitsuo Kawato[†],

[†]ATR Human Information Processing Research Laboratories Kyoto Japan

[‡]Massachusetts Institute of Technology Massachusetts USA, [*]NTT Basic Research Laboratories Kanagawa Japan,
[♯]Georgia Institute of Technology Atlanta USA, [**]Toyota Motor Corporation Aichi Japan,
[♯♯]Kawasaki Steel Corporation Chiba Japan

Abstract— **A general theory of movement pattern perception based on a dynamic optimization theory can be used for motion capture and learning by watching in robotics. We integrated three ingredients for Kendama executed by the SARCOS Dextrous Slave Arm, which has exactly the same kinematic structure as the human arm. The ingredients were (1) to extract via-points from a human movement trajectory using a Forward-Inverse Relaxation Model, (2) to treat via-points as a control variable while reconstructing the desired trajectory from all the via-points, and (3) to modify the via-points for successful execution.**

1   Introduction

Much progress has been made in the past decade regarding the computational understanding of motor learning in neuroscience [5, 6, 7]. A variety of cell types in the superior temporal sulcus of monkey brain that are selective for the sight of hand and body actions were found [13]. Neurons of the rostral part of the inferior premotor cortex of the monkey discharge during goal-directed hand movements, and also discharge when the monkey observes specific meaningful hand movements performed by the experimenters [3]. During the observation of hand movements, without actual movement, and during motor imagery, brain activation was mainly found in visual cortical areas, and also in areas related to the motor behavior of normal human subjects with Positron Emission Tomography [2]. These neurological data suggest that observations and mental images of motor behaviors might play an important role in motor learning.

In robotics, researchers' recent interest has been drawn to higher-level task learning [8, 11]. When we make a robot perform a task, it is difficult to tackle fluctuations and environmental uncertainty with only conventional teaching methods such as "teaching play back". It is hoped that "teaching by showing" (or learning by watching) will be effective in overcoming these difficulties.

Kawato [9] proposed a general computational theory that derives representations for a wide variety of motor behaviors. In order to examine their potential power, we control a robot arm to execute the Japanese toy Kendama using via-points extracted from a human demonstration.

2   Learning by Watching

Table 1 describes different strategies for learning by watching. If the learner had a perfect intelligence, one would be able to understand the will or motor intention of the teacher by movement perception, and would be able to translate this information into a stream of actual motor commands by taking into account laws of physics describing the mechanics of bodies and environments of the teacher and learner. There is another strategy based on imitating the position and force trajectory demonstrated by the teacher with accuracy. Indiscriminate imitation could be an efficient strategy if the following conditions are satisfied. (1) The teacher and the learner have exactly the same kinematic and dynamic properties. (2) The teacher and the learner have exactly the same environment. (3) The learner has extremely precise measurement and control ability. However, these requirements would not be satisfied in almost all realistic situations. In this case, a more abstract understanding of the teacher's motor behaviors at a higher level is essential.

Learning algorithms, such as reinforcement learning and genetic algorithms, can be efficiently used for task-level learning if adequate representations of the task are selected. However, this selection is the most difficult and critical part of motor learning, and if one assumes the pre-existence of proper representations, this amounts to abandoning plans to tackle a major part of the problem [14]. The representations should take into account the dynamics of the controlled object and the external world as well as computational principles adopted by the central nervous system in motor control. The via-points extracted from movement trajectories based on a dynamic optimization principle are attractive candidates for this representation.

2.1   Via-points extraction and trajectory formation

The problem of controlling goal-directed limb movements can be partitioned conceptually into a set of information-processing sub processes: trajectory planning, coordinate transformation from extracorporal space to intrinsic body coordinates, and motor command generation. These sub processes are required to

Table 1: Different strategies for learning by watching

Strategy of motor-task learning	Representations for motor primitives	Intelligence of learner	Difference in teacher and learner
Understanding motor intention	Movement intention	Perfect	Could be very different
Acquisition of emergent computation	Task dynamics	Good	Could be quite different
Task-level learning using abstract representations	Via-points	Poor	Quantitative difference
Indiscriminate imitation	Position and force trajectory	Little	Exactly the same

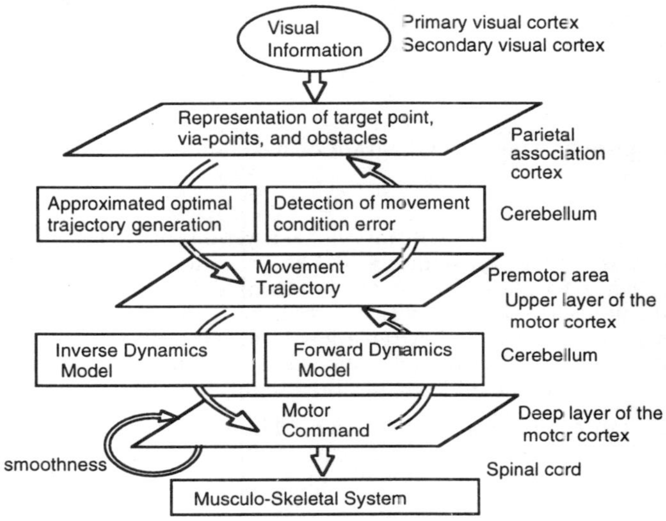

Figure 1: Bi-directional neural network model

translate the spatial characteristics of the target or goal of the movement into an appropriate pattern of muscle activation. Flash and Hogan [4] proposed a mathematical model called the "minimum jerk model" which predicted and reproduced multi-joint human arm movement. Uno et al. [15] took dynamics into account and proposed the "minimum torque change model". Recently, Kawato (1992) proposed a bi-directional neural network model (Figure 1) that derives representations for a wide variety of motor behaviors. Based on the bi-directional neural network model, Wada et al. [16] proposed the Forward-Inverse Relaxation Model (FIRM).

Using FIRM, we can extract the minimum number of via-points $S = P_1, P_2, \cdots, P_N$ from a given trajectory X_{data} with some level of error threshold δ. The via-point extraction problem is to find the minimum value of N giving a trajectory which satisfies $||X_{data} - X_{opt}(S)|| < \delta$. If a fixed number of via-points are given and the arm dynamics is known as $dX/dt = f(X, M)$, where M is motor command, we can calculate the optimal trajectory $X_{opt}(S)$ passing through these via-points and minimizing $\int_0^T || dM/dt ||^2 dt$.

2.2　Representation for task level learning

The controlled object is the SARCOS Dextrous Slave Arm which has almost the same kinematic structure (seven degrees-of-freedom) as the human arm. The kinematic parameters of the robot arm are different from the subject's arms. The robot's dynamic parameters, such as the mass, are very different from the human arm's (much heavier). And, because the robot arm is much stiffer than a human arm, even if the robot arm were able to follow exactly the same trajectory in Cartesian space as the human arm, it could not exert the same force to the environment and therefore could not perform the task. In general, we want to control the force trajectory in most interesting tasks. But, usually we can just perceive position trajectory.

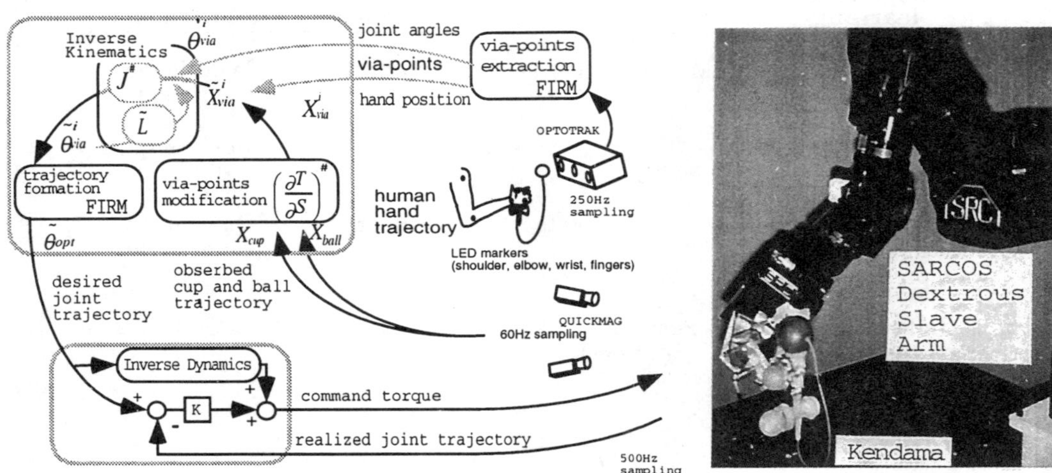

Figure 2: schematic diagram of Kendama learning robot

We chose Kendama as a task which enables simple task representation. The Japanese toy Kendama consists of two parts connected by a thin string: a ball and a handle equipped with three cups of different sizes. There are several ways to play Kendama. For simplicity, we consider the easiest one. In the initial condition, a player holds the handle with the ball hanging down. The player swings the handle up, yanking the ball to fly over the handle. After a few hundred millisec of flight, the ball is successfully caught in the cup. In order to play Kendama, quick and dynamic motion is required. A robotic arm which has complex link interferences could not perform highly precise trajectory following.

We extracted via-points from a human demonstration. The ball position trajectory was measured by a 3-D visual sensing system. To make the SARCOS arm yank the ball up properly and drop it on the cup, the via-points were modified by a Newton-like method.

3   Experiment

Figure 2 shows a schematic diagram of the Kendama learning experiment. While a subject was playing Kendama, we measured the positions of the shoulder, elbow, wrist and the back of the human hand by a 3-D vision system (OPTOTRAK: LED markers and 3 cameras). From these position data, we calculated the Cartesian hand position and orientation X_{data}, and seven joint angular position trajectories θ_{data}. We extracted via-points X_{via} and θ_{via} from these trajectories using the FIRM. For simplicity, the number of via-points were fixed at seven in this experiment. The extracted via-points were good representation of movement feature. For example, the FIRM selected a via-point at just before yanking the ball.

The Cartesian coordinates of the via-points of the robot arm are given as the hard constraint which must be strictly satisfied. For resolving the redundancy, the soft constraint is that the robot joint angles have to be as close as possible to those of the subject. To satisfy the above constraints, we use the following Newton-like method like Kawato et. al. [10].

$$^{n+1}\tilde{\theta}^i_{via} \;=\; {}^n\tilde{\theta}^i_{via} + J^\dagger({}^n\tilde{\theta}^i_{via})\left\{X^i_{via} - \tilde{L}({}^n\tilde{\theta}^i_{via})\right\} \tag{1}$$

where the left sided superscript n shows the iteration number of the Newton-like-method. We adopted the "singularity low-sensitive motion resolution matrix" proposed by Nakamura et. al. [12] $J^\dagger(\theta) = (\partial\tilde{L}(\theta)/\partial\theta)^\dagger$ as a generalized inverse matrix of the Jacobian. Since this matrix has a minimum norm property, we select the initial joint angle of the robot arm as $^0\tilde{\theta}^i_{via} =^0 \theta^i_{via}$. Therefore, $\tilde{\theta}^i_{via}$ are given as satisfying the above hard and soft constraints. The desired joint angular trajectory passing through via-points was generated by the FIRM.

If the SARCOS arm yanks the ball up properly, the ball will fall on the cup. Unfortunately, the robot arm can not reproduce the human kendama task exactly, because of the difference of dynamic and kinematic properties between the human and the robot. Moreover, some error remains even if the inverse dynamics model is used for feed-forward control with conventional feed-back control.

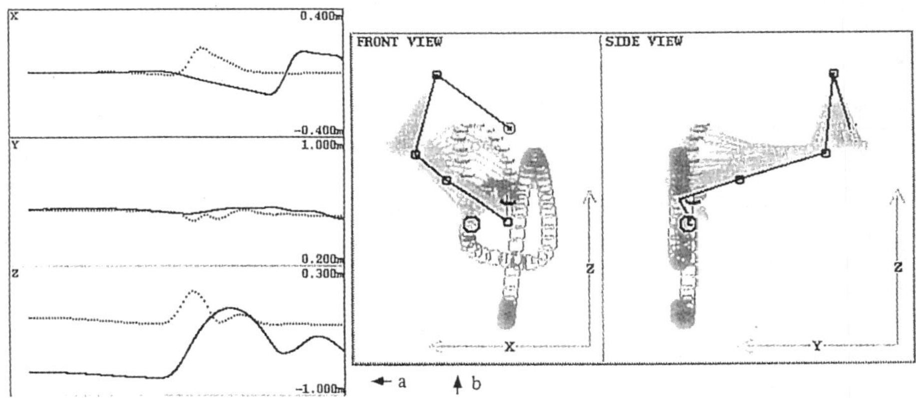

Figure 3: First trial of the Kendama task executed by the SARCOS arm. **a**: Time course of the cup (dotted line) and ball (solid line) trajectories. The abscissa shows time (2 seconds). **b**: Three-dimensional view.

By simply imitating the human Kendama motion, the SARCOS arm fails to perform the Kendama task as shown in Figure 3. To make the SARCOS arm successfully execute the task, we adopted the concept of task level learning. In this case, the control variables are via-points. The task variables are the vertical and horizontal distance between the peak and the bottom position of the ball. The diameters of the ball and the cup are about 58 mm and about 33 mm, respectively. The length of the string is about 395 mm.

Via-points were modified by the following Newton-like method. This learning scheme can be regarded as an extension of the task-level learning algorithm proposed by Aboaf et al. [1], in the sense that the control variables are not necessarily the task target but are as abstract as the task target.

$$S_{n+1} = S_n + \left(\frac{\partial T_n}{\partial S_n}\right)^{\#} T_{gain}(T_{desired} - T_n). \qquad (2)$$

Here, S_n is the via-points in n-th iteration. $T_{desired}$ and T_n are the desired and realized height and vertical and horizontal distance between the peak and the bottom positions of the ball. We use the matrix $(\partial T/\partial S)^{\#} = A^{\#} = (A^T A + kI)^{-1}A^T$. This matrix is the simply regularized g-inverse matrix which minimizes $\|I - AA^{\#}\|^2 + k\|A^{\#}\|^2$. The first term of this performance index requires that the inverse transformation is mathematically exact, and the second term requires that the via-points do not move too much. k is a weighting ratio of these two requirements. In this experiment, we set $k = 1$. Because it is very difficult to analytically compute the matrix $\partial T/\partial S$, we use matrix $\Delta T_{real}/\Delta X^i_{via}$ for $\partial T/\partial S$. To estimate the matrix, we observed the actual trials of the Kendama task ΔT_{real} when the fluctuation ΔX^i_{via} is added at the initial state. The amplitude of the Kendama movement along the vertical direction is larger than that of the horizontal direction. In order to adjust the amount of conversing errors, we added the diagonal matrix $T_{gain} = \text{diag}(0.2, 1, 1)$.

During the control of the SARCOS arm, the ball position was measured by a 3-D visual sensing system (QUICKMAG: tracking blob with two color cameras). We modified the via-points in accordance with Equation 2 for the next trial. After seven learning cycles as shown in Figure 4, the SARCOS arm executed Kendama successfully. Here, we tried several execution with this desired trajectory, and got two or three successful executions out of ten.

4 Conclusion

We demonstrated that a general theory of movement pattern perception based on a dynamic optimization theory can be used for motion capture and learning by watching in robotics. Although real time visual feedback control would be a powerful tool for a high success rate, we used a visual sensing system to allow Kendama to be done in a purely feedforward manner. In this experiment, we selected the Kendama task for simple task representation. We are planning to study more complicated tasks, such as a tennis serve.

Acknowledgments: We would like to thank Dr. Yoh'ichi Tohkura of ATR Human Information Processing Research Laboratories for his continuing encouragement. We would also like to thank Prof. Atkeson and the members of Department 3 of ATR Human Information Processing Research Laboratories for their useful discussions.

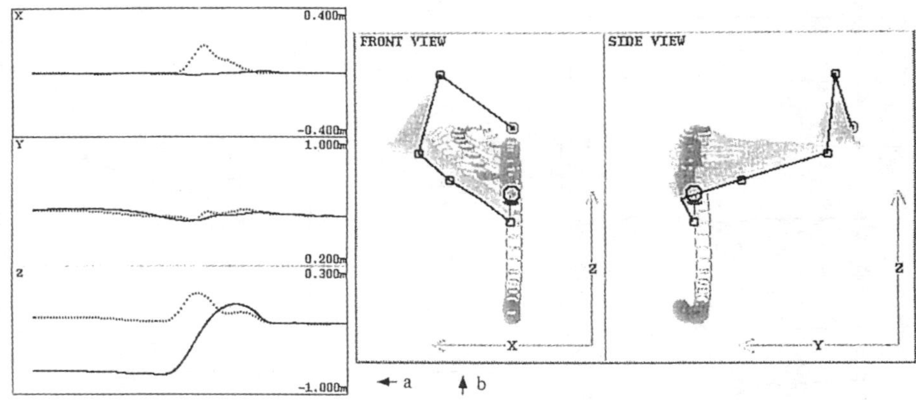

Figure 4: Seventh trial of the Kendama task executed by the SARCOS arm. **a**: Time course of the cup (dotted line) and ball (solid line) trajectories. The abscissa shows time (2 seconds). **b**: Three-dimensional view.

References

[1] E. W. Aboaf, C. G. Atkeson, and D. J. Reinkensmeyer. Task-level robot learning. *Proc IEEE Int Conf Robot Auto*, (Philadelphia), April 1988.

[2] J. Decety, D. Perani, M. Jeannerod, V. Bettinardi, B. Tadary, R. Woods, J. C. Mazziotta, and F. Fazio. Mapping motor representations with positron emission tomography. *Nature*, 371(13):600–603, 1994.

[3] G. di Pellegrino, L. Fadiga, L. Fogassi, V. Gallese, and G. Rizzolatti. Understanding motor events: a neurophysiological study. *Experimental Brain Research*, 91:176–180, 1992.

[4] T. Flash and N. Hogan. The coordination of arm movements: An experimentally confirmed mathematical model. *Journal of Neuroscience*, 5:1688–1703, 1985.

[5] M. Fujita. Adaptive filter model of the cerebellum. *Biological Cybernetics*, 45:195–206, 1982.

[6] M. Ito. Neurophysiological aspects of the cerebellar motor control system. *International Journal of Neurology*, 7:162–176, 1970.

[7] M. Ito. The cerebellum and neural control. *Raven Press, New York*, 1984.

[8] S. B. Kang and K. Ikeuchi. Toward automatic robot instruction from perception — recognizing a grasp from observation. *IEEE Trans. on Robotics and Automation*, 9:432–443, 1993.

[9] M. Kawato. Optimization and learning in neural networks for formation and control of coordinated movement. *Attention and Performance, XIV: Synergies in Experimental Psychology, Artificial Intelligence, and Cognitive Neuroscience - A Silver Jubilee*, (MIT press, Cambridge, Massachusetts):821–849, 1992.

[10] M. Kawato, M. Isobe, and R. Suzuki. Coordinates transformation and learning control for visually-guided voluntary movement with iteration: A Newton-like method in a function space. *Biological Cybernetics*, 59:161–177, 1988.

[11] Y. Kuniyoshi. The science of imitation — towards physically and socially grounded intelligence —. *RWC Tech. Rep.*, TR-94001:123–124, 1994.

[12] Y. Nakamura and H. Hanafusa. Singularity low-sensitive motion resolution of articulated robot arms. *Trans Soc Instrum Control Eng*, 20(5):453–459, 1984.

[13] D. I. Perrett, M. H. Harries, R. Bevan, S. Thomas, P. J. Benson, A. J. Mistlin, A. J. Chitty, J. K. Hietanen, and J. E. Ortega. Frameworks of analysis for the neural representation of animate objects and actions. *J. exp. Biol.*, 146:87–113, 1989.

[14] S. Schaal, C. G. Atkeson, and S. Botros. What should be learned? *Proc Seventh Yale Workshop on Adaptive and Learning Systems*:199–204, 1992.

[15] Y. Uno, M. Kawato, and R. Suzuki. Formation and control of optimal trajectory in human multijoint arm movement — minimum torque-change model. *Biological Cybernetics*, 61:89–101, 1989.

[16] Y. Wada and M. Kawato. A neural network model for arm trajectory formation using forward and inverse dynamics models. *Neural Networks*, 6:919–932, 1993.

Collision Detection in Robot Path Planning using Neural Networks

Jing Yuan
Department of Mechanical Engineering
University of Windsor
Windsor, Ontario, N9B 3P4, Canada

Abstract— **This paper presents a collision-identification neural network ($CINN$) to identify possible collisions between two convex polyhedra. It consists of a modified Hamming net and a constraint sub-net. The modified Hamming net is designed for point-to-polyhedron collision identification; and the constraint sub-net is designed to move a point within a polyhedron and detect possible collisions with another polyhedron. The mechanism of the $CINN$ is very similar to the well-known Hopfield net model. Its simple collective computing power accomplishes the relative complicated task of collision identification between convex polyhedra, rendering a suitable device for on-line path planning of robots.**

1   Introduction

Collision identification between two objects is of significant interest to computer-aided design, computer-aided manufacturing and robotics research, where computers are used to model, simulate and plan the movement of 3-D objects in the presence of obstacles. Generally, path planning is a constraint optimization problem. The cost function to be minimized is the length of the path or the energy consumed by the movement. An important constraint is to avoid collisions. Since a large number of collision constraints must be checked for each iteration, their computation has been recognized as the most costly part in path planning. An efficient algorithm to identify collision and compute an appropriate distance is a research focus in this field [9, 3, 16].

As pointed out by Gilbert (1985), the Euclidean distance is a natural way to measure a collision between two objects. The computation of the Euclidean distance between two objects is a topic in computational geometry [14]. The i-th object can be modeled by a polyhedron with M_i vertices. The computation of the distance itself is an optimization sub-problem — searching for two nearest points, which belong to the two objects. The number of operations is a function of $M = M_1 + M_2$. For 2-D problems, the asymptotic computational time is about $O(\log^2 M)$ by Schwartz's algorithm [20]. More efficient algorithms were reported by Chin and Wang [6] and Edelsbrunner [8]. When 3-D polyhedra are involved, the algorithms by Orlowski [18], and Dobkin and Kirkpatrick [7] require about $O(M \log M)$ and $O(M)$ operations respectively. Efficient algorithms were also reported by Barr [1], Barr and Gilbert [2], Wolf [22], Red [19], Buckley and Leifer [4], Cameron [5] and Gilbert *et al.* [10]. Recently, the gradient projection method was applied by Bobrow [3]; and quadratic programming method was reported by Liu and Mayne [16].

While it is a challenging topic to develop faster algorithms for collision detection, it is equally important to develop parallel algorithms to speed up the computation by exploring the advantages of VLSI techniques. Artificial neural networks provide a very economical approach. One of the advantages of neural networks is their ability to solve complex problems with extremely simple circuit structures. The well-known Hopfield model can solve the traveling-salesman-problem with a few hard-limiters as artificial neurons [11]. Several examples were given by Tank and Hopfield [21] which solve optimization problems using small numbers of inter-connected analog processors. The Hopfield model was applied by Lee and Bien [12] to collision-free control of robots, where the objects and robot arms are approximated by circles and line segments. A more sophisticated approach was recently reported by Lee and Park [13]. They introduce a collision penalty for point-to-polyhedron collision detection. When applied to 3-D path planning, a moving object is represented by a number of *via* points, which are somewhat similar to the vertices of polyhedra.

In this study, a collision identification neural network ($CINN$) is designed to detect collision between two convex polyhedra. It is hardware implementable with very simple circuit elements, such as analog integrators, linear operational amplifiers and hard-limiters. Compared with the traditional methods, the $CINN$ has a much higher speed/cost ratio.

2   Point-to-Polyhedron Collision Detection

This research focuses on a class of objects which can be approximated by convex polyhedra. Objects of this class have been common subjects in the trajectory planning research community — a non-convex object can be approximated by a combination of a number of convex polyhedra.

As the first step, collision detection between a point and a convex polyhedron is addressed in this section. A convex polyhedron is the intersection of N half-spaces defined by the corresponding boundary planes. One may attach a local Cartesian coordinate frame to each of the N boundary planes of a polyhedron. The x-y plane of a local coordinate frame coincides with a boundary plane. Its z axis is directed along the direction of the surface normal (pointing toward the outside of the object). The origin of the coordinate frame can be placed anywhere within the boundary of the plane.

An arbitrary point is represented by a 3-D vector $\mathbf{p} = [p_x, p_y, p_z]^T$. It can be expressed either in the global Cartesian coordinate or in the boundary coordinate frames. In order to distinguish the representation of a point with respect to an appropriate coordinate frame, one may use a subscript "n" to indicate that the vector is expressed in the n-th frame (attached to the n-th boundary plane). When the point is expressed with respect to the global coordinate frame, the subscript is dropped by default. According to the theory of geometric transformation, $\mathbf{p}_n$ is related to $\mathbf{p}$ by

$$\mathbf{p}_n = \mathbf{R}_n \mathbf{p} - \mathbf{t}_n \tag{1}$$

where $\mathbf{R}_n \in R^{3 \times 3}$ is a rotation matrix; $\mathbf{t}_n \in R^3$ is the offset vector representing the distance between the origins of the two coordinate frames.

The x-y plane of a coordinate frame cuts the whole space into two parts. One half of the space is characterized by a positive z coordinate. This half space does not contain the given polyhedron. The other half space is characterized by a negative z coordinate, in which the given polyhedron resides. Therefore only the z coordinates in the boundary frames are of interest. Equation (1) can be simplified to

$$p_{nz} = \mathbf{z}_n^T \mathbf{p} - t_{nz} \tag{2}$$

where $\mathbf{z}_n^T$ is the last row of the rotation matrix $\mathbf{R}_n$. The following two observations are essential to the new formulation:

1. Suppose the given convex polyhedron has N boundary planes, then p_{nz} are obtained for $1 \leq n \leq N$. If any one of $\{p_{nz}\}_{n=1}^N$ is positive, then there must exist at least one boundary plane separating point $\mathbf{p}$ from the convex polyhedron. Therefore point $\mathbf{p}$ is definitely outside the polyhedron.

2. On the other hand, if point $\mathbf{p}$ is inside the N-surface convex polyhedron, then $p_{nz} \leq 0$ for all $1 \leq n \leq N$.

On basis of these two observations, a indicator is defined as

$$p_{n^*z} = \max_{1 \leq n \leq N} \{p_{nz}\}. \tag{3}$$

The collision between point $\mathbf{p}$ and the N-surface polyhedron can be identified as follows:

$$\begin{cases} \text{If} \quad p_{n^*z} > 0, & \text{then collision free;} \\ \text{If} \quad p_{n^*z} \leq 0, & \text{then collision occurred; return direction vector } z_{n^*}. \end{cases} \tag{4}$$

Since p_{n^*z} has the minimum absolute value when all $\{p_{nz}\}_{n=1}^N$ are negative, the n^*-th boundary plane is the nearest to point $\mathbf{p}$. Consequently, the shortest way to push point $\mathbf{p}$ out of the polyhedron is to move along the z direction of the n^*-th boundary-frame.

A formulation for collision identification between a point $\mathbf{p}$ and a convex polyhedron is now completed by (2), (3) and (4). These three equations fit the mechanism of a Hamming net [15], which is one of the well-known neural network structures. A Hamming net has two layers. It stores N patterns in terms of 3-D connection weight vectors $\{\mathbf{w}_n\}_{n=1}^N$ and N thresholds $\{T_n\}_{n=1}^N$. Given an input feature vector $\mathbf{f} = [f_x, f_y, f_y]^T$, the first layer of the Hamming net matches the input with N patterns through N parallel inner product operations

$$ip_n = \mathbf{w}_n^T \mathbf{f} - T_n \quad (1 \leq n \leq N) \tag{5}$$

The resulting N inner products $\{ip_n\}_{n=1}^N$ are then fed into the second layer of the Hamming net, which is a MAXNET selecting the largest value from N inputs. One possible choice of the MAXNET is a Hopfield N flop [11]. Other possible candidates for the MAXNET are the "winner-take-all" neural net structures [15]. The final classification made by the MAXNET is given by

$$ip_{n^*} = \max_{1 \leq n \leq N} \{ ip_n \} \tag{6}$$

The input pattern $\mathbf{f} = [f_x, f_y, f_y]^T$ is thus attributed to the pre-stored vector $\mathbf{w}_{n^*}$, which has the largest inner product with $\mathbf{f}$.

The resemblance between (2), (3) and (5), (6) is evident. The computation of p_{nz} has exactly the same mathematic expression as that of ip_n. The selection of p_{n^*z} is exactly the same as that of ip_{n^*}. For point-to-polyhedron collision identification, the input is the point vector $\mathbf{p}$ instead of the feature vector $\mathbf{f}$. One can program the Hamming net by storing the $\{\mathbf{z}_n\}_{n=1}^N$ vectors instead of $\{\mathbf{w}_n\}_{n=1}^N$. The only modification needed here is some switching circuits to identify a possible collision according to (4). The indicator p_{n^*z} is returned as the distance when $p_{n^*z} > 0$. Otherwise, the direction vector $\mathbf{z}_{n^*}$ is output. This vector represents the optimum direction, along which point $\mathbf{p}$ can be pushed out of the polyhedron with a minimum distance.

3 Collision Detection Between Two Polyhedra

Compared with point-to-polyhedron collision identification, it is more involved to identify a possible collision between two polyhedra. On basis of the previous section, a new collision detecting measurement is introduced here. Given two convex polygons A and B. One may denote the numbers of boundary surfaces for the two polygons by N_A and N_B; and the z axes of the boundary frames are denoted by $\{\mathbf{z}_n^{(A)}\}_{n=1}^{N_A}$ and $\{\mathbf{z}_n^{(B)}\}_{n=1}^{N_B}$ respectively. The corresponding threshold sets are given by $\{t_n^{(A)}\}_{n=1}^{N_A}$ and $\{t_n^{(B)}\}_{n=1}^{N_B}$. A modified Hamming net can be programmed to identify a possible collision between a moving point $\mathbf{p}$ and polygon B. The indicator $p_{n \cdot z}$ and its direction index n^* in (3) are functions of vector $\mathbf{p}$. For this reason, they should be denoted explicitly as $p_{n \cdot z}(\mathbf{p})$ and $n^*(\mathbf{p})$. The new collision detecting measure is given by a constraint mini-maximum

$$p_{n \cdot z}^* = \inf_{\mathbf{p} \in A} \{p_{n \cdot z}(\mathbf{p})\} = \inf_{\mathbf{p} \in A} \{\max_{1 \leq k \leq N_B} [\mathbf{p}^T \mathbf{z}_k^{(B)} - t_k^{(B)}]\}. \tag{7}$$

$p_{n \cdot z}^*$ differs from $p_{n \cdot z}$ in the additional superscript "*". It is the indicator of point $\mathbf{p}^* \in A$, which has the smallest value compared with the indicators of any other points in polygon A. In this paper, $\mathbf{p}^*$ is called the "mini-maximum point".

The positive value of $p_{n \cdot z}^*$ signals the fact that no points of polyhedron A belong to polyhedron B. Therefore the two polygons do not contact nor collide with each other. In case any part of polygon A overlaps with a part of polygon B, then there must exist at least a point $\mathbf{p}_o$ which belongs to both polygons. Since $\mathbf{p}_o$ is inside polyhedron B, $p_{n \cdot z}(\mathbf{p}_o) = \max_{1 \leq k \leq N_B} [\mathbf{p}_o^T \mathbf{z}_k^{(B)} - t_k^{(B)}] \leq 0$. It follows that

$$p_{n \cdot z}^* = \inf_{\mathbf{p} \in A} \{p_{n \cdot z}(\mathbf{p})\} \leq p_{n \cdot z}(\mathbf{p}_o) \leq 0.$$

This in turn indicates that a collision has occurred. A possible collision between polygons A and B can be identified according to

$$\begin{cases} \text{If } p_{n \cdot z}^* > 0, & \text{then collision free;} \\ \text{If } p_{n \cdot z}^* \leq 0, & \text{then collision occurred.} \end{cases} \tag{8}$$

Since $p_{n \cdot z}^*$ is the result of a mini-maximization given by (7), it appears to be simular to the minimum translational distance (MTD) by Cameron and Culley [5], or the Δ function by Buckley [4]. However, there are significant differences between the two approaches. The first difference is reflected by the definitions of the two distance measures. The MTD or the Δ function is given by

$$\Delta = -\min_{\|\zeta\|=1} \{\max_{\mathbf{p}_1 \in A, \ \mathbf{p}_2 \in B} [\zeta^T (\mathbf{p}_1 - \mathbf{p}_2)]\}. \tag{9}$$

It differs from (7) in that

1. The maximization of (9) is over infinitely many choices of two points $\mathbf{p}_1 \in A$ and $\mathbf{p}_2 \in B$; whereas the maximization of (7) is over N_B possible unit vectors $\mathbf{z}_i^{(B)}$ and thresholds $t_i^{(B)}$, $1 \leq i \leq N_B$.

2. The minimization of (9) is over a <u>direction</u> vector ζ; whereas the minimization of (7) is over a <u>position</u> vector $\mathbf{p} \in A$.

In other words, the two mini-maximizations are conducted with respect to <u>different</u> sets and constraints. Therefore, the two measurements are not necessarily same.

Let C denote the set difference between A and B, then (9) may be simplified to

$$\Delta = -\min_{\|\zeta\|=1} \{\max_{\mathbf{p} \in C} [\zeta^T \mathbf{p}]\}.$$

The simplified version of Δ looks like of the same complexity as (7); however, it involves the set difference C whose construction is non-trivial. It requires $O(n)$ or $O(n^2 \log n)$ operations for 2-D or 3-D cases respectively [17]. A faster algorithm was developed by Cameron and Culley [5] to compute set difference. These operations are not required by (7), because it does not involve the set difference C.

A part from the difference in formulations, the computation method proposed here also differs from those by Cameron and Culley [5], or Buckley [4]. The method by Cameron and Culley is a dimension reduced search — It translates a boundary plane of one polyhedron to research another polyhedron. The approach of Buckley is similar to the method of Lagrange multipliers. The algorithm developed here, however, drives a point to move in a 3-D space to evaluate (7). It is tailored to suit a neural network implementation using very simple circuit elements. The hardware implementation and justifications of the idea are detailed in the next section.

4   The Collision-Identification Neural Network

The maximization of (7) can be implemented by a modified Hamming net which stores connection weights $\{\mathbf{z}_n^{(B)}\}_{n=1}^{N_B}$ and thresholds $\{t_n^{(B)}\}_{n=1}^{N_B}$. The modified Hamming net identifies a possible collision between an arbitrary point $\mathbf{p}$ and polygon B. To find the mini-maximum point $\mathbf{p}^*$, a 3-D analog integrator may be designed to drive $\mathbf{p}$ such that it converges to $\mathbf{p}^*$. A possible integrator design is given by

$$\dot{\mathbf{p}} = -\mathbf{z}_{k^*}^{(B)} \tag{10}$$

where k^* is the index returned by the MAXNET. It points to a direction vector $\mathbf{z}_{k^*}^{(B)}$ and the corresponding threshold $t_{k^*}^{(B)}$ such that

$$\mathbf{p}^T \mathbf{z}_{k^*}^{(B)} - t_{k^*}^{(B)} = \max_{1 \leq k \leq N_B} [\mathbf{p}^T \mathbf{z}_k^{(B)} - t_k^{(B)}]. \tag{11}$$

This direction vector $\mathbf{z}_{k\bullet}^{(B)}$ in (10) drives $\mathbf{p}$ along the steepest descendent of $p_{k\bullet z}$. The main problem with (10) is the absence of the constraint $\mathbf{p} \in A$. As a result, (10) will drive $\mathbf{p}$ all the way to the center of polygon B.

In order to keep the moving point $\mathbf{p}$ inside polygon A, $\mathbf{p}$ is fed into a constraint sub-net. This sub-net consists of N_A independent neurons. The output of the n-th neuron is denoted as o_i, which is obtained by a nonlinear operator

$$o_i = \left\{ \begin{array}{ll} 1 & \text{if } \mathbf{p}^T \mathbf{z}_i^{(A)} - t_i^{(A)} > 0; \\ 0 & \text{otherwise.} \end{array} \right. \tag{12}$$

Let $o = \bigcup_{i=1}^{N_A} o_i$ denote the logic union of all $\{o_i\}_{i=1}^{N_A}$, then (10) is modified to

$$\dot{\mathbf{p}} = -\sum_{i=1}^{N_A} o_i \mathbf{z}_i^{(A)} - \bar{o} \mathbf{z}_{k\bullet}^{(B)} \tag{13}$$

where $\bar{o}$ is the logic complement of $o = \bigcup_{i=1}^{N_A} o_i$. It satisfies $\bar{o} o_i = 0$ for $1 \le i \le N_A$.

The algorithm given by (13) has a very good feature. It can be implemented by three analog integrators whose inputs are controlled by $N_A + 1$ switching gates. There is no need to compute the direction vectors $\{\mathbf{z}_i^{(A)}\}_{i=1}^{N_A}$ and $\{\mathbf{z}_i^{(B)}\}_{i=1}^{N_B}$. Instead, they are set by a number of programable resistances connected to the power sources. The derivative of $\mathbf{p}$ is determined by the on/off states of artificial neurons $\{o_i\}_{i=1}^{N_A}$ and $\bar{o}$ respectively. The algorithm does not need a synchronization clock. No floating-point arithmetics are required. A hardware implementation is possible without using a CPU or any memory chips.

The inner product operations are, perhaps, the most complicated operations required to implement (13). They can be carried out simultaneously by $N_A + N_B$ linear operational amplifiers with programable input resistances. The resulting inner products are either fed to the MAXNET [15]; or hard-limited to form the switching signals $\{o_i\}_{i=1}^{N_A}$. These analog operations are comparison in nature — a hard-limiter can be viewed as a comparison of the input with a constant voltage representing 0. These operations are particularly suitable for a neural network implementation — a winner-take-all network obtains a maximum instantly without the exhaustive comparison required by traditional digital circuits. The effect of DC drift, a major treat to the accuracy of analog circuits, becomes relatively immaterial when all the analog elements are implemented on a single VLSI chip, since all elements have the equal amount of DC drifts and the DC drifts cancel each other in the comparison operations.

According to (13), the inputs of the integrators are on/off digital signals. In other words, the coupling between the integrators and the two sub-nets are digital in nature. Therefore the proposed neural network is an open-loop circuit with respect to analog signals, though it is a closed-loop circuit with respect to hybrid digital and analog signals. This is another measure intended to avoid the effect of DC drifts.

The *CINN*, is programable by setting two sets of connection weights and thresholds which, in turn, determine the two sets of inner product operations. The maximum numbers of elements of the two programable sets are N_A and N_B respectively. In general, N_A and N_B can be as large as allowed by the VLSI design and implementation standard. Each time the chip is used to detect collision between convex polyhedra A and B, its two sets of connection weights and thresholds must be programed to represent the surfaces of the two polyhedra respectively. If N_A or N_B is larger than the actual numbers of surfaces of the two polyhedra, then the connection weights of the redundant operational amplifiers may be set to zeros while their thresholds set to be a maximum positive value t_{max}. Thus, the outputs of all redundant operational amplifiers are uniformly $-t_{max}$. When these extreme negative values are fed into a MAXNET, they will never win the competition; when they are fed to the switching gates, their negative values will shut the corresponding gates off. In both cases, the redundant elements will not contribute to $\dot{\mathbf{p}}$, and hence bear no effect to the dynamics of the neural network system. They are implemented in the VLSI chip in case the chip is used to detect collisions between two convex polyhedra with large numbers of surfaces.

5   Conclusion

This study proposes a *CINN* for collision identification between two polyhedra. A *CINN* has a simple structure. One can program it by calculating and storing two sets of weights and thresholds. When the two polyhedra do not contact each other, the *CINN* returns a pseudo-distance measure; otherwise, it locates the deepest collision point and returns a direction vector to lead one of the polyhedra out of the collision.

References

[1] Barr, R.O., "An efficient computational procedure for a generalized quadratic programming problem", *SIAM J. Contr.*, vol. 7, pp. 415 – 429, 1969.

[2] Barr, R.O., and E. G. Gilbert, "Some efficient algorithms for a class of abstract optimization problems arising in optimal control", *IEEE Trans. Auto. Contr.*, vol. AC-14, pp. 640 – 652, 1969.

[3] Bobrow, J.E., "A direct minimization approach for obtaining the distance between convex polyhedra," *The International Journal of Robotics Research*, vol. 8, No. 3, June, pp. 65-76, 1989.

[4] Buckley, C.E., and L.J. Leifer, "A proximity metric for continuum path planning", *Proc. 9th Int. Joint Conf. Artificial Intelligence*, pp. 1096 – 1102, 1985.

[5] Cameron, S.A., and R.K. Culley, "Determining the minimum translation distance between two convex polyhedra", *Proc. IEEE Int. Conf. on Robotics and Automation*, pp. 591 – 596, 1986.

[6] Chin, F., and C.A. Wang, "Optimal algorithms for the intersection and minimum distance problems between planar polygons", *IEEE Trans. Compute.*, vol. C-32, pp. 1203 – 1207, 1984.

[7] Dobkin, D.P., and D.G. Kirkpatrick, "A linear algorithm for determining the separation of convex polyhedra", *J. Algorithms*, vol. 6, pp. 381 – 392, 1985.

[8] Edelsbrunner, H., "On computing the extreme distances between two convex polygons", *J. Algorithms*, vol. 6, pp. 515 – 542, 1985.

[9] Gilbert, E.G., and John, D.W., "Distance functions and their application to robot path planning in the presence of obstacles," *IEEE Journal of Robotics and Automation*, vol. RA-1, No. 1, pp. 21-30, 1985.

[10] Gilbert, E.G., D.W. Johnson, and S. Keerth, "A fast procedure for computing the distance between complex objects in three-dimensional space", *IEEE J. Robotics and Auto.*, vol. 4, pp. 193 – 203, 1988.

[11] Hopfield, J.J., "Neural networks and physical systems with emergent collective computational abilities," *Proc. Natl. Acad. Sci. USA*, vol. 79, April, pp. 2554-2558, 1982.

[12] Lee, D.T., and F.P. Preparata, "Computational geometry — A survey", *IEEE Trans. Compute.*, vol. C-33, pp. 1072 – 1101, 1984.

[13] Lee, J., and Bien, Z., "Collision-free trajectory control for multiple robots based on neural optimization network," *Robotica*, pp. 185 – 194, 1990.

[14] Lee, S., and J. Park, "Neural computation for collision-free path planning", *J. of Intelligent Manufacturing*, vol. 2, pp. 315 – 326, 1991.

[15] Lippmann, R. P., "An introduction to computing with neural nets", *IEEE ASSP Magazine*, April, pp. 4-22, 1987.

[16] Liu, C.Y., and Mayne, R.W., "Distance calculations in motion planning problems with interference situations," *Proc. of the 1990 ASME Design Tech. Conf.*, DE-vol. 23-1, pp. 145-152, 1990.

[17] Lozano-Perez, T., "Spatial planning: a configuration space approach," *IEEE Trans. Comput.*, vol. C-32, No. 2, pp. 108-120, 1983.

[18] Orlowski, M., "The computation of the distance between polyhedra in 3-space", presented at *SIAM conf. on Geometric Modeling and Robotics*, Albany, NY, 1985.

[19] Red, W.E., "Minimum distance for robot task simulation," *Robotica*, vol.1, pp. 231-238, 1983.

[20] Schwartz, J.T., "Finding the minimum distance between two convex polygons", *Inform. Processor. Lett.*, vol. 13, pp. 168 – 170, 1981.

[21] Tank, D.W., and J.J. Hopfield, "Analog processors interconnected to solve optimization problems", *IEEE Trans. Circuits and Systems*, vol. CAS-33, pp. 533 – 541, 1986.

[22] Wolf, P., "Finding the nearest point in a polytope", *Math. Programming*, vol. 11, pp. 128 – 149, 1976.

An Intelligent Navigator for Mobile Vehicles

N. H. C. Yung and C. Ye

Department of Electrical and Electronic Engineering
The University of Hong Kong
Pokfulam Road, Hong Kong
Tel: (852)28592685 Fax: (852)28598738 Email: nyung@hkueee.hku.hk

Abstract—**This paper presents an intelligent navigation method for navigation of a mobile vehicle in unknown environments. The proposed navigator consists of three modules: Obstacle Avoidor, Environment Evaluator and Navigation Supervisor. The Obstacle Avoidor is a fuzzy controller whose rule base is learnt through reinforcement learning. A new and powerful training method is proposed to construct the fuzzy rules automatically. The Navigation Supervisor determines the tactical requirement of avoiding obstacles or moving towards the goal location at each action step so that the vehicle can achieve its task without colliding with obstacles. The effectiveness of the learning method and the whole navigator are verified by simulation.**

1 Introduction

Path planning is an important issue in the navigation of mobile vehicles, which could be divided into two major categories: (1) global path planning, and (2) local path planning. Global path planning methods, such as roadmap [1], cell decomposition [2] are usually carried out in an off-line manner in a completely known environment. As a result, they are not suitable for navigation in complex, unknown or dynamic environments. On the other hand, local path planning techniques, also called obstacle avoidance methods which are carried out in an on-line manner are more efficient in the navigation of mobile vehicles in such environment.

Of the local path planning methods, potential field method [3, 4] seems quite efficient in obstacle avoidance, however it has two disadvantages: First, it is difficult to find the force coefficients influencing the velocity and direction of the mobile vehicle in a complicated environment, which are too complex to be embedded in a mathematical model. Second, the potential local minimum could cause the vehicle to be stuck and unable to get out. In order to overcome these problems, neural network and fuzzy logic approaches have been tried for this type of applications. Fuzzy logic approach [5, 6] seems promising, since it deals with various situations without requiring the construction of an analytical model of environment. While compared with the neural network approach [7], it has another distinct advantage that each rule of the rule base has a definite meaning and deals with a specific situation. This makes it possible to tune the rules manually. However, it is not easy to consistently construct the rules in the case of navigating the mobile vehicle in an unknown environment. To tackle this drawback, error back-propagation neural network was used to learn these rules[8]. Unfortunately, this method requires a sufficiently large set of representative patterns which can characterize the environment to train the network. To worsen the case, it is also difficult to obtain these training patterns which contain no contradictory input/output pairs. Thus reinforcement learning which requires only a scalar reinforcement signal as a performance feedback from the environment is quite attractive for constructing the fuzzy rule base. But due to the slow convergence speed of the reinforcement learning method, the Environment Exploration Methods (EEM), such as reference [9] which operates the mobile vehicle to explore a complex environment cmopletely and have the rules constructed is time consuming and cannot guarantee to end up with sufficiently learned rules.

In this paper, we introduce a new navigation method which uses fuzzy logic and reinforcement learning, and propose a powerful method for constructing the fuzzy rule base. When compared with the EEM, it has four distinct advantages: (1) high learning speed; (2) high number of learned rule; (3) high adaptability (4) reliable convergence of learning network.

2 Overview of the navigator

As shown in Fig. 1, we assume that the vehicle is equipped with a ultrasonic sensor ring in which five sensor are equally distributed in space on the front semicircle. Each sensor, $s_i (i = 1,2,\cdots,5)$ gives the distance to the obstacle $d_i (i = 1,2,...,5)$ in its field of view. Here we assume $4 \le d_i \le 200cm$ and each sensor covers a view of $\pi/4$. The control variables of the mobile vehicle are its linear velocity v and its steering angle $\Delta\theta$. In order to navigate the mobile vehicle to it's destination, we assume that the position vector of the mobile vehicle $p(X,Y)$

is always known from the internal sensor of the vehicle, and the goal vector $p_g(X,Y)$ is given. Therefore the navigation problem can be described as: given the input variables d_i, $p(X,Y)$ and $p_g(X,Y)$, control the output variables v and $\Delta\theta$ such that the vehicle avoids obstacles successfully and finally achieves its destination.

The structure of the proposed navigator is depicted in Fig. 2. The Navigation Supervisor, which is based on the If-Then rule, is a command module for controlling the mobile vehicle to move to its goal position or avoid obstacles. when the Obstacle Avoidor is activated, the Environment Evaluator performs an evaluation of the environment where the vehicle is, and determines the appropriate value of W for the Fuzzy Quantization. Further, input sensor readings are fuzzified and certain fuzzy inference is made. Finally the vehicle's action, v and $\Delta\theta$ are determined by defuzzifiction. In this paper we will focus on the Obstacle Avoidor and the method of constructing the fuzzy rule base.

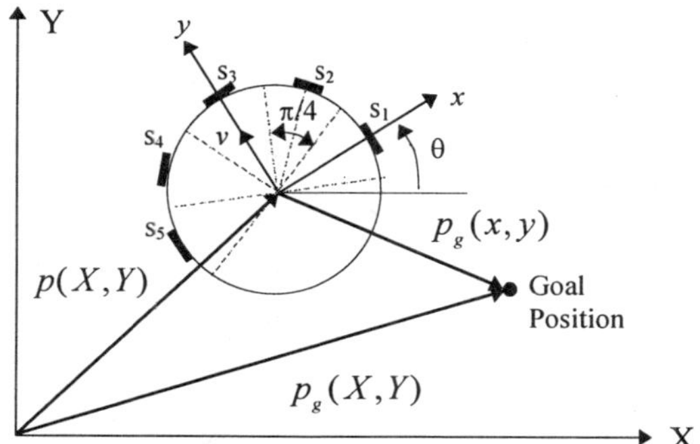

Fig. 1 Ultrasonic sensors and control variables

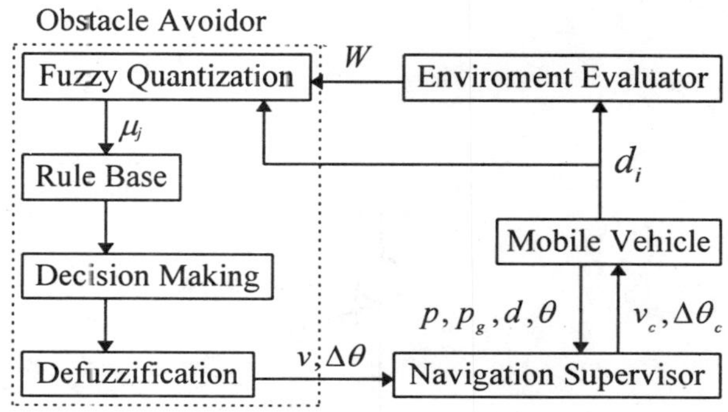

Fig. 2 Diagram of the proposed Navigator

3   Fuzzy control of obstacle avoidance

The Obstacle Avoidor is a fuzzy controller. The design steps of this module are as follows: (1) definition of membership functions for sensor input variables and control output variables; (2) fuzzification of the input variables; (3) rule base construction through reinforcement learning; (4) fuzzy inference; (5) defuzzification of the output variables.

Definition of the membership functions for the input/output variables and fuzzification of the input variables: The membership functions of the input and output variables are shown in Fig. 3. The crisp value of input variable d_i is fuzzified and expressed by the fuzzy sets - *VN, NR, FR*, which stand for very near, near and far, respectively. The fuzzy sets of the output variables v and $\Delta\theta$ have the definite membership functions, while their center positions (b_{1j} and b_{2j}, for $j = 1,2,\cdots,243$) are determined by the reinforcement learning.

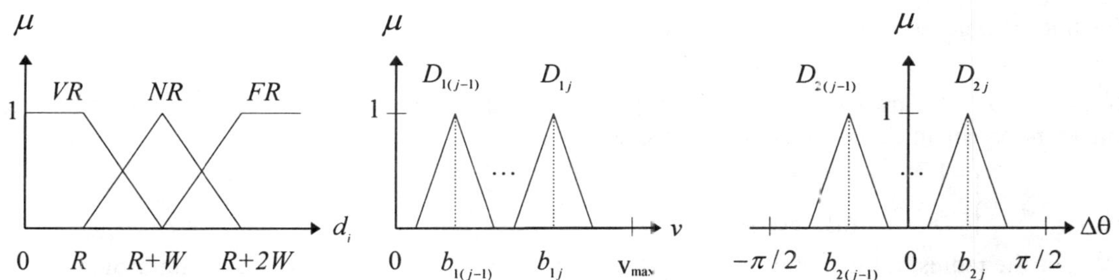

Fig. 3 The membership functions of input and output variables

Construction of the rule base and fuzzy reasoning: The fuzzy rules which play a role in mapping the sensor input space d_i to the mobile vehicle's action space v and $\Delta\theta$ are denoted by

Rule j: IF d_1 is D_{j1} AND ... AND d_s is D_{js} THEN v is V_j, $\Delta\theta$ is $\Delta\Theta_j$;   for $j = 1,\cdots,243$

where $d_i(i = 1,2,\cdots,5)$ stands for the sensor inputs; $D_{ji}(i = 1,\cdots,5)$ are the fuzzy sets for d_i in the jth rule, which take the linguistic value of *VN, NR* or *FR*; v and $\Delta\theta$ denote the output variables; and V_j and $\Delta\Theta_j$ are the fuzzy sets for v and $\Delta\theta$. These rules are constructed through the reinforcement learning.

Let the fire strength of the jth rule be denoted by μ_j. For the inputs $d_1 = d_1',\cdots,d_s = d_s'$, the fire strength of the jth rule can be written as

$$\mu_j = \mu_{D_{j1}}(d_1') \wedge \mu_{D_{j2}}(d_2') \wedge \mu_{D_{j3}}(d_3') \wedge \mu_{D_{j4}}(d_4') \wedge \mu_{D_{j5}}(d_5'); \quad \text{for } j = 1, \cdots, 243 \tag{1}$$

If Mamdani's minimum operation is used for fuzzy implication, the memberships of the inferred fuzzy control action, V_j' and $\Delta\Theta_j'$ are calculated by

$$\mu_{V'}(v) = \bigcup_{j=1}^{243} \mu_j \wedge \mu_{V_j}(v) \quad \text{and} \quad \mu_{\Delta\Theta'}(\Delta\theta) = \bigcup_{j=1}^{243} \mu_j \wedge \mu_{\Delta\Theta_j}(\Delta\theta) \tag{2}$$

Defuzzification of output variables: For the reason of lower computing cost, we use the method of height defuzzification. The crisp control action is given by

$$v = \frac{\sum_{j=1}^{243} \mu_j b_{1j}}{\sum_{j=1}^{243} \mu_j} \quad \text{and} \quad \Delta\theta = \frac{\sum_{j=1}^{243} \mu_j b_{2j}}{\sum_{j=1}^{243} \mu_j} \tag{3}$$

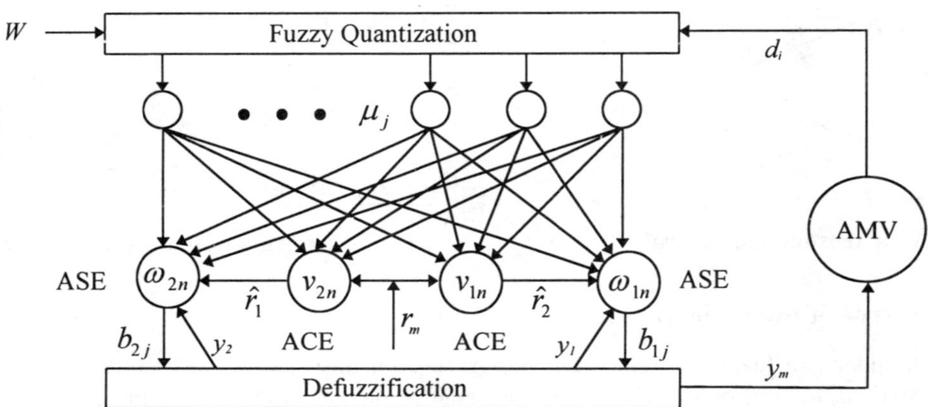

Fig. 4 Diagram of neural network to learn obstacle avoidance

4   Rule learning for obstacle avoidance

For convenience, we adopt the Sutton and Barto's model [10] in this paper. The structure of the learning algorithm is depicted in Fig. 4. The Fuzzy Quantization section encodes the input crisp value of sensors into μ_j by equation (1). In order to give the associativity in learning the rules, the trace, $\overline{\mu}_j(t)$ of the fired jth rule, is used. The trace at time step, $t+1$ is given by

$$\overline{\mu}_j(t+1) = \lambda\overline{\mu}_j(t) + (1-\lambda)\mu_j(t) \tag{4}$$

where λ, $0 \leq \lambda < 1$, is the trace decay rate. When a collision occurs, the associative critic element (ACE) receive an external reinforcement signal which is designed as

$$r_m = \begin{cases} -1 & \text{if } \min(d_i \mid i = 1, 2, \cdots, 5) < (R_{amv} + d_{s\min})(1+\varepsilon) \\ 0 & \text{otherwise} \end{cases} \quad \text{for } m = 1, 2 \tag{5}$$

where R_{amv} is the radius of the mobile vehicle, $d_{s\min}$ is the minimum distance which the ultrasonic sensor can detect, and ε, $0 < \varepsilon < 1$, is a safety factor. While using the temporal difference learning theory, the prediction of the external reinforcement signal is

$$p_m(t) = E\left(\sum_{t' \geq t} \gamma^{t'-t} r_m(t'+1) \right) \tag{6}$$

where $0 < \gamma < 1$, and $E(\bullet)$ denotes the expectation. Thus if $p_m(t)$ is correctly learned, then

$$p_m(t-1) = r_m(t) + \gamma p_m(t) \tag{7}$$

In the case of incorrect learning, an internal reinforcement signal will be generate by equation (7) to train the ACE, which is defined as

$$\hat{r}_m(t) = r_m(t) + \gamma p_m(t) - p_m(t-1) \tag{8}$$

The prediction value, $p_m(t)$ is implemented as follows:

$$p_m(t) = G\left(\sum_{j=1}^{243} v_{mj}(t)\mu_j(t)\right) \tag{9}$$

Where $G(x) = 2/(1+e^{-\xi x}) - 1$. In order to predict $p_m(t)$ correctly, the weights of ACE must be updated. It is expressed by

$$v_{mj}(t+1) = v_{mj}(t) + \beta \hat{r}_m(t)\overline{\mu}_j(t) \tag{10}$$

where β is a positive constant determining the rate of change of v_{mj}. In the same way, the weights of the associative search element (ASE) are updated by

$$\omega_{mj}(t+1) = \omega_{mj}(t) + \alpha \hat{r}_m(t)e_{mj}(t) \tag{11}$$

where α, $0 < \alpha \leq 1$, determines the learning rate, $e_{mj}(t)$ is the eligibility of the *jth* rule at time t, which is updated by

$$e_{mj}(t+1) = \delta e_{mj}(t) + (1-\delta)y_m(t)\mu_j(t) \tag{12}$$

where δ, $0 \leq \delta < 1$, is a trace decay rate, and $y_m(t) = (v, \Delta\theta)^T$ is the control action at time step t. Eventually, if the rules are sufficiently learnt in a specific environment, the weights of ASE will converge to fixed values. The center position of the fuzzy sets (Fig. 4) at each time step are determined by

$$b_{mj}(t) = b_m + \frac{\omega_{mj}(t)f_m}{k \max(|\omega_{mj}(t)|) + |\omega_{mj}(t)|} \tag{13}$$

where b_m, k and f_m are constants. When the learning process is terminated, the learned $b_{mj}(t)$ determined by equation (13) at the time step are used as the collision avoidance rule base for the mobile vehicle in its real navigation.

5 Simulation and results analysis

As we mentioned above, the reinforcement learning methods that have been proposed in the literature typically converge slowly. This drawback limits their capability on solving simple learning task. The EEM could be used to learn the rules for obstacle avoidance. But it cannot avoid the disadvantages that: (1) it is time consuming in exploring the environment; (2) whether the rules are sufficiently learnt or not cannot be ascertained when terminating the learning process; (3) it is not clear that an optimum environment for training the vehicle exists.

In this paper, we proposed a method to tackle this problem. Our key idea is to separate the rule learning and real navigation into two stages: (1) in the rule learning stage, we use a small value of W (Fig. 5), so the rule learning process could be implemented in a very small and simple environment; (2) in the real navigation stage, the Environment Evaluator is activated to generate an appropriate parameter-W of the current environment where the vehicle is. As a result, the fuzzy rule base learned in a small environment can be adaptively used in a new and fully unknown environment.

$R = 28cm$	$\delta = 0.85$	$\lambda = 0.5$	$b_1 = 15cm/s$	$b_2 = 0$	$\beta = 0.8$	$\alpha = 0.8$
$W = 20cm$	$\gamma = 0.95$	$\varepsilon = 0.2$	$f_1 = 15cm/s$	$f_2 = \pi/2$	$k = 0.2$	$\xi = 1.5$

Table 1. Parameter Used for simulation

A simple corridor-like environment (Fig. 5) was used to train the vehicle. Since the environment is regular, the trajectory of the vehicle has been kept unchanged when the learning method converges. The parameters for the simulation are shown in table 1. At the beginning of the simulation, $v_{mj}(t)$ was set to small non-zero values, while $\omega_{mj}(t)$, $\overline{\mu}_j(t)$, $p_m(t-1)$, $e_{mj}(t)$ were set to zero. The mobile vehicle began its first trial of the learning steps, which consists of a series of learning steps until a collision occurs. When a collision occurred, it backtracked 4 steps and the heading direction was reversed, then the next trial began. After several collisions, the vehicle navigated successfully in counter-clockwise (CCW) direction (which direction the vehicle takes in the environment depends on the start point.) and kept a constant trajectory. Then the CCW training was terminated and the clockwise (CW) direction was repeat. If a collision occurs, the vehicle will backtrack 40 steps and the heading angle turn $\pi/30$ in the CW direction, then the next trial began. After the vehicle navigated successfully in the CW direction and maintained its trajectory unchanged, the whole learning process was completed. The performance of the learning process could be expressed as the number of steps which was taken before a collision occurred. Simulation was carried out to compare our method with the EEM. In the EEM, the vehicle was trained in the environment shown in Fig. 8 with the same parameters as our method. The rules were almost sufficiently learnt (1.2% of the rules were blank) in our method after 34 trials, where CCW took up 22 trials since it began with a blank rule base, and CW took up 12 trials. On the other hand, the EEM took 100 trials and the rule base was far from sufficient (30% of the rules were blank). It only handled 3000 learning steps before a new collision occurred. Further simulation showed that the rule base was not constructed sufficiently at up to 40000 learning steps. Fig. 6 shows that the proposed method is quite efficient than EEM. In some situations where the EEM caused the vehicle to go into a dead loop, the performance of learning deteriorated significantly.

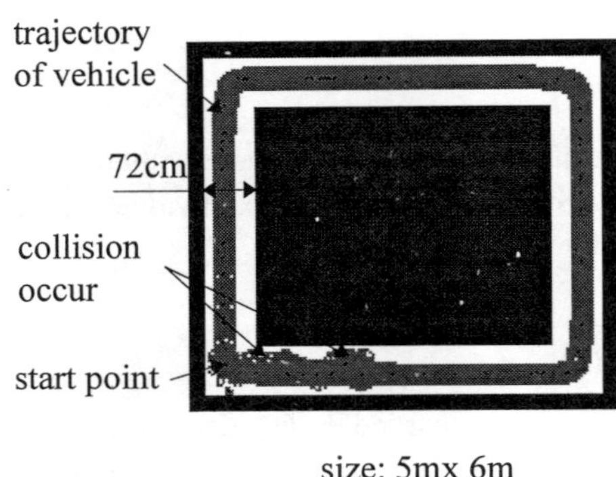

Fig. 5 Learning in a simple environment

Fig. 6 Performance of the proposed training method

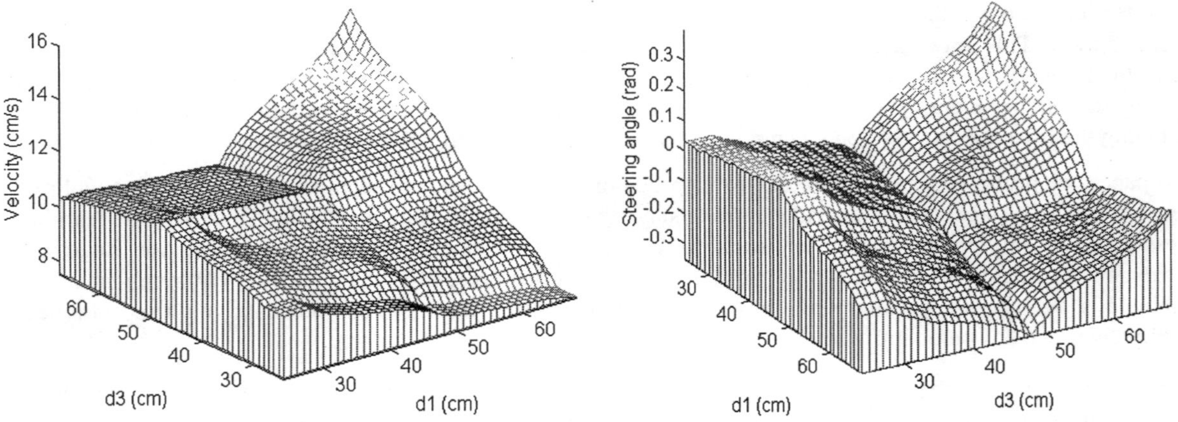

Fig. 7 Control surfaces of the collision avoidor

In the case of $W=20$cm, we found that the optimum width of the corridor for training the vehicle was 72cm. It means that we could get the largest number of rules in this case. For instance, there were only 3 blank rules for the width of 72cm while there were 18 blank rules for the width of 80cm. If the width is larger, it becomes more difficult to train the vehicle, as it turns in a zigzag trajectory along the corridor. For this reason, the rules learnt in the width of 72cm are used as the obstacle avoidance rule base. Furthermore, the three blank rules could be constructed in two ways: (1) re-train the vehicle in the situation associated with these rules until it learns to handle with the situation. (2) add the three rules manually. For convenience, the second method was adopted.

After the construction of the rule base, we plotted the control surfaces of the rule base. Whether the rules are learnt correctly and sufficiently could be shown by these control surfaces. Fig. 7 shows an example of $d_2=d_4=d_5=38$cm, it is indicated in this figure that if d_3 is near and d_1 is far, the vehicle will turn a negative $\Delta\theta$ (in the CW direction). This action enables it to move into a collision-free region. In addition, it is found that the velocity is reduced while d_1 or d_3 become small. The adaptability of the rule base was tested in an unknown environment (Fig. 8) by simulation. The vehicle navigated 300000 steps, completely explored the environment without a single collision. However, since the rules are learnt with a small W. this makes the obstacle avoidor rather nearsighted. So the Environment Evaluator was used in the proposed navigator to generate an appropriate W in the simulated navigation. The function of the Environment Evaluator is that it determines a large W in a environment of low obstacle density to ensure the vehicle "sees" farther and determines a small W in a environment with high obstacle density to ensure it is capable to navigate through this environment. The impact of the evaluator is that it reduces the average velocity (Fig. 9). The whole navigator is tested by simulation as shown in Fig. 8.

6 Conclusion

We have proposed an efficient method to learn the fuzzy rule base of collision avoidance. Based on this method, we have further proposed a new scheme for an intelligent navigator, in which an Environment Evaluator was introduced to tune the universe of discourse of the input variables. The learning algorithm and the scheme for the whole navigator have been verified and proved to be successful by a series of simulation. In our future research, The proposed method will find its application in multi-behavior navigation of mobile vehicle in a dynamic environment.

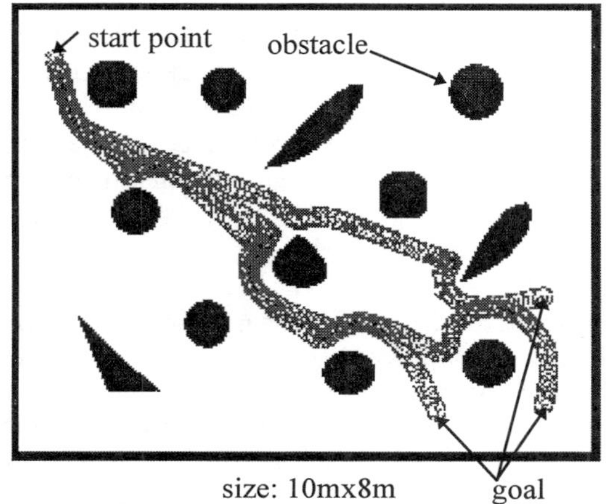

Fig. 8 Navigation in a complex environment

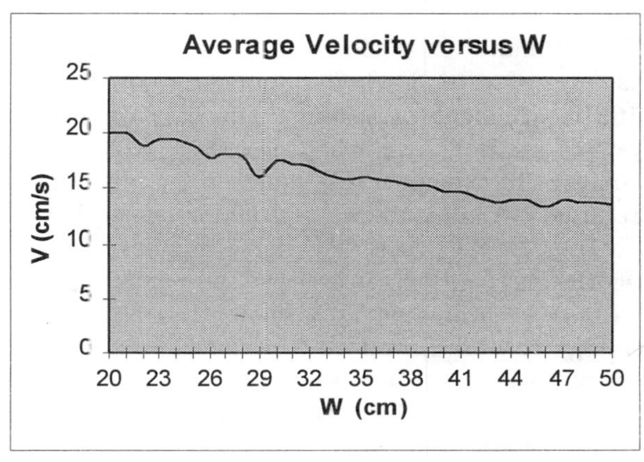

Fig. 9 Impact of tuning W

References

[1] Rohnert, H., "Shortest paths in the plane with convex polygonal obstacles", Information Processing Letters, 23,71-76,1986.

[2] Lozano-Perez, T., "Spatial planning: A configuration space approach", IEEE Trans. on Computers, C-32(2), 108-120, 1983.

[3] O. Khatib, "Real-time obstacle avoidance for manipulators and mobile robots", Int. J. of Robotics Research, vol. 5, no. 1, pp. 90-98, 1986.

[4] J. Borestein and Y. Koren, "Real-time obstacles avoidance for fast mobile robot", IEEE Trans. Syst. Man Cyber., vol. 19, no. 5, pp. 1179-1187, Sep./Oct. 1989.

[5] K. T. Song and J. C. Tai, "Fuzzy navigation of a mobile robot", Proc. of IEEE/RSJ International conference on Intelligent Robotics and Systems, pp. 621-627, 1992.

[6] F. G. Pin and H. Watanabe, "Using custom-designed VLSI fuzzy inferencing chips for the autonomous navigation of a mobile robot", Proc. of IEEE/RSJ International conference on Intelligent Robots and Systems, pp. 790-795, 1992.

[7] Prabir K. Pal and Asim Kar, "Mobile robot navigation using a neural net", Proc. of IEEE International Conference on Robotics and Automation, pp 1503-1508, 1995.

[8] C. Kozakiewwicz and M. Ejiri, "Neural network approach to path planning for two dimension robot motion", Proc. of IEEE/RSJ International Conference on Intelligent Robots and Systems, pp 818-823, 1991.

[9] H. R. Beom and H. S. Cho, "A sensor-based navigation for a mobile robot using fuzzy Logic and Reinforcement Learning", IEEE Trans. Syst. Man Cyber., vol. 25, No. 3, pp. 464-477, March, 1995.
Barto , R. S. Sutton, and C. W. Anderson, "neuronlike adaptive elements that can solve difficult learning control problems", IEEE Trans. Syst. Man Cyber., vol. SMC-13, no. 5, Sep./Oct.,1983.

On Integrating Domain Knowledge into Reinforcement Learning

Achim Hoffmann†, Bernd Freier† and ‡,
† School of Computer Science and Engineering, University of New South Wales
Sydney, Australia
‡ Student at the Australian Graduate School of Management, University of New South Wales
Sydney, Australia

Abstract— **Reinforcement learning attracted increasing interest in recent years. While reinforcement learners proved successful for certain problems with comparably small system state spaces, they tend to have severe problems when the system state space is larger. This paper introduces a method for integrating domain knowledge into the process of Q-learning, in order to allow significantly faster learning and good scale-up behavior for larger state spaces. We present experimental results in the domain of a simulated pole-and-cart system indicating the applicability and usefulness of the approach.**

1 Introduction

The automatic or semi-automatic generation of controllers for dynamic systems from a model of the system is of great practical importance. For complexity reasons, classical control theory deals essentially with linear models of systems. This limitation is perceived as an important issue because many practical systems are nonlinear when described in a 'natural way'. An example is the classical pole balancing problem. To overcome this shortcoming, different methods for coping with nonlinear systems have been proposed. Among them are Reinforcement Learning approaches, see e.g. [7, 11, 15] or recent NIPS, ICML or IJCAI proceedings for a number of papers, as well as Neural Networks, e.g. [1], and Genetic Algorithms, e.g. [14]. All these approaches face the problem of credit assignment: A control strategy can only be evaluated as a whole. If a strategy proves unsatisfactory, it is not clear how to alter the strategy to obtain improved performance. The mentioned learning approaches basically consider the system to be controlled as a black box. This appears in many cases unnecessarily restrictive. In [4] it has been shown, how learning can significantly be improved by employing qualitative together with causal domain knowledge. The learning algorithm employed, however, was not a reinforcement learner but rather tailored to exploit certain types of domain knowledge.

In this paper, we introduce an approach for the integration of causal domain knowledge into Reinforcement learning (Q-learning). The paper is organized as follows. The next section recalls Q-learning, which is the basis for our approach. Section 3 presents the types of domain knowledge which are used for augmenting Q-learning. Section 4 presents the novel approach of introducing domain knowledge into Q-learning. Section 5 presents a case study for applying the compiler where the basic concepts of the language will be illustrated. The conclusions are given in section 6.

2 Reinforcement learning

Reinforcement learning algorithms, such as the method of temporal differences (TD) [11] and Q-learning [15], were originally motivated by models of animal learning being inspired by the behavioral paradigms of classical and instrumental conditioning. Subsequently, these algorithms proved useful for solving problems of prediction and control in stochastic environments. Applications of reinforcement learning techniques currently being investigated range from noise-free game playing environments such as backgammon,[1] to possibly very noisy robotic environments [6].

There has been a variety of different reinforcement learning techniques proposed in the literature; a major class of such algorithms considered today is the class of temporal difference learners.

Temporal difference learners

Early work on temporal difference learners are found in [16, 2]. These temporal difference learners were all based on an evaluation of system states, where for each system state an estimate of the sum of all future rewards was determined. Q-learning, as it will be extended in this paper, was introduced in [15]. The

---

[1]In Backgammon reinforcement learning techniques have been successfully applied to develop systems capable of master-level play [12].

key advance here was to have an evaluation function of state/action pairs. This led to convergence and optimality proofs in Markov domains, which has the consequence, that the result of Q-learning becomes *experimentation insensitive* in such domains [15].

Q-Learning Q-learning is an algorithm which learns a table of reward estimates (Q-values) that are a mapping of state/action pairs to expected total future rewards (or payoffs).[2] I.e. the 'actual' Q-value for a state s and action a is given by

$$\hat{Q}(s,a) = E[\sum_{t=0}^{\infty} \gamma^t \cdot r(t)],$$

where $r(t)$ is the reward received at time step t given that an optimal policy of actions is followed. Q-learning learns the Q-values for each state/action pair by a successive approximation process. A current Q-value estimate $Q(s,a)$ is updated after a learning episode (an attempt to control the system using the current tabe of Q-values). The update takes place on the basis of the estimated payoff experienced after action a is executed from state s and its temporal difference to the respective estimate in state s for taking action a.

The update rule of 1-Step Q-learning is the following:

$$Q(s,a) := (1 - \beta)Q(s,a) + \beta y \tag{1}$$

where

$$y = r + \gamma \max_b Q(s',b) \tag{2}$$

where s' is the successor state of s after executing action a. The parameter γ is the discount factor indicating how a reward to be received one step later is valued at the time being. I.e. the value of a reward is considered to decrease exponentially the longer one has to wait for it. Finally, r is the immediate reward following the action a from state s. Rewards are received at each time-step, where rewards r may be 0. I.e. y represents the *accumulated discounted return* after the current time-step, also called the actual return.[3]

While Q-learning updates only those Q-values for state/action pairs actually taken in a learning trial, our new approach (see section 4) may also modify Q-values for state/action pairs which are not encountered but merely related to those encountered, according to the provided domain knowledge.

Intially, the table of state/action Q-values is set to 0. After an attempt to control the dynamic system, the achieved reward is used to update the Q-values. This is done by recalling the sequence of encountered states and the corresponding actions taken in reverse order using the formulas given above.

As the state/action Q-values $Q(s,a)$ estimate the payoff for taking action a in state s, a *policy action* for state s is the action with the highest estimated payoff (Q-value). As a consequence, an attempt to control a dynamic system using the current Q-value estimates uses normally the policy actions in each state. However, in order to allow also the exploration of new policies (control strategies), Q-learning deviates from the policy actions on a random basis. I.e. with a small probability a random action is taken instead of the policy action. Often, also in our experiments, a Boltzmann-like probability distribution is used, which takes the differences between the expected payoffs for different actions into account. I.e. the greater the differences, the less likely is the action taken with the worse estimate. In fact, the probability for taking a suboptimal action according to current estimates decreases exponentially with the difference in the estimates to the estimates for the policy action.

3 Domain knowledge

This section describes two types of domain knowledge which may be easy to be specified for a given dynamic system, even if the system in its detailed functionality is poorly understood. Such domain knowledge addresses both, constraining the set of admissible control strategies as well as guiding the order in which strategies are chosen for testing. These types of knowledge has been used initially in [4] for the pole balancing problem. In [5] it has been applied to the domain of trailer truck control. In this paper, it is used for the first time to support the process of reinforcement learning. Thus, the following recalls parts of [4].

---

[2] A state can also be considered to be defined by the currently perceived sensations, denoted by s.

[3] Of course, discounted future rewards assume that the optimal policy action will be taken in order to receive the respective rewards at a later stage.

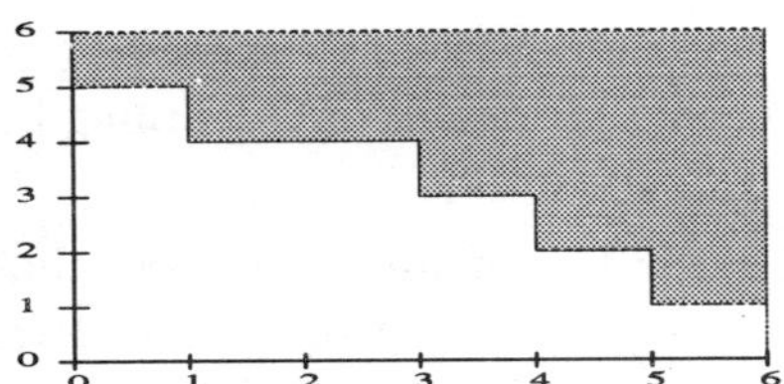 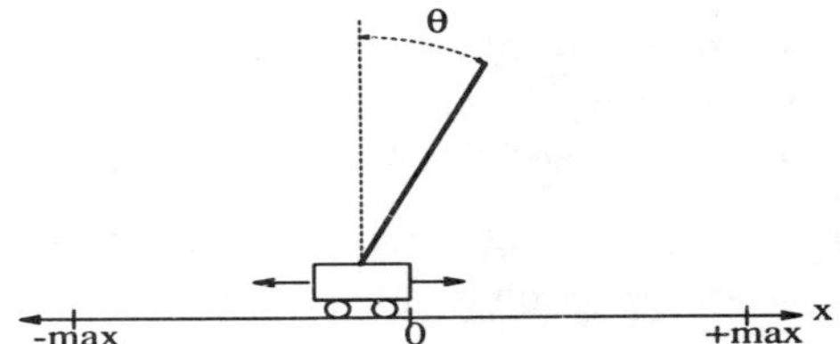

Figure 1: **Left:** The monotonicity constraint in the 2-dimensional variable space. The white area indicates the function value '0', while the shaded area represents '1'. The borderline is represented by a descending step function. The monotonicity is geometrically expressed by the fact that the shaded area extends uninterruptedly to the top and to the right. **Right:** The pole is hinged on the cart. The cart is moving and the control actions are to expose the cart to a fixed amount of force either to the left or to the right.

3.1   Qualitative knowledge for constraining the hypothesis space

The system allows to constrain the admissible control strategies by qualitative relationships between system states in which similar or equal control actions have to be taken. Recently, the problem of forming the class of considered control strategies by qualitative knowledge has been addressed, e.g. [13, 3, 14, 4]. In these investigations, not exclusively but mainly qualitative models *about the system* to be controlled were used. In the following, qualitative knowledge *about possible control strategies* is exploited without stating anything about the physics of the system.

In many domains, helpful restrictions of the set of control strategies which are common sense can be provided. The idea is to exclude strategies which are obviously absurd. For instance, in controlling a car on a curving road, the following monotonicity relation may be obvious: *If reducing speed is appropriate for taking a curve of radius r, then reducing speed is at least as appropriate for taking a curve of radius r', if $r' \leq r$.* In fact, it would be absurd attempting to take a curve of radius r', if it is already clear that a curve of radius r is too narrow for the current speed.

The mentioned type of monotonicity restrictions are treated in detail in [4]. We shortly sketch the multi-dimensional monotonicity constraints - see also Figure 1 (left), which can be defined as follows:

Definition 1 *We denote by $F_{mon,m}$ the set of functions f on m variables of the form $f : \{0, ..., k-1\}^m \rightarrow \{0, 1\}$ which are monotonic in all its variables. For all functions $f \in F_{mon,m}$ holds the following for all variables ranging in their respective domain:*

$$f(n_1, ..., n_m) = 1 \rightarrow f(n_1 + 1, n_2, ..., n_m) = 1 \ and$$

$$f(n_1, ..., n_m) = 1 \rightarrow f(n_1, n_2 + 1, ..., n_m) = 1 \ ... \ and \ ...$$

$$f(n_1, ..., n_m) = 1 \rightarrow f(n_1, n_2, ..., n_m + 1) = 1$$

Intuitively speaking, this generalization amounts to saying: *Everything else being equal (e.g. the road slope and surface, condition of car's tires and suspenders etc.), the smaller the radius, the slower the car has to go.*

3.2   Causal knowledge for guiding the choice of the next candidate

For guiding the credit (or blame) assignment, when a given control strategy turns out to be insufficient, obvious knowledge may be available, which can also be used for accelerating reinforcement learning significantly.

In the car example such domain knowledge may be as follows: *If the car is beginning to glide, then the speed was too high for the respective conditions of the car, the road, and the angle of the steering wheel.* Such knowledge may be very helpful in that it tells that a change of the control strategy resulting in even higher speed in the same situation is certainly no improvement.

More generally speaking, such knowledge may relate a class of possible states of failure to a class of control actions which had the potential to avoid the encountered failure. E.g. if the car is beginning to glide, some of the actions taken failed to slow down the car. The idea is, to provide knowledge which says for a particular state of failure what actions should have been taken. E.g. an applied force should be increased (decreased).

4 Integrating domain knowledge into Q-Learning

Temporal difference learners in general as well as Q-learning in particular appear not very suitable for taking domain knowledge as the one above into account. Reason for that is, that these algorithms maintain and incrementally approximate a state or state/action evaluations. If this process is disturbed by domain knowledge, their convergence properties are in jeopardy.

In the following, we introduce a cautious way of enhancing the normal update process of Q-learning in order to dramatically accelerate the overall learning speed.

The essential ideas are twofold:

1. The causal knowledge, as described above, can be used to determine for an action a_d for at least one encountered system state s, in which another action a_a has actually been taken. Thus, the Q-values for the actions of that state can be updated as follows: The action a_a, if it was the policy action, receives a slightly lower value than the desired action a_d currently has: I.e. $Q(s, a_a) \leftarrow (Q(s, a_d) - \varepsilon)$ for some small ε.

2. The qualitative knowledge for constraining the control strategies being considered can be integrated as follows: Whenever a Q-value is altered due to the causal knowledge as described above, all system states which need even more to ensure that the desired action a_d is taken, are respectively updated. I.e. let system state s' be required to take the same action a_d as in state s, then for all actions $a \neq a_d$: If $Q(s', a) \geq Q(s', a_d)$, then $Q(s, a) \leftarrow (Q(s, a_d) - \varepsilon)$. This ensures that for all system states specified by the qualitative knowledge will have the proper policy action.

The method above allows to modify the Q-values in accordance with the provided domain knowledge. These updates take place in addition to the normal updates of Q-learning. Thus, our method updates not only the Q-values for encountered state/action pairs, but may also update Q-values for state/action pairs related to those encountered, according to the provided domain knowledge.

First experimental evidence is provided in the following section, that the method does not disrupt the entire process of learning the Q-values based on temporal differences.[4]

5 Experimental results

The new approach has been tested on the problem of learning to balance a pole. The pole balancing problem is a popular domain for case studies on controlling nonlinear dynamic systems, as well as for reinforcement learning approaches. It is not only an attractive benchmark. It shows also similarities with control problems of practical importance, such as satellite altitude control [10]. A recent survey on approaches for learning to balance a pole can be found in [14]. The pole balancing system, see Figure 1 (right), consists of a pole which is hinged on a cart. The pole can swing in the vertical plane. The cart can be pushed to the right and left on a bounded track. The control task is to push the cart such that the pole stays balanced. The possible control actions are to apply a fixed force to the cart either to the left or to the right. This simple setting is also called *bang-bang regime*. The control decision can be made in small time intervals. Usually time intervals of a $\frac{1}{50}$ sec. are considered. A system state is described by the current position x of the cart on the track, its velocity $\dot{x}$ along the track, the angle θ of the pole and the pole's angle velocity $\dot{\theta}$.

In many papers, e.g. [1, 9, 8], this problem was used for experiments with the a state space representation of the system based on the division of the ranges of x, $\dot{x}$, θ into 3 intervals and 6 intervals for $\dot{\theta}$, resulting in 162 states. We ran standard Q-learning for comparison on this state space representation as well as on larger state spaces. In the following, the results are presented for two more state spaces, where the range of each variable is divided into 10 respectively 25 intervals. This led to state spaces of 10,000 and 390,625 states respectively.

Our approach clearly outperformed the standard Q-learning algorithm in all state spaces. All parameters of Q-learning were the same for the domain knowledge guided approach.

---

[4]This problem has been encountered in initial experiments when, e.g. selected Q-values where simply set to a fixed value.

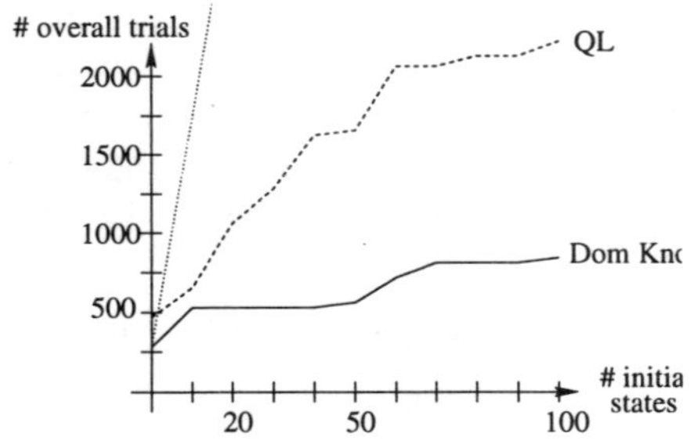

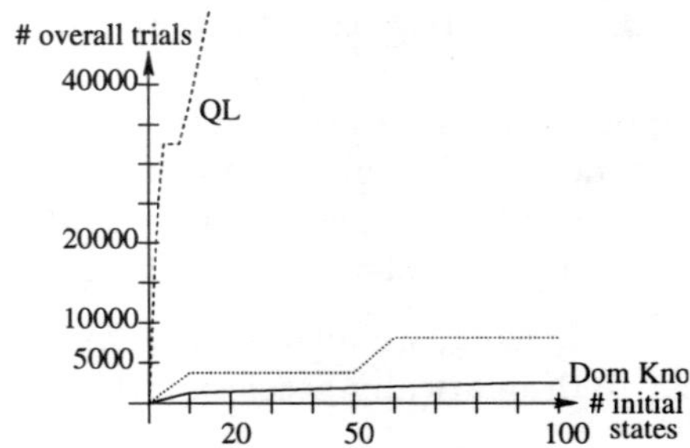

Figure 2: The charts show the overall number of trials before the nth initial system state was managed to be balanced. The left chart shows the results for the state space based on 10 intervals per variable, i.e. 10 000 states. The right chart shows the results for the state space based on 25 intervals per variable respectively, i.e. 390 625 states.. The solid lines show the results with the use of domain knowledge. The dashed lines show the Q-Learning results. The dotted lines give the results for Q-learning with the small state space of 162 states for comparison.

5.1   The domain knowledge used

The specified qualitative knowledge and causal knowledge is the same as in the experiments in [4] where a non-reinforcement approach was taken.

- **Causal knowledge:**
  - If the pole falls to the left side, then at least one control action which applied the force to accelerate the cart to the right has to be replaced by accelerating the cart to the left and vice versa.
  - If the cart exceeded the track to the left, then at least one control action which applied the force to accelerate the cart to the left has to be replaced by accelerating the cart to the right and vice versa.

- **Qualitative constraints:** If applying the force to the left is appropriate in a system state $S_0 = \langle x_0, \dot{x}_0, \theta_0, \dot{\theta}_0 \rangle$ *to balance the pole*, then it is also appropriate in each of the following four system states:

  1. $S_1 = \langle x_0, \dot{x}_0, \theta_0, \dot{\theta}_1 \rangle$, where $\dot{\theta}_1 < \dot{\theta}_0$, i.e. where the pole is even faster swinging to the left.
  2. $S_2 = \langle x_0, \dot{x}_0, \theta_2, \dot{\theta}_0 \rangle$, where $\theta_2 < \theta_0$, i.e. where the pole is even more inclined to the left.
  3. $S_3 = \langle x_0, \dot{x}_3, \theta_0, \dot{\theta}_0 \rangle$, where $\dot{x}_3 < \dot{x}_0$, i.e. where the cart is moving even faster to the left. (and therefore reaches earlier the left boundary of the track. Thus, it is even more important to move to the left, since a delayed movement would potentially exceed the boundary of the track.)
  4. $S_4 = \langle x_4, \dot{x}_0, \theta_0, \dot{\theta}_0 \rangle$, where $x_4 < x_0$, i.e. where the cart is even closer to the left boundary of the track. (Reason as above.)

  If applying the force to the left is appropriate in a system state $S_0 = \langle x_0, \dot{x}_0, \theta_0, \dot{\theta}_0 \rangle$ *to keep the cart on the track*, then it is also appropriate in each of the following two system states:

  1. $S_1 = \langle x_0, \dot{x}_1, \theta_0, \dot{\theta}_0 \rangle$, where $\dot{x}_1 > \dot{x}_0$, i.e. where the cart is moving even faster to the right.
  2. $S_2 = \langle x_2, \dot{x}_0, \theta_0, \dot{\theta}_0 \rangle$, where $x_2 > x_0$, i.e. where the cart is even closer to the right track boundary.

Initially the Q-values for both actions in all of the possible system states was set to 0. The system was initialized with a randomly chosen system state within the following intervals: $-0.5m \leq x \leq 0.5m$, $-6° \leq \theta \leq 6°$, $\dot{x}$ and $\dot{\theta}$ both zero.

The first simulation of the system resulted, as expected, in a pole fallen over to either side.

After each single learning step, the system was simulated again with the same initial state. This learning and test cycle was repeated until the pole was successfully balanced for a prespecified number of $100,000$ simulation steps ($2,000$ seconds). In each test run, the used learning algorithm had to manage to balance 100 different initial system states. Figure 2 shows, how many attempts were needed for balancing how many different initial system states.

6   Conclusions and Future Work

In this paper, we introduced a method for integrating qualitative and causal domain knowledge into reinforcement learning (Q-learning). We presented experimental evidence that the approach has the potential to significantly improve the learning speed and the reliability of the learning result. Furthermore, good scale-up potentials have been demonstrated as well. The taken approach, however, is not as generally applicable as Q-learning itself: It seems rather restricted to control tasks where the evaluation of a control policy is on a rather boolean scheme - either successful or not successful and that as a consequence, certain actions can sometimes be deemed 'absolutely inappropriate.' Future research will address the problem of allowing the integration of further types of domain knowledge in order to enhance the applicability of the approach to a larger class of problems. Another general problem is to deal with incorrect domain knowledge; reinforcement learning seems to be a particularly good framework for this problem.

Acknowledgement: The used pole-and-cart simulator was supplied by C. Sammut.

References

[1] C. W. Anderson. Strategy learning with multilayer connectionist representations. In *Proceedings of the 4th International Conference on Machine Learning*, pages 103–114. Morgan Kaufmann, 1987.

[2] A. Barto, R. Sutton, and C. Anderson. Neuronlike adaptive elements that can solve difficult learning control problems. *IEEE Transactions on Systems, Man, and Cybernetics,*

[3] I. Bratko. Deriving qualitative control for dynamic systems. In K. Furukawa and S. Muggleton, editors, *Machine Intelligence and Inductive Learning*. Oxford University Press. (new series of Machine Intelligence), to appear.

[4] A. G. Hoffmann. Exploiting causal domain knowledge for learning to control dynamic systems. In *Proceedings of the 11th European Conference on Artificial Intelligence*, pages 433–437, Amsterdam, The Netherlands, August 1994. Wiley & Sons.

[5] A. Hoffmann and S. Matsushima. Using easy-to-provide domain knowled ge for learning to control dynamic systems. In *Proceedings of the Australian Conference on Artificial Intelligence*, Canberra, Australia, November 1995.

[6] M. Mataric. Reward functions for accelerated learning. In W.Cohen and H.Hirsh, editors, *Proc. of Eleventh Int. Conf. on Machine Learning*. New Brunswick, New Jersey: Morgan Kaufmann, 1994.

[7] D. Michie and R. A. Chambers. BOXES: An experiment in adaptive control. In E. Dale and D. Michie, editors, *Machine Intelligence*, pages 137–152. Edinburgh: Oliver and Boyd, 1968.

[8] M. Pendrith, M. Ryan, and A. G. Hoffmann. Reinforcement learning algorithm for non-markovian and noisy domains reinforcement learning for cybernetic control. In *Proceedings of the 13th European Meeting on Cybernetics and Systems Research*, page to appear, Vienna, Austria, April 1996.

[9] C. Sammut. Experimental results from an evaluation of algorithms that learn to control dynamic systems. In *Proceedings of the 5th International Conference on Machine Learning*, pages 437–443. Morgan Kaufmann, 1988.

[10] C. Sammut and D. Michie. Controlling a "black box" simulation of a space craft. *AI Magazine*, (12):56–63, 1991.

[11] R. S. Sutton. Learning to predict by the methods of temporal difference. *Machine Learning*, (3):9–44, 1988.

[12] G. Tesauro. TD-Gammon, a self-teaching backgammon program, achieves master-level play. *Neural Computation*, 6:215–219, 1994.

[13] T. Urbancic and I. Bratko. Learning to control dynamic systems. In D. Michie and D. Spiegelhalter, editors, *Machine Learning, Neural and Statistical Classification*. Ellis Horwood, 1994.

[14] A. Varsek, T. Urbancic, and B. Filipic. Genetic algorithms in controller design and tuning. *IEEE Transactions on Systems, Man and Cybernetics*, SMC-23(6):1330–1339, 1993.

[15] C. J. Watkins. *Learning from delayed rewards*. PhD thesis, King's College, Cambridge, UK, 1989.

[16] I. Witten. An adaptive optimal controller for discrete-time Markov environments. *Information and Control*, 34:286–295, 1977.

Neuro-Adaptive Control of a Non-Minimum Phase System with Varying Time-Delay

Abdelmoumène TOUDEFT †&‡, Patrick GALLINARI †

† Laforia, BP 169, University of Paris 6
75252 Paris cedex 5, France
E-mail: gallinar@laforia.ibp.fr

‡ Irrigation Division, BP 5095, Cemagref
34033 Montpellier cedex 1, France
E-mail: moumene.toudeft@cemagref.fr

Abstract– **This paper deals with the control problem of a non-minimum phase discrete-time system with varying time-delay. The system we are dealing with is a simulated river. Regulation of such a system is usually performed under the assumption of a fixed time-delay. This is not realistic since the time taken by the water to go from the upstream to the downstream of the river is dependent on the average flow in the river. This paper shows that the use of neural networks in place of classical regulators allows to relax the assumption of a fixed time-delay and thus to build a more realistic controller.**

Since the plant is a non-minimum phase system, the command produced by the neural controller is highly oscillating. A controller structure is then proposed to solve this problem.

To deal with perturbations, a linear adaptive controller is added in parallel to the neural controller. A comparison with linear regulation is achieved.

1 Introduction

This paper deals with the neural control problem of a non-minimum phase discrete-time system with varying time-delay. Our system is a simulated river with perturbations corresponding to water withdrawals and unexpected inflows. The input and output are upstream and downstream flows, respectively. The goal of the controller is to propose the upstream flow so that the corresponding downstream flow is as close as possible to a reference trajectory defined in order to satisfy water users. Classical regulation of such a system is performed under the assumption of a fixed time-delay. Such an assumption causes several problems since the time taken by the water to go from upstream to downstream is dependent on the average flow in the river. This paper shows that the use of neural networks in place of classical regulators allows to overcome these problems.

Note that our plant is not a time-varying system but a nonlinear one, since the time-delay depends only on the region of operation.

Neural networks are known for their ability to model nonlinearities and have been recently widely used for the design of nonlinear controllers (eg. [1], [2]). They have been mainly used for learning control and in this sense are complementary to adaptive control techniques. The former allows to accomodate nonlinear dynamics, but is not adequate for time-varying dynamics and new situations. The latter is adequate for accomodating time-varying dynamics and new situations (like perturbations), but is not suitable for significant nonlinearities.

In this paper, a linear adaptive controller is used in parallel with a multi-layered neural network controller. The latter is used as a feedforward controller to compensate the variations of the time-delay. The adaptive controller is used as a feedback controller to deal with perturbations.

Because the plant is a non-minimum phase system, an adequate choice of the neural controller input vector is proposed so as to avoid oscillations of the command.

The plant is described in section 2. The problems mentionned above are illustrated in section 3 where a classical regulator is designed under the fixed time-delay assumption. In section 4, a neural network is used to model the plant and in section 5 the control problem is considered. A neural network open loop controller is first used to compensate the variations of the plant time-delay. To deal with perturbations a feedback adaptive controller is then added. The latter uses the predictions given by the model.

2 The plant

The plant considered here is a simulated river. It is a single input-single output system. The input u and the output y are the upstream and downstream flows, respectively. They are related by the following relation:

$$\frac{y}{u} = \frac{c + d.z^{-1}}{1 - a.z^{-1} + b.z^{-2}} . z^{-r(u_m)} \tag{1}$$

where: a=1.1692, b=-0.4102, c=0.1081, d=0.1318. $r(u_m)$ = truncated-value(delay(u_m)).

delay(u_m) = $\alpha . u_m^{\beta} . l$ α=0.55, β=-0.288, l=109 (km) is the river length (distance between upstream and downstream).

$u_m(t)$ is the average flow in the river:

$$u_m(t) = \frac{1}{2}\left(\frac{u(t-1)+\ldots+u(t-50)}{50} + \frac{y(t-1)+y(t-2)}{2} \right)$$

The considered region of operation is u,y $\in$ [5;10 m3/s]. All input/output data used in this study are moved to [-1;+1] by the transformation: T(x) = (x-7.5)/2.5

3 A reference controller: a pole placement regulator using a Smith predictor

In order to evaluate the neural controller, its performances are compared to the performances of a classical regulator designed for an average flow of 7.5 m3/s. For an optimal design of the regulator, equation (1) is supposed to be known in this section.

An exact linear model around 7.5 m3/s is obtained by replacing $r(u_m)$ by $r(7.5)=33$ in equation (1). A linear regulator (LR) defined by equation (2) is then incorporated into a Smith predictor scheme [3].

$$R(z^{-1}).z^{-33}.u = S(z^{-1}).y*(t) + T(z^{-1}).y_l(t) \qquad (2)$$

where $R(z^{-1})=1-r_1.z^{-1}$, $S(z^{-1})=s_1$, $T(z^{-1})=t_1.z^{-1}+t_2.z^{-2}$, y_l is the model output and $y*$ is the reference trajectory.

The pole-placement design is used to find values of the parameters of polynomials R, S and T such that the poles of the closed loop system (regulator+linear model) have pre-specified values. The dynamics of the closed-loop system depend on these pre-specified values. When these values are close to 0, fast dynamics are obtained but the command signal may contain strong transitions which can cause destruction of the control system. On the other hand, values close to 1 lead to slow dynamics. We have chosen the desired values of the poles equal to 0.5. Experiments have shown that this value achieves a good compromise. Figure 1(b,c,d) shows the performances of the corresponding regulator on the test reference trajectory y_t* corresponding to figure 1-a. The behaviour of this system clearly illustrates the varying time-delay problem when the fixed time-delay assumption is used. When the plant runs around 5 m3/s (Figure 1-b), 7.5 m3/s (Figure 1-c), and 10 m3/s (Figure 1-d), the water arrives to the river downstream respectively latter, at the same time, and earlier than desired. This is because the effective time-delay is respectively greater, equal, and smaller than the supposed one $r(7.5)=33$.

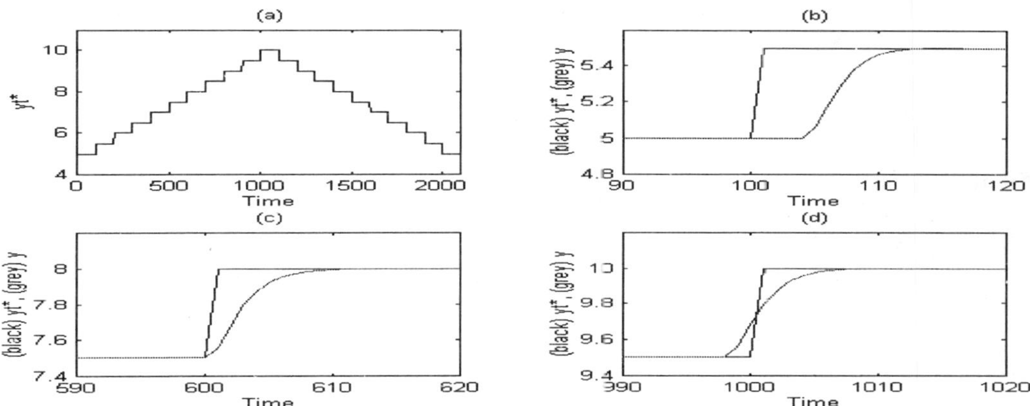

Figure 1. Performances of the linear regulator: (a) the whole test reference trajectory y_t*, and the plant output y and y_t*: (b) around 5 m3/s, (c) around 7.5 m3/s, (d) around 10 m3/s.

4 Plant Modeling

Simple simulations around 5 and 10 m3/s reveal that the plant output at time t can be affected by inputs which have been applied from (t-31) to (t-57). A multi-layered neural network with 10 sigmoïdal neurons in the hidden layer, one linear output neuron and 29 inputs is used to model the plant. The model equation is:

$$y_m(t)=F(y_m(t-1),y_m(t-2),u(t-31),...,u(t-57)) \qquad (3)$$

where F is the function implemented by the neural network model.

The back-propagation learning algorithm [4] is used with a constant learning rate of 0.001. The network parameters are adapted each time-step in order to minimize the error between plant and network outputs. This latter is computed when the plant and the network are run with an input signal u. When u was a sequence u_1 of steps with amplitudes and lengths uniformly distributed in [5;10] and [1;20] respectively, it was not possible to obtain a good model. This is because such a signal does not allow to span uniformly the region of operation. This problem was solved by changing u to u_2, a sum of two signals (figure 2): a sequence of steps x to x+1 with $x \in \{5; 5.2; 5.4;...;8.6;8.8;9\}$, where each step length is 100, is added to a sequence of steps with amplitudes and lengths uniformly distributed in [-0.5;+0.5] and [1;20], respectively. Figure 3 shows a comparison of the neural model and the linear model when the region of operation is close to 5 m3/s (a), 7.5 m3/s (b), and 10 m3/s (c). Although the neural model has been identified without any prior knowledge on the plant dynamics, its performances around 7.5 m3/s are similar to the exact linear model. Far from 7.5 m3/s, the neural model outperforms the linear model and appears to be able to learn the varying time-delay characteristic of the plant.

5 Plant Control

5.1 Feed-Forward Learning Control

The plant neural network model is now used to implement a distal learning approach [5]. The controller is a multi-layered neural network with 10 sigmoïdal neurons in the hidden layer and one linear output neuron. The controller output is the command u(t). According to equation (3), the network input vector was $[y*(t+31),y_m(t+30),y_m(t+29),u(t-1),...,u(t-26)]^T$.

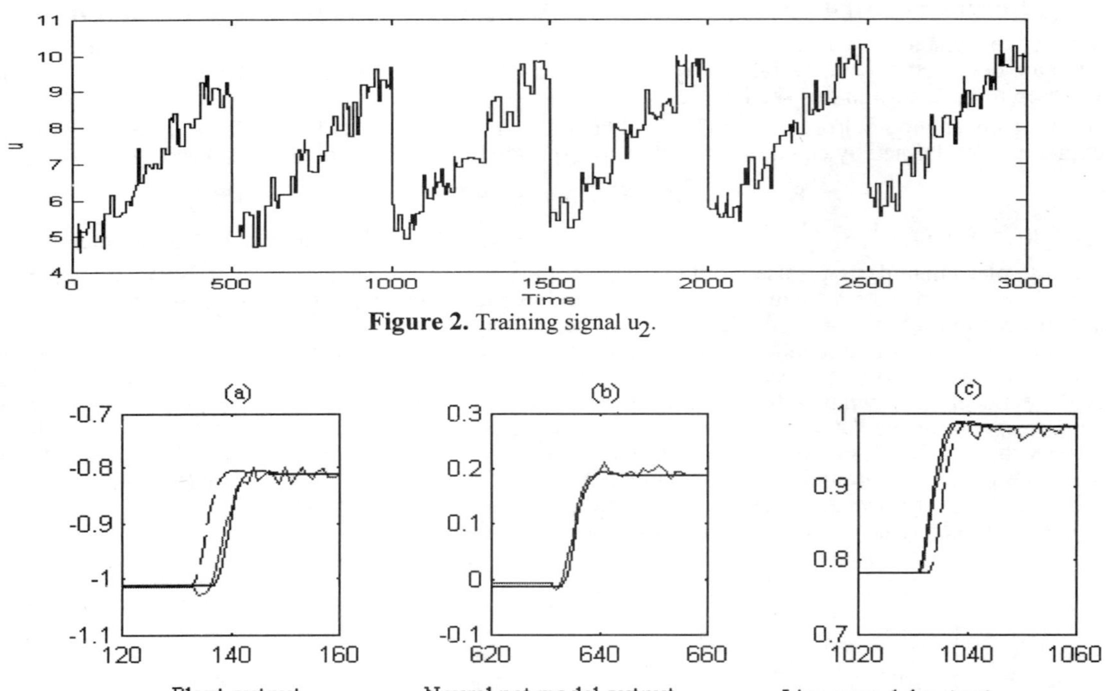

Figure 2. Training signal u_2.

Figure 3. Plant, neural and linear models outputs around: (a) 5m3/s, (b) 7.5 m3/s (plant and linear model outputs are identical), (c) 10 m3/s.

Let NNC denotes this controller structure.

The controller parameter vector w is adapted according to rule (4) where the gradient at the control level is obtained by back propagating the error through the model without modifying its parameters.

$$\Delta w(t) = -\alpha.(y(t)-y^*(t)).\frac{\partial y_m(t)}{\partial w(t)} \qquad (4) \qquad \Delta w(t) = -\alpha.(y_m(t)-y^*(t)).\frac{\partial y_m(t)}{\partial w(t)} \qquad (5)$$

The learning process is performed with a reference signal y* equal to the plant output when its input is u_2. This means that the ideal command is $u^*=u_2$. It can be used to evaluate the methods presented in this paper. u* is supposed to be unknown by the learning system.

In order to evaluate the controllers performances the following criteria are defined:

$$\text{TMSE} = \frac{1}{N}\sum_{t=1}^{N}(y_t^*(t)-y_t(t))^2 \qquad \text{LMSE} = \frac{1}{N}\sum_{t=1}^{N}(y^*(t)-y(t))^2$$

$$\text{MSTC} = \frac{1}{N}\sum_{t=1}^{N}(u_t(t)-u_t(t-1))^2 \qquad \left\|u^*-u\right\| = \sqrt{\sum_{t=1}^{N}(u^*(t)-u(t))^2}$$

where u, y are respectively the controller and the model outputs when the learning reference trajectory y* is used. u_t, y_t are the controller and the plant outputs when the test reference trajectory y_t^* is used.

Several experiments have been conducted with equation (4), with different learning rates and different initial weights values. The learning process did not converge (figure 4-a).

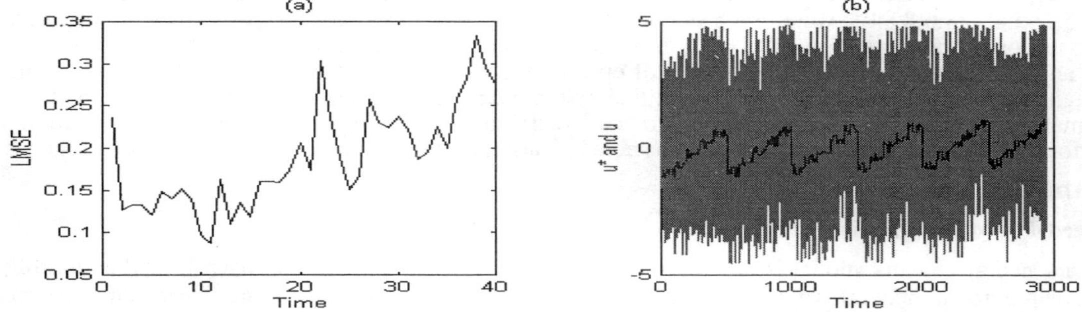

Figure 4. (a) Typical evolution of the learning mean-square error. (b) Ideal command u* and command u generated by the controller.

Because the plant is a non-minimum phase system, the command signal was highly oscillating and its range was out of the interval [-1;+1] where the model has been identified (figure 4-b).

When the learning rule was changed from (4) to (5), the learning process converged better than previously because the gradient used is now exactly that of the learning error $(y_m(t)-y^*(t))$. However, after the learning process was stopped, the command signal generated by the neural controller on the test reference trajectory y_t^* was still highly oscillating. For this reason, the controller input vector was changed as described below.

The plant output at time t can be affected by all inputs applied from (t-31) to (t-57). Conversely, the input at time t can affect all outputs from (t+31) to (t+57). The vector $[y^*(t+31),...,y^*(t+57)]^T$ is then used as input to the controller. This means that the command is computed in a non-recursive way. This controller structure is denoted NRC in the following.

Since the controller input vector contains more information, the control law is well defined and the learning process may converge better than previously. Table 1 summarises the performances of the linear regulator and the neural controllers obtained after 2000 learning iterations. The test was done on the test reference trajectory y_t^*.

	LMSE	$\|u^*-u\|$	TMSE	MSTC
NNC	0.0080	10.0910	28×10^{-4}	803×10^{-4}
NRC	0.0021	2.9787	2.1667×10^{-4}	7.5429×10^{-4}
LR	---	---	8.3429×10^{-4}	28×10^{-4}

Table1. Performances of linear and neural controllers.

The NRC structure appears to be superior to the NNC structure. The adequate choice of the controller input vector allows the learning process to converge and to avoid command oscillations during both the learning and the test. Also, the NRC outperforms the linear regulator LR.

However, the NRC being an open loop controller, it is not able to deal with perturbations. This problem is considered below.

5.2 Feedback Adaptive Control

In order to handle perturbations, we have added a feedback adaptive controller in parallel to the NRC. The command applied to the plant is then a sum of a feedforward command u_{ff} and a feedback command u_{fb}. The perturbations considered here are additive, i.e. the plant output is $y_s=y+p$, where y is given by equation (1). The perturbation p may correspond to a water withdrawal (p<0) or to a lateral inflow (p>0). p is also a sum of an expected perturbation p_e and an unexpected one p_u. Expected perturbations can be handled by simply using y^*-p_e as the NRC input instead of y^*. Unexpected perturbations are handled by the feedback controller.

Because the feedback command must be nonzero as long as the unexpected perturbation p_u is nonzero, the feedback controller input must be $-p_u=y-y_s+p_e$. Since y is not available, it is estimated via the model output. The control system then becomes sensitive to modeling errors and linear regulation leads to bad results even if $p_u=0$. This is because the linear model output can be far from y (see figure 3) which leads to a useless reaction of the feedback controller. The overall architecture is shown on figure 5.

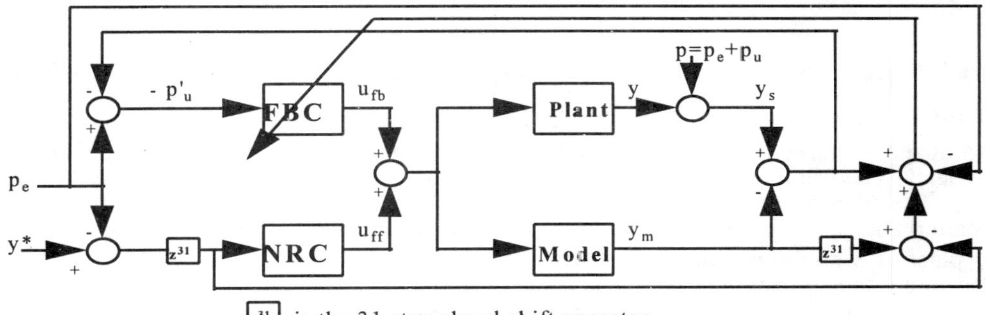

$\boxed{z^{31}}$ is the 31 step ahead shift operator.

Figure 5. Control system architecture: FBC=feedback adaptive controller, NRC=feedforward neural controller, p'_u is an estimation of p_u because unknown y is replaced by y_m. See text for details.

For the feedback controller, we have used a feedback gain w adapted by the Widrow-Hoff rule [6]. Note that the adaptation error was not backpropagated through the model because the sign of the plant static gain is known to be constant (positive). If this had not been the case, backpropagation through the model would have been necessary.

Suppose that the model is exact and the feedforward controller generates the command that leads to a zero output error in the abscence of perturbations. Then, under this assumption, an analysis similar to that given in [7] shows that for the overall system to be linear with respect to the perturbation, the gain adaptation rate has to be choosen equal to $\theta/(p_u^2)$, where θ is a constant. To avoid division by zero, this value is changed to $\theta/(p_u^2+\varepsilon)$, where ε is a small positive value (we have used $\theta=0.01$ and $\varepsilon=0.01$). The fact that the system is linear with respect to the perturbation guarantees that this latter is handled with the same dynamics, whatever its amplitude is. Consequently, it is sufficient to ensure the stability for only one value of p_u.

The neural control architecture was compared with a linear control architecture similar to that on figure 5 but where LR (eq. (2)) was used as a feedforward controller in parallel with a constant feedback gain equal to 1.

The comparison was done under the following conditions: the controller has to keep the plant output as close as possible to y*=-0.6 (recall that all the values are moved to [-1;+1]). We have considered the expected and unexpected perturbations shown on figure 6-a and 6-b, respectively. The adaptive gain was initialized to 0.8.

Figure 7 shows the results. Clearly, even in the absence of unexpected perturbations (i.e. when p_u=0), the feedback command is nonzero. This is due to the use of y_m-y_s+p_e as the feedback controller input instead of y-y_s+p_e. Consequently, the modelization errors cause useless reactions of the feedback controller. Because in the linear case these errors are large, large plant output errors are obtained. For dealing with unexpected perturbations, both controllers exhibit similar performances. However, the overall performances of the neuro-adaptive controller outperform the performances of the linear architecture. For example, in our experiment, the former allows to save on the average 119.2253 m3 each hour more than does the latter. Still, further theoritical analysis is needed to derive conditions on θ to insure stability.

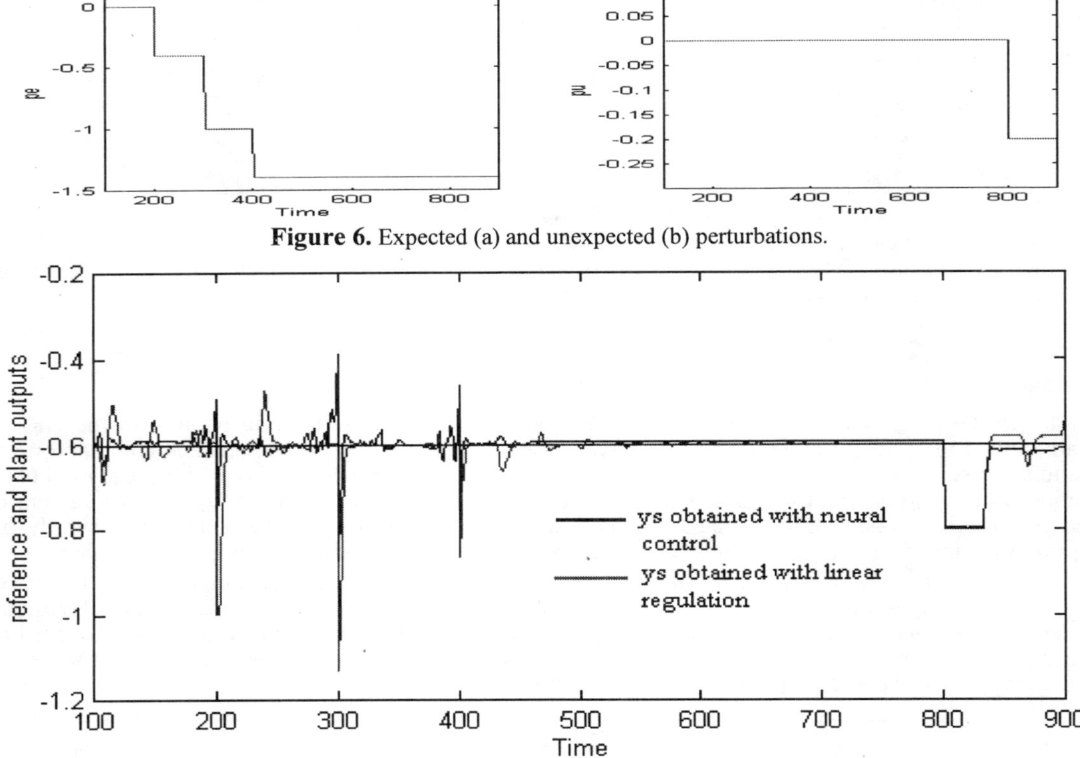

Figure 6. Expected (a) and unexpected (b) perturbations.

Figure 7. Constant reference output y*=-0.6 and the plant outputs when neural and linear control were used.

6 Conclusion

Learning and adaptive controllers are combined to control a non-minimum phase discrete-time system with varying time-delay. The learning controller is used as a feedforward controller to compensate the variations of the time-delay. The adaptive controller is used as a feedback controller to deal with perturbations. To detect unexpected perturbations, this latter uses predictions given by a neural network plant model.

Because the plant is a non-minimum phase system, its inverse dynamics are ill-defined. A suitable neural controller structure is then proposed to avoid command oscillations.

The neuro-adaptive control architecture is compared with a linear control architecture.

References

[1] D.A. White and D.A. Sofge, (Eds), *Handbook of Intelligent Control: Neural, Fuzzy, and adaptive approaches*. Van Nostrand Reinhold, 1992.

[2] W.T. Miller, R.S. Sutton, and P.J. Werbos, (Eds), *Neural Networks for Control*. MIT Press, 1990.

[3] O.J.M. Smith, "A controller to overcome dead-time", *Instrument Society of America Journal*, vol. 6, N°2, 1959.

[4] D.E. Rumelhart, G.E. Hinton and R. Williams, "Learning internal representations by propagation", in *Parallel Distributed Processing*, vol 1, D. Rumelhart, J. McClelland (eds.), MIT Press, 1986.

[5] M.I. Jordan, and D.E. Rumelhart, "Forward Models: Supervised Learning with a Distal Teacher", *Cognitive Science*, 16, pp. 307-354, 1992.

[6] B. Widrow, and M.E. Hoff, "Adaptive Switching Circuits", *Inst. of Radio Eng., West. Elect. Show and Convention, Convention record*, part 4, pp. 96-104, 1960.

[7] A. Toudeft, P. Kosuth and P. Gallinari, "A PID Neural Controller for Unstable Delayed Linear Systems", *Proc. Inter. Conf. on Artificial Neural Networks*, Sorrento, Italy, May 26-29, 1994.

Neural Dynamic Routing for Robust Teletraffic Control

W. K. Felix Lor and K. Y. Michael Wong
Department of Physics, The Hong Kong University of Science and Technology,
Clear Water Bay, Kowloon, Hong Kong.
E-mail addresses: phfelix@usthk.ust.hk, phkywong@usthk.ust.hk

Abstract— **We study the performance of a neural dynamic routing algorithm on the circuit-switched network under critical network situations. It consists of a teacher generating examples for supervised learning in a group of student neural controllers. Simulations show that the method is robust and superior to conventional routing techniques.**

1   Introduction

In telecommunications networks, resources (such as links, bandwidths or buffers) have to be allocated among a large number of interacting components to accommodate a dynamical and evolving demand. Its optimization is often too complicated for real-time computation. Effective control are especially essential during critical situations such as sudden rise in demand, link failures and unbalanced load. Recently, neural computing became an attractive approach in this area, since neural networks are adaptable to an evolving environment, and are able to make a quick decision once they have learned the control function. Most work in this area involve the reinforcement learning approach, but their responses are slow. Since in many cases model-based control algorithms are available, we propose a supervised learning approach, in which examples for optimal control are collected and used to train the controllers.

Many centralized and decentralized algorithms for dynamic routing have been proposed. In centralized algorithms, networkwide information are collected and a globally optimal decision can be made. However, this approach may involve heavy computational load, heavy load in the signaling network, and is susceptible to network breakdown. On the other hand, decentralized algorithms assign the control task to a group of local controllers, and thus reduce the computational load and the risks of network breakdown, but the local routing decisions may not be globally optimal. We propose to use neural networks to combine the strengths of both approaches. Given a training set of globally optimal decisions, a local neural controller learns to infer decisions based on locally available information. Recent work showed that such an approach reduces blocking and crankback probabilities in equilibrium situations [1]. Here we consider critical network situations such as high traffic profile, network breakdown, bursty traffic and unbalanced load, and demonstrate that the neural controllers have robust performances.

2   The Network Model

Consider the hierarchical circuit-switched network, which consists of serving stations connecting directly to the subscribers, and the tandems which are intermediate stations to accommodate the traffic between the serving stations. There are direct links between the serving stations, and indirect ones to and from the serving stations and tandems, each link consisting of many channels. To connect an attempted call, a channel in the direct link is first searched. If all channels are occupied, a channel through a tandem will be sought according to the routing algorithm. If the indirect path of first choice is full, the call will be crankbacked to a path of second choice and so on. When all choices are exhausted, the call is blocked. In our model, we assume all the links are uni-directional. Calls are randomly generated from station i to k at a rate of v_{ik}, and randomly terminated at a rate of μ.

3   Dynamic Routing Methods

In dynamic routing, the routing algorithm is updated periodically according to the network condition, the updating period T being typically 5 seconds. Many dynamic routing schemes were proposed for circuit-switched networks. The most common types are Least Loaded Path (LLP) based [2] and Markov Decision Process (MDP) based [3] routing schemes. One of the LLP based routing algorithm is Maximum Free Circuit Routing (MFC) [4] which is the foundation of Real Time Network Routing (RTNR) [5] used in AT&T telephone network. It sets up an alternate call by selecting the least congested path. Chan and Yum proposed an improved routing method called the Maximum Mean Time to Blocking (MTB) [6]. It is an MDP based routing scheme. It considers not only the trunk status, but also the traffic. According to trunk status and call arrival rate, the time that the link is first blocked is calculated at the equilibrium condition. This method involves rather heavy matrix computation.

Recently, we proposed the Decentralized Neural Routing [7]. This routing scheme is an adapative robust control which can deal with various overload situations. Instead of using fixed routing tables during the period T, the method uses routing ratios to increase the flexibility in distributing calls throughout the network. It composes of two parts: teacher routing and student routing. The teacher samples the global trunk and traffic information, and compute the optimal control decisions off-line. These examples are then fed to the students for supervised learning, each located at a serving station.

3.1   The Teacher Routing Algorithm

Consider a network configuration whose links have the capacities D_{ik} for the direct link from station i to k, $N_{ij}^{(i)}$ for the link from station i ingoing to tandem j, and $N_{jk}^{(o)}$ from tandem j outgoing to station k. Suppose that at the beginning of an updating period, the number of vacancies in the respective links are d_{ik}, $n_{ij}^{(i)}$ and $n_{jk}^{(o)}$. To estimate the number of available channels in the indirect links in the next period, we take into account the averaged disconnection rate and arrive at

$$\tilde{n}_{ij}^{(i)} = n_{ij}^{(i)} + \frac{1}{2}\left(N_{ij}^{(i)} - n_{ij}^{(i)}\right)T\mu, \quad \tilde{n}_{jk}^{(o)} = n_{jk}^{(o)} + \frac{1}{2}\left(N_{jk}^{(o)} - n_{jk}^{(o)}\right)T\mu. \tag{1}$$

Similarly, the effective call arrival rate for the indirect links are, taking into account the connection and disconnection rates in the direct links,

$$\tilde{v}_{ik} = \max\left(v_{ik} - \frac{d_{ik}}{T} - \frac{1}{2}(D_{ik} - d_{ik})\mu, 0\right). \tag{2}$$

Let r_{ik}^j be the routing ratio originating from node i linking through tandem j and terminating at node k. The time-to-blocking $\tau_{ij}^{(i)}$ and $\tau_{jk}^{(o)}$, respectively of the links from station i to tandem j and from tandem j to station k, are estimated as

$$\tau_{ij}^{(i)} = \frac{\tilde{n}_{ij}^{(i)}}{\sum_k \tilde{v}_{ik} r_{ik}^j}, \quad \tau_{jk}^{(o)} = \frac{\tilde{n}_{jk}^{(o)}}{\sum_i \tilde{v}_{ik} r_{ik}^j}. \tag{3}$$

The routing ratios are calculated by maximizing the minimum time-to-blocking with the use of the simplex algorithm. In most cases, the number of routing ratios is more than the number of independent constraints, hence the routing ratios cannot be uniquely determined. This degeneracy is broken by maximizing the second minimum time-to-blocking in the degenerate solution space, and so on.

3.2   The Student Routing Algorithm

After collecting examples of routing ratios generated by centralized simplex routing, we can use them to train the neural students. A single-layered neural network is implemented at each serving station. The inputs of neural controllers are their local information of trunk status and call arrival rate. All the inputs are normalized by their averages. To increase their weighting near congestion, we use the quadratic function of the trunk status as inputs. For an input vector $\vec{\sigma}$, the local field for a path from i to k through j is given by:

$$h_{ik}^j = \sum_l J_{(ijk)l}\sigma_l \tag{4}$$

where $J_{(ijk)l}$ is the synaptic matrix to be determined by the training process. The output for each path O_{ik}^j is the routing ratio computed by the neural controller. It is normalized with a partition function so that the routing ratios through all tandems between a pair of nodes sum up to 1.

$$O_{ik}^j = \frac{e^{h_{ik}^j}}{\sum_{j'\in J'} e^{h_{ik}^{j'}}}, \tag{5}$$

where J' is the index set of all indirect links of the node pair i & k. Learning is done by gradient descent of an energy function E with a learning rate η.

$$E = \frac{1}{2}\sum_{ijk}(r_{ik}^j - O_{ik}^j)^2. \tag{6}$$

$$\Delta J_{(IJK)L} = \eta\sigma_L O_{IK}^J[(r_{IK}^J - O_{IK}^J) - \sum_j (r_{IK}^j - O_{IK}^j)O_{IK}^j]. \tag{7}$$

4   Simulations Results

We apply the decentralized neural routing to several critical situations. For comparison, MFC routing is also tested. The following simulations are executed for 50,000 seconds and the data points are averaged over 10 samples.

4.1   High Traffic

The simulation was done on a network with 7 stations and 4 tandems (7-4-7), with dimensions and traffic based on part of the Hong Kong metropolitan network. We train the neural controllers using examples generated at the load of 25 calls per second. During operation the network traffic is increased from 23 to 33 calls per second. Figs. 1 & 2 show the blocking probability and crankback percentage. They yield performances better than MFC routing and comparable to the centralized simplex routing algorithm. Therefore, the low traffic controller can adapt to high traffic situations.

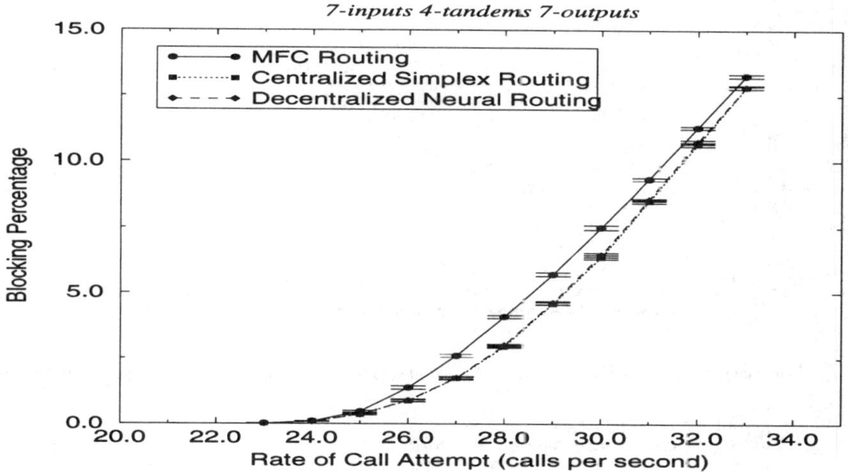

Figure 1: Blocking probability of a 7-4-7 network with the use of low traffic controller.

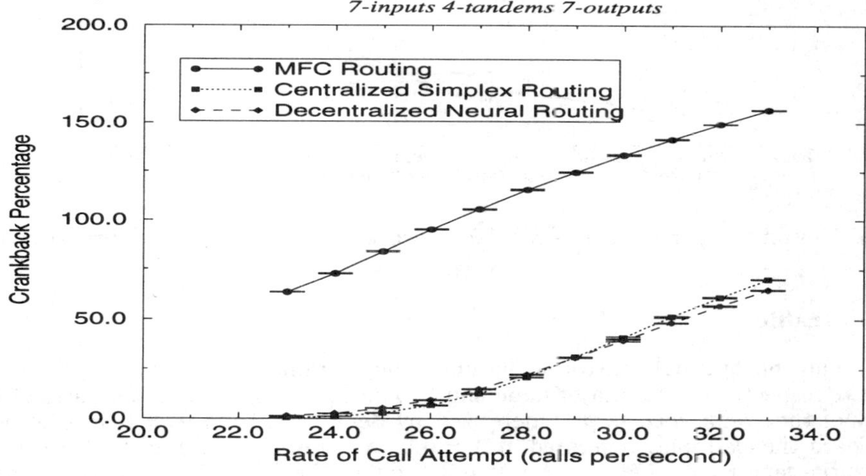

Figure 2: Crankback percentage of a 7-4-7 network with the use of low traffic controller.

4.2 Network Breakdown

We consider the 7-4-7 network and implement the neural controllers trained at normal network situations. Figs. 3 & 4 show the situation when a link from a major station to a tandem breaks down. Decentralized neural routing yields a blocking probability and crankback percentage better than MFC routing and comparable with centralized simplex routing.

4.3 Bursty Traffic

In reality, there are a lot of unpredicted catastrophes that suddenly affect the traffic. For example, when a typhoon signal is hoisted, swarms of people dial a phone call to notify their family, and the teletraffic will be increased abruptly. Most routing schemes cannot respond fast enough to accommodate this disturbed environment. However, decentralized neural routing can still minimize the blocking and crankback events under such a situation, as shown in Fig. 5. The blocking probabilities for MFC, simplex and neural routing are 1.5%, 1.2% and 1.0% respectively. The crankback percentage for MFC is 77% while for simplex and neural are 8% and 7% only.

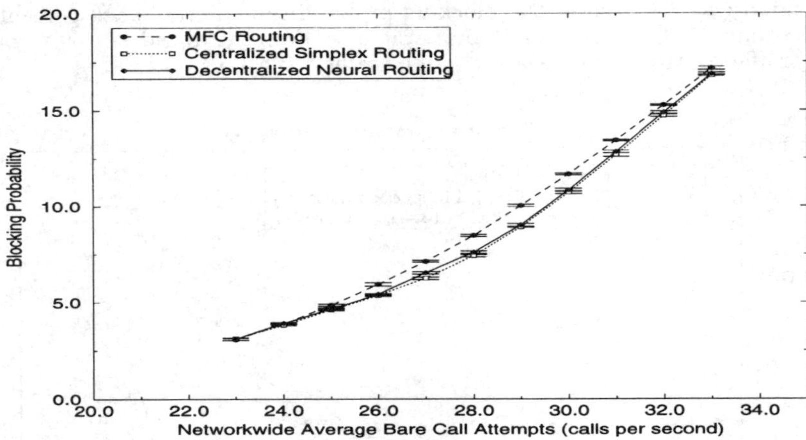

Figure 3: Blocking probability of a 7-4-7 network during a major link breakdown.

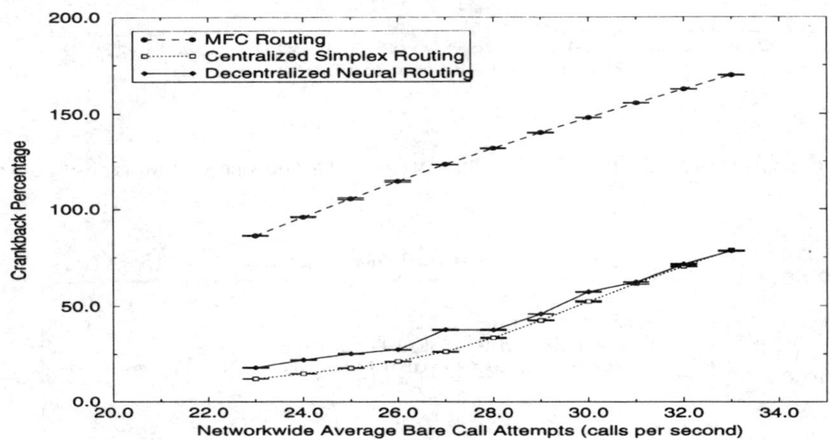

Figure 4: Crankback percentage of a 7-4-7 network during a major link breakdown.

4.4 Unbalanced Traffic

Another situation requiring optimal control is the unbalanced traffic. We simulate a 2-2-3 network, in which calls terminate respectively at a major node and two background nodes in the ratio of $1 : \lambda : 1 - \lambda$. The asymmetricity of the traffic load is parameterized by deviations from $\lambda = 0.5$. The decentralized neural controllers learn the examples generated at $\lambda = 0.3$. As shown in the Fig. 6, decentralized neural routing They give surpassing results between $\lambda = 0$ and $\lambda = 0.6$. For $\lambda > 0.6$, they also give performances comparable with simplex.

5 Conclusions

We have studied the performance of a decentralized neural routing in the circuit-switched network and showed that it can adapt its control function to various critical network situations such as high traffic, network breakdown, bursty traffic and unbalanced load. The neural controllers are single-layered neural networks, and it is unlikely that it can learn the complete control function taught by the teacher algorithm. Yet its success is based on the provision of a training set generated by a teacher controller dealing with the most common traffic scenarios. Further improvement in versatility is possible by combining the training examples of various traffic and network scenarios, normal and abnormal. In such cases, a multi-layered network or a committee of networks may be necessary. Research along this direction is in progress.

We thank Hong Kong Telecom for providing dimensioning and traffic data on part of the Hong Kong metropolitan network. This work was supported by the Hong Kong Telecom Institute of Information Technology, HKUST.

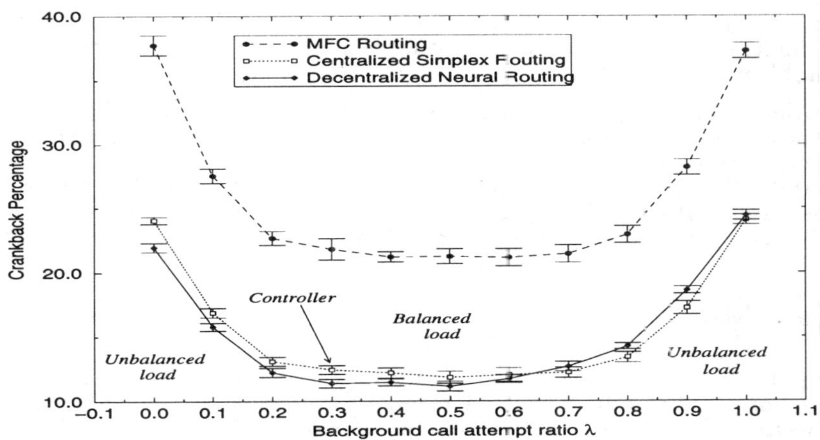

Figure 5: Network performance of bursty traffic profile during typhoon.

Figure 6: Crankback percentage of a 2-2-3 network with asymmetric traffic.

References

[1] W. K. Felix Lor, and K. Y. Michael Wong, "Decentralized Neural Dynamic Routing in Circuit-Switched Networks," *Proceedings of International Workshop on Applications of Neural Networks in Telecommunications (IWANNT*95)*, pp. 137–144, 1995.

[2] J. Regnier, P. Blodeau, and W. H. Cameron, "Grade of Service of a Dynamic Call Routing System," presented at the *Tenth International Teletraffic Congress*, June, 1983.

[3] T. J. Ott, and K. R. Krishnan, "State Dependent Routing of Telephone Traffic and the Use of Separable Routing Schemes," presented st the *Eleventh International Teletraffic Congress*, September, 1985.

[4] Eric W. M. Wong, and Peter T. S. Yum, "Maximum Free Circuit Routing in Circuit-Switched Networks," in *Proceedings of the Conference on IEEE INFOCOM '90*, vol. 3, pp. 934–937, 1990.

[5] G. R. Ash, J. S. Chen, A. E. Frey, and B. D. Huang, "Real-time Network Routing in a Dynamic Class-of-service Network," presented at the *Thirteenth International Teletraffic Congress*, Copenhagen, Demark, June 19-26, 1991.

[6] K. M. Chan, and Peter T. S. Yum, "The Maximum Mean Time to Blocking Routing in Circuit-Switched Networks," *IEEE Journal on Selected Areas in Communications*, vol. 12, no. 2, pp. 313–321, February, 1994.

[7] Felix W. K. Lor, "Neural Routing in Circuit-Switched Networks," *MPhil. thesis*, The Hong Kong University of Science & Technology, 1995.

Recursive Neural Networks as an Hypothesis Tester for Deinterleaving Repetitive Sequences

G. Noone, S. D. Howard

Electronic Warfare Division, Defence Science and Technology Organisation

PO Box 1500 Salisbury, South Australia 5108

email: Greg.Noone@dsto.defence.gov.au & Stephen.Howard@dsto.defence.gov.au

Abstract— Conventional algorithms for deinterleaving repetitive sequences, such as radar pulse trains, experience great difficulties when two or more of the sequences are significantly jittered. Such algorithms are usually variations of simple sequence search type techniques which are unable to intelligently test whether the captured sequence is actually periodic or not. In addition, such scenarios tend to lead to overwhelming ambiguity and fragmentation difficulties when using traditional techniques. In this paper we propose a modified sequence search technique combined with a novel recursive neural network approach. The sequence search forms the hypothesis that a given chain of events is periodic and the neural network is used to intelligently test this hypothesis. This approach has been used to allow the satisfactory deinterleaving of multiple jittered radar pulse trains.

1   Introduction

An obvious, but quite general, example of a repetitive sequence is a radar pulse train. Each radar emits a sequence of pulses whose times of arrivals (TOAs) are regularly spaced. The interception of several such signals leads to an interleaved sequence of times of arrivals. From this interleaved mixture, the individual pulse trains need to be separated out (i.e. deinterleaved). This is often referred to as the TOA deinterleaving problem.

Traditionally, variations of simple sequence search type techniques have been used with some success [2], [3]. However, as with all sequence search type algorithms, there appears to be overwhelming ambiguity and fragmentation problems when the scenario contains more than one pulse train with significant *timing jitter*. We are not aware of any such algorithm reporting the successful *deinterleaving* of two or more pulse trains with *significant* amounts of jitter. Hence we are provided with the motivation of "robustifying" the standard deinterleaving algorithm to cope with real life complexities.

2   Pulse Train Model

A general radar pulse train model is given in Figure 1. We assume that the pulse train is either strictly periodic, staggered or cumulatively jittered. A recursive expression which can describe such pulse trains is, where y_t is the *time of arrival* of the t'th pulse of a train:

$$(1) \qquad y_t = y_{t-1} + T_{t \bmod M} + \nu_t$$

where an M level staggered pulse train consists of M interleaved periodic pulse trains with the same Pulse Repetition Interval (PRI) offset from each other by time amounts of $T_1, .., T_M$ and ν_t represents any cumulative jitter that may distort the TOA measurements. The source of this jitter noise may be from the receiver, the emitter or both, and may be intentional or unintentional. Note that equation (1) describes, in effect, a general noisy discrete period M function.

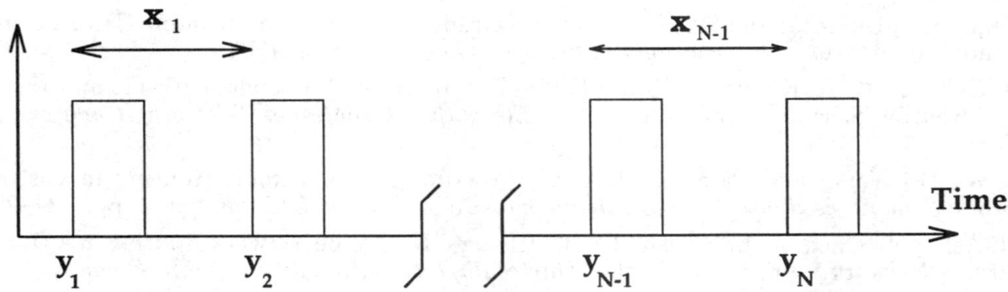

Figure 1: A general pulse train description. In the ideal problem where there is complete data and no jitter, the x_i's refer to the stagger offsets. If there is a "1-level" stagger, we recover a simple periodic pulse train where the Pulse Repetition Interval= x_i.

3 Pulse Train Deinterleaving

It is a common Electronic Warfare problem to experience radar pulse trains from multiple emitters being received at the one electronic site. From this interleaved mixture, the individual pulse trains need to be separated out (i.e. deinterleaved). It is usually not possible to infer directly from the interleaved data set the number of emitters present except for the most simple of cases. The final stage of the problem is to then extract the individual pulse train signal parameters and to identify the signal. A simple block description of the problem is given in Figure 2

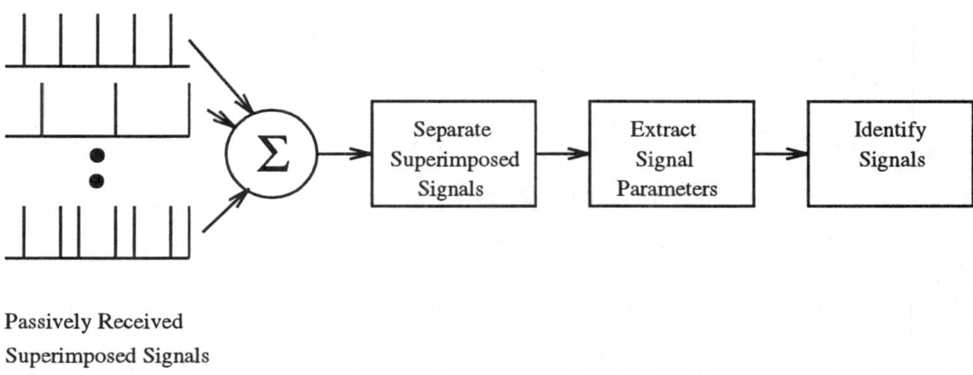

Figure 2: Pulse train TOA deinterleaving description.

In this challenging radar deinterleaving problem, certain sequence search type algorithms have been traditionally used for separating out individual pulse trains from an initial complex interleaved set (see for instance [2], [3]). However, certain complications arising from the receiver and/or emitter can make the radar deinterleaving process a difficult one.

First, when two or more radar pulses overlap at the electronic receiver, only the first pulse is recorded. Or simply the emitter may occasionally fail to fire a pulse at all. This leads to potentially many *missing pulses*, especially in an emitter dense environment. Occasionally, a radar may fire an unintended pulse or the receiver itself may spuriously record a pulse when there is only noise present. This leads to *spurious pulses* being recorded which the deinterleaving algorithm may invariably try to assign to a particular pulse train.

However, most importantly in so far as this paper is concerned, the TOA values may be subject to jitter noise, either intentionally or unintentionally. The source of this noise may be from the receiver, the emitter or both. Finally, many modern radars are able to change PRI modes discontinuously. All these factors can mask the periodicities of the pulse trains and make deinterleaving extremely difficult. A more intelligent form of the sequence search algorithm is clearly required for the general problem.

4 The Sequence Search Algorithm

As mentioned earlier, full descriptions of the sequence search algorithm can be found in [2] and [3]. However, a very brief description follows. In essence, the sequence search algorithm works by forming trial pulse trains from an initial pulse pair. This initial pulse pair is hypothesised to be the PRI of a periodic pulse train within a given window of tolerance. The input buffer is searched for additional pulses by projecting forward in the file using this estimated PRI interval.

We advance and seek for hits a given number of times. Provided there are a sufficient number of successes, we conclude a periodic pulse train exists. If not we choose another pulse pair and repeat the process. The estimated PRI is refined and updated and we then sweep forward and backward through the TOA file and flag any matching pulses. Once this is completed, all the flagged pulses are removed from the sequence and stored as a chain. This process is continually repeated until there are less than a specified number of pulses left.

Initially, we search for chains with stable *PRIs*. Once this option has been exhausted and all such chains removed from the TOA file, we then search for jittered PRI chains. The window of tolerance is increased to allow for increasing amounts of jitter. This often leads to the formation of sub-harmonics and fragmentation of pulse chains. As the window size is increased, the more likely we are to produce chains that do not actually constitute a periodic sequence. In practice, this process works well for stable PRIs but a more intelligent approach is required for capturing periodic but jittered pulse chains.

5 Recursive Neural Network Algorithm

Neural networks have been shown to have the ability to reasonably *track* highly non-linear time series, even when the data is *noisy* [1,6]. A simple recurrent back-propagation neural network based on a simple

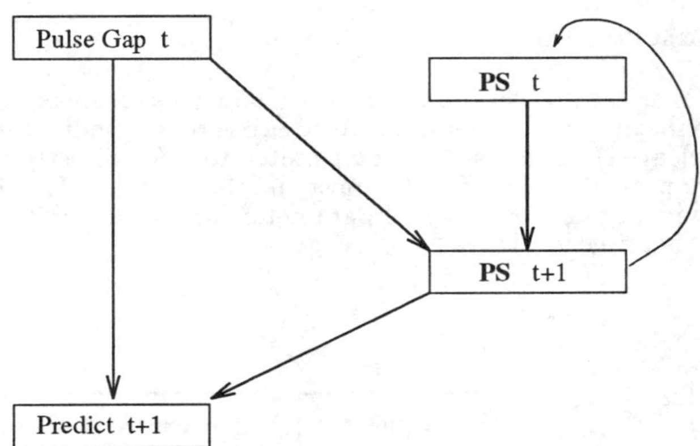

Figure 3: A 4-layer recurrent backpropagation network

state space time series formulation of the radar problem has been designed to track a single regular pulse train. A detailed explanation of this approach is contained within [4] and [5]. A brief summary of this approach follows.

According to the formulation in [4] and [6] we have for the radar pulse train problem:

(2) $$x_{t+1} = F(\boldsymbol{PS}_{t+1}, x_t) + N_{t+1}$$

(3) $$\boldsymbol{PS}_{t+1} = G(\boldsymbol{PS}_t, x_t)$$

where N_{t+1} represents a random noise component at time $t+1$ and $\boldsymbol{PS}$ is the so called Parameter Storage vector which contains the relevant information pertaining to all the T_i's of the pulse train (see equation 1).

Based on the above state space formulation, a 4 layer recurrent back propagation network with 4 interconnecting matrices is shown in Figure 3. The two "input" layers (the current Pulse Gap encoded vector and the current Parameter Storage vector) are "transformed" to form the next Parameter Storage vector (c.f. equation (3)) which then is fed forward, together with the current pulse gap vector, to predict the next pulse gap vector (c.f. equation (2)).

A novel heuristic adaptive error threshold is incorporated into the network that allows simultaneously good tracking and parameter estimating abilities even when using noisy data. The adaptive threshold should be stable when the network error is stable but should rapidly respond to changes in E_t in such a way that minimises noise bias effects (including jitter and missing and spurious pulses) and maximises the learning speed of the sequence in terms of the amount of data required. Thus we found that a suitable functional form to adapt the error threshold was:

(4) $$\epsilon_{t+1} = \epsilon_t \exp \kappa (E_{t+1} - E_t).$$

The *gain* parameter κ is set at some value above one and ϵ_0 is set at a value $<< 1$. The limit we impose on ϵ typically represents 10% jitter of the initial time series value.We can expect the adaptive error threshold to converge once it has "locked" onto a pulse train's PRI pattern. The network can be rapidly and continuously updated as each new time series value is encountered. Each recursive update also leads to an update in the estimates of the parameter values of the pulse train. Memory of the previous inputs and predictions is contained within the $\boldsymbol{PS}$ layer. The network is able to track various kinds of radar pulse trains, even with large amounts of jitter and missing and spurious pulses as well as high stagger levels where $M > 1$ (see [4] and [5]).

6   Integrated Algorithm

We present the novel idea of combining a sequence search with the recursive neural network to produce a single integrated algorithm. We hope to build an intelligent sequence search type deinterleaver by utilising the robust and adaptive properties of the above recursive neural network. When presented with an interleaved TOA data set, the algorithm performs as a simple sequence search deinterleaver to initially remove all the stable PRI pulse trains. The remaining pulse trains are considered to be jittered (or overly noisy) which the simple sequence search algorithm has failed to separate. We now utilise the integrated algorithm.

The fundamental idea is that a modified sequence search through jittered pulse train TOA values will still form chains of data. However, we can intelligently deduce if these candidate chains of data are actually part of a periodic pulse train by processing each chain through the above recursive neural network. In other words, the sequence search forms the hypothesis that a given chain of pulses is periodic and we use the recursive neural network to intelligently test this hypothesis. With this application, each of the four neural network layers consist of just 2 neurons interconnected by 2×2 weight matrices.

We look for network convergence in terms of its estimate of T (i.e. PRI) for that chain. If convergence occurs, we can reasonably deduce that the chain forms part of a given PRI pulse train (with associated jitter). The network is robust to highly corrupted data and will still converge even when there are many missing and spurious pulses and significant jitter [4], [5]. This is an important point and justifies the use of a robust neural network approach, instead of using a simple least squares approach to estimating T. In any case, this robustness substantially reduces the likelihood of chain fragmentation.

We assume the maximum amount of jitter, in terms of its Gaussian standard deviation, that a pulse train has is 10% of its mean PRI value. Hence the width of the "window of tolerance" is initially set at ± 0.3 times the current best estimate of the chain's PRI. This represents $\pm$ three Gaussian standard deviations from the mean. Any pulses outside of this window could not therefore be reasonably considered as part of the chain. The use of such a Gaussian window further reduces the possibility of chain fragmentation as well as sub-harmonic selection (i.e. multiples of PRI).

As with the standard sequence search algorithm, we initially choose a pair of pulses and hypothesise that the TOA difference is representative of a periodic jittered pulse train. The integrated algorithm is:

- 0. Start. Set $N = 0$
- 1. Select sample pair ensuring smaller pulse gaps are chosen first. Calculate maximum window of tolerance based on 10% jitter. Process initial pulse gap through the neural network and assume this is initial PRI estimate.
- 2. Advance using initial PRI estimate and seek a "hit" within tolerance. Flag each hit pulse. If multiple pulses within window, choose nearest neighbour. If no pulses within tolerance, advance another PRI estimate. Allow at most two consecutive missing pulses before returning to 0. Process pulse gap through neural network and update PRI estimate and adaptive error threshold. $N = N + 1$.
- 3. Check for network convergence. If no convergence and $N > N^*$ (where N^* is some critical value defining the existence of a periodic chain and varies with the level of jitter), return to 0. If no convergence and $N < N^*$, goto 2. If convergence, goto 4. For the maximum 10% jitter, $N^* \approx 15$.
- 4. With current PRI estimate, advance and seek hits within tolerance and continue to track the periodic chain through the interleaved data. Remove "flagged" pulses from data set.
- 5. Continue advancing in time with network filter until PRI chain vanishes or changes parameters. This will be obvious in the sudden fluctuations in the PRI estimate and adaptive error threshold value. Return to 0.

It should be mentioned that we can leave one recursive neural network running for the life of each PRI chain, once the existence of that periodic chain has been established. This is ideal for real-time applications when one pulse is being received at a time and rapid recursive updates are required. In addition, it effectively means we are able to continuously track and predict the next pulse event of the interleaved environment, which is another advantage over the traditional algorithm.

7 Examples

Two simple examples, both involving 250 pulses, are given to illustrate how the integrated approach can work successfully in a multiple jittered pulse train environment. The first example involves an interleaved data set consisting of two pulse trains with mean PRI values of 1.10 and 6.15, with cumulative Gaussian jitter of 7.0% and 1.5% respectively. The second, and more challenging, example involves an interleaved data set consisting of three pulse trains with mean PRI values of 1.00, 1.31 and 1.67, each with cumulative Gaussian jitter of approximately 4%.

The appropriate network parameters were chosen to allow a period one function ($M = 1$) to be recognised amidst reasonably large amounts of Gaussian jitter (up to 10% of its PRI value) without overtraining on any one pulse gap. In this way we are able to minimise noise bias. We also allow the condition that the minimum adaptive error threshold value does not come into existence until after the processing of 3 pulse gaps, allowing the network to quickly deduce a course approximation of the mean pulse gap.

For the first example, several different candidate chains were passed through the network. Figure 4 shows just three of these candidates chosen from three different initial pulse pairs. These pulse pairs correspond to the initial PRI estimates for the hypothesised pulse trains. The encoded input for all the chains is normalised so as to lie between the values of 0 and 1. The maximum encoded value for the pulse gaps was set to four times the initial pulse gap value which allows for up to two consecutive missing pulses. This assumes the initial pulse gap is a fair initial approximation of the mean pulse gap. This must be true otherwise the sequence search would not have formed the candidate chain.

The solid lines show the recursive mean pulse gap estimates (i.e. the PRIs) and the labels "+" and "o" show the actual pulse gaps. The two chains labelled "+" and "o" in Figure 4 clearly converge very quickly to their actual PRI values. This is because the initial estimates, 1.11 and 6.13, are sufficiently close to the true values of 1.10 and 6.15 respectively. The PRI convergences confirms the hypotheses of periodic sequences with PRIs 1.10 and 6.13. The chain labelled "*" with an initial PRI estimate of 3.68 does not converge and can be discarded. The scale of the graph may give an *impression* of convergence,

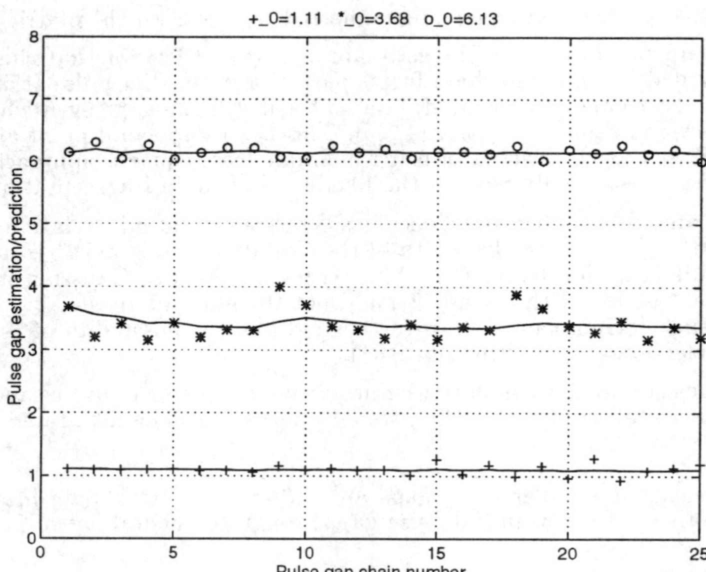

Figure 4: Pulse Gap Convergence or otherwise of jittered candidate chains in an interleaved two jittered pulse train environment. The solid lines represent the recursive estimates of the mean pulse gaps.

but numerically this is clearly not the case. Even a pulse train with the maximum 10% jitter will clearly converge within 25 pulse gaps.

We now consider the second example involving three jittered interleaved pulse trains. The results are shown in Figure 5 where the convergence or otherwise of five candidate chains are shown. The convergence of the three chains labelled "+", "x" and "o" corresponding to the actual PRIs are clearly seen. The other two chains labelled "$*$" and "$\bullet$" clearly do not converge, even after 25 pulse gaps, and can be discarded.

In practice, sub-harmonic chains, which plague the traditional sequence search algorithm, do not seem to prove a problem. We ensure that we initially exhaust our search for smaller pulse gap values and as long as they correspond to actual chains, convergence is almost inevitable within the limits of feasible jitter and missing and spurious pulses. This also means that fragmentation is minimised as the neural network is essentially a robust pulse train tracker. Combined with a Gaussian window for the sequence search, there is hence no need to increase the level of tolerance by increments to cope with increasing levels of jitter.

Note also that we have actually solved the *more* challenging problem of tracking each pulse chain through the full interleaved data. Usually, we remove periodic chains as they are captured, making it an easier exercise to separate out the remaining chains. Once the robust algorithm has track of a periodic chain, even within a dense and jittered interleaved environment, only an unusual amount of noise allows us to lose this track. In our two examples, the integrated algorithm was able to track all periodic sequences without a single fragmentation.

It is interesting to note that the standard sequence search on its own could not have satisfactory converged to this solution due to its simplistic definition of a periodic pulse chain and lack of robustness. This standard algorithm was, in fact, unable to arrive at a sensible solution and resulted in severe fragmentation problems, as well as choosing chains that were in fact not periodic.

For the first example of two jittered pulse trains, 14 "periodic" chains were formed. There were two short chains that did constitute the actual pulse trains. There were also several other chains that could be interpreted as sub-harmonics of the $PRI = 1.10$ train, but with with large variations of their jitter value. There were also "periodic" chains captured that had no relationship to either of the $PRIs$ present. Using the standard sequence search, those pulses that could not be classified at smaller jitter levels will eventually be classified as the jitter level is increased leading to totally spurious results.

With the second example of three jittered interleaved pulse trains, the standard algorithm had even less success. Of the three $PRIs$ present, only two short chains corresponding to $PRI = 1.31$ were captured. There were 15 "periodic" chains captured in total, again with with a mixture of some being sub-harmonics and others completely spurious. It would indeed take a very intelligent expert system to put all the pieces back into their original order.

We were careful to ensure that these results were not merely because of a possible poor implementation of the standard sequence search algorithm. Hence, we verified the authenticity of our own implementation by testing it on all the examples given in [2]. It was entirely successful and in general gave very good results, even in a very dense environment, *so long as at most one of the pulse trains had significant timing*

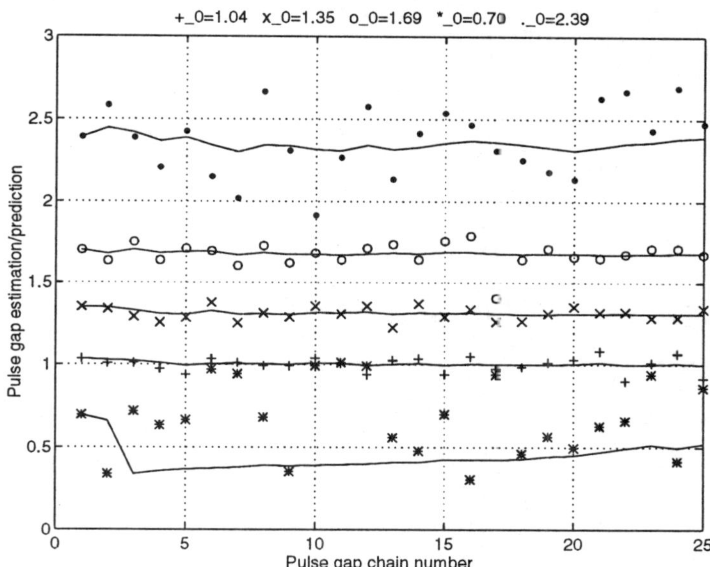

Figure 5: Pulse Gap Convergence or otherwise of jittered candidate chains in an interleaved three jittered pulse train environment.

jitter associated with it.

8 Conclusions

A new integrated algorithm is discussed here that leads to a more general approach to time of arrival deinterleaving, particularly of a multiple jittered pulse train environment. In particular, a recursive neural network with adaptive error thresholding is used as a hypothesis tester to assist in the pulse train processing. This allows a sequence search type algorithm to make more intelligent decisions as to whether a periodic jittered pulse train may exist or not, even in a noisy environment. Importantly, the problems of sub-harmonic detection and chain fragmentation is minimised using the robust integrated approach.

For each identified periodic chain we can build a recursive network filter. Each filter is left running to track the designated periodic chain through the interleaved data. Hence, the potential is there to be able to satisfactory deinterleave a multiple jittered pulse train environment in a real time manner. In addition, this also allows us to effectively track the entire interleaved environment by predicting the next pulse event. Indeed, the recursive network used here could even be applied to a quite general noisy time series prediction problem.

Acknowledgements

The authors wish to acknowledge the funding of the activities of the Cooperative Research Centre for Robust and Adaptive Systems by the Australian Government under the Cooperative Research Centres Program.

References

[1] C.R. Gent and C.P. Sheppard, A general purpose neural network architecture for time series prediction. In *Proc. IEE ICANN'92*, pp. 323–327, IEE, 1992.

[2] H.K. Mardia, New techniques for the deinterleaving of repetitive sequences. *IEE Proc. F (Radar & Signal Processing)*, vol. 136, pp. 149–154, 1989.

[3] D.J. Milojevic and B.M. Popovic, Improved algorithm for the deinterleaving of radar pulses. *IEE Proceedings F (Radar & Signal Processing)*, vol. 139, pp. 98–104, Febuary 1992.

[4] G. Noone, Radar pulse train parameter estimation and tracking using neural networks. In *Proc. Inter. Conf. Artificial Neural Networks and Expert Systems*, New Zealand, Nov. 1995, pp. 95-98.

[5] G. Noone and S.D. Howard, Investigation of periodic time series using neural networks with adaptive error thresholds. In *Proc. Inter. Conf. Neural Networks*, Australia, Nov. 1995, pp. 1541-45.

[6] A.S. Weigend and N.A. Gershenfeld, *Time Series Prediction: Forecasting the Future and Understanding the Past.*, volume Proc. Vol XV of *Studies in the Sciences of Complexities*. Santa Fe Institute, 1992.

Neural Control and Robotics
(Poster Presentation)

Comparison of Three Different Neuro-Compensation Schemes
for Adaptive Control of Robot Manipulators

*S. K. Tso   **N. L. Lin
*Centre for Intelligent Design, Automation and Manufacturing, City University of Hong Kong, Hong Kong
**Dept. of Electrical and Electronic Engineering, The University of Hong Kong, Hong Kong

Abstract—Two control schemes using feedforward multi-layer neural networks (NN) to compensate for uncertainties (parametric and/or structural) of the robot manipulator are presented in this paper. The closed-loop system is shown to be stable in the Lyapunov sense. Novel adaptive learning algorithms for tuning the NN weights are derived. With suitable assumptions made, these two schemes will lead to the feedback-error-learning scheme as a special case. Comparison of the performance of the three kinds of control schemes is presented.

1. Introduction

The robot manipulator is a complex controlled plant. The existence of parametric and/or structural uncertainties makes the controller design difficult.

In recent years, neural networks (NN) have been widely used as a new approach to adaptive control. Most of approaches aim at providing an inverse dynamics model of the controlled plant using the neural networks [1-4]. The stability of the approaches is hard to establish in general. From the control viewpoint, it is not a good practice to design a control system without using any *a priori* knowledge of the controlled plant. Ozaki et al. [5] discussed the use of a neural network to adaptively compensate for the uncertainties of the robot manipulator, so that both *a priori* knowledge of the controlled plant and the learning ability of the neural network can be effectively combined to achieve superior tracking performance. Chen et al. [6] presented the stability analysis for the iterative process.

In this paper, two approaches of using the NN to adaptively compensate for the uncertainties of the robot manipulator are presented. The closed-loop system stability with the NN adjusted on-line is discussed in detail based on the Lyapunov stability approach. The weights-adaptive-learning algorithms different from the widely used back-propagation (B-P) algorithm for the neural network are obtained based on the above stability analysis. The error signals for training the neural-network compensator can be directly obtained from the controlled system without using any partial derivatives of the controlled robot manipulator variables. We also show that feedback-error learning [3-4] is a very special case of both approaches.

2. Background

Given $X \in R^n$, a three-layer feedforward NN described in matrix format has an output: $v = w_3 f[w_2 g(w_1 X)]$, where f(.) and g(.) are the nonlinear hyperbolic-tangent activation functions, and w_1, w_2, w_3, are the interconnection weights. X is the state of the robot system used as input for the NN.

In order to study the stability of the closed-loop system with the NN used as an adaptive compensator, we make the following assumptions:

1. The neural-network compensator with the constant or slowly-varying desired weights can represent the entire system uncertainties with a bounded error, $v(w^*, X) = \eta(X) + \varepsilon, \|\varepsilon\| \le \varepsilon_{max}$.

2. The ideal weights are bounded by known positive values so that $\|w^*\| < w_{max}$.

3. Control Scheme I
3.1 Control Law and System Uncertainties

The dynamics of the robot manipulator can be written in the form

$$M(\theta)\ddot{\theta} + h(\theta,\dot{\theta}) = \tau \tag{1}$$

$M(\theta)$ is the $n \times n$ inertia matrix. $h(\theta,\dot{\theta})$ is an $n \times 1$ vector associated with the centrifugal, Coriolis, gravitational and frictional torque components. τ is the $n \times 1$ input torque vector.

According to the well-known computed torque method

$$\tau = \hat{M}(\theta)u + \hat{h}(\theta,\dot{\theta}) \tag{2}$$

$\hat{M}(\theta,\dot{\theta})$ is the estimate of the actual $M(\theta)$. $\hat{h}(\theta,\dot{\theta})$ is the estimate of the actual $h(\theta,\dot{\theta})$.

With an NN compensator added, u in (2) is given by

$$u = \ddot{\theta}_d + K_v \dot{e} + K_p e + v(w,\theta,\dot{\theta},\ddot{\theta}) \tag{3}$$

$e = \theta_d - \theta$ is the joint position error. $v(w,\theta,\dot{\theta},\ddot{\theta})$ is the output of the NN compensator. w represents the weights of the NN compensator.

Then the closed-loop dynamics of the robot control system with the NN compensator tuned on-line is expressed as:

$$\ddot{e} + K_v \dot{e} + K_p e = \Delta v \tag{4}$$

where $\Delta v(w, \theta, \dot{\theta}, \ddot{\theta}) = (\hat{M}^{-1}(\theta)M(\theta) - I)\ddot{\theta} + \hat{M}^{-1}(\theta)(h(\theta, \dot{\theta}) - \hat{h}(\theta, \dot{\theta})) - v(w, \theta, \dot{\theta}, \ddot{\theta}) = \eta(\theta, \dot{\theta}, \ddot{\theta}) - v(w, \theta, \dot{\theta}, \ddot{\theta})$.
The uncertainties are represented as a complicated function of the closed-loop system state $X = [\theta, \dot{\theta}, \ddot{\theta}]^T$.

We define: $e_f = \dot{e} + \Lambda e$, where Λ is a constant diagonal matrix. The filtered error e_f is used to ensure that the closed-loop system is strictly positive real.

Equation (4) may be written in the state-space form as,

$$\dot{Y} = AY + B\Delta v; \quad e_f = CY \tag{5}$$

where $Y = [e\ \dot{e}]^T$, $A = \begin{bmatrix} 0 & I \\ -k_p & -k_v \end{bmatrix}$, $B = [0\ \ I]^T$, $C = [\Lambda\ \ I]$.

From the linear control system theory, there exist two symmetric positive-definite matrices P and Q satisfying

$$A^T P + PA = -Q$$
$$PB = C^T \tag{6}$$

The difference between the system uncertainties and the NN compensation may be expressed in terms of the difference of the desired weights and the actual weights [7-8]

$$\Delta v = \eta(\theta, \dot{\theta}, \ddot{\theta}) - v(w, \theta, \dot{\theta}, \ddot{\theta}) = F(w^*, X) - F(w, X) + \varepsilon = w_3^* f[w_2^* g(w_1^* X)] - w_3 f[w_2 g(w_1 X)] + \varepsilon$$
$$= (w_3^* - w_3)f[w_2 g(w_1 X)] + w_3 f_a'[w_2 g(w_1 X)](w_2^* - w_2)g(w_1 X)$$
$$+ w_3 f_a'[w_2 g(w_1 X)]w_2 g_a'(w_1 X)(w_1^* - w_1)X + \varepsilon \tag{7}$$

3.2 Stability Analysis and the Adaptive Learning Algorithm

We choose the Lyapunov candidate function as follows:

$$L(Y, w_{n1}, w_{n2}, w_{n3}) = Y^T PY + tr(w_{n1}^T \Gamma_1^{-1} w_{n1}) + tr(w_{n2}^T \Gamma_2^{-1} w_{n2}) + tr(w_{n3}^T \Gamma_3^{-1} w_{n3}) \tag{8}$$

Γ_1: $h_1 \times h_1$ diagonal positive-definite matrix. Γ_2: $h_2 \times h_2$ diagonal positive-definite matrix. Γ_3: $n \times n$ diagonal positive-definite matrix. h_1 and h_2: number of neurons in the first and the second hidden layer respectively. $w_{n1} = w_1^* - w_1$, $w_{n2} = w_2^* - w_2$ and $w_{n3} = w_3^* - w_3$.

Differentiating L and substituting $\dot{Y}$ from (5) and (7) leads to

$$\dot{L} = \dot{Y}^T PY + Y^T P\dot{Y} + 2tr(\dot{w}_{n1}^T \Gamma_1^{-1} w_{n1}) + 2tr(\dot{w}_{n2}^T \Gamma_2^{-1} w_{n2}) + 2tr(\dot{w}_{n3}^T \Gamma_3^{-1} w_{n3}) \tag{9}$$

Note that $C^T = PB$, $C = B^T P^T = B^T P$, and that every term in the equation is a scalar. Equation (9) may be finally written as:

$$\dot{L} = Y^T(A^T P + PA)Y + 2tr(\dot{w}_{n1}^T \Gamma_1^{-1} w_{n1} + XY^T C^T w_3 f_a'[w_2 g(w_1 X)]w_2 g_a'(w_1 X)(w_1^* - w_1))$$
$$+ 2tr(\dot{w}_{n2}^T \Gamma_1^{-1} w_{n2} + g(w_1 X)Y^T C^T w_3 f_a'[w_2 g(w_1 X)](w_2^* - w_2))$$
$$+ 2tr(\dot{w}_{n3}^T \Gamma_3^{-1} w_{n3} + f[w_2 g(w_1 X)]Y^T C^T (w_3^* - w_3)) + 2Y^T P\varepsilon \tag{10}$$

If we choose by design

$$\dot{w}_{n1} = -\Gamma_1 g_a'^T(w_1 X)w_2^T f_a'^T[w_2 g(w_1 X)]w_3^T CYX^T$$
$$\dot{w}_{n2} = -\Gamma_2 f_a'^T[w_2 g(w_1 X)]w_3^T CYg^T(w_1 X)$$
$$\dot{w}_{n3} = -\Gamma_3 CYf^T[w_2 g(w_1 X)] \tag{11}$$

there results

$$\dot{L}(Y, w_{n1}, w_{n2}, w_{n3}) = -Y^T QY + 2Y^T P\varepsilon \tag{12}$$

If

$$\|Y\|_2 \geq 2\frac{\lambda_{p\,max}}{\lambda_{q\,min}}\varepsilon_{max}, \tag{13}$$

where $\lambda_{p\,max}$ is the maximum eigenvalue of P, $\lambda_{q\,min}$ is the minimum eigenvalue of Q, then

$$\dot{L}(Y, w_{n1}, w_{n2}, w_{n3}) \leq 0. \tag{14}$$

Equation (13) implies that there exist constants e_{max} and $\dot{e}_{max}$ such that $\|e\| < e_{max}$, $\|\dot{e}\| < \dot{e}_{max}$. That is to say, the error signals are bounded. The system is stable in the Lyapunov sense. It then follows from equation (4), that another constant $\ddot{e}_{max}$ exists such that $\|\ddot{e}\| < \ddot{e}_{max}$.

The adaptive learning law for w_1, w_2 and w_3 is hence

$$\dot{w}_1 = \Gamma_1 g_a'^T(w_1 X) w_2^T f_a'^T [w_2 g(w_1 X)] w_3^T CYX^T$$
$$\dot{w}_2 = \Gamma_2 f_a'^T [w_2 g(w_1 X)] w_3^T CYg^T(w_1 X)$$
$$\dot{w}_3 = \Gamma_3 CYf^T [w_2 g(w_1 X)] \tag{15}$$

The adaptive learning law for a two-layer and radial-basis-function NN compensator can be obtained in a similar way. More detailed discussion about the control scheme and the adaptive learning law can be found in [7-8].

4. Control Scheme II
4.1 Control Law and System Uncertainties
The dynamics of the robot manipulator is represented by

$$M(\theta)\ddot{\theta} + h(\theta,\dot{\theta}) = \tau \tag{16}$$

If the NN compensator term is added as a torque correction instead, we have

$$\tau = \hat{M}(\theta)u + \hat{h}(\theta,\dot{\theta}) + v(w,\theta,\dot{\theta},\ddot{\theta}) \tag{17}$$
$$u = \ddot{\theta}_d + K_v\dot{e} + K_p e \tag{18}$$

Then the closed-loop dynamics of the robot control system with the neural-network compensator tuned on-line is expressed as:

$$\ddot{e} + K_v\dot{e} + K_p e = \hat{M}^{-1}(\theta)\Delta v \tag{19}$$

where $\Delta v(w,\theta,\dot{\theta},\ddot{\theta}) = (\hat{M}^{-1}(\theta) - M(\theta))\ddot{\theta} + (h(\theta,\dot{\theta}) - \hat{h}(\theta,\dot{\theta})) - v(w,\theta,\dot{\theta},\ddot{\theta}) = \eta(\theta,\dot{\theta},\ddot{\theta}) - v(w,\theta,\dot{\theta},\ddot{\theta})$

It is important to note that the uncertainties defined in equation (19) are different from that in equation (4). Following the same procedure as that in control scheme I, equation (19) may be written as,

$$\dot{Y} = AY + B\hat{M}^{-1}(\theta)\Delta v$$
$$e_f = CY \tag{20}$$

4.2 Stability Analysis and the Adaptive Learning Algorithm
Choosing the same Lyapunov candidate function as before, we have

$$L(Y, w_{n1}, w_{n2}, w_{n3}) = Y^T PY + tr(w_{n1}^T \Gamma_1^{-1} w_{n1}) + tr(w_{n2}^T \Gamma_2^{-1} w_{n2}) + tr(w_{n3}^T \Gamma_3^{-1} w_{n3}) \tag{21}$$
$$\dot{L} = \dot{Y}^T PY + Y^T P\dot{Y} + 2tr(\dot{w}_{n1}^T \Gamma_1^{-1} w_{n1}) + 2tr(\dot{w}_{n2}^T \Gamma_2^{-1} w_{r2}) + 2tr(\dot{w}_{n3}^T \Gamma_3^{-1} w_{n3}) \tag{22}$$

Expanding,

$$\dot{L} = Y^T(A^T P + PA)Y + 2tr(\dot{w}_{n1}^T \Gamma_1^{-1} w_{n1} + XY^T C^T \hat{M}^{-1}(\theta) w_3 f_a'[w_2 g(w_1 X)] w_2 g_a'(w_1 X)(w_1^* - w_1))$$
$$+ 2tr(\dot{w}_{n2}^T \Gamma_1^{-1} w_{n2} + g(w_1 X)Y^T C^T \hat{M}^{-1}(\theta) w_3 f_a'[w_2 g(w_1 X)](w_2^* - w_2))$$
$$+ 2tr(\dot{w}_{n3}^T \Gamma_3^{-1} w_{n3} + f[w_2 g(w_1 X)]Y^T C^T \hat{M}^{-1}(\theta)(w_3^* - w_3)) + 2Y^T P\varepsilon \tag{23}$$

Stability will result if the adaptive learning laws for w_1, w_2 and w_3 are selected as

$$\dot{w}_1 = \Gamma_1 g_a'^T(w_1 X) w_2^T f_a'^T [w_2 g(w_1 X)] w_3^T \hat{M}^{-1}(\theta) CYX^T$$
$$\dot{w}_2 = \Gamma_2 f_a'^T [w_2 g(w_1 X)] w_3^T \hat{M}^{-1}(\theta) CYg^T(w_1 X)$$
$$\dot{w}_3 = \Gamma_3 \hat{M}^{-1}(\theta) CYf^T [w_2 g(w_1 X)] \tag{24}$$

It can be similarly proved that $\|e\| < e_{\max}$, $\|\dot{e}\| < \dot{e}_{\max}$ and $\|\ddot{e}\| < \ddot{e}_{\max}$. The system is stable in the Lyapunov sense. Other discussions are similar to those in control scheme I.

5. Comparison of Three Control Schemes
5.1 Feedback-Error-Learning Scheme
The feedback-error-learning scheme of Kawato et al. may be expressed in the form:

Output of Controller = Feedback Controller Output + Neural-Network's Output $\qquad$ (25)

With learning, the neural-network will get closer to the inverse model of the robot. As the error becomes smaller, so does the feedback controller output. This scheme represents an inverse-dynamics-model approach. If the feedback controller is selected to be a P-D controller, equation (25) will lead to

$$\tau = K_v\dot{e} + K_p e + v(w,\theta,\dot{\theta},\ddot{\theta}) \tag{26}$$

5.2 Discussion
For the control law in equations (17) and (18) and the adaptive-learning law for weights in equation (24) (or control law in equations (2) and (3) and the adaptive-learning law for weights in equation (15)), suppose that the estimate $\hat{M}(\theta)$ is chosen as a constant unit matrix, $\hat{M}(\theta) = I$, and $\hat{h}(\theta,\dot{\theta}) = 0$. Suppose also that the desired trajectory does not vary not too fast, and $\ddot{\theta}_d \to 0$. What will be the effect? The control law turns out to be that of the feedback-error-learning scheme of Kawato et al. in equation (26), with $C = k_p\begin{bmatrix} I & k_v / k_p \end{bmatrix}$. The

feedback-error-learning scheme is of course simpler than the above two control schemes, without using any *a priori* model knowledge of the robot manipulator $\hat{M}(\theta)$ and $\hat{h}(\theta,\dot{\theta})$. The above stability analysis also explains why the feedback-error-learning scheme would be convergent provided that the assumed conditions are satisfied. In the feedback-error-learning scheme, the uncertainty for the NN to compensate is usually larger, a larger number of neural-network nodes is required, and the learning time is generally longer.

In control scheme I, the estimated $\hat{M}(\theta)$ may be selected to be as close to the actual $M(\theta)$ as possible to achieve good control performance. In control scheme II, in order to guarantee closed-loop system stability and to simplify mathematical manipulation, the estimated $\hat{M}(\theta)$ is normally selected to be a diagonal matrix. Insofar as $\hat{M}(\theta)$ does not represent $M(\theta)$ faithfully, the uncertainty for the NN to compensate is larger than that in control scheme I. For the same NN structure and performance, it is required that more neurons be included in the NN compensator in control scheme II than in control scheme I.

5.3 Simulation

Consider a two-link robot working always on a horizontal plane. The dynamic-motion equation of link 2 and 3 of the Unimation PUMA 560 arm is:

$$M(\theta)\ddot{\theta} + h(\theta,\dot{\theta}) = \tau$$

$$\text{where} \quad M(\theta) = \begin{bmatrix} a_1 + a_2 \cos\theta_2 & a_3 + \dfrac{a_2}{2}\cos\theta_2 \\ a_3 + \dfrac{a_2}{2}\cos\theta_2 & a_3 \end{bmatrix} \quad h(\theta,\dot{\theta}) = \begin{bmatrix} (-a_2\sin\theta_2)(\dot{\theta}_1\dot{\theta}_2 + \dfrac{\dot{\theta}_2^2}{2}) + v_1\dot{\theta}_1 \\ (a_2\sin\theta_2)\dfrac{\dot{\theta}_2^2}{2} + v_2\dot{\theta}_2 \end{bmatrix}.$$

The trajectories for the robot to track are specified to be $\theta_{id}(t) = \sin(2\pi t/6)$ $(i=1,2)$. The cycle period is $T = 6s$. The actual values for the model parameters are taken to be $a_1 = 6.64$, $a_2 = 4.24$, $a_3 = 1.42$, $v_1 = v_2 = 1.0$.

For the three-layer NN adaptive compensator, there are 2 neurons in the second hidden layer. and the output weight matrix is fixed at $w_3 = 10I$; this will reduce the nonlinearity of NN compensator and speed up the learning process. For control scheme I, there are 30 neurons in the first hidden layer. For control scheme II and feedback-error-learning scheme, there are 80 neurons in the first hidden layer. The initial values of the weights w_1 and w_2 are given from -0.01 to 0.01 randomly. The learning algorithm of (15) is used to tune the weights w_1 and w_2 of the neural-network compensator in control scheme I. The learning algorithm of (24) is used to tune the weights w_1 and w_2 of the neural-network compensator in control scheme II and the feedback-error-learning scheme.

For all the three control schemes considered, the estimated values $\hat{a}_1 = 3.82$, $\hat{a}_2 = 2.12$, $\hat{a}_3 = 0.71$, $v_1 = v_2 = 1.0$ and $\Lambda = 1$, $K_p = 25$, $K_v = 26$ are used in constructing a computed-torque-method controller.

For control scheme II, $\hat{M}(\theta)$ is selected to be a diagonal matrix, $\hat{M}(\theta) = \begin{bmatrix} \hat{a}_1 + \hat{a}_2\cos\theta_2 & 0 \\ 0 & \hat{a}_3 \end{bmatrix}$. For the feedback-error-learning scheme, we have $\hat{M}(\theta) = I$, $\hat{P}(\theta,\dot{\theta}) = 0$, and $C = \begin{bmatrix} k_p & k_v \end{bmatrix}$. Reasonably large gains are necessary for control scheme II and the feedback-error-learning scheme, although less essential for control scheme I.

Fig.1-3 show the results for control scheme I, scheme II and the feedback-error-learning scheme respectively. The sum-of-errors is defined as $\dfrac{1}{T}\displaystyle\int_0^T [e_1^2(t) + e_2^2(t) + \dot{e}_1^2(t) + \dot{e}_2^2(t)]dt$ in its discretised form,. It is seen that with the learning in progress, the output errors in all the three schemes become smaller and smaller, and the learning process is fast. Error convergence is achieved even though the initial weights are not close to the desired values.

As *a prior* knowledge has been properly used in control scheme I, the uncertainties of the system for the NN to compensate is relatively small. The K_p and K_v can be selected to be smaller values, and the size of the NN made smaller. Fig. 4(a) shows the effective convergence even with $K_p = 5$, $K_v = 6$ in control scheme I. Were the reduced gains applied, the other two schemes would not work satisfactorily (see Fig. 4(b) and Fig. 4(c)). The uncertainties of the system for the NN to compensate are larger for control scheme II and the feedback-error-learning scheme, hence much larger values of K_p and K_v are required to keep the errors small and for successful NN learning. But very large values of K_p and K_v should not be used to avoid undue excitation of noises in practical applications. Increasing the number of neurons will not only increase the computation time, but also slow down the learning process. Fig.1 (c) shows that the weights converge quickly in control scheme I, while Fig.2 (c) and Fig.3 (c) show that the weights converge very slowly in control scheme II and the feedback-error-learning scheme respectively.

6. Conclusion

This paper compares the performance of three different schemes of NN-based adaptive control for robot manipulators. As *a priori* knowledge of the robot manipulator is effectively used in control scheme I, it shows some advantages over control scheme II and the feedback-error-learning scheme. Simulation results support the theoretical work developed.

References

[1] D. Psaltis, A. Sideris, and A. Yamamura, "A Multilayer Neural Network Controller," IEEE Control System Magazine, pp. 17-21, April 1988.

[2] M. I. Jordan, "Generic Constraints on Underspecified Target Trajectories," Proc. of the 1989 International Joint Conference on Neural Networks, Vol. 1, pp. 217-225, 1989.

[3] H. Gomi, and M. Kawato: " Learning Control for a Closed Loop System using Feedback-Error-Learning," Proc. of the 29th Conference on Decision and Control, Honolulu, Hawaii, pp. 3289-3294, Dec. 1990.

[4] M. Kawato, K. Furukawa, and R. Suzuki., "A Hierarchical Neural-Network Model for Control and Learning of Voluntary Movement," Biological Cybernetics, Vol. 57, pp. 169-185, 1987.

[5] T. Ozaki, T. Suzuki, T. Turuhashi, and S. Okuma., "Trajectory Control of Robotic Manipulator Using Neural Networks," IEEE Trans. on Industrial Electronics, Vol. 38, No. 3, pp. 195-202, June 1991.

[6] P.C.Y. Chen, J.K. Mills, and K.S. Smith: "Parameter Uncertainty Compensation in Robot Trajectory Tracking: a Neural Network Approach," Proc. of 1993 IEEE International Conference on System, Man & Cybernetics, France, Vol. 4, pp. 317-322, 1993.

[7] S.K. Tso and N.L. Lin, "Adaptive Neural Network Controller for Robot Manipulator System," Proc. of the 1995 IEEE International Conference on Neural Networks, Australia, Vol. 5, pp. 2320-2325, 1995.

[8] S.K. Tso and N.L. Lin, "Neural-Network-Based Adaptive Controller for Uncertainty Compensation of Robot Manipulators," Proc. of the 13th IFAC World Congress, USA, 1996 (to appear).

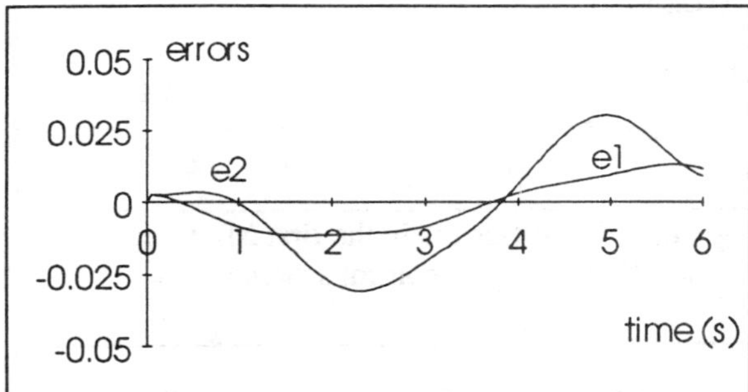

Fig. 1(a). Error response in the 1st cycle (without NN compensator) - control scheme I

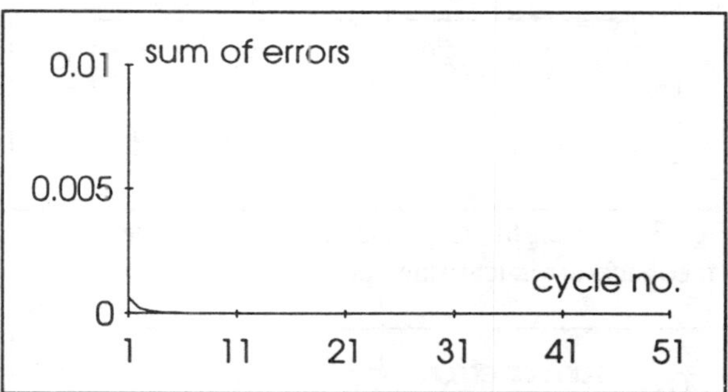

Fig. 1(b). Sum-of-errors in the first 51 cycles (with NN compensator) - control scheme I

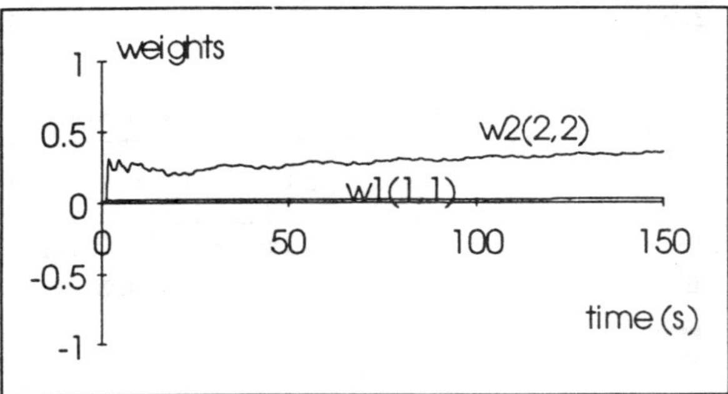

Fig. 1(c). Weights response (with NN compensator)- control scheme I

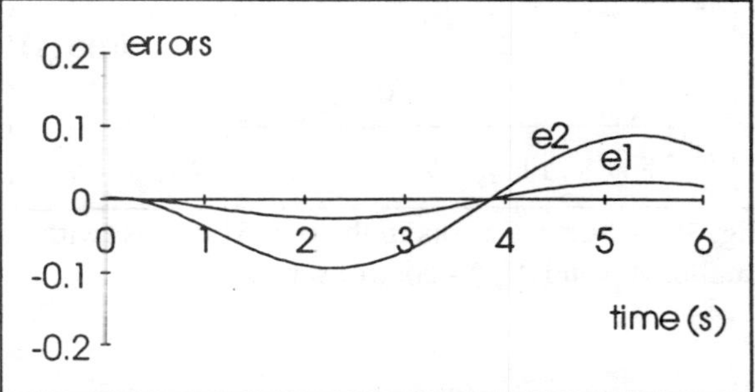

Fig. 2(a). Error response in the 1st cycle (without NN compensator) - control scheme II

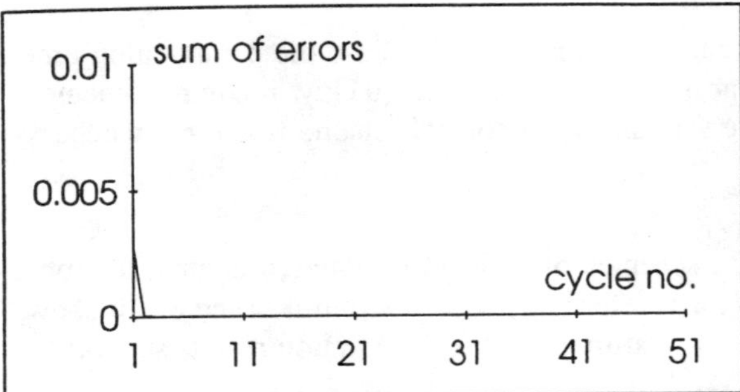

Fig. 2(b). Sum-of-errors in the first 51 cycles (with NN compensator)- control scheme II

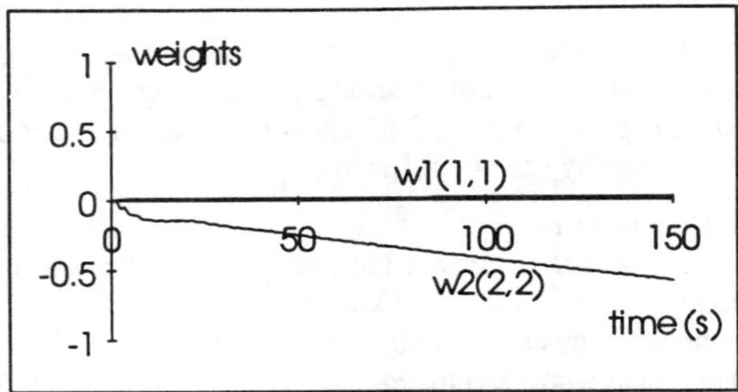

Fig. 2(c). Weights response (with NN compensator) - control scheme II

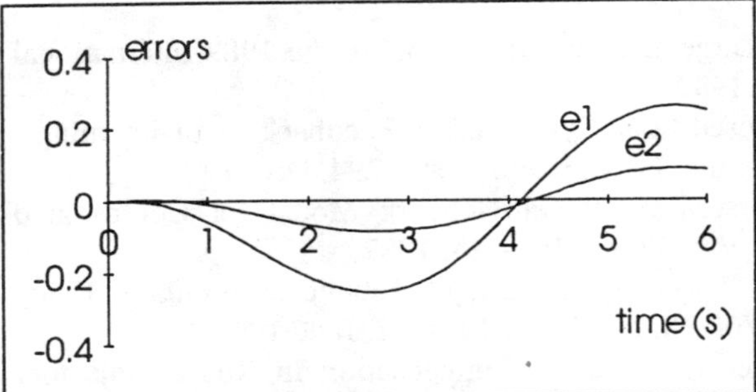

Fig. 3(a). Error response in the 1st cycle (without NN compensator) - feedback-error-learning scheme

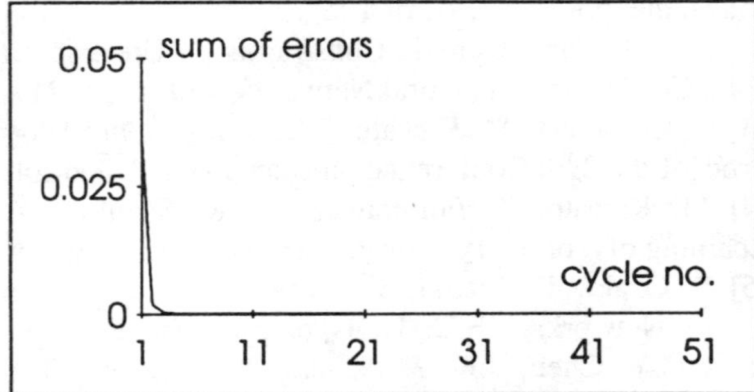

Fig. 3(b). Sum-of-errors in the first 51 cycles (with NN compensator) - feedback-error-learning scheme

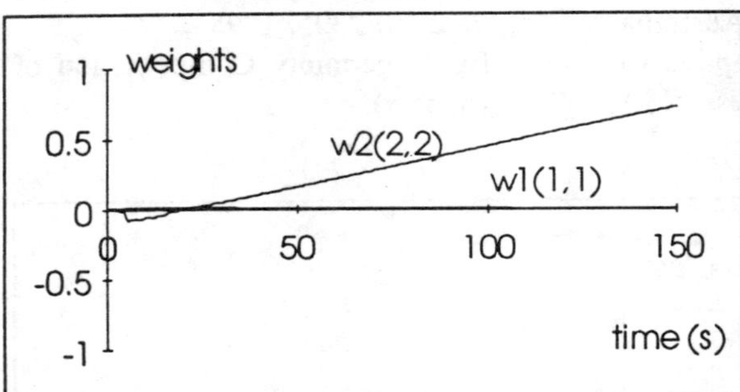

Fig. 3(c). Weights response (with NN compensator) - feedback-error-learning scheme

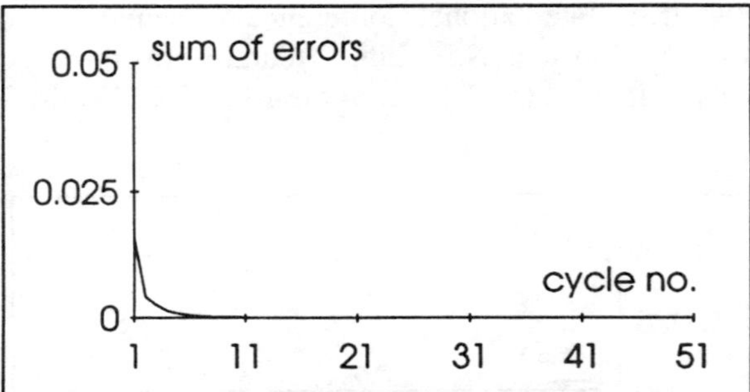

Fig. 4(a). Sum-of-errors in the first 51 cycles (with smaller K_p and K_v) - control scheme I

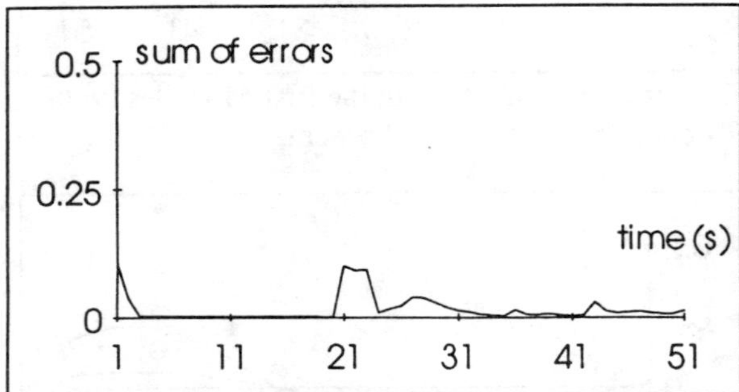

Fig. 4(b). Sum-of-errors in the first 51 cycles (with smaller K_p and K_v) - control scheme II

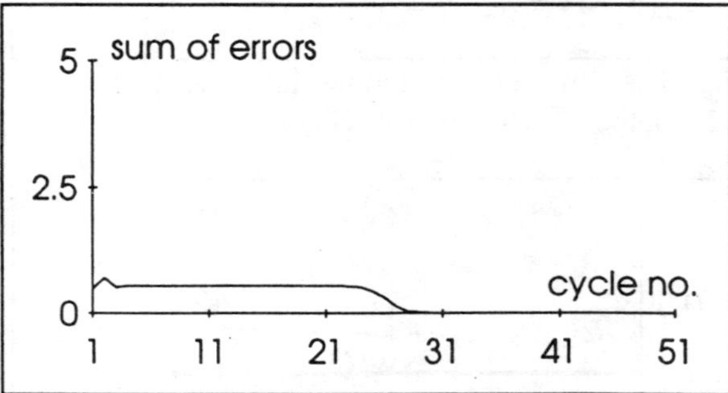

Fig. 4(c). Sum-of-errors in the first 51 cycles (with smaller K_p and K_v) - feedback-error-learning scheme

A Neural Network for Industrial Robot Collision Avoidance

Ulrich Borgolte
Department of Electrical Engineering, FernUniversität Hagen
P.O. Box 940
D 58084 Hagen, Germany
Email: ulrich.borgolte@fernuni-hagen.de

Abstract— An Artificial neural network doing online collision detection as well as collision avoidance is described. The input layer of the network gets the states of the robot doing collision avoidance as well the states of possible obstacles. These obstacles can be of stationary type, but also moving. Special attention is given to robots as obstacles. The output layer generates new interpolation points for the robot doing collision avoidance. This is done while the robots are moving, i.e. every single interpolation cycle. Therefore it is possible to detect deviations from the programmed paths and to react immediately.

The training of the neural network is done in an offline simulation phase. Within this phase, special features of the robots, e.g. velocities, accelerations, kinematic constraints etc., can be given to the software. After training of a network for a special kind of robot, this can be integrated to every robot controller.

1   Introduction

In the last years, the application of robots in industries has increased all over the world. Nevertheless, the enthusiastic forecasts have not become true. Besides the low level of programming techniques, and the missing multi-sensor integrations, a main reason for this is the lack of multi-robot systems, especially in manufacturing and in the wide range of assembly. Above all, CIM will need these systems of several robots and/or peripheral devices in coordinated operation. In this context, collision avoidance strategies, which have to be superimposed on all coordinated operations, become a basic requirement.

An obvious approach to avoid collisions is the generation of secure paths before starting of the actual movements or parts of them. The basis for this can be methods like the Configuration Space or Potential Field Approach [1], [2]. These are computed offline and are able to generate optimized trajectories. But they are insufficient if the environment is changing unpredictably or it is not completely known. Furthermore, this is due to sensor driven changes of the trajectories and possible failures in mechanical or electrical devices. Therefore, even if global planning and programming is done in multi-robot-workcells, in real-world applications it is important to supervise the actual movements and to influence them if necessary by online collision detection and avoidance.

The goal is the coordination of a working cell with an arbitrary number of robots and stationary or moving obstacles. Therefore it is necessary to generate desired values for all axes which let the arm move without collisions. This is done with regard to the position and velocity as well as the dynamic behaviour of each axis. If there is no danger of collision, the original trajectory given by the path-planning module has to be driven. Due to the very limited computation time in an online application, the only criterion for optimization is the avoidance of collisions.

The paper presents an artificial neural network doing online collision detection as well as collision avoidance.

The network considers the danger of collision for every single axis. This is due to the fact, that even if one axis is critical the whole arm may not be in danger (e.g. if the arms are crossing in the (x,y)-plane but they are far enough in the z-direction). After leaving a dangerous situation the original trajectory will be reentered as fast as possible.

2   Problem description

In this paper, robots with the main axes rotation-translation-translation are considered. The axes are denoted as φ, r, and z, respectively (fig. 1). The method proposed enables an easy way to adapt different kinematic structures, thus it is not restricted to a special type of robot.

Within a system of r robots, we are considering the robots j and k. Robot k has the right-of-way, i.e. robot j has to avoid collisions. With this, a neural network is assigned to robot j, getting inputs from the axis controllers of both robots. If a predefined danger of collision is reached, the output of the net will change the desired output vector for the axis control of robot j.

Considering the given kinematic structure, collision avoidance can be done by changing the height of the third link (z), decreasing the length of the third axis (r), or by rotating away from the arm of robot k (φ).

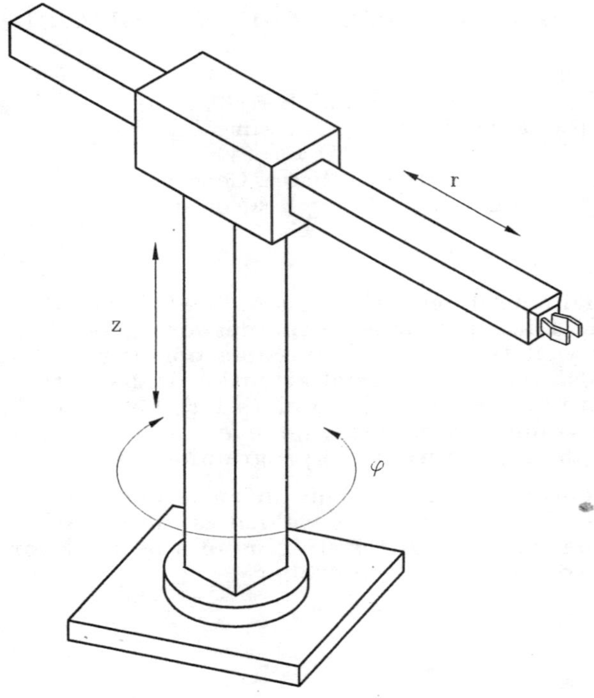

Figure 1: Robot configuration

As the third link is of fixed length, it just slides forward and backward with respect to the second link. Thus a reduction of r (i.e. a reduction of the distance between z-axis and TCP - Tool-Center-Point) results in an increasing of its backside part. This has to be considered, and a decision is made whether the TCP or the backside part of the third link is taken into account. A thorough overview on the geometric considerations, including the computation of the distance, is given in [3]. The architecture of the complete system is shown in fig. 2. First of all, from the data coming from the robot controllers (i.e. state space vectors), geometric information is extracted. This is given to the neural net. The output from the net is adapted to the needs of the robot control and given back to the controller of robot j.

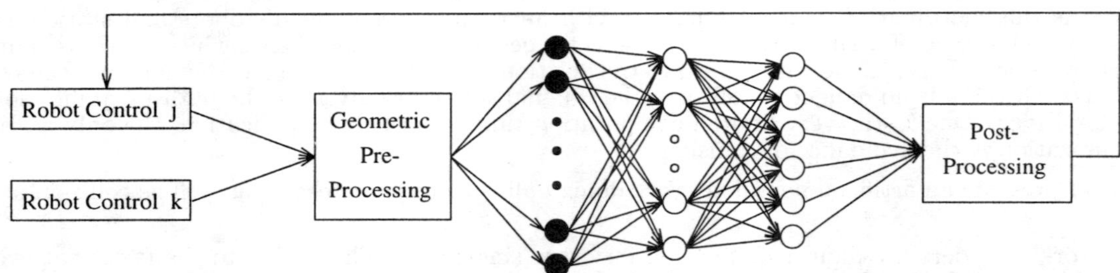

Figure 2: System architecture with data flow

3   Network architecture

The network architecture used is a feedforward net with one hidden layer. The input layer consists of 9 neurons:

Input	Description of input
1	Distance of robot arms
2/3	Height-relation of robot arms: (1,0) if $z_j < z_k$, (0,1) else
4/5	Relevant part of third link: (1,0) if TCP, (0,1) else
6/7	direction of rotation: (1,0) if $\dot{\varphi} > 0$, (0,1) else
8/9	(1,0) if z-axis is at upper or lower stop, (0,1) else

There is a single hidden layer with 10 neurons in it. The output layer consists of 6 neurons:

Output	Description of output
1/2	collision avoidance by z-axis
3/4	collision avoidance by r-axis
5/6	collision avoidance by φ-axis

The activation function used is the binary sigmoid:

$$f(net_i) = \frac{1}{1 + e^{-(net_i - K)}} \tag{1}$$

with K=5. As learning rule, the Relative Payoff Procedure [4] has been applied. The learning algorithm is as follows:

1. Initial setting of the connection weights by a random function. The values should be in the interval [0,1]:
$$w_{ij} = \mathcal{R}(0, 1) \tag{2}$$
with $\mathcal{R}(0, 1)$ a random value from the interval (0,1).

2. A second random function defines the initial state of the connections. If the value of the second function is greater than that of the connection, the connection will be set to *open*, otherwise to *closed*:
$$w_{ij}^* = \left\{ \begin{array}{ll} 1 & \text{if } w_{ij} > \mathcal{R}(0, 1) \\ 0 & \text{otherwise} \end{array} \right. \tag{3}$$

3. A sample pattern is given to the input layer, from this the output is calculated. If the distance between the robot arms is under a given threshold, the output layer is activated. In that case the trajectory of the robot is altered.

4. The error E is computed as difference between minimal distance with (r_{kj}^{net}) resp. without (r_{kj}) collision avoidance:
$$E = r_{kj}^{net} - r_{kj} \tag{4}$$
The minimal distance is taken from [3].

5. Now the weights of the connections are updated. The weights of the closed connections are increased, the weights of the open connections are decreased:
$$w_{ij} = \left\{ \begin{array}{ll} w_{ij} + \gamma E(1 - w_{ij}) & \text{if } w_{ij}^* = 1 \\ w_{ij} - \gamma E w_{ij} & \text{otherwise} \end{array} \right. \tag{5}$$
with γ as learning rate.

6. Steps 2 – 5 are repeated until a given value of E is reached. If γ is small (e.g. 1), the algorithm converges.

The learning is done without moving the robots, just by simulating their movements. This can be done within a robot simulation system, e.g. ROBCAD.

4 Simulation example

The example in fig. 3 shows a typical situation for collision avoidance. Robot 1 (on the left) turns around (-0.8,0.0) and starts at (-0.8,1.2), robot 2 turns around (1.0,0.0) and starts at (0.8,-1.0). The lower right window shows the top view of the final situation (i.e. after execution of the movements). The r-axis of robot 1 is shown in the upper left window, the z-axis in the upper right one, and the φ-axis in the middle left window. The planned trajectories are drawn in black, the actual ones in grey. Robot 1 does collision avoidance by altering all axes while robot 2 is moving his predefined path. The distance is shown in the lower left window, a secure distance is always kept.

The simulation is done with path interpolation as well as dynamic modeling and nonlinear decoupling and control. The learning of the net took 1000 cycles, the computation of the net during the application phase is neglectible with regard to the interpolation cycle of the robot control.

5 Conclusion

Even if global planning is done in multi-robot workcells, in real-world applications it is important to supervise the movements and to influence them if necessary. This is due to sensor driven changes of the trajectories, incomplete information of the environment and possible failures in devices. Therefore, precautions have to be taken for online collision detection and avoidance.

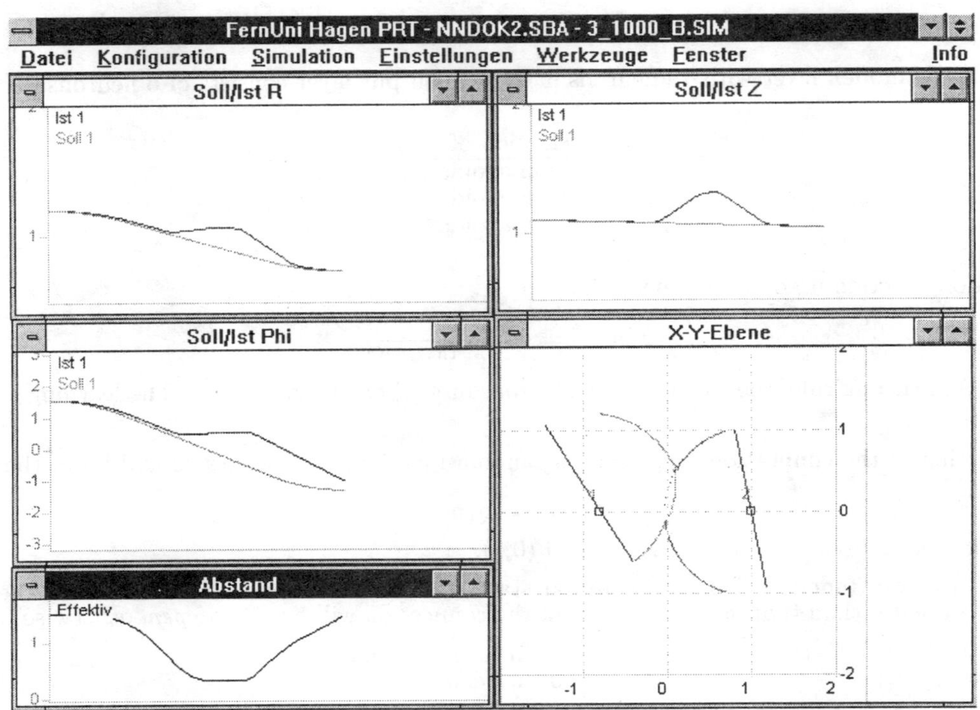

Figure 3: Example of collision avoidance

The method presented gives a new solution to this problem. A neural network is presented which can be trained to supervise the robot's motion. If a critical situation occurs, the trajectory will be altered. The network is easy to implement and fast to compute. It detects the danger of collisions and generates collision free trajectories while the robots are moving. Their dynamic behaviour and constraints are considered, too. The network can be adapted to different types of robot kinematic. This as well as the practical application to robot systems is currently in action in our laboratories.

References

[1] V.J. Lumelsky, "Effect of kinematics on motion planning for planar robot arms moving amidst unknown obstacles", *IEEE Journal of Robotics and Automation*, Vol. RA-3, pp. 207–223, 1987.

[2] O. Khatib, "Real-time obstacle avoidance for manipulators and mobile robots", *International Journal of Robotics Research*, Vol. 5, No. 1, pp. 90–98, 1986.

[3] U. Borgolte, "An online algorithm for three degrees-of-freedom collision avoidance", Proc. 2nd Singapore Int. Conf. on Intelligent Systems (SPICIS'94), Singapore 1994, pp. B454-B459.

[4] M. Köhle, *Neuronale Netze*. Berlin: Springer, 1990.

Population Coding of Hand Locational Direction in Proprioceptive Cortex

Min Jang and Sungzoon Cho
Department of Computer Science and Engineering
POSTECH Information Research Laboratories(PIRL)
Pohang University of Science and Technology(POSTECH)
San 31 Hyojadong, Pohang, 790–784, Korea
jmin@albireo.postech.ac.kr, zoon@vision.postech.ac.kr

Abstract— Proprioceptive information such as muscle length is conveyed to a part of somatosensory cortex which we call "proprioceptive cortex". A computational model of the proprioceptive cortex was recently developed. Using the model arm and the neural network, muscle length and tension information was found to be coded in the cortex. In this paper, we propose a hypothesis that the hand locational direction is populationally coded. Each unit has its preferred direction along which it is maximally activated. As the hand or the end point of the model arm moves in three dimensional space, the population vector of the weighted sum of the directionally tuned units in the model cortex is computed. Simulation results show that the population vector predicts the directional vector of the hand location with 95% confidence.

1 Introduction

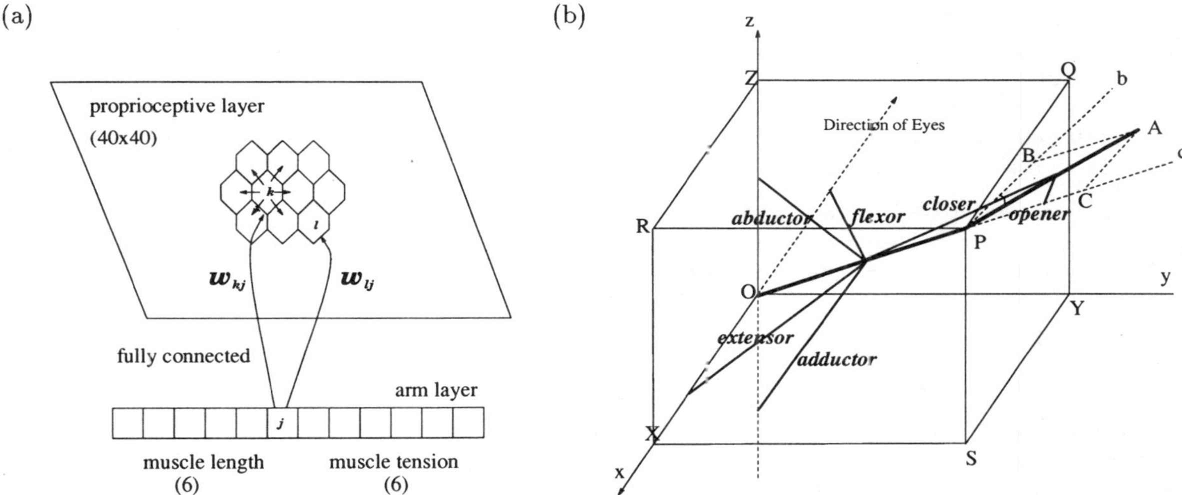

Figure 1: (a) The network has two separate layers of units, the arm layer and proprioceptive layer. The arm layer contains six length units and six tension units. The proprioceptive layer consists of a grid of 40×40 laterally connected units in hexagonal tessellation. Competitive distribution of activation was used to induce lateral inhibition among units without using inhibitory connections. (b) The model arm is considered as the right arm of a human facing the negative x-axis and controlled by three pairs of antagonistic muscles (or groups of muscles), extensor, flexor, abductor, adductor, opener and closer. The points O, P and A denote the locations of the shoulder, elbow and hand of the idealized model arm, respectively.

Proprioception refers to sensory input from the musculoskeletal system, which includes the input from muscle and tendon receptors as well as joint receptors [5]. Proprioceptive cortex as a part of somatosensory cortex plays an important role to transfer the proprioceptive senses from muscles to the motor cortex. Recently a model of computational feature map formation in proprioceptive cortex was developed (see Fig. 1(a)) [2]. Given an arbitrary neuronal input from motor cortex, the corresponding muscle length and tension information is computed according to the geometry of the model arm, and provided as the input to proprioceptive layer. After repeated presentation of various input patterns, the cortical layer developed a feature map consisting of regularly spaced clusters of cortical columns tuned to stretch and to tension of individual muscles (see Fig. 2).

In addition, muscle length was found to be coded by the number of active tuned units [4]. That is, as a muscle stretches (increased muscle length), the number of active units tuned to that muscle increases and that of active units tuned to its antagonistic muscle decreases. In [2], we also concluded that hand location information is encoded in the cortex. Stripes of units tuned to certain hand locations in 3-D space were found. We propose in this paper that the hand location direction of the model arm is encoded by a population of directionally tuned units. Numerical simulation was carried out to support the hypothesis.

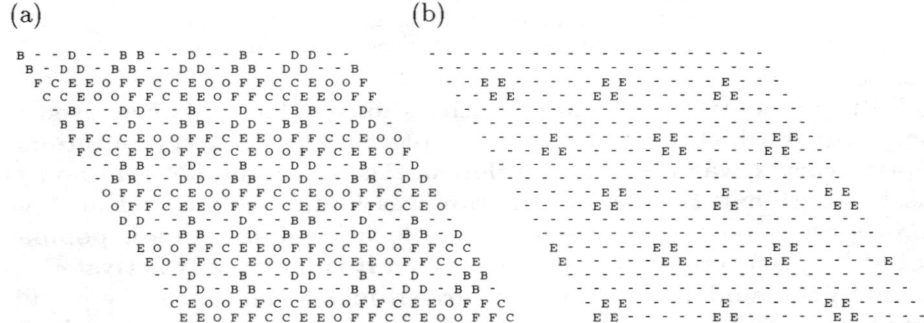

Figure 2: (a) Tuning of cotical units to the maximally stretched muscle length in a 20×20 proprioceptive layer. Labels E, F, B, D, O and C represent upper arm extensor and flexor, upper arm abductor and adductor, lower arm opener and closer, respectively. Units marked with "-" character were not found tuned to any muscle. (b) Tuning of cortical units to only extensor length.

The population coding scheme was originally proposed by Georgeopoulos and his colleagues as a mechanism in the motor cortex to represent hand movement direction of a primate arm. He found that each neuron in motor cortex was tuned to its preferred direction along which each neuron was maximally activated [3]. Given an arm movement direction, he could compute the population vector by a weighted sum of preferred direction vectors of all neurons. It was then verified that the population vector could predict the direction of an arm movement with 95% confidence.

In the next section, a brief introduction of the model arm, cortical network, activation dynamics and learning rule is given. Then we present the way to identify preferred direction of each unit and to compute population vector. Simulation results are followed by conclusions.

2   Methods

The model arm which is a great simplification of biological reality consists of two segments we call the upper arm and the lower arm, connected at the elbow (see Fig. 1(b)). The model arm is fixed at the shoulder and has six generic muscles or muscle groups. We assume that there are four muscles that control the upper arm and two muscles that control the lower arm. These "muscles" correspond to multiple muscles in a real arm. Since there is no motor cortex in the model, input activation to muscles to control the arm is randomly generated. Given this input activation, the expected proprioceptive information from muscle, i.e., muscle length and tension is computed. The length and tension values of six muscles represent proprioceptive inputs of the model.

The neural network has two separate layers of units. The arm layer consists of 12 units which represent six muscle length and six tension values. How to compute length and tension values is in [2]. The proprioceptive layer consists of a grid of 40×40 which represents proprioceptive cortex and each unit is connected to its laterally connected neighboring units forming a hexagonal tessellation.

Both arm layer units and proprioceptive layer units distribute activation "competitively". The activation level of unit k at time t, $a_k(t)$ is determined by

$$\frac{da_k(t)}{dt} = -4a_k(t) + (5 - a_k(t)) \sum_{j \in N_k} 0.9 \frac{a_k(k)w_{kj}}{\sum_{j \in N_l} a_l(t)w_{lj}} a_j(t), \tag{1}$$

where N_k denotes the set of all neighboring units within the lateral connection radius distance of 3 from unit k. The numbers of units within distance 1, 2, and 3 from unit k are 6, 12 and 18, respectively. Thus, the total number of units in N_k is 36.

Connection weights are modified according to the competitive learning, a variant of Hebbian learning. The particular learning rule used is adapted from [6].

$$\Delta w_{kj} = -\eta[a_j - w_{kj}]a_k^*$$

(2)

$$a_k^* = \begin{cases} a_k - \theta & \text{if } a_k > \theta \\ 0 & \text{otherwise} \end{cases}$$

(3)

where learning rate η and threshold θ are set to 0.1 and 0.32, respectively.

(a)   (b)

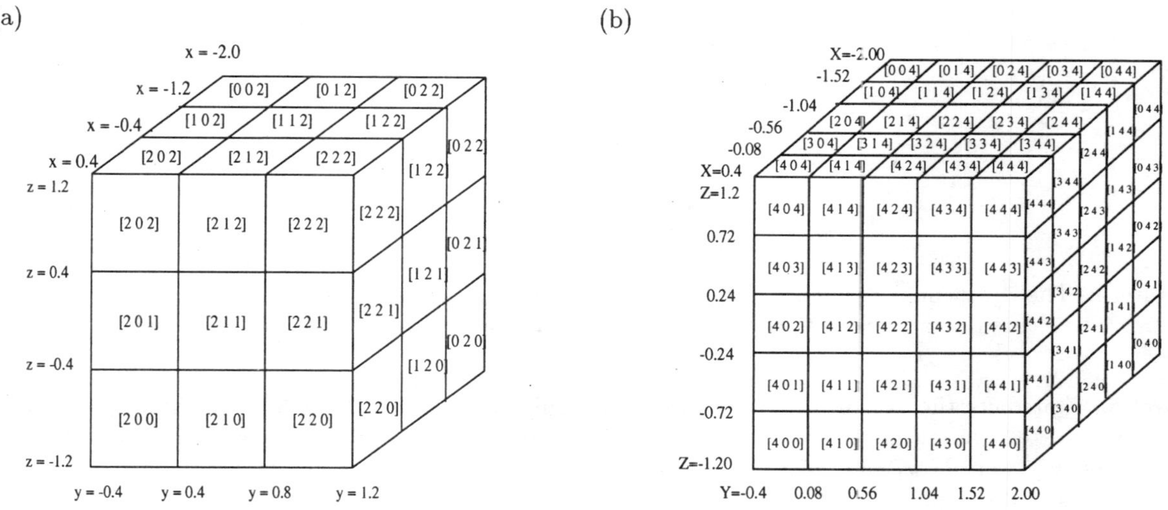

Figure 3: Partitioning of the 3-D hand movement space when the number of cubicles is (a) 3^3 and (b) 5^3

If unit k is maximally activated when the hand of the model arm is located at $\vec{x}_k$, $\vec{x}_k$ is defined as the "preferred direction" of unit k. For each unit, we identify the preferred direction vector. In order to reduce the computational cost involved in continuously varying directions in 3-D space, we chose a discretized approximation scheme. The 3-D space where the model arm's hand moves was divided into 3^3 and 5^3 equally sized cubicles (see Fig. 3). Then the preferred directions were determined among the center locations of the cubicles.

The activation level of unit k when the hand was located at $\vec{l}(l_x, l_y, l_x)$ is denoted by $a_k(\vec{l})$. If a given vector $\vec{l}$ equals $\vec{x}_k$, unit k will be maximally activated. If, on the other hand, $\vec{l}$ is opposite to $\vec{x}_k$, unit k will be minimally activated or at its resting level. For those intermediate directions, unit k will be activated accordingly, i.e., somewhere between maximal and minimal values.

Finally, the population vector $\vec{p}(\vec{l})$ with the hand located at $\vec{l}$, is defined as a weighted sum of preferred directions of all units in the cortex,

$$\vec{p}(\vec{l}) = \sum_{i=1}^{1600} a_k(\vec{l})\vec{x}_k.$$

(4)

3   Simulation Results

We placed the hand at the center of each cubicle, thus $\vec{l}$ at a total of 26 and 98 different locations for 3^3 and 5^3 cubicle cases, respectively. The corresponding population vector $\vec{p}(\vec{l})$ was computed and compared with the actual locational direction $\vec{l}$. Two prediction measures introduced by Georgeopoulos were used. One is *directional difference* ϕ in degree between two vectors $\vec{l}$ and $\vec{p}(\vec{l})$. The other is *confidence*, defined as one minus the ratio of the surface area of the cone formed by $\vec{l}$ and $\vec{p}(\vec{l})$ and the surface area of a unit sphere (see Fig. 4). If the two vectors are equal, ϕ becomes $0°$ and confidence becomes 100%. If, on the other hand, the two vectors are of an opposite direction, ϕ becomes $360°$ and confidence becomes 0%. A smaller ϕ and a higher confidence level imply strong congruence of the two vectors, thus high prediction ability of $\vec{l}$ by $\vec{p}(\vec{l})$.

Fig. 5 shows a typical prediction of $\vec{l}$ by $\vec{p}(\vec{l})$ with the locational direction, population vector and weighted preferred direction vectors when the hand was located at the center of cubicles [3 0 2]. The populational

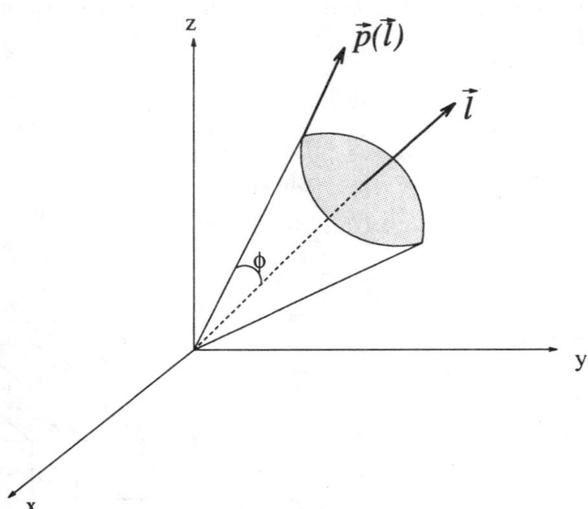

Figure 4: The directional difference defined as the difference between $\vec{l}$ and $\vec{p}(\vec{l})$ is the angle ϕ in the figure. The shaded area represents the surface area of the cone formed by the two vectors.

direction $\vec{p}$ predicts the actual locational direction $\vec{l}$ quite well. Table 1 for 3^3 case shows all 26 hand locations, corresponding population vectors and predictability measures. Average directional difference and confidence were 17.97° and 95.01%, respectively. Both locational direction and population direction were normalized. A given locational direction was predicted by a populational direction with a high confidence level. The difference in the predictability of the population vector seems to be accounted for by the difference in the frequency of cubicles. Those cubicles with a high frequency value tend to have a smaller ϕ and higher confidence level as exemplified by cubicle [1 0 1]. The worst predictability case, on the other hand, came from cubicle [2 0 0] which has one of the lowest frequency values.

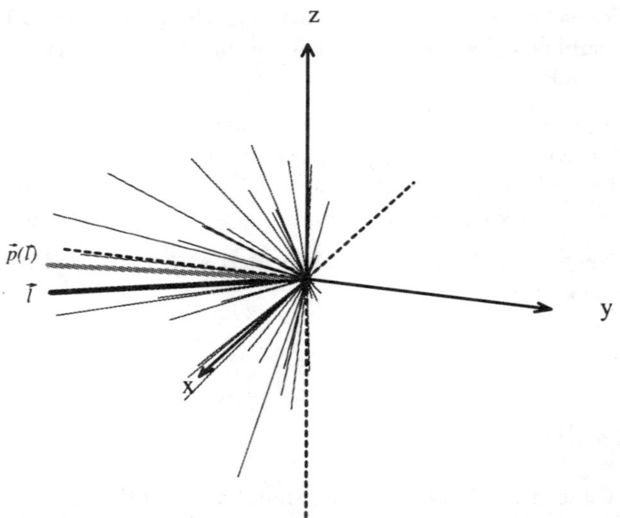

Figure 5: A Typical prediction of $\vec{l}$ by $\vec{p}(\vec{l})$. The thick black line represents the hand locational direction vector $\vec{l}$ (0.493, −0.870, 0.002) (the center of cubicle [3, 0, 2]). The thick gray line represents the corresponding population direction vector $\vec{p}(\vec{l})$ (0.387, −0.919, 0.074). Both $\vec{l}$ and $\vec{p}(\vec{l})$ are normalized. Thin lines represent the weighted preferred direction vectors of all the units. The directional difference ϕ between $\vec{l}$ and $\vec{p}(\vec{l})$ was 13.0° and confidence was 96%.

When the number of cubicles is 5^3, the average directional difference and confidence increased to 37.7° and decreased to 89.5%, respectively. The lower predictability with 5^3 cubicles seems to be caused by the lack of cortical units, or the low resolution of preferred direction space. When the space is divided too densely, there are not enough units to specialize on individual cubicles. Use of a larger network could alleviate this problem.

Table 1: To each of 26 cubicle centers does locational vector correspond. Frequency represents how likely a randomly generated hand location is placed in that cubicle. The resultant population vector, the directional difference and confidence values are shown. Maximum, minimum and average confidence are 99.06% (cubicle [1 0 1]), 82.12% (cubicle [2 0 0]) and 95.01%, respectively. Cubicles are labeled according to its positional ordering as shown in Fig. 3.

cubicle	frequency(%)	hand direction $\vec{l}$	population direction $\vec{p}(\vec{l})$	ϕ (degree)	confidence (%)
[0 0 0]	0.45	(-0.57, -0.51, -0.65)	(-0.50, -0.36, -0.79)	12.373	96.56
[0 0 1]	9.12	(-0.68, -0.73, -0.00)	(-0.69, -0.71, 0.14)	8.478	97.64
[0 0 2]	0.39	(-0.56, -0.56, 0.61)	(-0.65, -0.55, 0.53)	6.836	98.10
[0 1 0]	1.90	(-0.64, -0.02, -0.77)	(-0.33, 0.35, -0.88)	28.063	92.20
[0 1 1]	6.37	(-1.00, -0.05, 0.02)	(-0.85, 0.46, 0.26)	34.272	90.48
[0 1 2]	2.01	(-0.65, -0.02, 0.76)	(-0.78, -0.17, 0.60)	14.768	95.90
[0 2 0]	0.20	(-0.51, 0.60, -0.62)	(-0.58, 0.79, -0.21)	26.395	92.67
[0 2 1]	0.55	(-0.63, 0.78, -0.02)	(-0.75, 0.65, 0.09)	12.214	96.61
[0 2 2]	0.06	(-0.60, 0.55, 0.58)	(-0.87, 0.35, 0.35)	23.495	93.47
[1 0 0]	2.42	(-0.08, -0.58, -0.81)	(-0.01, -0.13, -0.99)	28.396	92.11
[1 0 1]$^{+}$	17.54	(0.03, -1.00, -0.01)	(0.08, -1.00, 0.03)	3.376	99.06
[1 0 2]	2.45	(-0.07, -0.60, 0.80)	(0.04, -0.31, 0.95)	19.677	94.53
[1 1 0]	6.55	(-0.03, 0.02, -1.00)	(0.10, -0.04, -0.99)	8.372	97.67
[1 1 2]	6.45	(-0.03, 0.06, 1.00)	(0.11, -0.17, 0.98)	15.519	95.69
[1 2 0]	2.29	(0.10, 0.70, -0.71)	(-0.14, 0.67, -0.73)	14.323	96.02
[1 2 1]	5.10	(0.07, 1.00, 0.02)	(-0.02, 0.99, -0.14)	10.334	97.13
[1 2 2]	2.60	(0.08, 0.68, 0.73)	(-0.22, 0.63, 0.75)	17.980	95.01
[2 0 0]$^{-}$	0.07	(0.59, -0.60, -0.54)	(0.74, 0.45, -0.50)	64.368	82.12
[2 0 1]	5.36	(0.64, -0.77, 0.00)	(0.42, -0.89, 0.17)	17.506	95.14
[2 0 2]	0.02	(0.47, -0.42, 0.78)	(0.43, -0.12, 0.89)	18.389	94.89
[2 1 0]	1.60	(0.68, 0.13, -0.72)	(0.70, 0.45, -0.55)	21.090	94.14
[2 1 1]	3.07	(1.00, 0.09, -0.03)	(0.90, 0.43, -0.09)	20.623	94.27
[2 1 2]	1.56	(0.67, 0.12, 0.74)	(0.70, -0.06, 0.71)	10.539	97.07
[2 2 0]	2.73	(0.58, 0.60, -0.55)	(0.67, 0.60, -0.44)	8.027	97.77
[2 2 1]	4.29	(0.68, 0.73, 0.02)	(0.70, 0.69, -0.18)	11.701	96.75
[2 2 2]	2.35	(0.61, 0.57, 0.55)	(0.62, 0.67, 0.41)	10.005	97.22

4 Conclusions

In this paper, we showed by simulation that hand locational direction might be coded by a population of directionally tuned units in the proprioceptive cortex. We first identified the preferred locational direction of each unit, to which the unit was maximally activated. Given an arbitrary hand locational direction, the populational direction vector was computed by summing the weighted preferred directions of active cortical units. Then the population vector was compared with the hand location vector and found to predict the latter with 95% confidence on average. The result could not be validated against physiological data, unfortunately, due to lack of the available data. However, future biological study could test the prediction. As movement direction was shown to be coded by a population of directionally tuned neurons in motor cortex, it is likely that a similar coding mechanism is also present in a sensory area of the cortex. We plan to examine the coding properties of the motor cortex model developed alongside the proprioceptive cortex in [1]. In particular, we will investigate the movement direction in the motor cortex of the combined model.

Acknowledgement

This study was supported by KOSEF grant 941-0900-031-02.

References

[1] Y. Chen and J. Reggia. Alignment of coexisting cortical maps in a motor control model. *Neural Computation*, 1995. submitted.

[2] S. Cho and J. Reggia. Map formation in proprioceptive cortex. *International Journal of Neural Systems*, 5(2):87–101, 1994.

[3] A. Georgeopoulos, A. Schwartz, and R. Kettner. Neuronal population coding of movement direction. *Science*, 233:1416–1419, 1986.

[4] M. Jang and S. Cho. Population coding properties of muscle length in proprioceptive cortex. In *Proceedings of the International Conference on Artifical Neural Networks*, pages 531–534, 1995.

[5] G. Shepherd. *Neurobiology*. Oxford University Press, Oxford, UK, 1988.

[6] C. von der Malsburg. Self-organization of orientation sensitive cells in the striate cortex. *Kybernetic*, pages 85–100, 1973.

Optimal Trajectory Generation for an Industrial Robot by Markovian Networks*

Jan Puzicha†, Nils Goerke‡ and Rolf Eckmiller‡
† Institut für Informatik III, jan@cs.uni-bonn.de
‡ Institut für Informatik VI, {goerke,eckmiller}@nero.uni-bonn.de
University of Bonn, F. R. Germany

Abstract— Optimal trajectory generation can be represented as a constrained variational problem posed simultaneously in cartesian and joint coordinate spaces. Markovian Networks are presented as a class of neural networks especially suited for solving general constrained variational problems. By incorporation of the kinematic map an iterative network dynamic is created, which gradually converges to an optimal solution. The capability of this approach is demonstrated by generating optimal 6–DOF movements along surfaces for an industrial robot arm with remarkable improvements compared to a standard algorithm.

1 Introduction

The generation of optimal robot trajectories is difficult for two reasons. First, optimality conditions are posed simultaneously in cartesian and joint spaces, as constraints like constant distance to a surface or approximately constant tool velocity as well as maximal values for position, velocity and acceleration of joints have to be satisfied [3]. The special property of the selected algorithm is its ability to optimize simultaneously in both spaces. Second, there is a growing need for fulfilling abstract quality demands specified through a priori unknown cost functions, e.g. minimal variation in film thickness in spray coating of complex surfaces [1]. We thus take an abstracting step towards high level planning by specifying the optimal trajectory as a general constrained variational problem.

Markovian Networks are presented as a class of neural networks with local interactions and iterative dynamics (like the dynamics of Hopfield–Nets or Boltzmann–Machines) [4, 7, 11]. They are closely related to the statistical framework of Markov–Random–Fields [4], which has been used to solve complex optimization problems with topological structured variables [5]. In this work we develop Markovian Networks for solving constraint variational problems and apply them on the formation of optimal trajectories by incorporating the forward kinematic map in the definition of a network dynamic. The neural algorithms are tested by generating trajectories along surfaces for a 6–DOF industrial manipulator, as it is important in industrial applications like welding or spray coating [1].

2 Trajectory Generation

Most tasks of a manipulator require one of the following types of movements: point–to–point, pick–and–place, path tracking (no time specification), trajectory tracking (with time specification) and movements along surfaces. The different tasks need different optimality conditions like approximately constant distance to a surface or minimal cartesian accelerations to be fulfilled for the executed trajectory. The robotic hardware dynamic limits possible movements, e.g. by means of maximal values for position, velocity and acceleration of each joint. The example constraints can be stated as in a variational formulation using some distance measure D (including orientation deviation) and denoting the cartesian trajectory by $Y(t)$ and the corresponding joint trajectory by $\Theta(t)$:

$$J_1[Y] \;=\; \int_a^b \left(Y''(t)\right)^2 dt \qquad\qquad \text{(minimal cartesian acceleration)}, \qquad (1)$$

$$J_2[Y] \;=\; \int_a^b D\left(Y(t), \text{surface} + c \cdot \text{surface-normal}\right) dt \qquad \text{(distance to surface)}.$$

The robot specific hard constraint can be expressed by the condition $G[\Theta] = 0$ with

$$G[\Theta] \;=\; \int_a^b \sum_{i \text{ is joint}} \Big[(\Theta_i(t) - \Theta_{i,max})_+ + (\Theta_i'(t) - \Theta_{i,max}')_+ + (\Theta_i''(t) - \Theta_{i,max}'')_+ \qquad (2)$$

$$+ (\Theta_{i,max} - \Theta_i(t))_+ + (\Theta_{i,max}' - \Theta_i'(t))_+ + (\Theta_{i,max}'' - \Theta_i''(t))_+ \Big] dt.$$

*Supported by the Federal Ministry for Education, Science, Research, and Technology (BMBF) for project DEMON and partially by the German Research Foundation (DFG).

The formalism is easily extended to further constraints. By a weighted summation $J[Y] = \sum_i w_i J_i[Y]$ of competing optimality conditions this defines a general (constrained) variational problem in two coupled coordinate spaces [11]: minimize

$$J[Y] = \int_a^b F(t, Y(t), Y'(t), \ldots, Y^{(n)}(t))dt \tag{3}$$

with a vector valued function $Y \in C^2(a, b)$ as the variational parameter, given boundary values $a, b, Y(a) = y_a, Y(b) = y_b$ and a differentiable function F under the constraint $G[\Theta] = 0$.

The tasks of a manipulator can be classified according to their difficulty:

- Tasks with optimality conditions exclusively in the joint domain can often be solved easily [3].

- For time optimal movements there exists a large number of approaches (see the references in [11]).

- Cartesian path tracking can be solved by recursive pointwise mapping using a differential inverse kinematic map and applying interpolation [3] and rescaling [8] techniques in the joint domain.

- Time dependent cartesian movements, especially when the type of deviation is crucial (as in the surface scenario), have to be optimized simultaneously in both spaces [3].

There exist a vast amount of heuristic approaches to trajectory formation, but these hardly solve the last type of problems, because they decouple kinematic map and optimization and thus lead to sub–optimal or useless trajectories (see discussion and references in [11]). We thus focus on tasks of this type.

3   Markovian Networks

A Markovian Network constitutes itself of *state variables*, called neurons or nodes, and a *local neighborhood* defining possible dependencies among the variables. The state of a neuron changes during the optimization process depending on the state of neighboring neurons according to an asynchronous stochastic or deterministic update rule, called the *dynamic* of the Markovian Network. The local neighborhood guarantees a parallel update yielding fast, iterative algorithms. In the robotic application the position of the robot at a specific time instant is coded through a (vectoriell) state of a neuron. During optimization the manipulator position at a time instant is asynchronously optimized given the positions before and after.

Using the nomenclature known from the MRF–framework [5] a Markovian Network can be stated as a tuple $(\mathcal{S}, \mathcal{G}, T, V, D_i)$ with a *graph* $(\mathcal{S}, \mathcal{G})$, a realization of a family of (random) variables $T := (T_s)_{s \in \mathcal{S}}$ with state space $\Omega := \bigotimes_{s \in \mathcal{S}} \Lambda_s$ and a network dynamic defined by a *site visitation schedule* $V : I\!N \to \mathcal{S}$ and a stochastic or deterministic map $D : I\!N \times \Omega \to \Omega$ with the following properties:

1. $D_l(\vec{t}) = D(l, \{t_1, \ldots, t_n\}) = \{t_1, \ldots, t_{V(l-1)}, \tilde{t}_{V(l)}, t_{V(l+1)}, \ldots, t_n\}$. This defines an asynchronous update rule of the network by changing solely $t_{V(l)}$.

2. $D_l(\{t_s : s \in \mathcal{S}\}) = D_l(\{t_s : s \in \mathcal{G}_{V(l)}\})$. The state change of the neuron $V(l)$ thus depends only on the current state of the neighborhood $\mathcal{G}_{V(l)}$ of that neuron.

Let $\mathcal{S} = \{t_i : i = 1, \ldots, n\}$ be a discretization of $[a, b]$. Approximating the derivatives by symmetric differences [6] the function F in (3) can then be approximated by the variational function values at t_i and at a neighborhood of t_i:

$$F\left(t_i, Y(t_i), Y'(t_i), \ldots, Y^{(n)}(t_i)\right) \approx F_i\left(t_i, Y(t_i), Y(t_j)|t_j \in \mathcal{G}_{t_i}\right). \tag{4}$$

The neighborhood $\mathcal{G}_{t_i}$ depends only on the chosen approximation for the derivatives and is typically small. $(\mathcal{G}_i)_{t \in \mathcal{S}}$ as a neighborhood system of $\mathcal{S}$ thus defines a graph. Approximating functional (3) yields a sum of (clique–dependent) potentials.

$$J[Y] \approx \sum_{t_i \in \mathcal{S}} F_i(t_i, Y(t_i), Y(t_j)|t_j \in \mathcal{G}_{t_i}). \tag{5}$$

Using the ICM–algorithm [2] this can be used to define a network dynamic gradually converging to the solution:

$$D_{l,V(l)}(\vec{t}) = \arg \min_{w \in \Lambda_{V(l)}} J(t_1, \ldots, t_{V(l-1)}, w, t_{V(l+1)}, \ldots, t_n) \tag{6}$$

with $D_l(\vec{t}) = (D_{l,k}(\vec{t}))_{k=1,\ldots,n}$. In the robotic application the minimization in (6) solely has to be carried out varying the robot position at one time instant. For this low–dimensional optimization we decided to use the Method of Powell as described in [10].

For trajectory optimization we use the joint representation $\Theta_i = \Theta(t_i)$ and incorporate the (fast computable) forward kinematic map in the network dynamic to compute the cartesian representation Y. To satisfy the hard constraint (2) we apply a penalty function method [6] by choosing a monotonically increasing schedule $L : \mathbb{N} \to \mathbb{R}$ with $\lim_{l \to \infty} L(l) = \infty$. Adding the discretization of (2) to (5) we define a potential function J_l

$$J_l[Y] \approx \sum_{t_i \in \mathcal{S}} F_i(t_i, Y(t_i), Y(t_j)|t_j \in \mathcal{G}_{t_i}) + L(l) \cdot G[t_i, \Theta_i, \Theta_j | j \in \tilde{\mathcal{G}}_{t_i}]] \tag{7}$$

relative to a modified Graph $\left(\mathcal{S}, (\tilde{\mathcal{G}}_t \cup \mathcal{G}_t)_{t \in \mathcal{S}} \right)$. Note that J_l depends on the iterating index l of the network dynamic.

Plugging (7) into (6) defines a Markovian Network $\left(\{t_i\}, (\tilde{\mathcal{G}}_t \cup \mathcal{G}_t)_{t \in \mathcal{S}}, \{y_i\}, D_l(J_l) \right)$ gradually converging to a solution of the constrained variational problem.

4   Results

We tested the neural algorithms by generating movements along surfaces for the industrial robot Manutec r2. As examples we present here the the drawing of an '8' specified by 21 via-points on a table as illustrated in Fig. 1a and drawing the letter 'b' specified by 81 via-points on a hemisphere as illustrated in Fig. 2a. The optimal movement is specified by integrating over the distance between trajectory and surface (with higher weighting of points in the interior of the object) and summing over distance and orientation angle (as illustrated in Fig. 2a) between trajectory and via-points.

The generated trajectories are subject to constraint (2) with maximal values specified by the controller of the manipulator. Note that the algorithms are easily extendible to more complex dynamic models of the robot. The network was initialized by splining the via-points together and computing the corresponding joint trajectory using a regularized differential inverse kinematic. This is an elaborated 'state of the art' method for trajectory generation from a sequence of via-points [9].

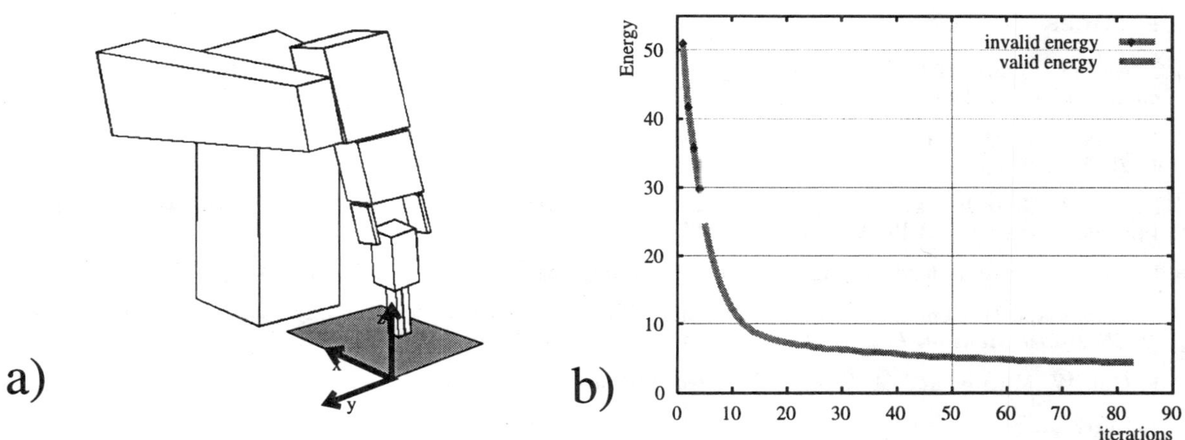

Figure 1: In (a) the robot drawing on a table is illustrated. In (b) the optimization progress for the chosen example is depicted. It demonstrates a significant improvement of the initial solution. Especially the computed solution becomes kinematically valid after a few iterations.

In Fig. 1b the optimization progress for the table example is illustrated. We like to point out that the initialization computed by a 'state of the art' method is kinematically invalid, thus not executable on the robot. After a few iterations the trajectory becomes valid. In Fig. 2b the optimization progress for the hemisphere example is illustrated. It corresponds to an improvement of the average distance of the trajectory to the object from 3.9mm to 0.1mm and of the maximal distance from 16.8mm to 0.8mm. The average distance from the via-points was improved from 1.6mm to 0.16mm. Improvements of this order of magnitude are crucial to enable industrial applications like welding or spray coating. The technical details as well as many more examples and an empirical analysis of the behavior of the algorithms can be found in [11]. The presented examples were validated with the real robot.

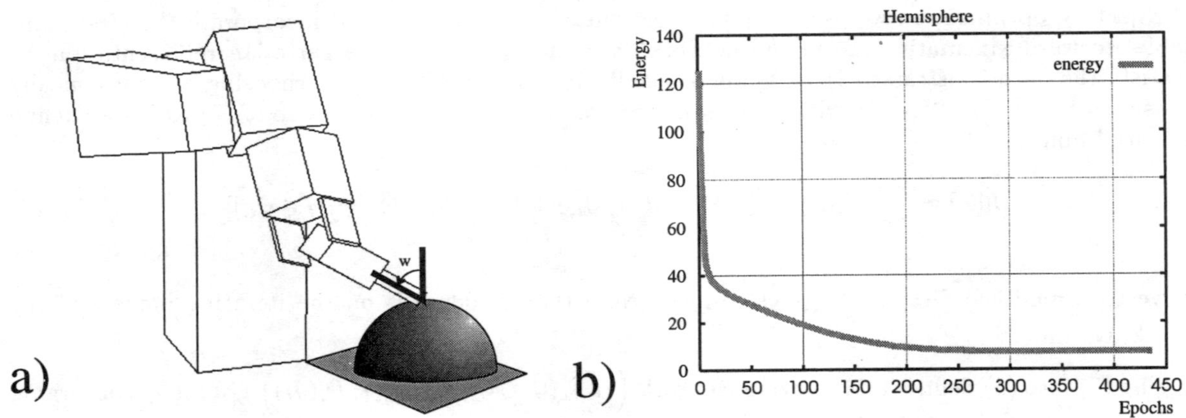

Figure 2: In (a) the scenario of the robot drawing on a hemisphere is illustrated. The angle w illustrates a deviation of the optimal orientation. In (b) the optimization progress for the chosen example is shown. It demonstrates a significant improvement of the initial solution.

5 Conclusion

By posing the task of optimal trajectory generation as a general constrained variational problem simultaneously operating in cartesian and joint space we make an abstracting step towards high level planning. This formulation is well–suited for manipulator applications requiring time dependent cartesian optimality conditions as e.g. welding or spray coating.

We applied Markovian Networks to gradually compute optimal trajectories by extending the definition of the iterative network dynamic to solve constraint variational problems. We used the neural algorithms for the computation of optimal movement trajectories for an industrial robot with remarkable improvements compared to standard algorithms, as demanded by important industrial applications.

References

[1] J. Antonio. Optimal trajectory planning for spray coating. In *Proceedings of the International Conference on Robotics and Automation*, pages 2570–2577, 1994.

[2] J. Besag. On the statistical analysis of dirty pictures. *Journal of the Royal Statistical Society, Series B*, 48:25–37, 1986.

[3] K. Fu, R. Gonzales, and C. Lee. *Robotics: Control, Sensing, Vision and Intelligence*, chapter 4, pages 149–200. McGraw-Hill Book Company, 1987.

[4] D. Geman. Random fields and inverse problems in imaging. *Lecture Notes Mathematics*, 1427:117–193, 1990.

[5] S. Geman and D. Geman. Stochastic relaxation, Gibbs distributions, and the Bayesian restoration of images. *IEEE Transactions on Pattern Analysis and Machine Intelligence*, 6(6):721–741, 1984.

[6] P. Gill, W. Murray, and M. Wright. *Practical Optimization*. Academic Press, 1981.

[7] J. Hertz, A. Krogh, and R. Palmer. *Introduction to the Theory of Neural Computation*. Addis. Wesley, 1991.

[8] J. Hollerbach. Dynamic scaling of manipulator trajectories. Technical report, MIT AI–Memo 700, 1983.

[9] Y. Nakamura. *Advanced Robotics, Redundancy and Optimisation*. Addison–Wesley, 1991.

[10] W. Press, S. Teukolsky, W. Vetterling, and B. Flannery. *Numerical Recipes in C*. Cambridge University Press, 2. edition, 1992.

[11] J. Puzicha. Neuronale Generierung von Trajektorien aus Bewegungsanforderungen. Diploma thesis, University of Bonn, 1995.

A New Component Architecture Approach for CBP Neural Networks

Chan-ho Park*   Hyon-soo Lee**

*,**Dept. of Computer Engineering,KyungHee University,
Kyunggi-Do,Youngin-Kun,Kihueng-Eup,Sochon-Ri 1,Korea.
E-mail : chpark@ss-10.kyunghee.ac.kr

ABSTRACT

Multi Layer Perceptron(MLP) with Error Backpropagation algorithm has generalization capability and nonlinearity. It has been applied to solve some pattern recognition and classification problems successfully. The size of this network is determined by the number of neurons and connections of each layers. But connections between the layers are fully connected so this topological overhead bring about increase of network size and slow learning convergence time.

In order to solve above disadvantages , we have proposed new component neural network which perform independent learning in each component networks by dividing MLP network structure. But that network has a weakness of generalization capability and it has same problems of EBP algorithms that are used in each component network.

In this paper , we propose new CBP network. Here, input and output pattern vectors are patitioned into abstract vectors for component networks. For improving of generalization capability of CBP, we add AOG (Abstract Output Generator) instead of TG. Simulation results shows better results compared to CBP[1] and EBP.

1. INTRODUCTION

Multilayer perpectron network with error backpropagation algorithm has fully connections between the upper and lower layer. This structure incurs difficulty of learning because all the trainig patterns are expressed as complex functions in a network. In other words , all the weights should be adapted to train given patterns in common. So, as given pattern's functional complexity of a problem is high, more and more difficult to solve a problem on only one weight domain.

There exists some methods that decompose training patterns into several clustered patterns according to similarities of that and these networks learn patterns by adapting adequate parameters. The representative networks are CMAC(Cellular Model Arithmatic Computer)[2] ,RBF(Radial Basis Function)[3], and Modular Network[4]. Among above networks , CMAC network needs a lot of memory capacity. In case of RBF, it has adventages of fast learning but the numbers of reactive region very increase as data size and has low generalization capability. Modular Networks has high ganeralization capability and fast speeds for learning but because the number of input and output neurons of each modular networks are large that it has a problem of networks size overhead.

Another approach is Pao's FUN(Functional Link Network)[5]. this network perform linear classification of training patterns like one layer perceptrons by adding combinational logic units to input layer. But if the size of input patterns are large then many combinational logic units are needed. In this case, this network is hard to use in practice.

For solve above problems , we have already proposed CBP network[1] by partitioning ordinary MLP network into small component netwroks and this netwroks showed enhanced network's performance results. But CBP network has critical problems on generalization capability. Beacause threshold values which are used for same input patterns in component network are minutely determined in case of large data , learning speeds decrease.   And each component networks with using EBP algorithm have same weaknesses of that algorithm.

In this paper , we peropose new CBP network and algorithm by analyzing CBP network[1]. In CBP , original input and output pattern vectors are partitioned and partitioned training patterns perform fast learning procedure in small component networks. But because each partitioned patterns are learned independently and each weights of component networks are adapted by it's own partitioned input patterns only that if partitioned input is unknown then component networks can not produce correct output when threshold values of each correct and unknown input patterns are same and this unknown input pattern is already trained to produce different output . To overcome this, all the input pattern vector values should be adapted by each component networks.

In proposed network , we increase generalizaton capability by using AOG(Abstract Output Generator) instead of TG[1]. Original input patterns and abstract output patterns are used in AOG and these outputs are propagated into each component networks. In component networks, abstract output patterns of AOG are used as inputs and partitioned original outputs are used. Here , same input patterns can not exists in component networks and TG is not used. In this network , small component network can be reused in a problem or in another problems if required training patterns are same in a network. These adventages are efficiently applied to hardware implementation and weight memory size can decreas. In addition to, each component network can use FUN algorithm instead of EBP algorithm in order to increase learning speed.

2. CBP(Component Back Propagation) Algorithm

We have proposed CBP network[1] composed of two different structures. One is component networks that perform learning for partitioned input and output patterns. The other is threshold generator that output threshold values which are used in components networks during learning and recall procedure. The number of output neurons are same that the number of component networks and the single threshold value is propagated to hidden neurons in each component networks. Fig1. shows the structure of CBP neural network. In fig.1 the network topology of each component networks and threshold generator are same that of MLP.

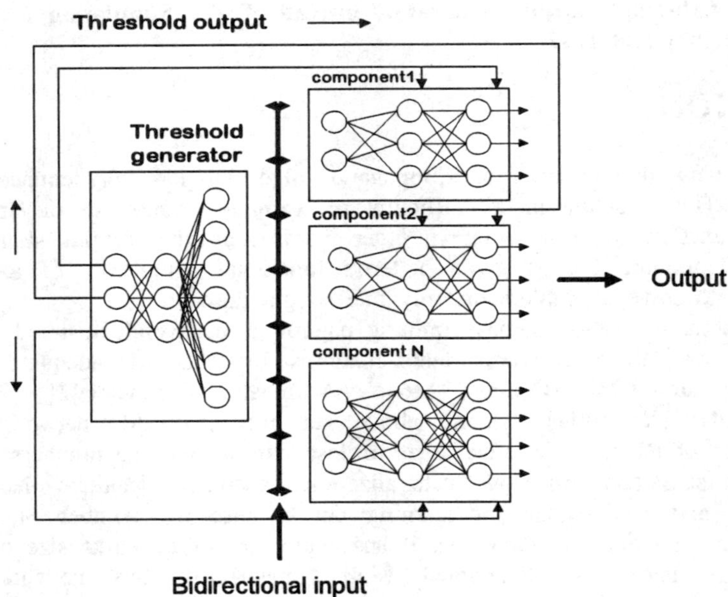

Figure 1. Component BackPropagation network architecture[1].

A ordinary CBP learning algorithm follows next strategy. first. each component networks and TG perform learning independently. Since the convergence time of learning of each components networks and TG are different , we determine total convergence time as the time of latest convergence time among component networks and TG. Second, partitioned input and output pattern pairs should be determined before learning. Methods of pattern partitioning can be written like belows.

Let I_i is input pattern vector and O_i is output pattern vector. Then the set of input output pattern pair T can be described by eq1.

$$T = \{ (I_1,O_1),(I_2,O_2),(I_3,O_3),...,(I_i,O_i)\} \qquad (1)$$

Input pattern vector I_i which have n neurons and output pattern vector O_j which have q neurons can be decribed by eqs2-3.

$$I_i = (i_1, i_2, i_3, ..., i_l, .., i_m, ..., i_n) \tag{2}$$
$$O_j = (o_1, o_2, o_3, ..., o_o, .., o_p, ..., o_q) \tag{3}$$

And each component C_i can be written as set of input output pairs as follows :

$$C_1 = \{ \ (i_1, i_2, .., i_l), (o_1, o_2, .., o_o,) \ \}$$
$$... \qquad\qquad ...$$
$$C_2 = \{ \ (i_{l+1}, i_{l+2}, .., i_m), (o_{o+1}, o_{o+2}, .., o_p) \ \} \tag{4}$$
$$... \qquad\qquad ...$$
$$C_i = \{ \ (i_{m+1}, i_{m+2}, .., i_n), (o_{p+1}, o_{p+2}, .., o_q) \ \}$$

Disadvantages of proposed CBP[1] can be explained like this. First, if number of same patterns are increased then the differences of threshold values of that patterns become minute that it results in slow learning convergence. And because of each component networks perform it's learning independently without communicating each other , generalization capability can be weaked than that of EBP. For example , let's consider first input I_1 = { 000000000 } , and it's output O_1 = { 001 } and second input I_2 = { 111000000 } , and it's output O_2 = { 000 } are learned in EBP networks. Next, consider that new untrained pattern I_3 = { 000000001 } produce output O_3 = { 001 } that are same first output O_1 during recall procedure. If these patterns are learned and recalled in CBP networks which are composed of three component networks (a component network's number of input neuron are three and output is one) with a threshold generator then the 3rd component networks will produce output O_{c3} = { 0 } or unknown ouput during recall procedure in case of it's input is I_{c3} = { 001 } which is partitioned input pattern of input I_3. The reason is that already I_{c3} = { 001 } pattern is learned to produce output O_{c3} = { 0 } in learning procedure. So , although threshold values are different for partitioned input I_{c3} = { 000 } and input I_{c3} = { 001 } , it is hard to produce partitioned output pattern O_{c3} to { 1 } of original output O_3 = { 001 } for partitioned input pattern I_{c3} = { 001 } of original input pattern I_3 = { 000000001 }.

3. NEW CBP Architecture Design

Network size of EBP can be determined by it's number of neurons and by it's connections. Input neurons can expressed as input pattern vectors by the characteristics of input patterns and output neurons as the output pattern vectors by numbers of desired output patterns when input patterns are presented. But because EBP algorithm use supervised learning , the size of output pattern vector can be varied by network designer. For example, if desired output pattern numbers are N then minimum size of output pattern vector is $\lceil \log_2 N \rceil$ for represent binary output patterns of vector. But in order to learn simply , we often determine or use the size of N input vector. In the former case , complexity of network is large and number of hidden neuron is also. So it results in slow learning convergence. The latter case have advantages of fast learning convergence but the numbers of output neurons become increase and network size also. In general , the latter case is widely used for solve practical problems. let's consider input pattern vecor is presented to 1 X M , output pattern vector is 1 X N , and the desired classified patterns are N. At this , maximum number of desired classified patterns are 2^N. For example , if we consider N = 10 then maximum enable output patterns are 2^N = 1024. But among this, only 10 output patterns are used to classify input patterns. So, minimum output pattern vector size is $\lceil \log_2 10 \rceil$ = 4. If we partiton output pattern vector into or more sub pattern vectors then desired output patterns of that will be small and it's vector size also. As a result, if input and output pattern vectors are partitioned and desired output patterns are smaller then total partitioned output pattern vectors size will be smaller than that of original output vector.

In this paper, we propose new learning method that use abstract output vector for component network by partitioning input and output pattern vector into several sub pattern vectors. And we add AOG (Abstract Output Generator) for produce abstract output patterns from original input patterns. Fig2.

shows newly proposed component network structure.

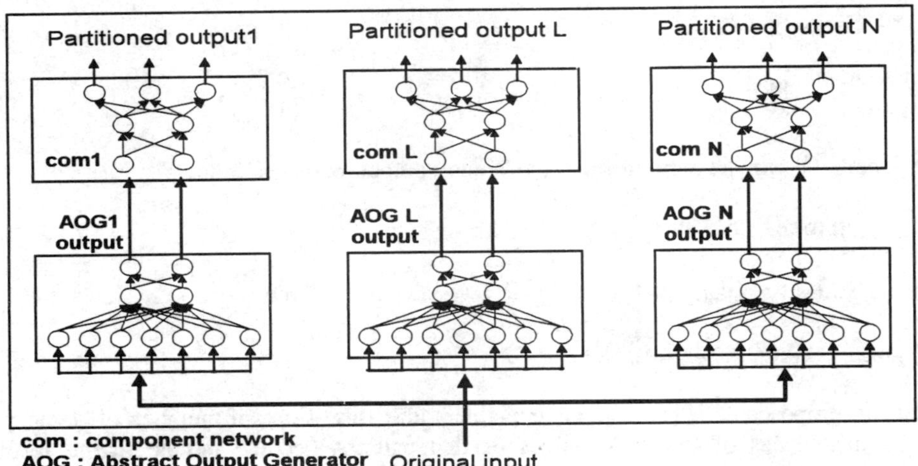

Figure2. Newly Proposed Component Network Structure.

4. Learning Algorithm on Proposed Component network.

Learning procedure of proposed network can be written like this :

step1) Determine Number of component network.
step2) Partition of original input and output pattern vector.
step3) Determine abstract output vector and patterns.
step4) Determine number of output neurons of AOG
       and of input neurons of component networks.
step5) Learning of AOG and component networks.
step6) Recall

Each AOG perform learning for original input patterns and it produce abstract output patterns. Each component network perform learning for abstract output patterns of AOG and it produce original output patterns. At this, abstract output patterns are determined like this. If number of desired output patterns are N in set of partiotioned input output pattern pairs then output pattern vector size is $\lceil log_2N \rceil$. For example , if 4 desired output patterns are exists in one of partitioned input output pattern pairs then new abstract output vector of that will be 2 and 00,01,10,11 patterns are used to each 4 different desired output pattern pairs. Above definition can be described like this.. Let input pattern vector is I_i and output pattern vector is O_i. Then the set of input and output pattern pair T can be described as eq.1 and Input pattern vector I_i which have n neurons and output pattern vector O_j which have q neurons can be described as eqs.2-3. By partition input and output vectors of eqs2-3, we can define new input output pairs as C_i and each set of partitioned input and output pattern pairs can be described like eq4. In eq4., we should produce new abstract output patterns $K_x \sim M_z$ from C_1 to C_i and at this, each network's input, output pattern pairs of AOG and Component network can be described likes:

1) AOG

$$AOG_1 = \{ \ (i_1,i_2,i_3,...,i_l,..,i_m,...,i_n),(k_1,k_2,..,k_x) \ \}$$
$$...\qquad\qquad...$$
$$AOG_2 = \{ \ (i_1,i_2,i_3,...,i_l,..,i_m,...,i_n),(l_1,l_2,..,l_y) \ \} \qquad (5)$$
$$...\qquad\qquad...$$
$$AOG_i = \{ \ (i_1,i_2,i_3,...,i_l,..,i_m,...,i_n),(m_1,m_2,..,m_z) \ \}$$

2) Component network

$$Com_1 = \{ \ (k_1,k_2,..,k_x),(o_1,o_2,..,o_o) \ \}$$
$$...\qquad\qquad...$$
$$Com_2 = \{ \ (l_1,l_2,..,l_y),(o_{o+1},o_{o+2},..,o_p) \ \} \qquad (6)$$
$$...\qquad\qquad...$$
$$Com_i = \{ \ (m_1,m_2,..,m_z),(o_{p+1},o_{p+2},..,o_q) \ \}$$

At this, we should consider that although large numbers of component network may efficiently perform it's learning with partitioned small training patterns but total network size increase because number of AOG become large. So, network designer ought to carefully consider the determination the number of component networks and partitioning original input and output patterns.

5. SIMULATION RESULT AND DISCUSSION

To compare the performance of proposed network with CBP[1] and EBP network, we simulate two simple application problems. and that simulation is performed on 386DX IBM PC. First simulation, total network size and learning convergence speed was compared for seven segment display problem. Table 1. shows the results of networks size of each networks. Here, most fast learning networks were selected among many network structures and simulated. In table 1., connection number of proposed network is same that of CBP network. But in proposed network, two same component network COM1 are used. So if this network is implemented on hardware, real connection size will be 108. Table2. shows compared results of iteration steps and its learning convergence time. In Table2 , proposed networks shows similar results as CBP networks. But it almost 5 times fast than that of EBP networks.

Table1. Network size comparision results for seven segment display.

Network	Network Structure					Connection No.
	TG or CG			com1	com2	com3	
EBP	X			7 * 10 * 10			170
CBP	7*6*3			2*3*3	2*3*3	3*4*4	118
Proposed	AOG 1	AOG 2	AOG 3	com1	com1	com2	118(108)
	7*2*2	7*2*2	7*5*3	2*2*3	2*2*3	3*4*4	

TG : Thresholg Generator   AOG : Abstract Output Generator
Com : Component neural network   ( ) : real number of weights

Table2   Network Learning speed comparision results for seven segment display

Network	EBP	CBP	Proposed
iterations avg.	190.1	110.4	110.4
learning time	14.755 sec	3.297 sec	3.038 sec

Next simulationis is alphabet character recognition. Table3. shows the results of networks size of each networks. Here, the most fast learning networks are selected among simulated networks for compare with the the other networks. In Table3. The numbers of connections of proposed network are 692 but because 4 same component networks are used in a network, real numbers of weights on hardware equal 622. Table4. shows the result of iteration steps and convergence time of networks. In table4. proposed network shows superior result than that of CBP[1] and EBP. To compare with other networks , convergence time is over twice fast than that cf CBP and about 11 times fast than that of EBP.

This simulation results shows that proposed network can perform fast learning in small networks than CBP and EBP. And this network have better generalization capability than that of CBP because all the original input patterns affects to produce output patterns. If we can adequately partition input and output patterns then that speeds of learning will be more fast in small networks.

Table3. Network size comparision results for alpahabet character recognition.

<table>
<tr><td rowspan="2">Network</td><td colspan="6" align="center">Network Structure</td><td rowspan="2">Connection No.</td></tr>
<tr><td>TG or CG</td><td>com1</td><td>com2</td><td>com3</td><td>com4</td><td>com5</td></tr>
<tr><td>EBP</td><td>X</td><td colspan="5" align="center">25 * 15 * 26</td><td>765</td></tr>
<tr><td>CBP</td><td>25*9*5</td><td>5*4*5</td><td>5*4*5</td><td>5*4*5</td><td>5*4*5</td><td>5*5*6</td><td>485</td></tr>
<tr><td rowspan="2">proposed</td><td>AOG 1</td><td>AOG 2</td><td>AOG 3</td><td>AOG 4</td><td>AOG 5</td><td>com1 X 4</td><td>com2</td><td></td></tr>
<tr><td>25*4*3</td><td>25*4*3</td><td>25*4*3</td><td>25*4*3</td><td>25*4*3</td><td>(3*3*5)X4</td><td>3*4*6</td><td>692(622)</td></tr>
</table>

TG : Thresholg Generator   AOG : Abstract Output Generator
Com : Component neural network   ( ) : real number of weights

Table4. Network Learning speed comarision results for alpahabet character recognition

Network	EBP	CBP	proposed
iterations avg.	310	178.3	168.66
learning time	231.55 sec	45.753 sec	20.26 sec

6. CONCLUSION

In this paper, we propose new component networks that overcome disadvantages of CBP[1] and shows better performance results. Simulation results represents fast learning speed and small network size. In addition to, we can efficiently acquire small size of memory or registors for storing weights on hardware implementation. And for component networks, FUN algorithm can be used instead of EBP algorithm for it's fast learning speed. But input patterns of each AOG are original input patterns that this may incurs network size overhead in case of big problems. Our future works will be performed for solving above problems and to find advanced optimum methods for partitioning input and output patterns.

REFERENCE

[1] C.H.Park,H.S.Lee,"EBP Neural Network Component Architecture Using Threshold Generator", ICONIP'95 , vol2,pp840-844,1995.

[2] W.T.Miller,F.H.Glanz and L.G.Kraft,"CMAC:An associative neural network alternative to Backpropagation , " Proc.of the IEEE vol.78,No.10.,pp1561-1567,1990

[3] J.Park and I.W.Sandberg."Universal Approximation using Radial Basis-Function Networks." ,Neural Computation.,vol3,pp246-257,1991

[4] R.A.Jacobs,and M.I.Jordan,"A Competitive modular connectionist Architecture," Advance Neural Information Processing System3,pp767-773.San Mateo,CA;Morgan Kaufmann,1991

[5] Y.H.Pao,"Adaptive Pattern Recognition and Neural Networks",Addison Wesley com., pp197-222 ,1989.

[6] S.Haykin,"Neural Network a Comprehensive Foundation," McMillan College Publishing Company ,1993.

Hardware Implementations

(Oral Presentation)

An Implementation of BP ANNs on a ILLIAC Connected Multiple Processors System

Wai-Yip Chan, Chi-Kwong Li and Huiwei Guan

Department of Electronic Engineering,
The Hong Kong Polytechnic University,
Hung Hom Kowloon, Hong Hong.

Abstract— This paper illustrates the techniques of mapping and the implementation of an artificial neural networks (ANNs) on an ILLIAC connected massively parallel multiple processor system. A parallel computation framework of the Back-propagation learning algorithm and ILLIAC connected multiple processor system are described. Method for partition of these processors and mapping of neurons are discussed. An efficient dynamic broadcast algorithm is proposed and is found that it can be obtained an optimum broadcast communication in ILLIAC connected network. Simulation studies of the algorithm are presented and performance of the algorithms are discussed.

1   Introduction

Applications of multi-layer artificial neural networks(ANNs) are growing explosively in the past few years. It is proved that such kind of ANNs can be employed in various engineering applications such as pattern classification, image processing, voice recognition and many others. However, since the back-propagation learning algorithm [1] requires high computation power the application of ANNs is retarded. To reduce the training time, various parallel schemes have been proposed by S.Y. Kung and J.N. Hwang and many others [2]-[7].

An ANNs implemented on mesh-connected multiprocessors which based on weight matrices was proposed in [8]. In this paper, other approaches of neurons partitioning strategies and a dynamic broadcast algorithm under ILLIAC network are proposed. Then the ANNs is shown to be implemented using the Distributed Back-Propagation algorithm(DBP) proposed by [2]. Finally, the performance of which will be studied.

2   Background

2.1   Back-propagation learning algorithm

The Back-propagation learning algorithm [1] is one of the most often used in training multi-layer ANNs. This method trains the ANNs by repetitive adjustment of connection weights according to the corresponding output error. The algorithm can be divided into three phases; forward execution of activation, back-propagation of error, and weight update, which can be formulated by equations 1 to 4.

$$a(l,k) = f(\sum_{j=0}^{N_{l-1}-1} w(l-j,j,k) \times a(l-1,j)) \quad where \; k = 0..N, \; l = 1..L \tag{1}$$

$$e(l,j) = [y(l,j) - a(l,j)] \times [a(l,j) \times (1 - a(l,j)], \quad where \; l = L \tag{2}$$

$$e(l,j) = [\sum_{k=0}^{N_{l+1}-1} (e(l+1,k) \times w(l,j,k))] \times [a(l,j) \times (1 - a(l,j)], \quad where \; l = L-1..0 \tag{3}$$

$$\delta w_{ij} = \alpha \times e(l,j) \times a(l-1,j), \quad where \; \alpha = learning \; rate \tag{4}$$

where $a(l,k)$ is the activation value of a neuron k on layer l, f is a nonlinear sigmoid function of the form of , $w(l-1,j,k)$ is the weight value between the neuron j on layer $l-1$ and the neuron k on layer l, $e(l,j)$ is the error value of neuron j on layer l and $Y(l,j)$ is the desired value of neuron j in the output layer, and is the weight value updated.

2.2   The ILLIAC connected multiprocessors network

The ILLIAC topology is a subset of a two-dimensional mesh connected processor array with $P = p \times q$ PE's where p and q is the number of row and column of a two dimension array of processors. For each PE has four communication links as shown in figure 1a. However, it was redrawn as a ring format called ILLIAC network shown in figure 1b. For such network, it takes $C \leq \sqrt{p} - 1$ communication steps to broadcast data from a particular PE to all the other PEs where P is the number of processors in the network.

3   DBP algorithm on ILLIAC topology

3.1   Mapping of neurons: - Horizontal neurons mapping

There are two primary factors that can improve the computation performance of DBP learning algorithm: one is neuron partition method and the other is allocation of data in each processor. In this session, a horizontal neurons partition strategy is adopted.

Consider a ILLIAC connected multi-processor network shown in figure 1b which consists of P processors, there is no shared memory and they can communicate by message passing through point-to-point links. For each layer of n_l neurons are partitioned according to the equation 5. As a result, n_l/P neurons are assigned to each processor in each layer shown in figure 2a. Moreover, each processor maintains in its local memory the activation values the back error values and the input and output weight vectors of the assigned neurons. The philology behind such partitioning is to facilitate the dynamic broadcast algorithm which will be discussed in session 3.3.

$$n_i \; map \; to \; PE(i_{mod}P), \quad for \; i = 0..L \tag{5}$$

Where L is the number of neuron in a ANNs layer.

3.2   Implementation of DBP learning in ILLIAC topology

The DBP is proposed and implemented on a multi-transputer system with ring topology [2], where the neural network is partitioned into N sub-networks and mapped onto P processors. It consists of three phases: forward execution of activation, back-propagation of error and weight update. The computation of each phase based on the Back-Propagation algorithm equated by equations 1-4.

In forward execution of activation, the activation value of $l - 1$ layer are broadcast to all neurons in l Layer from the input layer to output layer. Afterwards, each processor computes their activation value in accordance with equation 1. In the back-propagation phase, each processor calculates its back error value by equation 2-3 and the back-error values are broadcasted to each processor from output layer down to input layer. Finally, the weight value in each processor is updated by equation 4 using the back-error value and activation value obtained from the pervious phase.

It is found that the DBP algorithm consists of two broadcast activities: it broadcasts the activation value in $l - 1$ layer to l Layer at the forward execution phase and also the back-error value from output layer down to input layer. Since each processor maintains their local connection weight and back-error values, there is no need to broadcast the weight and back-error values in weight update phase. Therefore, the communication overhead is dominated by activation value and back error broadcasting.

3.3   Dynamic ILLIAC Broadcast Algorithm (DIB)

Each processor of an ILLIAC-connected architecture has four communication links connected to their neighbor processors as shown in fig 1b. The objective of an efficient broadcast algorithm in a ILLIAC topology is to minimize the communication redundancy and reduce the complexity of algorithm so that the software and hardware overhead can be minimized. The proposed Dynamic ILLIAC Broadcast algorithm (DIB) is based on communication redundancy minimization, so that the four communication links can be fully utilized.

As mentioned in the pervious session, each neuron in any layer is mapped into the processors according to the mapping function (5) which is shown in figure 2. In the figure, it is conceptually regarded as a disc, each processor in this disc has four communication links that are connected to PE_{i+1}, PE_{i+r} and PE_{i-1}, PE_{i-r} where PE_i is the PE number i and . We proposed a disc rotation and broadcast method to broadcast data in each PE to all other PEs with minimum communication redundancy.

The disc rotation and broadcast method is divided into two disc phases: a left rotating disc figure 3a and a right rotating disc figure 3b. In each rotating disc, the value is sent to other PEs with the sending direction that the left rotating disc in PEi sends to the links PE_{i+1}, PE_{i+r}, and the right rotating disc sends to the links PE_{i-1}, PE_{i-r}. The discs rotate until all data in each PE are broadcasted to all other PEs. The pseudo-code implementation is shown below:

```
if   P is even number then K=P/4;      /* Where K is defined as the broadcast limit */
if   P is odd  number then K=(P-1)/4;  /* Where P = total number of PEs in the network */

for   j=0 to j=K-1
   {        Parallel_for  i =0 to P-1
                    {              Send [LeftDisc [PEi] ] to [PEi+1];
                                   Send [LeftDisc [PEi] ] to [PEi+r];
                                   Send [RightDisc[PEi]] to [PEi-1] ;
                                   Send [RightDisc[PEi]] to [PEi-r];    }
             Rotate_Left__By_One_Unit( LeftDisc[] );
             Rotate_Right_By_One_Unit( RightDisc[] );

if (   (j mod sqrt(p)-1 ) = 0 )
       {
 for i = 0 to i = (sqrt(p) -1)        /* Virtually rotate both disk by  unit */
       {  Rotate_Left__By_One_Unit( LeftDisc[] );
            Rotate_Right_By_One_Unit( RightDisc[] ); }
       }
   }
```

For example, an ILLIAC network connected to P processors and each of which was mapped with a neuron. Because the network is symmetric, we only have to analysis the right hand side of the network. In order to broadcast an activation value of neuron n_0 to all upper layer neurons, the disc rotating and broadcast scheme can be adopted, At the first broadcast cycle $(i = 0)$, PEi sends n_0 to PE_{i+1}, PE_{i+r}. At the next cycle $(i = 1)$, both discs rotate by one step and broadcast again, then PE_i send n_0 to PE_{i+1}, PE_{i+r}. The discs rotate until $i = \sqrt{p} - 1$ is reached (note $r = \sqrt{p}$).

In this stage the disc is located on PE_{r-1} , and PE_0 to PE_{2r} receive the activation value n_0. Since PE_{r-1} to PE_{2r} has already received the activation value n_0, if the disc rotate and broadcast operation continues; this will generate an unnecessary broadcast of data to PE_{r-1} to PE_{2r} . In order to minimize the redundancy of communication, the disc rotates from PE_{r-1} to PE_{2r} without broadcast and then repeat the above rotate and broadcast procedures again. The whole operation will be repeated unit the broadcast limit K is reached. Finally, the activation value n_0 will be broadcasted to PE_0 to $PE_{\frac{p}{2}}$. Owing to the network is symmetric, all PEs in the network receive the activation value.

It is observed that the total communication steps required to broadcast n_l neurons on a layer to P processors are :

$$C_{odd} = \frac{p-1}{4} \times \frac{n_l}{p} = \frac{n_l(p-1)}{4p} \quad and \quad C_{even} = \frac{p}{4} \times \frac{n_l}{p} = \frac{n_l}{4} \tag{6}$$

where C_{odd} and C_{even} are the communication count in a odd and even number processors network respectively.

It is found that by using the DIB is matched well with the optimum solution found mathematically [9][10]. Finally, the total number of communication steps for all neurons of one layer to complete a learning cycle are

$$C_{odd} = \frac{n_l(p-1)}{2P} \quad and \quad C_{even} = \frac{n_l}{2} \tag{7}$$

4   Performance analysis

In this session, we would like to analysis the performance of DIB algorithm as compare with difference approaches of communication scheme.

As mentioned in session 2.2, the ILLIAC network requires $C \leq \sqrt{p} - 1$ steps to broadcast data on a PE to all other PEs. There are P processor in the network and with n_l neurons in each ANNs layers, so the total number of communication steps for original broadcast scheme to complete one layer learning needs is

$$C_1 = (\sqrt{p} - 1) \times p \times 2 \times \frac{n_l}{p} = 2n_l(\sqrt{p} - 1) \tag{8}$$

Using the DIB algorithm, total communication steps required is described in equation 7. It shows find that

$$C_1 \gg C_{odd} \quad and \quad C1 \gg C_{even} \tag{9}$$

In figure 4a-b, the DIB reduces the communication overhead as compare with the traditional broadcasting approach.

A simulation study of the DBP learning algorithm with DIB was implemented. It is proved that this model can be executed in parallel on the ILLIAC topology as the number of processors connected on the network is changed. The speed-up ratio of which is closed to $3P/4$, where P is the number of processors in the network.

5   Conclusion

A mapping and computation framework for paralleling the back-propagation algorithm of ANNs under ILLIAC connected multiple-processor network has been illustrated. In this implementation, the neurons on each layer of ANN are partitioned in a horizontal basis in order to improve communication efficiency. Moreover, a Dynamic ILLIAC Broadcast (DIB) algorithm has been proposed and shown without prove that it is an optimum broadcast algorithm in the ILLIAC network. The DIB is not only applicable on the ANNs application, but also suitable for other parallel applications using the ILLIAC topology.

References

[1] Rumelhart, G.E. Hinton and R.J. Williams, "Learning Internal Representation by Error Propagation", in Parallel Distributed Processing, Vol 1, pp. 318-362, MIT press, 1986.

[2] Huiwei Guan, Chi-Kwong Li and Wai-Yip Chan, "A Parallel Implementation of BP Neural Network on a Multiple Processor System", in ISANN'95, pp. E2-19-24.

[3] S.Y. Kung and J.N. Hwang, "Parallel Architecture for Artifical Neural Nets" Proc. IEEE International Conference on Neural Networks, pp.II-165-172, 1988.

[4] Y.Fujimoto, "An Enhanced Parallel Planar Lattice Architecture for Large Scale NeuralNetworks", in Proc. International Joint Conference on Neural Networks, pp. II-581-II586, 1990.

[5] Y.Suzuki and L.E. Atlas, "A Study of Regular Architectures for Digital Implementation of Neural Networks", in Proc. IEEE International Symposium on Circuits and Systems, pp.82-85, 1989.

[6] S.W.Aiken, M.W.Koch and M.W.Roberts, "A Parallel Neural Network Simulator", in Proc. International Joint Conference on Nerual Netowks, pp. II-611-II611, 1990.

[7] D.Jackson and D.Hammerstrom, "Distributing Back Propagation Networks Over the Intel iPCS/860 Hypercube", in Proc. International Joint Conference on Neural Networks, pp.I-569-I-574, 1991.

[8] Takashi YUKAWA and Tsutomu ISHIKAWA, "Optimal Parallel Back-Propagation Schemes for ILLIAC-connected and Bus-connected Multiprocessors", in IEEE International conference on Neural Networks. PP.1748-53 vol.3., 1993

[9] C. Ozveren, "Communication aspects of parallel processing". Laboratory for Information and Decision Systems Report LIDS-P-1721, Massachusetts Institute of Technology, Cambridge, MA, 1987.

[10] A. Varvarigos Emmanouel and P. Bertsekas Dimitri P. Bertsekas, "Partial Multinode Broadcast and Partial Exchange Algorithm for d-Dimensional Meshes, in Journal of Parallel and Distributed Computing, 00 177-189, vol.23, 1994.

Figure List

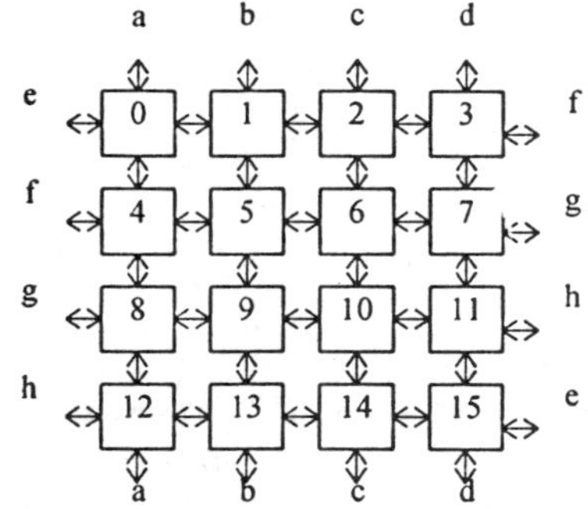

Figure 1a, A mesh connected network

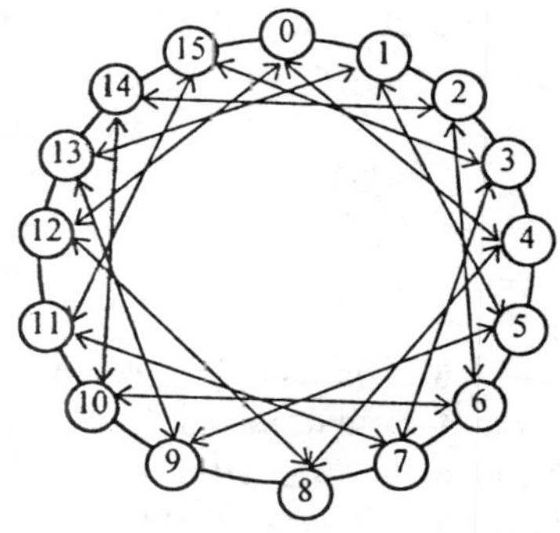

Figure 1b, An ILLIAC network

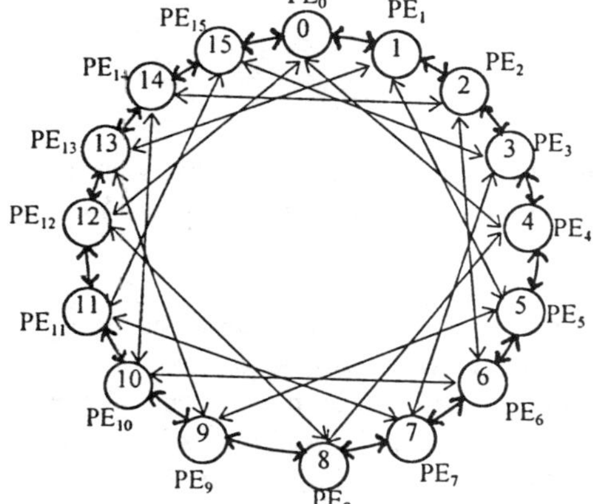

Figure 2, A mapped PE origination

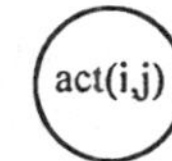

- Where the value inside the circle represented the activation value located on that PE

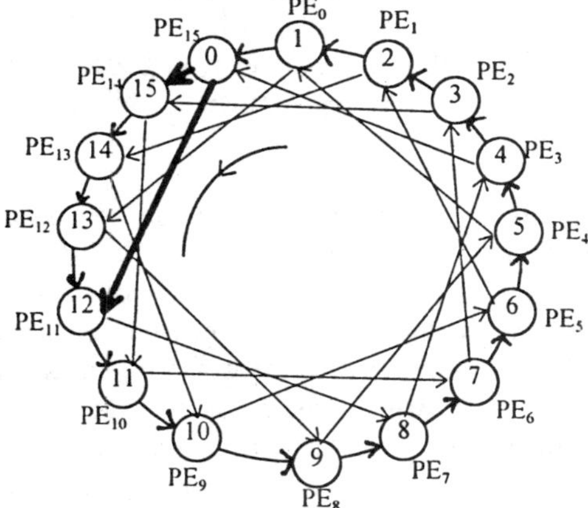

Figure 3a, A left rotating broadcast disc

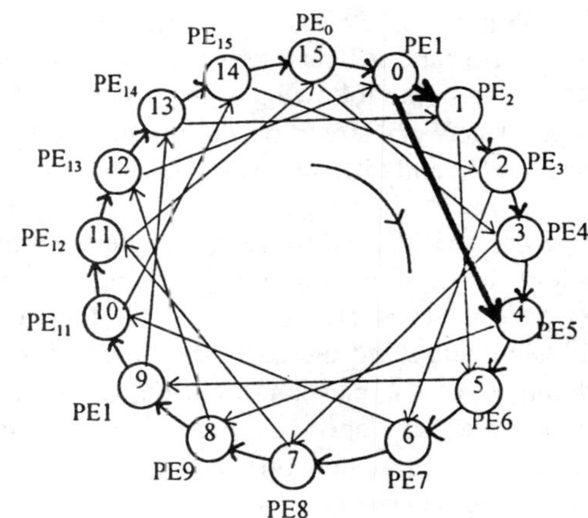

Figure 3b, A right rotating broadcast disc

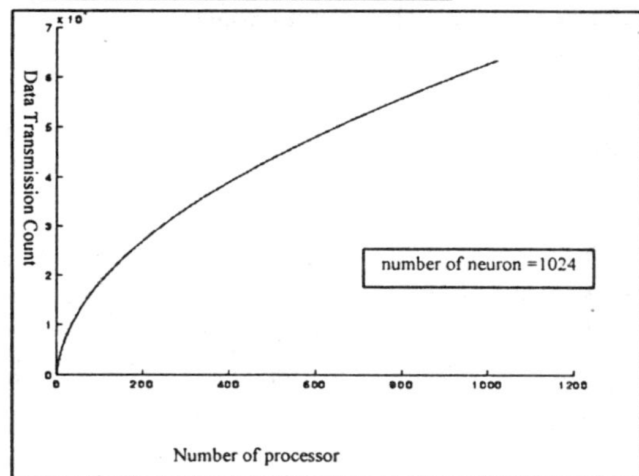

Figure 4a, Data transmission count of traditional approach broadcast

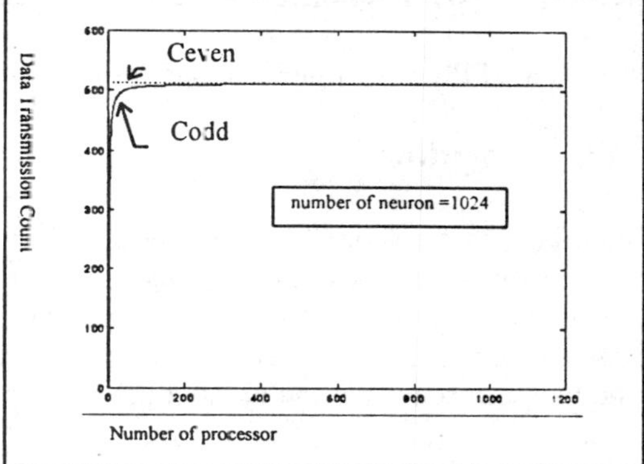

Figure 4b, Data transmission count using DIB algorithm

ASIC Structure Research and Design of FP-Based Neural Networks

Ling Liu   Yannan Zhao   Bo Zhang
Department of Computer Science & Technology, Tsinghua University
Beijing, China
email: dcsjpf@tsinghua.edu.cn

Abstract — **In this paper we present a real full-parallel architecture ASIC implementation for multilayered feedforward neural network. Due to the intrinsic attributes of the learning algorithm (Forward Propagation Algorithm) we adapted, our neuron structure is quite simple and costs little hardware resource. No timing duplex or pipeline technology are involved, all of the neurons work parallelly and independently. Network expansion is easy and adds no complexity on neuron connection. The function simulation of our design has proved to be successful.**

1   Introduction

In recent years, artificial neural networks have been widely applied in several research areas such as image processing, speech processing and medical diagnoses due to their high classification power and learning ability [5].

At present time most of these networks are simulated by software programs or fabricated using VLSI technology [4]. The software simulation based on traditional serial processors is unable to make full use of the parallel advantage of neurons. With the development of Neural Network research work and the pressing demand for practical products, the network scale and complexity increases rapidly. Software simulation can no longer meet the requirements on speed and storing capacity. As a result, hardware implementation is inevitable.

Although there have been many research on the hardware implementation of neural network now [2]-[4], there is no general and efficient solution for hardware implementation of large-scaled neural network. The major problems lie in the following aspects: complexity of the multiplier; connection between PEs; swift and flexible change of network structure; the modification and store of weight. They make the hardware implementation very complex and difficult, especially for large-scaled neural network.

As we can see, the hardware architecture complexity are determined by the learning algorithm and network topology. Most of the traditional learning algorithm need recurrence and multiply calculation, so timing duplex or systolic structure are used frequently for efficiency improvement. However, timing duplex is still a kind of serial simulation and increases the difficulty of control, especially when the number of recurrence increases with the network expansion, the learning speed slows down rapidly to an intolerable extent. On the other hand, systolic structure depends too much on the corporation of each node, which decreases the fault-tolerant character of neural network. For these reasons, we adapt a new learning algorithm-FP algorithm for our research. No recurrence exist in this algorithm, no multiply operation, all the computation can be converted to the calculation of Hamming distance and accumulation operation. Learning speed is very fast. We use bus to connect neurons. As a result, a real full-parallel neural network is easy to construct and expand.

We use Xilinx FPGA to implement our design with WORKVIEW for design entry.

2   FP Algorithm

For multilayered feed-forward neural network, most popular learning algorithms such as BP algorithm have several drawbacks such as low learning speed, emergence of spurious attractive centers, etc. Besides, so far there is no effective synthesis tool for constructing such a neural network. A new learning algorithm -- Forward Propagation (FP) of multilayered feedforward neural networks can overcome the shortages of the BP algorithm and the like. Consequently, an optimal network structure can be obtained as soon as the new learning process finishes.

As contrasted with the BP algorithm, the new learning process starts from the first layer of a neural network. Based on the data given by a set of training samples, the number of elements in the first layer and their weights and thresholds are first determined. Assume that the number of given sample is p, the input of each sample is n-dimensional, input vectors of given samples are transformed into p vertices of an orthogonal simplex in (p-1)-dimensional space. Then, regarding the outputs of the first layer elements as the inputs of the second layer elements, the number of elements in the second layer and their weights and thresholds are determined. Through them, the origin and p-1 unit vectors of the coordinate system are transformed into p m-dimensional output vectors of the given samples. Thus, the whole network is constructed and we have an associative memory corresponding to the given samples.

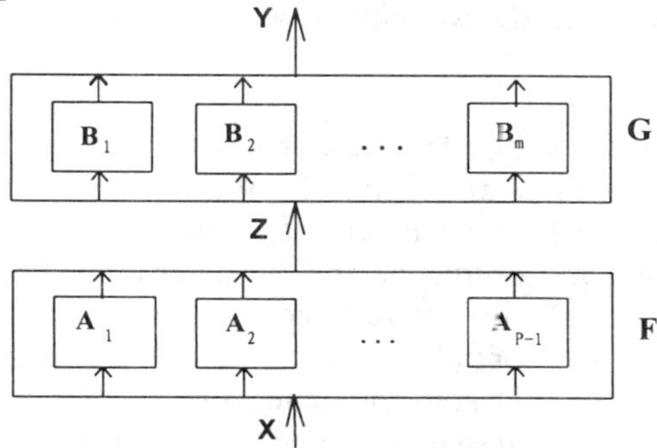

Fig1. Network Architecture

The structure of neural network is shown in Fig1.

Assume that element A_i has n inputs and one output. The domain of each component of input (output) vectors is $\{-1,+1\}$. The relationship between input X and output Y of the first layer network A is

$$Y = sgn(W * X - \theta)$$

where W is a weight matrix of the first layer network **A**, θ a threshold vector.

A set $K = \{r^0 = (x^0, y^0), r^1 = (x^1, y^1), \cdots, r^{P-1} = (x^{P-1}, y^{P-1})\}$ of training samples is given. Let

$$Z^0 = (-1, -1, \cdots, -1)$$

$$Z^1 = (+1, -1, \cdots, -1)$$

$$\cdots$$

$$Z^{P-1} = (-1, -1, \cdots, +1)$$

there exists a $(P-1) \times N$ matrix W and a threshold θ such that

$$Z^i = F(X^i), i = 0, 1, \cdots, p-1$$

It can be proved that

$$W^i = (X^i)^T$$

$$\theta_i = \begin{cases} n - d_i + 1 & \text{if } d_i \text{ is even} \\ n - d_i & \text{if } d_i \text{ is odd} \end{cases}$$

$$i = 1, 2, ..., P-1$$

Where $d_i = \min_{i \neq j} d(x^i, x^j), i = 1, 2, \cdots P-1, j = 0, 1, 2, \cdots P-1$, $d(x,y)$ denotes the Hamming distance between x and y.

For **P** given m-dimension output vectors $\{y^0, y^1, ..., y^{P-1}\}$ there exists a $M \times (P-1)$-matrix **U** and a threshold vector ξ such that

$$y^j = G(z^j), j = 0, 1, 2, \cdots P-1$$

The FP-based neural network has several advantages: (1) The order of learning complexity is minimal, (2) The number of elements of the network is minimal, (3) Each sample is an attractive center and its attractive radius is maximal (in average sense), (4) There is no spurious attractive center, (5) FP is not only a learning algorithm but also a synthesis tool of neural network.

3   System Architecture Overview

We use two different kinds of chips to implement the two layers of the network respectively, thus each chip contains single type of PE (processing element) or neurons, so that control of both chips is easier and network structure can be configured dynamically . As we can see from the above algorithm, the second layer converts the matching results of the first layer into corresponding sample output vector, this is quite similar to the function of memory chips. So common memory chip can fulfill the task of the second layer , using the output of the first layer as the address. Consequently, we only need to integrate the first layer of the neural network into a FPGA chip.

Fig 2 shows the general architecture of the chip. The most important parts of it are PEs. All the PEs have same structure and can run parallelly. The chip is programmable. We divide the function of the chip into several basic operations and define a small User Instruction Set, each instruction is associated with a basic operation. The Instruction Register keeps current user instruction and select corresponding operation. Users can program the chip through writing the Instruction Register so as to control the training and application of the network. While the controller generate all of the control signals to control the running process inside each basic operation,. In addition, there are several counters to corporate with the controller in timing control. As the 4 or 5K FPGA's series contains on-chip memory resources, weight matrix   can be stored inside the chip (W-RAM) when input the sample vectors.

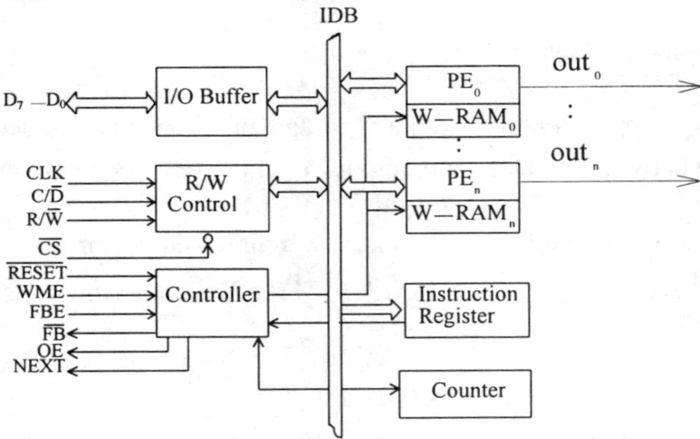

Fig2. General Architecture

Fig3 illustrates the block diagram of PE. It is the heart of the chip. Its functions include : store a sample vector into the weight ram; calculate the attractive radius, store it into the THR after some pre-processing. During the application period, it calculate the inner product of input vector and weight vector, output the sign bit. Only one of $OUT_n - OUT_0$ can be high (for example, OUT_i) ,which means the input vector is most similar to sample *i.*

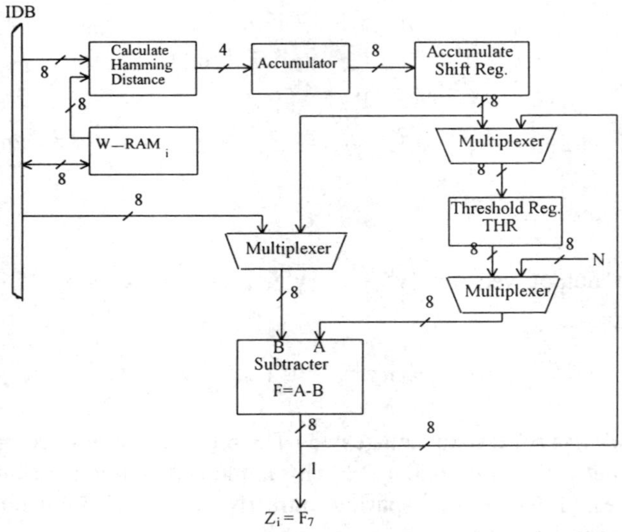

Fig3. Architecture of PE

4   System Features

4.1   Real Full-Parallel Processing

When the network scale enlarges, the number of connection between PEs increases tremendously, so most of the general purpose neural network system today adopt serial-parallel implementation. That is, by the means of time-duplexing, use a few PEs to simulate a large scale network. This kind of method sacrifice certain network connection speed to gain the enlargement of scale. On the other hand, full-parallel process system has real physical unit corresponding to each PE of the network model. When the scale enlarges, complex connection problem arises. The solution is to develop a new method of system architecture.

In our design, PEs connect with each other through Internal Data Bus (IDB), so it is easy to control, convenient to expand and cost little hardware resources. As only the training period needs communication between PEs to compute the attractive radius , while in a well-trained network, all PEs can run independently and parallelly, we use broadcasting method to pass data to PEs. During the period of network training, the host should input the sample vectors twice, one time to store the sample vectors into appropriate weight ram and the other time to broadcast them to each PE so they can calculate the Hamming distances and update the minimal value. At the end of the second input, each PE would have got its attractive radius. As there is not any recurrence in FP algorithm, two-times input of sample vectors can still ensure a fast learning speed and it will not have any effect on the application of the network.

4.2   Flexibility

Our system is flexible in several aspects. Firstly, the network structure is reconfigurable. PEs of the first layer is activated successively with the input of sample vectors. The dimension of input vectors can be programmed by users. With two different kinds of chips playing the function of the two layers, it is quite easy to form variety of networks. Secondly, as weight matrix is the transposition of input matrix, it is modified automatically when input the samples. We use FPGA's on-chip memory resources to store it distributely inside the chip. Thirdly, the chip is programmable. Users can control the training and application process through User Instruction Set.

4.3   Easy Expansion

The number of PEs in one chip is limited by the number of gates in the FPGAs. For larger scale network, it is necessary for the chip to expand itself. The upper limit of the input dimensions depends on the maxim capacity of weight ram. On the other hand, when the number of sample vectors increase, more PEs are need to store and manage the samples, this can be implemented by connect several chips together. As the PEs are connected by bus and communicate through broadcasting, the cascade is very simple. The only problem is the counting of the PE, when the PE in the first chip is used up, the second chip is activated and begins to work. This is similar to the expansion of common counters.

4.4   Greatly-Reduced hardware cost

Since the domain of the input and output vector is {-1,+1}, it can be proved that the inner product can be converted to the calculation of Hamming distance. Thus the core of both training and application of the network is unified into the basic operation of computing Hamming distance and the complex multiplier is omitted here.

Besides, with bus connecting PEs, and no timing duplex needed, the control becomes very simple.

As a result, hardware cost is reduced greatly and large-scaled network will not be too expensive.

5   Conclusion

We have finished the logic design entry using Viewlogic to draw schematics and Viewsim to achieve the function simulation. The simulation results and timing diagram shows that our design functions well and has right timing.

Fig4 illustrates the typical timing diagram of the application process. The input vector is defined as 16 dimension. The positive pulse of signal $OUT_4 - OUT_3$ shows four application result respectively. We can see that the network gives us a result every 7 clock cycles.

An implementation using XC4013 has been made. The result shows that each PEs costs 60 CLBs and each weight Ram costs 10 CLBs. The rest control part costs 53 CLBs. It is evident that our aim of reducing hardware resources has been reached. XC4013 contains about 13,000 gates, that is, 576 CLBs. It is suitable for integrating 4 PEs into one chip. With higher density FPGA's, we can expand the network easily by just adding more PE and weight Ram nodes with the same design.

It is convenient to form variety of networks, with general memory chips act as the second layer, both the cost and complexity of the network are reduced greatly. The interior structure of the first layer chip is quite simple but flexible. It cost little hardware resources but achieve rich functionality. Users can program the input dimensions and the number of samples, as well as control the training and application courses. Network is constructed automatically.

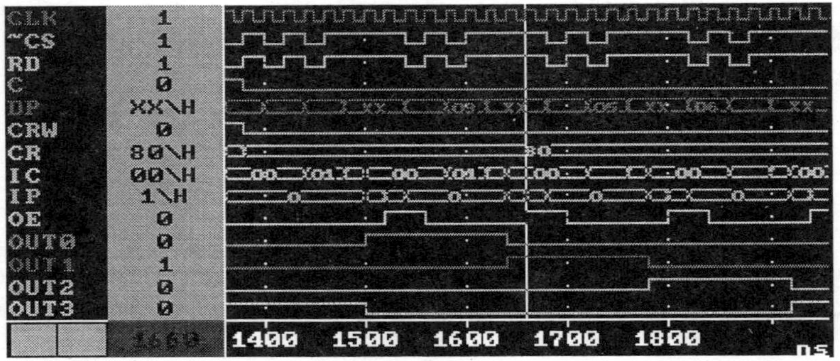

Fig4. Typical timing diagram of application process

References

[1] Bo Zhang, Ling Zhang and FuChao Wu, "A Learning and Synthesis Algorithm of Multilayered Feedforward Neural Networks", *Journal of Software*, Vol. 6, No. 7, 1995.

[2] C. E. Cox and W. Ekkehard Blanz, "Ganglon-A fast hardware implementation of a connectionist classifier", *IEEE-CICC,* Phoenix, AZ, 1991.

[3] N.Botros and M. Abdul-Aziz, "Hardware implementation of an artificial neural net*work,"* in *Proc. IEEE Int. Conf. on Neural Networks*, San Francisco, CA, March 1993, vol. 2, pp. 1252-1257.

[4] S. Satranarayana, Y. Tsividis, and P. Graf, "A reconfigurable VLSI neural network," *IEEE J. Solid-State Circuits*, vol. 25, pp.849-55, June 1990.

[5] R. Lippmann, "An introduction to computing with neural nets," *IEEE-ASSP*, Mag., pp.4-22, April 1987.

Implementing Backpropagation Training on a Reconfigurable Computer Using Pipelining of the Training Patterns

Jim Torresen
jimtoer@idt.unit.no

Jon Gunnar Solheim
jon@idt.unit.no

Department of Computer Systems and Telematics
Norwegian University of Science and Technology
N-7034 Trondheim, Norway

Abstract— This paper describes implementations of backpropagation training on the reconfigurable neurocomputer RENNS (REconfigurable Neural Network Server). We have experimented with different task-to-processors assigments to find the best parallelization of a given neural network application.

The results show that we can obtain performance improvements by splitting the backpropagation training into two sub-tasks, one for the hidden layer computation and one for the output layer computation. We also suggest a method on how to assign the appropriate number of modules to each sub-task.

1 Introduction

During recent years, several different approaches have been exploited to reduce simulation time for artificial neural networks (ANN). The backpropagation algorithm (BP) [1] has been used in many applications, but one of its weaknesses is the time consuming computation. To be able to reduce the long training time and get acceptable performance for real-time applications, parallel processing is mandatory. In this work, we study the two layer perceptron network consisting of a hidden layer and an output layer.

One approach is to implement the algorithm on a general purpose parallel computer [2]. This gives good flexibility and the computer can be applied to many applications, but does not obtain the same performance as the recently developed neurocomputers [3, 4]. This is specially designed hardware made to compute the neural networks (i.e. matrix vector multiplication) at high speed. However, the problem is often that fast special purpose hardware lacks reconfigurability.

Some neurocomputers have been designed as a compromize, between speed and reconfigurability. One of these is RENNS, REconfigurable Neural Network Server, designed at the Norwegian University of Science and Technology [5]. This is a general purpose neurocomputer, designed with a reconfigurable communication system. In this paper, several different BP implementations/system configurations on RENNS are described and evaluated.

In the following section a brief description of the RENNS architecture is given. Section 3 outlines the different aspects of parallel BP. The implementations undertaken on RENNS are described in section 4, followed by the performance results in section 5. Conclusions are given in section 6.

2 The RENNS Computer System

The main building block of the RENNS Computer System, the RENNS Module, consists of a Processor Module and a Communication Subsystem. A block diagram of the RENNS Module is shown in Figure 1.

The Processor Module is built around a digital signal processor, the TMS320C30 — with a maximum performance of 32 MFLOPS. The memory requirements of an ANN-algorithm tend to be very large. To hold connection-matrices and input/output-data, the Processor Modules are equipped with up to 16 MByte of DRAM, and up to 1 MByte of SRAM. In addition, the processor has 8 KByte of fast, internal SRAM. A VME-interface gives access to a Sun Sparc compatible host, and the local area network.

An efficient implementation of parallel algorithms is dependent on the inter-processor communication scheme. The RENNS Communication Subsystem is implemented in field programmable gate arrays (FPGAs), thus it can be reconfigured in-system to meet the different requirements from ANN algorithms. Each subsystem has eight individually programmable channels connected to other subsystems. The communication bandwidth is 5 MBytes/second on each channel.

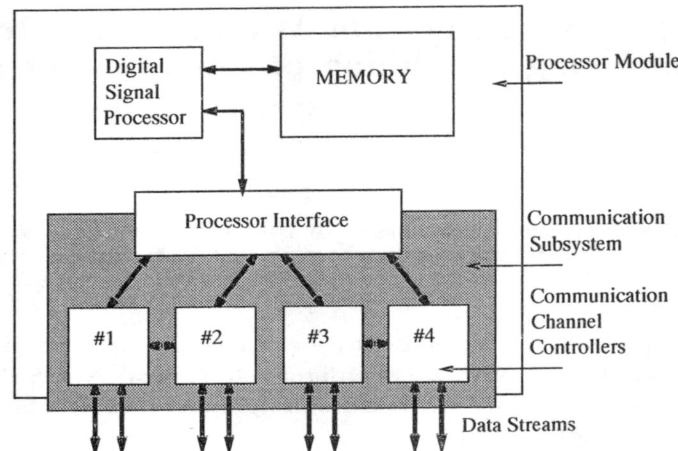

Figure 1: **Block diagram of the RENNS Module**

3   Parallel implementation of BP

Several different degrees of BP parallelism exists [6]: training set parallelism, node parallelism and pipelining of the training patterns.

3.1   Node parallelism

Node parallelism is the most fine grained level of parallelism in the BP algorithm. The degree can be further subdivided into two sub-degrees: synapse parallelism and neuron parallelism. The former splits the computation of a single neuron onto several processors, while the latter compute neurons in parallel. A synapse-based parallel implementation will usually also include neuron parallelism. In this paper, we are only applying neuron parallelism, which is presented in Figure 2. The network is split vertically into as many slices as there are processor-modules. The connection values (weights) are stored on the processor-module holding the receiving neuron. All processors store the *whole* hidden layer input vector.

3.2   Training set parallelism

Another parallelizing approach, is to put a local copy of the complete weight matrices on each processor module together with a subset of the training set. Each processor accumulates weight change values for its given training patterns. When the weights are to be updated, the weight change values from each processor are summed and the result is used to update all the local weight matrices.

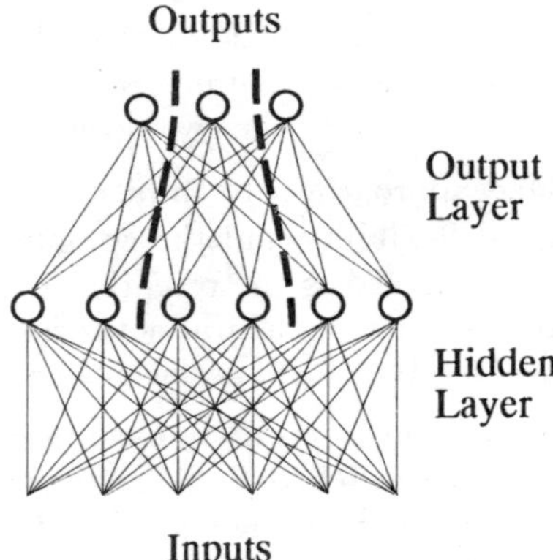

Figure 2: **Neuron parallelism example for a system of 3 processors. The neural network is split into equal slices, as indicated by the dotted lines. Each slice is computed on one processor.**

This method is well suited for parallelization, but usually implies slower convergence rate than updating the weights after every training pattern and is not used in this work.

3.3   Pipelining

Two processors (for a two layer neural network) pipeline the training patterns. That is, while the output layer processor calculates output and error values, the hidden layer processor concurrently processes the *next* training pattern. Pipelining requires a delayed weight update of the hidden weight matrix. Experiments show that the effect of the delay on the converge is marginal. This is reasonable since the delta weight change values are small compared to the weights. Thus, the convergence should be very close to the convergence of ordinary pattern weight updates.

3.4 Parallelizing problems

The two major concerns in parallel implementations are:

Load balancing, To minimize idle time in each module it is necessary to keep the processors active. Each module should be given the *same* amount of computation load.

Communication, To maximize the time processors actually perform computation, communication has to be minimized.

As the number of processors gets larger, these problems will become more prominent. One way to reduce them is to combine different degrees of parallelism [2]. Moreover, when using a reconfigurable computer, we can easily make a system configuration that fits well to the ANN.

4 Implementation of BP on RENNS

Based on the previous section, two implementations on RENNS are described in this section. First, a solution using neuron parallelism is briefly described. Then, another solution is proposed, which rearranges the processor assignments according to the given neural network application.

4.1 Neuron parallelism

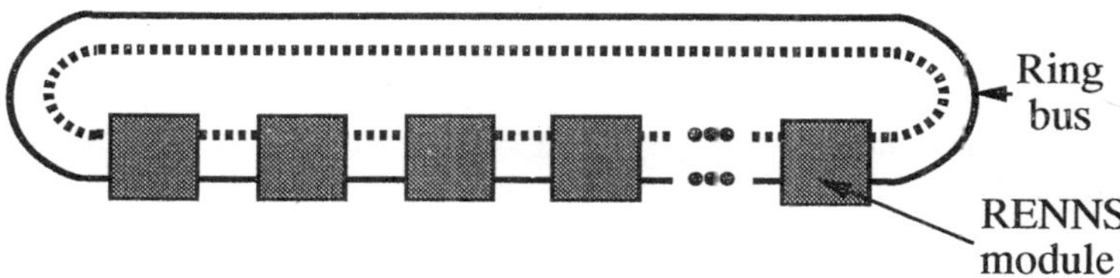

Figure 3: **The RENNS modules connected by one ring bus. An optional bus is shown by the dotted line.**

One or two ring buses connects the modules, see Figure 3. Each module contains one slice of the network weight matrices. For each pattern presented during training, two communication phases are required. First, all processor-modules must broadcast its local hidden layer ouput values to all other modules. Second, partial sums of the error to be used for updating the hidden layer weights have to be distributed to the dedicated processors. Since the two phases are different, separate ring buses were used for each of these two communication phases to reduce the total communication overhead.

4.2 Neuron parallelism and pipelining combined

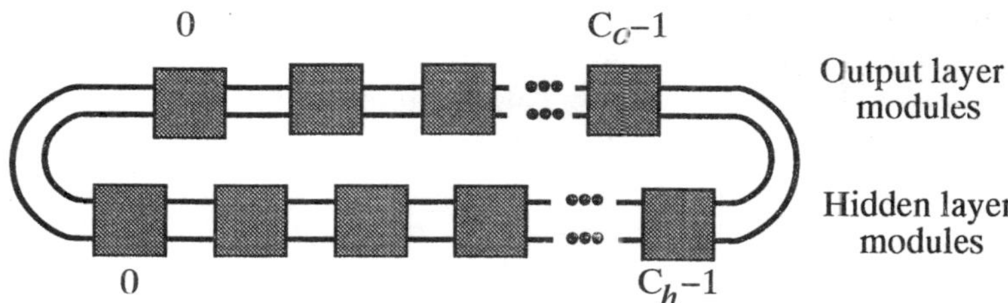

Figure 4: **The RENNS modules connected by two ring buses for combining neuron parallelism and pipelining.**

Based on the neuron parallel implementation, a combined solution is here proposed with neuron parallelism and pipelining of the training patterns as shown in Figure 4. The upper RENNS modules do the output layer computation, while the lower row do the hidden layer computation. To avoid an interleaving of hidden-to-output communication with output error communication two ring buses are used. C_h RENNS modules are used for the hidden layer calculation and C_o for the output layer calculation. The number of available modules is $C = C_h + C_o$.

The motivation for this method is that

- More computation (in double for-loops) is undertaken between communication steps, since less number of processors are used for each layer. It can be shown that this implies reduced communication.

- Reduction of the program code size implies more space for data in fast memory.

This implementation differs from the one described in [7] by not using a separate processor message handling and using delayed weight update instead of training set parallelism. Moreover, the communication strategy is different and is based on equal sized packages sent around the ring. The token ring protocol implemented on RENNS requires a package to be sent around the ring before a new one can be sent. Thus, broadcast is more efficient than accumulation of values along the ring.

To obtain the best distribution of modules, the algorithm in Figure 5 can be used. The algorithm starts with an equal number ($C/2$) of hidden and output modules. Then, it alters the number of modules assigned to each layer by comparing $T_h(C_h)$ and $T_o(C_o)$. If the hidden layer processor needs most time, it increases the number of hidden modules. In many cases, this will make a better load balance, since most ANN applications require a much larger number of input neurons than output neurons. However, if this is not the case, it tries to use a larger number of modules in the output layer. The timing required (T_h and T_o) is measured by actual execution on RENNS. A neural application usually requires training of several hundred iterations of the whole training set. Thus for a small system ($C < 16$), the initial time measurements to find the best configuration do not add much to the total execution time. The algorithm can be improved by use of binary search.

```
T_h(C_h): Time for computing hidden layer for 1 pattern
T_o(C_o): Time for computing output layer for 1 pattern
C_h = C/2;
C_o = C/2;
T_m = max(T_h(C_h), T_o(C_o));
if (T_h(C_h) > T_o(C_o)) then
    whiie ((t= max(T_h(C_h + 1), T_o(C_o - 1))) < T_m) {
        C_h = C_h + 1;
        C_o = C_o - 1;
        T_m = t;
    }
else
    while ((t= max(T_h(C_h - 1), T_o(C_o + 1))) < T_m) {
        C_h = C_h - 1;
        C_o = C_o + 1;
        T_m = t;
    }
ConfigureSystem(C_h, C_o);
```

Figure 5: **Heuristic to find the best assignment of PEs to the computation of each neural network layer.**

It is possible to execute the forward and backward phase in parallel [8]. Hence, make a three stage pipeline for a two layer network. However, then the output weights would have to be stored and updated twice, since they are necessary both for forward output computation and hidden delta error computation. This increases the interprocessor communication and has not been further studied in this work.

5   Results

The performance on RENNS of the algorithms described in the previous section is given below and is measured in MCUPS (Million Connections (Weights) Updated Per Second).

Figure 6 shows the training performance of the neuron parallel implementation for the NETtalk network[1] and a speech recognition network[2]. The training performance increases for up to 8 modules. For the largest network – speech recognition, the performance can be further improved on larger systems, while this is not the case for the NETtalk network. The leap in the measures between 4 and 5 modules for a NETtalk network with 30 hidden units is due to the ability to store more of the data arrays in fast SRAM. On 5 modules the data arrays are smaller than when 4 modules is used.

---

[1] A two weight layer network that transforms text to phonemes using 203 input units and 26 output units.
[2] 256 input units and 64 output units.

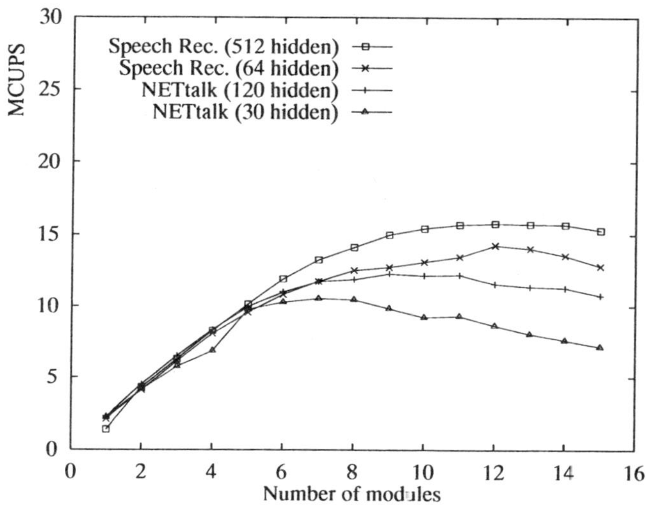

Figure 6: **Neuron parallel NETtalk training on 1 to 15 processing modules.**

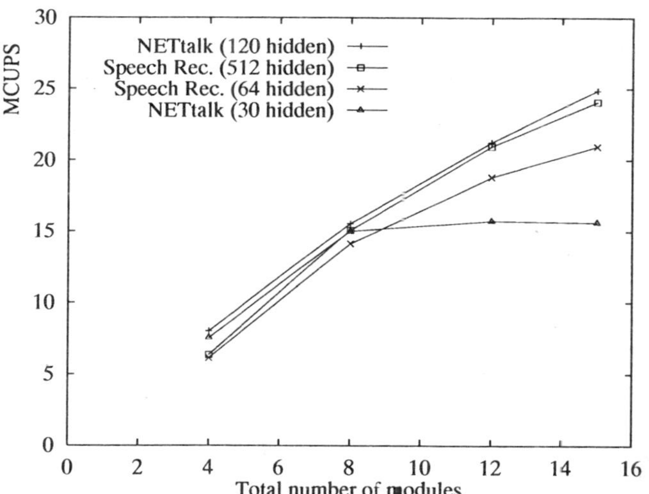

Figure 7: **Pipelined training performance of NETtalk and speech recognition.**

Figure 7 shows the training speed for the pipeline implementation as a function of the total number of modules ($C_o + C_h$). That is, the performance of the pipelined configuration with highest training speed for each total number of modules is plotted in the figure.

Except for NETtalk with 30 hidden units the scaling is promising and better than for only neuron parallelism, as seen in Figure 6. The difference in performance between the two implementations increases as the number of modules increases. The results emphasize the importance of including pipelining for a large number of modules. On 15 modules, pipelined training of NETtalk network for 120 hidden units is 131% faster than non-pipelined training.

Figure 8 shows the performance of the pipeline implementation on 15 modules. The x-axis represents the number of hidden modules employed, C_h. The corresponding number of output modules is given by $C_o = 15 - C_h$. The performance is highly dependent on the number of modules assigned for each layer. The best performance is achieved when $C_h > C_o$. This is due to the much larger number of input (203) and hidden neurons compared to output neurons (26).

This shows the benefit of using more processors on the hidden layer computation (computation intensive) and less on the output layer computation (communication intensive).

Some small networks were also trained. The difference in performance was less between the two implementation compared to for the larger networks.

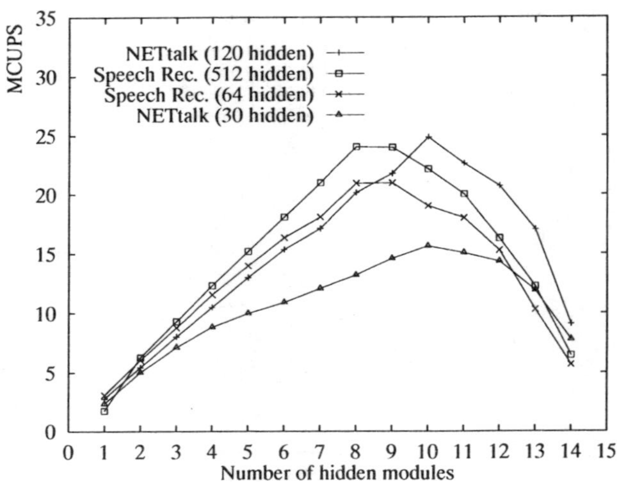

Figure 8: **Pipelined training of NETtalk. The horizontal axis shows the number of modules involved for hidden layer computation. The total number of modules is 15.**

6   Conclusions

A description of two mappings of BP on the reconfigurable neurocomputer RENNS has been given. The reconfigurability makes it possible to connect the modules by ring buses. We have proposed a method to divides the processors into two groups. Each of them are computing different parts of the backpropagation training. By making several implementations, it was posible to show that the pipelined partitioning is beneficial for BP networks of various sizes, especially for an increasing number of processors. The ring busses allows us to obtain good load balance for two non-equal sized computations.

References

[1] D.E. Rumelhart, G.E. Hinton, and R.J. Williams. Learning internal representation by error propagation. In *Parallel Distributed Processing*, volume 1, pages 318–362. The MIT Press, 1986.

[2] Jim Torresen, Shin-ichiro Mori, Hiroshi Nakashima, Shinji Tomita, and Olav Landsverk. Parallel back propagation training algorithm for MIMD computer with 2D-torus network. In *Proceedings of International Conference On Neural Information Processing, Seoul, Korea*, volume 1, pages 140–145, October 1994.

[3] Robert W. Means. High speed parallel hardware performance issues for neural network applications. In *Proc. of IEEE Int. Conference on Neural Networks*, 1994.

[4] Dan Hammerstrom. A VLSI architecture for high-performance, low cost, on-chip learning. In *Proc. of Int. Joint Conference on Neural Networks*, volume 2, pages 537–542, 1990.

[5] O.Landsverk et al. RENNS - a reconfigurable computer system for simulating artificial neural network algorithms. In *Proceedings of the ISMM International Conference. Parallel and Distributed Computing and Systems*, pages 251–256, October 1992. ISBN: 1-880843-02-1.

[6] Alexander Singer. Implementation of artificial neural networks on the Connection Machine. *Parallel Computing*, 14:305–315, Summer 1990.

[7] Wayne Allen and Avijit Saha. Parallel neural-network simulation using back-propagation for the ES-kit environment. In *Proc. of 1989 Conf. Hypercubes, Concurrent Computers and Application*, pages 1097–1102, 1989.

[8] C.R. Rosenberg and G. Blelloch. An implementation of network learning on the Connection Machine. In D. Walz and J. Feldman, editors, *Connectionist Models and their Implications.*, pages 329–340. Ablex, Norwood, NJ, 1988.

Design of 12 Bit Multiplier
Using the Redundant Binary Representation

DonHee Jung*, TaeIn Yun**, and Duckjin Chung**
*Associate DSP Team Samsumg Electronics Co., LTD
Suwon P.O. Box 105 Kyungki-Do Korea 440-600
**Department of Electronic Materials & Devices
College of Engineering, Inha University
#253, Younghyun-Dong Nam-Ku Inchon 402-751, South of Korea
e-mail : djchung@munhak.inha.ac.kr

Abstract

In this paper we design the 12-bit parallel multiplier for the neural network. In order to improve the performance, we use Radix 8 Booth Algorithm for reducing the partial product and the Redundant Binary Adder for fast adding without carry propagation. Radix 8 Booth Algorithm requires the value of three times of multiplicand and Redundant Binary Adder also requires the scheme of converting to binary. In order to implement, this paper propose a adaptable converter/adder in 12bit multiplier. This proposed converter/adder has faster than conventional carry lookahead adder, and similar area as that of carry ripple adder.

1. Introduction

A multiplier is a .very important element in all the processor. It is area and speed to be considered in designing a multiplier. We are endeavoring to decrease the area and increase speed. Speaking generally, there are 2 methods. First, we decrease the partial products, so we can obtain the gain of speed and area. In order to do this, we usually use the Booth algorithm, especially the radix-4 Booth algorithm. Actually the radix-8 Booth algorithm is better than the radix-4 but the disadvantage to triple the multiplicand prevents us from using it. The second is using the high-speed adder, tree structure, and no carry propagation[1][2]. Wallace suggested the fast tree structure but it is not practical because of the complexity of data propagation. In this paper we use the redundant binary adder to add the partial product fast, which use the redundant binary representation without carry propagation. We modify the converter which changes the redundant binary number to the pure binary number. This converter examines the carry propagation with the MOS switches. We show that the suggested converter/adder is 1/3 faster than the carry lookahead adder with the spice simulation. The area of this is 1/5 smaller than that.

2. Redundant Binary Representation

The general binary number represents only 0 and 1, but the redundant number system can represent the sign so it is useful in adding or subtraction. For example, the radix-2 sign digit binary includes -1 representation.

$$\sum_{i=0}^{n-1} x_i \cdot 2^i \, (단, \; x_i \in \{0, 1, -1\})$$

It is possible to add in redundant binary representation without carry propagation.

2.1 Redundant Binary Converting Skill

It is easy to change the redundant binary number to general binary number in coding -1, 0, 0, 1 as 00, 01, 10, and 11, respectively[1]. The redundant binary representation zi is coding to (zi- zi+), meaning $z_i = z_i^+ - \overline{z_i^-}$

$$Z = Z^+ - (\overline{Z^-})$$
$$= Z^+ + (\overline{\overline{Z^-}} + 1)$$
$$= Z^+ + (Z^- + 1)$$

We see that the general addition can represent the 2's complement, which the carry is 1. In this paper we convert the redundant binary number to the pure binary number.

3. Design of 12 Bit Multiplier

It is known that the minimum bit to be able to learn is 12 in the neural network[3]. When we design the neuron, we usually use a parallel circuit to increase the operation speed. In the case of the 12-bit neuron the performance is improved very much so we design the 12-bit parallel multiplier.

The radix-8 Booth algorithm scan each 4 bit, and is better than radix-4 Booth algorithm scanning 3 bit.

Table 1 Radix 4 Vs Radix 8

	radix 4	radix 8
partial product	6 layer	4 layer
RB adder layer	2 layer	1 layer
gate count	about 1695	about 1262

The radix-8 need to triple the multiplicand and we modify the converter. We use the redundant binary adder. Fig.1 shows the full block diagram of 12 bit multiplier.

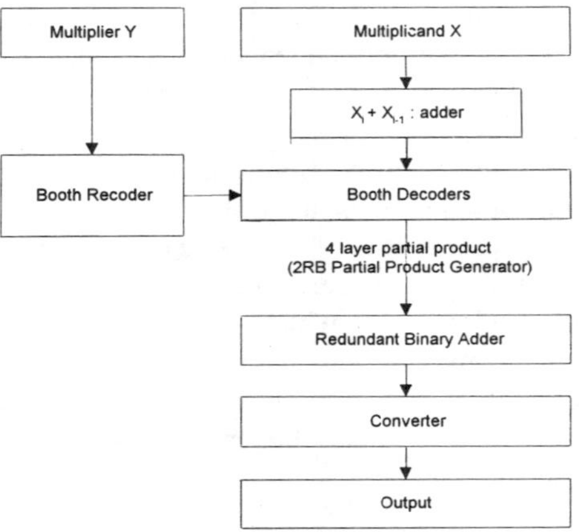

Fig.1 Full block diagram

The multiplier and the multiplicand input at the same time. The multiplicand input to the Booth recoder each 4bit with the radix-8 Booth algorithm[4] and then the coding data go to the Booth decoder. We can obtain the important data in each layer. When the inputs are 12 bit, 4 layers are generated. Those are changed to 2 layer redundant binary so we finish the operation with just one redundant binary adding.

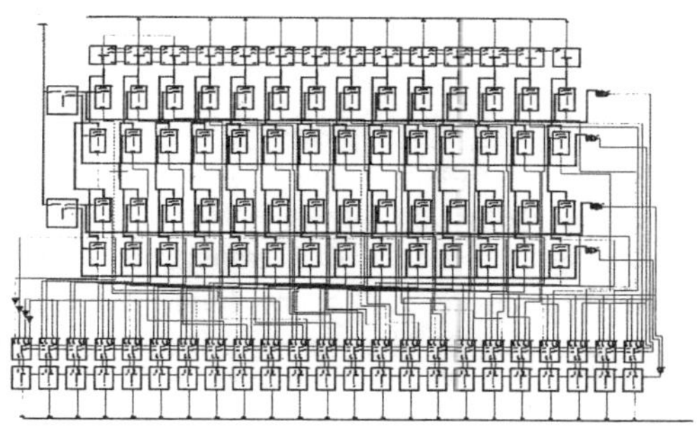

Fig.2 Full schematic

4. The Proposed Converting Method

When we separate the positive and the negative number in the redundant binary representation, in the case of -1 the carry propagate to the first 0. If there is 1, the carry doesn't propagate any more and the binary data keeps the same during that time. Considering this, we design the converter on the switch level.

input		mean	
0	0	T	generate the sign
0	1	0	propagate the sign
1	0	0	
1	1	1	kill the sign

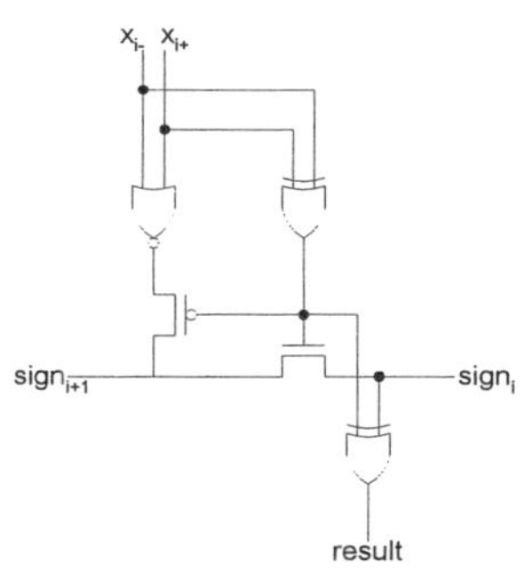

Fig.3 The Proposed Converter

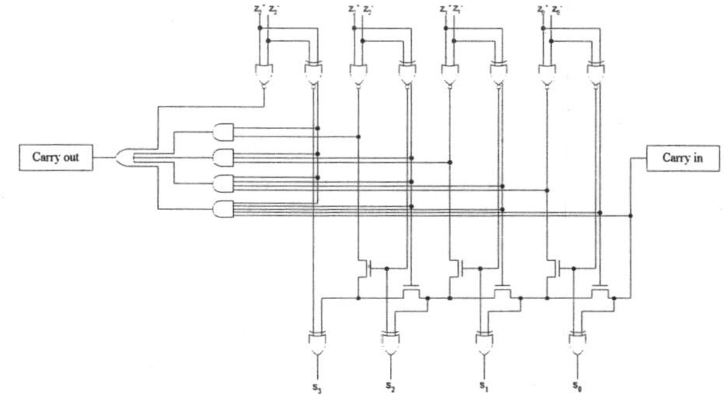

Fig.4 The proposed converter block

In Fig.3, the result of Ex-OR is 1 in case of carry propagation. Otherwise, NMOS is closed and PMOS is open to change the sign. NMOS is open and PMOS is closed and then the previous sign keep propagating. In this paper, we simulate the sign propagation with only NMOS. We use the inverter to examine the sign propagation. To compensate the delay, voltage dissipation and poor voltage, we use the 4-bit carry lookahead block. The disadvantage of using only NMOS is disappeared.

4.1 The Proposed Adder

We design the adder to triple the multiplicand in the radix-8 Booth algorithm using the suggested converter. Instead of NOR gate to examine the sign, we design the adder similar to converter using AND gate. We devide 12 input bit into each 4 bit so we increase the operating speed.

5. Simulation

We used SPICE3 ver. 3D2 to simulate the proposed converter/adder. We simulated the case of tripling the multiplicand different from X.Huang et al.[1] and passing one more redundant adder. Fig.5 shows the time of adding operation using the radix-8 Booth algorithm. Computing the XOR gate delay at 1.5[1], we know that it passes 7 gates and 3 transistors to triple the multiplicand. In Fig.6, we simulate the time of passing one more redundant binary circuit to connect the Booth recoder serially using the radix-4 Booth algorithm. The result of the simulation shows that the suggested adder is 0.4ns faster.

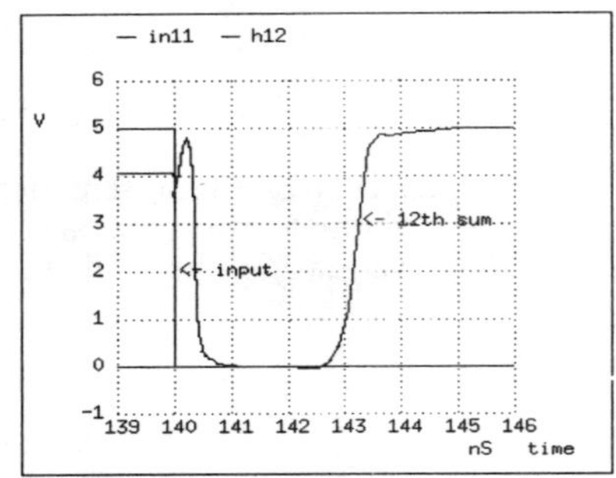

Fig.5 The result of the proposed 12 bit adder

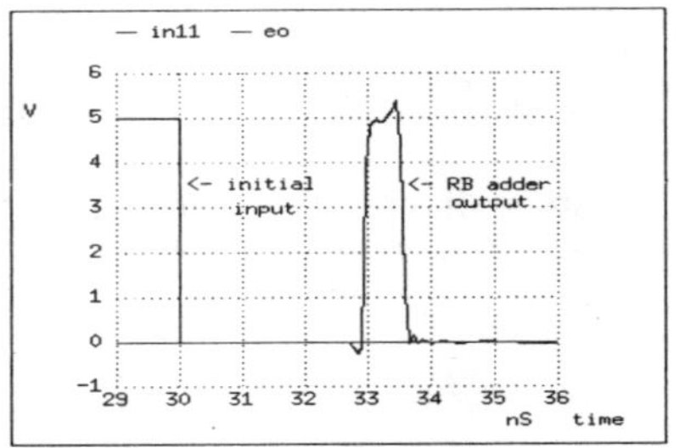

Fig.6 The time of operation in the extra layer using the radix-4 Booth algorithm

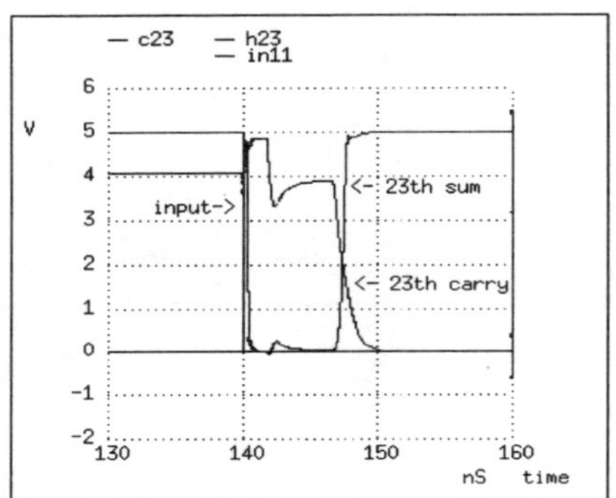

Fig.7 Proposed adder
-Maximum delay time of summation input to 23rd

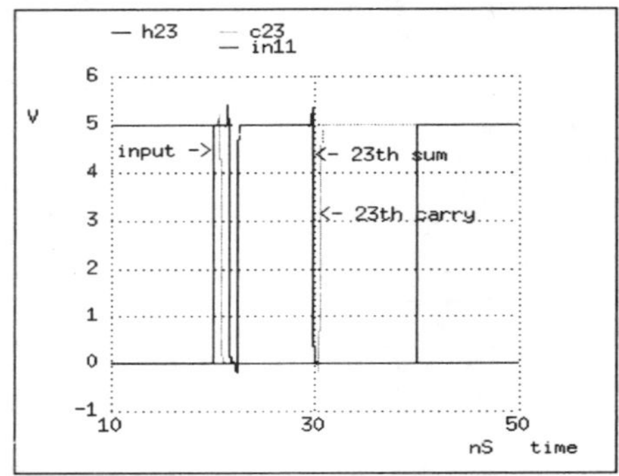

Fig.8 Carry lookahead adder
-Maximum delay time of summation input to 23rd

We also simulated the converter in comparison with the conventional adder. The criteria of size of MOS is 2u. Table.2 shows the size and the speed. The conventional means the general carry ripple adder, and carry lookahead means a carry lookahead adder. In the worst case, we show the time of operation and count the number of gate with CMOS3 Cell Library[5].

Table 2 time interval between input & output of 23th sum in the worst case

	time interval(10^{-9}sec)	gate count
conventional	21.37	161
carry lookahead	10.84	225
proposed adder	7.25	175

Next figures show the simulation of the output 23 bit to convert. They plot the 23rd summation and the carry. In Fig.7, we show the carry which is generated by connecting the full adder serially. Fig.8 shows the carry of 4 bit carry lookahead adder block. In Fig.9, we simulated the result of Fig.6, designing the lookahead block to propagate the sign. While X.Huang's MAC pass 13.5 gates till changing to binary, in this paper it passes 10.5 gates and 3 transistors.

6. Conclusion

In this paper we suggest the modified convert using the redundant binary adder without carry propagation and increase the speed and decrease the area. Using the radix-8 Booth algorithm, we reduce the number of the redundant binary adder layer by decreasing the number of the partial product layer. The modified converter is more efficient than the conventional. Especially, we show that the modified converter is 32% faster than the carry lookahead adder with SPICE simulation which is known to be fast. This 12-bit parallel multiplier increase the speed of neuron operation using the redundant binary representation.

7. Reference

1. Xiaoping Huang, Wen-Jung Liu, and Belle W. Y. Wei, Member, IEEE, A High-Performance CMOS Redundant Binary Multiplication-and- Accumulation (MAC) Unit, IEEE Trans on Circuit and Systems-I : Fundamental Theory and Applications, Vol. 41, NO. 1, Jan. 1994, pp. 33 - 39.

2. Yoshihisa Harata, Yoshio Nakamura, Hiroshi Nagase, Mitsuharu Takigawa, and Naofumi Takagi, A High-Speed Multiplier Using a Redundant Binary Adder Tree, IEEE J. of Solid-State Circuits, Vol. sc-22, NO. 1, Feb. 1987, pp. 28 - 34.

3. S. Eberhardt, T. Duong, and A. Thakoor, A VLSI Analog Synapse 'Building-Block' Chip for Hardware Neural Network Implementations, Proc. Third Annual Parallel Processing Symposium, Fullerton, Cal., Mar. 1989, pp. 29 - 31.

4. H.Sam, A. Gupta, A Generalized Multibit Recoding of Two's Complement Binary Numbers and Its Procf with Application in Multiplier Implementations, IEEE Trans. on Computers, VOL. 39. No. 8, Aug. 1990, pp. 1006 - 1015.

5. Dennis V. Heinbuch, CMOS3 Cell Library, Addison-Wesley Publishing Company, 1988.

A Switched–Capacitor Fuzzy Processor[*]

Liusheng Liu, Bingxue Shi and Zhijian Li

Institute of Microelectronics, Tsinghua University
Beijing, 100084, P. R. China
email: imewsd@tsinghua.edu.cn

Abstract

A multi-input switched-capacitor fuzzy processor is proposed. It focuses on pattern classification and pattern recognition. Multiple inputs that represent multiple features of an unknown pattern are inputted to the processor in time-shared way. Membership function generators generate memberships corresponding to each standard pattern according to the input features. Switched-capacitor accumulators sum multiple memberships to get synthetic memberships. Finally, WTA (Winner-Take-All) circuit finds the maximum synthetic membership and the recognition result is obtained.

1. Introduction

After thirty years of development, fuzzy theory has been greatly promoted. Especially, in the nearest decade, it has found applications in expert system, pattern recognition, robotics and industrial control, etc. It is predicted that fuzzy theory will become one of the kernel technology in information science.

Of course, fuzzy information can be handled in a digital computer, grades of membership function are transformed to many sets of binary codes. The binary coded grades are stored, transferred and operated in electronic binary circuits over and over again in accordance with the stored program. Therefore, it takes a large number of periods to process fuzzy information by digital system. Moreover, the binary coded grades require large number of storing and operating elements. It is not suitable for some applications. Researchers devote themselves to grope for another type of machine which is able to process fuzzy information effectively and at high speed.

Fuzzy hardware can be implemented in analog or digital circuits. Digital fuzzy system is a special computer system, it takes advantage of mature digital VLSI technology, but its scale is large. Fuzzy inference engine fabricated by Bell Lab[1] is its typical representative. Analog fuzzy system is composed of multiple-valued logic (MVL) circuit elements. MVL circuits have two kinds of mode, current-mode and voltage-mode. Yamakawa's fuzzy computer[2-4] is a kind of voltage-mode fuzzy system. It adopts binary process, completes fuzzy inference function through MIN and MAX operation. Current-mode circuit is easy to realize sum and difference operation, has large current range and high integration density[5~12]. But poor precision and high power consumption are its vital weakness. In addition, it must has V-I and I-V converter circuits in order to interface with other circuits.

In this paper, a switched-capacitor fuzzy processor for pattern recognition is proposed, which has the following features:

- Multiple inputs in time-shared way, having greatly process ability;
- Employing switched-capacitor circuits, analog/digital mixed integration;
- Compatible with standard CMOS process, can be easily implemented in VLSI;
- Using for pattern classification and pattern recognition.

2. Principle Of Fuzzy Pattern Recognition

The feature of objective things often has some ambiguity and can be demonstrated in fuzzy set characterized by a membership function. The grade of membership is represented by a number ranging from 0.0 to 1.0. The fundamental principle of fuzzy pattern recognition is maximum membership[13].

Assume $\widetilde{A}_1, \widetilde{A}_2, ..., \widetilde{A}_V$ be V standard patterns, u_0 be the object to be recognized, if

$$\mu_{\widetilde{A}_i}(u_0) = \max\left\{\mu_{\widetilde{A}_1}(u_0), \mu_{\widetilde{A}_2}(u_0), ..., \mu_{\widetilde{A}_V}(u_0)\right\} \tag{1}$$

---

[*] This project is supported by National Natural Science Foundation of China

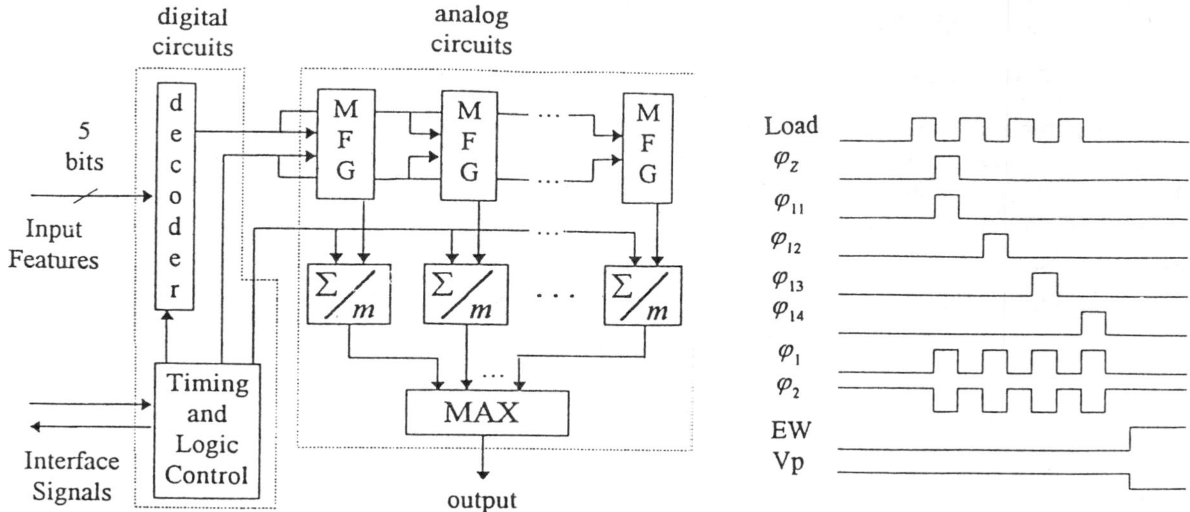

Fig. 1 The structure and timing of fuzzy processor

then, it is decided that u_0 relatively belongs to $\widetilde{A}_i$. $\mu_{\widetilde{A}_i}(u_0)$ is the membership that u_0 belongs to $\widetilde{A}_i$.

In fact, a standard pattern is often with multiple fuzzy features. Let each of V standard patterns be with N fuzzy features. $\widetilde{A}_{ij}$, $i = 1,2,...,V$; $j = 1,2,...,N$, represents the jth fuzzy feature of the ith pattern. Then, each standard pattern becomes a fuzzy vector (or multifactorial fuzzy set):

$$\widetilde{A}_i = \dot{A}_i = \left\langle \widetilde{A}_{i1}, \widetilde{A}_{i2},...,\widetilde{A}_{iN} \right\rangle , \qquad 1 \le i \le V \tag{2}$$

$u^0 = \left(u_1^0, u_2^0,...,u_N^0\right)$ is the object to be recognized, its each element u_j^0, $j = 1,2,...,N$, corresponds to a fuzzy feature, and each feature can get a set of membership relative to each standard pattern. A multifactorial function $M_N(\ )$ should be defined to get a synthetic membership [13,14].

$$\mu_{\widetilde{A}_i}\left(u^0\right) = M_N\left(\mu_{\widetilde{A}_{i1}}\left(u_1^0\right), \mu_{\widetilde{A}_{i2}}\left(u_2^0\right),...,\mu_{\widetilde{A}_{iN}}\left(u_N^0\right)\right) \tag{3}$$

then, we can still get recognition result according to equation (1).
Multifactorial function is manifold, the following two is used most often.

$$\text{Min function: } X \rightarrow \bigwedge_j (X) = \bigwedge_{j=1}^{N} x_j \tag{4}$$

$$\text{Sum function: } X \rightarrow \sum X = \sum_{j=1}^{N} a_j x_j \tag{5}$$

where $X = (x_1, x_2,...,x_N)$, $a_j \in [0,1]$ and $\sum_{j=1}^{N} a_j = 1$. Usually $a_j = 1/N$. Min function combined with Max function is adopted by existing fuzzy hardware by now [1-3], it is fit for fuzzy inference. For fuzzy pattern recognition, our experiments show that Sum function is more suitable because of its good memorization ability and generalization ability [15]. Hence, our fuzzy processor adopts Sum function as multifactorial function.

3. The Structure Of Fuzzy Processor

Our fuzzy processor is a voltage mode digital/analog mixed integrated system. Its structure and timing are shown in Fig. 1.

The input features are coded in 5 bits, i.e. each feature has 32 values. Multiple features (in our system, $N=4$) are inputted to the processor in time-shared way controlled by the timing and logic controller (*Load* signal). In this way, input pins can be reduced and one decoder can be shared. These features are decoded by the decoder, then enter the membership function generators (MFG). Thus, memberships of these features belong to V (in our system, $V = 11$) standard patterns are gotten. The accumulators sum multiple memberships, which are generated by multiple features, up to a set of synthetic memberships. Maximum circuit finds the maximum membership and the recognition result is gotten.

3.1 Membership Function Generator

Membership function generators are shown in Fig. 2. The membership is quantized to 11 values by a resistor string. Different voltages represent different membership value. A group of analog switches are linked to different voltage to form membership function for each standard pattern. Analog switches are controlled by the output of the decoder, c_d, $0 \leq d \leq 31$, and the timing signal $\overline{P1} \sim \overline{P4}$. $\overline{P1} \sim \overline{P4}$ are four unlapped, successive pulses, each pulse corresponds to a input feature. In the figure, $M_{i1} \sim M_{i4}$, $1 \leq i \leq V$, individually stand for the membership values, that four input features belong to standard pattern i.

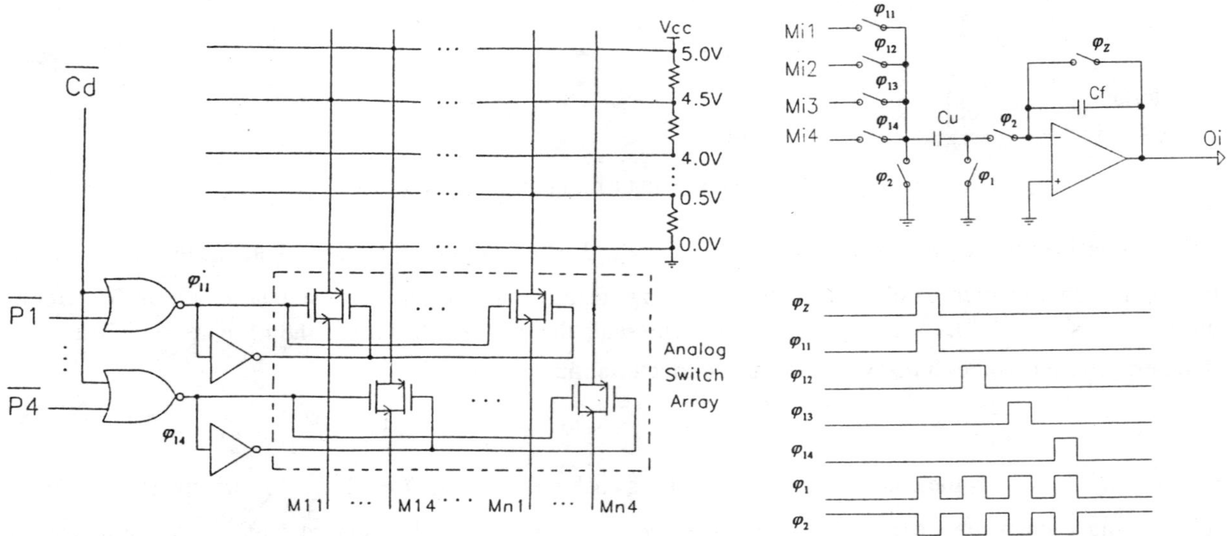

Fig. 2 Membership function generators   Fig. 3 Switched-capacitor accumulator

3.2 Switched-capacitor Accumulator

Switched-capacitor circuit is employed to perform the accumulation of the memberships. Fig. 3 shows the structure of the accumulator. During φ_1, $M_{ij}, 1 \leq i \leq V, 1 \leq j \leq 4$, charge the capacitor C_u; During φ_2, charges are transferred to capacitor C_f and stored on it. Therefore, multiple memberships are accumulated step by step under the control of timing signal φ_1 and φ_2. Obviously

$$O_i = \sum_{j=1}^{N} \left(C_u / C_f \right) M_{ij} , \quad 1 \leq i \leq V \tag{6}$$

Comparing with equation (5), it can be determined that $C_u / C_f = 1/N = 1/4$. When the accumulated synthetic membership equals 1 (maximum value, its corresponding voltage is 5V), the output of the accumulator should be 5V. However, the power supply of the system is ±5V, so a rail-to-rail cascaded op-amp is used [16].

3.3 Maximum Circuit

WTA (Winner-Take-All) circuit proposed in [17,18] is taken as the maximum circuit. It is of high resolution and high speed, and it can perform defuzziness automatically. Fig. 4 demonstrates a four terminals WTA circuit (the really designed circuit is of V terminals).
This circuit is a laterally inhibitory interconnected network. Before the signal EW and Vp are effective, the negative feedback branches of the network is not activated, and all terminals are at initial potential. After EW and Vp are effective, the network is turned from the initial unstable state to a stable state under the action of competitive inhibition. The potential of each terminal turns on the pull-down NMOS transistors at all other terminals to lower their potential. Only the terminal with maximum initial potential can pull other terminals

down to the ground. So, the pull-down NMOS transistors which are linked to this terminal are turned off, and itself is enhanced to *Vcc* by the pull-up PMOS transistor.

3.4 Simulation Results

Fig. 5 gives a typical case of a 6 terminals system. It is evidently that during φ_1 、 φ_2, the voltage of all terminals are accumulated and promoted step by step. After *EW* and *Vp* are activated, the maximum voltage (4.5V) is pulled up to *Vcc* and the others are pull down to the ground.

SPICE simulation results shown that resolution of a ten terminals WTA circuit is better than *15mV*. In our system, the minimum interval is *0.5V/4=125mV*. Hence, WTA circuit is competent and the system works well.

Fig. 6 shows the layout of the fuzzy processor. The processor is designed in 3μm double poly, N-well CMOS process. It is now under fabrication.

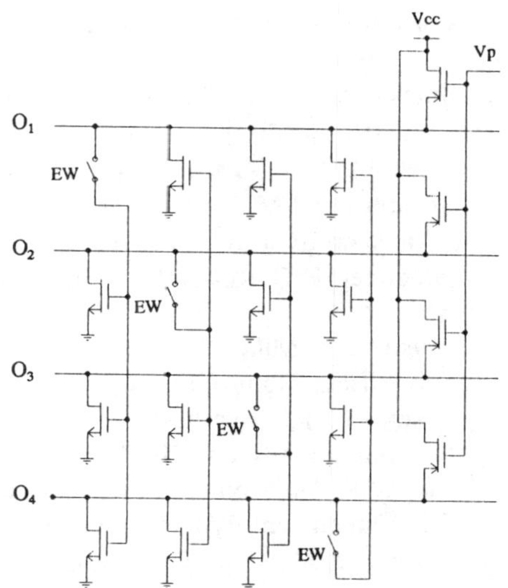

Fig. 4 A four terminals WTA circuit

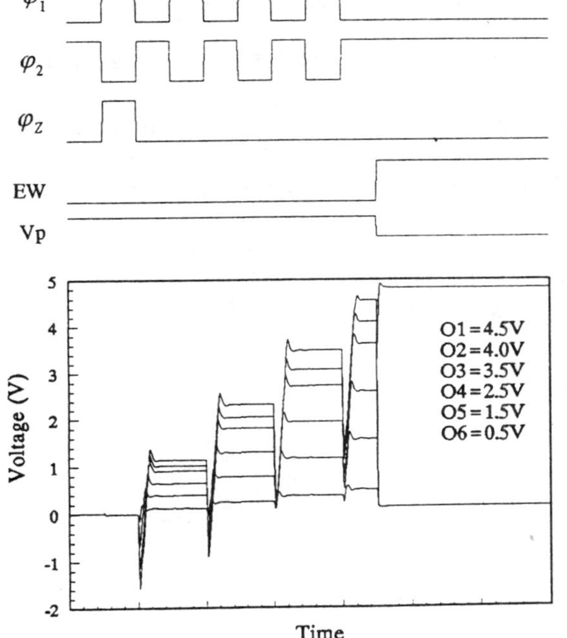

Fig. 5 A typical simulation result of a 6 terminals system

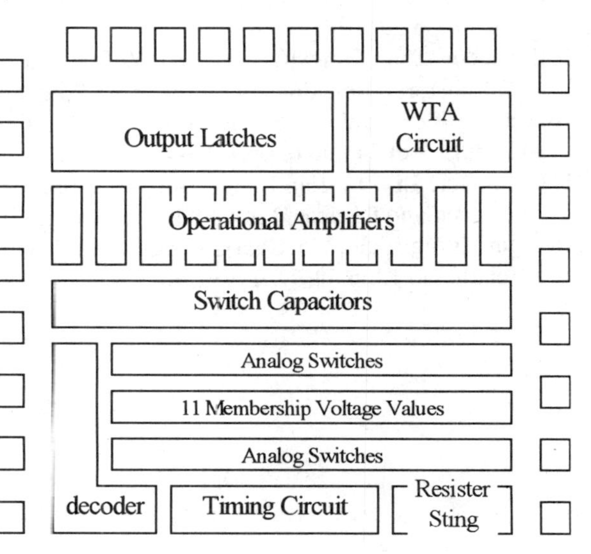

Fig. 6 Layout of the fuzzy Processor

4. Summary

The proposed fuzzy processor focuses on pattern recognition. It accepts multiple inputs in time shared way. In this way, its process ability is improved and its application can be expanded. Switched-capacitor circuits is used as accumulators, and is compatible with standard CMOS technology, so the whole system can be easily implemented in VLSI technology.

References

[1] M. Togai, H. Watanable, "A VLSI implementation of a fuzzy inference engine: toward an expert system on a chip", Information Sciences, Vol.38, No.2, pp.147–164, 1986.

[2] T. Yamakawa, "A simple fuzzy computer hardware system employing MIN & MAX operations — a challenge to 6th generation computer", Priprints of Second IFSA Congress, 1987, Vol.2, pp.823–830.

[3] T. Yamakawa, "An approach to a fuzzy computer hardware system", Proc. 2nd Int. Conf. on Artificial Intelligence, Marseille, Japan, 1986.

[4] T. Yamakawa, K. Sasaki, "Fuzzy memory device", Priprints of 2nd IFSA Congress, 1987, Vol.2, pp.551–555.

[5] T. Yamakawa, et al., "The design and fabrication of the current mode fuzzy logic semi–custom", Proc. 15th. ISMVL, pp.76–82, 1985.

[6] T. Yamakawa, "CMOS multivalued circuits in hybrid mode", Proc. 15th. ISMVL, pp.144–150, 1985.

[7] T. Yamakawa and M. Einaga, "Hybrid–mode multiple–valued logic circuits based on Nyquist expansion", The Trans. on IECE of Japan, Vol.E69, No.4, pp.497–500, 1986.

[8] S.P. Onneweer, H.G. Kerkhoff, "Current–mode CMOS high–radix circuits", Proc. 16th. ISMVL, pp.60–69, 1986.

[9] T. Yamakawa, T. Miki, "The current mode fuzzy logic integrated circuits fabricated by the standard CMOS Process," IEEE Trans. on Computer, Vol.C–35, No.2, pp.161–167, 1986.

[10] F. Ueno, et al., "Synthesis of fuzzy membership function circuits with multiple inputs and their applications", Trans. on IEICE of Japan, Vol.E71, No.1, pp.77–87, 1988.

[11]F. Ueno, et al, "A maximum and minimum circuits with multiple inputs in current mode", Trans. of the IEICE of Japan, Vol.E70, No.4, pp.392–395, 1987.

[12] M. Sasaki, et al., "Fuzzy multiple–input maximum and minimum circuits in current mode and their analysis using bounded–difference equations", IEEE Trans. on Computers, Vol.39, No.6, pp.768–774, 1990.

[13] LI Hongxing, WANG Peizhuang, "Fuzzy mathematics ", National Defense Industry Press, 1994. (in Chinese)

[14] LI Hongxing, "Multifactorial Fuzzy sets and Multifactorial Degree of Nearness", Fuzzy Sets and Systems, Vol.19, pp.291-297, 1986.

[15]Liusheng Liu, Bingxue Shi and Zhijian Li, "A Comparison of Two Kinds of Memberships and Multifactorial Functions in Fuzzy Logic Speech Recognition", ICONIP'95, Vol.2, pp.890–893, 1995.

[16]Terri S. Fiez, et al, "A Family of High-Swing CMOS Operational Amplifier", IEEE Journal of Solid-State Circuits, Vol.24, No.6, pp.1683-1687, 1989.

[17] Bin–Qiao Li, Zhi–Jian Li and Bing–Xue Shi, "An analog integrated circuit of a hamming neural network designed and fabricated in CMOS technology", IJCNN'93, Vol.1, pp.879–882, 1993.

[18]Ugur Cilingiroglu, " A Charge-Based Neural Hamming Classifier", IEEE Journal of Solid-State Circuits, Vol.28, No.1, pp.59-67, 1993.

NeuDB'95: An SQL Based Neural Network Environment

Erich Schikuta
Institute of Applied Computer Science and Information Systems, Dept. of Data Engineering,
University of Vienna, Rathausstr. 19/4, A-1010, Vienna, Austria,
schiki@ifs.univie.ac.at

Abstract— **The NeuDB'95 system is a novel approach to the physical and conceptual integration of neural networks into an object-oriented database systems. In the context of the database system neural networks are seen as basic objects and are administrated by the standardized SQL interface of the system. The network paradigm of a neural network object is defined by the type hierarchy of the general neural net database type. The structural information is stored using a data oriented approach. The dynamic components of the neural networks are triggered by conventional SQL statements for insertion, update, deletion and access. They are processed by an independently running artificial neural network simulator.**

1   Introduction

In the last few years many different systems for the easy and software supported creation and administration of neural networks were presented. Some of the system tackle only special types of neural networks as for example Aspirin/MIGRAINES [5] or SOM-PAK [13]. Other try to deliver a comprehensive tool as AXON [3], SNNS [15] or NeurDS [14].

In general all systems provide the user with a proprietary software environment, which reaches from highly sophisticated interactive systems to programming language extensions. They confront the user with the problem to cope with a new and/or complex tool. Further most of these systems present a standalone environment, which is not capable to interconnect to other software systems. A further problem of all these systems is the lack of a generalized framework for handling data sets and neural networks homogenously. During the training phase and the evaluation phase of a neural net the user has to feed the net with large amounts of data. Conventionally data sets are mostly supported via sequential files only and the definition of the input stream, output or target stream into a neural net is often extremely clumsy, static and complex.

2   Database Approach

Object oriented database systems have proven very valuable at handling and administrating complex objects. The object-oriented approach seams (and in our opinion has proven) the most comfortable and natural design model for neural networks [4]. In the context of object-oriented database systems neural networks are treated generally as complex objects. These systems showed very valuable at handling and administrating such objects in different areas, as computer aided design, geographic databases, administration of component structures, etc. It is our objective to consider neural networks as conventional data in the database system. From the logical point of view a neural network is a complex data value and can be stored as a normal data object.

The usage of a database system as an environment for neural networks provides both quantitative and qualitative advantages.

- **Quantitative Advantages.** Modern database systems allow the administration of objects efficiently. This is provided by a 'smart' internal level of the system, which exploits well studied and well known data structures, access paths, etc. A whole bunch of further concepts is inherent to these systems, like models for transaction handling, recovery, multi-user capability, concurrent access etc. This places an unchallenged platform in speed and security for the definition and manipulation of large data sets at users disposal.

- **Qualitative Advantages.** The user has powerful tools and models at hand, like data definition and manipulation languages, report generators or transaction processing. These tools provide a unified framework for both handling neural networks and the input/output data streams of these networks. A homogeneous and comprehensive user interface is provided to the user. This spares awkward tricks to analyze the data of his database with a separate network simulator system.

A further important aspect (which is beyond the scope of this paper) is the usage of neural networks as part of the rule component of a knowledge base database system [9]. Neural networks represent inherently knowledge by the processing in the nodes [6]. Trained neural networks are similar to rules in the conventional symbolic sense. A very promising approach is therefore the embedding of neural networks directly into the generalized knowledge framework of a knowledge based database system.

3 The NeuDB'95 System

The NeuDB'95 system is based on the Postgres'95 database system [7] and an adapted version of the NeurDS neural network simulator [14]. The predecessor to the NeuDB'95 System was the original NeuDB System [10]. This was the first approach of integrating neural networks into a database system. The main drawback of this system was the propriatory interface language of the Postgres 2.0 database system, called Postquel, which was difficult to understand and to use (in spite of or, maybe due to, its logical soundness). The user acceptance of the whole system suffered from the clumsy interface language. This led to the replacement of the Postquel language by the SQL[2] interface in the latest Postgres'95 system. The replacement of the interface language of the Postgres system triggered a comprehensive redesign of the NeuDB system too and resulted into the new SQL based NeuDB'95 system.

3.1 System design

Postgres'95 is a highly extensible database system with object oriented features, like type inheritance. The data model of Postgres'95 consists of classes (relations) containing tuples, which represent real-world entities. A class has attributes of a fixed type that represent properties of the objects stored in the class. The type inheritance feature allows a natural and comfortable modeling of the neural network data type according to our embedding framework. A neural network class is embedded into the Postgres'95 class system and the rule system of Postgres'95 is heavily exploited to emulate the dynamic neural network component.

We chose Postgres'95 because of its capability to define triggering rules on database operations [12]. Using the rule system a data-driven request-action strategy was established. The insertion or update of neural network objects notifies the neural network simulator by inserting a request record into a dedicated communication class the server is listening to. This approach realizes represent the dynamic component of the system.

The Artificial Neural network simulator runs as an independent server process (ANNSserver) to the database system in parallel and performs the actual network evaluation and training. It provides a user interface, which allows to monitor the state of the simulator. This proved extremely useful for the training phase of a network. The user can create trace files, which can be used for the design of succeding training phases. The following figure shows the process structure of the NeuDB'95 system.

Figure 1: The NeuDB'95 process structure

The Postgres'95 database server administrates the data on disk and requests actions of the ANNSserver corresponding to database commands (insert, update, eval). The ANNSserver creates an artificial neural network according to the data description, performs the requested actions and updates the database accordingly. The user at the computer console directs both processes and controls interactively the system status.

The distribution of the tasks to 2 separate and independently running servers gives the advantage of exploiting the inherent parallelism of the system. While the ANNSserver is processing the neural networks (training or evaluation), the database server is providing the input data streams in parallel. Generally it can be seen as a pipelined process structure. Postgres'95 is designed to support the database server paradigm, where an independent database server runs on a dedicated machine and communicates with the front-end processes via the network.

We exploit this paradigm by a 'request - action' strategy. The user connects to the database via a front-end process (this can be the usual Postgres'95 'monitor' or any other available front-end program). User inputs trigger actions (e.g. the insertion of a training object triggers a training phase), which are resolved by a call to the ANNSserver. The server processes the requests (e.g. the training phase) and performs dependent data actions (e.g. the insertion of link weights).

The ANNSserver can physically distribute its tasks among available processing units of the underlying network. So it can exploit idle workstations of the network to perform the very time consuming neural network actions. The user has not to wait for the accomplishment his requested actions; he just initiates it and continues with his work. This allows to parallelizes the requests, for example multiple training phases.

The whole NeuDB'95 design exploits heavily parallelism to speed-up the program execution. More specific we distinguish between three levels of parallelism, the processes(user monitor, database system, ANN server), inter-operation (SQL requests), intra-operation parallelism (training). A comprehensive description and performance analysis can be found in [11].

3.2   Data types

The 'NeuralNet' type is a subtype of the general object type of the database system. Subtypes of this NeuralNet type can be classified into specialized neural network types according to their network paradigm. It is also possible that a network paradigm is the supertype of another more specialized paradigm. In the NeuDB'95 system a neural network is generally defined by the 'NeuralNet' class, which provides a unique identifier for referencing the neural network object. It also describes the basic structure of the network by a Layer attribute. This attribute contains a sequence (basically an array) of integer values, which defines the number of processing elements in each layer. In the following we give the SQL statement for the respective class creation for clarification. These are no user actions. The classes are predefined in NeuDB'95.

```
create table NeuralNet ( NNId char16, Layer int4[] );
```

At this definition level nothing is said about the network paradigm. It is defined by a specialization, a subtype of 'NeuralNet'. This subtype (which inherits all characteristics of its supertype) provides the specific and necessary attributes dependent on the network paradigm. Combined with the definition of the paradigm is the dynamic behavior of the network. For example, a feedforward network paradigm with backpropagation training algorithm is provided by the system class,

```
create table BPN ( ConnectInToOutput bool ) inherits ( NeuralNet );
```

The characteristics of a trained network is defined by the 'Train' class. This class provides all attributes for the training phase of the referenced neural network object. It is organized as a hierarchical type structure similar to the basic neural network class. Generally a 'Train' class consists of the neural object reference (NNId), a unique 'Train' object identifier (TId) and a definition of the input and target data stream. The notation '[ ]' denotes an array of values.

```
create table Train
        ( TId char16, NNId char16, InputA float8[],
        TargetA float8[], InputF text, TargetF text );
```

The data values can be defined explicitly by a value sequence or implicitly by an SQL statement (see the following section). A 'Train' sub-class provides object characteristics dependent on the network paradigm.

```
create table TrainBPN
        ( InitWeight float8, ActivationF char16, ... )  inherits ( Train );
```

This class defines all describing attributes for the training phase respective to the network paradigm. The training action is started by the insertion of a training object into the specialized class. After a completed training phase the user can use the 'trained' neural network object to analyze his data sets. This can be done via two mechanisms, the creation of an 'Eval' (evaluate) object or the use of the 'eval'-function. The 'eval' function allows the user to evaluate a neural network object according to the training characteristics responding to an input data stream. This function can be seen as an embedded operator and can be used in any SQL statements. The second possibility is the insertion of an 'Eval' object into the respective class. The insertion triggers an eval action, which is resolved by the ANNSserver. The result is inserted into a result class. The user can directly access this class or via a composed 'Output' attribute (an SQL function) defined on 'Eval'. The creation of an 'Eval' object has the advantage that the result of the neural network evaluation is stored in the database and has not to be calculated again. It can easily be accessed via the conventional database operations.

3.3 Functional data stream definition

The functional data stream definition allows to specify the data sets in a comfortable way. It is not necessary to specify the data values explicitly, but the data streams can be described by SQL statements. The well known apparatus of the SQL database manipulation language is at hand. Thus the same tool can both be used for administration and analysis of the stored information. So it is easily possible to use 'real world' data sets as training set for neural networks and to analyze other (or the same) data with trained networks (see Section 4).

The main design principle of the NeuDB'95 system is that the handling of a neural network has to be simple. That means that there has not to be a complex or artificial procedure to use it. In contrary the environment has to supply functions to manipulate neural network in a natural and (more important) commonly known way. In the formalism of the database system both types of information (the 'real-world' data and the neural networks) are 'just' data. These data objects are therefore administrated and handled homogeneously within the same framework.

To perform a useful training phase the user has to provide certain training phase controlling parameters. The type and the number of parameters are highly dependent on the network paradigm. All paradigms expect input and target data. In an increasing number of neural network applications these data sets show tremendous sizes, like in cluster analysis, pattern recognition, and others. Therefore the access costs can not be neglected and have to be considered in the processing times. In these cases the database facilities of the NeuDB'95 system can improve the performance of the data analysis process tremendously. Besides the mentioned data pipelining of the independent processes, the access mechanisms of the database system provide a powerful tool for the handling of these large data sets.

4 An example: The XOR problem

The following section gives an example of the creation, training and usage of a neural network object which solves the well known XOR-problem [1]. All user inputs are marked by a preceding ' >' prompt. The shown examples represent actual screen dumps. The sometimes intricate format is a 'specialty' of the basic Postgres'95 monitor program.

4.1 Creation and administration

To solve the XOR-problem we use a feedforward multi-layer network with the backpropagation training algorithm [8]. First we have to create a neural network object within the database system. This is easily done by an insert to the back-propagation network class BPN. We define the network identifier (for future references to this object), the number of layers (3), and the number of processing elements for each layer (3, 1, 1 respectively).

```
> insert into BPN values ( 'XOR-Net', ' 3, 1, 1 ', 't' );
```

The links between the processing nodes can be inserted explicitly. In can also be done automatically by setting the 'ConnectInToOutput' flag to true. This triggers a Postgres'95 rule, which inserts the correct links to the Link class automatically. Actually the ANNSserver performs these insertions. The status of the new neural network object is untrained. Via the network identifier NNId the object can be referenced and administrative database tasks can be performed, like updating

```
> update BPN set Layer = ' 3, 5, 1 ' where BPN.NNId = 'XOR-Net';
```

or deleting

```
> delete from BPN where NNId = 'XOR-Net'; .
```

During the update and the delete operation the consistency is kept in the database system in accordance to the status or properties of the neural network. Both operaticns trigger rules, which change the operation dependent objects accordingly. This can be an update of the connections of the processing elements represented by entries in the Link class (see 'update' example) or the deletion of training characteristics of neural network objects (see 'delete' example). All these 'ccnsistency-keeping' operations are performed automatically without a forced activity by the user.

4.2 Training

The training phase is started by the insertion of a training object. This object contains the necessary training parameter as attribute values. Besides the neural network identifier, the training identifier and the Input and Target data stream the other values are set to default values. Thus it is not necessary to specify all values explicitly (but it is good programming practice).

```
> insert into TrainBPN ( NNId, TId, InputA, TargetA, ... )  values
    ('Train1', 'XOR-Net',
    '{ 1.0, 0.0, 0.0, 1.0, 0.0, 1.0, 1.0, 1.0, 0.0, 1.0, 1.0, 1.0 }',
    '{ 0.0, 1.0, 1.0, 0.0 }', ... );
```

The above example uses input and target values explicitly. But as mentioned in Section 3.3, it is also possible to apply a functional data stream definition and use input and/or target functions. These functions are SQL statements. The result of these statements are sequential data streams with the same properties as the respective explicit value definition. A training object with a functional data stream definition can therefore be inserted by (comments are denoted by '- -' in SQL)

```
> insert TrainingBPN ( NNId, TId, InputF, TargetF, ... )  values
    'XOR-Net', 'Train2',
    'retrieve(A.x, A.y) from A in InputValues', -- input function
    'retrieve(B.z) from B in TargetValues',    -- target function
    ... );
```

The result of a training phase is a new object in the 'weight' class. This object can be accessed by the following select statement

```
> select * from weight where NNId = 'XOR-Net' and TID = 'Train2';
```

which produces as result

```
------------------------------------------------------------
| NNId        | TId         | Weights       | cWeights     |
------------------------------------------------------------
| XOR-Net     | Train2      | '{1.93072,4.76279,-5.74234,
-3.07542,-5.74085,-3.075,-7.72916}'|
'{0.000641426,0.00224068,-0.00127401,-0.00165155,-0.00126514,
-0.00171889,-0.00279093}'|
------------------------------------------------------------
```

4.3 Usage

As mentioned above, neural networks can be used to analyze test data by the insertion of an 'Eval' object,

```
> insert into Eval ( EId, NNId, TId, InputA ) values
    ( 'E1', 'XOR-Net', 'Train1', '{ 1.0, 1.0, 1.0 }' );
```

or by the 'eval' function,

```
> select eval('XOR-Net', 'Train1', '{ 1.0, 1.0, 1.0 }');
```

which produces

```
      ---------------
     | x             |
      ---------------
     | '0.199699'    |
      ---------------
```

We have the possibility to use a functional data stream definition (an SQL statement) instead of explicit input values, too.

5 Conclusions

We used the NeuDB'95 system, and its predecessor, for a certain while and it proved extremely well with practical applications. We tested it with the administration and analysis of medical data sets and it reached a high degree of acceptance throughout the group of test user. The homogeneity of the database and neural network simulator interface found general acceptance and a high attraction.

The next milestone will be the replacement of the NeurDS based neural network simulator with a novel parallelizing artificial neural network simulation system. We aim for a highly parallel system design, which can employ equally well a underlying workstation cluster environment or a specialized parallel hardware architecture.

References

[1] Beale R., Neural Computing: an introduction, Hilger, 1990

[2] Melton J., Simon A.R., Understanding the new SQL: A Complete Guide, Morgan Kaufmann Publishers, 1993

[3] Hecht-Nielsen R., Neurocomputing, Addison/Wesley, 1989

[4] Heileman G., et al., A General Framework for Concurrent Simulation of Neural Networks Models, IEEE Trans. Software Engineering, 18, 7, pp. 551-562, 1992

[5] Leighton R., The Aspirin/MIGRAINES Neural Network Software, user manual, MITRE Corp., 1992

[6] Pao Y.-H., Sobajic D.J., Neural networks and Knowledge Engineering, IEEE Knowledge and Data Engineering, 3, 2, pp. 185 - 192, June 1991

[7] Rowe L., Stonebraker M., The POSTGRES data model, Proc. 1987 Conference on Very Large Database Systems, Brighton, 1987

[8] Rumelhardt, D.E. et al., Learning internal Representation by Error Propagation, in Rumelhardt D.E. et al., Parallel Distributed Processing: Explorations in the Microstructure of Cognition, Vol 1, MIT Press, 1986

[9] Schikuta E., The Role of Neural Networks in Knowledge Based Systems, In Proc. Int. Symp. on nonlinear theory and applications, IEICE, Hawaii, Dec. 1993

[10] Schikuta E., The NeuDB-system: Towards the Integration of Neural Networks and Database Systems, In Proc. KI'94, Saarbruecken, Springer-Verlag, Sept. 1994

[11] Schikuta A., Parallelism in the NeuDB System, In Proc. 2nd Int. Conf. on Massively Parallel Computing Systems, Ischia, IEEE Computer Society Press, May 1996

[12] Stonebraker M., et. al., On Rules, Procedures, Caching and Views in Database Systems, In Proc. 1990 ACM-SIGMOD Conf. on Management of Data, Atlantic City, June 1990

[13] SOM Team, SOM-PAK, The Self-Organizing Map Program Package, user guide, Helsinki, 1992

[14] Wecker D.B., The Neural Design and Simulation System (NeurDS), Digi TR. 589, May 1989

[15] Zell A. et al., SNNS, Stuttgart Neural Network Simulator, User Manual, Tech.Rep.No. 3/92, Univ. Stuttgart, 1992

High Performance VLSI Compressors for Large Data Matrix in Digital Neural Networks Implementation

D. Zhang

Department of Computer Science, City University of Hong Kong
Kowloon, Hong Kong, dapeng@cs.cityu.edu.hk

Abstract

A key problem for implementing high performance, high capacity digital neural networks (DNN) is to design effective VLSI compressors to reduce the impact of carry propagation of large data matrix. In this paper, such a compressor design based on complex complementary pass-transistor logic (C^2PL) is presented. Some types of 3-2 compressors in C^2PL are implemented and a number of experiments are conducted to optimize their performance. Two typical building blocks, 4-2 and 7-3 compressor, are developed and their DNN applications are discussed. Compared with the complementary pass-transistor logic (CPL) and the conventional direct logic (CDL), our simulations show that the C^2PL compressors have the best performance in power, delay and number of transistors.

1   INTRODUCTION

Numerous studies have shown that the complexity of digital neural network (DNN) does not stem from the complexity of its nodes but rather from the multitude of ways in which a large collection of these nodes can interact [1-2]. As an example, for a fully connected layered network with two layers and n neurons per layer, each neuron is required to form an inner product of n elements using 1-bit binary input lines and m-bit weights (e.g., m=16), where carry propagation is an expensive operation in digital arithmetic of the inner product. Thus, a key problem for implementing high performance, high capacity DNN is to build effective compressors to reduce the impact of carry propagation.

CMOS digital technology can be used to design such compressors due to high noise immunity, low power dissipation, relatively high speed, and compatibility to other logic families [3]. There are many CMOS logic design styles to choose for DNN implementation. Some typical logic design styles are pseudo-NMOS CMOS logic, CMOS non-threshold logic (NTL), cascode voltage switch logic (CVSL), differential cascode voltage switch logic (DCVS), differential split-level logic (DSL), and Zipper CMOS logic. They achieve different tradeoffs in speed, power, and area. The highest speed logic families also tend to consume the most power. The most compact tend to be slow.

Complementary pass-transistor logic (CPL) proposed by K. Yano, et al. in [4] seems to offer modest performance, is compact, and low power. The CPL circuit is twice as fast as conventional CMOS because of lower input capacitance and higher logic functionality. However, CPL design needs more area in silicon like the conventional CMOS due to the mixed interconnection. In addition, CPL implementation must take into account noise margin and speed degradation caused by mismatched input signal level and the logic threshold voltage of the CMOS driver [5]. A variation, swing restored pass-transistor logic (SRPL) [6], is developed to improve the performance of CPL, but it has still high area drawback. In this paper, a new member of CPL family, called complex complementary pass-transistor logic (C^2PL), will be presented to design the more effective VLSI compressors with applications to DNN.

2 C^2PL MODEL

A basic CPL model consists of complementary inputs / outputs, an NMOS pass transistor logic network, and CMOS output inverters [4]. Complementary input space is defined as $R = R^{(G)} + R^{(D)}$, where $R^{(G)}$ and $R^{(D)}$ are gate input space and drain input space, respectively. The pass transistors function as pull-down and pull-up devices. The output inverters are necessary because of amplifying the output signals, shifting the logic threshold voltage and driving the capacitive load.

Notice that the NMOS pass transistor logic network in CPL is built by some logic layers, where each achieves a given function. Assuming that these logic layers are symbolized as L_i (i = 1, 2, ..., n), and n is the number of the layers in the network, a CPL circuit can be designed by the following rules: (1) Only NMOS pass transistors are used in the logic network; (2) All complementary gate inputs receive data from $R^{(G)}$; (3) The drain inputs of Layer L_i come from Layer L_{i-1} except for L_1. Obviously, these rules limit CPL to use in DNN implementations, which require both flexible design and effective computation.

In order to obtain the high performance, we supplement a new member, C^2PL, to CPL family. The basic concept of C^2PL model is to regard each layer in the network as an independent logic layer built by NMOS or PMOS / NMOS pass transistor logic. The connection between the logic layers may be not only in serial, but also in parallel. This means that both complementary drain and gate input for logic layer L_i may receive data from either R or previous layer L_{i-1}, and the complementary outputs of L_i connects to L_{i+1} or directly network output units, CMOS or BiCMOS driver. It is evident that CPL is a special example of C^2PL.

3   3-2 COMPRESSOR DESIGN

<u>A. Basic Structure</u>   Let the complementary input space R = { a, a', b, b', c, c' }, and the complementary output space Q = { S, S', C, C' }. Their relations can be represented as: S (sum) = (a $\oplus$ c) b' + (a $\oplus$ c)' b and C (carry) = (a $\oplus$ c) b + (a $\oplus$ c)' c, where $\oplus$ is a XOR operator. We can extract two essential cells, (a $\oplus$ c) and (a $\oplus$ c)'. Let F = a $\oplus$ c. Thus, the relations can be rewritten as S = F $\oplus$ b and C = F b + F' c.

Using C^2PL to design such a 3-2 compressor, a simple logic structure with two logic layers can be obtained in Fig. 1. Their input / output spaces are R1 = {a, a', c, c'} / Q1= { F, F' } and R2 = {F, F', b, b', c, c'} / Q2 = { S, S', C, C' }, respectively. Note that two types of logic processing elements, an XOR / XNOR element and a wired-AND / NAND element, are used in the design. Analyzing the logic structure in Fig. 1, some useful characteristics can be obtained as follows:

a.   Only two complementary inputs in R, { a, a', c, c' }, are required in the first logic layer. This characteristic is superior in multi-layer design. It can be proved by designing typical building blocks to DNN applications in Section IV.

b.   The complementary output space Q1 of the first logic layer are directly used as the gate input $R2^{(G)}$ to the next layer. Since both $R1^{(D)}$ and $R2^{(D)}$ can be obtained at the same time, a key to enhance the performance of the compressor is how to provide $R2^{(G)}$ current paths for any pull-down or pull-up operation.

Two kinds of 3-2 compressors to improve $R2^{(G)}$ in C^2PL are given in Fig. 2, where the second logic layers are the same, but PMOS latch approach ($C^2PL(1)$) and PMOS / NMOS device approach ($C^2PL(2)$) are used in the first layer, respectively. It is evident that $C^2PL(2)$ has the symmetry of both the PMOS and the NMOS devices. Independent of the voltage level of the input space R1, its delay time is approximately the same. However, $C^2PL(1)$ can be built with the less transistors.

A number of experiments based on HSPICE simulation have been achieved to optimize these compressors, and some useful results are: (a) the gate width ratio between logic layers, $\zeta = W_{up} / W_{down}$, is chosen at the ratio of about 2; (b) the gate width ratio between PMOS and NMOS in CMOS output driver, $\phi = W_p / W_n$, exists at the ratio of about 1.25. Notice that these ratios are different from CPL and ordinary CMOS drivers in [4] because we adopt a power-delay product as our measurement, which is more reasonable than only delay time.

<u>B. Comparison with CPL</u>   Area, power and delay estimations are used as our measurements between the CPL and the C^2PL. The circuit simulations are performed using the 0.8μ device parameters at a supply voltage of 5V. The worst delay time, T, refers to situations where the inputs are such that circuit operation is slowest and the average power, P, is defined as 0.5 x C_{load} x $(V_{cc})^2/T_{cyc}$ x E(switching), where C_{load} is the load

capacitance in the circuit, V_{cc} is the supply voltage, T_{cyc} is the clock cycle time, and E(switching) is the expected value of the number of output transition per global clock cycle. The simulated T (P) of three 3-2 compressors, i.e., the CPL in [4], the $C^2PL(1)$ and the $C^2PL(2)$ in Fig. 2, are 0.56ns (1.95mw), 0.58ns (1.89mw) and 0.55ns (1.78mw). The simulated power-delay product, T x P, as a function of supply voltage and output load shows that the 3-2 compressors in C^2PL, especially $C^2PL(2)$, is about 10% less power-delay product than one in CPL mainly due to less transistor and smaller input capacitance.

Based on the 0.8μ design rules, layout results of the basic 3-2 compressor structure show that the areas required are $1245.44\mu m^2$ for CPL, $865.18\mu m^2$ for $C^2PL(1)$ and $867.57\mu m^2$ $C^2PL(2)$ (See Fig. 3). Obviously, the area of 3-2 compressors in C^2PL can be reduced by about one-thirds. The results mentioned above are summarized in Table I. It shows that the 3-2 compressor in C^2PL has the lower area complexity in silicon and the smaller power while maintaining the same high computing speed.

4   DNN APPLICATIONS

<u>A. Building Block Definition</u>   Using the 3-2 compressors in C^2PL, two typical building blocks, i.e., 4-2 compressor (Fig. 4(a)) and 7-3 compressor (Fig. 4(b)), can be built to DNN applications. Since some data flow paths between the 3-2 compressors are not crucial for signal degradation of each building block, they are connected without buffering to reduce the total count of transistors. In addition, based on the characteristic of the 3-2 compressor structure obtained in Section III, the numbers of the logic layers required for the longest data flow paths, as shown as dashed lines in Fig. 4, can be reduced from 4 to 3 for 4-2 compressor and 6 to 5 for 7-3 compressor, respectively.

These two compressor building blocks in C^2PL are comparable in power, delay and number of transistors to the same building blocks in both CPL and CDL (Conventional Direct Logic [7-8]). Their comparisons are shown in Table II and Table III, respectively. Notice that $C^2PL(3)$ is represented as a design approach in C^2PL, where a 3-2 compressor is built by full PMOS / NMOS device in the both layers. The results show that the building blocks in C^2PL can offer the highest performance in VLSI design.

<u>B. Row Matrix Reduction</u>   As an example in DNN application, we assume that a perceptron sums the 1010 data inputs, each with one bit. A reduction process is to use 7-3 compressor to reduce the initial 1010 row matrix to a matrix with no more than three elements in each column.

The whole reduction process is shown in Fig. 5, where 252 7-3 compressors and 6 processing stages are needed. Based on the different logic design styles in Table III, our simulations show that the required parameters (i.e., power, delay and number of transistor) are: 0.66w, 9.3n and 27,216 ($C^2PL(3)$); 1.14w, 10.44n and 28,224 (CPL), and 0.69w, 18n and 28,224 (CDL), respectively. This means that power and delay in C^2PL are only about half as much as one in CPL and in CDL, respectively.

<u>C. Wallace Tree Reduction</u>   Fast multipliers with Wallace tree adders are essential part of DNN implementation. Assuming that a perceptron sums the M data inputs, each with N bits. A reduction process for this Wallace tree is to compress the initial M x N matrix to 2 x K matrix, where $K \geq N$. Using 4-2 compressor as a building block, the height of Wallace tree, h, can be reduced in the following series: $\cdots \rightarrow 32 \rightarrow 16 \rightarrow 8 \rightarrow 4 \rightarrow 2$, i.e., the number of 4-2 compressors required by each column is $\lceil h / 4 \rceil$.

Assuming that Wallace tree with h = 16 is reduced by 32 x 7 (= 224) 4-2 compressors. Using the different logic design styles listed in Table II, the simulation results show that the three measurements (power, delay and number of transistor) are: 0.44w, 2.1n and 10,304 for $C^2PL(2)$; 0.59w, 3.2n and 12,544 for CPL, and 0.47w, 5.1n and 12,992 for CDL, respectively. It is evident that the C^2PL compressor still has the best performance compared with the other designs.

5   CONCLUSIONS

In this paper, we presented a new complementary pass-transistor logic design style, C^2PL, to DNN applications. Applying the C^2PL model to compressor designs, some types of 3-2 compressors are developed and a number of experiments are conducted to optimize their performances. As examples of DNN applications, two typical building blocks, i.e., 4-2 and 7-3 compressors, are defined, and their parallel structures are discussed.

Compared with the CPL and the CDL, our simulation results show that the C^2PL compressors have the best performance in power, delay and number of transistors.

REFERENCES

[1]   M.I. Elmasry (ed.), *VLSI Artificial Neural Networks Engineering*. MA: Kluwer Academic, 1994.

[2]   J.B. Burr, "Digital neural network implementation", in *Neural Networks, Concepts, Applications, and Implementations*, Prentice Hall, pp. 237-285, 1991.

[3]   M.I. Elmasry (ed.), *Digital MOS Integrated Circuits II with Applications to Processors and Memory Design*. New York: IEEE Press, 1992.

[4]   K. Yano, et al., "A 3.8-ns CMOS 16x16-b multiplier using complementary pass-transistor logic", *IEEE Journal of Solid-State Circuits* 25, 2, pp. 388-395, 1990.

[5]   A.P. Chandrakasan, S. Sheng and R.W. Brodesen, "Low-power CMOS digital design", *IEEE Journal of Solid-State Circuits* 27, 4, pp. 473-483, 1992.

[6]   A. Parameswar, et al., "A high speed, low power, swing restored pass-transistor logic based multiply and accumulate circuit for multimedia applications", *CICC 94*, pp. 278-281, 1994.

[7]   J. Mori, et al., "A 10-ns 54x54-b parallel structured full array multiplier with 0.5-μm CMOS technology", *IEEE Journal of Solid-State Circuits* 26, 4, pp. 600-605, 1991.

[8]   E. Hokenek, R.K. Montoye and P.W. Cook, "Second-generation RISC floating point with multiply-add fused", *IEEE Journal of Solid-State Circuits* 25, 5, pp. 1207-1213, 1990.

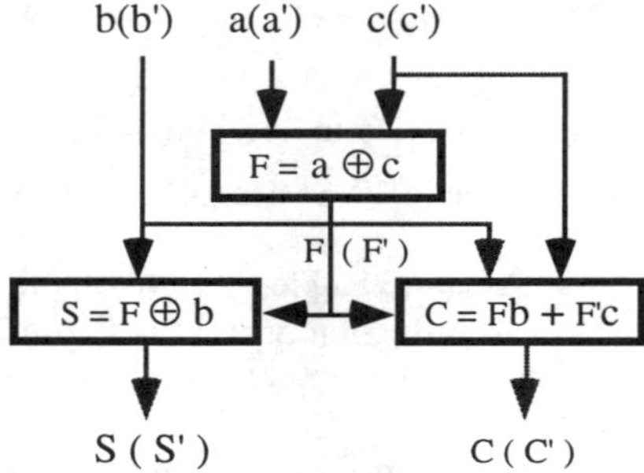

Fig. 1. 3-2 compressor logic structure with two kinds of logic processing elements

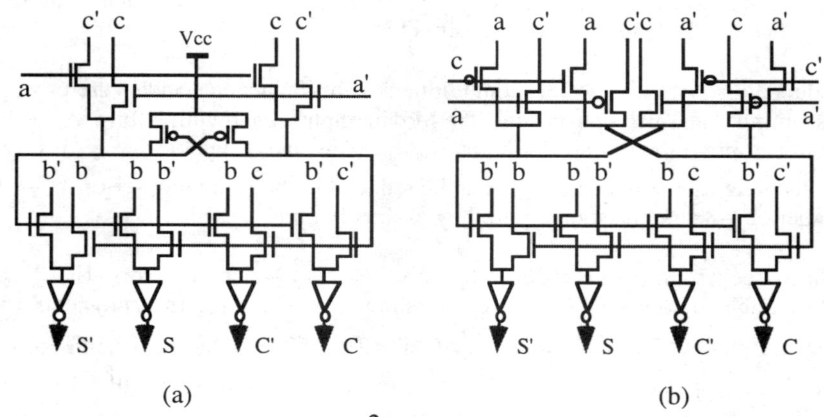

Fig. 2. Two typical 3-2 compressors in C^2PL with (a) PMOS latch approach; and (b) PMOS / NMOS device approach

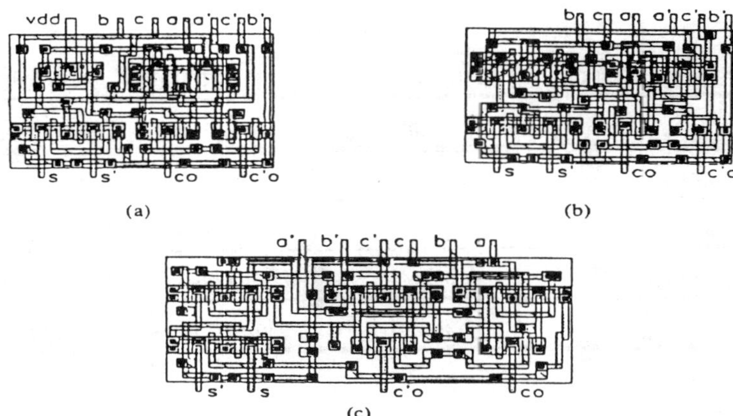

Fig. 3.   Layout results for 3-2 compressor logic structure in (a) $C^2PL(1)$, (b) $C^2PL(2)$ and (c) CPL

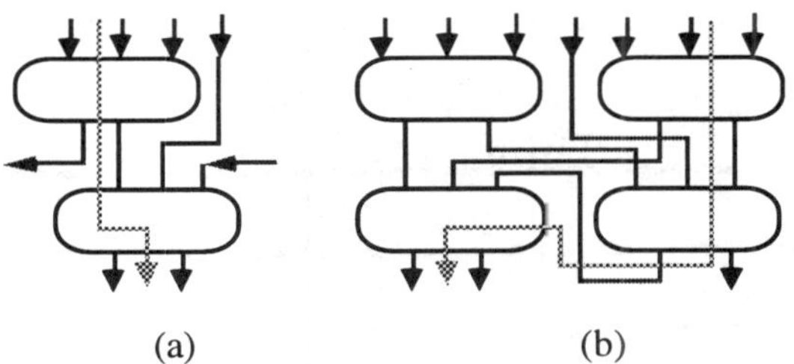

Fig.4. Two typical compressor building blocks to DNN applications (a) 4-2 compressor and (b) 7-3 compressor

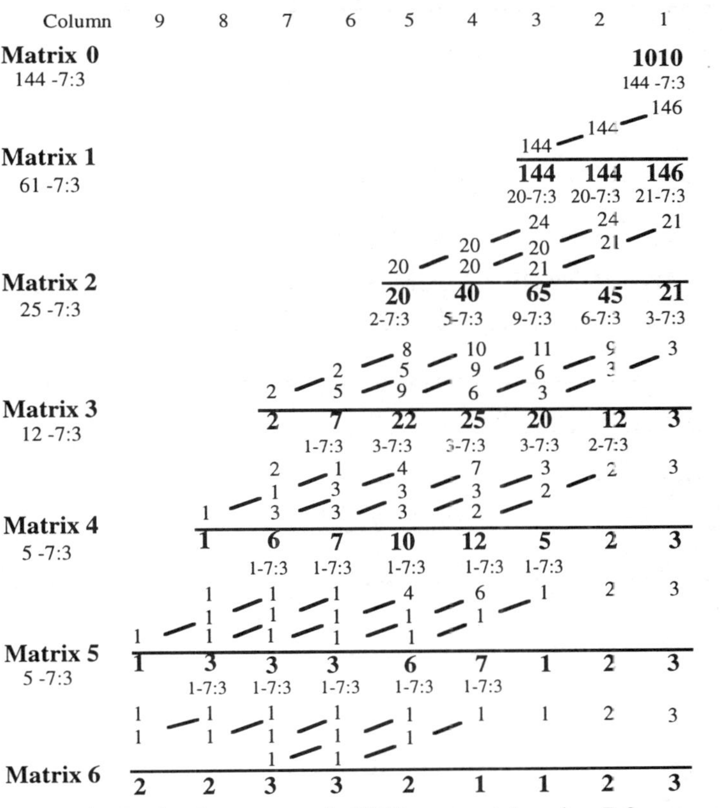

Fig. 5.   Reduction process in 1010 row matrix using 7-3 compressors

TABLE I

COMPARISON OF 3-2 COMPRESSORS BETWEEN CPL AND C^2PL

	CPL	C^2PL(1)	C^2PL(2)
No. of Transistors	28	22	24
Delay Time	0.56ns	0.58ns	0.55ns
Power	1.95mw	1.89mw	1.78mw
Area	1245.44μm^2	865.18μm^2	867.57μm^2

TABLE II

COMPARISON OF 4-2 COMPRESSORS FOR THE DIFFERENT
LOGIC DESIGN STYLES

	Power	Delay	# Tran.
C^2PL(3)	1.83mw	0.73n	60
C^2PL(2)	1.97mw	0.70n	46
CPL	2.66mw	1.07n	56
CDL [7]	2.1mw	1.70n	58

TABLE III

COMPARISON OF 7-3 COMPRESSORS FOR THE DIFFERENT
LOGIC DESIGN STYLES

	Power	Delay	# Tran.
C^2PL(3)	2.61mw	1.55n	108
C^2PL(2)	3.37mw	1.45n	94
CPL	4.54mw	1.74n	112
CDL [8]	2.74mw	3.0n	112

A Floating-Gate "Synapse" Circuit and its Application to a Neural Network Integrated Circuit with On-Chip Learning

P.A. Shoemaker[1], C.G. Hutchens[2], J.E. Cooper[3], I. Lagnado[1]

[1] U.S. Naval Command, Control, and Ocean Surveillance Center, RDT&E Div. 891
San Diego, CA 92152 USA
shoe@cod.nosc.mil

[2] Oklahoma State University Dept. of Electrical and Computer Engineering, Stillwater, OK 74078 USA
hutchen@master.ceat.okstate.edu

[3] James Cooper Consulting, 2012 Applewood Ln. , Vista, CA 92083 USA
CooperJim@aol.com

Abstract - We report a "synapse" circuit, fabricated in silicon-on-sapphire, for use in analog artificial neural network integrated circuits with on-chip learning. For non-volatile analog memory, it uses a floating gate with symmetric injection capacitors and a simple charging regulation circuit. A compact four-quadrant multiplier performs the weighting function. We describe integration of this cell into a "neural layer" which implements a modified form of the back-propagation learning rule, and which has been demonstrated to learn linearly separable problems.

1   Introduction

Artificial neural network models have exhibited some success in the last decade in application to signal processing, control, and other problems at which biological neural systems excel. In addition, learning algorithms developed for these models allow acquisition of function by examples, and/or adaptation to nonstationary environments. Analog integrated circuits offer the potential for high-density, low-power implementations of neural networks, but many technical issues must be addressed before such devices can become generally useful. Long-term storage of "synaptic" or interconnection weights, and practicable approaches to real-time, on-chip "learning" are two such problems. We report a weight or "synapse" cell designed to address these particular issues, and discuss its integration into an analog "neural layer" integrated circuit with on-chip, parallel learning capability.

2   Process and Devices

Circuits were fabricated in a complementary metal-oxide semiconductor (CMOS) process using thin-film silicon-on-sapphire (SOS) [1] . While SOS has primarily found application in radiation-hard and very high-speed digital CMOS circuits, it has several characteristics which are exploited in designs for our analog neural network application, as well. Transistors are formed in isolated silicon islands etched on the insulating sapphire substrate, allowing full dielectric isolation between devices. Enhancement mode CMOS transistors are fabricated in the usual fashion. Fabrication of depletion-mode CMOS transistors is straightforward, using channel doping of the same type as the source/drains, without the complications of buried channels encountered in bulk silicon. MOS capacitors are fabricated using lower (crystalline silicon) plates doped with the n-type depletion-mode doping. As in most modern CMOS processes, gates are formed from highly doped polycrystalline silicon (poly) rather than metal.

3   "Synapse" Circuit

The "synapse" circuit, depicted in Fig. 1 below, comprises a floating gate with charge injection circuitry [2,3], an integrator for regulating the process of charge injection, and a simple analog four-quadrant multiplier [4]. The floating gate is used for a non-volatile analog memory to hold a "synaptic" weight value. It comprises a dielectrically isolated structure, which may be charged or discharged by a relatively high programming voltage applied to the charge injection circuit, but which retains the charge for long periods when the programming voltage is removed. Because the gate oxides are 250nm thick, and a thinner tunneling oxide is not available, the charge injection is accomplished by a pair of MOS injection capacitors [2,3]. In each capacitor, if a sufficiently large positive voltage is applied to the upper poly plate relative to the crystalline silicon lower plate, charge (electrons) will be injected from a deep depletion region in the lower plate through the oxide onto the upper plate [2]. In order to both charge and discharge the gate, two injection capacitors with opposing orientations must be used; in one of these, the silicon island plate must contact the floating gate, requiring dielectric isolation of the island. The two capacitors allow symmetric injection of charge onto or off of the floating gate, depending on the polarity of the voltage applied across them. Useful currents without destructive changes in the oxide are obtained with 14-18V. A bias capacitor C_b is used in practice to bias the floating gate during programming or learning.

The floating gate is connected to an integrator via an MOS transistor which acts as a decouple switch: when the stored charge is to be modified, the switch is opened and a high-voltage programming pulse applied across the PGM+ and PGM-/REF terminals in Fig. 1. Afterward, the switch is closed and the injected charge is integrated onto the storage capacitor C_S, bringing the floating gate potential back to a reference (applied at the PGM-/REF terminal). In this way, a charge increment/decrement of the same size is obtained at each pulse, as long as the output voltage of the integrator remains within its operating range. This method is used to regulate the charging characteristics of the floating gate against the strongly nonlinear charge transfer mechanism of the injectors, and is necessary to enable learning by the algorithm discussed below.

The integrator output drives the gates of a multipier circuit that performs the "synaptic" function of weighting an input signal. The multiplier consists of a complementary pair of long-channel depletion mode transistors. These supply an output current I_{OUT} to a virtual ground proportional to the product of gate voltage V_1 and an input voltage V_2 (provided along with its inverse) [4]. The circuit deviates from an ideal multiplier in a soft manner when subject to device mismatches and second-order effects, and is intended for use in applications like neural networks in which the importance of precise bilinearity is secondary to compactness.

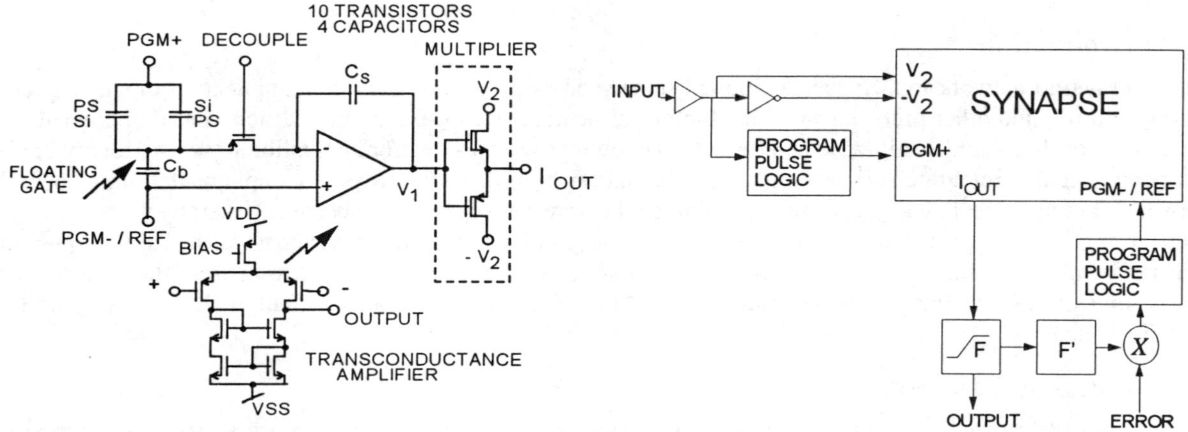

Figure 1. "Synapse" cell schematic diagram. The labels PS and Si refer to polysilicon and crystalline silicon, respectively.

Figure 2. Block diagram of input/output path through a synapse cell in a "neural layer" chip.

4 Integration into "Neural Layer" with Modified Back-Propagation Learning

The weight cell has been integrated into a fully interconnected "neural layer" of the sigmoid perceptron type, with 100 inputs and outputs, and a matrix of 10K weights. A block diagram of a single input/output path is shown in Fig. 2. The "neurons" are current-summing transimpedance amplifiers, with nonlinear feedback to give a sigmoidal input/output relation.

The chip also contains circuitry to implement a modified version [5-7] of on-line back-propagation [8], an algorithm for supervised learning by stochastic approximation. Some of these circuits perform the "error back-propagation" as defined in the original algorithm; the circuit labeled F' in Fig. 2, which approximates the derivative of the sigmoid (F) function, is part of this subsystem. However, in contrast with the original algorithm, changes that are made to the weights during learning are trinary or Manhattan in nature (i.e., fixed increment, decrement, or zero). Although the resulting learning rule does not follow local gradients of an error measure in the weight space, it nevertheless performs a local descent and can be used for stochastic approximation, as shown by convergence on solutions to a number of test problems [5,6]. The trinary version of the delta rule may be implemented in parallel with switching circuitry associated with each input block and output "neuron," which (taken pairwise) perform the equivalent of an exclusive-or function: the sign of a weight update is the product of the signs of the input to the synapse and error in output of the neuron associated with the synapse (with thresholds allowing for no update). Of central importance is that the controlling circuitry is located at the input blocks and neurons rather than the synapses, which contain only the charging regulation described above. This permits a compact synapse design (4800 μm^2 in the existing circuit, with a 3025 μm^2 redesign completed), which may be contrasted with synapses designed to implement full gradient back-propagation, *e.g.*, the 70,000 μm^2 cell reported by Cho *et al.* [9]. Rather than adapt an analog design to an algorithm developed through simulation on floating-point digital computers, we have made an adaptation of the algorithm requiring considerably less complexity and accuracy in analog hardware. (This statement must be accompanied by the caveat that offset errors in the back-propagation path are generally fatal to convergence and provision must be made in the circuitry to trim them to zero.)

5 Experimental Results and Conclusions

Fig.3 depicts a family of curves from an isolated multiplier circuit, with externally connected gates allowing direct application of the voltage V_1. Fig. 4 shows programming of a floating-gate synapse as alternate trains of positive and negative programming pulses are applied. The ordinate represents the output of the multiplier in the synapse with fixed input V_2, as measured between programming pulses. The effects of charging regulation -- nearly constant and equal rates of increase and decrease of the output -- are clear. While floating-gate charge retention has not yet been measured in high-temperature experiments, weight values have been observed to be held for at least several months when input/output curves are measured for individual "neurons."

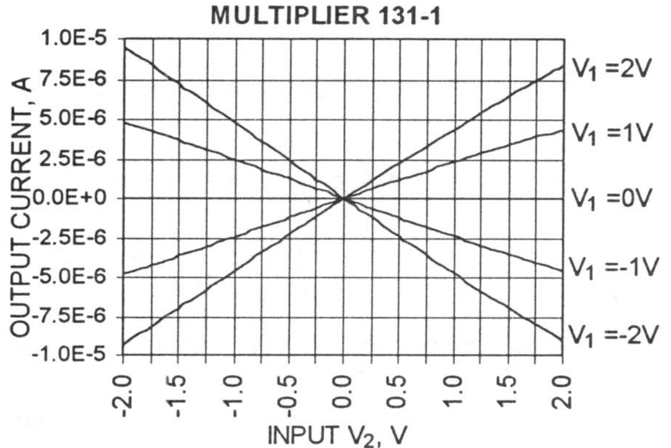

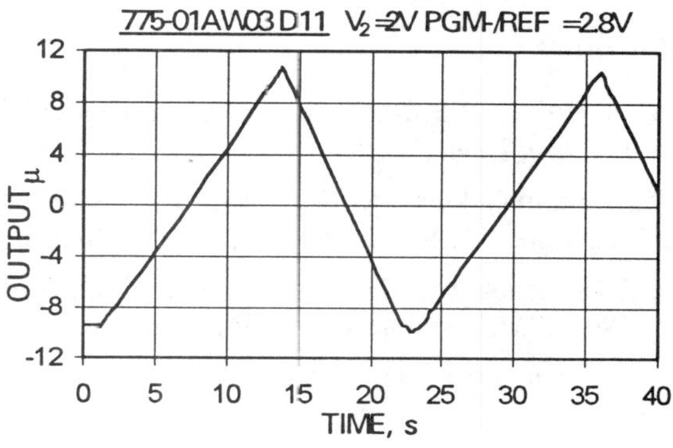

Figure 3. Experimental family of curves taken from a multiplier circuit.

Figure 4. Bidirectional programming of a floating-gate synapse cell with pulse trains of alternating sign. Programming pulse duty cycle is 1%.

Several design and process deficiencies were identified and found to affect the functionality of the full neural network chip. In particular, the back-propagation circuitry is not completely functional, which precludes cascading chips into multilayer learning networks. Nevertheless, with some difficulty, parallel learning has been demonstrated with individual chips on simple problems which can be computed by a single layer. When input and target vectors consist of alternating positive and negative components, the synapses organize into a checkerboard of alternating positive and negative weights, as measured after learning. This test is used to screen the synapse arrays for programmability and multiplier functionality; on wafers with good parametrics, synapse yields in excess of 96% are typically obtained.

Among the other linearly-separable test problems that have been successfully learned on subsets of the chip are the separation of vectors in an orthogonal set, and computation of all the linearly separable two-input logic functions. In Fig. 5, the response functions of a neuron over its two-dimensional input space (horizontal plane) is displayed at several times during training as it is trained on data representing the AND function, after previously having learned the NOR function. Noise on the signal is particularly evident in the high-gain region of the neuron, and irregularities in the separatrices between positive and negative responses are due to deviations from bilinearity in the synaptic multipliers, as well as an identified deficiency in the summing amplifier design. This last also contributes the unwanted peak in the response on the left side of the final graph.

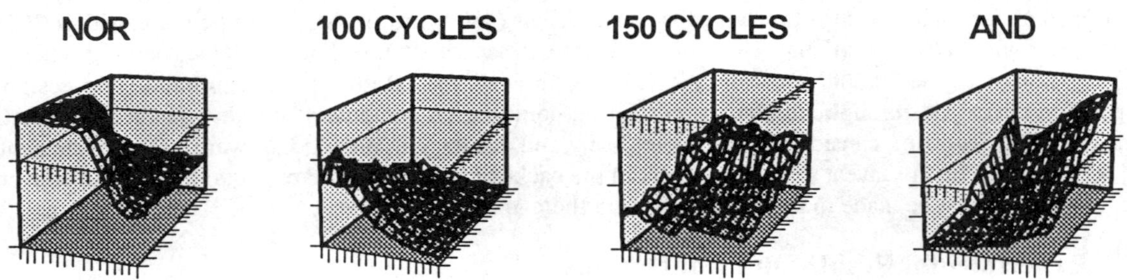

Fig. 5 Response functions of a neuron over its input space as it is trained on data representing the AND function after previously learning the NOR function

---

Acknowledgments: This work was supported by the U.S. Office of Naval Research. Hughes Aircraft Company Technology Center (Carlsbad, CA) fabricated the devices.

References

[1] G.A. Garcia, R.E. Reedy, and M.L. Burgener, " High-quality CMOS in thin (100nm) silicon on sapphire," *IEEE Electron Device Letters*, vol. 9, pp. 32-34, 1988.

[2] R.L. Shimabukuro, M.E. Stewart, P.A. Shoemaker, and G.A. Garcia, "MOS Analog memory with Injection Capacitors," U.S. Patent No. 5,253,196, issued Oct. 1993.

[3] R.L. Shimabukuro, M.E. Wood, and P.A. Shoemaker, "A neural network synapse cell in 90nm SOS," *Proc. 1991 IEEE International SOI Conference*, Vail, Colorado, Oct. 1-3, 1991, pp. 162-163.

[4] P.A. Shoemaker, G.L. Haviland, and R.L. Shimabukuro, "A simple CMOS analog four-quadrant multiplier," *Analog Integrated Circuits and Signal Processing* , vol. 1, no. 2, pp. 107-117, 1991.

[5] P.A. Shoemaker, M.J. Carlin, and R.L. Shimabukuro, "Back-propagation learning with trinary quantization of weight updates," *Neural Networks*, vol. 4, no. 2, pp. 231-241, 1991.

[6] P.A. Shoemaker, M.J. Carlin, and R.L. Shimabukuro, "Back-propagation learning with coarse quantization of weight updates," *Proc. International Joint Conference on Neural Networks*, Washington, Jan. 15-19, 1990, vol. 1, pp. 573-576.

[7] R.L Shimabukuro, P.A. Shoemaker, C.C. Guest, and M.J. Carlin, "Effect of circuit parameters on convergence of trinary update back-propagation," *Proc. Connectionist Models Summer School*, Touretzky, D.S., Elman, J.L., Sejnowski, T.J., and Hinton, G.E., eds., pp. 152-158. San Mateo, Calif.: Morgan Kaufmann, 1991.

[8] D.E. Rumelhart, G.E. Hinton, and R.J. Williams, "Learning internal representations by error propagation," in *Parallel Distributed Processing, Explorations in the Microstructure of Cognition*, 1 (pp. 318-362). Cambridge, Mass.: MIT Press, 1986.

[9] J.-W. Cho, Y.K. Choi, S.-O. Kwon, S.-Y. Lee, "Expandable Analog Neural Network Chip Set with On-Chip Learning by Error Back-Propagation and Hebbian Learning Rules, " *Proc. World Congress on Neural Networks*, Washington, July 17-21, 1995, vol. II, pp. 468-471.

"CAM-BRAIN"
ATR's BILLION NEURON
ARTIFICIAL BRAIN PROJECT

Hugo de Garis

Brain Builder Group, Evolutionary Systems Department,
ATR Human Information Processing Research Laboratories,
2-2 Hikaridai, Seika-cho, Soraku-gun,
Kansai Science City, Kyoto, 619-02, Japan.
tel. + 81 7749 5 1079, fax. + 81 7749 5 1008
degaris@hip.atr.co.jp

Abstract - **This paper reports on progress made in the first 3 years of ATR's "CAM-Brain" Project, which aims to use "evolutionary engineering" techniques to build/grow/evolve a RAM-and-cellular-automata based artificial brain consisting of thousands of interconnected neural network modules inside special hardware such as MIT's Cellular Automata Machine "CAM-8", or NTT's Content Addressable Memory System "CAM-System". The states of a billion (later a trillion) 3D cellular automata cells, and millions of cellular automata rules which govern their state changes, can be stored relatively cheaply in giga(tera)bytes of RAM. After 3 years work, the CA rules are almost ready. MIT's "CAM-8" (essentially a serial device) can update 200 million CA cells a second. It is likely that NTT's "CAM-System" (essentially a massively parallel device) will be able to update a *hundred billion* CA cells a second. Hence all the ingredients will soon be ready to create a revolutionary new technology which will allow thousands of evolved neural network modules to be assembled into artificial brains. This in turn will probably create not only a new research field, but hopefully a whole new industry, namely "brain building". Building artificial brains with a billion neurons is the aim of ATR's 8 year "CAM-Brain" research project, ending in 2001.**

1.   Introduction

ATR's CAM-Brain project resulted from the experience of the author's thesis work, in which he evolved neural net modules (using concatenated bit-string weights) to control the behavior of a simulated quadruped called "LIZZY", which could walk straight, turn left, turn right, peck at food and mate [6]. Each of these behaviors was controlled by the time varying outputs of a single evolved neural network module, and applied to the angles of the leg components of LIZZY. (As far as he is aware, the author was the first person to evolve neural net dynamics [3], (in the form of walking stick-legs "Walker")). Switching between behaviors involved taking the outputs from one neural net module and feeding them into the inputs of the next module. The next step was to evolve neural net detectors, e.g. for frequency, signal strength, signal strength difference, etc. Finally, neural net "production rule" modules were evolved which could map conditional inputs from detectors to output behaviors. Thus an "intelligent" artificial creature was built, which could detect prey, mates and predators, and then approach and eat or mate, or turn away and flee. Virtually every neural net that the author tried to evolve, evolved successfully. *The evolution of these fully connected neural network modules proved to be a very powerful technique.* This success made a deep impression on the author, reinforcing his dream of being able to build much more complex artificial nervous systems, even artificial brains. However, every time the author added a neural net module to the Lizzy simulation, its speed on the screen was slowed (on a Mac II computer). Gradually, the necessity dawned on the author that some kind of evolvable hardware solution [5] would be needed to evolve large numbers of neural net modules and at great speed (i.e. electronic speed) in special machines the author calls "Darwin Machines" [5]. Evolving artificial brains directly in hardware remains the ultimate future goal of the author, but in the meantime (since the field of evolvable hardware (EHW, E-Hard) is today only in its infancy), the author compromises by using cellular automata to grow/evolve neural nets in large numbers in RAM, which is cheap and plentiful. (In a year or so, it will be quite possible to have a gigabyte of RAM in one's work-station). By using cellular automata based neural nets which grow and evolve in gigabytes of RAM, it should be possible to evolve large numbers (thousands) of neural net modules, and then assemble them (or even evolve their interconnections) to build an artificial brain. The bottleneck is the speed of the processor which updates the CA cells. State of the art in such processors is MIT's "CAM-8" machine, which can update 200,000,000 CA cells a second. Very recently, it has been suggested by the author's ATR colleague Hemmi, that NTT's Content Addressable Memory System (CAM-System) might be able to update CA cells at a rate *thousands* of times faster than the MIT machine, i.e. at a *hundred billion* CA cells per second. NTT's machine is massively parallel. Hemmi and his programmer assistant Yoshikawa are now (December 1995) busily engaged in writing software to convert the author's CA rules (in 2D form) into Boolean expressions suitable for the NTT machine. If they succeed in applying this machine to CAM-Brain, then a new era of brain building can begin, because the ability to evolve thousands of neural net modules would become realistic and very practical (for example, to evolve a neural net module inside a cubic space of a million CA cells, i.e. 100 cells on a side, at a hundred billion cells a second, would take at most about 500 clock cycles, i.e. about five milliseconds. *So the evolution of a population of 100 chromosomes over 100 generations could all be done in about one minute.)* All the essential ingredients for brain building would be available (lots of RAM, the CA rules, and fast CA processors). Even if Hemmi does not succeed, then a new machine can be designed to be thousands of times faster than the CAM-8 machine. The author believes the CAM-Brain breakthrough is either less than a year away, or at most only a few years away (the time necessary to design and build a "Super-CAM" machine, probably with the help of NTT).

The above gives an overview of the CAM-Brain research project. What now follows is a more detailed description of CAM-Brain, showing how one grows and evolves CA based neural net modules in 2D and 3D. We begin with the essential idea. Imagine a 2D CA trail which is 3 cells wide (e.g. Fig. 2). Down the middle of the trail, send growth signals. When a growth signal hits the end of the trail, it makes the trail extend, or turn left, or right, or split etc., depending upon the nature of the signal (e.g. see Fig. 3). It was the author who hand coded the CA rules which make these extensions, turns, splits etc. happen. The CA rules themselves are *not* evolved. It is the *sequence* of these signals (fed continuously over time into an initialized short trail) that is evolved. This sequence of growth signals is the "chromosome" of a genetic algorithm, and it is this sequence that maps to a cellular automata network. When trails collide, they can form "synapses" (e.g. see Fig. 5). Once the CA network has been formed in the initial "growth phase", it is later used in a second "neural signaling phase". Neural signals move along CA-based axons and dendrites, and across synapses etc.

The CA network is made to behave like a conventional artificial neural network (see Fig. 5). The outputs of some of the neurons of the complex recurrent networks which result can be used to control complex time dependent behaviors whose fitnesses can be measured. These fitness values can be used to drive the evolution. By growing/evolving thousands of neural net modules and their interconnections in an incremental evolutionary way, it will be possible to build artificial brains. According to the CAM developers at MIT, it is likely that the next generation of CAMs will achieve an increase in performance of the order of thousands, within 5 years. However, to be able to evolve a billion neuron artificial brain by 2001 (ATR's goal), it is likely that a "nano-CAM" machine (i.e. one which uses nano-scale electronic speeds and densities) will need to be developed. To this end, we are collaborating with an NTT researcher who has developed a nanoscale electronics device, who wants to combine huge numbers of them to behave as nano-scale cellular automata machines.

In the summer of 1994, a two dimensional CAM-Brain simulation was completed which required 11,000 hand crafted CA state transition rules. It was successfully applied to the evolution of maximizing the number of synapses, outputting an arbitrary constant neural signal value, outputting a sine wave of a desired arbitrary period and amplitude and to the evolution of a simple artificial retina which could output the vector velocity of a "white line" which "moved" across an array of "detector" neurons. Work on the 3D simulation should be completed by early 1996, and is expected to take about 150,000 hand crafted CA rules. The Brain Builder Group of ATR took possession of one of MIT's CAM8 machines in the fall of 1994. At the time of writing (December 1995) the porting of the 2D rules from a Sparc20 workstation to the CAM8 is nearing completion. If the porting of the rules of the 3D simulation to this machine is not possible, then a "SuperCAM" machine will be designed specifically for CAM-Brain, with the collaboration of the Evolutionary Technologies (ET) group of NTT, with whom our Brain Builder group of ATR's Evolutionary Systems (ES) group, collaborates closely. The complexity of CAM-Brain will make it largely undesignable, so a (directed) evolutionary approach called "evolutionary engineering" is being used. Neural networks based on cellular automata [1], can be grown and evolved at electronic speeds inside state of the art cellular automata machines, e.g. MIT's "CAM8" machine, which can update 200 million cells per second [10].

Since RAM is cheap, gigabytes of RAM can be used to store the states of the CA cells used to grow the neural networks. CA based neural net modules are evolved in a two phase process. Three cell wide CA trails are grown by sending a sequence of growth signals (extend, turn left, turn right, fork left, fork right, T fork) down the middle of the trail. When an instruction hits the end of the trail it executes its function. This sequence of growth instructions is treated as a chromosome in a Genetic Algorithm [9] and is evolved. Once gigabytes of RAM and electronic evolutionary speeds can be used, genuine brain building, involving millions and later billions of artificial neurons, becomes realistic, and should become concrete within a year or two. The CAM-Brain Project should revolutionize the fields of neural networks and artificial life, and in time help create a new specialty called "Brain Building", with its own conferences and journals.

2.   Cellular Automata Based Neural   Networks

Building an artificial brain containing billions of artificial neurons is probably too complex a task to be humanly designable. The author felt that brain building would be a suitable task for the application of evolutionary engineering techniques. As mentioned briefly in the introduction, the key ideas are the following. Use evolutionary techniques to evolve neural circuits in some electronic medium, so as to take advantage of electronic speeds. The medium chosen by the author was that of cellular automata (CA) [1], using special machines, called "Cellular Automata Machines (CAMs)", which can update hundreds of millions of CA cells a second [10]. CAMs can be used to evolve the CA based neural networks at electronic speeds. The states of the cellular automata cells can be stored in RAM, which is cheap, so one can have gigabytes of RAM to store the states of billions of CA cells. This space is large enough to contain an artificial brain. MIT's Information Mechanics Group (Toffoli and Margolus) believe that within a few years it will be technically possible to update a trillion CA cells in about 0.1 nanoseconds [p221, 10]. Thus, if CA state transition rules can be found to make CA cells behave like neural networks, and if such CA based networks prove to be readily evolvable, then a potentially revolutionary new technology becomes possible. The CAM-Brain Project is based on the above ideas and aims to build artificial brains before the completion of the project in 2001. The potential is felt to be so great that it is likely that a new specialty will be formed, called "Brain Building".

For the first 18 months of the CAM-Brain Project, the author simulated a two dimensional version of CAM-Brain on a Sparc 10 workstation. This work was completed in the summer of 1994. The 2D version was used briefly (before work on the 3D version was started) to undertake some evolutionary tests, whose results will be presented in the next section. The 2D version served only as a feasibility and educational device. Since trails are obliged to collide in 2D, the 2D version was not taken very seriously. Work was begun rather quickly on the more interesting 3D version almost immediately after the 2D version was ready. Proper evolutionary tests will be undertaken once the 3D version is ready, which should be by early 1996. To begin to understand how cellular automata [1] can be used as the basis for the growth and evolution of neural networks, consider Fig. 1 which shows an example of a 2D CA state transition rule, and Fig. 2 which shows a 2D CA trail, 3 cells wide. All cells in a CA system update the state of their cells synchronously. The new state of a given cell depends upon its present state and the states of its nearest neighbors. Down the middle of the 3 cell wide CA trail, move "signal or growth cells" as shown in Fig. 2 As an example of a state transition rule which makes a signal cell move to the right one square, consider the right hand most signal cell in Fig. 2, which has a state of 5. The cell immediately to its right has a state of 1, which we want to become a 5. Therefore the 2D state transition rule to turn the 1 into a 5 is 1.2.2.2.5-->5. These signal or growth cells are used to generate the CA trails, by causing them to extend, turn left or right, split left or right, and Tsplit. When trails collide, they can form synapses. It is the sequence of these signal cells which determines the configuration of the CA trails, thus forming a CA network.

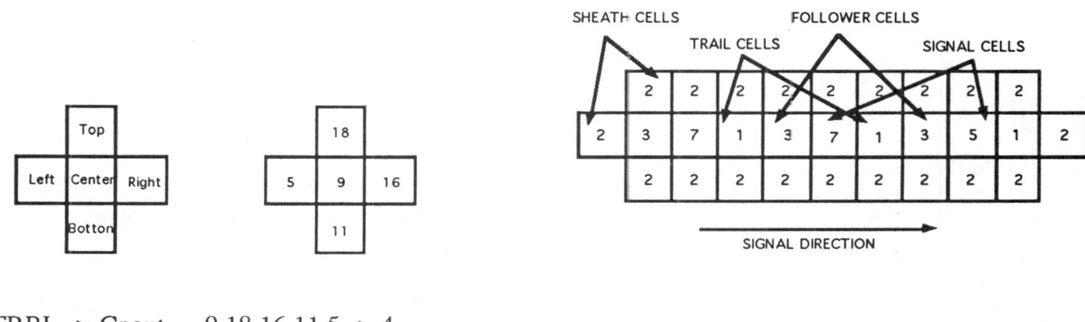

CTRBL -> Cnext   9.18.16.11.5 -> 4

Fig.1   A 2D CA State Transition Rule   **Fig.   2   Signal Cells Move Along a Cellular Automata Trail**

It is these CA trails which later are used as neural network trails of axons and dendrites. Neural signals are sent down the middle of these CA trails. Thus there are two major phases in this process. Firstly, the CA trails are grown, using the sequence of signal cells. Secondly, the resulting CA trail network is used as a neural network, whose fitness at controlling some system can be measured and used to evolve the original growth sequence. To make this more explicit, it is the sequence of growth cells which is evolved. By modifying the sequence, one alters the CA network configuration, and hence the fitness of the configuration when it functions as a neural net in the second phase. From a genetic algorithm (GA) point of view, the format of the GA "chromosome" is the sequence of integers which code for the signaling (growth) instructions. By mutating and crossing over these integers, one obtains new CA networks, and hence new neural networks. By performing this growth at electronic speeds in CAMs, and in parallel, with one CAM per GA chromosome, and attaching a conventional programmable microprocessor to each CAM to measure the user defined fitness of the CA based neural circuit, one has a means to evolve large numbers of neural modules very quickly. Using CAMs to evolve neural circuits, is an example of a type of machine that the author labels a "Darwin Machine", i.e. one which evolves its own structure or architecture. A related idea of the author concerns the concept of "Evolvable Hardware (EHW)" [5] where the software instructions used to configure programmable logic devices (PLDs) are treated as chromosomes in a Genetic Algorithm [9]. One then rewrites the circuit for each chromosome.

[Note added, June 1996] Figs. 5 and 6 show results from porting the 2D version of CAM-Brain to the CAM-8 machine, plus some goals my colleague Felix Gers and I want to reach.

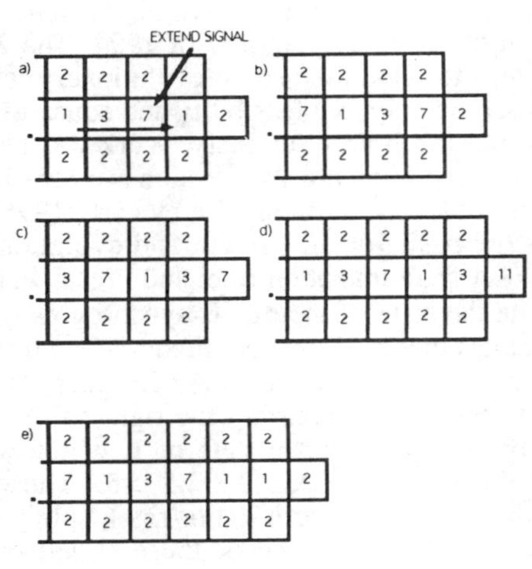

Fig. 3   Extend the Trail

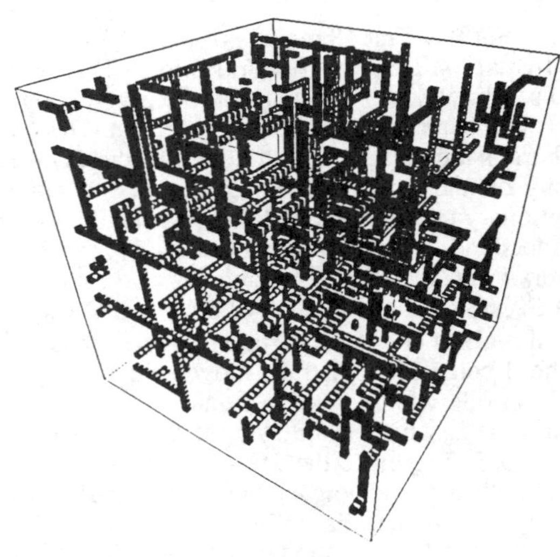

**Fig. 4   3D CAM-Brain
Non-Synaptic   Growth**

References

[1] E.F. Codd, *Cellular Automata*, Academic Press, NY, 1968.
[2] Hugo de Garis, "Genetic Programming: Modular Evolution for Darwin Machines", *ICNN-90WASH-DC*, (Int.Joint Conf. on Neural Networks), January 1990, Washington DC, USA.
[3] Hugo de Garis, "Genetic Programming", Ch.8 in book *Neural and IntelligentSystems Integration*, ed. Branko Soucek, Wiley, NY, 1991.
[4] Hugo de Garis, "Artificial Embryology : The Genetic Programming of an Artificial Embryo", Ch.14 in book *Dynamic,Genetic,and Chaotic Programming*, ed. Branko Soucek and the IRIS Group, Wiley, NY, 1992.
[5] Hugo de Garis, "Evolvable Hardware : Genetic Programming of a Darwin Machine", in *Artificial Neural Nets and Genetic Algorithms*, R.F. Albrecht, C.R. Reeves, N.C. Steele (eds.), Springer, NY, 1993.
[6] Hugo de Garis, "Genetic Programming : Evolutionary Approaches to Multistrategy Learning", Ch.21 in book "Machine Learning : A Multistrategy Approach, Vol.4", R.S. Michalski & G. Tecuci (eds), Morgan Kauffman, 1994.
[7] Hugo de Garis, "Cosmism : Nano Electronics and 21st Century Global Warfare", (to appear in a future nanotech book).
[8] K.E. Drexler, *Nanosystems : Molecular Machinery, Manufacturing and Computation*, Wiley, NY, 1992.
[9] D.E. Goldberg, *Genetic Algorithms in Search, Optimization, and Machine Learning*, Addison-Wesley, Reading, MA, 1989.
[10] T. Toffoli & N. Margolus, *Cellular Automata Machines*, MIT Press, Cambridge, MA, 1987; and *Cellular Automata Machines*, in Lattice Gas Methods for Partial Differential Equations, SFISISOC, eds. Doolen et al, Addison-Wesley, 1990.

Initial Pattern

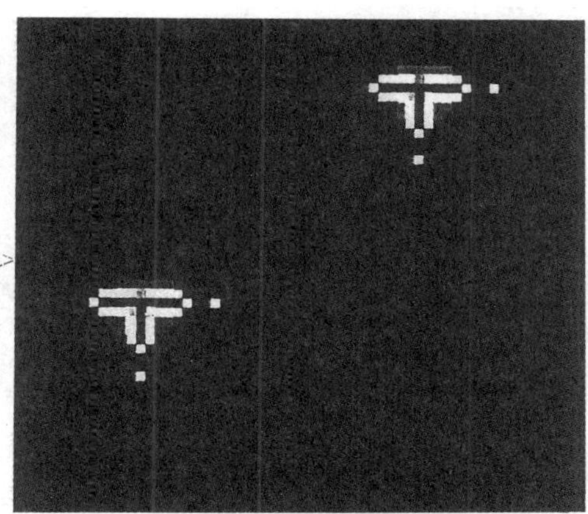

**Growth of
Neuron Bodies**

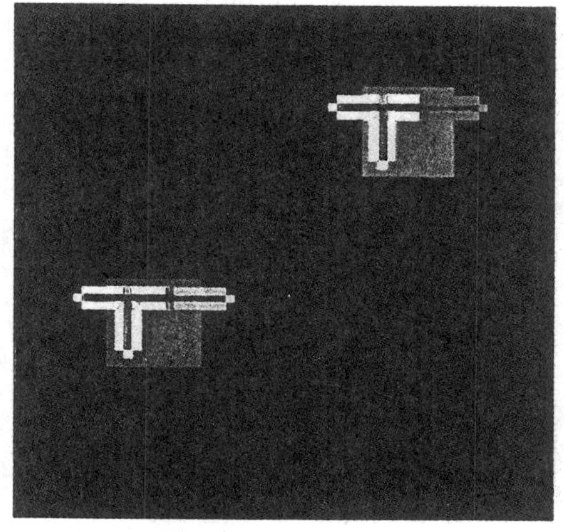

**Excitatory and
Inhibitory Neurons**

Chromosomes

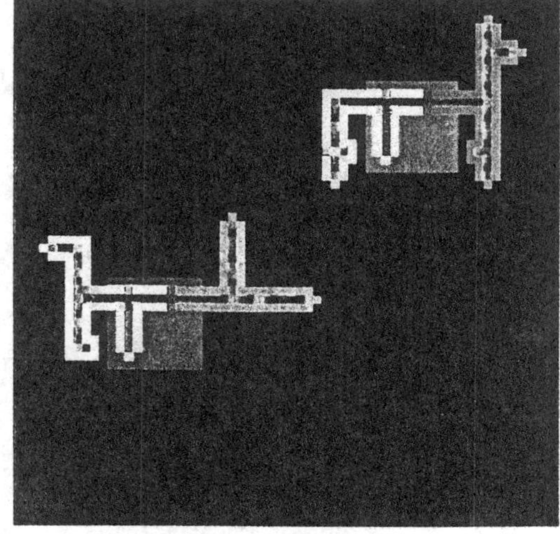

**Growth Phase of
Axons and Dendrites**

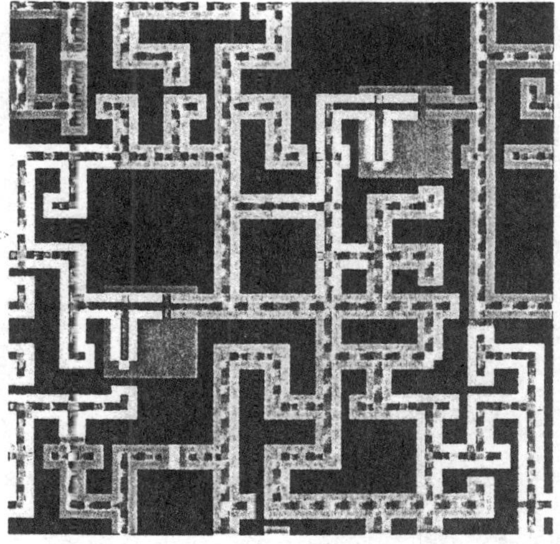

Grown Neural Network

Fig. 5   2D CAM-Brain on MIT's CAM-8 Machine

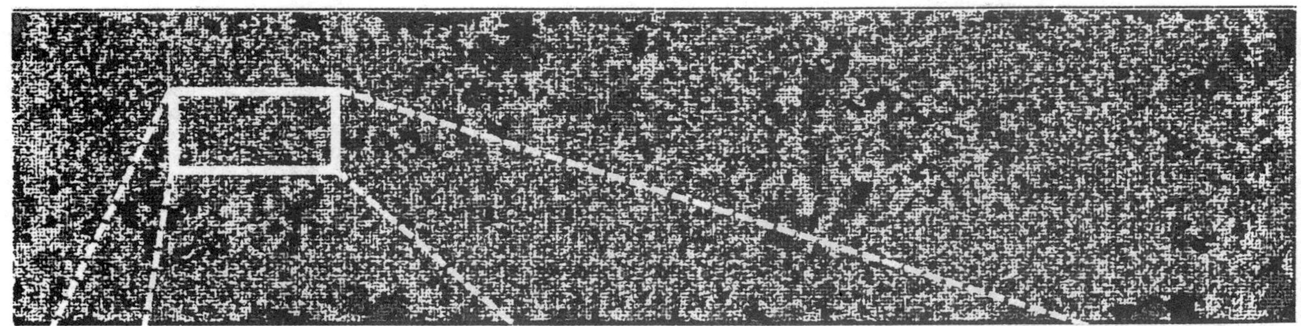

ATR's CAM-Brain Project Highlights

Dr. Hugo de Garis, Felix Gers;   ATR Labs, Kyoto, Japan

1996 - 10,000,000 neurons on MIT's "CAM-8" machine
             (updating   200,000,000   cells/sec)
1997 - 50,000,000 neurons on new "CAM-9" machine
             (updating   100,000,000,000   cells/sec)
1998 - an artificial brain with 1,000,000 evolvable neural modules
2001 - (goal) a billion neuron artificial brain evolving directly in
             hardware at hardware speeds

Fig. 6   Doubly Zoomed 2D CAM-Brain on CAM-8

Hardware Implementations

(Poster Presentation)

Study of Neuron Model using the Stochastic Processing

KuyTae Kim*, ByoungKwan Kim**, and Duckjin Chung**
*Design Department1 LG Semicon Co., Ltd.
#171, Imsoo-dong Gumi Kyung-buk 730-350, Korea
e-mail : 76men@gumi.gsen goldstar.co.kr
**Department of Electronic Materials & Devices
College of Engineering, Inha University
#253, Younghyun-Dong Nam-Ku Inchon 402-751, South of Korea
e-mail : djchung@munhax.inha.ac.kr

Abstract

In the stochastic processing, if the number of inputs is increasing, the output error is increasing because the output can be decided by an input and an weight. So we suggest the magnitude control factor α, which controls the multiplied result from inputs and weights. Using α, we suggest the new hardware model that improves the accuracy against large inputs, and show the new statistical model that can induce the proposed stochastic model.

1. Introduction

The neural network imitates the brain of a higher animal . It has the enormous assemblage of the processing elements that has a simple structure and the parallel communication of the informations.

The previous implementation methods of the neural network can be divided by analog, digital and hybrid methods. The stochastic processing is used to reduce the complexity of parallel circuit and the size of VLSI chip.

The stochastic processing is summarized like this. If we have n random-pulse sequences in which two pulses coincide. These sequences are therefore, statistically dependent. Let the distribution be done according to probabilities k_1, k_2, $\cdots$, k_n assigned to each line. Each sequence K_i will then represent a constant k_i. Assume n variables x_1, x_2, $\cdots$, x_n are given and that, through and AND-OR network, we form the function

$$Z = K_1 X_1 \bigvee K_2 X_2 \bigvee \cdots \bigvee K_n X_n \tag{1}$$

The corresponding transfer function will be a straight linear combination, since addend pulses never coincide[1]:

$$z = k_1 x_1 + k_2 x_2 + \cdots + k_n x_n \tag{2}$$

2. The basic structure of stochastic method

2.1. The basic of the neural networks

The neural networks is the complicated network which operates the multiple outputs with multiple inputs. The general neural networks which have an input layer, an hidden layer, and an output layer like Fig. 1.

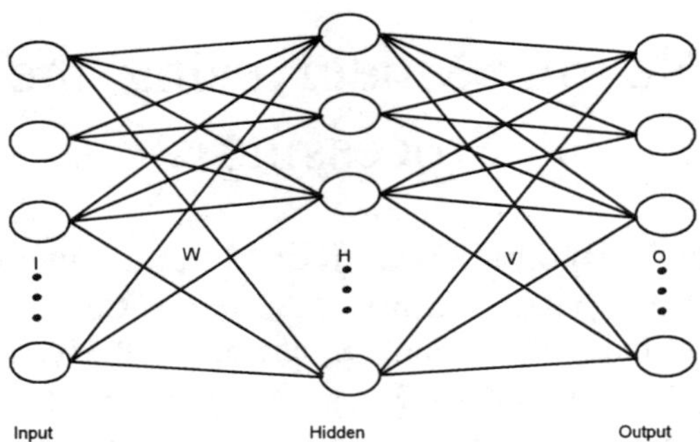

Fig. 1. The general neural networks
scheme

In Fig. 1, the each input I modified by the weight W, summate to the hidden layer H, and using same way, the output layer O calculate by the hidden layer H. This basic calculation can be defined by the equation (5).

$$out = f\left(\sum_{n=0}^{N} w_n i_n \right) \tag{5}$$

At equation (5), f(x) is the transmit function(in the general neural networks it is f(x)=tanh x). In stochastic processing, the AND gate replaces the multiplier, and the OR gate replaces the adder and the sigmoid transmit function. So basic neuron processor can be translated like Fig 2.

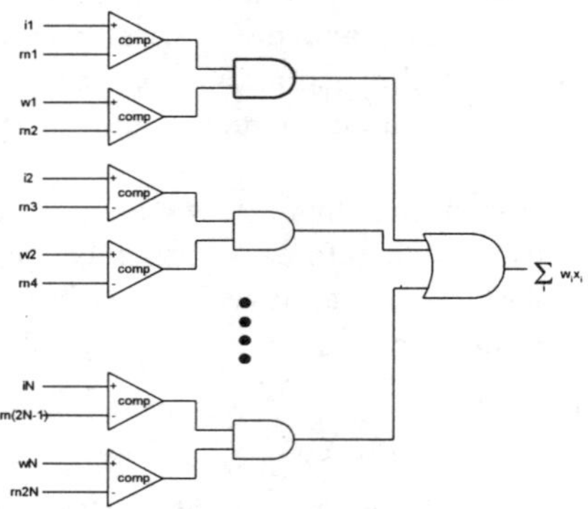

Fig. 2. The basic neuron processor
using   the   stochastic
processing.

In Fig. 2 rn means the random numbers of each input, when i is the input. The input number can be translate to the pulse stream using the random number by comparator. In Fig. 2 to calculate N inputs, the basic neuron needs 2N random numbers(one for input number, and the other for weight value), and to stochastic processing these random numbers must be independent.
The neuron in Fig. 2 can be translated to equation 6[2].

$$\sum_{n=1}^{N} w_n i_n = P(w_1 i_1 = 1) \bigvee P(w_2 i_2 = 1) \cdots \bigvee P(w_N i_N = 1)$$

$$\tag{6}$$

$$= 1 - \prod_{n=1}^{N} (1 - w_n i_n)$$

In equation 6, if any $w_n i_n$ has the value 1, the output must be 1 without relation to the other value. So if N is increased, the output is closed to 1.

2.2. The suggested structure

In this paper, to compensate the effect of one input and one weight, we suggest the modified equation include the magnitude control factor α.

$$\sum_{n=1}^{N} w_n i_n = aP(w_1 i_1 = 1) \bigvee aP(w_2 i_2 = 1) \cdots \bigvee aP(w_N i_N = 1)$$

$$= 1 - \prod_{n=1}^{N}(1 - aw_n i_n) \tag{7}$$

If α has one value in (0, 1), the value of $1 - \alpha w_n i_n$ is larger than 0. So it can prevent the output fixed by one input and one weight. Extending to the bipolar equation, the calculation result is separated into the plus part and minus part and the output is subtract the minus value from the plus value. So equation 7 can be expressed to equation 8.

$$\sum_{n=1}^{N} w_n i_n = plus - minus$$

$$plus = as_1 P(w_1 i_1 = 1) \bigvee as_2 P(w_2 i_2 = 1)$$

$$\cdots \bigvee as_N P(w_N i_N = 1)$$

$$= 1 - \prod_{n=1}^{N}(1 - as_n w_n i_n) \tag{8}$$

$$minus = a(1 - s_1)P(w_1 i_1 = 1) \bigvee a(1 - s_2)P(w_2 i_2 = 1)$$

$$\cdots \bigvee a(1 - s_N)P(w_N i_N = 1)$$

$$= 1 - \prod_{n=1}^{N}(1 - a(1 - s_n)w_n i_n)$$

In equation 8, the plus and minus part is gathered by the sign factor s of each input and weight(XOR). The equation 8 is changed to the Fig. 4 using the stochastic processing

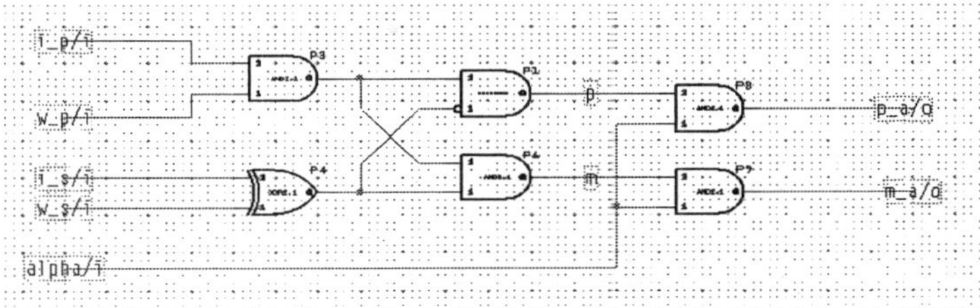

Fig. 4. The gate structure of the stochastic schematic for one input and one weight.

The output of Fig. 4 can be added by the each OR gate, and using up-down counter the result translate to the binary number and the sign signal.

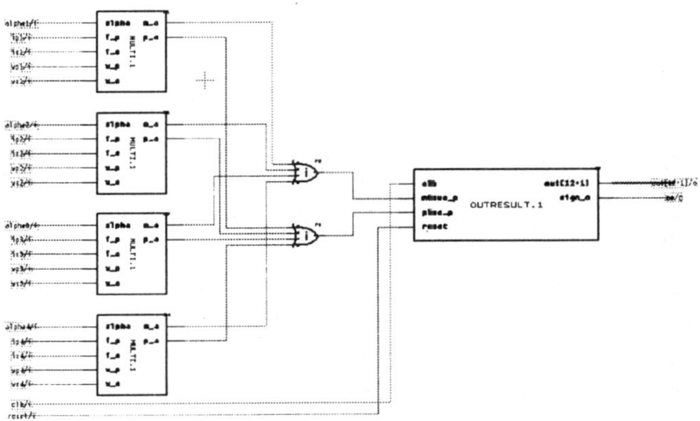

Fig. 5. The neuron stochastic schematics using pulse stream.

In Fig. 5, the OUTRESULT has the 12 bit up-down counter.

3. The effect of α for the adjustment of output

To test the effect of α in the suggested method, it was simulated using C programming language. In simulation we test the neuron of four inputs which change from 0 to 1 of interval 0.4(-1, -0.6, -0.2, 0.2, 0.6, 1) with the accuracy 2^{12}. When α change from 0.1 to 1 of interval 0.1, the results are like Fig. 6.

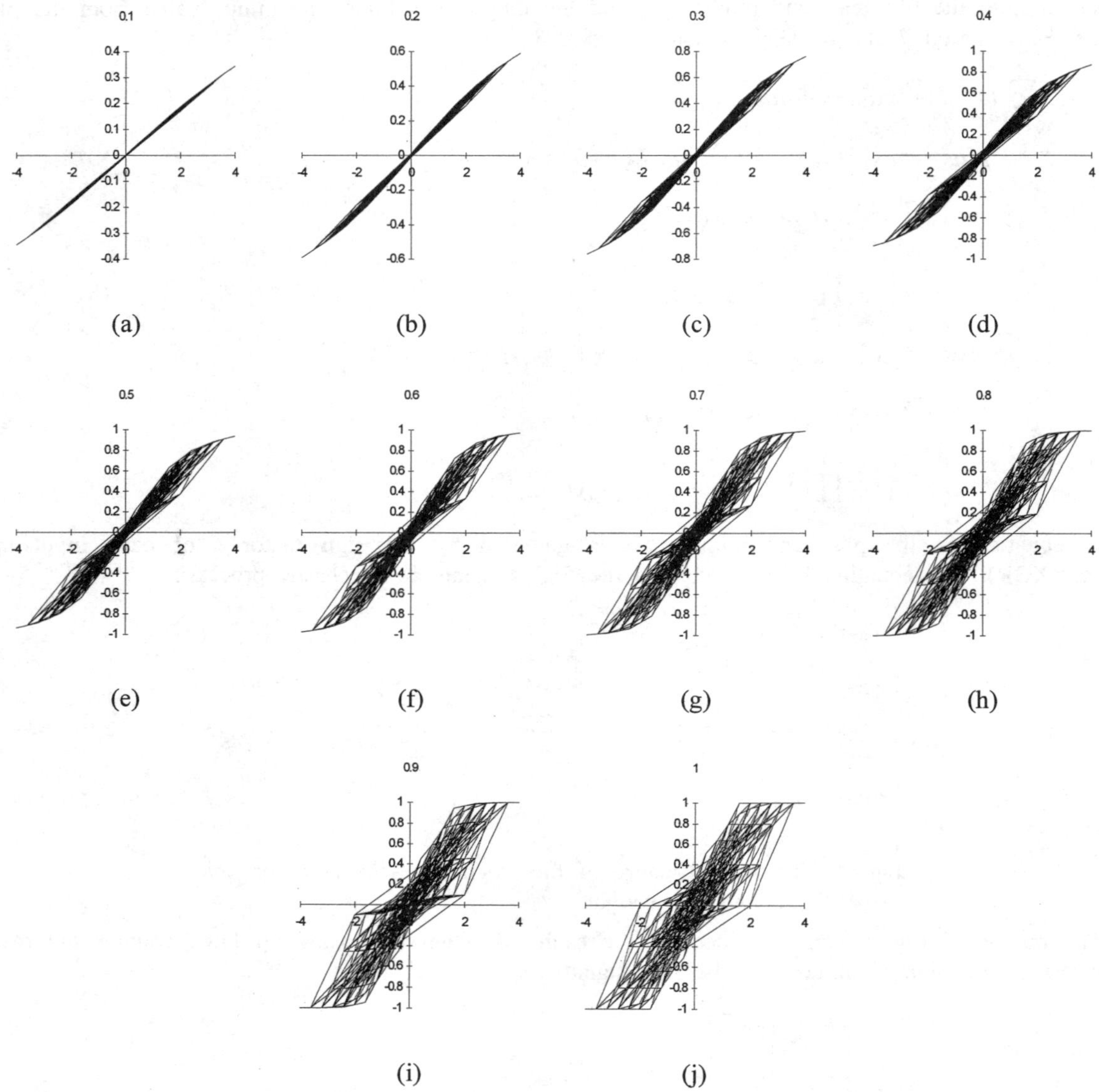

Fig. 6. The results about the magnitude control factor α. x-axis means the arithmetic calculation. y-axis is the stochastic calculation; when α is (a) 0.1, (b) 0.2, (c) 0.3, (d) 0.4, (e) 0.5, (f) 0.6, (g) 0.7, (h) 0.8, (i) 0.9, (j) 1.

In Fig. 6, the result of plot (a) is like linear calculation, but the output range is from -0.4 to 0.4. That of plot (j) spreads too broad in x-range nearby 0. It's because one calculated result is dominated without the another result. Fig. 6 shows that the increase of α more broaden the output results, so α is the factor for changing the slope of sigmoid function

4. The simulation results

To simulate the stochastic neuron, we construct the system, which has four inputs and weights.

This system is shown in Fig. 7.

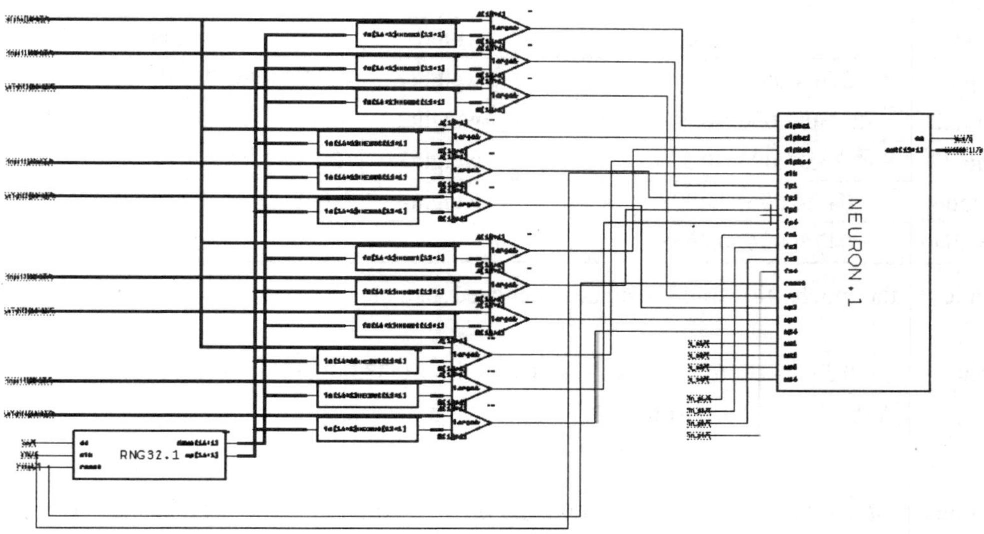

Fig. 7. The schematic of the stochastic neuron.

In Fig. 7. total 12 random numbers are generated by one 32 bit random number generator[3]. For neural network learning the estimated calculation time is $4096(2^{12})$. By using MyCAD, it is simulated, and result is shown Fig. 8.

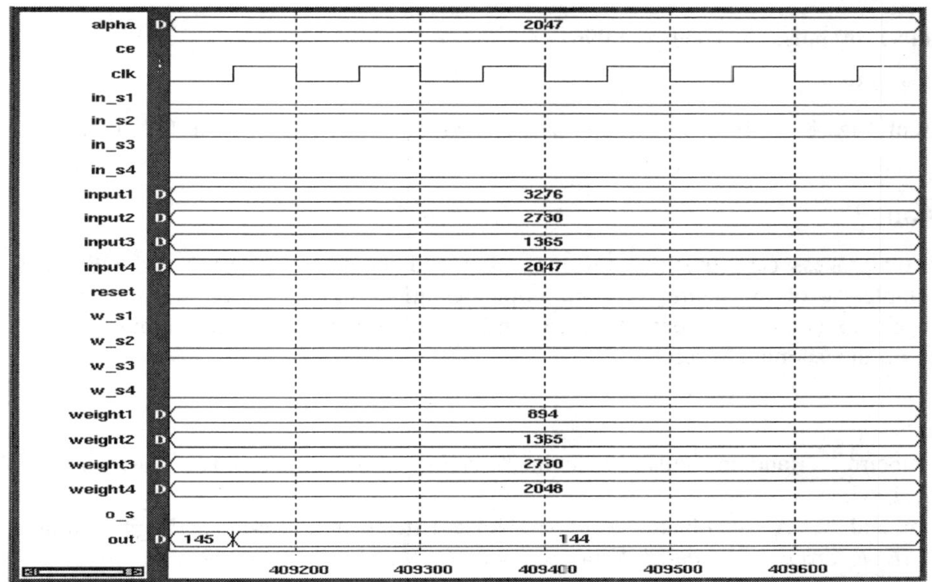

Fig. 8. The simulated result of the schematic in Fig. 7.

In Fig. 8, the accuracy is $1/2^{12}$ and the random number generator's method is the 32 bits MCA method. And also each random numbers randomly selected 12 bits in 32 bits MCA[3]. The value of inputs, weights, and alpha in Fig. 8 is shown in Table 1.

Table 1. The input values in Fig. 8

kind	value	kind	value
input1	3,276/4,096=0.8	weight1	-894/4,096=-0.218
input2	-2,730/4,096=-0.666	weight2	1,365/4,096=0.333
input3	-1,365/4,096=-0.333	weight3	-2,730/4,096=-0.666
input4	2,047/4,096=0.4998	weight4	2,048/4,096=0.5
alpha	2,047/4,096=0.4998		

Using table 1, the stochastic results can be calculated like this.

$$\text{plus} = \alpha \times -0.333 \times -0.666 + \alpha \times 0.4998 \times 0.5 - \alpha^2 \times (-0.333 \times -0.666 \times 0.4998 \times 0.5)$$

$$= 0.111 + 0.125 - 0.0139$$

$$= 0.222$$

$$\text{minus} = -(\alpha \times 0.8 \times -0.218 + \alpha \times -0.666 \times 0.333 - \alpha^2 \times (0.8 \times -0.218 \times -0.666 \times 0.333)$$

$$= 0.087 + 0.111 - 0.0097$$

$$= 0.188$$

$$\text{sum} = 0.222 - 0.188$$

$$= 0.034$$

$$\text{Number of pulse} = 0.034 \times 4,096$$

$$= 139$$

The output of Fig. 8. is 144, so the compared error is $(144-139)/4096 \times 100 = 0.12\%$.

5. Conclusion

The stochastic process can substitute the multiplier and the adder to AND and OR gates, so it can reduce the complexity of the neural network implementation. In this paper, we suggest the magnitude control factor(α) to control the output range, and examine the result. Controling α, we can easily get the linear or the sigmoid result.

Reference

[1] S. T. Ribeiro, "Random Pulse Machine," *IEEE Trans. Electronic Computer*, vol. EC-16, pp.261-276, 1967.
[2] Y. C. Kim and M. A. Shanblatt, "Random Noise Effects in Pulse-mode Digital Multiplier Neural Networks," *IEEE Trans. on Neural Networks*, vol. 6, No. 1, pp. 220-229, Jan. 1995.
[3] Kuytae Kim, Duckjin Jung, "Pseudorandom Number Generators for Neural Networks", *International Conference on Neural Information Processing*, vol. 1, pp. 643-648, 1994.

Discrete Walsh Transform Neuro Chip Using OTA Circuits

Takeshi KAMIO   Haruyasu ADACHI   Hiroshi NINOMIYA   Hideki ASAI

Department of System Eng., Faculty of Engineering, Shizuoka University,
3-5-1,Johoku, Hamamatsu, 432 Japan
hideasai@eng.shizuoka.ac.jp

Abstract— Discrete Walsh transform (DWT) is one of the most important techniques as well as the discrete Fourier transform (DFT) in the field of signal processing. We have proposed the theoretical circuit model of the DWT processor based on Hopfield linear programming neural networks.

This paper describes the practical design of DWT neuro chip using the operational transconductance amplifier (OTA) circuits which is fabricated in a 2-μm CMOS process. Finally, it is confirmed by SPICE simulations that our neuro chip is useful and practical.

I. Introduction

Neural networks have been shown to have capability to handle problems in a number of applications and in a variety of areas. Especially, simple analog processors proposed by Tank and Hopfield are famous as highly interconnected neural networks [1] [2]. Furthermore it has been shown that DFT can be performed by neural networks for the linear programming [3]. They are able to deal with some optimization problems more effectively than digital computers. We have also shown theoretical designs of digital sequential circuits [6] and the discrete Walsh transform (DWT) processor using Hopfield linear programming neural networks [7]. This DWT processor can be regarded as the analog circuit to solve the linear equations by steepest descent (SD) method. Although it is well-known that the convergence rate of SD method for a general problem is slow, we have proved the rapid convergence and high accuracy of DWT processor both analytically and by simulation[8][9]. However, it has been found by the experimental measurements that our DWT processor fabricated on the breadboard requires several micro seconds for convergence, which is caused from the propagation delay of the operational amplifiers[10].

In this paper, we show the DWT neuro chip using operational transconductance amplifier (OTA) circuits which is fabricated in a 2-μm CMOS process. At the same time, we achieve both simplification and structural modularity of our processor through some modifications. Finally, it is confirmed by SPICE simulations that our neuro chip is useful and practical.

II. DWT Processor Composed of Hopfield Linear Programming Neural Networks

The DWT is one of the most significant techniques as well as the DFT in signal processing. The DWT works well for digital signal due to the fundamental function called the Walsh function. The Walsh function has only ±1 in the range [0,1], and is the system of orthogonal functions. In general, the Walsh function is generated by the Kronecker's product of the Hadamard matrix $\boldsymbol{H}$, and is expressed as each row of $\boldsymbol{H}$. Therefore DWT is known as a kind of the Hadamard transform (HT), where $\boldsymbol{H}$ has some useful following characteristics.

$$\text{i)} \quad \boldsymbol{H} = \boldsymbol{H}^T \quad (\boldsymbol{H} \text{ is symmetric.}) \tag{1}$$

$$\text{ii)} \quad \boldsymbol{H}\boldsymbol{H}^T = \boldsymbol{H}^T\boldsymbol{H} = n\boldsymbol{I} \quad (\boldsymbol{H} \text{ is orthogonal.}) \tag{2}$$

Therefore, the DWT and the inverse DWT are defined as follows:

$$\boldsymbol{V} = \frac{1}{n}\boldsymbol{H}\boldsymbol{B}, \tag{3}$$

$$\boldsymbol{B} = \boldsymbol{H}\boldsymbol{V}, \tag{4}$$

where n is the number of sampled points, $\boldsymbol{B}$ is the sampled data vector, $\boldsymbol{V}$ is the DWT of $\boldsymbol{B}$, and $\boldsymbol{H}$ is Hadamard matrix. (That is to say, Hadamard-ordered Walsh functions.)

We have proposed the theoretical design of DWT processor, using Hopfield linear programming neural networks[7], which is shown in Fig.1.

In this circuit, B_j is the input current which is regarded as an element of the sampled data vector $\boldsymbol{B}$. H_{ji} is an interconnect conductance to reflect our transform kernel $\boldsymbol{H}$ (the Hadamard matrix). V_i and ϕ_j are the outputs of amplifiers which are called the variable (neuron) amplifier g and the constraint amplifier f respectively. Each of the g amplifiers has an input capacitor C and an input resistor R in parallel, which connect the input line to the ground. The output V_i of the amplifier g_i is expressed as a linear function of the input u_i as follows,

$$V_i = g_i(u_i) = \beta_g u_i \quad (\beta_g > 0), \tag{5}$$

where β_g is dimensionless, u has the unit of voltage. Furthermore the output ϕ_j of the amplifier f_j is also given by a linear function of the input u'_j, namely,

$$\phi_j = f(u'_j) = \beta_f u'_j \quad (\beta_f > 0), \tag{6}$$

where β_f has the unit of resistance, u'_j has the unit of current. Therefore we can ideally regard the variable amplifier and the constraint amplifier as Voltage Controlled Voltage Source (VCVS) and Current Controlled Voltage Source (CCVS) respectively.

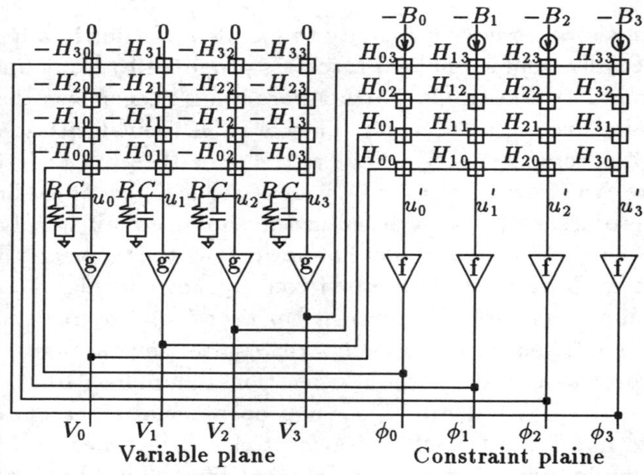

Fig.1 DWT processor composed of Hopfield neural networks.

Therefore, the circuit equation of DWT processor is given by

$$C\frac{du}{dt} = -\frac{u}{R} - \beta_f \boldsymbol{H}^T(\boldsymbol{H}\boldsymbol{V} - \boldsymbol{B}). \tag{7}$$

Transforming (7) into the equation with respect to $\boldsymbol{V}$ using (2) and (5), we can have

$$C\frac{d\boldsymbol{V}}{dt} = a\boldsymbol{H}^T(b\boldsymbol{B} - \boldsymbol{H}\boldsymbol{V}), \tag{8}$$

where

$$a = \frac{1}{Rn} + \beta_g\beta_f, \tag{9}$$

$$b = \frac{\beta_g\beta_f}{a} = \frac{1}{1 + 1/Rn\beta_g\beta_f}. \tag{10}$$

Applying Forward Euler method to (8), the iterative formula is given by

$$\boldsymbol{V}_{k+1} = \boldsymbol{V}_k + \underbrace{\frac{a}{C}\Delta t}_{\alpha_k} \underbrace{\boldsymbol{H}^T(b\boldsymbol{B} - \boldsymbol{H}\boldsymbol{V}_k)}_{\boldsymbol{p}_k}. \tag{11}$$

The energy function of this DWT processor is given by

$$E = \frac{\beta_f}{2}\|\boldsymbol{H}\boldsymbol{V} - \boldsymbol{B}\|_2^2 + \frac{1}{2\beta_g R}\|\boldsymbol{V}\|_2^2. \tag{12}$$

Furthermore, the energy function (12) can be rewritten by,

$$E = \frac{a}{2\beta_g}\|b\boldsymbol{B} - \boldsymbol{H}\boldsymbol{V}\|_2^2 + b(1 - b)\|\boldsymbol{B}\|_2^2, \tag{13}$$

and its partial differential equation is given by

$$\frac{\partial E}{\partial \boldsymbol{V}} = -\frac{a}{\beta_g}\boldsymbol{H}^T(b\boldsymbol{B} - \boldsymbol{H}\boldsymbol{V}). \tag{14}$$

The steepest gradient direction of the energy function is $\boldsymbol{p}_k$ in (11) because $\partial E/\partial \boldsymbol{V}$ multiplied by $-\beta_g/a$ is $\boldsymbol{p}_k$. Therefore, the solution by the iterative formula (11) is equivalent to seeking the global minimum of the energy function by SD method.

Pay attention to the energy function (13), and we can find that $\boldsymbol{V}$ at the global minimum satisfies $\boldsymbol{H}\boldsymbol{V} = b\boldsymbol{B}$. This shows that DWT processor actually solves not $\boldsymbol{H}\boldsymbol{V} = \boldsymbol{B}$ but $\boldsymbol{H}\boldsymbol{V} = b\boldsymbol{B}$ by SD method. Furthermore, as the Hadamard matrix $\boldsymbol{H}$ is orthogonal and symmetric, it is clear that the solution of DWT processor is obtained by only once iteration regardless of initial vector $\boldsymbol{V}_0$ according to the characteristics of SD method for the orthonormal matrix[8][9], and the solution is given by

$$\boldsymbol{V} = b\boldsymbol{H}^{-1}\boldsymbol{B} = \frac{1}{1 + 1/Rn\beta_g\beta_f}\boldsymbol{H}^{-1}\boldsymbol{B}. \tag{15}$$

This solution includes an error due to $1/Rn\beta_g\beta_f$. Therefore, we must make the product of four parameters (R, n, β_g, β_f) large enough to regard (15) as the exact solution of DWT. In addition, the optimal step size α_k of the SD method to compute the iterative formula (11) effectively is given by

$$\alpha_k = \frac{(\boldsymbol{r}_k, \boldsymbol{H}\boldsymbol{p}_k)}{(\boldsymbol{H}\boldsymbol{p}_k, \boldsymbol{H}\boldsymbol{p}_k)} = \frac{1}{n}, \tag{16}$$

where $\boldsymbol{r}_k = b\boldsymbol{B} - \boldsymbol{H}\boldsymbol{V}_k$ is the residual vector. From $\alpha_k(= a\Delta t/C)$ in (11) and (16), the optimal time step is given by

$$\Delta t = \frac{C}{na} = \frac{C}{1/R + n\beta_g\beta_f}. \tag{17}$$

We can regard this optimal time step as the time required for convergence because the solution is given by the once iteration. That is to say, the above equation shows that the convergence of DWT processor is very rapid when R and C are small or n, β_g and β_f are large. Therefore, both the accuracy and the convergence are improved only when n, β_g and β_f are large. If R is very large, the accuracy is improved but the time required for convergence increases. Additionally, we emphasize that the efficient DWT processor can be realized by increment of the number n of sampled points.

III. Design of Discrete Walsh Transform Neuro Chip

A. Structural modularity of DWT processor

It is significant that the network structure is simplified for VLSI implementations. Moreover, we must consider structural modularity which is required to design DWT neuro chip for transforming a large number of samples.

The dynamics of our DWT processor shown in Fig.1 is determined by the interaction between the variable plane and the constraint plane of the network. Since each of two planes has the same conductance matrix $\boldsymbol{H}$, we can simplify the structure of this network by removing one of them. Furthermore, if the global feedback of the RC pairs is replaced with the local feedbacks for each RC pair, we can achieve structural modularity, therefore the structure will be simpler for implementation[4]. Concretely, they are achieved as follows.

Using (2) and $\beta_f = 1$, the circuit equation (7) can be rewritten by

$$C\frac{d\boldsymbol{u}}{dt} = -\frac{\boldsymbol{u}}{R} - n\boldsymbol{V} + \boldsymbol{H}\boldsymbol{B}. \tag{18}$$

The above equation describes that the DWT processor has only $-n\boldsymbol{V} + \boldsymbol{H}\boldsymbol{B}$ as the input current of RC pairs. Therefore the network in Fig.1 can be transformed into the circuit illustrated in Fig.2. However, n and B_i in Fig.2 represent the interconnected conductance and the input voltage unlike Fig.1, respectively. Although Fig.2 is much simpler than Fig.1, the network shown in Fig.2 also keeps the characteristics described in II, because the circuit equation (18) is equivalent to (7).

B. OTA circuit for DWT neuro chip fabricated in CMOS process

As mentioned above, we have implemented the DWT processor shown in Fig.1 on the breadboard. As the result of SPICE simulations and the experimental measurements, we have verified that the experimental DWT processor has the similar characteristics to the theoretical DWT processor. However, we have also found that the experimental DWT processor requires much larger convergence time, several micro seconds, than the theoretical DWT processor, which is caused from the propagation delay of the operational amplifiers. The DWT processor shown in Fig.2 also has the same problem.

In order to cope with this problem, we design DWT neuro chip, using CMOS-OTAs[5]. (The OTA circuit is a kind of operational amplifiers whose output current increases in proportion as the differential mode input voltage, and the characteristics are controlled by the bias voltage.)

We use the circuit shown in Fig.3 as a synapse. In this circuit, V_B is the bias voltage to control the characteristics. V_{in} is the input voltage and I_{out} is the output current. The channel length and channel width of MOSFET M_k are L_k and W_k respectively. Fig.4 shows the input-output relation of the circuit in Fig.3 by SPICE simulation, where $V_B = 0$, W1/L1=3(μm)/3(μm) and W2/L2=100(μm)/2(μm). We get the current generated from a synapse in the linear area around $V_{in} = 0$ as shown in Fig.4.

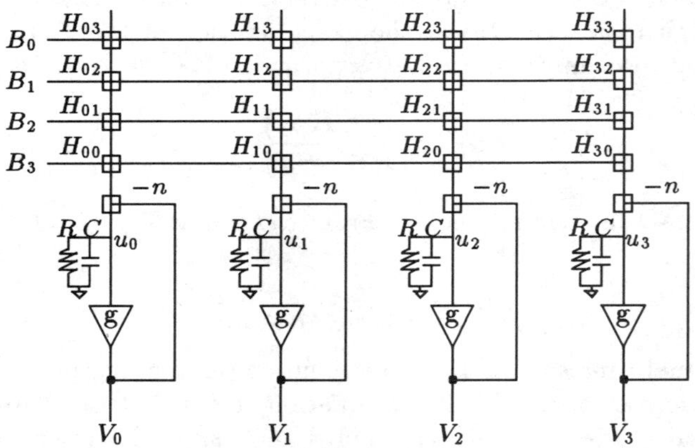

Fig.2 Modular DWT processor.

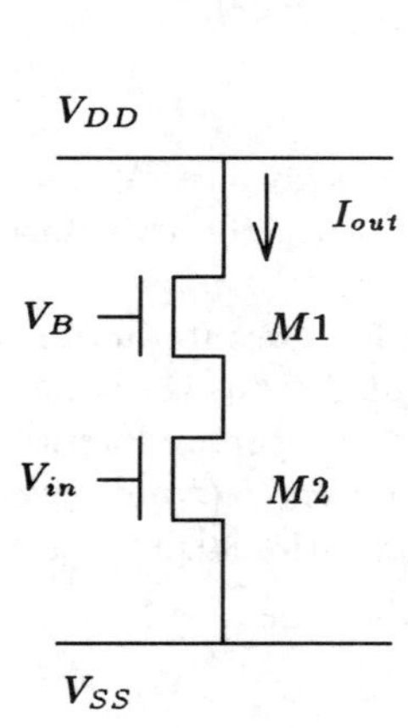

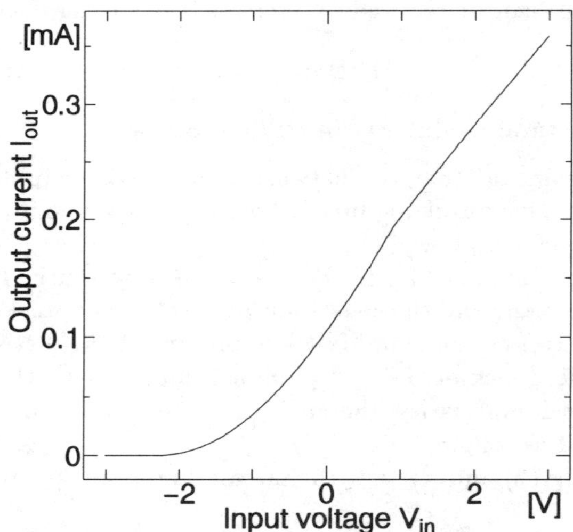

Fig.3 A synapse using MOSFET.   Fig.4 Input-output relation of the circuit in Fig.3.

Furthermore, we use the current-voltage (I-V) converter shown in Fig.5 as the part which consists of an RC pair and a variable amplifier. The output voltage V_{out} of the I-V converter is expressed as a linear function of the input current I_{in} as follows,

$$V_{out} = \frac{I_{in}}{2k(V_B - 2V_T)} = \beta I_{in},$$

(19)

where k is the gain of MOSFET, V_T and V_B are the threshold voltage and the bias voltage respectively.

Using a unity gain current mirror circuit and these two units, the OTA circuit for DWT shown in Fig.6 is constructed, where V_{off} shows the offset voltage. When this network reaches the steady state, the output voltage is given by

$$V = \frac{1}{1 - 1/\beta n} H^{-1} B \tag{20}$$

Therefore, (20) is regarded as the exact solution of DWT when the product of n and β is large.

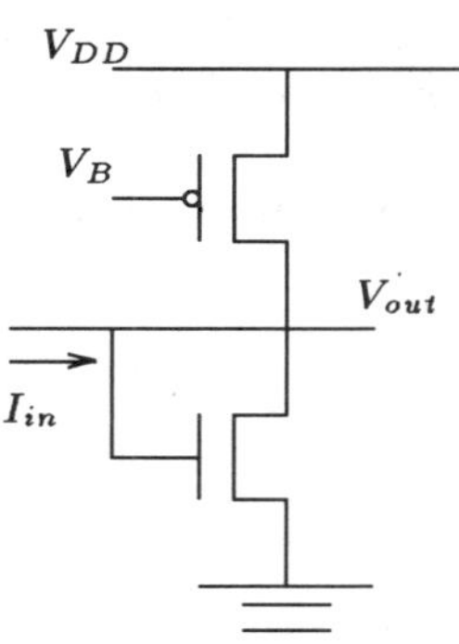

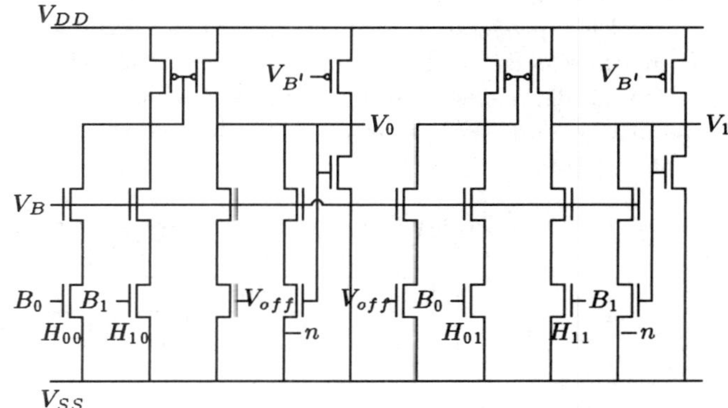

Fig.5 I-V converter.

Fig.6 DWT processor using OTAs.

IV. SIMULATION RESULTS

Using an interactive system MAGIC[13] for creating and modifying VLSI circuit layouts, we have designed the DWT neuro chip ($n = 8$) based on OTA circuits shown in Fig.6. Fig.7 shows the Magic layout of the DWT neuro chip using OTAs. This DWT neuro chip has been simulated by SPICE. We have used a unit down-step function ($B[mV] = [100, 100, 100, 100, 0, 0, 0, 0]^T$) as the input signal to be transformed.

The simulation results are illustrated in Fig.8, and summarized in Table 1. Fig.8 shows the transient behaviors of the variable V_0 and the input B_0, where the exact solution V_0 is 50[mV]. Table1 shows both the exact solutions and simulation results of $V_0 \sim V_7$.

From these simulation results, it is confirmed that our chip keeps the error less than 1% and carries out the DWT within 30 nano-seconds.

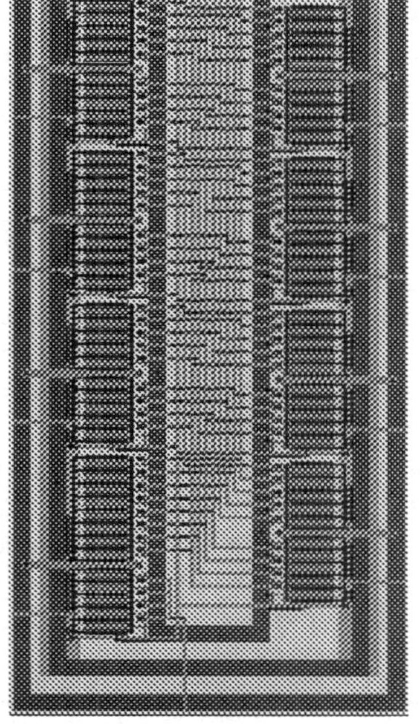

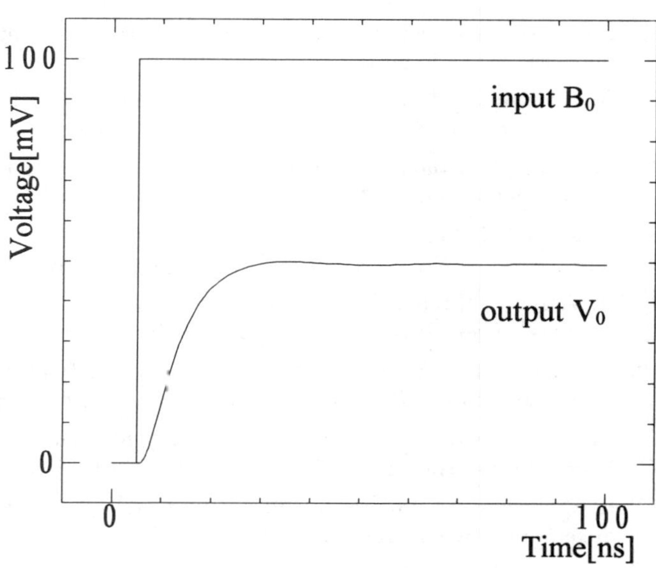

Fig.7 Magic layout of the DWT neuro chip using OTAs ($n = 8$).

Fig.8 SPICE simulations of V_0 and B_0 for the DWT neuro chip.

V. Conclusions

After we have simplified the DWT processor composed of Hopfield linear programming neural networks, we have designed the DWT neuro chip using CMOS-OTA circuits. As the result of SPICE simulations, we have found that our DWT neuro chip has only the error less than 1% and can complete the DWT within 30ns. Comparing the DWT neuro chip with the DWT processor fabricated on the breadboard, it is verified that the former can carry out the DWT $100 \sim 200$ times as fast as the latter.

It is significant to compare our DWT neuro chip with other implementations. Unfortunately, we can't find out the literature on the fabrication of DWT processor. As the references, we show a few examples of DFT and FFT processors. Ref.[11] describes an implementation which enables DFT of 840 complex numbers in 100 ms. Ref.[12] gives an implementation which can perform a complex FFT with $n = 512$ in $276.5\mu s$. Ref.[3] describes an implementation which can perform DFT from 50ns to 500ns, regardless of n. Consequently, our DWT neuro chip can be regarded as a high performance processor, compared with other implementations.

Table1 Exact solutions versus simulation results of $V_0 \sim V_7$.

	exact solutions [volt]	output solutions [volt]
V_0	50m	50.010m
V_1	0	258.735μ
V_2	0	258.735μ
V_3	0	258.735μ
V_4	50m	50.449m
V_5	0	258.735μ
V_6	0	258.735μ
V_7	0	258.735μ

References

[1] J. J. Hopfield, "Neurons with great response have collective computational properties like those of two-state neurons", *Proc. Natl. Acad. Sci. USA*, vol.81, pp.3088-3092, May 1984.

[2] D. W. Tank and J. J. Hopfield, "Simple 'neural' optimization networks: An A/D converter, signal decision circuit, and a linear programming circuit ", *IEEE Trans. CAS*, vol. CAS-36, pp.533-541, May 1986.

[3] Andrew D. Culhane, Martin C. Peckerar and C. R. K. Marrian, "A Neural Net Approach to Discrete Hartley and Fourier Transforms", *IEEE Trans. CAS*, vol. CAS-36, pp.695-703, May 1989.

[4] Shaohua Tan and Joos Vandewalle, "Comments on "A Neural Net Approach to Discrete Hartley and Fourier Transforms"", *IEEE Trans. CAS - II: Analog and Signal Processing*, vol. 39, no.10, pp.756-757, October 1992.

[5] Russel D. Reed and Randall L. Geiger, "A Multiple-input OTA Circuit for Neural Networks",*IEEE Trans. CAS*, vol.36, no.5, pp.767-769, May 1989.

[6] H. Ninomiya and H. Asai, "Design and Simulation of Neural Network Digital Sequential Circuits", *IEICE Trans. Fundamentals.*, vol.E77-A, no.6, pp. 968-976, June 1994.

[7] T. Kamio, H. Ninomiya and H. Asai, "A Neural Net Approach to Discrete Walsh Transform", *IEICE Trans. Fundamentals*, vol. E77-A, no.11 pp.1882-1886, Nov. 1994.

[8] T. Kamio, H. Ninomiya and H. Asai, "Convergence of Hopfield Neural Network for Orthogonal Transformation", *Proc. IEEE ISCAS'95*, vol.1, pp.493-496, May 1995.

[9] H. Asai, T. Kamio, and H. Ninomiya, "Discrete Walsh Transform Processor Based on Hopfield Neural Network" *Proc. IEEE Instrumentation/Measurement Tech. Conf*, pp.317-322, April 1995.

[10] T. Kamio, H. Ninomiya and H. Asai, "Design and Implementation of Neuro-Based Discrete Walsh Transform Processor", *Proc. IEEE International Conference on Neural Networks*, June 1996 (to appear).

[11] R. M. Owens and J. Ja'Ja', "A VLSI chip for Winogard/prime factor algorithm to compute the discrete Fourier transform," *IEEE Trans. Acoust. Speech, Signal Processing*, vol. ASSP-34, Aug. 1986.

[12] R. E. Owens, "A 15 nanosecond complex multiplier-accumulator for FFTs," *Proc. IEEE Conf. Acoustics, Speech and Signal Processing*, 1986.

[13] Robert N. Mayo, Michael H. Arnold, Walter S. Scott, Don Stark and Gordon T. Hamachi, "1990 DECWRL / Livermore Magic Release", Western Reserch Laboratory, Sep. 1990.

A Neural Network Visualization and Sensitivity Analysis Toolkit

Yuansong Liao and John Moody
Department of Computer Science, Oregon Graduate Institute, Portland, OR 97291-1000
liao@cse.ogi.edu and moody@cse.ogi.edu

Abstract— **In this paper, we present a neural network visualization and sensitivity analysis toolkit developed at OGI. The functions of this tool include: network parameter visualization, activation and projection plots for hidden units, and sensitivity analysis for input and hidden variables. This tool is characterized by the following features: (1)The graphical representation of a network directly reflects both the network topology and weight connections between units; (2) The activation and projection views of hidden units offer useful information about network behavior and are very useful for understanding the network learning procedure; (3) The graphical display of several sensitivity measures aids in selecting input features and pruning hidden units.**

1   Introduction

Representing information-bearing data using visual methods provides a highly efficient way to transfer information to the data interpreter (Tufte 1985). A good visualization tool can be a tremendously useful aid to research, development, and education.

Although a lot of effort has been put into artificial neural network research, network visualization has not gained much attention. Previous reports include the Hinton diagram in (Rumelhart & McClelland 1986) and the bond diagram developed by Wejchert and Tesauro (Wejchert & Tesauro 1991).

In this paper, we present a system for network visualization and input and hidden unit sensitivity analysis. The whole system takes trained network parameters and training/testing data as input. The network visualization mechanism of the system displays neural network parameters graphically. It produces activation and projection plots of hidden units, and visual displays of network variables. These graphics allow users to observe network behavior directly. The sensitivity analysis mechanism of the system performs four types of model-dependent sensitivity analyses. The outputs of these analyses give information about which input features and hidden units are important to the learning task, and guide pruning.

2   Framework of the Toolkit

The framework of the tool is shown in Figure 1. Inputs to the system include a training or testing data file, a neural network parameter file, and display and sensitivity analysis selections. Outputs of the system include graphical representations of trained networks, plots for hidden units, and sensitivity analysis results which are output either in graphical or in numerical format.

3   Visualization Mechanism

Given display setups, the visualization mechanism may produce two windows. One of the windows, called TrainedNet, gives a graphical representation of the trained network which is specified by a network parameter file. An example of this window is shown in Figure 2. Another output window is the HiddenActivity window. In the HiddenActivity window, either the HiddenActivity view or the ProjectionPlot view is displayed. Examples of the HiddenActivity window are shown in Figure 4 and Figure 5.

The graphical representation of a trained network (shown in Figure 2) explicitly reveals the network topology. Interpretation of the graphical representation is given in Figure 3. Values of network variables, weights, biases, gains, and sensitivities, are displayed with both gray level and square size. All variables are normalized between -1 and 1 for display. The stronger the connection between two units, the larger the square. Black, the gray level used for background, and white correspond to values -1, 0 and 1 respectively. By pressing a square in the graph using the left mouse button, the actual value and the gray level of the parameter represented by the square are displayed. Four different kinds of sensitivity measures (defined in Section 4) can be selected. The input and hidden units are

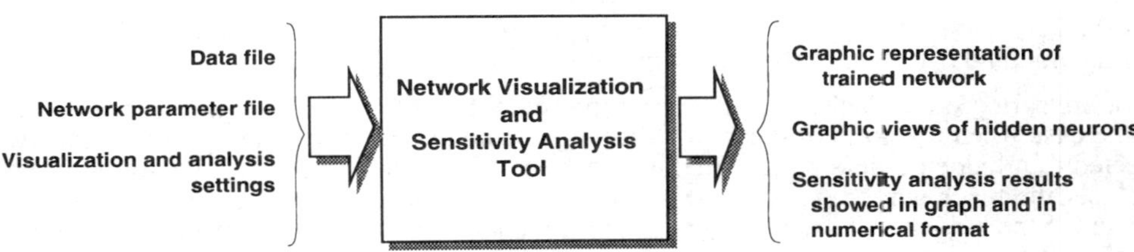

Figure 1: Framework of the toolkit.

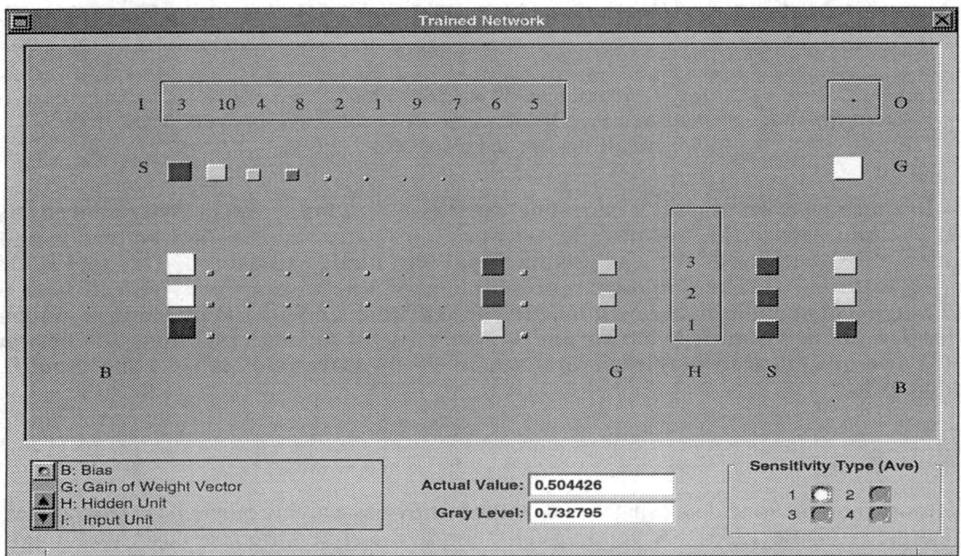

Figure 2: Graphical representation of a neural network. The 10-3-1 network was trained to predict the U.S. Index of Industrial Production (Moody *et al.* 1993).

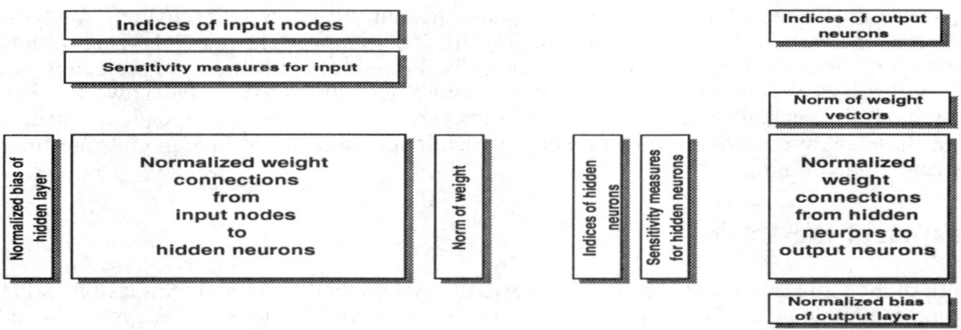

Figure 3: Interpretation of the graphical representation of a network. (In the case of multiple hidden layers, multiple pages are used to display network parameters.)

sorted according to their sensitivity levels for a selected sensitivity measure. The absolute sensitivity decreases from left to right for input units, and decreases from top to bottom for hidden units. The example given in Figure 2 shows that there exist large positive weight connections between the input unit with index 3 and the hidden units with indices 2 and 3, and a large negative weight connection between that input unit and the hidden unit with index 1. This example also shows that the input variables with indices 5, 6, 7 and 9 have small sensitivity measurements, which means these variables may be not important to the learning task, and can be removed from the input feature sets.

In a HiddenActivity view (an example shown in Figure 4), a coordinate axis corresponds to a hidden unit. The black curve in a coordinate axis is the hidden unit's response function to the normalized weighted sum of its inputs. For a hidden unit, its black curve is obtained using

$$y \quad = \quad f(\alpha x)$$
$$x \quad = \quad \frac{1}{\alpha}\mathbf{X}^T\mathbf{W},$$

where $f(\cdot)$ is the activation function of the hidden unit, $\mathbf{X}$ is the input vector to the unit, $\mathbf{W}$ is the weight vector connected to the unit, and α is the norm of the weight vector $\mathbf{W}$ ($\alpha = \|\mathbf{W}\|$).

The white dot appearing on a black curve is the current output of the unit. The gray curve is the hidden unit function for the case when the norm of the weight vector is equal to one. The absolute norm of the weight vector that is connected to a hidden unit is represented by the slope of the black curve relative to the slope of the gray curve. The closer the black curve is to the x-axis, the smaller the norm is. For example, in Figure 4, the weight vector connected to the hidden unit shown in the upper right corner has norm less than one, and the weight vectors connected to the other three hidden units have norms larger than one. If the norm of the weight vector connected to a hidden unit is very small (close to zero), the hidden unit will mostly operate in its linear region. If the norm of the weight vector is large (greater than one), the hidden unit will operate in its nonlinear or saturated region.

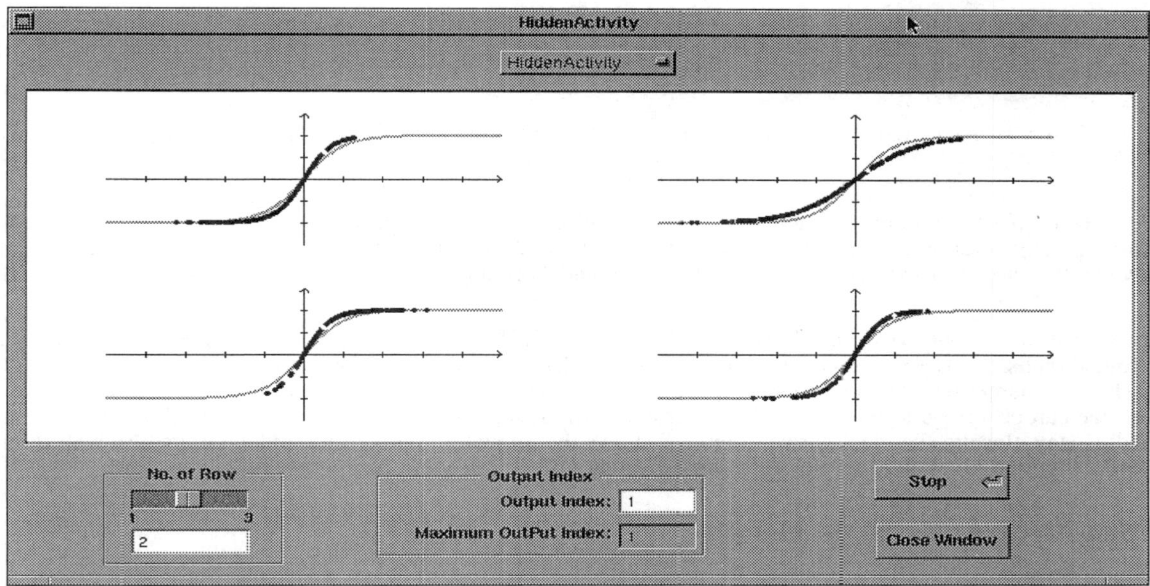

Figure 4: Hidden Activity Window – Activation plots of hidden units. (For multiple output units, multiple pages are used to display.) This view is for a 12-4-1 network which was trained to predict the sunspots time series.

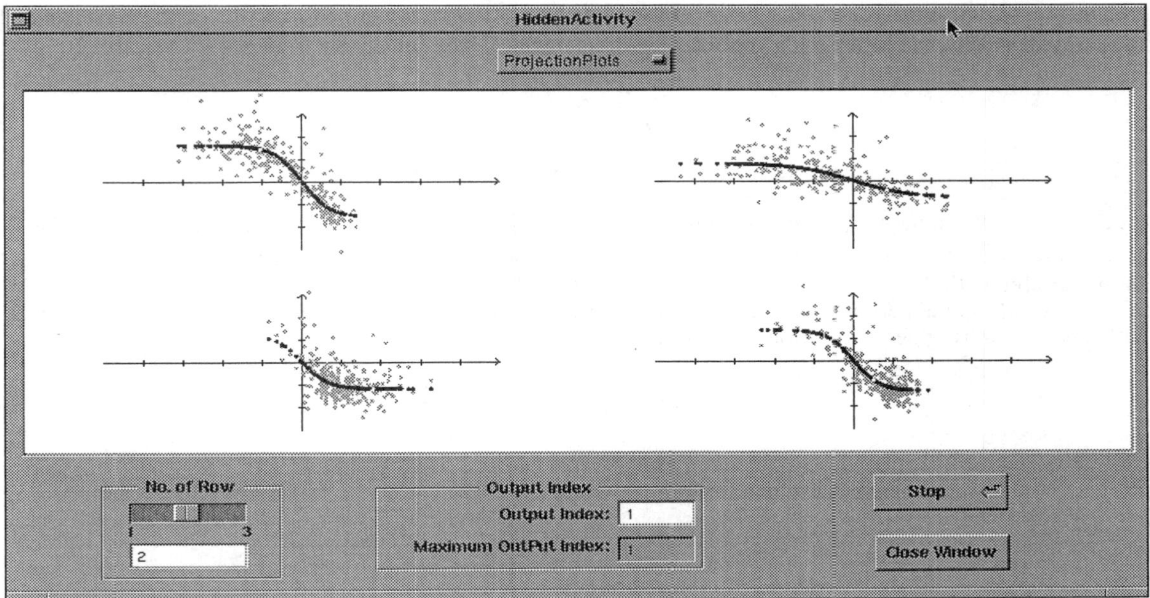

Figure 5: Hidden Activity Window – Projection plots of hidden units. (Multiple pages are used to display if there are multiple output units.) This view is for a 12-4-1 network which was trained to predict the sunspots time series.

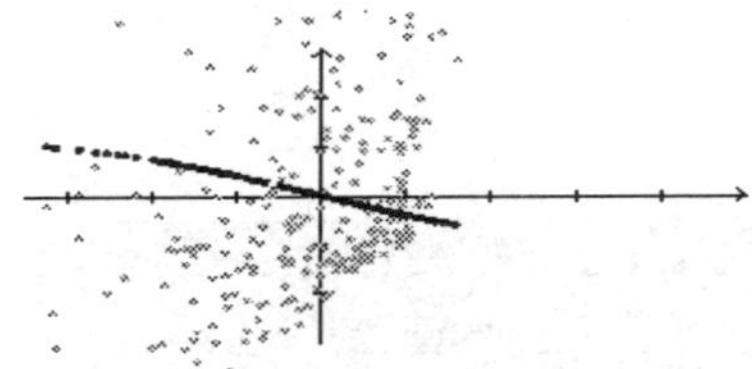

Figure 6: An example of a poor fit. The output of the hidden unit does not fit the residuals well.

We can easily observe the operating region of each hidden unit from the HiddenActivity view. Both the trained network graphical representation and the hidden activity view can guide pruning. Using these graphics, we can easily identify those units which have constant outputs, and those units which are highly correlated with each other.

In the ProjectionPlot view, (Moody & Yarvin 1992), the x-axis is a projection of the multi-dimensional input space onto one dimension. The y-axis is the fit to data. The black curve is the actual output of a hidden unit and the gray dots show the target data residuals added to the sigmoid. When the hidden unit response function fits well to its target, we can observe that the gray dots cluster and form a shape which is similar to the black curve, and most gray dots stay close to the black curve. Figure 5 shows the projection plots of the hidden units of a well trained network. Figure 6 gives an example of the projection plot of a hidden unit of a poorly trained network.

4   Sensitivity Analysis Mechanism

Selecting good input feature sets is very important for classification and regression. Input features which are irrelevant to the task may add noise to outputs and result in worse performance. Sometimes, collecting data may be very expensive. When we construct a feature set for a task, we therefore try to include the useful features and eliminate any unnecessary ones. The sensitivity analysis mechanism of the toolkit computes four types of model-dependent sensitivity measures using the whole data set, and two sensitivity measures for individual exemplars. These measures can be used to guide input feature selection and the pruning of hidden layer units. The sensitivities for individual exemplars can provide insight into which factors are important for specific predictions.

Input and Hidden Sensitivity Analysis (Average)

The sensitivity measures discussed in the section are calculated using the whole data set. We define four types of sensitivity measures.

One of the sensitivity measures, *delta error*, (Moody & Utans 1994), is defined in terms of the increase of the average square-error when replacing a variable x with its mean $\overline{x}$. The sensitivity S_i of the ith variable is:

$$S_i \;=\; \frac{1}{N}\sum_{n=1}^{N} S_i^{(n)} \,,$$

$$S_i^{(n)} \;=\; \mathrm{SE}(\overline{x}_i, \mathbf{W}) - \mathrm{SE}(x_i^{(n)}, \mathbf{W}) \,,$$

where SE denotes the square-error which is a function of network weights and data exemplars, and $S_i^{(n)}$ is the *delta error* measure of the nth data exemplar. If S_i is large, the network error will be largely changed by replacing the ith input variable with its mean. If S_i is small, we need the help of other measures to decide whether the ith input variable is useful. Three additional sensitivity measures are computed based on perturbating an input or a hidden variable and monitoring network output variations:

$$\textbf{Average Gradient (AG)} \qquad S_i = \frac{1}{N}\sum_{n=1}^{N} \frac{\partial f^{(n)}}{\partial x_i} \,,$$

$$\textbf{Average Absolute Gradient (AAG)} \qquad S_i = \frac{1}{N}\sum_{n=1}^{N} |\frac{\partial f^{(n)}}{\partial x_i}| \,,$$

$$\textbf{RMS Gradient (RMSG)} \qquad S_i = \sqrt{\frac{1}{N}\sum_{n=1}^{N} \left[\frac{\partial f^{(n)}}{\partial x_i}\right]^2} \,,$$

where $f^{(n)} = f(x_1^{(n)}, \dots, x_i^{(n)}, \dots, x_d^{(n)})$ is the network output given the nth input data pattern.

These three sensitivity measures together offer useful information. If $S_i^{\mathbf{AG}}$ is positive and large, then on average the change of the direction of the network output f is the same as that of the ith input variable. If $S_i^{\mathbf{AG}}$ is negative and has large magnitude, on average the change of the direction of f is opposite to that of the ith input variable.

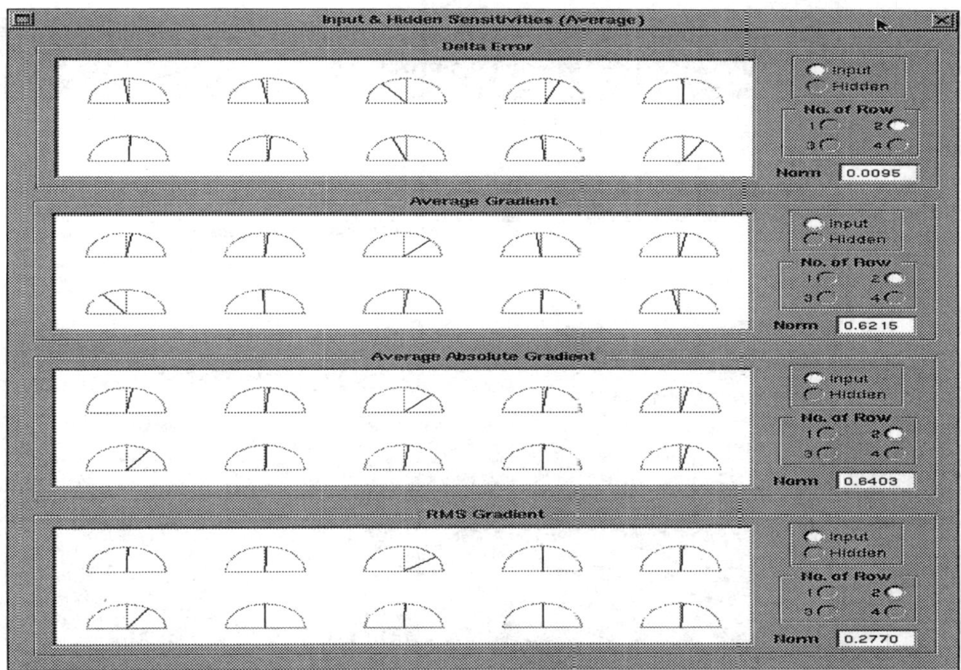

Figure 7: Sensitivity analysis results. Results for the four different average sensitivity methods are displayed in four views. The norm of each sensitivity vector is computed and displayed. In a view, each half-circle corresponds to an input or a hidden unit. The angle between the black arm and the y-axis in a half-circle represents the magnitude of the unit's sensitivity value. The location of the black arm in a half-circle exhibits the sign of the sensitivity value. In a half-circle, if the black arm is at the right side of the y-axis, the sensitivity value of the variable is negative. If it is at the left side of the y-axis, the value is positive. Consistency between the four measures increases our confidence in identifying irrelevant inputs or hidden nodes.

When $S_i^{\mathbf{AG}}$ is close to zero, we can not get much information from this measure. If $S_i^{\mathbf{AAG}}$ is large, the output f is sensitive to the ith input variable. if $S_i^{\mathbf{AAG}}$ is small, f is not sensitive to the ith input variable. If $S_i^{\mathbf{RMSG}}$ is very different from $S_i^{\mathbf{AAG}}$, the ith input series could be very noisy and have a lot of outliers.

The sensitivity analysis mechanism produces results either in numerical format or in graphical format depending on the user's selection. In the graphical format, the four different sensitivity measures are displayed in four views. In a view, each half-circle corresponds to an input or a hidden unit. The angle between the black arm and the y-axis in a half-circle represents the magnitude of the unit's sensitivity value. The location of the black arm in a half-circle exhibits the sign of the sensitivity value. In a half-circle, if the black arm is at the right side of the y-axis, the sensitivity value of the variable is negative. If it is at the left side of the y-axis, the value is positive. Figure 7 shows an example, in which all the four sensitivity measures identify that the third input variable plays an important role in the modeling task.

Sensitivities for Individual Exemplars

When we apply a data exemplar to a trained neural network, the network outputs a result. Sensitivity analysis performed for an individual exemplar provides information about which input features play an important role in producing the current network output. This helps the user interpret how the network is making a prediction. Two types of sensitivity measures for individual exemplars are calculated. These measures are defined as

$$\textbf{Delta Output (DO)} \qquad S_i = \Delta f_i = f(x_1^{(n)}, \dots, x_i^{(n)}, \dots, x_d^{(n)}) - f(x_1^{(n)}, \dots, \overline{x_i}, \dots, x_d^{(n)}),$$

$$\textbf{Output Gradient (OG)} \qquad S_i = \frac{\partial f^{(n)}}{\partial x_i}.$$

where $f^{(n)} = f(x_1^{(n)}, \dots, x_i^{(n)}, \dots, x_d^{(n)})$.

Presenting the nth exemplar to the network, if $S_i^{\mathbf{DO}}$ or $S_i^{\mathbf{OG}}$ is large then the ith variable plays an important role in the current network output, and slightly changing the value of the variable may cause a large change in the network output. Figure 8 gives an example of the graphical output of the individual exemplar sensitivity analysis. Black and gray represent negative and positive respectively. The size of a rectangle represents the magnitude of a sensitivity value. The indices of exemplars change along the horizontal direction, and the indices of input variables change along the vertical direction.

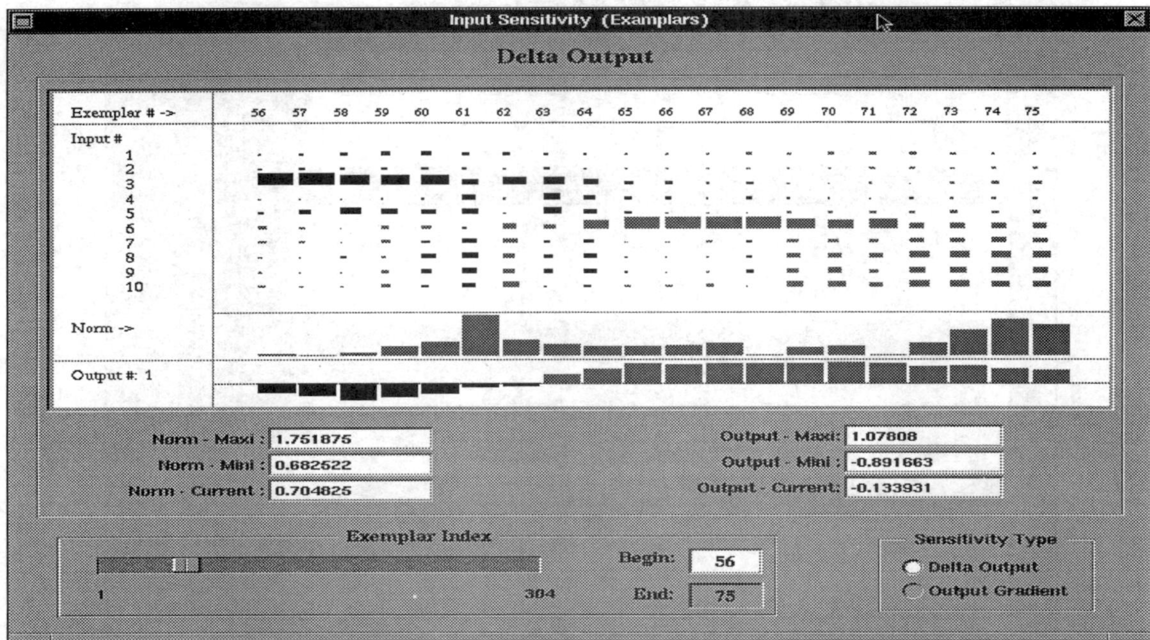

Figure 8: Sensitivity analysis results for individual exemplars. Black and gray represent negative and positive respectively. The size of a rectangle represents the magnitude of a value. The indices of exemplars change along the horizontal direction. The indices of input variables change along the vertical direction.

Using this graphical display, we can easily observe which input variables play important roles on the current network output, or which input variables, when we change them, can largely increase or decrease errors. If individual exemplars are part of a time series, we can easily observe how the roles of different input variables change through time. For example, in Figure 8, for exemplars with indices from 56 to 60, the third input variable has large negative sensitivity measures. Starting with the 65th exemplar, the sixth input variable starts to play an important role, and this lasts until the 71th exemplar.

5   Summary

We have described a neural network visualization and sensitivity analysis toolkit in this paper. This tool is characterized by the following features: (1) The network graphical representation directly reflects both the network topology and weight connections between units; (2) The activation and projection views of the hidden units offer useful information about network behavior and are useful for understanding the network learning procedure; (3) The average sensitivity measures are a useful aid for selecting input features and pruning hidden units. (4) The exemplar sensitivity measures assist in understanding which inputs are important for a specific prediction.

Acknowledgements

Both authors thank Matthew Saffell for his useful feedback about the system and the paper. We gratefully acknowledge support for this work from ARPA and ONR(grant N00014-92-J-4062).

References

Moody, J. E. & Yarvin, N. (1992), Networks with learned unit response functions, *in* J. E. Moody, S. J. Hanson & R. P. Lippmann, eds, 'Advances in Neural Information Processing Systems 4', Morgan Kaufmann Publishers, San Mateo, CA, pp. 1048–55.

Moody, J. & Utans, J. (1994), Architecture selection strategies for neural networks: Application to corporate bond rating prediction, *in* A. N. Refenes, ed., 'Neural Networks in the Captial Markets', John Wiley & Sons.

Moody, J., Levin, A. & Rehfuss, S. (1993), Predicting the U.S. index of industrial production, *in* 'Neural Networks in the Captial Markets', John Wiley & Sons.

Rumelhart, D. & McClelland, J. (1986), *Parallel Distributed Processing: Exploration in the microstructure of cognition*, MIT Press.

Tufte, E. (1985), *The Visual Display of Quantitative Information*, Graphics Press.

Wejchert, J. & Tesauro, G. (1991), 'Visualizing processes in neural networks', *IBM Journal of Research and Development* **35**, 244–253.

Parallel Implementation of the
Confluent Preorder Parser on DECmpp

HO Kei Shiu Edward, LUK Wai Shing, CHAN Lai Wan
Department of Computer Science and Engineering, The Chinese University of Hong Kong
Shatin, New Territories, Hong Kong

Abstract— In this paper, we discuss and implement a parallel version of the Confluent Preorder Parser (CPP) on DECmpp which has an SIMD architecture. CPP has been reported to have excellent generalization performance in syntactic parsing and it is also capable of parsing erroneous sentences as well as resolving syntactic ambiguity. In this parallel CPP, the control parallelism inherent in the backpropagation training algorithm is exploited. In addition, based on a data-flow analysis, independent training patterns can be spotted out to extract their underlying data parallelism. Tens of folds in speedup is realized which greatly enhances the practicality of CPP.

1 Introduction

Syntactic parsing addresses the problem of finding the hierarchical relationship between the terminals or words in a sequential sentence. Traditionally, this relationship is manifested in the form of a tree – the parse tree. For example, by classifying the words in the sentence "the boy takes the apple on the table", we form a sequence $\langle$ D N V D N P D N $\rangle$ where the terminal D stands for $\underline{D}$eterminer, N for $\underline{N}$oun, V for $\underline{V}$erb and P for $\underline{P}$reposition. Upon successful parsing, the parse tree in Figure 1 is produced, where the non-terminal np stands for $\underline{n}$oun $\underline{p}$hrase, vp for $\underline{v}$erb $\underline{p}$hrase, pp for $\underline{p}$repositional $\underline{p}$hrase and s for $\underline{s}$entence. Alternatively, it can also be represented by the Lisp-like structure ((D N) (V ((D N) (P (D N))))).

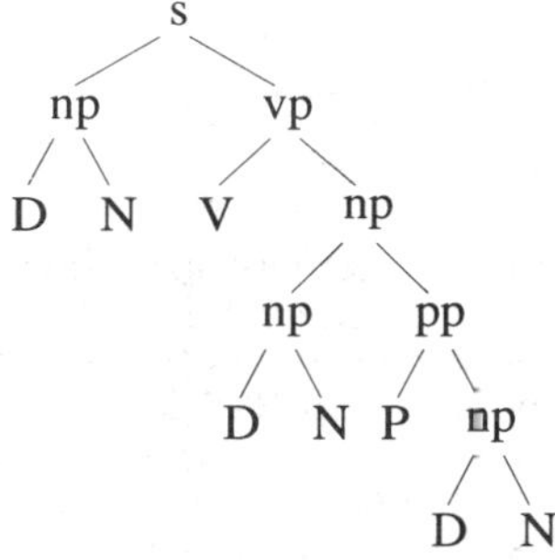

Figure 1: The parse tree of the sentence $\langle$ D N V D N P D N $\rangle$

In this paper, we present a parallel implementation of the Confluent Preorder Parser (CPP) which was previously proposed for syntactic parsing [9]. Functionally, CPP behaves like a recurrent network for sequence encoding. Weights are updated after reading each terminal, instead of waiting until the entire sequence is scanned (similar to the Simple Recurrent Network (SRN) [5]). Training of this model is a hybrid between SRN [5] and the auto-associative encoder (that is, the backpropagation network [13]). However, the sequences are broken down into static training patterns. Hence, temporal causality constraint exists among the patterns which encode the same sequence. This dictates that all patterns be presented to the network one-by-one in a strictly sequential manner. In this parallel CPP, we make use of a data-flow analysis to identify independent training patterns and have them processed together in the same batch. As a result, unnecessary causality constraint can be eliminated. In addition, the parallelizable operations in the backpropagation algorithm are also extracted. Together, significant speedup is realized by this parallel CPP.

2 Confluent Preorder Parser

Previously, the holistic parsing paradigm was proposed [12, 1, 10]. Instead of an algorithmic approach, parsing is achieved via a holistic transformation [2, 3] from the connectionist representation of the sentence to the connectionist representation of the parse tree. Since these data structures are recursive, hierarchical and possibly infinite, distributed representations of fixed length must be used which have to be developed using functional composition techniques [14]. In this respect, the traditional convention to encode a parse tree as a hierarchical data structure (as in [12, 1, 10]) has been found inefficient. The structure of the parse tree is only implicitly reflected by the order/manner in which different components and terminals of it are "amalgamated" together. The representation obtained simply fails to capture the structural characteristics of the data structure encoded. Poor generalization is thus resulted.

In view of this, we propose to linearize the parse tree by preorder traversal and encode the preorder traversal sequence instead of the parse tree. Parsing is thus implemented as a sequence-to-sequence transformation – from the sentence sequence to the preorder traversal sequence. Both types of sequences are encoded using SRAAM (Sequential Recursive Auto-Associative Memory [11]). To further promote the generalization performance, confluent inference [4] is applied. The two SRAAMs are trained together consistently such that an identical representation is developed for the sentence and the preorder traversal. Realization of these two techniques gives rise to the Confluent Preorder Parser (CPP) [9] (see Figure 2). Two versions of CPP have been examined, CPP1 and CPP2. CPP1 is trained with complete sentences only, whereas CPP2 is trained to parse phrases to produce the corresponding sub-parse-trees, in addition to complete sentences.

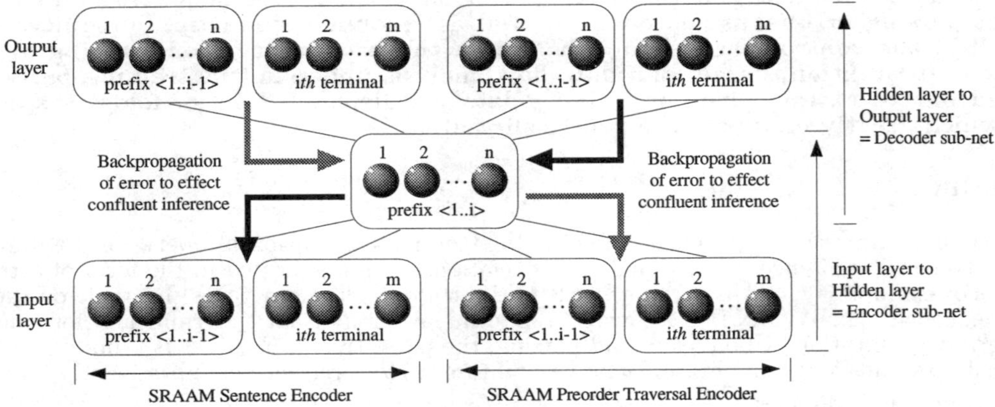

Figure 2: Confluent Preorder Parser (CPP)

3   The Performance of CPP

To evaluate the performance of CPP, the context-free grammar in Table 1 is used (which is adopted from [11]). A total of 112 syntactically well-formed sentences (and their parse trees) are generated using s as the root. The length of the longest sentence is equal to 13 and the height of the highest tree is equal to 5. Among them, 80 sentences are randomly selected for training, while the remaining 32 sentences are reserved for testing. Table 2 summarizes the results. As depicted, CPP has excellent generalization ability and it is also capable of parsing erroneous sentences and resolving syntactic ambiguities (see [6] for a detailed discussion). Analysis reveals that the representational space as a whole exhibits a regularly nested structure. Systematicity is observed among the parse tree representations which accounts for its better performance [8]. A model has been suggested which elucidates the operations of CPP as governed by a finite state automata [7]. Based on this formalism, the holistic parsing mechanism, the generalization and the error recovery capability of CPP can all be explained in terms of state transitions.

Sentence	*Noun phrase*	*Verb phrase*	*Prepositional phrase*	*Adjectival phrase*
s → np vp s → np V	np → D ap np → D N np → np pp	vp → V np vp → V pp	pp → P np	ap → A ap ap → A N

Table 1: The context-free grammar used to evaluate the performance of CPP

			CPP1	*CPP2*
Generalization		*Training*	100%	100%
		Testing	81.25%	93.75%
Error Recovery		*Wrong terminal*	91.21%	94.72%
		Missing terminal	69.94%	70.93%
		Extra terminal	46.64%	50.80%
		Swapped terminal	63.65%	66.88%
Syntactic Disambiguation		*1 ambiguity*	98.24%	99.65%
		3 ambiguities	91.89%	97.31%

Table 2: The performance of CPP

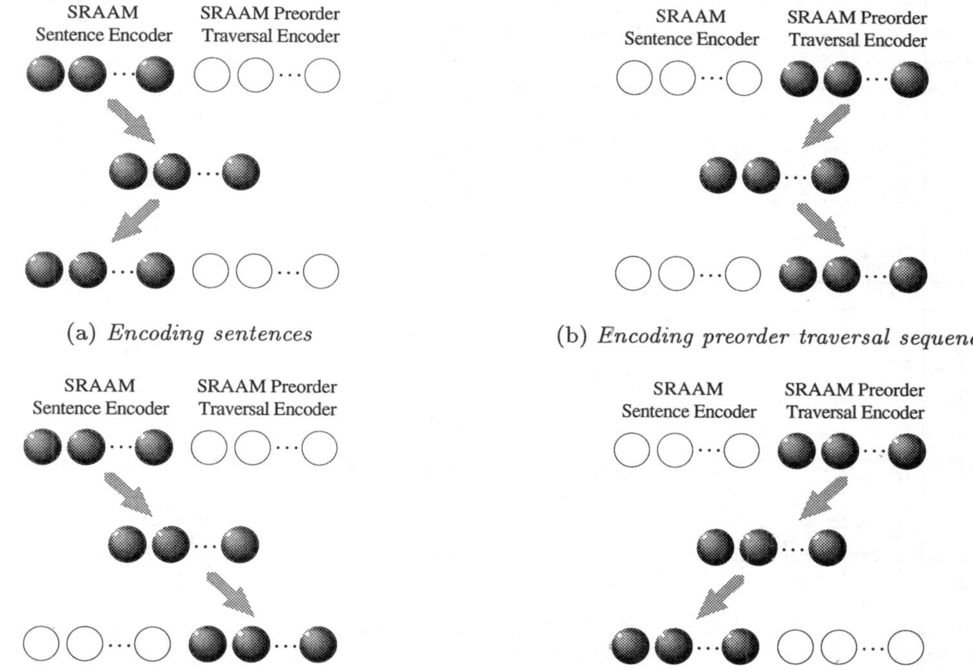

Figure 3: Different parts (shaded) of CPP are adapted for different types of training patterns. The arrows show the direction which the error is backpropagated during training.

4 Sequential Training

In CPP, three types of training patterns are needed :

1. those for encoding the sentence sequence itself (see Figure 3(a)),

2. those for encoding the preorder traversal sequence of the parse tree (see Figure 3(b)), and

3. those required for enforcing confluent inference. Depending on the particular weights of CPP that are adapted during training, they can be further classified into two types :

   (a) training patterns that modify only those weights which connect the input layer of the Sentence Encoder and the hidden layer, as well as those connecting the hidden layer to the output layer of the Preorder Traversal Encoder (see Figure 3(c)), and

   (b) training patterns that modify only those weights which connect the input layer of the Preorder Traversal Encoder and the hidden layer, as well as those connecting the hidden layer to the output layer of the Sentence Encoder (see Figure 3(d)).

For example, to learn parsing the two sentences ⟨ D A N V ⟩ (which corresponds to the parse tree ((D (A N)) V) with preorder traversal ⟨ s np D ap A N V ⟩) and ⟨ D N V ⟩ (which corresponds to the parse tree ((D N) V) with preorder traversal ⟨ s np D N V ⟩, the training patterns as shown in Table 3 are needed (assuming that CPP1 is used). As depicted, there exists a part-whole relationship between the patterns in which the sub-sequence encoded in the hidden layer for one pattern (such as ⟨ D A N ⟩ in pattern 3) will act as the input component or prefix of the next (correspondingly ⟨ D A N V ⟩). A causality constraint of this type dictates that the former pattern should be presented to the network before the latter. In the sequential implementation, training patterns are processed in a strictly sequential order, with one sentence following the other. And for each sentence, patterns of type 1 are trained first, followed by patterns of type 2, and finally patterns of type 3. Thus, the training patterns in Table 3 will be fed to CPP in the top-down order as presented. This guarantees the satisfaction of the causality constraint. Training then proceeds using the backpropagation algorithm [13] with the real-time weight updating mode – after the presentation of each pattern, the necessary weight change is calculated and the weights are modified before the next pattern is processed.

5 Parallel Implementation on DECmpp

To accelerate training, we have implemented the CPP model on DECmpp which has an SIMD architecture. The model we are working with has 8K processors and each processor has 64K local memory.

	Number	Type	Input	Hidden layer	Target
Time 1	1	1	# + D	⟨ D ⟩	# + D
Time 2	2	1	⟨ D ⟩ + A	⟨ D A ⟩	⟨ D ⟩ + A
Time 3	3	1	⟨ D A ⟩ + N	⟨ D A N ⟩	⟨ D A ⟩ + N
Time 4	4	1	⟨ D A N ⟩ + V	⟨ D A N V ⟩	⟨ D A N ⟩ + V
Time 5	5	2	# + s	⟨ s ⟩	# + s
Time 6	6	2	⟨ s ⟩ + np	⟨ s np ⟩	⟨ s ⟩ + np
Time 7	7	2	⟨ s np ⟩ + D	⟨ s np D ⟩	⟨ s np ⟩ + D
Time 8	8	2	⟨ s np D ⟩ + ap	⟨ s np D ap ⟩	⟨ s np D ⟩ + ap
Time 9	9	2	⟨ s np D ap ⟩ + A	⟨ s np D ap A ⟩	⟨ s np D ap ⟩ + A
Time 10	10	2	⟨ s np D ap A ⟩ + N	⟨ s np D ap A N ⟩	⟨ s np D ap A ⟩ + N
Time 11	11	2	⟨ s np D ap A N ⟩ + V	⟨ s np D ap A N V ⟩	⟨ s np D ap A N ⟩ + V
Time 12	12	3(a)	⟨ D A N ⟩ + V	⟨ D A N V ⟩	⟨ s np D ap A N ⟩ + V
Time 13	13	3(b)	⟨ s np D ap A N ⟩ + V	⟨ s np D ap A N V ⟩	⟨ D A N ⟩ + V
Time 14	14	1	⟨ D ⟩ + N	⟨ D N ⟩	⟨ D ⟩ + N
Time 15	15	1	⟨ D N ⟩ + V	⟨ D N V ⟩	⟨ D N ⟩ + V
Time 16	16	2	⟨ s np D ⟩ + N	⟨ s np D N ⟩	⟨ s np D ⟩ + N
Time 17	17	2	⟨ s np D N ⟩ + V	⟨ s np D N V ⟩	⟨ s np D N ⟩ + V
Time 18	18	3(a)	⟨ D N ⟩ + V	⟨ s np D N V ⟩	⟨ s np D N ⟩ + V
Time 19	19	3(b)	⟨ s np D N ⟩ + V	⟨ D N V ⟩	⟨ D N ⟩ + V

Table 3: Training patterns for teaching a CPP1 to parse the sentences ⟨ D A N V ⟩ and ⟨ D N V ⟩. In the sequential implementation, they are presented to the parser in a strictly top-down order.

Two sources of parallelism have been exploited. Firstly, given the fact that CPP is an ordinary back-propagation network, the calculations of individual neurons/units in the same layer, being independent of each other, can proceed in parallel.

Secondly, there is an enormous data parallelism inherent across different training examples. Recall our discussion in Section 4 that training patterns (such as those in Table 3) are presented to the CPP network in a strictly sequential order. This ordering is in fact too "conservative". Two or more training patterns can be grouped and processed together so long as no conflict can result, even if they are from different sentences. Precisely, only the following three types of constraints are really necessary :

- *Data Dependency* : A training pattern should wait for those patterns which encode its inputs and targets to finish first (this is exactly the causality constraint mentioned in Section 4).

- *Consistency Constraint* : Two patterns cannot be processed together it they encode the same sub-sequence in their hidden layers (e.g. pattern 17 and pattern 18 in Table 3).

- *Weight Constraint* : Two patterns can be trained together only if they involve the same set of weights (see Figure 3). In other words, they must be of the same type.

Observing these, "pattern scheduling" (as software preprocessing) is applied such that the original training schedule in Table 3 can now be changed from a linear list into a Directed Acyclic Graph (DAG), as depicted in Figure 4. Patterns represented by nodes on the same level of this DAG can be processed concurrently. In actual training, these independent pattern vectors will be packed together column-by-column into an augmented matrix and presented to the network as a whole. Effectively, the weight updating necessary for each pattern is calculated independently and in parallel with the weights fixed. The total accumulated changes in weights are then used to modify the weights in the network, and processing continues with the set of training patterns in the next time-step (or level) of the DAG. Intuitively, weight updating now proceeds in a "semi-batch" manner, with the "batch size" (which is the number of patterns presented to the network between two weight updates) varies in each time step.

5.1 The Performance of the Parallel CPP

In the parallel CPP, the total duration for each training epoch is equal to the length of the critical path of the DAG, which depends on the length of the longest sequence only (probably, it is a preorder traversal sequence). But in the strictly sequential implementation, it is proportional to the number of training sentences times the average length of the training sentences.

As shown in Table 3, the two sentences ⟨ D A N V ⟩ and ⟨ D N V ⟩ originally require 19 time steps to finish one training epoch in the sequential schedule. But now, it takes 13 time steps only, as depicted in Figure 4. In other words, a speedup of more than 31% has been realized. More importantly, it can be expected that this gain in efficiency will be further magnified as the network size is scaled up, since the increase will be offset by the large number of parallel processors available. Also, when more training examples are to be learned, a greater amount of potential data parallelism will be provided. The speedup will thus become more significant.

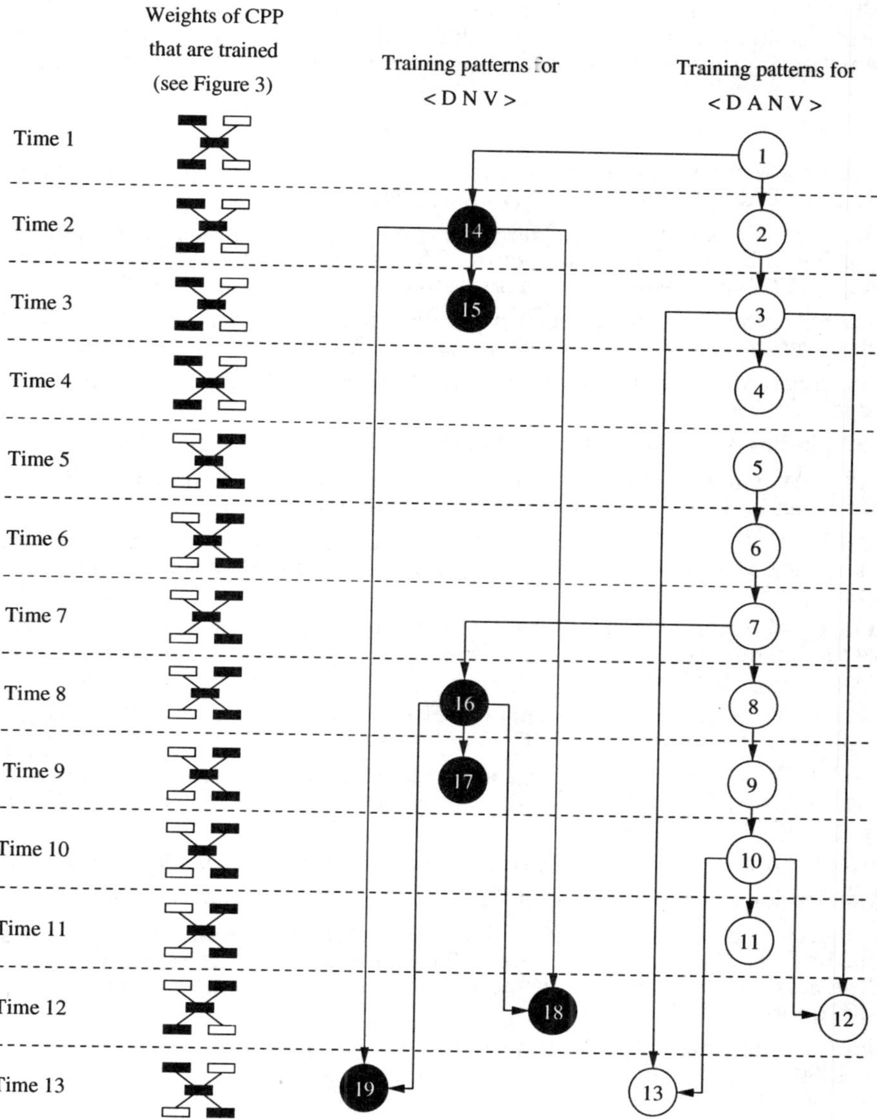

Figure 4: The parallel training schedule for learning the two sentences ⟨ D A N V ⟩ and ⟨ D N V ⟩ as represented by a Direct Acyclic Graph (DAG). The numbers which label the nodes correspond to the pattern numbers appearing in Table 3. An arrow represents a data dependency constraint between a pair of training patterns.

As a comparison, the 80 training sentences in Section 3 when processed by this parallel CPP needed only about 13 seconds to finish one iteration (which accounts for a complete sweep of 864 training patterns), with the degree of parallelism equal to 35 (meaning that a maximum of 35 patterns can be processed together in the same time step). But in the original sequential implementation using a SPARC-20 computer, one single iteration took more than 12 minutes to complete.

6   Conclusion

In this paper, a parallel implementation of CPP on DECmpp has been presented. Tens of folds in speedup is achieved for the training process. For the future work, it remains interesting to examine the exact effect of the "semi-batch" training paradigm on the stability of the backpropagation algorithm as well as the "quality" of the network produced (measured in terms of its generalization performance).

References

[1] G. Berg. Learning recursive phrase structure : Combining the strengths of PDP and X-bar syntax. Technical Report TR91-5, University at Albany, 1991.

[2] D. S. Blank, L.A. Meeden, and J. B. Marshall. Exploring the symbolic/subsymbolic continuum: A case study of RAAM. In J. Dinsmore, editor, *The Symbolic and Connectionist Paradigms: Closing the Gap*, pages 113–148. Lawrence Erlbaum Associates, Hillsdale, NJ, 1992.

[3] D. J. Chalmers. Syntactic transformations of distributed representations. In N. Sharkey, editor, *Connectionist Natural Language Processing*, pages 46–55. Intellect Books, 1992.

[4] L. Chrisman. Learning recursive distributed representations for holistic computation. *Connection Science*, 3:345–366, 1991.

[5] J. L. Elman. Finding structure in time. *Cognitive Science*, 14:179–211, 1990.

[6] K. S. Ho and L. W. Chan. Confluent Preorder Parsing. Technical Report CS-TR-95-03, Department of Computer Science, The Chinese University of Hong Kong, 1995.

[7] K. S. Ho and L. W. Chan. Efficient Connectionist Representations of Parse Trees for Grammatical Inference. Technical Report CS-TR-95-15, Department of Computer Science, The Chinese University of Hong Kong, 1995.

[8] K. S. Ho and L. W. Chan. Linearization + Confluent = Efficient Connectionist Representations of Parse Trees for Grammatical Inference. In *Proc. 1995 International Symposium on Artificial Neural Networks*, pages IS24–IS31, 1995.

[9] K. S. Ho and L. W. Chan. Syntactic parsing using RAAM. In *Proc. World Congress on Neural Networks*, volume 1, pages 485–488, 1995.

[10] K. S. Ho and L.W. Chan. Representing sentence structures in neural networks. In M. W. Kim and S. Y Lee, editors, *Proc. International Conference in Neural Information Processing Systems*, volume 3, pages 1462–1467, 1994.

[11] J. B. Pollack. Recursive distributed representations. *Artificial Intelligence*, 46:77–105, 1990.

[12] R. Reily. Connectionist techniques for on-line parsing. *Network*, 3:37–45, 1990.

[13] D. E. Rumelhart, G. E. Hinton, and R.J. Williams. Learning internal representations through error propagation. In D. E. Rumelhart, J. L. McClelland, and The PDP Research Group, editors, *Parallel distributed processing: Experiments in the microstructure of cognition*, volume 1, pages 318–362. MIT Press, Cambridge, MA, 1986.

[14] T. van Gelder. Compositionality: a connectionist variation on a classical theme. *Cognitive Science*, 14:355–384, 1990.

Hybrid Systems and Applications

(Oral Presentation)

Asymptotic Stability Of Feedback Additive Fuzzy Systems

Bart Kosko
Signal and Image Processing Institute
Department of Electrical Engineering
University of Southern California
Los Angeles, California 90089-2564

Abstract. **Feedback fuzzy systems take their own output as input and define nonlinear rulebased dynamical systems. They use a fixed number of rules to model other dynamical systems while feedforward fuzzy systems suffer from exponential rule explosion. But most feedback fuzzy systems are not themselves stable. Generalized additive fuzzy systems are a special class of feedback fuzzy systems that compute a system output as a convex sum of linear operators. A matrix replaces each then-part fuzzy set function in a standard fuzzy system. The paper proves that continuous versions of these feedback systems are globally asymptotically stable if all rule matrices are stable. This does not hold for the better-known discrete version of Tanaka. A corollary shows that it does hold for a special but practical case of the discrete additive model.**

1. Feedback Fuzzy Systems and Rule Explosion

Feedback fuzzy systems take their own output as input. They use a set of if-then rules to define continuous or discrete autonomous dynamical systems on a real vector space:

$$\dot{x} \;=\; F(x) \tag{1}$$

$$x(k+1) \;=\; F(x(k)) \tag{2}$$

The feedback fuzzy system F is a vector field $F: R^n \to R^n$ that has the origin as a fixed point: $F(0) = 0$. Feedback fuzzy systems can arise in control or in signal processing or in models of complex social or medical processes where subsystems affect one another in closed causal loops.

The feedback structure often arises because a feedforward fuzzy system $F: R^n \to R^p$ suffers from rule explosion in high dimensions [3]. Fuzzy systems are universal function approximators just as are feedforward neural networks [2]. But fuzzy systems need on the order of k^{n+p-1} rules to approximate a continuous or bounded measurable function $f: R^n \to R^p$ on a compact domain.

This paper gives sufficient conditions for the stability of (1) and (2) when the feedback fuzzy system F is a simple type of additive fuzzy system [1, 4]. These nonlinear systems compute the global output $F(x)$ as a convex sum of the rule outputs:

$$F(x) = \sum_{j=1}^{m} p_j(x)\, B_j x \text{ for square matrix or linear operator } B_j.$$ Each rule acts as a linear

subsystem as in the feedback scheme of Tanaka and Sugeno [5 - 6]. The system itself is nonlinear because the convex coefficents $p_1(x),\ldots,p_m(x)$ change with each input or state vector x. The system becomes a standard linear system in the special case when the system has just one rule (when $m = 1$).

We prove that the continuous system (1) is globally asymptotically stable if each rule matrix is negative definite and thus if each local subsystem is stable. Tanaka [5 - 6] has shown that this result does not hold in the discrete case (2) and has applied his feedback model to the neural-fuzzy test problem of backing up a truck and one or more trailers. Stable subsystems can still lead to global instability. We present Tanaka's result in the framework of a generalized additive system and prove a corollary that gives a practical criterion for global stability of the discrete feedback fuzzy system (2).

2. Global Asymptotic Stability of Generalized Additive Fuzzy Systems

We first prove the asymptotic global stability of the unforced continuous fuzzy

system $$\dot{x} \;=\; F(x) \;=\; \sum_{j=1}^{m} p_j(x)\, B_j x \qquad\qquad\qquad (3)$$

A control input column vector $u \in R^p$ can steer the generalized standard additive model (SAM) [4] feedback system (3) through m n-by-p control matrices $C_j \in R^{n \times p}$:

$$\dot{x} \;=\; \sum_{j=1}^{m} p_j(x)[B_j x + C_j u] \qquad\qquad\qquad (4)$$

A like convex sum holds for the forced discrete generalized SAM:

$$x(k+1) \;=\; \sum_{j=1}^{m} p_j(x(k))\,[B_j x(k) + C_j u(k)] \qquad\qquad\qquad (5)$$

The unforced case assumes $u = 0$ and lets us look at the stability of the equilibrium vector $x_e = \lim_{k \to \infty} x(k)$ if it exists. We take the equilibrium vector to be the origin: $x_e = 0$.

The structure of a SAM comes from the SAM Theorem [4] that expands the

centroidal additive structure of the SAM output in $F(x) = \sum_{j=1}^{m} w_j\, a_j(x)\, B_j$. Here the if-

part fuzzy set $A_j \subset R^n$ has the joint set function $a_j : R^n \to [0,1]$ that in practice may

factor into a product of n scalar if-part set functions. The then-part term is not here a

matrix but a proper fuzzy set $B_j \subset R^p$ with joint set function $b_j : R^p \to [0,1]$. We can

take integrals based on this then-part set function to compute the set's finite positive volume V_j and centroid $c_j \in R^p$. The scalar $w_j \geq 0$ acts as the weight of the jth rule. Then the SAM Theorem gives the centroidal output as a simple ratio or convex sum:

$$F(x) = \frac{\sum_{j=1}^{m} w_j \, a_j(x) V_j \, c_j}{\sum_{j=1}^{m} w \, a_j(x) V_j}$$

$$= \sum_{j=1}^{m} p_j(x) \, c_j$$

The convex coefficients or discrete probability weights $p_1(x), ..., p_m(x)$ depend on the input x through the ratios

$$p_j(x) = \frac{w_j \, a_j(x) V_j}{\sum_{k=1}^{m} w_k \, a_k(x) V_k}$$

Unsupervised and supervised learning can tune all the parameters in the SAM system. The use of delta pulses in the SAM Theorem shows [4] that a generalized additive fuzzy system has the form of (3) above or (6) below when the then-part terms are square matrices with real coefficients. The rule weights can also change with the input x.

The equilibrium point x_e is *stable* in the sense of Lyapunov if small changes in the initial conditions lead to only small changes in the state trajectory: for all k_0 and all $\varepsilon > 0$ there is a $\delta > 0$ such that $\|x(k_0) - x_e\| < \delta$ implies $\|x(k) - x_e\| < \varepsilon$ for all $k \geq k_0$. The norm stands for the Euclidean norm: $\|x\|^2 = x_1^2 + \cdots - x_n^2$. The point x_e is *asymptotically stable* if it is stable and if it attracts the state trajectory: for all k_0 there is a $\delta' > 0$ such that $\|x(k_0) - x_e\| < \delta'$ implies $\lim_{k \to \infty} \|x(k) - x_e\| = 0$. The equilibrium is *globally asymptotically stable* if we can pick δ' to be arbitrarily large. When these results hold they hold uniformly for the autonomous system (3) and its discrete version (5).

We seek a smooth Lyapunov function $L : R^n \to R$ for the continuous feedback SAM model (3) that is positive definite $L(x) > 0$ when $x \neq 0$ and that obeys $L(x) = 0$ when $x = 0$ and that grows to infinity as the vector squared norm $\|x\|^2$ grows to infinity: $L(x) \to \infty$ as $x^T x \to \infty$. This holds if we take L as the quadratic form $x^T x$ or as the more general quadratic form $x^T P x$ for some n-by-n positive definite matrix P. Then standard results in Lyapunov stability theory imply that the dynamical system (3) has a stable equilibrium $x_e = 0$ if $\dot{L} \leq 0$ and has a globally asymptotically stable equilibrium $x_e = 0$ if $\dot{L} < 0$ along system trajectories for all $x \neq 0$. A discrete Lyapunov function $L(x(k))$ leads to stability for the unforced version of the discrete dynamical system in (5) and (11) below if $\Delta L \leq 0$ and leads to global asymptotic stability if $\Delta L < 0$ along system trajectories.

We can now prove the main result of this paper: The generalized SAM in (3) is globally asymptotically stable if all the local rule matrices B_j are stable. A stable matrix B_j in the continous case means that B_j is negative definite: $x^T B_j x < 0$ for all nonnull state vectors $x \neq 0$. This result extends the usual stability result for linear systems and reduces to it in the one-rule case when $m = 1$.

Theorem 1 (*Continuous SAM Stability*).   The generalized feedback SAM system

$$\dot{x} \;=\; \sum_{j=1}^{m} p_j(x)\, B_j x \tag{6}$$

with convex coefficients $\quad p_j(x) \;=\; \dfrac{w_j(x)\, a_j(x)}{\displaystyle\sum_{i=1}^{m} w_i(x)\, a_i(x)} \tag{7}$

is globally asymptotically stable if each then-part rule matrix B_j is negative definite. The if-part fuzzy set $A_j \subset R^n$ has joint set function $a_j : R^n \to [0,1]$ and rule weight w_j. In practice engineers often work with factored set functions $a_j(x) = a_j^1(x_1) \cdots a_j^n(x_n)$.

Proof. Choose the Lyapunov function L as the quadratic form $L(t) = x^T(t)\, x(t)$. Then

$$\dot{L} \quad = \quad 2x^T \dot{x} \tag{8}$$

$$= \quad 2x^T \sum_{j=1}^{m} p_j(x)\, B_j x \tag{9}$$

$$= \quad 2 \sum_{j=1}^{m} p_j(x)\, x^T B_j x \tag{10}$$

At all times t there is some convex coefficient that obeys $p_k(x(t)) > 0$. So $\dot{L} < 0$ along trajectories if each then-part matrix B_j is negative definite. *Q.E.D.*

The proof of Theorem 1 extends the stability proof of the continuous-time linear system or one-rule case. The feedback SAM F in (3) is nonlinear since the convex coefficients $p_j(x)$ change with each input x. The fact that at each time t at least one term obeys $p_k(x(t)) > 0$ lets us treat the convex sum of matrices as if it were a simple sum with constant coefficients. This does not hold in the discrete case.

We next look at the stability of the unforced discrete feedback systems of the form

$$x(k+1) \quad = \quad F(x(k)) \quad = \quad \sum_{j=1}^{m} p_j(x(k))\, B_j x(k) \tag{11}$$

A stable matrix B_j in this discrete case means that the linear subsystem $x(k+1) = B_j x(k)$ is asymptotically stable and thus that all n eigenvalues $\lambda_j^1, \ldots, \lambda_j^n$ of B_j lie in the unit circle in the complex z-plane: $\lim_{k \to \infty} B_j^k = \varnothing$ iff $|\lambda_j^i| < 1$ for all i.

Is the discrete system (11) stable if each rule matrix B_j is stable? Tanaka [5 - 6] first showed that the answer is no for a slightly simpler unweighted SAM model. But we show below that this does hold in the special case where each rule matrix B_j is not only stable but diagonal. Tanaka showed that stability did not hold for a simple two-rule system with then-part "set" matrices

$$B_1 = \begin{pmatrix} 1 & -\frac{1}{2} \\ 1 & 0 \end{pmatrix} \quad \text{and} \quad B_2 = \begin{pmatrix} -1 & -\frac{1}{2} \\ 1 & 0 \end{pmatrix} .$$

Matrix B_1 has the two eigenvalues $\lambda_i = \frac{1}{2} \pm i\frac{1}{2}$ and B_2 has the two eigenvalues $\lambda_i = -\frac{1}{2} \pm i\frac{1}{2}$. All four eigenvalues lie in the unit circle. So both matrices or linear subsystems are stable. Tanaka showed that the unweighted convex sum (4) is unstable for trapezoidal if-part sets A_1 and A_2 and constant or unity rule weights $w_1 = w_2 > 0$. He did find a sufficient condition for stability of (11) and we restate it here in the more general SAM case without proof.

Theorem 2. (*Discrete SAM Stability (Tanaka)*). The generalized discrete-time feedback SAM system

$$x(k+1) = \sum_{j=1}^{m} p_j(x(k)) B_j x(k) \tag{12}$$

with convex coefficients

$$p_j(x(k)) = \frac{w_j(x(k)) \, a_j(x(k))}{\sum_{i=1}^{m} w_i(x(k)) \, a_i(x(k))} \tag{13}$$

is globally asymptotically stable if there exists a common positive definite matrix P such that all m of the then-part matrices $B_j^T P B_j - P$ are negative definite.

There is no known way to find such a common positive definite matrix P. The odds of finding such a P fall with each new rule one adds to the system. Exponential rule explosion offers little hope of finding such a P for largescale systems. We next present a corollary to Theorem 2 that gives a sufficient condition for the identity choice $P = I$. Then the discrete system (11) will be globally asymptotically stable if each rule matrix B_j is stable and if each B_j is *diagonal* with real coefficients.

Corollary (*Discrete Diagonal SAM Stability*). The generalized discrete-time feedback SAM system

$$x(k+1) \;=\; \sum_{j=1}^{m} p_j(x(k))\, B_j x(k) \tag{14}$$

is globally asymptotically stable if all m then-part matrices B_j are diagonal and stable.

Proof. The diagonal matrix $B_j = Diag[b_j(1,1),\ldots,b_j(n,n)]$ is symmetric and lists its eigenvalues along its main diagonal. So the choice $P = I$ in Theorem 2 gives

$$B_j^T P B_j - P \;=\; B_j^2 - I \tag{15}$$

The diagonal matrix $B_j^2 - I$ is negative definite iff all its eigenvalues are negative. This holds iff each diagonal entry obeys $b_j^2(i,i) - 1 < 0$ iff $b_j^2(i,i) < 1$ iff $|b_j(i,i)| < 1$. The last condition is just that of stability for matrix B_j. Q.E.D.

This practical result holds for any positive definite matrix P of the form $P = cI$ with constant $c > 0$. For then $B_j^T P B_j - P \;=\; cB_j^2 - cI$. So the diagonal condition $cb_j^2(i,i) - c < 0$ still leads to the stability condition $|b_j(i,i)| < 1$.

References

[1] Kosko, B., *Neural Networks and Fuzzy Systems: A Dynamical Systems Approach to Machine Intelligence*, Prentice Hall, 1991.

[2] Kosko, B., "Fuzzy Systems as Universal Approximators," *IEEE Transactions on Computers*, vol. 43, no. 11, 1329 - 1333, November 1994; an earlier version appears in the *Proceedings of the First IEEE International Conference on Fuzzy Systems (IEEE FUZZ-92)*, 1153 - 1162, March 1992.

[3] Kosko, B., "Optimal Fuzzy Rules Cover Extrema," *International Journal of Intelligent Systems*, vol. 10, no. 2, 249 - 255, February 1995; an earlier version appears in the *Proceedings of the 1994 World Congress on Neural Networks (INNS WCNN-94)*, vol. I, 697 - 698, June 1994.

[4] Kosko, B., *Fuzzy Engineering*, Prentice Hall, 1996.

[5] Tanaka, K., and Sugeno, M., "Stability Analysis and Design of Fuzzy Control Systems," *Fuzzy Sets and Systems*, vol. 45, no. 2, 135 - 156, 24 January 1992.

[6] Tanaka, K., "Stability and Stabilizability of Fuzzy-Neural-Linear Control Systems," *IEEE Transactions on Fuzzy Systems*, vol. 3, no. 4, 438 - 447, November 1995.

Neural Networks for Detecting Conflicts on Real Vector Sets

Yasuo Matsuyama† and Kouichi Ogura‡

† Department of Electrical, Electronics and Computer Engineering,
Waseda University, Tokyo 169, Japan
† Also with Sympat Committee of the RWC Partnership of Japan
‡ NTT Data Communications Systems, Co., Tokyo 135, Japan

Abstract— This paper gives evidences that layered neural networks can detect conflicts among real vector representations. Such an ability includes mechanical theorem proving via refutation for crisp logic processing. Traditional crisp operations correspond to detections of conflicts among binary vectors. The introduction of the real number is one possible way of softening and adapting the crisp logic towards subsymbols and patterns. First in the text, a neural network architecture to realize logic reasoning is specified. This network is trained to acquire inference of the propositional logic. Then, generalization ability for non-binary cases is verified. Next, applications to the first order logic is examined. Inclusion of the Herbrand base is tried here. The total system becomes a hybrid of neural networks and crisp symbolic processing. Thus, experimental results of this paper pioneers the step towards joint processing of symbols, subsymbols and patterns.

1   Introduction

Symbols, subsymbols and patterns are fundamental sophistications refined from raw data for intelligent information processing. However, the classification by {raw data, patterns, subsymbols, symbols} can not be "monolithic." Symbols and subsymbols may be treated as just patterns at more abstract or higher levels of processing. Fig. 1 illustrates such a notion of this hierarchy. Symbols expressible by $\{0,1\}^m$ are the most crisp ones. They are considered to reside in the upper right corner of this figure.

Symbol manipulation has a long history and has been successfully used in traditional data processing. However, it suffers from lots of difficulties on ill-conditioned problems and pattern processing. Thus, information integration [4] has become an urgent field of study.

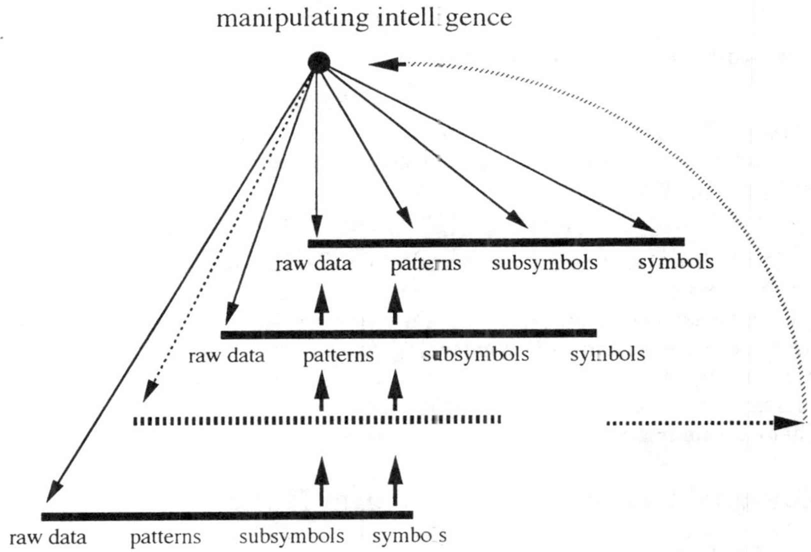

Fig. 1. Refinement of raw data towards symbols.

As is illustrated in Fig. 1, there are many subfields on the information integration according to the level of abstraction. In this paper, we discuss one possible softening of the most crisp symbols. This problem is found around the upper-right corner of Fig. 1 with the direction of "from crisp symbols to raw data." For this problem, we choose an approach of embedding logic operations into neural networks. Here, we have a clue that the crisp logic operations correspond to calculations on integers. Since neural networks process real numbers, all logic operations can be computed on the real number set which includes the integer set. Thus, the domain of input/output data is extended from integers to real numbers. This is a necessary step towards continuous interface with lower level entities of Fig. 1. The next important step is to fix which properties are verified using the neural network. Among various important crisp logic operations, we select inference and refutation since they are the main tools for logic reasoning. Thus, resolution for the refutation on real numbers is tried in this paper using neural networks. This corresponds to a detection of conflicts on real vector sets. The main text first discusses the propositional logic for the neural network training. Then, obtained real number structures are used to process the first order logic with the Herbrand universe of a finite set. Examples starting from raw data towards symbols on the bottom level of Fig. 1 are found in [1], [2].

2   Resolution on Disjunctive Expressions

2.1   Disjunctive forms and resolution for the propositional logic

First, we review relevant logic operations which are related to our symbol softening of this paper. Propositional logic is a fundamental system which uses conjunction "$\wedge$", disjunction "$\vee$", negation "$\neg$", implication "$\rightarrow$" and equivalence "$\leftrightarrow$". Note that "$p \rightarrow q$" is equivalent to "$\neg p \vee q$." Basic propositions are expressed by disjunctions of products of literals, e.g., "$q = \neg p q \vee p q$." In our actual situation, there are many propositions given conjunctively. Thus, the conjunction of disjunctions is adopted (the conjunctive normal form). The conjunction is simply denoted by ",".

Resolution is a process of deleting literals by using

$$\frac{\neg p \vee q, \ p}{q} \quad \text{or} \quad \frac{\neg p \vee q, \ \neg q \vee r}{\neg p \vee r}. \tag{1}$$

This is a forward reasoning. On the other hand, refutation is a strategy of formal theorem proving in terms of a backward reasoning. This process adds the negation of the proving proposition. If a contradiction is derived by the resolution, the proposition is proved.

2.2   Extensions of Range and Domain

Every logic variable or constant takes a value of either "F" or "T". These values correspond to the binary set $\{0, 1\}$. We extend this set to the interval $[0, 1] = \{0, 1\} \cup (0, 1)$. Consider the case that each basic proposition is expressed by disjunctions of products of n literals: Let $a_i^{\alpha_i}$, $(i = 1, \ldots, n)$, be n literals corresponding to the basic propositions such as p, q and r. Here,

$$a_i^{\alpha_i} = \begin{cases} \neg a_i \stackrel{\text{def}}{=} \bar{a}_i \ ; & \alpha_i = 0, \\ a_i \ ; & \alpha_i = 1. \end{cases}$$

Then, a product atom (min-term) is expressed by

$$\prod_{i=1}^{n} a_i^{\alpha_i}. \tag{2}$$

Thus, we have $m = 2^n$ product atoms starting from $\bar{a}_1, \ldots, \bar{a}_n$ to $a_1, \ldots, a_n$. Each proposition can be expressed by a binary vector $(b_1, \ldots, b_m)$. Here, $b_j = 0$ or 1, $(j = 1, \ldots, m)$. This is the case of the crisp logic. Next, we try the following extension:

$$(b_1, \ldots, b_m) \in \{0, 1\}^m \quad \Longrightarrow \quad (b_1, \ldots, b_m) \in [0, 1]^m. \tag{3}$$

Thus, our idea starts from allowing a real number coefficient to each min-term. This is compatible with Tsukimoto's multilinear function approach on the topological logic model [5], [6]. But, our approach in this paper is totally based on training of neural networks by given samples. That is, our purpose is to show evidences that the extension (3) concerning to the refutation by resolution is realizable by layered neural networks through learning on a finite data set. Thus, preparation of the data set and training of neural networks are important issues. Decisions on unlearned data, i.e., generalizations are expected as usual requirement on neural networks after the learning.

3   Embedding of Resolution into Neural Networks

3.1   Data Set for Learning

First, we prepare a training data set for the crisp logic.

Step 1   (crisp logic) Let A and B are propositions expressed by binary vectors a and b. These vectors are inputs to the neural network. For the training of the network, we prepare three types of teacher signals.

   1. (resolution)   If "$A \wedge B$" derives a proposition C such as in (1), a binary vector c corresponding to C is given as a teacher signal. For an identification of successful resolution, a flag F is taught to output the value 1.

2. (refutation) The refutation is a process of deducting a contradiction between the propositions A and B. This corresponds to $c = \mathbf{o}$, i.e., a null vector. We teach that $F = 1$ so that the refutation is achieved.

3. (don't care) Given propositions A and B, neither resolution nor refutation can be derived. In reality, this is the most likely occasion. In such a case, we select the teacher signal of $c = \mathbf{b}$ and $F = 0$. That is, the second input-cluster is simply reproduced at the output terminal. The flag of zero tells that proposition B is not used.

Step 2 (real number logic) Besides Step 1 of the crisp-valued logic, real number data can be given to the network. In this case , a, b and c are vectors in $[0,1]^m$. We regard $\|c\| < 1$ is the condition for the contradiction (c.f., [5]).

The above training set is actually applied to the neural network in the next section.

3.2 Input-output specifications to layered networks

Fig. 2 illustrates input-output terminals of the layered network for the real-number resolution for refutation. This figure is the case of two basic propositions ($n = 2$, $m = 2^n = 4$).

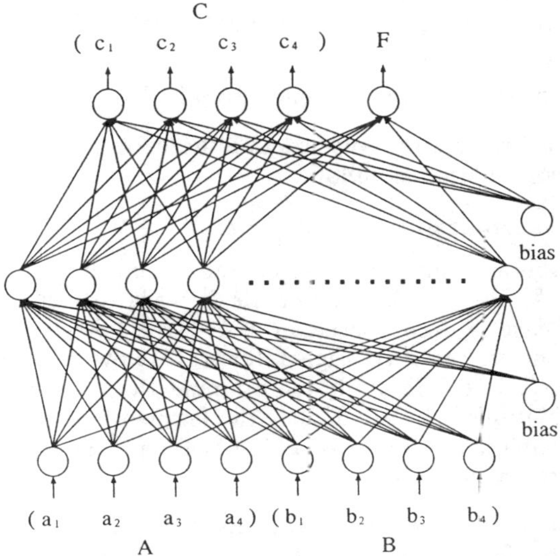

Fig. 2. Input-output terminals for real-number resolution via refutation.

Given a proposition A (vector a), another proposition B (vector b) is supplied. Then, the network produces a resolvent C (vector c). If a contradiction is detected, $C = \emptyset$ ($\|c\| < 1$) is produced as the refutation. In these cases, the flag F is on. Otherwise, this flag is off and $C = B$ ($c = b$). The training for weight modification is done by usual backpropagation (e.g., [3]).

Next, we explain the process of recall, i.e., the use of the learned network.

1. The set of axioms $\mathcal{W}$ and the negation $\neg w$ of the theorem to be proved are given. Append $\neg w$ to $\mathcal{W}$. Transform each logic expression to a conjunctive normal form. Then, express such forms by vectors.

2. Choose two vectors from the vector pool of $\mathcal{W}$ as a and b. Propagate them forward in the network.

3. If $F \geq 1 - \varepsilon = \theta$ (a threshold) and $C \neq \emptyset$, a resolution is made. The output C (the vector c) is appended to the set $\mathcal{W}$. Otherwise, do nothing. The condition $C \neq \emptyset$ is detected by $\|c\| \geq 1$.

4. Repeat the above two procedures until $C = \emptyset$ is achieved, or until no possible combination for the resolution is left. The condition $C = \emptyset$ is detected by $\|c\| < 1$ and $F \geq \theta$.

5. If a contradiction $C = \emptyset$ is derived, the theorem w is proved. Otherwise, conclude that the proof was not derived.

3.3 Verification of learned results and interpretation of real vectors

The procedure in Section 3.2 can be verified as follows. We take an example of three basic propositions ($n = 3$). Since $m = 2^n = 8$, the network in this case has a structure of $(2m) \mapsto (2 \times 2m) \mapsto (m + 1)$.

[Verification Example 1 (crisp logic)]

Given the set of axioms $\mathcal{W} = \{p \vee q \vee r, \neg q, \neg r\}$, prove the theorem $w = p$.

1. $\mathcal{W} \cup \neg w = \{p \vee q \vee r, \neg q, \neg r, \neg p\}$
   $= \{(1.00, 1.00, 1.00, 1.00, 0.00, 0.00, 0.00, 0.00), (0.00, 1.00, 1.00, 1.00, 1.00, 1.00, 1.00, 1.00),$
   $(1.00, 1.00, 0.00, 0.00, 1.00, 1.00, 0.00, 0.00), (1.00, 0.00, 1.00, 0.00, 1.00, 0.00, 1.00, 0.00)\}.$
   is given.

2. From $(0.00, 1.00, 1.00, 1.00, 1.00, 1.00, 1.00, 1.00) \wedge (1.00, 1.00, 1.00, 1.00, 0.00, 0.00, 0.00, 0.00)$,
   a resolvent of $(0.01, 1.00, 1.00, 1.00, 1.00, 0.00, 0.99, 0.98)$ is derived. This resolvent is used in 5.

3. From $(1.00, 1.00, 1.00, 1.00, 1.00, 1.00, 1.00, 0.00) \wedge (1.00, 1.00, 0.00, 0.00, 1.00, 1.00, 0.00, 0.00)$,
   a resolvent of $(0.01, 1.00, 0.00, 0.99, 0.98, 1.00, 0.98, 1.00)$ is derived. This resolvent is not used for
   further resolution.

4. From $(0.00, 1.00, 1.00, 1.00, 1.00, 1.00, 1.00, 1.00) \wedge (1.00, 0.00, 1.00, 0.00, 1.00, 0.00, 1.00, 0.00)$,
   a resolvent of $(0.01, 0.01, 1.00, 0.99, 0.99, 0.99, 1.00, 0.99)$ is derived. This resolvent is not used for
   further resolution.

5. From $(0.01, 1.00, 1.00, 1.00, 1.00, 0.00, 0.99, 0.98) \wedge (1.00, 1.00, 0.00, 0.00, 1.00, 1.00, 0.00, 0.00)$,
   a resolvent of $(0.00, 1.00, 0.00, 0.98, 0.01, 1.00, 0.00, 1.00)$ is obtained. This resolvent is used in 6.

6. From $(1.00, 0.00, 1.00, 0.00, 1.00, 0.00, 1.00, 0.00) \wedge (0.00, 1.00, 0.00, 0.98, 0.01, 1.00, 0.00, 1.00)$,
   a contradiction $(0.00, 0.01, 0.01, 0.01, 0.00, 0.00, 0.00, 0.02)$ is obtained. Thus, the refutation is
   completed.

7. The above process verifies that the theorem $w = p$ is derived from the original $\mathcal{W}$.

The procedure 1 to 7 is a verification only around the crisp logic. Usage of non-crisp symbols, i.e., a
grounding of $c_j \in (0, 1)$ can be tried as follows.

[Verification Example 2 (generalization to real vectors)]

Here, we check to see if there exists a proper generalization. It is necessary to apply non-crisp data to
the learned neural network. We use the case of the forward reasoning "$(A \to B) \wedge A$ implies B." Each
basic proposition of this case is decomposed by $\neg A \neg B$, $\neg AB$, $A \neg B$ and AB. The crisp logic gives a
binary vector "0101" for the resulting B. Fig. 3 illustrates how this "0101" is softened if the premise A's
feasibility is reduced from 1.0 to 0.75 while maintaining that $A \vee \neg A$ is true. Note that the feasibility
of 0.5 means "totally ambiguous." In this figure, the learned feasibilities of $\neg A \neg B$, $\neg AB$, $A \neg B$ and AB
are plotted. One finds that only AB shows a significantly decreasing feasibility from 1.0 to 0.5. This
tendency can be interpreted as follows.

1. The feasibility of A is decreased (from mow on, "feasibility" is omitted). On the contrary, $\neg A$ is
   increased. These are premises. Then, B is decreased because of "$A \to B$."

2. The following changes on individual terms are compatible with the above fact.

   $\neg A \neg B$: $\neg A$ is increasing. But, only little can be judged on $\neg B$. Thus, $\neg A \neg B$ remains almost unchanged
         around 0.0.

   $\neg AB$: $\neg A$ is increasing. But, only little can be judged on B. Thus, $\neg AB$ remains almost unchanged
         around 1.0.

   $A \neg B$: A is decreasing. But, little can be judged on $\neg B$. Thus, $A \neg B$ remains almost unchanged
         around 0.0.

   AB : A is decreasing. Also, B is decreasing. Thus, AB is decreasing from 1.0.

The above generalization can be understood by the following inerpretation. Let the proposition A be
"it is an airplane." Let the proposition B be "it flies." Since A is decreased and $\neg A$ is increased, the
proposition A is shifting to "it is almost an airplane" and "it is perhaps an airplane." Then, it is natural
that AB, i.e., "it is an airplane and it flies" decreases significantly.

The experiments of the above were on the feasibility of the *fact*. It is possible to use the real number
property on a *rule*

[Usage of Real Numbers for Rules]

We consider a problem of exceptions. Let the basic proposition p mean "bird." Let q specify "flies."
Usually, "$p \to q$" holds. But, we want to be more precise. Let r_θ be the critical wing/body ratio. Let s
be a proposition to specify a species of a bird. Then,

$$s \to p, \qquad s \to r_s, \qquad p \wedge (r_s > r_\theta) \to q$$

are given as a set of propositions. Obviously, r_θ and r_s are a real numbers. Given such a set of database
including an object s and its measurement r_s, we can derive if an ostrich, an emu or a kiwi can fly. If we
add $r_s > r_\theta$ or $r_s \leq r_\theta$ as a proposition, the above set is reduced to a crisp one. However, this is rather

a rare instance. Consider the case that the decision boundary is at least two dimensional and obtainable by learning. Then, the usage of real numbers matches well to express the judgement on "files."

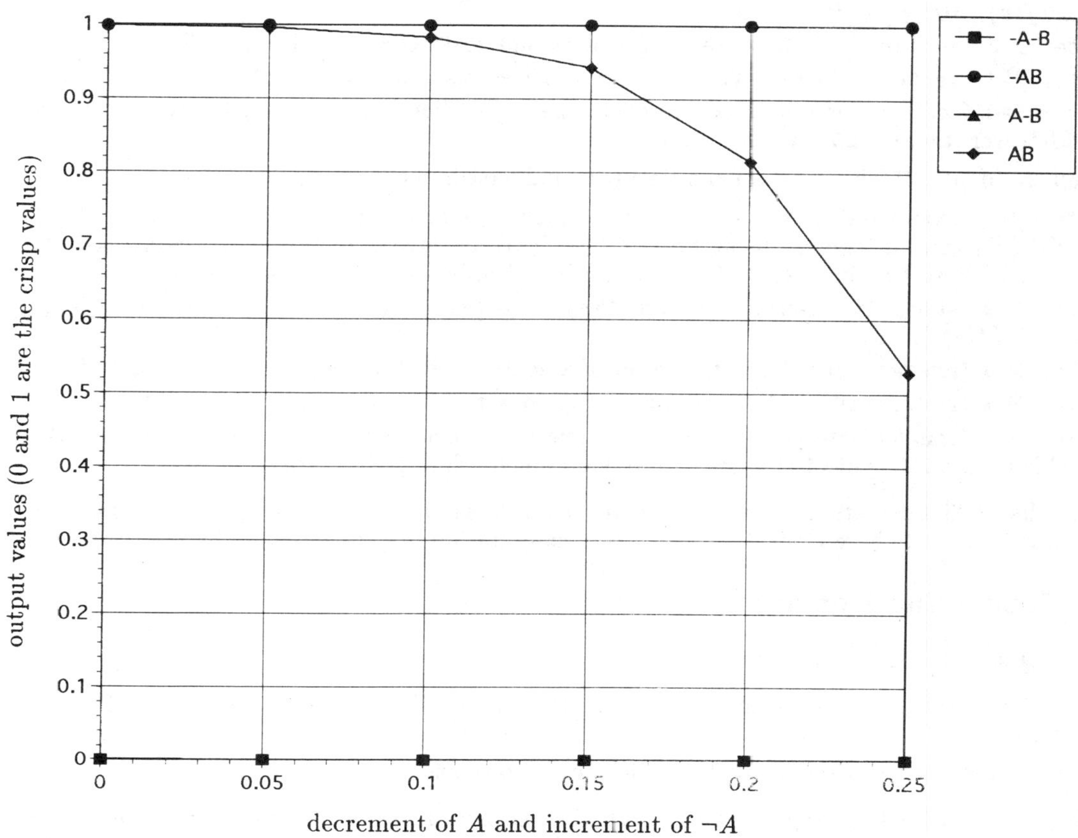

Fig. 3 Output values affected by decreasing feasibilities on premises.

4　Applications of the Trained Neural Network to Predicates

4.1　First order predicate logic on finite sets

Predicates have arguments such as $P(x)$ and $P(a)$. If $f(a)$ is allowed as an argument of P, then the following Herbrand universe is necessary:

$$\mathcal{H}_U = \{a, \; f(a), \; f(f(a)), \; f(f(f(a))), \; \ldots\}.$$

This corresponds to "a person a's farther's farther's farther's $\cdots$." Then, resolutions need to use the Herbrand base:

$$\mathcal{H}_B = \{P(a), \; P(f(a)), \; P(f(f(a))), \; P(f(f(f(a)))), \; \ldots\}.$$

Since $\mathcal{H}_B$ is an infinite set, truncation to a finite set is necessary. In the above example, there is only one constant "a". We can extend the problem class up to having a finite number of constants. The experiment in Section 3.3 shows that the neural networks can be trained and used for real domain conflict detection for the propositional logic. However, the predicate logic (the first order) is more powerful and is regarded as corresponding to "softwares." Thus, we have to check if the neural network can handle important properties of the predicate logic. In what follows, we check if the Herbrand base can be handled by the trained neural network.

4.2　Applications of trained neural networks to conflict detection for the Herbrand base

Instead of giving an abstract description of the conflict detection, we describe the total procedure by the following example. Although the description uses terminologies of the crisp case (integers and pure predicates), the domain is the real number as is in Section 3.3. The total process is illustrated by Fig. 4.

[Example of Herbrand Base Processing]

Step 1. (depth 1)

Step 1-1 (axiom set $\mathcal{W}$ and a theorem w; `herbrand.exe`): An axiom set of $\mathcal{W} = \{P(a), \neg P(x) \vee P(f(x))\}$ and a theorem to be proved $w = P(f(f(a)))$ are given. Here, "a" is the only constant.

Step 1-2 (`substitute.exe`): Pick up elements of the Herbrand universe to obtain $P(a), \neg P(a) \vee P(f(a)), \neg P(f(f(a)))$.

Step 1-3 (`assign.exe`): Rewrite the set of axioms to $\mathcal{W} \cup \neg w = \{A, \neg A \vee B, \neg C\}$.

Step 1-4 (`vectorize.exe`): Vectorize the above set as is in Section 3.3.

Step 1-5 (conflict detection; `resolution.exe`): Conflict detection similar to Section 3.3 is tried. However, there is no conflict detected.

Step 2. (depth 2) The depth of the Herbrand universe is increased by one.

Step 2-1 (axiom set $\mathcal{W}$ and a theorem w; `herbrand.exe`): An axiom set of $\mathcal{W} = \{P(a), \neg P(x) \vee P(f(x))\}$ and a theorem to be proved $P(f(f(a)))$ are given. In this step, we increase the depth by one. Pick up "a" and "$f(a)$" from the Herbrand universe as the constants.

Step 2-2 (`substitute.exe`): Obtain $P(a), \quad \neg P(a) \vee P(f(a)), \quad \neg P(f(a)) \vee P(f(f(a))),$ and $\neg P(f(f(a)))$.

Step 2-3 (`assign.exe`): Rewrite the set of axioms to $\mathcal{W} \cup \neg w = \{A, \neg A \vee B, \neg B \vee C, \neg C\}$.

Step 2-4 (`vectorize.exe`): Vectorize the above set as is in Section 3.3.

Step 2-5 (conflict detection; `resolution.exe`): Conflict detection similar to Section 3.3 is tried. In this case, an output of almost all zero is obtained. That is $P(f(f(a)))$ holds.

Thus, the conflict detection on the real domain was successful for the case including the Herbrand universe. It is worthy to note here again that the above computation uses real vectors by the neural network.

5   Concluding Remarks

Our target is itemized as follows:

1. To give a set of evidences and theories to connect two diagonal corners of Fig. 1: From raw data to symbols.

2. To embed a part of the external intelligence onto the the elements of Fig. 1.

This paper is a starting step around the top right corner of Fig. 1. As was observed in the experiments of the text, the total system is already a hybrid of neural networks and usual crisp symbol processing. A pattern-oriented approach starting from the bottom left corner is given in [1], [2]. Strategies of this paper, [1] and [2] will lead to the usage of patterns as guard parts of inferences. Methods and evidences to make these two opposite corners will appear succeedingly and connect them more smoothly.

Acknowledgments

The authors are grateful to Mr. M. Shibata for his data processing supports and discussions at the early stage of the study.

References

[1] Y. Matsuyama, "Learning algorithms associated with penalties and human intelligence: From performance improvement to animation coding," *Proc. Int. Symp. of Artificial Neural Networks*, Tainan, Dec. 14-16, 1994, pp. 547-560.

[2] Y. Matsuyama, "Morphing of self-organized patterns combined with human intelligence: Quantization applicable to intellectual multimedia processing," *Proc. RWCP: Beyond Divide and Conquer Strategy*, Tsukuba, Apr. 26-28, 1995, RWC TR-95010, pp. 162-171.

[3] D. E. Rumelhart, J. L. McClelland and the PDP Research Group, *Parallel Distributed Processing*, vol. 1, Boston: MIT Press, 1986.

[4] Real World Computing Partnership, *Information Integration Workshop'95: Beyond Divide and Conquer Strategy*, Tsukuba: RWCP, TR-95010, 1995.

[5] H. Tsukimoto, "A topological model for propositional logics," *J. IPSJ*, vol. 31, pp. 783-791, June 1990.

[6] H. Tsukimoto, "On continuously valued logical functions satisfying all axioms of classical logic," *Trans. IEICE*, vol. J77-D-I, pp. 247-252, Mar. 1994.

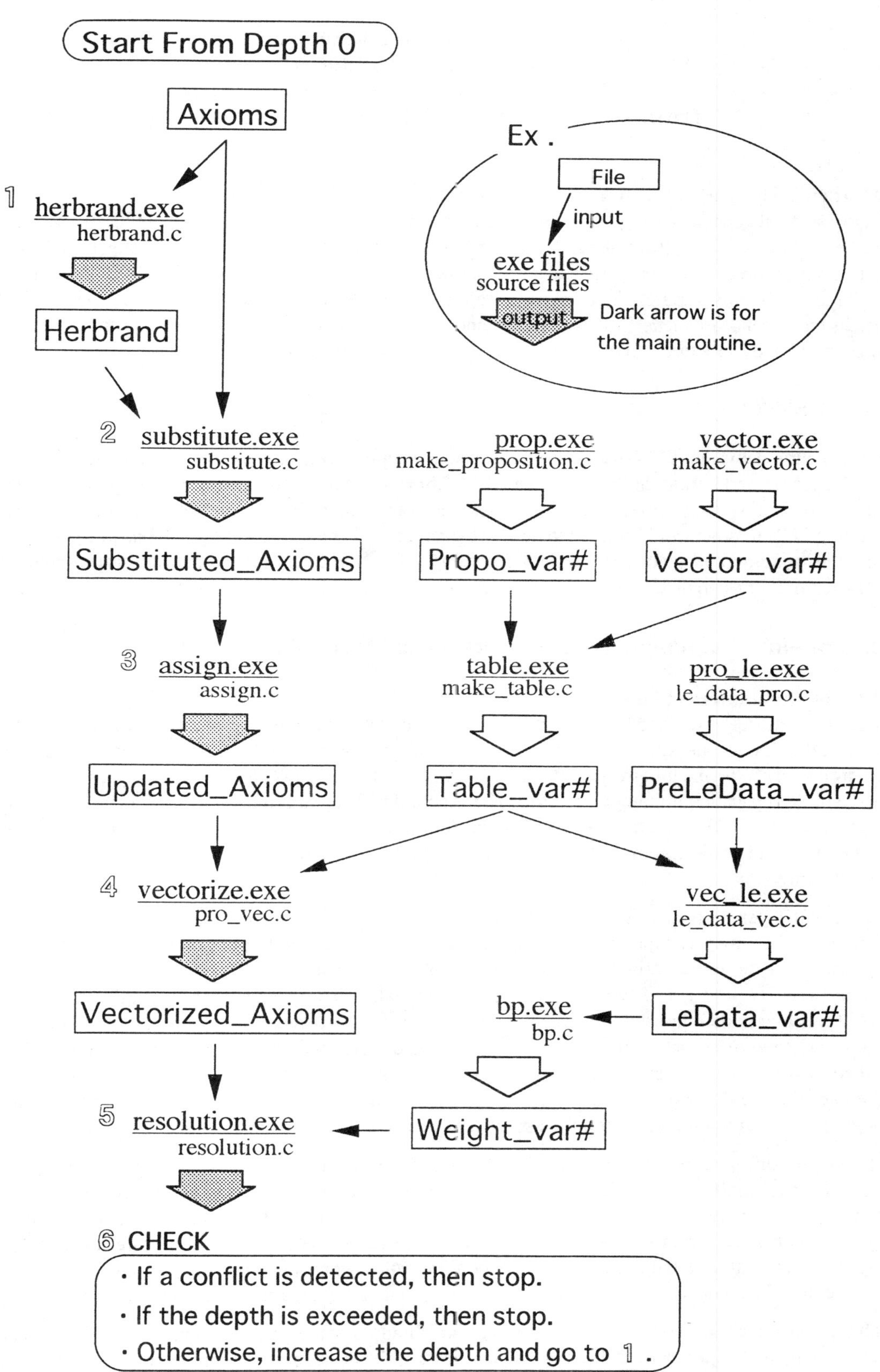

Fig. 4 Procedure of the hybrid computation using the neural network and symbolic processing.

Adaptive Learning in Modular Fuzzy Neural Networks

Nikola K Kasabov

Department of Information Science

University of Otago, P.O.Box 56, Dunedin, New Zealand

Phone: +64 3 479 8319, Fax: +64 3 479 8311, email: nkasabov@otago.ac.nz

Abstract   Fuzzy neural networks have features which make them useful for knowledge engineering, namely: fast learning; good generalisation; good explanation facilities in the form of fuzzy rules; abilities to accommodate both data and existing fuzzy knowledge about the problem under consideration. This paper investigates adaptive learning, rules extraction and reasoning for a particular model of fuzzy neural networks, called FuNN. A multimodular structure, which consists of several FuNNs, makes learning and rules extraction easier and more flexible. Experiments on two bench-mark data, a chaotic time-series data and a classification data, are used to illustrate the effectiveness of the suggested FuNN structure and the proposed adaptive learning strategies.

1. Introduction

Fuzzy neural networks (FNN) have been suggested and applied by several authors, among them Yamakawa and Uchino [1], Uchikawa and Furuhashi [2], and others [3,4,5,6]. These FNN have been successfully used for learning and tuning fuzzy rules and solving classification, prediction and control problems. Some recent publications suggest methods for training FNN in order to adjust them to new or dynamically changing data and situations [4,5]. This paper investigates some learning and adaptation strategies for one type of FNN, called FuNN, and illustrates them on a bench mark chaotic time-series prediction problem and on a static data classification problem.

2. Training Adaptation, Rules Extraction and Reasoning in FuNN

2.1. The Architecture of FuNN

The FuNN model is designed to facilitate learning from data, fuzzy rules extraction, fuzzy rules insertion, using both data and rules in one system, approximate reasoning, adaptation (adaptive learning in a dynamically changing environment), experimenting with different adaptation strategies. FuNN uses a multi-layer perceptron (MLP) network and a backpropagation training algorithm. The general FuNN architecture consists of 5 layers as shown in fig. 1(a). It is an adaptable FNN where the membership functions of the fuzzy predicates, as well as the fuzzy rules inserted before training or adaptation, may adapt and change according to new data. Here, a brief description of the FuNN architecture is given.

The input layer represents the input variables. The condition element layer represents triangular membership functions. The layer is expandable during the adaptation phase with more nodes representing more membership functions for the input variables. Simple activation functions are used for the nodes here, $a = 1 - |\text{Net}|$, where Net$= x.w + Bw$; $w=1/b$; $Bw=-c/b$; x is the input signal, c is the center of the triangle and b is its width. In the rule layer one node represents one fuzzy rule. The layer is expandable, ie. more nodes can be added to represent more existing rules or potential rules to be learned during training. The activation function is the logistic function with a variable gain coefficient g (a default value of 1 is used; values larger than 5 will make it close to the hard limited thresholding function). The semantic meaning of the activation of a node is that it represents the degree to which input data match the antecedent part of the corresponding rule.

In the action element layer a node represents a fuzzy label from the fuzzy quantisation space of an output variable, eg. small. medium, large. The activation of the node represents the degree to which this membership function is supported by all fuzzy rules together, so this is the level to which the membership function for this label is 'cut' according to the rules and current facts. The connections from the rule layer to the action element layer represent the certainties of the corresponding rules when inferring output values. The activation function for the nodes of this layer is the logistic function with a variable gain factor (as in the previous layer).

The output layer performs COG defuzzification. Singletons are used as membership functions for the output labels, which is equivalent to having the centres c only of triangular membership functions. Linear activation function is used. The singletons are attached as connection weights to the corresponding connections. For example, small, medium and large are represented as 0, 0.5 and 1.0 as connection weights from the output range of [0,1] if normalised outputs are considered. Non-normalised outputs can also be used.

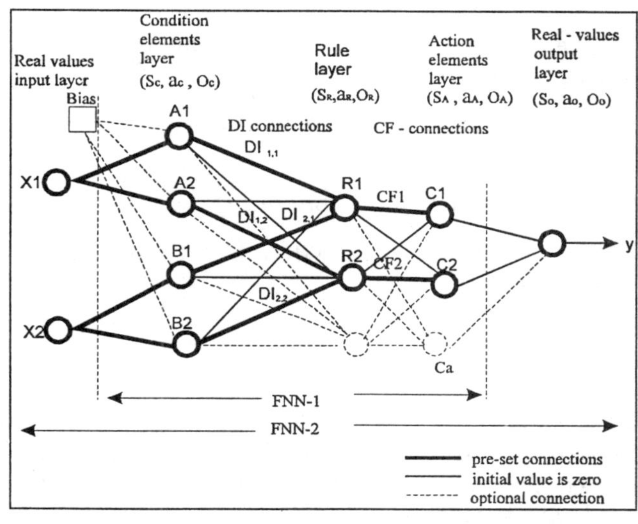

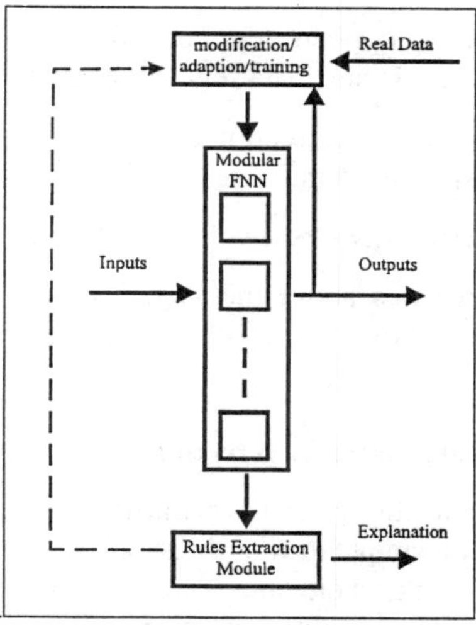

(a)   (b)

Fig. 1 (a) A FuNN structure for two initial fuzzy rules: R_1: IF x_1 is A_1 $(DI_{1,1})$ and x_2 is B_1 $(DI_{2,1})$ THEN y is C_1 (CF_1); R_2: IF x_1 is A_2 $(DI_{1,2})$ and x2 is B_2 $(DI_{2,2})$ THEN y is C_2 (CF_2), where DIs are degrees of importance attached to the condition elements and CFs are confidence factors attached to the consequent parts of the rules; **(b)** A general architecture of an adaptive intelligent multi-modular system

2.2. Training and adaptation in FuNN

The following is a procedure for training and adaptation in FuNN:

1. Initialisation: uniformly distributed triangular MF can be used as initial values for the input variables, and uniformly distributed singletons - as initial values for the output variables. If initial set of rules is available, it is used for initialisation of the FuNN structure as explained in [3].

2. Training the FuNN can be accomplished either for the inner three layers, in which case the system adapts its fuzzy rules but does not adapt the membership functions, or - for the five layers, in which case the system adapts both the rules and the membership functions. The connections in the fuzzification and defuzzification layers are "frozen" in the former case and they are subject to change in the latter case. The network is trained with the use of the method of training and zeroing based on the backpropagation algorithm [4,5].

The following is a typical procedure for training a FuNN on a given data set (or on consecutive segments of dynamically changing data). It uses a gradual change of the threshold for regular zeroing of small connection weights and a gradual change of the gain factor in the logistic activation function for the sake of better rules extraction. An exemplar procedure is given below:

(a) (a-0) set the gain factor g in the logistic activation function g=1; train the FuNN for a small number of epochs (eg. 50)

 (a-1) zero the small connection weights by using a threshold, say of 0.5; in this case all the positive and negative weights which modulus is smaller than 0.5 are zeroed.

 (a-2) increase g to g=2; train the FuNN

 (a-3) repeat (a-1) and (a-2) several times until satisfactory training and test error are obtained

(b) (b-0) mask the trained FuNN; masking is a procedure which keeps the significant connections to the rule layer in order to later on extract fuzzy rules such that one rule node represents one fuzzy rule and the connections only which contribute to this rule are kept in the masked FuNN structure. The rest of the connections are cut off or set to 0 and "frozen" for further change during further training.

 (b-1) extract initial set of fuzzy rules

 (b-2) train the FuNN further on

 (b-3) extract refined rules

After having applied steps (a) and (b) above these two steps are repeated for a new data segment. Depending on the size of this new data segment two general learning strategies can be distinguished:

- *aggressive* - a section of new data is used for further training and adaptation without using any of the old, previously used data;

- *conservative* - a new data is added to a portion of the old data and training is performed.

 In both cases above the system adapts its previous rules and membership functions to the new data. The strategies above are illustrated on two bench mark problems below.

2.3. Rules extraction from trained FuNN

Different methods for rules extraction are applicable on FuNN. One of them, called REFuNN, is published in [3,4]. It is based on a simple idea of thresholding connection weights according to a pre-set threshold. The weights, which are above the threshold are represented as condition, or action elements in the extracted fuzzy rules with their corresponding weights representing degrees of importance and confidence factors.

Here, another algorithm for interpreting a FuNN structure in terms of fuzzy rules is presented. Each rule node is represented as one fuzzy rule. The strongest connection from a condition element node to the rule node, along with the neighbouring condition element nodes, are represented in the corresponding rule. The connection weights of these connections are interpreted as degrees of importance attached to the corresponding condition elements. One rule has in general as many consequent elements as the number of the nodes in the action element layer, each action (class) inferred with a certainty degree (confidence factor) defined by the connection weights from this rule node to that class node. An example of a rule set extracted from a FuNN trained with the bench-mark gas-furnace data, as presented in [5], is given in fig. 2.

RULES

if <Input1 is A 2.88> and <Input1 is not C 5.69> and <Input2 is not A 1.57> and <Input2 is not B 1.66>

then <Output1 is not A 2.21> and <is not B 3.98> and <is C 2.08>

else

if <Input1 is not A 6.27909> and <Input1 is not B 2.75163> and <Input1 is D 1.13242> and <Input1 is E 2.51647> and <Input2 is A 2.85492> and <Input2 is not C 4.99544> and <Input2 is not D 7.41543> and <Input2 is E 3.13044>

then <Output1 is A 2.59163> and <is B 1.22> and <is not C 4.84>and<is not D 4.04>and <is E 2.36>

Fig. 2. Two of the eight fuzzy rules extracted from FuNN2 trained with the gas-furnace data when aggressive training was applied (see section 4)

2.4. Evidential Reasoning over extracted fuzzy rules from FuNNs

The following fuzzy reasoning method was used to test the validity of the extracted from FuNNs fuzzy rules:

Step 1 . Fuzzify input data using pre-defined membership functions for the input variables.

Step 2. Find the support from the input data to each of the antecedent parts of the fuzzy rules. Weighted sum is used, ie the membership degrees, to which the input values belong to the fuzzy labels, are multiplied to the degrees of importance attached to the condition elements in a rule Ri, and then added together for the whole antecedent part of the rule Ri producing a net support Neti. A term of support is added with a minus sign if the corresponding antecedent element takes part in the rule with a *not* connective (hedge) in front.

Step 3. Find the degree Di to which the whole antecedent part of a rule Ri is matched by the input data; a *matching function g* is used to calculate this value on the basis of the whole support Neti to the antecedent part of the rule,

$$Di= g \ (Neti) \ .$$

Step 4. Calculate the support Sj from all the fuzzy rules Ri (i=1,2,...,m) to a particular consequent element Cj (action element) which represents an output fuzzy value. The following formula is used for this purpose,

$$Sj=f \ (\Sigma \ Di.CFij), \ i=1,2,...,numb\_rules$$

where: f is an *inference function*, Di is the matching degree to which the antecedent part of a rule Ri is matched; CFij is the confidence with which rule Ri infers action (consequent) element Cj.

Step 5. Defuzzification; centre of gravity method (COG) or the mean-of- maxima are used here depending on the application.

The above described method depends on two types of functions, ie. the matching function and the inference function. Different functions may suit different applications. Hard-limiter function can be used in   classification tasks, but smooth functions would be more appropriate to use in time-series prediction tasks.

3. Adaptive Multi-Modular Systems

Here, multi-modular systems which consist of several FuNN modules, a rule extraction module and a module for adaptation, are discussed (see fig.1b). Such systems can efficiently be used for classification tasks when one FuNN is trained to classify examples of one particular class. This structure allows for fine individual tuning of each of the class FuNN units according to test results. Initially, all the modules are trained with identical data for a small number of epochs. After that, each of the units can be tuned using specific variant of the general learning and adaptation technique presented in section 2.

A classical example is the Iris classification problem. Here, the Iris data set is used to train three FuNNs, one for each of the classes Setosa, Versicolour and Virginica. Five triangular, uniformly distributed membership functions are used to represent each of the four input variables (sepal length, sepal width, petal length, petal width). Two membership functions (no and yes) are used to represent each of the output classes. Four hidden rule nodes are used in each of the FuNN structures which are randomly initialised in the beginning. After a brief training of all the FuNNs for 10 epochs, the Setosa's FuNN recognises all the examples, but the other two FuNNs misclassify examples. Only these two FuNNs are further trained with doubled number of examples of the misclassified classes for 50 more epochs. Then a perfect correct classification is achieved by using both the FuNNs and the extracted fuzzy rules from them with the use of the rules extraction method and the evidential reasoning method described in section 2.

 This is a simple example of efficient use of multimodular FuNN structures on static classification data. If the task is for the system to adapt to dynamically changing time-series data, more complicated variants of the learning and rules extraction techniques from section 2 can be applied as illustrated in the example given in the next section.

4. Time Series Prediction based on FuNN

Here the well-known bench mark gas-furnace chaotic time-series data set is used [6]. The data consists of 292 consecutive values of Methane(t-4) at a time moment (t-4) and the produced in a furnace CO_2(t-1) as input variables and the produced CO_2(t) at the moment (t) as an output variable. Five membership functions for the input and output variables are used here and 8 rule nodes in the rule layer of the FuNN architecture. The whole data set was divided into 4 consecutive sub-sets on equal time intervals. Two experiments with the use of the aggressive and the conservative training strategies are presented here. The following four steps were performed for adaptive aggressive training and testing of a FuNN:

 Step 1.gas-frn subset one; set g=0.5; train for 100 epochs; zero the weights with Thr=0.5; set g=1.0; train for 100 epochs; mask; set g=1; train for 100 epochs and obtain FuNN1; test it; extract rules: gas-frn.rul1, test rules

Step 2. gas-frn sub-set 2: set g=0.5; train for 100 epochs; zero the weights with Thr=0.5; set g=1.0; train for 100 epochs; zero the weights with Thr=1.0 and obtain FuNN2; test it; extract rules: gas-frn.rul2, test rules

Step 3. Set all the weights that have been "frozen" in FuNN2 to zero and allow them to change during training; use gas-frn third sub-set: g=0.5; train for 100 epochs; zero the weights with Thr=0.5; g=1.0; train for 100 epochs; mask; set g=1.0; train for 100 epochs and obtain the FuNN3; test it; extract rules: gas-frn.rul3, test rules

Step 4. data-set used: gas-frn sub-set 4: g=0.5; train for 100 epochs; zero the weights with Thr=0.5; set g=1.0; train for 100 epochs; zero the weights with Thr=1.0 and obtain FuNN4; test it; extract rules: gas-frn.rul4, and test them.

The test results of the *aggressively* trained FuNN on consecutive sub-sets of the time series data and the test results for the correspondingly extracted fuzzy rules with the evidential reasoning method, are given in fig.3. The FuNN obviously "forgets" about previously used time-series data patterns, for example section t=43 to t=47. This is because this pattern of data is in contrast to new data patterns in sections t=115-119; t=202-206 and t=232-240. The more the FuNN adapts to new data, the better it generalises over the next segments, but the more it forgets about the "strange" data patterns seen in the past (t=43-47). The test results from the fuzzy rules are very similar to those of the corresponding FuNNs

A *conservative* training on the same data with the use of one previous data segment to which the new one is added before the next training is performed, shows an expected result that the FuNN does not forget much about the previous patterns in data even if they are in conflict with the new ones. In this case a longer term generalisation may not be as good as in the case of aggressive training.

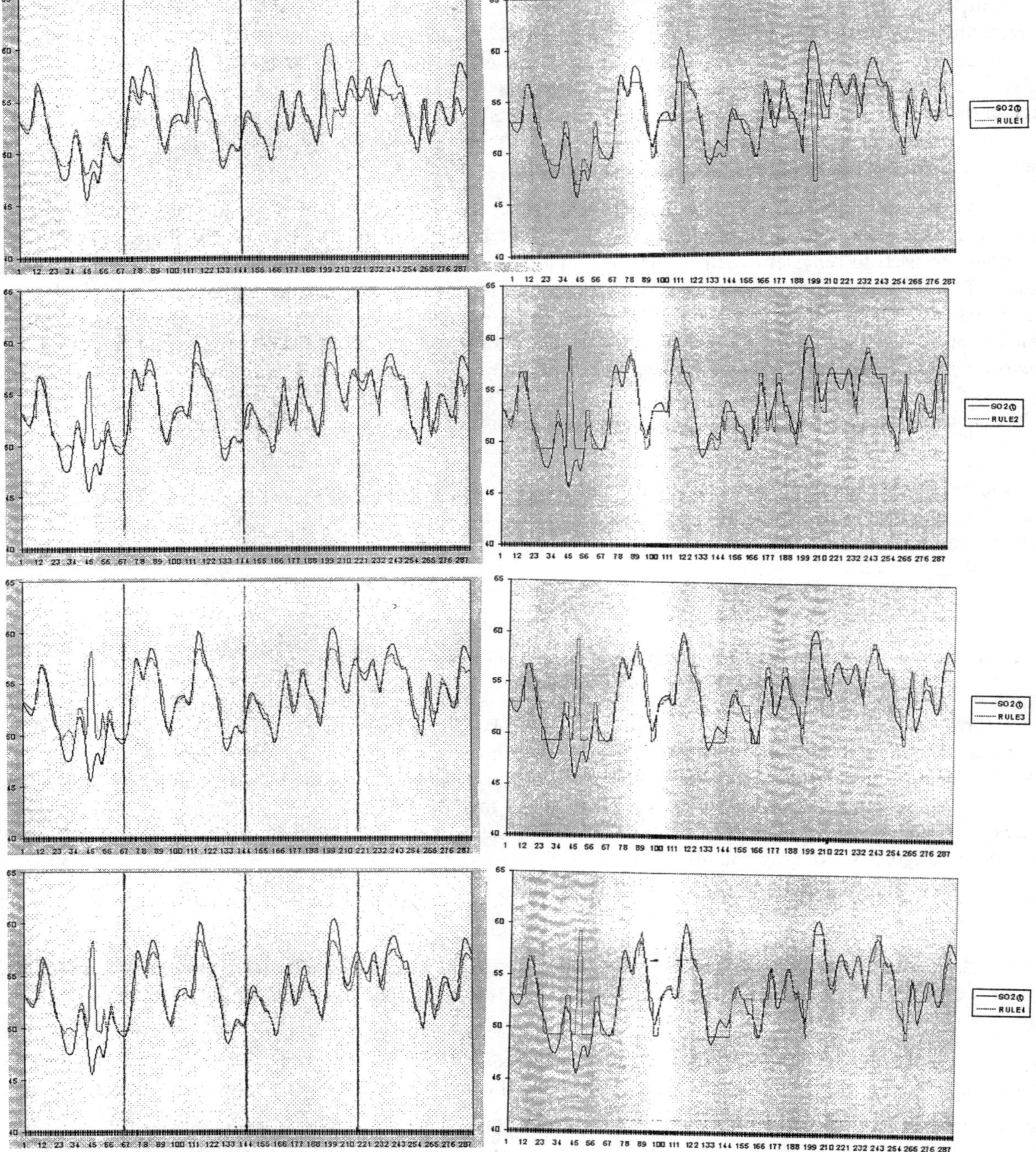

Fig.3. Test results from testing FuNNs, adaptively trained with the use of the *aggressive* strategy on the gas-furnace data, shown on the left side, and testing the corresponding extracted rules with the use of the evidential reasoning, results shown on the right side: (a) FuNN1; (b) FuNN2; (c) FuNN3 and (d) FuNN4,

Fig.4 shows experimental results of using a *conservative* adaptive learning strategy. The steps taken are similar to steps 1 and 2 above, but here all the cut-off connections during masking of the FuNN1 were recovered with initial weights of 0 and were allowed to change during the training in step 2. The first and the second data segments are used to train the FuNN2 network.

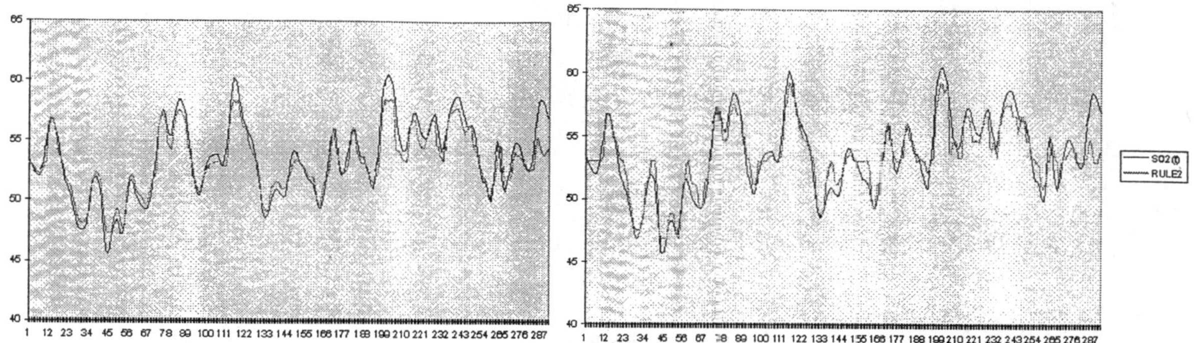

Fig 4. Test results from the FuNN2 trained on the gas-furnace data (the first two sub-sections) with the use of the conservative strategy (shown on the left side) and the test results from the evidential reasoning over the extracted fuzzy rules (on the right side).

5. Conclusions

The introduced here adaptive learning algorithm along with the rules extraction technique and evidential reasoning method for a particular structure of fuzzy neural network, called FuNN, show that this is a promising approach to building adaptive intelligent information processing systems. More research has to be done for developing algorithms for on-line decision about which strategy should be used at each of the training steps of the FuNN and whether there is a need of new nodes in the membership layers and rule layers. Genetic algorithms are suitable techniques to be employed for this purpose.

Acknowledgment
 Some of the experiments used as illustrations in this paper, were done by Feng Zhang. I thank Martin Purvis and Andrew Gray for the fruitful discussions during the preparation of the paper.

References
[1] T.Yamakawa, H.Kusanagi, E.Uchino and T.Miki, "A new Effective Algorithm for Neo Fuzzy Neuron Model", in: Proceedings of Fifth IFSA World Congress, (1993) 1017-1020.
[2] T.Hashiyama, T.Furuhashi, Y.Uchikawa, "A Decision Making Model Using a Fuzzy Neural Network", in: Proceedings of the 2nd International Conference on Fuzzy Logic & Neural Networks, Iizuka, Japan, (1992) 1057-1060.
[3] N. Kasabov, "Learning fuzzy rules and approximate reasoning in neuro-fuzzy hybrid systems", Fuzzy Sets and Systems,1995, Special Issue edited by N.Kasabov and T.Yamakawa
[4] N. Kasabov, Neural Networks, Fuzzy Systems and Knowledge Engineering, The MIT Pres, CA, MA, 1996
[5] N.Kasabov, "Investigating the adaptation and forgetting in fuzzy neural networks by using the method of training and zeroing", in: Proceedings of the International Conference on Neural Networks ICNN'96, IEEE Press, Washington DC, June 3-6, 1996
[6] W. Hauptmann, K. Heesche, A Neural Net Topology for Bidirectional Fuzzy-Neuro Transformation, in: Proceedings of the FUZZ-IEEE/IFES, Yokohama, Japan, (IEEE, 1995), 1511-1518.

Recognition–Based Extraction of Characters in Printed Documents

Jin Hak Bae, Min Ho Park and Hang Joon Kim

Dept. of Computer Engineering, Kyung–Pook National Univ.

Taegu, 702–701 Korea

E-mail : kimhj@bh.kyungpook.ac.kr

Abstract   In this paper, we propose a character extraction method from documents written in both Hangul and Alphanumeric characters. To segment touching characters, character segmentation and recognition are done in parallel. Character segmenter is implemented by neural network. As the neural network is trained for many kinds of touching characters in documents, it can segment all touching characters by itself. We use recognizer to test whether the touching character is correctly segmented or not. Experimental result shows that the proposed method achieves high segmentation rate in documents written in both Hangul and Alphanumeric characters.

1. Introduction

To deal with information conveniently, people frequently use computer systems. However, information is mostly saved on papers in the form of books, newspapers and magazines. The manual keying is time consuming and error prone. Today, character recognition systems facilitate the transfer of information into computer systems without intensive manual keying.

It is not much difficult to make a system which recognizes well–formed and well–spaced printed texts. If there are many touching characters in document, it is difficult to segment these touching characters. In these documents, a great part of recognition errors is due to segmentation errors.

To segment touching characters correctly and to make a practical recognition system, some investigators have attempted to develop segmentation techniques[1-4,6,7]. These techniques segment touching characters before recognition. Once the touching character is incorrectly segmented, the character recognizer cannot recognize these characters and this may affect the next characters.

In this paper, we propose a method of character extraction from a document in which both Hangul and Alphanumeric characters are written. We do character segmentation and recognition in parallel. Several candidate cutting points are generated from the neural network based segmenter, then the character recognizer recognizes the character cut at the candidate cutting point to test whether the candidate is correct or not. Fig. 1 shows the flowchart of the proposed system.

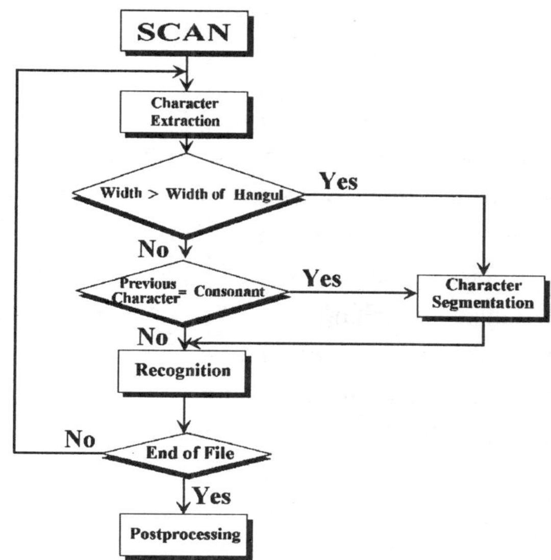

Fig. 1   Flowchart of Character extraction and recognition system

2. Touching types

There are many kinds of touches in documents written in both Hangul and Alphanumeric characters. In this paper, we defined 11 touching types. Fig. 2 shows touching types which are frequently seen in documents. Among them, (h),(i),(k) are touching types those can be seen in document written in both Hangul and Alphanumeric character.

Fig. 2   11 Touching types

In general, the width of Alphanumeric character is as half as that of Hangul. If a character width is bigger than the width of normal Hangul character, we know that character touch occurred. But type (e),(i),(j),(k) have the same width with normal Hangul character though these are touching characters. In type (b), because the character is divided into two components, the width of each components is similar to that of Alphanumeric character. In this paper, we treat these divided components and Alphanumeric characters in the same manner.

3. Character Segmentation

3.1 Structure of the multi-layer perceptron

Fig. 3 shows the structure of the multi-layer perceptron. It has 72 input nodes, 70 hidden nodes and 60 output nodes. It is fully-connected between input layer and hidden layer and between hidden layer and output layer. We used the backpropagation learning algorithm. The input to the network is 72-order mesh vector extracted from 30*60 normalized character image. The example of normalized touching character images is shown in Fig. 4. The number of pixels in each 5*5 local window is counted and the 72 integer values are obtained. The resulting 25 intensities are normalized to the range of [0.0,1.0]. A desired cutting point is determined manually and saved behind the 72-order mesh vector.

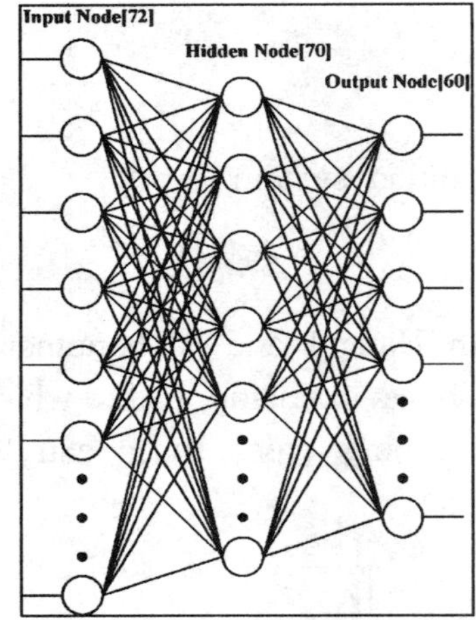

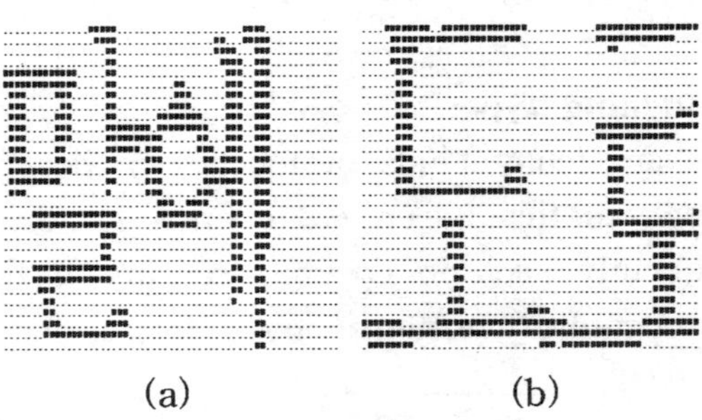

Fig. 3   Structure of the multi-layer perceptron   Fig. 4   Normalized touching character image

3.2 Character Segmentation

If the width of the character is bigger than that of normal Hangul character, or if previous character is the consonant and the width of this character is equal to that of normal Hangul character, it is a touching character. When a touching character is detected, we segment it using neural network. Fig. 5 shows touching character images and values of neural output. 60 output nodes of neural network have values within the range of [0,1]. In Fig. 5 the height of each line represents the output value. We keep selecting the node number with the highest output value as a cutting point until segmented characters are recognized. Fig. 6 shows the example of segmented images which are cut at the candidate cutting points. As the character images at the first candidate cutting point are not recognized and the images at the second are correctly recognized, we select the second candidate cutting point as a correct one in the example.

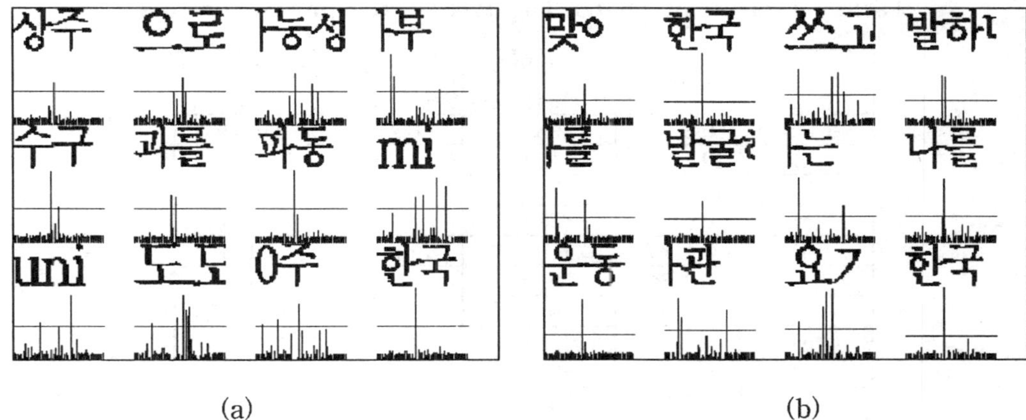

(a)   (b)

Fig. 5   Touching character images and neural output

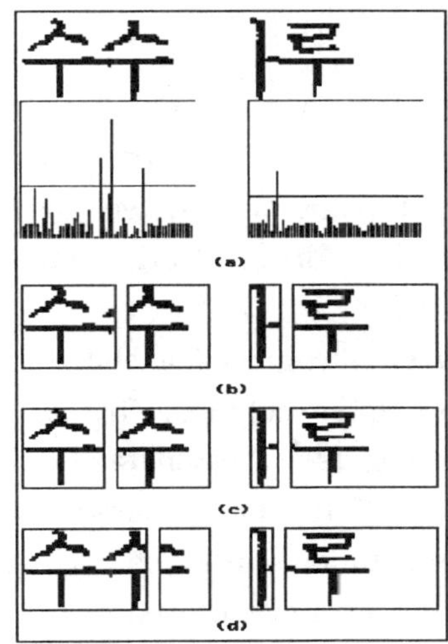

Fig. 6   Segmented images which are cut at the candidate cutting points

4. The experimental result and analysis.

The system is implemented in C language on PC. 30 pages of document are scanned using HP flatbed scanner at 300dpi. We used 20 pages for training of the character segmentation neural network. The number of training pattern was 2045. The rest 10 pages were used for testing. Documents used in this experiment contain about 20% touching characters. It is assumed that a line of text has already been extracted. The segmentation accuracy is 92.2% for touching characters and 99.2% for all characters in documents. When Hangul and Hangul characters are touched, it is segmented with high accuracy, but Alphanumeric and Hangul characters are touched, it is segmented with lower accuracy than that of between Hangul characters. I think it is caused by insufficient number of training patterns when compared with the number of touching characters between Hangul characters.

Table 1 Proportions of touching types and segmentation rate

	Proportion	The number of characters	Correctly Segmented	Segmentation rate
No touch	66.8 %	6985	6985	100 %
(a)	10.7 %	1120	1113	99.4 %
(b)	12.7 %	1323	1323	100 %
(c)	4.6 %	480	469	97.7 %
(d)	1.1 %	119	101	84.9 %
(e)	0.3 %	35	31	88.6 %
(f)	0.2 %	20	17	85.0 %
(g)	1.5 %	154	131	85.1 %
(h)	0.4 %	38	34	89.5 %
(i)	0.1 %	14	10	71.4 %
(j)	1.3 %	141	135	95.7 %
(k)	0.3 %	29	22	75.7 %
Total	100 %	10458	10371	99.2 %

5. Conclusion

In this paper, we proposed a method which extracts characters from document in which both Hangul and Alphanumeric characters are written. To test the cutting point whether the touching character is cut at the right point or not, we use character recognizer. This method enables us to segment touch between Alphanumeric and Hangul character as well as the touch between two Hangul characters.

We used a Hangul recognizer which recognizes a character by using the information of the shape of strokes and positional relationship between strokes, and has about 95% of recognition rate. So, the recognizer cannot recognize the character if the touching character is not segmented exactly. As the segmenter of touching characters uses the result of recognizer, the performance of the character segmentation is much influenced by the performance of the character recognizer. Fig. 7 shows the example of segmentation errors.

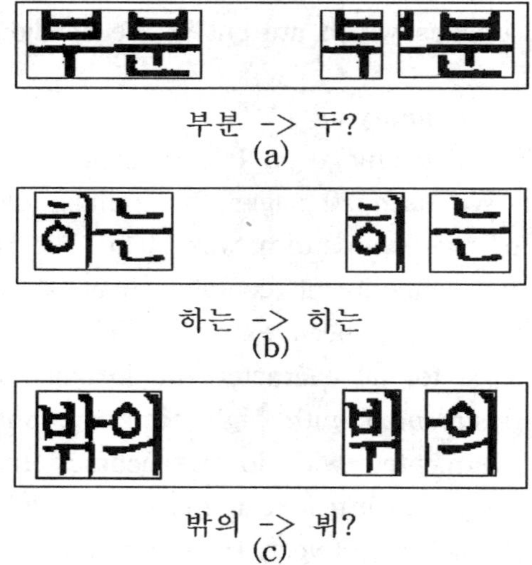

Fig. 7 Example of segmentation errors

References

[1]Friedrich M. Wahl, Kwan Y. Wong and Richard G. Casey, Block Segmentation and Text Extraction in Mixed Text/Image Documents, Computer Graphics and Image Processing, Vol. 20, pp. 375-390, 1982.

[2]J.C.Namkung, H.B.Ryou, Y.Namkung, A Study on the Korean Character Segmentation and Picture Extraction from a Document, KITE, Vol.25, No.9, pp. 1091-1100, 1988.

[3]I.D.Lee, O.S.Kwon, T.K.Kim, An Algorithm for Extraction of Block Images in a Document, KISS, Vol.18, No.2, pp.218-226, 1991.

[4]M.W.Jang, D.N.Chun and H.S.yang, Segmentation and Recognition of Document Images based on Connected Component, KITE, Vol.20, No.12, pp. 1741-1751, 1993.

[5]K.C.Kim and S.W.Lee, A Knowledge-Based System for Address Block Location on Envelop Images, proc. of KITE, Vol.20, No.1, pp. 183-186, 1993.

[6]J.I.Doh, A Study on the Letter Segmentation of Hangul Characters for Printed Hangul Character Recognition, proc. of KITE, Vol.17, No.2, pp. 175-178, 1990.

[7]E.J.Kim and T.K.Kim, A Study on the Extraction of Characters for Printed Documents Recognition, 2nd Workshop of Character Recognition, pp. 171-179, 1994.

INTERACTIVE CONNECTIONIST SYSTEM
FOR RHYTMIC PREDICTION

Alejandro Pazos. Ph. D. email: *ciapazos@udc.es*
J. J. Romero-Cardalda. Post-graduate student. email: jj@udc.es
Antonino Santos del Riego. Post-graduate student. email: nino@udc.es
Julián Dorado. Post-gradute student. email: julian@udc.es

Laboratory for Artificial Neural Networks and Adaptative Systems
Department of Computing. School of Computer Science. University of A Coruña.
15071 A Coruña. Spain.

ABSTRACT: As M. Minsky states, "clearly, people use music for directing their mental activities. After all, that's what it means when we speak of music as stimuling, or as soothing, as like an opiate for relieving pain or anxiety. Or encouraging us to march and fight, or to sorrow at a funeral" [1]. The Interactive Connectionist System for Rhytmic Prediction (ICSRP from here on) fits into the domain of musical computer science. This system has a double use: on the one hand, it is a powerful, practical tool for generating musical phrases in real time and, on the other hand, it makes up a novel connectionist system for rhythmic prediction. The first module, the phrase generator, is in charge of generating melodies in real time by using two methods: the arpeggiator and the harmonizer. The second module takes care of the perception and subsequent prediction of tempo (rhythm) of a musical piece though a connectionist system.

INTRODUCTION

Ever since computer science made its first attack upon the music world, the idea underway has been to incorporate computers into close collaboration with musicians in the performance of musical works [2]. One of the main problems with such collaboration is that of rhythmic synchronization. Traditionally, this problem was solved by giving the computer a superior role, forcing the musician to submit himself to a rhythmic "tyranny". For this reason, one of the most important areas of research in applying Artificial Intelligence (AI) to music, is that of prediction and perception of rhythm. In this article, we present a new view by using a connectionist system to overcome many of the limitations which are present in other approaches, those of AI as well as conventional computer science, which do not have learning capacity or which do not have learning capacity or which require an explicit representation of knowledge in order to acquire learning capacity.

In this investigation, an extensive study has been made on modelization of the inputs and outputs used in the training of the Artificial Neural Network (ANN), establishing two possible hypothesis at the time of selecting the examples to be used:

- Absolute magnitudes (temporal distance)
- Relative magnitudes (accelerations and decelerations)

The ANN developed is a feed-forward type; it uses second-type relative inputs (at float points), and presents 7, 5 and 1 processing elements at its input, hidden and output layers, respectively.

The system developed allows for its use in real time (its main application), as well as a high level of specialization when adjusting itself to the parameters which are characteristic of the performance being given by the musicians [3].

In order to illustrate the performance of the ANN, we developed a system, in MOXC [4], which generates musical phrases from interaction with the musician.

JUSTIFICATION OF THE APPLICATION OF ARTIFICIAL NEURAL NETWORKS TO THE FIELD OF RHYTHMIC PERCEPTION AND PREDICTION

To provide computer support to the generation of training files and to the subsequent testing of the ANN´s which have been developed, we have implemented an interactive, musical phrase-generating system.

The world of rhythmic perception and prediction (and music in general) is subject to three big problems:

1. Limitations in the use of prediction systems in real time. This is due to the impossibility of using backtracking, since the execution time of the routines involved is not predictable [5]. Neither can we apply other methods, such as statistics, since the response time would be too long.
2. There is no clear representation of the information (communication is carried out by way of musical performances). "Communication between musicians, verbal as well as musical, assumes certain shared concepts and experiences. Observing, for example, a rehearsal of chamber music, or a piano lesson, one might her a comment such as, "Broaden the end of the phrase". Interpreting that instruction engages a compless collection of listening and performing skills, which must be related to each other in a reasonably precise way. The neccesary relations are rarely described verbally beyond the use of just such admonitions; if a student were to share the phrase poorly, a typical next response for the teacher would be simply to play or sing it" [6]. The rhythm is the most irrational and subjective part of music, therefore, it is where this phenomenon can be most widely observed.
3. High rate of error in data, making it difficult to work with non-connectionist systems.

As a result, the ANN application is justifiable, solving these three problems, since:

1. The response time of execution satisfies the requirements of this type of system in real time.
2. Explicit expert knowledge is not necessary nor is it availabe. The system works from examples.
3. ANN´s can work with partially incomplete informaticn and/or errors or noise.

Another one of the problems that arise with applications of this kind is that of specialization. Each musician has his own appreciation of rhythm, therefore, it is necessary to adapt the system to each particular musician. This problem, along with the ones already mentioned, justifies the use of AI methods and techniques, such as the ones which we present here.

MODEL OF THE PROPOSED ANN

One of the most important decisions that had to be made was that concerning modelization of the inputs and outputs of the ANN. With respect to modelization of the input patterns, it was decided to use, as had been mentioned, relative magnitudes (accelerations and decelerations of rhythm). We rejected the option of using absolute magnitudes in the inputs, among other things, because of their execution limitations in real time and for the need of independent learning of global 'tempo'.

The ANN analizes a temporal window which indicates the latest accelerations and decelerations produced throughout the performance of the music. The final objective of the connectionist system is to predict, based on these data, the next acceleration/deceleration. To do this, the output of the ANN consists of single processing unit which represents the aforementioned value. We determine the size of the temporal windows, which is used as input, experimentally, with seven accelerations/cecelerations, each one of them represented by a processing element in the input layer of the ANN.

$$I_{\substack{7 \\ i=1}} = \frac{t_{i_t} - t_{i_{t-1}}}{t_{i_{t-1}}}$$

where I_i is the input for the processing element

t_{i_t} is the inter-onset interval

As far as the range of variation used in the input data, we obtained, by way of experimentation, a margin of ± 20% between every two samples. These values normalized within the range between -1, +1 for its use in the training phase of the ANN. The format obtained for the output of the ANN was the same as that of the input.

Thus, once all decisions were made concerning the characteristics of the input and output of the ANN, we tried out various architectures, and found the best of those tried to be the one which contained 7, 5 and 1 processing elements [7] in the input layer, the hidden layer and the output layer, respectively (figure 1) [8].

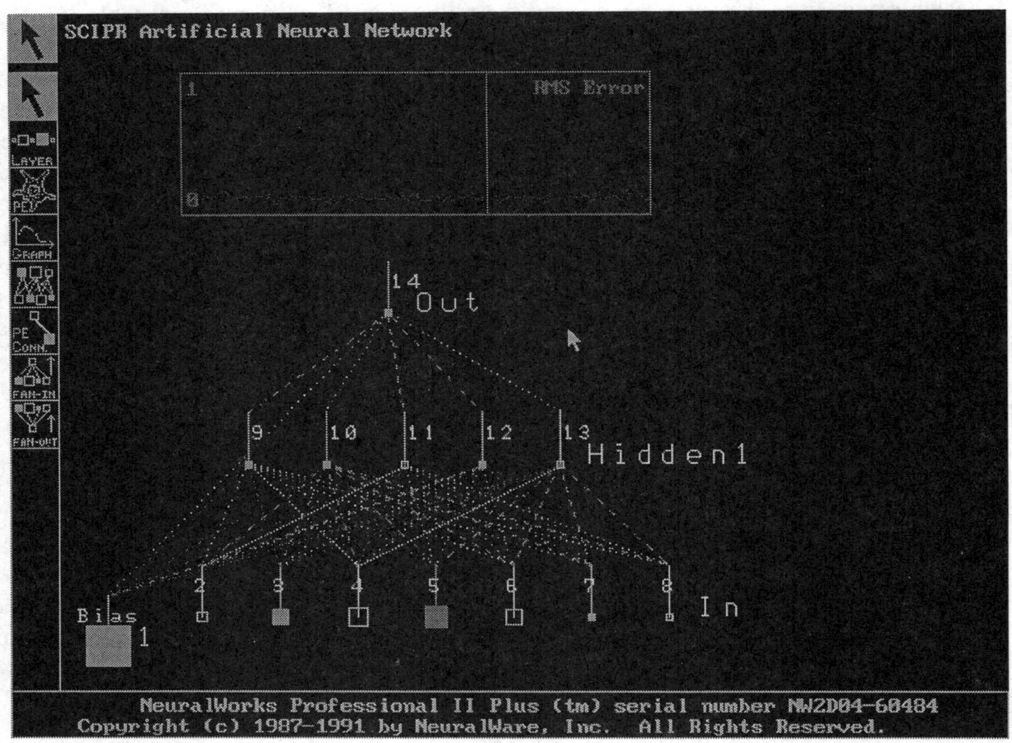

Figure 1.- ICSRP Artificial Neural Network.

As far as choosing the transfer function, we tested the sigmoid and the hyperbolic tangent [9]. The first kept obtaining a constant mean value and did not adapt to the variations of the training set. For this reason, we opted for the second choice, which adapted much better to the changes which came about in the input. This probably occurs from dealing with data which could take on positive or negative values, which better adapt to the use of the hyperbolic tangent function in the processing elements.

The ANN of the ICSRP is multilayer with forward feeding, and the interconnection between the processing elements is complete. The training file is made up of 330 patterns, which have been obtained the capture of the pulsations exerted upon a pedal during the accompaniment of a musician.

For this, a previously designed interactive system is used to carry out this capture and to do a test afterwards [3].

On the other hand, we used for the learning process the Delta Normal rule with an epoch of 16. The hardware platform used was a PC-486 at 66 Mhz, taking 2 minutes to obtain a convergence criteria of 0.065. Throughtout the training period, 57705 patterns were presented to the ANN.

CONCLUSIONS

The system developed here allows us to predict the time intervals of musical rhythm with the aim of adapting the system to the musician during the performance of a theme.

The ANN´s proved to be efficient at the task which they intended to execute, generation of musical phrases in real time and prediction of rhythm. This is deduced from the degree of convergence obtained, 0.065, and from we were able to verify, experimentally, on how the ANN, once trained, tends to maintain a basic rhythm without permitting brusque fluctuations. The functional character of the ANN depends, in great measure, on the musician who´s recorded the rehearsal and on the diverse conditions in which the recording has been made (method and pulsation). Thus, the training is improved if the recording is made in a "conditioned" manner, that is, with a reference (metronome, another musician, etc)

DISCUSSION AND FUTURE WORKS

Once the effectivity of the ANN´s in this domain has been verified, we can study the possiblity of including other parameters in the training process (tonal information, intensity of pulsations, harmony, etc.) in order to improve the two objectives previously mentioned (generation of musical phrases in real time and prediction of rhythm; to try to study the human perception of rhythm).

The search for a better prediction will still be an open field of exploration. Moreover, introducing a preprocessing of the data which is entered into the ANN, with some type of filtering, or the use of an ANN with non-supervised learning as a previous stage to using the predictor ANN, are paths which are still unexplored and can lead us to a better solution.

ACKNOWLEDGEMENTS

This work has been supported in part by the "Xunta de Galicia" (Spanish Goverment) under project XUGA-10501B95. We would like to thank Miss Lisa Marie Shectman for her active participation in the translation of this paper.

REFERENCES

[1].- M. Balaban, K. Ebciagly & O. Laske. "Understanding Music with AI. Perspectives on Music Cognition. Foreword: A Conversation with Marvin Misky". The AAAI Press/Mit Press. Cambridge, 1992.

[2].- N. P. Todd. "A Model of Expresive Timing in Tonal Music". Music Perception 3 (1), 1985.

[3].- J. J. Romero Cardalda. "Generador Interactivo de Frases Musicales". Trabajo fin de Diplomatura. Dep Computación. Fac Informática. Univ. da Coruña, 1996.

[4].- Dannenberg, B. Roger. "The CMU MIDI Toolkit". (ftp://ftp.g.gp.cs.cmu.edu/usrg1/rbd/public/cmt), 1993.

[5].- P. Desain & H. Honing. "Quantization of Musical Time A Connectionist Approach". Computer Music Journal 13 (3), 1991.

[6].- R. Rowe. "Interactive Music Systems: Machine listening and composing". The MIT Press. Cambridge, 1993.

[7].- A. Pazos. y col. "Estructura, dinámica y aplicaciones de la Redes de Neuronas Artificiales". Ed. Centro de Estudios Ramón Areces, S.A., 1991.

[8].- NeuralWare. "NeuralWorks Professional II/Plus and NeuralWorks Explorer", 1991.

[9].- D. E. Rumelhart & J. L. McClelland. "Parallel Distributed Processing". Foundations, Cambridge MA. MIT Press. Vol.1, 1986.

Three Valued Logic Neural Network[*]

Wang Guoyin[+], Shi Hongbao[++]

[+] Department of Computer
Chongqing University of Posts & Telecommunications
Huangjiaoya, Nanan, Chongqing, P.R.China, 630065
[++] Department of Computer
Shanghai Tiedao University
Shanghai, P.R.China, 200333

Abstract

The problem of expressing and dealing with logic knowledge using neural network is discussed. A novel neuron model (three valued logic neuron, or TLN) is presented. It can express three valued logic knowledge. A multi-layer neural network (TLNN) made up of TLNs can be used as a three valued logic inference system. TLNN is a base for expressing logic knowledge using neural network.
Keywords: Neural Network, Neuron, Logic Inference, Knowledge Representation

1   Introduction

Neural network is a new method and tool for storing and dealing with information. It simulates the organization style of human nervous system and it is made up of many simple neurons that are linked to each other. It has many good characteristics such as large scale, parallel, robust, self-organization and self-learning. It is applied in such domains as automatic control, fuzzy processing, pattern recognition, knowledge acquisition & representation, etc.

Many scholars expect to implement logic symbol processing using neural network, and present some plots and methods such as extracting rules from neural network[1,2] and implementation of logic neural network[3]. They all have the same drawback of not being able to express and deal with uncertain or unknown cases in logic inference. They can only be applied in two valued logic.

Fuzzy logic is very useful in many areas. There are also some scholars working to implement fuzzy inference systems (FIS) with neural network. P.Magrez and A. Rousseau interpreted the symbolic meaning of output value of a back-propagation neural network based on possibility theory defined by Zadeh[5,6]. Jyh-Shing Roger Jang presented an adaptive-network-based fuzzy inference system (ANFIS)[7,8]. Yoichi Hayashi proved that any fuzzy expert system employing one block of rules can be approximated by a neural network and any neural network (feed forward, multi-layer) can be approximated by a fuzzy expert system[9]. So, a neural network can not only be used in exact logic but also be used in fuzzy logic successfully.

Three valued logic is another useful logic. It can deal with uncertain and unknown cases that often happens in logic problems and is very hard to be dealt with by the classical logic. There are few scholars studding the problem of three valued logic neural network until now. Chan S.C. has studied this problem and presented a neural logic network' model(NLN)[10]. Each neuron in a NLN of Chan S.C. is not a neuron but a compressed expression of a multi-layer perceptron based neural network[11]. So, the problem of three valued logic neural network is still unresolved. In this paper, a novel neuron model (three valued logic neuron, or TLN) is presented to deal with three valued logic problems. Multi-layer neural network made up of TLNs (TLNN) can be used to solve any three valued logic problem.

In section 2, we will discuss the limitation of perceptron in logic expressing and processing. In section 3, we will present the model of three valued logic neuron(TLN). In section 4, we will discuss how to represent and implement three valued logics with TLN. In section 5, we will draw some conclusion about TLN and TLNN.

2   Limitation of perceptron in logic expressing and processing

Perceptron model, which is shown in fig.1, was presented by Rosenblatt in 1957 and it has been used in many domains successfully. Its internal activation function $f(\alpha)$ can be any of hard limiting activation function, threshold logic activation function and sigmoid activation function. It can express and deal with two valued

[*] This project is supported by N.S.F. of P.R.China.

logic very well. Now, let's analyze whether it can be used to deal with three valued logic problems.

The true value table of a three valued two element logic expression is shown in table 1.

Generally speaking, a three valued n element logic expression can be expressed by the following three formulas:

$$Y = \overline{X} : Y = \begin{cases} -1, X = 1 \\ 0, X = 0 \\ 1, X = -1 \end{cases} \tag{2.1}$$

$$Y = \overset{n}{\underset{i=1}{\wedge}} (X_i) : Y = \overset{n}{\underset{i=1}{Min}} (X_i) \tag{2.2}$$

$$Y = \overset{n}{\underset{i=1}{\vee}} (X_i) : Y = \overset{n}{\underset{i=1}{Max}} (X_i) \tag{2.3}$$

One (1) means true while minus one (-1) means fault and zero (0) means unknown (uncertain) in this paper. Because all inputs (premises) to a perceptron are of the same importance (equal effect) to its output (conclusion), the following stipulations might as well be made for a perceptron:

$$|W_1| = |W_2| = \cdots = |W_n| = W \tag{2.4}$$

where, $W>0$. Now, let's discuss its logic characteristics.

Suppose a perceptron is used to express the following three valued logic expressions:

$$Y = X_1 \wedge X_2 \wedge \cdots \wedge X_n \tag{2.5}$$

If there are p unknown premises and q fault premises, the perceptron will output

$$Y = f(nw - 2qw - pw) \tag{2.6}$$

where, f is the internal activation function of a perceptron.

The following two formulas can be derived from (2.2) and (2.6).

if p=2 and q=0, then

Y=f(nw-2qw-pw)=f(nw-2w)=0   (2.7)

if p=0 and q=1, then

Y=f(nw-2qw-pw)=f(nw-2w)=-1   (2.8)

There must be contradiction between (2.7) and (2.8) whatever f be selected. So, a perceptron can not express and deal with three valued logic problems.

3   Three valued logic neuron model (TLN)

The mode of three valued logic neuron(TLN) is shown in fig.2. Its structure is similar to that of a perceptron shown in fig.1. Its internal activation function, the effect of inputs to output, has varied. The internal activation function of TLN can be expressed with the following formula:

$$f(I) = f(\sum_{i=1}^{n} W_i X_i - \sum_{i=1}^{n} ((1 - \frac{|W_i|}{\sum_{i=1}^{n}|W_i|})|W_i X_i|)) \tag{3.1}$$

It can be interpreted as followings.

The activation of neuron Xi to neuron Y is WiXi, which may be a positive activation (WiXi>0) or a negative activation (inhibition, WiXi<0). Once neuron Xi generates an activation WiXi, it will generate an inhibition value to the activation value of every input neuron Xj of neuron Y except Xi itself. The inhibition value to neuron Xj (j ≠ i) is

$$\frac{|W_j|}{\sum_{i=1}^{n}|W_i|}|W_i X_i|, j \neq i \tag{3.2}$$

So, the total inhibition value generated by Xi is

$$\sum_{j=1,(j \neq i)}^{n} \frac{|W_j|}{\sum_{i=1}^{n}|W_i|}|W_i X_i| = \frac{|W_i X_i|}{\sum_{i=1}^{n}|W_i|}(\sum_{j=1}^{n}|W_j| - |W_i|) \tag{3.3}$$

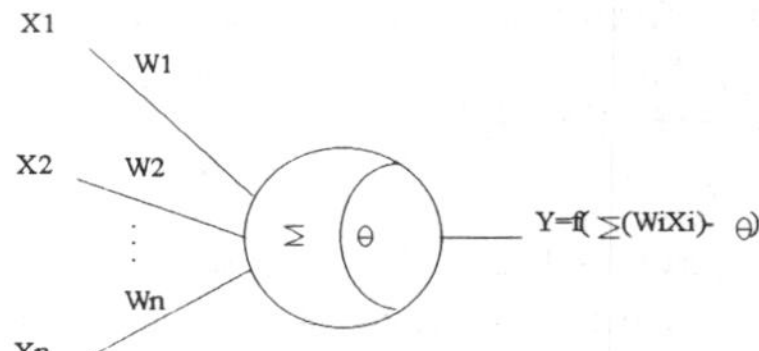

Fig. 1. Perceptron

Table 1. True value table of a three valued two element logic expression

A	B	$\overline{A}$	$\overline{B}$	A ∨ B	A ∧ B
-1	-1	1	1	-1	-1
-1	0	1	0	0	-1
-1	1	1	-1	1	-1
0	-1	0	1	0	-1
0	0	0	0	0	0
0	1	0	-1	1	0
1	-1	-1	1	1	-1
1	0	-1	0	1	0
1	1	-1	-1	1	1

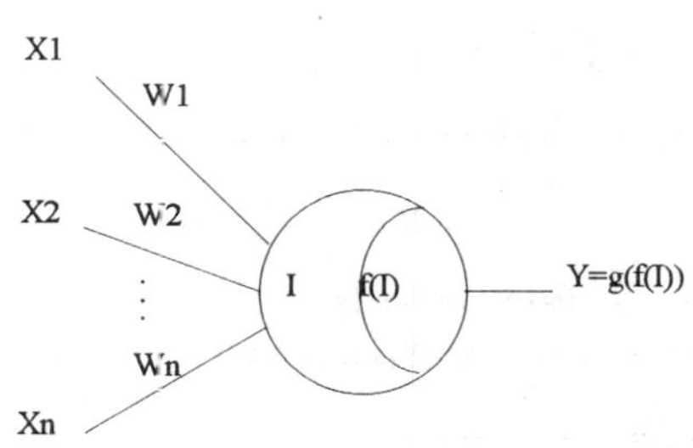

Fig. 2. Three valued logic neuron (TLN)

The total inhibition value generated by all input neurons of neuron Y is

$$\sum_{i=1}^{n}\left(\frac{|W_i X_i|}{\sum_{i=1}^{n}|W_i|}\left(\sum_{j=1}^{n}|W_j|-|W_i|\right)\right)=\sum_{i=1}^{n}\left(\left(1-\frac{|W_i|}{\sum_{i=1}^{n}|W_i|}\right)|W_i X_i|\right) \tag{3.4}$$

From (3.1) and (3.4), we can find that the input (I) of neuron Y is equal to the difference between the sum of activation of all input neurons and the sum of inhibition values of all input neurons to all other input neurons of neuron Y. The internal activation state f(I) of neuron Y can be gotten from I and the output g(f(I)) of Y can be gotten from f(I).

The internal activation function f can be selected as any of linearity activation function, sigmoid activation function, threshed logic activation function and hard limiting non linearity activation function while the output function g can be chosen according to the neediness of problem. In this paper, f is chosen as a sigmoid function (3.5) and g is chosen as a hard limiting non linearity function (3.6) in three valued logic but a segmented linearity function (3.7) in many valued logic. Many valued logic neural network is discussed in [11,12]. We will not discuss it here. Readers who are interested in it can refer to [11,12].

$$f(\alpha)=\frac{2}{1+\ell^{-\lambda\alpha}}- \tag{3.5}$$

$$g(\alpha)=\begin{cases}1,\alpha\geq\theta_1\\0,\theta_2<\alpha<\theta_1\\-1,\alpha\leq\theta_2\end{cases} \tag{3.6}$$

$$g(\alpha)=\begin{cases}1,\alpha\geq\theta_1\\\alpha,\theta_2<\alpha<\theta_1\\-1,\alpha\leq\theta_2\end{cases} \tag{3.7}$$

4   Represention and implemention of three valued logics

Let's consider the following three valued logic expression.

$$Y=X_1\wedge\cdots\wedge X_n\wedge\overline{X_{n+1}}\wedge\cdots\wedge\overline{X_{n+m}} \tag{4.1}$$

It can be expressed and implemented by the TLN shown in fig.3. Each premise neuron has the same importance to conclusion neuron. So, we might as well suppose all weights between premise neurons and conclusion neuron are the same heavy, for instance, they are all either +1 or -1 for positive premise or negative premise separately.

The internal activation state of this TLN is

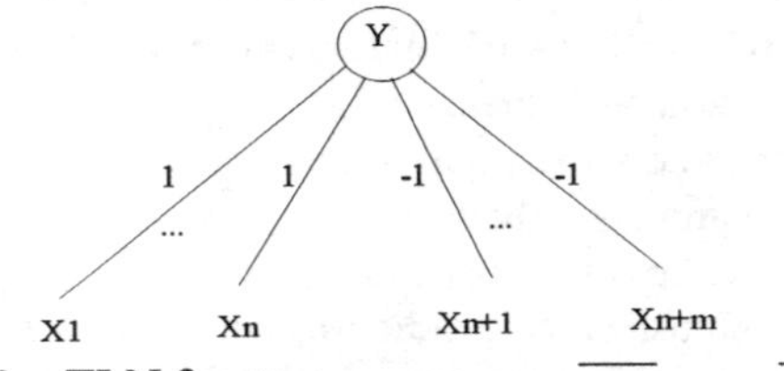

Fig. 3.   TLN for $Y=X_1\wedge\cdots\wedge X_n\wedge\overline{X_{n+1}}\wedge\cdots\wedge\overline{X_{n+m}}$

$$f(I)=f\left(\sum_{i=1}^{n}X_i-\sum_{i=n+1}^{n+m}X_i-\left(1-\frac{1}{m+n}\right)\sum_{i=1}^{n+m}|X_i|\right) \tag{4.2}$$

where, f is a sigmoid function as (3.5). g is a hard limiting non linearity function as (3.6).

Let $\theta_1=\frac{2}{1+\ell^{-\lambda}}-1,\theta_2=\frac{2}{1+\ell^{\lambda}}-1,\lambda>0$. Now look at the logic ability of this neuron.

Suppose there are q fault premises (positive premise takes -1 (value of fault) or negative premise takes +1 (value of true)) and p unknown premises (premise takes 0 (value of unknown)). So,

$$f(I)=\frac{2}{1+\ell^{-\lambda(m+n-p-2q-(1-\frac{1}{m+n})(m+n-p))}}-=\frac{2}{1+\ell^{-\lambda(1-2q-\frac{p}{m+n})}}- \tag{4.3}$$

1) If q=0 (without any fault premise), then

$$f(I)=\frac{2}{1+\ell^{-\lambda(1-\frac{p}{m+n})}}-1 \tag{4.4}$$

The following conclusion can be drawn under this condition.

If p=0, then $f(I)=\frac{2}{1+\ell^{-\lambda}}-1=\theta_1$ $\qquad\qquad$ (4.5)

If 0<p<m+n, then $0<f(I)<\theta_1$ $\qquad\qquad$ (4.6)

If p=m+n, then $f(I)=0$ $\qquad\qquad$ (4.7)

2) If q>0 (with some fault premises), then

$$f(I) = \frac{2}{1 + \ell^{-\lambda(1-2q-\frac{p}{m+n})}} - 1 \tag{4.8}$$

$$\leq \frac{2}{1 + \ell^{-\lambda(1-2q)}} - 1 \leq \frac{2}{1 + \ell^{\lambda}} - 1 = \theta_2$$

So, the following conclusions can be drawn.

If outputs of premise neurons are all correct (p=q=0), then $\quad$ g=1 $\hfill$ (4.9)

If there are no mistake in outputs of all premise neurons (q=0) and there are outputs of some premise neurons which are unknown (p>0), then $\quad$ g=0 $\hfill$ (4.10)

Once there is a premise neuron which output is fault (q>0), then $\quad$ g=-1 $\hfill$ (4.11)

We can find from (4.9-4.11) that the function of this TLN satisfies the relation of three valued "logic and". The following theorem holds in logic.

Theorem 1: $\{\neg, \wedge\}, \{\neg, \vee\}$ and $\{\neg, \rightarrow\}$ are all complete.

TLN can express "logic not ($\neg$)" if there is only one premise neuron and the connecting weight between the premise neuron and the conclusion neuron is less than zero. It can express "logic and ($\wedge$)" if there are more than one premise neurons. So, any three logic expression can be expressed by some TLN neurons according to the theorem above.

5 Conclusion

The limitation of perceptron for expressing three valued logic problems is analyzed. A novel model of neuron (TLN) that is suit for expressing three valued logic problems is presented. TLNN made up of TLNs can be used to express any three valued logic rules and implement three valued logic inferences. Unknown (uncertain) conception can be expressed and dealt with successfully using TLN and TLNN. The model of TLN can be considered as a theoretical base for integration of neural networks and symbolic inference systems.

References

[1] LiMin Fu, Rule Generation From Neural Network, IEEE TRANSACTIONS ON SYSTEMS, MAN,AND CYBERNECTICS, VOL.24, NO.8, AUGUST 1994, P1114-1124.

[2] Wang Guoyin, Shi Hongbao, Specially-Structured Rule Knowledge Acquisition With Feedforward Neural Network, JOURNAL OF XI'AN JIAOTONG UNIVERSITY, P.R.CHINA, Vol.30, No.1, 1996, P120-126.

[3] Cheng Hui, Logic Neuron Network, Pattern Recognition & Artificial Intelligence, P.R.China, Vol.6, No.4, December 1993, P300-306.

[4] Wang Guoyin, Shi Hongbao, Logic Symbol Inference System Based on Recurrent Multi-layer Perceptron Neural Network, submitted to International Conference on Neural Network 96'.

[5] P.Magrez, A.Rousseau, A Symbolic Interpretation for Back-Propagation Network, International Journal of Intelligent Systems, Vol.7, 339-360, 1992.

[6] L.A.Zadeh, Fuzzy sets as a basis for a theory of possibility, Fuzzy Sets and System,1, 3-38, 1978.

[7] Jyh-Shing Roger Jang, ANFIS: Adaptive-Network-Based Fuzzy Inference System, IEEE Transaction on Systems, Man, and Cybernetics, Vol.23, No.3, May/June 1993.

[8] Jyh-Shing Roger Jang, Self-Learning Fuzzy Controllers Based on Temporal Back Propagation, IEEE Transaction on Neural Network, Vol.3, No.5, September 1992.

[9] Yoichi Hayashi, James J.Buckley, Ernest Czogala, Fuzzy Expert Systems Versus Neural Network, IEEE Conf. on Neural Network, II720-726, 1992.

[10] Chan S.C., Hsu L.S., Brody S., Teh H.H., On neural logic network, neural Network Journal, 1(supplement 1), 428, 1988.

[11] Wang Guoyin, Study of the neural network models and algorithms in an integrated intelligent system, Ph. D. Thesis, Xi'an Jiaotong University, P.R.China, 1996.

[12] Wang Guoyin, Shi Hongbao, TMLNNs: Three or Many Valued Logic Neural Networks, Chinese Journal of Computer, to appear.

Neural Network Based Automatic Grammatical Annotation of Chinese Text

Weiquan LIU and Yixin ZHONG

Department of Information Engineering
Beijing University of Posts and Telecommunications
Beijing 100088, China
b9300726@bupt.edu.cn

Abstract

In NLP study, corpus of sentences requires to be annotated with syntactic and semantic labels. This paper focus on tagging words with correct part-of-speech labels by neural networks. Firstly, the tagging problem is described, then the structure and training procedure of two neural network models, namely, SHDN and AARN are addressed. Experiments show that their accuracy in tagging a small scale Chinese corpus achieves more than 92% and 95% respectively. Finally, the performance of the two models is analyzed and compared.

1   Introduction

The subject of Natural Language Processing (NLP) research is how to build computer systems that are capable of analyzing natural language text automatically. In the literature of last two decades, corpus study draws much attention of researchers. Corpus means a large scale collection of text or discourses written down in words. Because of its wide scale, a corpus may contain various usage of language. This made it possible to serve as an ideal linguistic knowledge base. The way of converting the simply stacked raw material into a corpus KB is to annotate the text with suitable labels, enabling the syntactic structure of sentences and the semantic item that each word takes be explicit.

To annotate a mandarin Chinese corpus, the operation is commonly divided into four levels. The first one is word segmentation. The second one is to label each word with its part-of-speech tag according to the context. This is to eliminate the grammatical category ambiguity that is common in natural language. The third one is to annotate syntactic structures on sentences with phase-structure tree or other convenient methods. Finally in the fourth step, predicate case frame will be marked, in order to generate a semantic representation for each sentence.

Techniques of word segmentation are relatively mature. Now the corpus annotation research is focusing on the second and third level, that is how to label words with their part-of-speech tags and how to mark a sentence with its syntactic structure. Of the two operations, the former is more crucial, which is the premise of descendent steps. So in this paper efforts will be made to tackle this problem, mainly by ANN models.

Those existing tagging schemes lie in three catalogues according to the strategies they follow: a) rule-based scheme[1], b) statistics-based scheme[2] and c) the combination of a and b[3]. In [4], a MLP model is proposed to assign grammatical categories to words of an English corpus. But it is unfit to tag Chinese text. In the next section of this paper, we will characterize the procedure of part-of-speech tagging of Chinese text. In section 3, two ANN models, SHDN and AARN respectively, are proposed, their structures and training algorithms are also discussed. Then in section 4 and 5, we trained the two models and made them perform tagging automatically. It is concluded that both SHDN and AARN can be used to resolve the grammatical ambiguity in corpus annotation or they can be combined with rule-based and/or statistics-based methods.

2   Description of Part-of-Speech Tagging

A same word may present different kinds of grammatical categories in different context. Statistics drawn from a corpus show that about 13% of lexicon words have more than one categories, but in running text, above 35% of all the words are multi-cat ones. That is because the frequently used words have more grammatical ambiguity than those that are less frequently used. For instance, the Chinese word "连" belongs to adverb, preposition, verb, noun or qualifier, totally five kinds of categories.

Suppose according to their grammatical function, all the words can be grouped into M kinds of categories, and each category is labeled by a shorthand tag. Let **T** be the set of all tags. For a sentence S= $w_1w_2...w_N$, any word $w_i \in$ **W**(**W** is the lexicon) in S may have m_i tags. That is to say an ambiguity tag set $T_{wi}=\{t_{i1}, t_{i2},...,t_{im_i}\}$, ($t_{ij} \in$ **T**, $1 \leqslant i \leqslant N$, $1 \leqslant j \leqslant m_i$) is defined for each w_i. In an annotated Chinese corpus it is found that there will be N consecutive multi-cat words in a sentence. N never exceeds 8, in most cases N is between 1~3[1].

The task of part-of-speech tagging is for every w_i ($1 \leqslant i \leqslant N$), assign the correct tag t_i to it. The result is just the tag sequence of S: $T_S= t_1t_2...t_i...t_N$; ($t_i \in T_{wi}$). T_S is chosen from $\prod_{i=1}^{N} m_i$ possible kinds of tagging paths for a sentence with N words (Fig. 1). Let the tagging procedure be noted as Φ, Φ is a mapping relation from S to T_S:

$$\Phi: \quad S \rightarrow T_S = \Phi(S)$$

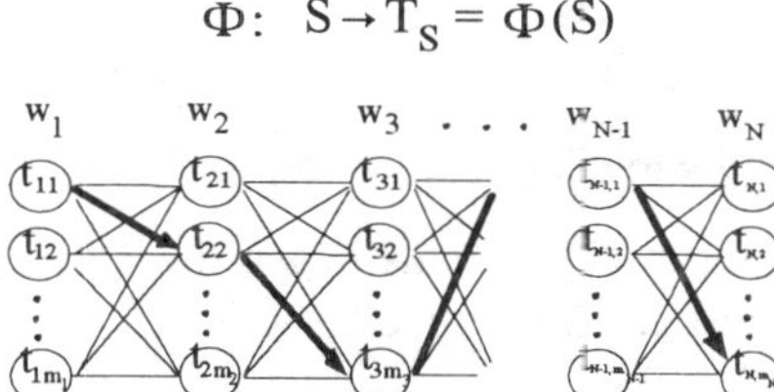

Fig. 1 Tagging paths of S. T_S is shown as a bold line with arrows.

In this study, set **T** has 61 tags. All the words are grouped as noun(n), verb(v), adjective(a), adverb(d), conjunction(c), etc., totally 18 coarse categories. some of them are further refined into 2~8 sub-cats.

3   ANN Models for Part-of-Speech Tagging

Both of the two ANN models proposed in this section are supervised learning networks. For each model, a training algorithm is devised to make them simulate the mapping function Φ. To find the T_S for a given S, there are generally two possible ways: a) All the tagging paths are either legal or illegal, let a neural network to classify them. If there is only one legal path, it is T_S. b) Feed each T_{wi} of S to a network, which directly generate T_S as the output.

3.1 Single-layer Higher-order Dynamic Network (SHDN)

SHDN works as a classifier. There are only two output neurons which are marked "YES" and "NO" to represent the inputting tagging path is legal or illegal respectively. As shown in Fig. 2, the computing performed by the two output neurons is just summation, whilst complicated non-linear activation functions are avoided. This makes the network easy to realize.

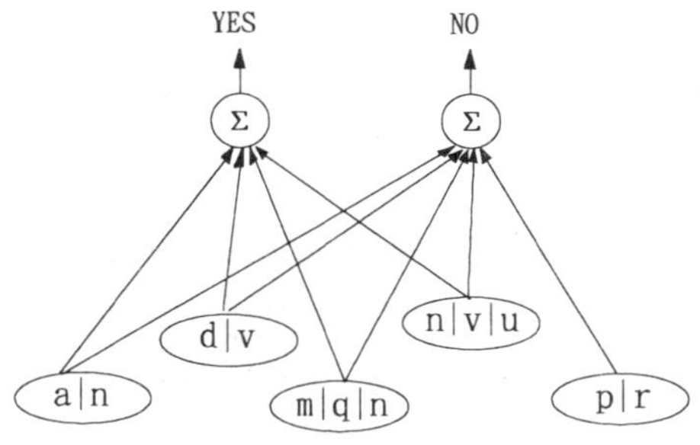

Fig. 2 Structure of SHDN

The input neurons don't need to perform any computing (so the network is habitually regarded as having a single-layer structure), they are used to code the information in the inputting sequence of part-of-speech tags. Each of the neurons maps to a certain sub-string of length from 1 to a maximum number taken from the tag sequence. Suppose T'_S is a possible tagging path of S, $T'_S = t'_1 t'_2... t'_i...t'_N$, sub-strings of length 1 are $t'_1,t'_2,t'_3,...$, sub-strings of length 2 are $t'_1t'_2,t'_2t'_3,...$, and sub-strings of length 3 are $t'_1t'_2t'_3,...$, etc. In order to reduce

the perplexity of network structure, the maximal length is usually set to 2 or 3 (pair or triple of tags). To a single input neuron, when its corresponding sub-string appears in the inputting sequence, it is ignited and outputs 1, otherwise it outputs 0. Higher-order means one neuron relates to more than one consecutive tags. After initialization there are no input neurons, all of them are dynamically generated during the training process. The construction of neurons and weights adjustment is depicted in the following supervised learning algorithm:

① Take the next tagging path from training set as input sequence.

② Activate corresponding input neurons representing each sub-string in the sequence of length from 1 to maximal length.

③ For both of the output neurons, compute the weighted sum:

$$O_i = \sum_j W_{ij} I_j \qquad i=1,2. \quad 1 \leqslant j \leqslant \text{current num. of input neurons.}$$

④ Of the two outputs O_1 and O_2, the larger one is called the actual winner. When it is the same as the expected winner say the network makes a correct classification.

⑤ For the sub-strings appear in inputting sequence but without corresponding input neurons, create new nodes for them. Add weight connections between the newly added nodes and the expected winner, the initial values are all set to 1.

⑥ If expected winner is different to the actual winner, adjust the weight matrix:

$$\Delta W_{ij} = \frac{\delta e^{-\beta|W_{ij}-1|}}{1+e^{-\beta|W_{ij}-1|}} \qquad \text{for i=1,2} \quad I_j=1, \quad \text{and empirically } \beta =0.1\sim0.5 \tag{1}$$

⑦ While the classification error to the entire training set is satisfactorily small exit this algorithm , otherwise go to ①.

The weight matrix is adjusted according to Eq.(1) only when the network makes a mistake in classification. When i, the first subscript in W_{ij}, stands for the expected winner, let $\delta =+2$ (teach); while i stands for the actual winner (fraud) let $\delta = -2$ (punish). ΔW_{ij} decided by Eq.(1) is within [-1, 1]. ΔW_{ij} reaches its maximum as W_{ij} closes to 1, and approaches to 0 as W_{ij} escapes from 1. This guarantees all elements in weight matrix are not divergent too much.

3.2 Auto Associative Recurrent Network (AARN)

This model is the enhancement of Simple Recurrent Network (SRN) originally proposed by Elman[7]. SRN has a three-layer feed-forward structure, the nodes in its first layer are divided into state nodes $S(k)$ and input nodes $X(k)$. $S(k)$ is the copy of hidden nodes with an unit delay, $S(k)=H(k-1)$. The output of hidden neurons is function vector of state and input $I(k)=[S(k)X(k)]$:

$$H(k) = \Psi(I(k)) = \Psi(H(k-1), X(k))$$

Similarly output of SRN is:
$$O(k) = \Xi(H(k)) = \Xi(\Psi(H(k-1), X(k)))$$

$S(k)$ records the information in the first k-1 inputting signals, so $O(k)$ is a function of $X(1)X(2)\cdots X(k)$.

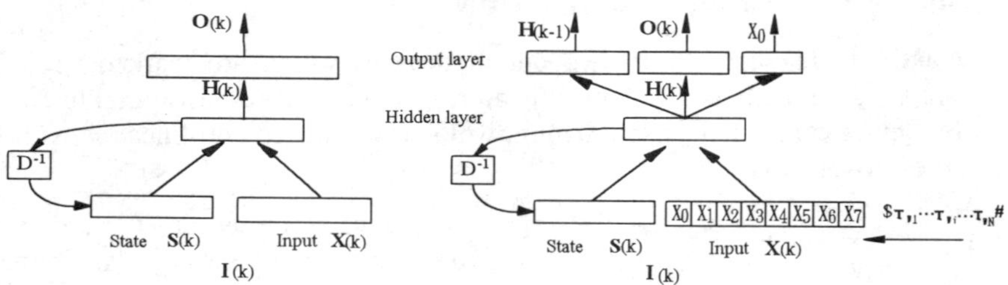

Fig. 3   (a) Structure of SRN   (b) Structure of AARN

In part-of-speech tagging, suppose w_k is the k-th word in sentence S, let $X(k)$ to be the coding form of T_{wk}. As the network is trained under supervision, let $O(k)$ to represent the correct tag t_i for w_k. Well learned network will simulate Φ, that is $\Xi(\Psi(\cdot)) \approx \Phi(\cdot)$. But under the following two conditions SRN cannot be sufficiently learned due to the limitation in its structure. (Fig. 3(a))

Condition 1: Suppose the tagging paths of S_1 and S_2 are *Pxu $\cdots$w* and *Pyu $\cdots$v* respectively. *P* is the common handle of two sequences. After *Px* or *Py* is fed into network, note current hidden layer output as h(*Px*) or h(*Py*). To both S_1 and S_2, next input signal is the same *u*, so h(*Px*) and h(*Py*) will be very similar. The difference among *x* and *y* disappears here. When *w* or *v* reaches, output layer will fail to differentiate them and a same tag is generated for both *w* and *v*. To deal with this circumstance, nodes representing current inputs should be added to the output layer. (See X_0 of the output layer in Fig. 3(b))

Condition 2: Suppose tagging sequence *Px₁ $\cdots$ xᵣw* and *Qx₁ $\cdots$ xᵣv* correspond to S_3 and S_4 respectively. As *P* or *Q* is fed into input layer, the output of hidden layer is noted as h(*P*) or h(*Q*). Then *x₁* reaches, hidden layer outputs h(Px_1) or h(Qx_1), they are more similar to each other than h(P) and h(Q). After x_r appears at input layer, h($Px_1 \cdots x_r$) and h($Qx_1 \cdots x_r$) will be so close that output layer will also give out a same tag for the subsequent w and v . In this case state of current hidden layer should be expressed by additional nodes in output layer to buffer the difference occurs before current input. (See **H**(k-1) of the output layer in Fig. 3(b))

SRN with the above improvement is called Auto Associative Recurrent Network. Training algorithm takes the error back propagation strategy. Weights from hidden nodes to the state nodes are all constant 1 with a unit delay. Other weights between any two layers are modified after each epoch by Δw :

$$\Delta w(k) = -\varepsilon \frac{\partial E}{\partial w(k)} + \alpha \Delta w(k-1) \qquad \varepsilon : \text{learning rate} \quad \alpha : \text{momentum} \quad E: \text{error energy}$$

Since in any sentence S, the maximal number of consecutive multi-cat words $N_{max}=8$, so the input nodes in AARN are divided into 8 groups: $\mathbf{X}=\mathbf{X_0}\mathbf{X_1} \cdots \mathbf{X_7}$. Each group represents an ambiguity tag set $\mathbf{T_w}$ with distributed coding scheme. Inputting tag sequence for S is $\mathbf{T_{w1}}\mathbf{T_{w2}} \cdots \mathbf{T_{wN}}$#. \$ and # are attached to initialize network internal state and mark the ending of sequence. The sequence is moved along the direction shown by an arrow in Fig. 3(b). At the moment the token $\mathbf{T_{wk}}$ reaches $\mathbf{X_0}$, $\mathbf{O}$(k) is decoded as the tag t_k for w_k. As each $\mathbf{T_{wk}}$ (k=1,2,...,N) is fed into AARN, it generates t_k one by one, until the whole $\mathbf{T_S}$ is got after $\mathbf{T_{wN}}$ reaches $\mathbf{X_0}$.

4 Experiment Results

The original corpus to be tagged is composed of 650 mandarin Chinese sentences, words of them are previously segmented. The average length is 15.3 words per sentence. After segmentation, each word is labeled by hand with its part-of-speech tag to make templates for further examining ($|\mathbf{T}|$=61). 400 out of all the sentences are randomly chosen to form the training set, the remaining 250 as the test set to evaluate the performance.

The final training data for SHDN is derived from all the possible tagging paths of the sentences in training set. Only the T_S for each S possessing a legal state, all the other paths are illegal. Each of the paths is fed into SHDN as a sequence of tag. Nodes in the input layer are activated when their corresponding sub-strings exist in the sequence. The output layer judges the state of the path.

The training of SHDN is performed with four different configurations of its input layer. The first one is to set the nodes in input layer represent all the sub-strings of length from 1 to 3. In the second configuration nodes for single tags are deleted, just remaining nodes for pairs (2) and triples (3) of tags in the sequence. Then in the next two stories, only nodes for pairs or triples are kept respectively, thus making the network more slim. Each configuration is trained using the algorithm introduced in section 3.1. Training process stops when the classification accuracy on training data no more increases.

After training, performance of the four configurations is evaluated with both training and test set. Results are shown in table 1 and 2. "Tag selection" means the network mistakenly marked an illegal path as a legal one, T_S is also legal. So at least one word in S has more than one tags, which should be selected by hand. "tag change" means the network gives one or more words in S incorrect tags but without the correct one.

Tab. 1 Tagging accuracy of SHDN on training set

length of sub-string	1, 2, 3	2, 3	2	3
num. of input nodes	203	181	57	124
tag selection	0.7%	2.2%	5.0%	4.2%
tag change	0.6%	1.5%	2.9%	5.1%
tagging accuracy	98.7%	96.3%	92.1%	90.7%

Tab. 2 Tagging accuracy of SHDN on test set

length of sub-string	1, 2, 3	2, 3	2	3
num. of input nodes	203	181	57	124
tag selection	1.9%	3.8%	7.4%	5.2%
tag change	5.2%	5.6%	3.5%	7.6%
tagging accuracy	92.9%	90.6%	89.1%	87.2%

The output layer of AARN represents the certainty of assigning a tag to the current input word of S. Local coding scheme is employed here allowing each neuron corresponds to a single tag in **T**. While in each of the input node groups of X_0–X_7 there are 6 nodes to represent T_w with distributed coding.

In the training of AARN, we tried to let the entire training set input to network at a same batch. But it was found that the error energy vibrates all the time, the weights didn't converge steadily. The resulting performance was also sensitive to different learning rate ε. Then incremental training is used. The training has several stages. At the first stage, only a small portion of training set is inputted, and at each other successive stage, enlarge the data inputted with another portion from the training set, until the entire set is used. Incremental training reduced the total amount of time needed in training to achieve a similar result. At the end of each stage, the network performance can also be tested.

The tagging accuracy of AARN on both the training and test set can be found in table 3. Because AARN generates T_S directly from the sequence of ambiguity tag sets of S: $T_{w1} \cdots T_{wN}$, for each w_i, the node with the highest activation in output layer indicates its tag t_i. When network made a tagging mistake, "tag change" will record the percentage of words that got a wrong tag. There is no need to select among several tags for w_i by hand, so the "tag selection" is always 0 in table 3.

Tab. 3 Tagging accuracy of AARN

num. of sent in training set \ test set	current training set			test set (250 sentences)		
	tag selection	tag change	tagging accuracy	tag selection	tag change	tagging accuracy
100	0	1.6%	98.4%	0	28.7%	71.3%
200	0	2.9%	97.1%	0	12.3%	87.7%
300	0	3.5%	96.5%	0	7.5%	92.5%
400	0	3.8%	96.2%	0	4.6%	95.4%

5 Conclusions

From the results reported above we find both SHDN and AARN can be used for part-of-speech tagging of Chinese Sentences with high accuracy. The relatively simpler structure of SHDN promises it can be trained with less amount of computation. We also tried to set the maximal length of sub-strings to be 4. Too many combinations of tags are generated due to this, which consequently beyond the capacity of the network. When the length takes 1,2 and 3, SHDN reaches its best performance.

AARN is a feed forward network with feedback copying connections. It is suitable for the case of on-line tagging of text. The training is complicated with incremental strategy. At the end of each stage, it can be found that the tagging accuracy on current training set is declining, because new combinations of tags are introduced; while the accuracy on test set is climbing showing the network is learning.

References

[1] ZHOU Lina. Acquisition Techniques of Rules for Grammatical Tagging for Chinese Corpus. *Computational Linguistics: Research and Applications*. BILC Publishing House, 1993.

[2] BAI Shuanhu. A Statistics Approach of Tagging Chinese Corpus. *Master Thesis of Tsinghua Univ.*, 1992

[3] ZHOU Qiang. Chinese Corpus Tagging Using Rule Techniques and Statistics Techniques. *Journal of Chinese Information Processing*, 9(3):1-10, 1995.

[4] Julia Benello *et al.* Syntactic Category Disambiguation with Neural Network. *Computer Speech and Language*, 3:203-217, 1989.

[5] Wyard P. T. Nightingale C. A Single Layer Higher Order Neural Net and its Application to Context Free Grammar Recognition. In Sharkey N. eds. *Connectionist Natural Language Processing*. Klumer Academic Publishers, 1992.

[6] Maskara A. Noetzel A. Sequence Recognition with Recurrent Neural Networks. *Connection Science*, 5(2):139-152, 1993.

[7] Elman J. L. Distributed Representations, Simple Recurrent Networks, and Grammatical Structure. *Machine Learning*, 7:195-225, 1991.

Self-organized Segmentation of Hormone Pulsatility:
Separating Growth Hormone Secretion in Health and Disease

Klaus Prank†, Mirko Kloppstech†, Steven J. Nowlan‡, Terrence J. Sejnowski§¶, and Georg Brabant†

†Department of Clinical Endocrinology
Medical School Hannover
D-30623 Hannover, Germany
ndxdpran@rrzn-user.uni-hannover.de
‡Lexicus Inc.
San Jose, California 95134, U.S.A.
steven@lexicus.mot.com
§Howard Hughes Medical Institute and Computational Neurobiology Laboratory
The Salk Institute
San Diego, California 92186-5800, U.S.A.
¶ Department of Biology
University of California, San Diego
La Jolla, California 92093, U.S.A.
terry@salk.edu

Abstract **The pulsatile pattern of growth hormone (GH) secretion was assessed over 24 hours in 10 healthy subjects and in 6 patients with a GH producing pituitary tumor (acromegaly) before treatment with the somatostatin analogue octreotide by sampling blood every 10 min. Time series prediction based on a single feedback neural network has recently been demonstrated to separate the secretory dynamics of parathyroid hormone (PTH) in healthy controls from patients with osteoporosis, a severe bone disease. To reveal possible differences of GH secretory dynamics in healthy controls and patients with acromegaly we tested time series prediction based on a single feedforward neural network and a system of multiple neural networks acting in parallel (*adaptive mixtures of local experts*). Both approaches significantly separated GH dynamics under the various conditions. By performing a self-organized quantification of hormone pulsatility of GH the *adaptive mixtures of local experts* performed significantly better than the single network approach. It thus may represent a potential tool to characterize alterations of the dynamic regulation in hormonal systems associated with diseased states.**

1 Introduction

Pulsatile hormone secretion has been demonstrated in a large number of different endocrine systems with pulse frequencies ranging from approximately 6 to 140 pulses in 24 hours [1]. This dynamic mode of secretion has important effects on the regulation of target cells and organs in health and disease [1].
Time series prediction has been used to capture regularities in the temporal pattern of complex time series particularly in the context of nonlinear dynamical systems and to separate deterministic from random behavior [2-4]. This technique tries to predict the future dynamics of a time series from a number of past values. Differences in the temporal dynamics of a system are then reflected in an altered predictability. Such predictive approaches have been effectively used in several biological systems [5-10] and may be applied for short time series containing a very limited number of data points [2, 3]. We recently applied neural networks to the prediction of hormone concentration time series to clearly separate the secretory dynamics of parathyroid hormone (PTH) in a group of osteoporotic patients from that in healthy controls, demonstrating a significantly higher predictability of the PTH secretory dynamics in healthy subjects than in the osteoporotic group [11]. In 24h profiles of PTH serum concentrations we could additionally demonstrate a switching behavior between two dynamic phases, a phase of high and one of low predictability. Based on these results a single neural network predictor might not been optimal for the prediction of time series with different switching dynamics.

2 Subjects

Ten male young lean subjects and six patients with clinical and biochemical diagnosis of acromegaly not cured by previous surgical and/or radiation therapies took part in this study. The studies were approved by the local

Committee on Medical Ethics, and all subjects and patients gave their informed written consent. Blood samples were taken every 10 minutes over 24 hours starting at 1800 h. Healthy controls were studied under normal nutrition. The 24h GH secretory profile in the acromegalic group was studied without any medication. The study design has been described in more detail previously and some of the data of these studies have been included in the present data set [12, 13].

3   Methods

3.1 Time series prediction

In the present study we used feedforward neural networks to predict future values of the time series of GH serum concentrations. This form of a predictive model was chosen since it is relatively easy to control over-fitting using regularization functions and cross-validation. The next value $x(t_i)$ of each GH concentration time series was predicted from m past values $x(t_i) = f(x(t_{i-1}), x(t_{i-2}), ..., x(t_{i-m})) + \epsilon_i$, where $x(t_{i-1})$ is the preceeding value, and ϵ_i corresponds to noise or fitting error. The function f represents feedforward neural networks with linear or nonlinear (sigmoidal) activation functions. The neural networks were trained (fitting the model f to data by using a conjugate gradient descent technique) to predict 10 min. into the future within either group. Prior to training the original data sets were normalized to a [0,1] interval to account for the nonlinearities in the activation functions and different mean GH levels between the healthy controls and acromegalic patients. The training within each group was performed using a "leave one out technique" where the time series being tested for prediction is left out of the training procedure. To predict multiple time steps ahead the value $x(t_i)$ predicted one time step ahead was iterated back to predict two steps into the future. This procedure can be iteratively repeated to predict any given number of time steps ahead. We used the average relative variance (arv) as prediction error estimate to decorrelate it from the variance of the respective time series: $arv = \langle (x_i - x'_i)^2 \rangle / \sigma^2(x_i)$, where the angle brackets denote the mean over all predicted values and $\sigma^2(x_i)$ denotes the variance of the measured time series. The simulations were performed on a Sun SPARCstation 20 using customized C-code. A large variety of neural network architectures was explored. We found a 7 input units, 10 hidden units, 1 output unit network with sigmoidal activation functions as the best predictor within the control group and a 5 input units, 8 hidden units, 1 output unit network with sigmoidal activation functions for the acromegalic group.

3.2 Mixture of experts

Divide-and-conquer strategies are effective methods for solving complex problems by dividing it into simpler problems whose solutions can be combined to yield a solution to the complex problem [14-17]. The mixture of experts is a modular neural network system composed of several different "expert" networks plus a gating network that decides which of the experts should be used for each input (Fig. 1). During the training procedure the experts compete to generate the desired output for each input pattern, and adapt to a particular input pattern in proportion to their performance relative to the other expert networks. When an expert has less error than the weighted average of the errors of all experts, its responsibility for that case is increased, and when it does worse, its responsibility is decreased. In this way, individual experts specialize for specific subsets of the input pattern. The experts are therefore local since the weights in one expert are decoupled from the weights in other experts. At the same time, the gating network learns to select the best performing expert for a given case by adjusting the mixing proportions of the experts. Simulations on a complex vowel classification task have shown that adaptive mixtures of local experts are able to effectively decompose a problem to yield higher classification performance than a single network[18]. The mixtures of experts also generalizes better from limited amounts of training data.

In our simulations we varied the number of local experts between 2 and 6 and the input window size between 7 and 16 data values. Each expert consisted of a feedforward linear network without hidden units. We trained the best predictive mixture of experts system using pooled reference data from 5 healthy controls. This system consisted of 5 linear experts with 9 input units each and a gating network with 3 hidden units and sigmoidal activation functions. It was tested for its predictive ability on the remaining control and acromegalic GH time series. The number of the respective expert selected to predict a given value of the time series was recorded versus time. Finally, a frequency distribution of the expert selection was computed for each subgroup. Adaptive mixtures of local experts were simulated with customized C-code on a Sun SPARCstation 20.

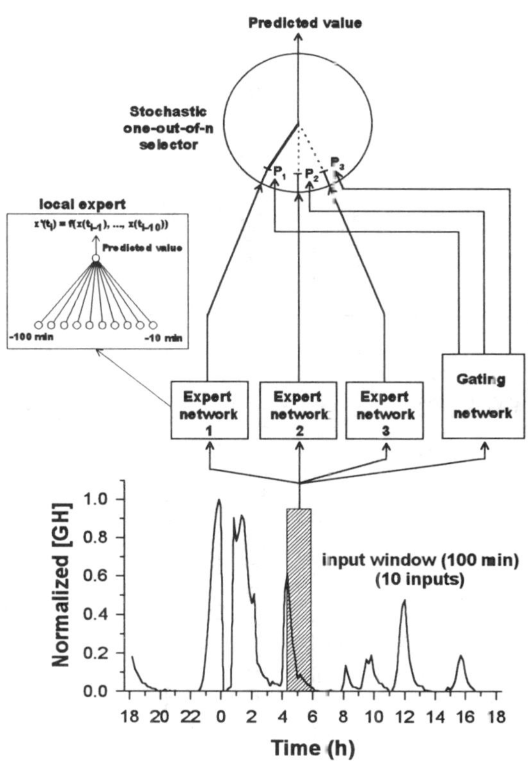

Figure 1. Schematic architecture of adaptive mixtures of local experts used for time series prediction. Each local expert is a feedforward neural network which all have the same architecture and receive the same input. The gating network is also feedforward and receives the same input as the expert networks. It has normalized outputs $p_j = exp(x_j) / \sum_i exp(x_i)$, where x_j is the total weighted input received by output unit j of the gating network. The selector acts like a multiple input, single output stochastic switch. The probability that the switch will select the output from expert j is P_j, which is the jth output of the gating network. These local experts are trained in parallel to perform time series prediction one time step ahead. During testing the weighted average of the expert outputs (with weights assigned by the gating network) is used as the output of the mixture of experts.

4 Results

The one-step ahead prediction error (arv) was found to be significantly ($p < 0.002$) lower in healthy controls (arv$=0.14\pm0.07$) than in acromegalic patients (arv$=0.51\pm0.29$). This was reflected in correctly predicting the pulsatile features of the 24h GH profile in healthy controls for 100 minutes ahead (Fig. 2b), in contrast to a significant predictability of only 10 min. in acromegaly (Fig. 2c). Compared to a single neural network predictor the predictive performance of the modular approach was superior for both groups resulting in a significantly smaller one-step ahead prediction error (controls: arv $= 0.07\pm0.03$, $p<0.01$; acromegaly: arv$=0.24\pm0.13$, $p<0.01$). Analyzing the temporal pattern of the selected local expert for each predicted GH value we found that the mutiple network approach had performed a self-organized segmentation of the pulsatile secretory pattern (SOPUL) in healthy controls and acromegalic patients reflected in a switching between distinct expert networks. The selection pattern of the local experts easily separates acromegalic patients healthy controls. During the training phase, each expert network specialized to predict certain parts of a GH pulse. Expert 1 focussed its performance on predicting the decrease of a hormonal pulse whereas expert 5 was best in predicting the increase of a GH pulse and the GH baseline. Although experts 2 to 4 contributed significantly to the predictive performance of this modular approach they were selected in only about 1 % of the cases in healthy controls and in about 5 to 8 % of the cases in the patient group. The frequency distributions of these most probable experts significantly differ in acromegalic patients from those in healthy controls. Expert 1 was chosen in 2.5 % in normal controls compared to 12.7 % in acromegaly, which separated the controls from acromegaly with high confidence ($p<0.01$).

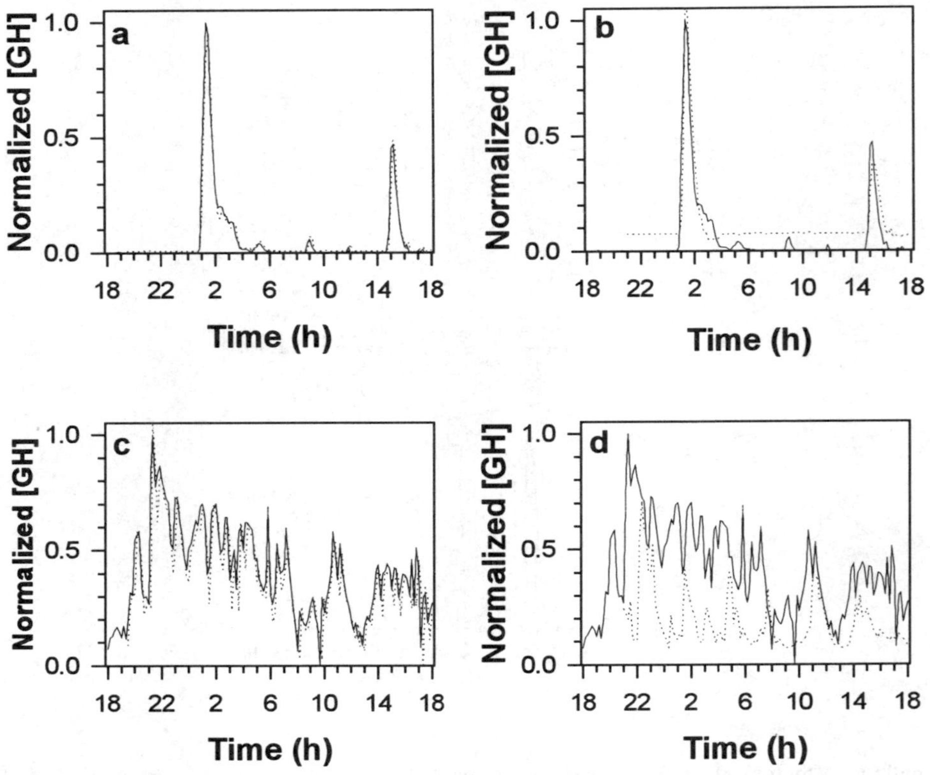

Figure 2. One and ten-step ahead prediction using an adaptive mixture of five local experts with nine input units each (nonlinear gating network with three hidden units). Solid line: original time series of normalized GH serum concentration, dotted line: predicted time series. Healthy control: (a) one step ahead (10 minutes) prediction, (b) ten steps ahead (100 minutes) prediction; acromegalic patient: (c) one step ahead (10 minutes) prediction, (d) ten steps ahead (100 minutes) prediction.

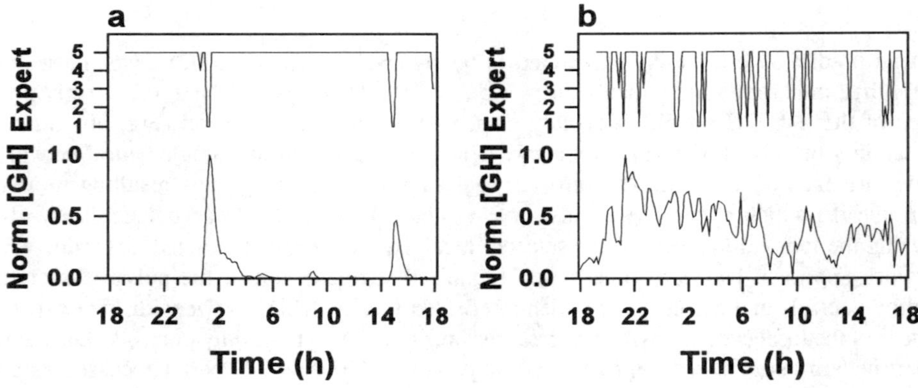

Figure 3. Self-organized segmentation of the pulsatile pattern of secretion (SOPUL). Normalized original GH time series and selection pattern of local experts used for prediction. (a) healthy control (b) acromegalic patient.

5 Discussion

Using time series prediction with a single feedforward neural network we were able to separate the secretory dynamics of GH of healthy subjects from acromegalic patients. We previously used the same analytical approach successfully to predict PTH serum levels and to separate healthy controls from osteoporotic patients where standard methods of time series analysis as computing the mean, the variance, or the power spectrum failed [11]. However, such a single neural network predictor has distinct disadvantages when applied to the prediction of time series with nonuniform local dynamics as described for episodic hormone release in most endocrine systems with phases of secretory bursts and quienscence [1]. This may elicit strong interference effects in single feedforward neural networks and result in slow learning and poor generalization. To circumvent these problems we used adaptive mixtures of local experts in the present study. The modular neural network architecture reduces interference by a mixture of several distinct expert neural networks which are chosen by a gating network to optimally adapt for each training and testing case. By this approach each experimental group was predicted much better than using the single neural network. Each expert specializes on distinct parts of a time series. The switching between local experts may be used to perform a self-organized segmentation of the pulsatile pattern of hormone secretion (SOPUL). We show that in acromegalic patients the expert specialized on predicting the decrease of a GH pulse contributed significantly more to the overall prediction of the GH time series than in healthy controls. Thus, histograms of selected expert networks may be used to separate temporal rhythms in health and disease.

In contrast to standard methods for the analysis of pulsatile patterns of secretion [19] our SOPUL approach does not require any previous knowledge of the physiological characteristics of the system. Therefore it may reflect better the "true" pattern of endocrine information transfer than the approaches published so far which all rely on certain assumptions on the nature of a pulse. The approach discussed here may help to expand standard techniques for the analysis of hormonal time series beyond counting pulse frequency and amplitude. Our approach using multiple adaptive neural networks may form an analytical basis to test the potential importance of temporal coding in the endocrine system.

Acknowledgements

This work was supported by Deutsche Forschungsgemeinschaft (KP, MK, GB) and by Howard Hughes Medical Institute (TJS).

References

[1] G. Brabant *et al.*, ``Pulsatile patterns in hormone secretion,'' *Trends Endocrinol. Metab.*, vol. 3, pp. 183-190, 1992.

[2] G. Sugihara and R. M. May, ``Nonlinear forecasting as a way of distinguishing chaos from measurement error in time series,'' *Nature*, vol. 344, pp. 734-741, 1990.

[3] A. A. Tsonis and J. B. Elsner, ``Nonlinear prediction as a way of distinguishing chaos from random fractal sequences,'' *Nature*, vol. 358, pp. 217-220, 1992.

[4] A. S. Weigend and N. A. Gershenfeld, *Time Series Prediction: Forecasting the Future and Understanding the Past.* SFI studies in the sciences of complexity, Proc. Vol. XV, Reading: Addison-Wesley, 1993.

[5] K. J. Blinowska and M. Malinowski, ``Non-linear and linear forecasting of the EEG time series,'' *Biol. Cybern.*, vol. 66, pp. 159-165, 1991.

[6] T. Chang *et al.*, ``Stochastic versus deterministic variability in simple neuronal circuits. I. Monosynaptic spinal cord reflexes,'' *Biophys. J.*, vol. 67, pp. 671-683, 1994.

[7] J. H. Lefebvre *et al.*, ``Predictability of normal heart rhythms and deterministic chaos,'' *Chaos*, vol. 3, pp. 267-276, 1993.

[8] S. J. Schiff *et al.*, ``Stochastic versus deterministic variability in simple neuronal circuits. II. Hippocampal slices,'' *Biophys. J.*, vol. 6pp. 684-691, 1994.

[9] G. Sugihara, ``Nonlinear forecasting for the classification of natural time series,'' *Phil. Trans. R. Soc. Lond. A*, vol. 348, 477-495, 1994.

[10] D. A. Scott and S. J. Schiff, ``Predictability of EEG interictal spikes,'' *Biophys. J.*, vol. 69, 1748-1757, 1995.

[11] K. Prank *et al.*, ``Time series prediction of plasma hormone concentration: Evidence for differences in predictability of parathyroid hormone secretion between osteoporotic patients and normal controls,'' *J. Clin. Invest.*, vol. 95, 2910-2919, 1995.

[12] M. Riedel *et al.*, ``The pulsatile GH secretion in acromegaly: hypothalamic or pituitary origin?'' *Clin. Endocrinol. (Oxf.)*, vol. 37, pp. 233-239, 1992.

[13] M. Riedel *et al.*, ``Pulsatile growth hormone (GH) secretion in lean, and obese men: differential metabolic regulation of GH release during energy restriction," *Metabolism* , vol. 44, pp. 605-610, 1995.

[14] R. A. Jacobs *et al.*, ``Adaptive mixtures of local experts," *Neural Comp.*, vol. 3, pp. 79-87, 1991.

[15] M. I. Jordan and R. A. Jacobs, ``Hierachical mixtures of experts and the EM algorithm," *Neural Comp.*, vol. 6, pp. 181-214, 1994.

[16] S. J. Nowlan, ``Competing experts: an experimental investigation of associative mixture models," *Technical Report CRG-TR-90-5*, Department of Computer Science, University of Toronto, Toronto, Canada, 1990.

[17] K. Pawelzik *et al.*, ``Annealed competition of experts for a segmentation and classification of switching dynamics," *Neural Comp.*, vol. 8, pp. 340-356, 1996.

[18] S. J. Nowlan, ``Soft competitive adaptation: neural network learning algorithms based on fitting statistical mixtures," *Ph.D. thesis, CMU-CS-91-126*, School of Computer Science, Carnegie Mellon University, Pittsburgh, PA. pp. 110-130, 1991.

[19] K. Prank and G. Brabant, ``Estimating thyrotropin secretory activity by a deconvolution procedure," *Methods in Neurosci.*, vol. 20, 377-389, 1994.

Radial Basis Network for Facial Expression Synthesis*

I. King   H. T. Hou
{king,hthou}@cs.cuhk.edu.hk

Department of Computer Science & Engineering
The Chinese University of Hong Kong
Shatin, New Territories, Hong Kong

Abstract— **Many multimedia applications require the synthesis of facial expressions. We demonstrate the synthesis of different degrees of various 2D grayscale facial expressions using the Radial Basis Function (RBF) neural network. The RBF network is used to generate spatial displacement of a set of facial feature points as in multidimensional density interpolation. We have implemented two RBF networks for synthesizing facial expressions. One network generates the spatial displacement of facial feature points for different degrees of expressions and the other generates the spatial displacement of facial feature points of mixed facial expressions. The predicted facial landmark displacement information is then fed into our image warping algorithm along with the expressionless facial image to produce the final synthesized facial image. We discuss the method used and demonstrate the results.**

1   Introduction

Facial expressions play an important role in non-verbal communications. Furthermore, we use facial gestures to convey our mood and express our feeling. Moreover, to make an intelligent, friendly, and effective machine-human interface we need to synthesize facial expressions for a variety of applications, e.g., graphics, animation, security, teleconference, and facial data compression.

Suppose we are given a 2D grayscale expressionless face image of a person, how can we synthesize different expressions of that person? One of the ways to synthesize facial expressions is to find the "approximate" displacement of prominent facial feature points. This problem is similar to non-parametric multivariate density estimation since we do not know the underlying multidimensional facial landmark displacement function. Moreover, we often cannot obtain accurate facial landmark displacement information due to inherently inaccurate input data. This is because: (1) it is hard to generate a set of standardized expressions, e.g., each person may "smile" differently, (2) it is hard to produce accurately the precise degree of a particular expression, e.g., how to generate a "20% smile"?, and (3) it is difficult to mix various facial expressions, e.g., how to gesture a "happy and sad" face?

Current approaches in synthesizing facial expressions include texture mapping approach to 3D facial image synthesis [11] and the use of 3D model of facial muscles and tissues [4]. These methods proves to be tedious in determining the actual parameter values for synthesizing and animating facial expressions. An alternative approach has been investigated by Nur Arad et al. [9], which demonstrated the use of Radial Basis Function (RBF) in interpolating the anchor points for 2D image warping, which can be applied to synthesize facial expressions. However, it does not provide a mechanism to determine the appropriate destination of the anchor points for each particular facial expression.

We have obtained a set of prominent facial landmarks which have greater potentials in revealing changes in displaying a particular facial expression. The spatial displacement of these landmarks for the facial expressions is used to generate control points in the image warping procedure for synthesizing various facial expressions.

We construct the RBF neural network that maps the relationship between necessary patterns of movements of these landmarks and the six universal facial expressions described in [3]. The distinctive difference between this method and that of [9] is that, we use the RBF in the network description for finding the necessary changes of the landmarks, rather than in interpolating the anchor points in image warping.

The next section will briefly introduce the facial expression recognition process which is crucial in understanding the facial expression synthesis process. We will then formulate the RBF network in Section 3. Lastly, we will demonstrate our results and end with some discussions.

2   Reverse of Facial Expression Recognition

Before we deal with the synthesis of facial expressions, we briefly summarize the process of facial expression recognition since each process is the inverse of the other.

---

*This work is supported in part by RGC Earmark Grant # 221500620, Direct Grant 220500910, and Direct Grant 220500720. A preliminary version was presented in ICNN'96 [8].

2.1   Facial Expression Recognition

In [7], Kobuyashi & Hara presented a method of classifying the six universal facial expressions using neural network. A set of 30 facial landmarks located near the eye-brows, eyes and the mouth are defined as the Facial Characteristic Points(FCPs) as shown in Figure 1(a). These points are extracted semi-automatically from a 2D grayscale expressionless face image as shown in Figure 2(a)-(c). These FCPs are selected since they have the largest variance among facial expressions; hence, they are the best candidate in revealing the changes in facial expressions.

The basic idea is to find out the spatial differences between the FCPs of the normal face and that of the expressive face. Thus, the differences of those 30 pairs of position information will constitute the 60 inputs to the two-layered neural network as shown in Figure 1(b). The number of output layer unit is six, the position of which corresponds to each of the six emotion labels in the order HAPPY, SAD, ANGRY, FEAR, SURPRISED and DISGUSTED.

Since each 2D grayscale input face image is different, we must perform several pre-processing steps. To compensate for the differences in the size, orientation and position of the faces in the image as well as the size of the face components, we have to transform the coordinates of the FCPs so that they are comparable across the set of individual faces. Therefore, the absolute coordinates of the FCPs have to undergo the following four transformations:

Translation - It is employed to translate the origin of coordinate system to the nose top of the individual as the absolute pixel coordinates of the FCPs are obtained relative to the lower left corner of the image. A quantity called *base* is introduced, which should not be varied for each of the facial expressions,

$$base = \sqrt{(xb_2 - xb_1)^2 + (yb_2 - yb1)^2}$$

where (xb_1, yb_1) and (xb_2, yb_2) are the pixel position of inner corners of left eye and right eye respectively. The mid-point, (x_0, y_0), between (xb_1, yb_1) and (xb_2, yb_2) is also calculated using the mid-point formula, $x_0 = (xb_1 + xb_2)/2$ and $y_0 = (yb_1 + yb_2)/2$. The origin of the new coordinate system $(origin_x, origin_y)$ is calculated as $(x_0 - base * \sin\theta, y_0 - base * \cos\theta)$.

Rotation - It is employed to correct the inclination of the face so that the coordinates are expressed with respect to the vertical axis of the face in the new coordinate system. The inclination of the face with respect to the horizontal line, θ, is defined as

$$\tan^{-1} \frac{(yb_2 - yb1)}{(xb_2 - xb_1)}.$$

Normalization - It is introduced to compensate the distance effect between the client's face and the camera. The landmarks of the normal and expressive face after rotation are divided by the value *base*. These normalized values of the expressive face are subtracted from those of the normal one.

Standardization - As those subtracted values are indeed the absolute displacements of the FCPs from their normal position, thus these magnitudes are subject to individual variations. Standardization is needed to find out the relative displacement of the landmarks from their normal position. From the normal face, we determine the standard values as follows: openness of eyes: $((yn_7 - yn_5) + (yn_8 - yn_6))/2$, width of eyes: $((xn_1 - xn_3) + (xn_4 - xn_2))/2$ height of eyebrows: $((yn_{19} - yn_1) + (yn_{20} - yn_2))/2$ openness of mouth: $(yn_{26} - yn_{25})$ width of mouth: $(xn_{24} - xn_{23})$ where (xn_i, yn_i) is the *i-th* FCP of the normal face after normalization.

After the above pre-processing steps are performed, the filtered data is ready for both facial expression classification and synthesis.

3   Synthesis as a Reverse Process

The recognition of facial expressions is a classification process. The reverse of it is a multidimensional interpolation problem.

3.1   The Radial Basis Function Network

The basic principle of synthesizing facial expressions is to find out the necessary relative spatial displacement of the FCPs for each facial expression. This is similar to a nonparametric multidimensional density estimation problem. The RBF network is ideal for interpolation since it uses a radial basis function, e.g., Gaussian function, for smoothing out and predict missing and inaccurate inputs.

Given a set of n-dimensional training data, $(\vec{x}_i, \vec{d}_i), \vec{x}_i \in R^n, \vec{d}_i \in R^{n'}$ for $i = 1, \cdots, m$, find a function $F : R^n \mapsto R^{n'}$ which satisfies the interpolation conditions

$$F_k(\vec{x}_i) = d_{ik}, \qquad i = 1, \cdots, m; k = 1, \cdots, n' \text{ with } n' < m. \tag{1}$$

We would consider interpolating functions of the form

$$F_k(\vec{x}) = \sum_{j=1}^{m} w_{jk} \, g(\| \vec{x} - \vec{\mu}_j \|), \qquad \vec{x} \in R^n, k = 1, \cdots, n'$$

where $\|\cdot\|$ denotes the usual Euclidean norm on R^n and $\vec{\mu}_j \in R^{n'}$, $j = 1, 2, \cdots, m$ denotes the *centers* of the radial-basis functions which are given as the known data points.

Often, the $g(\cdot)$ is the normalized Gaussian activation function defined as

$$g(\vec{x}) = \frac{\exp[-(\vec{x} - \vec{\mu}_j)^2/2\sigma_j^2]}{\sum_k \exp[-(\vec{x} - \vec{\mu}_k)^2/2\sigma_k^2]}$$

where x is the input vector, μ is a set of weights and σ is the width of the RBF.

Hence, the determination of the nonlinear map $F(\vec{x})$ has been reduced to the problem of solving the following set of linear equations for the coefficients w_j,

$$\begin{pmatrix} f_{1k} \\ \vdots \\ f_{mk} \end{pmatrix} = \begin{pmatrix} A_{11} & \cdots & A_{1m} \\ \vdots & \ddots & \vdots \\ A_{m1} & \cdots & A_{mm} \end{pmatrix} \begin{pmatrix} w_{1k} \\ \vdots \\ w_{mk} \end{pmatrix}, \quad k = 1, 2, ..., n'$$

where $A_{ij} = g(\|\vec{x}_i - \vec{\mu}_j\|)$, $i, j = 1, 2, \cdots, m$.

The basic architecture of our two-layered RBF network is shown in Figure 1(b). The input layer units of the neural network is 60 since we have 30 pairs of FCP position information, and the number of output layer unit is six, the position of which corresponds to each of the six universal facial expressions in the order **HAPPY, SAD, ANGRY, FEAR, SURPRISED**, and **DISGUSTED**. The training phase of the RBF network constitutes the optimization of a fitting procedure on known spatial displacement data points of various facial expressions presented to the network in the form of input-output examples.

The x in the Gaussian function corresponds to the facial expression label for the neural network while the output of the network is a vector of movements of FCPs. The σ corresponds to the spread constants set in the training setup. The only real design decision for RBF network is to find a good value of σ, which determines the generalization ability of the RBFs. The variable σ should be large enough to allow the overlapping of the input regions of radial basis functions. This makes the network function smoother and results in better generalization for new input vectors occurring between input vectors. However, σ should not be so large that each neuron responds in essentially the same manner, i.e., any information presented to the network becomes lost. Our σ is picked manually by trial and error, within maximum and minimum of distances of input vectors. After training, 2 sets of weights, $\vec{\mu}$ and w, are obtained. This is used to produce the spatial displacement of facial landmark points.

The generalization phase is then the interpolation between the data points along the constrained surface generated during the training phase. Here the generalization will allow the user to specify various degrees of a facial expression.

We now will perform post-processing on the facial feature displacement data to synthesize facial expressions.

3.2 Mapping the Output to the Image

As the output from the RBF network is a vector that consists of relative displacements of FCPs for a facial expression, the displacement vectors have to be de-standardized, de-normalized and transformed back according to the FCPs of the normal face.

Let the output vector be in the form $(x_1, ..., x_{30}, y_1, ..., y_{30})$ where (x_i, y_i) denotes the displacement of the *i-th* FCP. To perform de-standardization, the elements of the output vector should be multiplied by their corresponding standard value: y_1 to y_{16} are multiplied by (openness of eyes), x_1 to x_{16} are multiplied by (width of eyes), y_{17} to y_{22} are multiplied by (height of eyebrows), x_{17} to x_{22} are multiplied by (height of eyebrows), y_{23} to y_{30} are multiplied by (openness of mouth), and x_{23} to x_{30} are multiplied by (width of mouth).

To de-standardize, the elements of the output vector are multiplied by their corresponding standard values as defined in [7] and then added to the normalized values of the FCPs of the normal face image:

$$x_i := x_i + normal\_x_i, \qquad y_i := y_i + normal\_y_i$$

These values are then de-normalized by the *base* value:

$$rotx_i := x_i * base, \qquad roty_i := y_i * base$$

and then rotated and translated back:

$$x_i := rotx_i * \cos\theta - roty_i * \sin\theta, \qquad y_i := rotx_i * \sin\theta + roty_i * \cos\theta$$

$$xb_i := x_i + origin_x, \qquad yb_i := y_i + origin_y$$

(xb_i, yb_i) is then the new position of the *i-th* FCP on the normal face image.

To generate an expressive face image from the normal face image, we used 2D image warping [5]. Both of the FCPs of the normal face and that of the expressive face are connected to form triangular patches as shown on Figure 1(c). Image warping is then performed by scan-converting each triangle.

4   Training by Radial Basis Network and Results

Now the remaining problem is how we obtain the displacements of the FCPs corresponding to a certain emotion. We have made use of Radial Basis Network (RBN) to carry out two sets of training: (1) training with different degrees of six universal facial expressions; (2) training with a set of six universal facial expressions.

4.1   Experimental Results

We have carried out 2 sets of training using the Neural Network Toolbox of Matlab running on Sun Sparc20 and C programs on SGI INDY machines. A set of 128×128 grayscale images are used in our experiment. We set $\sigma = 0.5$ and 1 for RBN1 and RBN2 respectively. The total time for facial feature extraction, pre-processing, neural network calculation, and image warping takes less than 15 seconds.

4.1.1   Training with Different Degrees of Six Universal Facial Expressions

Facial expressions can have different strengths, e.g, the degree of happiness ranges from smile to grin to laugh. Therefore, we used five images with different degrees for each of the six universal facial expressions, thus a total of 30 images are used as the training set. For each expression, we manually arrange the images in the order of decreasing strength and assign to each of them the value 1.0, 0.9, 0.8, 0.7 and 0.6 accordingly. Thus the input vector would be in the form $(0.6, 0, 0, 0, 0, 0)$ for the weakest degree of happiness among the five images.

After training, the network is able to generate the six universal facial expressions, plus different degrees of variation for each facial expression (RBN1). Figure 3(a)-(f) illustrate how the neural network is able to capture the features of the facial expressions: for happy face, the upward movement of mouth corners is captured; for sad face, the inner eyebrows raise and mouth corners go down; for surprise the whole eyebrows raise and the mouth widely open, etc. Figure 4(a)-(e) display five degrees of happy faces generated. We find that this process is certainly not a linear one.

4.1.2   Training with a Set of Six Universal Facial Expressions

We find that the above network is unable to generate mixed expressions, i.e., if we specify the input as a mix of some degrees of sadness and happiness, the network cannot generate the output as a mixed expression. Hence, we trained another RBF network with a set of six universal expressions which we denote as RBN2. When mixed inputs such as $(1.0, 1.0, 0, 0, 0, 0)$ are applied, the output shows a dependence on the mixed input, resulting in a mixed expression. However, this network is unable to generate different degree for each expression. Figure 5(a)-(e) show the results obtained from this network.

4.2   Discussions

Although the experimental results are encouraging, we briefly outline the shortcoming of this facial synthesis method using the RBF network.

1. **Hard to obtain accurate FCPs for training.** – From our experimental results, one main problem we faced is that we were unable to unify the two RBF network into one network capable in generating both mixed expressions and different degrees of each expression. This is due to the highly inaccurate and hard-to-obtain training information.

2. **The basic parameters are hand-tuned.** – We have mentioned that the input vectors of RBN1 consist of arbitrarily assigned values that represent the degree of emotion. These distinct data points are required for different degrees of variation for each expression. Therefore there is a need to adjust the inputs for the training to be successful. This is a highly subjective judgement; hence, an adaptive one would be better.

3. **Cannot generate artificial features.** – Apart from the movements and shapes of the facial components, wrinkles such as naso-labial folds or crow's-feet wrinkles on the face contribute significantly to facial expressions. However, our system only uses normal face images where the face is free from any wrinkle, and simple warping technique is employed. Special technique such as texture mapping should be adopted to add such wrinkles to the final image.

4. **Additional FCPs are needed.** – Also, more FCPs need to be added near the eyebrows and mouth region to obtain smooth, detailed, and better warped images.

5   Conclusion

We have built a system for synthesizing mixture and various degrees of facial expressions. Radial Basis Function networks are used to map the emotion labels to the displacements of the set of FCPs. Depending on the positions of the sample data points, the RBF approach constructs a nonlinear function space according to an arbitrary distance measure. Thus an interpolating surface which exactly passes through all the pairs of the training set can be produced so that when data points not in the training set are

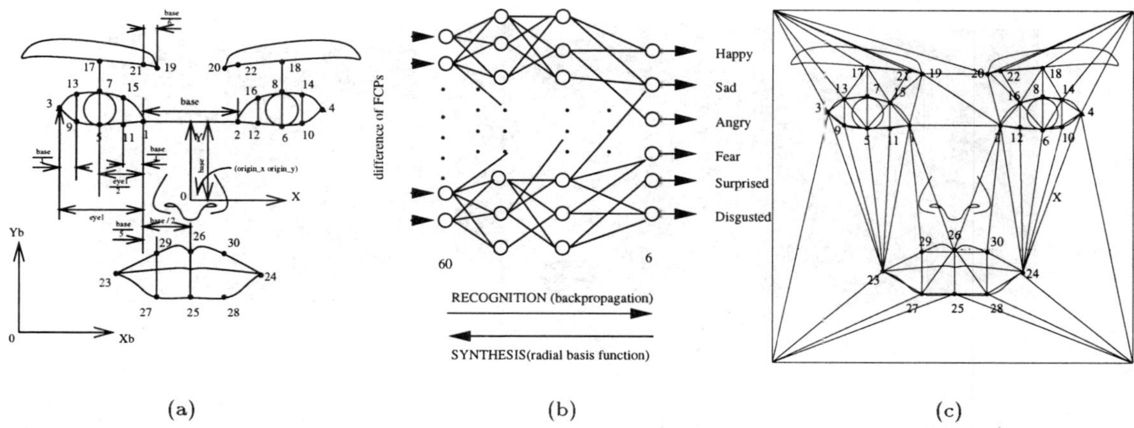

Figure 1: (a) The 30 facial characteristic points, (b) the neural network for facial expression classification and synthesis, and (c) the FCPs are connected to form patches for image warping.

presented to the RBF network, the mapping can also be interpolated. Since facial expressions have different degrees and are often mixed with one another, the use of RBF network for high dimensional interpolation makes the synthesis of facial expressions possible.

Acknowledgments

The authors gratefully acknowledge Ms. Mary Y.Y. Leung and Ms. Yen-Hui Hung for their initial design and implementation of the image warping software program at the Neural Computing & Engineering Lab.

References

[1] P. J. Benson. Morph transformation of the face image. *Image and Vision Computing*, 12:691–696, 1994.

[2] D. Broomhead and D. Lowe. Multivariable functional interpolation and adaptive networks. *Complex Systems*, 2:321–355, 1988.

[3] P. Ekman and W. V. Friesen. *Unmasking the Face*. Consulting Psychologists Press, Inc., 1975.

[4] F. Hara and H. Kobayashi. Computer graphics for expressing robot-artificial emotions. IEEE International Workshop on Robot and Human Communication, 1992.

[5] P. Heckbert. Graphics gems. pages 65–77, 1990.

[6] K. Hertz and Palmer. *Introduction to the theory of neural computation*. Addison Wesley, 1991.

[7] H. Kobayashi and F. Hara. Recognition of six basic facial expressions and their strength by neural network. IEEE International Workshop on Robot and Human Communication, 1992.

[8] Mary Y.Y. Leung, H. Y. Hung, and I. King. Facial expression synthesis by radial basis function network and image warping. In *IEEE International Conference on Neural Networks*, volume III, pages 1400–1405, Washington D.C., 1996. IEEE Computer Society.

[9] D. R. Nur Arad, Nira Dyn and Y. Yeshurun. Image warping by radial basis functions: Application to facial expressions. *CVGIP: Graphical Models and Image Processing*, 56, No. 2:161–172, 1994.

[10] G. Wolberg. *Digital Image Warping*. IEEE Computer Society Press Monograph, 1990.

[11] J. Yau and A. Duffy. *A Texture mapping approach to 3D facial image synthesis*. 1988.

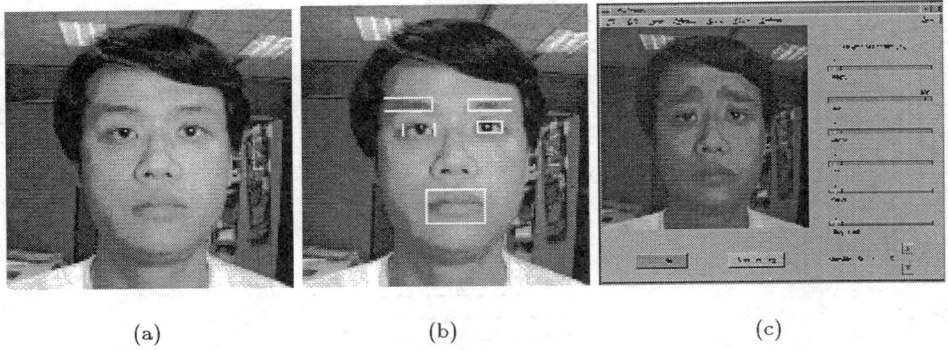

Figure 2: (a) The NORMAL face, (b) the FCPs are extracted semi-automatically from the expressionless face by first marking the facial feature area in white rectangles, and (c) a window view of the system.

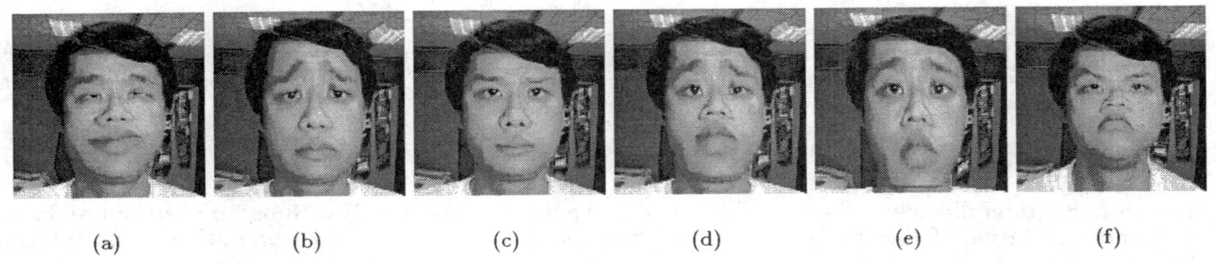

Figure 3: The six universal facial expressions generated by RBN1: (a) NORMAL, (b) HAPPY, (c) SAD, (d) ANGRY, (e) FEAR, (f) SURPRISED and (g) DISGUSTED.

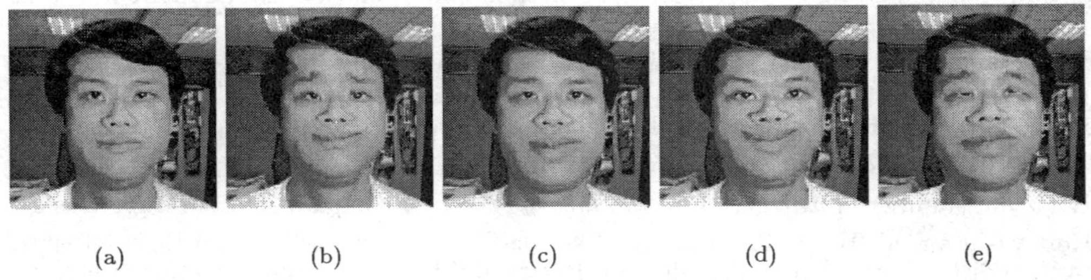

Figure 4: Various degrees of the "HAPPY" expression increasing from left to right.

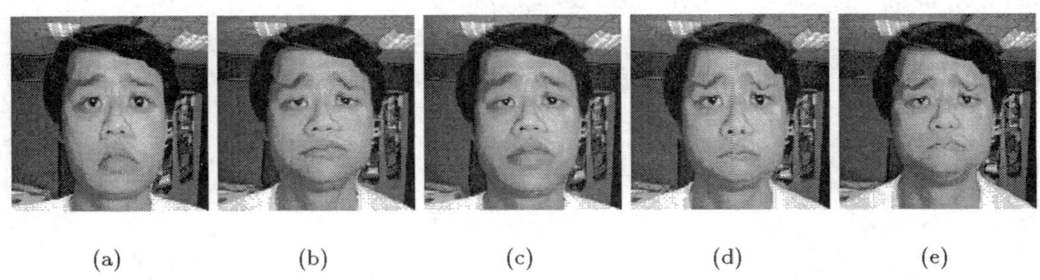

Figure 5: A mixture of various expressions: (a) FEAR–SURPRISED, (b) HAPPY–SAD, (c) HAPPY–SURPRISED, (d) SAD–ANGRY, and (e) SAD–DISGUSTED.

Hybrid Systems and Applications

(Poster Presentation)

Neural Network Model with Pointer Loop for STM

Huang Bingxian

Institute of Automation, Academia Sinica, Beijing , China, 100080

Abstract:

Human short-term memory (STM) is characterized by capacity limited and chunking for information storage. In this paper, a neural network model for STM was proposed. The model consists of two neural networks, one is the network of represetation of information content that share with long-term memory, the other is the STM pionter loop. Computer simulation that mimic the chess board position reproduction task are performed, it shows that the model's behaviour are same as that of the persons in the task. So, the model grasp two main characteristics of STM.

Ⅰ. Introduction

Cognitive psychological studies shown that: Human memory accorging to storing duration, can divided into sensory memory, short-term memory (STM) and long-term memory (LTM). They have different memory mechanism and storage site[1][2]. The length of time during which a memory is retained in STM is few seconds to half a minute. The capacity of STM is limited, it is generally asserted that the capacity is only 7 ± 2 chunks. The information content in a chunk depend on the information encoding.

Capacity limited and chunking are two fundamental charateristics of STM. For example, in the chess board reproduction experiment, The subject is shown a position from a actural chess game with about 25 pieces on the board for 5 seconds. and then reproduces the position from memory, a weaker player will replace few pieces on the board, but a master can perform this task with twenty or more pieces correctly. It is because the average person regard the position of a piece as a chunk, and the master regard the configuration of pieces as a chunk [3]. This result indicates that STM probably is pointer like. The master's STM pointer is point to the configuration which have been stored in LTM. In this paper a neural network model with pointer loop is proposed for STM. and computer simulation of the model show that the model grasp of two main characteristics of STM.

Ⅱ. Neural network model of STM

According to the pointer like hypothesis of STM, the neural network model of STM was proposed. The model consists of two neural network, one is the pointer loop, it consists of many neuron closed loops which have limited capacity. The other is a hierarchical neuron network with huge capacity. It is the representation area of event's content that corresponding to the association area of neocortices. An activative pattern of neurons of this area represent an event that is perceived. We assert that LTM and STM occupy same representation area. The LTM is realized by synaptic connections between neurons of representation area, and STM is realized by establishing of synaptic connections between neurons of pointer loop and neurons of representation area. Because there are many pointer loops, any area of representation can be linked to a pointer loop, and pointer loops are inhibitive each other, so that only one loop can be activated at a time, this loop became the pointer of the event in STM. The neurons in a loop are activated in order and link with the activated neuron of the representation area at that time. Fig. 1 is the architecture of STM neural network model we proposed, where each block is an neural network. F is the neural network of pointer loops. A_1 and A_2 is a two levels associative memory network. It is representation area of memory content. Activated patterns of neurons of A_2 represent the events and activated patterns of neurons of A_1 represent the higher level events or abstract concept [4]. Each pointer loop in F are connected with corresponding area of A_1 or A_2, W_{FA1}, W_{FA2}, W_{A12}, denote the synaptic weights between F and A_1, F and A_2, A_1 and A_2 respectively. In our model, we assume that LTM have been established by previous experiences, so W_{A12} is determinate. When an event is stored in STM, W_{FA1} or W_{FA2} increase rapidly according Hebbian rule and then decay gradually. We also assume that higher level take priority of lower level area, so, if some patterns in A_1 are activated, the pointer point to A_1; W_{FA1} is increased and W_{FA2} is not. When information retrieve from STM, the pointer loop is activated first, and then, corresponding neural pattern of representation area is activated. So the content that was stored in STM is retrieved. Because neurons in pointer loop is limited, so that the capacity of the model of STM is limited.

Ⅲ. Computer Simulation

For verifing availability of the model, the computer simulation was performed. It mimicked the chess board position reproduction task, in experiment the subject is shown a position from a actual chess game with about 25 pieces on the board for 5 sec, and 5 seconds is not enough to form LTM. After showing the board , the subject was ordered to reproduce the position from STM. Two different conditions corresponding to a weaker player and master were corried out.

Real nervous system is work parallelly, the pieces and the configurations of chess board should be represented by neural assembly. For simplifing, in our preliminary simulation, we use a neuron instead of the neural assembly for the representation. It may lose some glaceful perfrormances of parallel system, but the fundamental characteristics of the model still maintain. We assumed that there are 100 positions and 6 configurations on the board, so that, there are 100 neurons in A_2 and 6 neurons in A_1. When a position was occupied by a piece, the corresponding neuron on A_2 is activated; a neuron in A_1 is activated, it means a corresponding configuration appear in the board. We also assumed that there are two pointer loop, each loop consists of 5 neurons, one pointer loop corresponding to the chess board area. We use linear threshold function as the characteristics of a neuron, and A_2 is denoted by 100 dimensions vector X, A_1 is denoted by 6 dimensons vector X_1, F is denoted by 5 dimension vector X_F, and x_i denote the ith element of X, x_{1i} denote the ith element of X_1 and then the moving equations of the model as follow:

$$x_{f,i} = 1[x_{f,i-1}(t-1) - \theta_f]$$
$$X_1(t) = 1[W_{A1_2} \cdot X(t-1) + W_{FA_1} \cdot X_F(t-1) - \theta_1]$$
$$X(t) = 1[W_{A1_2} \cdot X_1(t-1) + W_{FA_2} \cdot X_F(t-1) - \theta_2]$$

where x_{f_i} is the ith element of X_F, θ_f, θ_1, θ_2 is the threshold of neuron in F, A_1, A_2 respectively and the learning equation of the model are:

$$w_{FA_2}(i,j) = 0 \qquad\qquad\qquad \text{if } X_i \in X_{1_g} \neq 0$$
$$\qquad = x_i \cdot x_{f_j} - k_1 \cdot w_{FA_2}(i,j) \qquad \text{otherwise}$$
$$w_{FA_1}(i,j) = x_{1_i} \cdot x_{f\_} w_{FA_1}(i,j) \cdot K_2$$

where $w_{FAZ}(i,j)$ is the ij-th element of matrix W_{FAZ}, $w_{FA1}(i,j)$ is the ij-th element of martrix W_{FA1} and k_1, k_2, is the forgotten factor. $X_i \in X_{1_g}$ denote that the $i-$th piece is belong to $g-$th configuration.

In simulation firstly the positions of pieces on the board produce randomly with $p = 0.25$, p is the probability of a position that occupy by a piece. So that, about $20-30$ neurons are activated in A_2, it corresponding 20-30 pieces was shown on the board for STM.

First condition is corresponding to average person, he cann't recognize the configurations, so $W_{A12} = 0$. Run the model in this condition, the result is shown in Fig.2 the left side is the position for memory, and the right side is the pieces that replace by the model, only few pieces was retrieved. This behaviour same as that of weaker player.

Another condition also simulated in computer, it corresponding to the master, because he recognize all configurations; so that, W_{A12} is known. In this condition, pointer connet to A_1 and then X is retrieved according W_{A12}. Fig.3 is the position of the condition, the left side of Fig.3 is the positions for memory, the right side is the pieces that retrieved by the model. You can see, almost all pieces are replaced correctly. and this result is same as that of the master in chess board reproduce task. The simulations as above shown that the model capture two main characteristic of STM: capacity limited and chunking.

IV. Discussion

There are different models about relationship between STM and LTM. Traditional view assert that STM is the gateway to LTM. The information content to be registesed in LTM or to be retrieved from LTM must pass through STM. and the representation site of LTM and that of STM are different. Recently Fuster[5] has been point out that LTM and STM may be deposited and represented in the same neocortex. In our model, we assume that two kind of memory share the same representation area. From the point of view of information storing, it is unreasonable that STM and LTM occupy different representation area. If STM used different memory space for representation, it will need as huge resources as LTM for encoding the rich information content; and information in STM are unvalued for long time retension. By using few neurons that constitute the pointer loop. Short-time storing of information can be performed in our model. Pointer loop link with the representation area of LTM. then very rich information can be stored in STM. and by using LTM memory, capacity of STM can be increased by suitable chunking. Computer simulation shows that proposed model is functionally similar to human STM system, we believe that the neural network model of STM proposed here hold the basic characteristics of human STM, it will help to understanding the principle of human memory.

Recently, Neuro psycholgical researches include recording from single cell in behaviors, metabolic mapping and PET observation, show that prefrontal cortex is involved in STM[6]. it is not yet clear what its role is neural activity in prefrontal cortex possibility is itself the representation of information, It also possible that the prefrontal activity represent a pointer or index[7], our model supports the pointer hypothesis.

This work is supported by Chinese Natural Sciences Foundation and Chinese National Key Project of Fundamental Reasearch climbing Program.

References

[1] Anderson J. R. Cognitive Pychology and Implication, 3rd edition, W. H. Freman and company, N. Y. 1990.

[2] Parkin A. J. : Memory and Amnesia, Basil Blockwell, 1987.

[3] Chase W. C. & Simon H. A. : Cognitive Psychology, 4:55 – 81, 1973.

[4] Huang Bingxian: Associative Memory and Brain Model, In Biological Science References Vol·25:145 – 166, Scientific Publishing House, Beijing, 1988.

[5] Fuster J. M. : Memory in Cerebral Cortex, MIT Press, Cambridge, 1995.

[6] Goldman – Rakic P. S. : Scientific American 267(3):73 – 80, 1992.

[7] Jonides J. etal: Nature, 363:623 – 625, 1993.

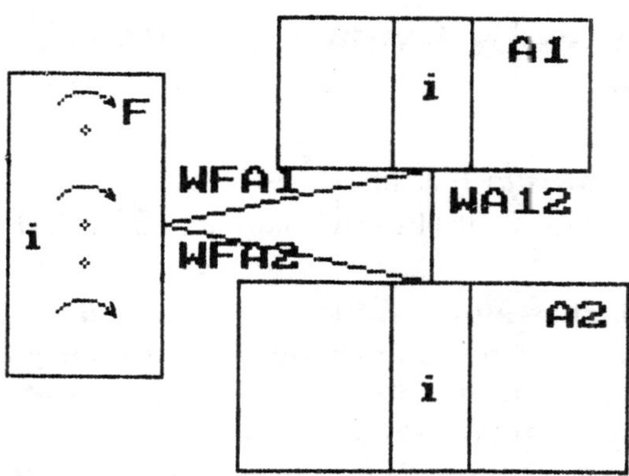

Figure 1

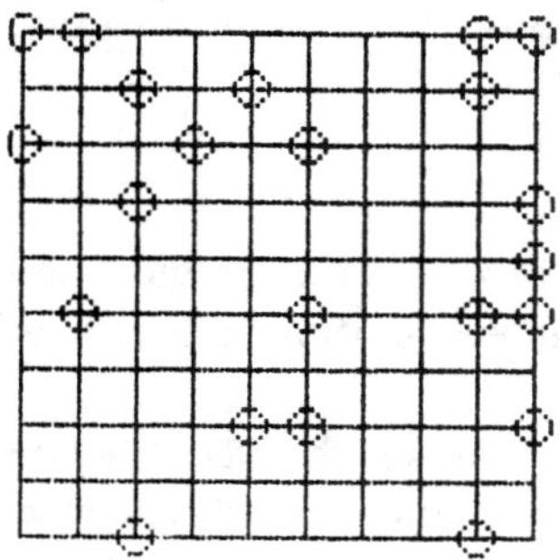
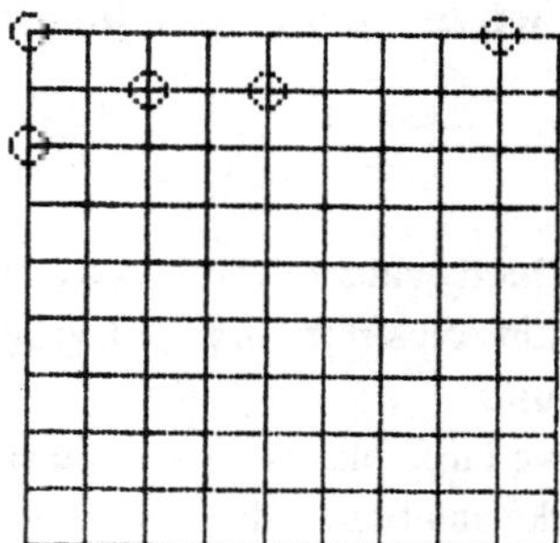

Figure 2

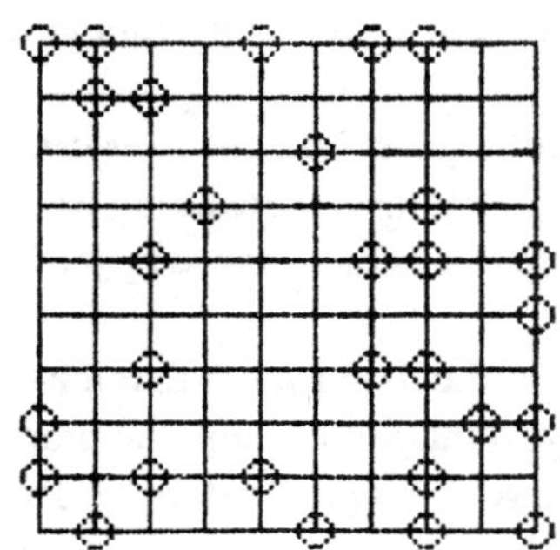
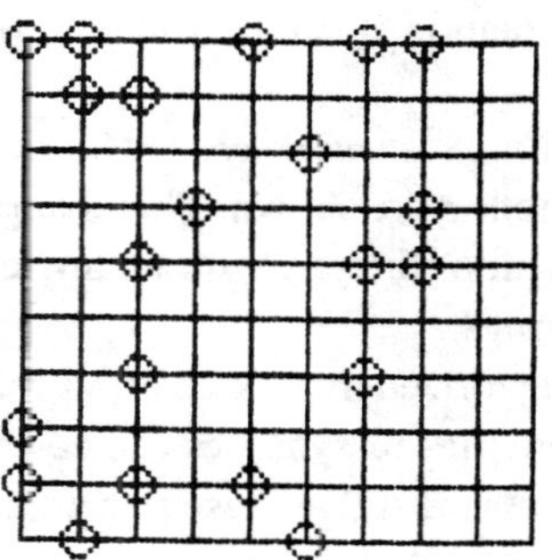

Figure 3

Creation of Evaluation Axes by Evolution and their Roles for Mind in Neural Networks

Mitsuo Takase
3013-1-503 Futoo-cho Kouhoku-ku Yokohama 222, JAPAN

Abstract —Evaluation axes, which evaluate value, are created in the vector space of cells in the process of evolution. They play important roles not only for living things to continue to exist for generations, but also for creation of a part of mind. They can not be created by learning, but by evolution. They memorize necessary states, which are made essential through evolution, for living things to continue to exist by patterns and can be stimulated by input patterns or by themselves from mutual connection. When the values of states or patterns are evaluated by the axes, actions to approach to get them or to avoid them are always accompanied. Then part to transmit and strengthen informations from evaluation axes to part to act becomes important and can contribute as a part of mind when part to act has multiple components and can do many types of responses.

1 Introduction

Evaluation axes, which evaluate value, are created in the vector space of cells in the process of evolution. They can play important roles not only for living things to continue to exist for generations, but also for creation of a part of mind.

Neural networks have large plasticity and are changeable by learning. On the other hand there can be many parts of neural networks and brain which can not be changed in their structures, neural connections and even synapse conductivities. Because there are necessary things for living things to live like food and preferable things and many of them are memorized by nature. So it is thought that these things are memorized in gene through evolution and transmitted to offsprings.

Evaluation axes mean memorized patterns. They memorize necessary states, which are made essential through evolution, for living things to continue to exist for generations by patterns and can be stimulated by input patterns or by themselves from mutual connection. The living thing is created to be driven to take actions to approach and get the state (or avoid from sense of crisis with minus value) when one of the axes is stimulated. In this situation it can be said that the axes evaluate the value of the state from the definition shown in section 2.

Here how evaluation axes can be created by evolution, not by learning and how the axes can contribute as a part of mind like emotion are shown. Then I suppose that patterns memorized by learning can not be connected to cause actions directly without any evaluation and that patterns memorized by learning can not be transmitted to offsprings.

Patterns can be memorized in gene and transmitted to offsprings in the assumption that the structure of cells and the conductivities of synapses can be changed gradually by mutation through the process of evolution. It is also assumed that these structures of cells and synapse conductivities are hardly changed through the lifetime of each living thing.

If a pattern newly created through evolution process as an evaluation axis makes probability for living things to continue to exist higher, the pattern continues to exist with the living things with the heightened probability. Patterns memorized in this way are transmitted to offsprings through evolution and these patterns continue to be memorized in gene through evolution for a long time. In this process multiple evaluation axes can be created through evolution and the space of evaluation axes can be created through evolution in gene. Evaluation axes can not be created by learning, but by evolution. This is explained in section 3 and 4. Comparison and priority among multiple values can be also made. (section 5.4)

When a pattern created in evolution at least affects to actions (whatever actions they may be.) taken by the living things to heighten the probability for them to continue to exist for generations, the pattern can continue to exist with the living things. In the case of value when a state or an input pattern is recognized as a valuable pattern by stimulating an evaluation axis of a living thing, actions to approach and to get the state are taken. In this case the pattern memorized in the axis can be thought to evaluate value. Here I mention about the case of *value* and the definition of *value* is explained in section 2. There is the definition of value in [1] and value is analyzed in [2].

Then part (part B in fig.2,3) to transmit and strengthen informations from evaluation axes to part (part C in fig.2,3) to act is important and can contribute as a part of mind when part to act has multiple components and can do many types of responses. This is shown in section 5. Evaluation axis necessarily accompanies the part (part B in fig.2,3).

Here living things with neural networks mean things with neural networks, which behave like animal (as complex living things) etc.. Input patterns mean informations of things or states.

2 Definition of value and models of living things with evaluation axis

2.1 About the definition of value (What is the evaluation of value in living things?)

Not only the memorization of necessary states(for example eating foods), but also doing actions to seek the states are necessary as evaluation axes. Because the memorization of necessary states is only memorization of patterns and there is nothing to show that they are valuable. For example there is the definition of value in [1]. Following definition can be applied to consider what kinds of parts are necessary for the system of living things to evaluate value to continue to exist. It is thought reasonable to apply this definition of value to our purpose.

[Definition of value]

(1)There is a purpose for living things, for example, to continue to exist and flourish.

(2)Necessary states for the purpose are memorized.

(3)There are actions to approach to get the states when the states are recalled. (There are actions to avoid from sense of crisis when the states are recalled and have minus value.)

2.2 Models with evaluation function and the behavior of models

Some living things, which can evaluate necessary patterns, can be shown in simple models of fig.1,2 thinking from the definition of value. Model 1 means simple living things and model 2 means more complex living things. In these models there are three main parts. Part A memorizes necessary states by patterns and can be stimulated by input patterns or by themselves from mutual connection. Part B is transmission part from the information of part A to part C in model 1. Part B strengthens the information from part A and transmits it to part C in model 2.

Part C takes actions to approach to the states and get them (or avoid from sense of crisis). Part C has only one component and there can be only one way of response to approach to the states in model 1. On the other hand part C in Model 2 consists of multiple components and the living things can do various responses like movement for various directions, hearing some information, telling to information, etc.. These actions are taken to heighten the probability to be able to get the states, so they have generalized meaning to approach to a nearer position to get the states even in model 2. Responses by part C are not only patterns, but also spatiotemporal patterns.

In Model 2 part E is for thinking or planning and can be thought one of components in part C, since part E can be one of ways of responses to approach to necessary states.

3 Simplified mechanism as rule of evolution to show creation of evaluation axes

Here as rule of evolution a simple logic is used to explain how evaluation axes are created. Evaluation axes need be obtained from the time of birth or destined to be obtained in a time of lifetime by nature. The axes, which memorize necessary patterns, can be made by repeated creations of mutation and selections from testing through evolution.

[Assumption of changes of both network structure and synapse conductivities in evolution]

Patterns can be memorized in gene and transmitted to offsprings in the assumption that the network structure of cells and the conductivities of synapses can be changed gradually by mutation through the process of evolution. It is also assumed that these network structures of cells and synapse conductivities are not changed through the lifetime of each living thing.

[Axes, which heighten probability for living things to continue to exist, can be created and continue to exist in evolution.]

If a pattern newly created through evolution process makes probability for living things to continue to exist higher, the pattern continues to exist with the living things with the heightened probability as an evaluation axis.

(1)Case where probability, by which the number of living things increases in a generation, is greater than or equal to 1 (1 means not increasing and not decreasing.) before having the newly created evaluation axis.

The difference between the number of living things, which have the newly created axis and heighten probability to continue to exist, and the number of living things, which have not this newly created axis, can be increased infinitely by repetitive multiplication of the probability and the new probability for generations. Actually this difference will saturate, but at least the living things, which have the newly created axis, will be prevalent and the axis continues to exist in gene.

(2)Case where probability, by which the number of living things increases in a generation, is less than 1 before having the newly created evaluation axis.

In this case the number of the living things decreases in each lifetime. If the average probability for the living things to continue to exist is not heightened greater than or equal to 1, the newly created axis will disappear and will not continue to be memorized in gene in generations. If the average probability is heightened greater than or equal to 1 by the newly created axis, the axis will continue to exist in gene with the living things.

Patterns memorized in this way are transmitted to offsprings through evolution and these patterns continue to be memorized in gene through evolution for a long time. In this process multiple evaluation axes can be created through evolution and the space of evaluation axes can be created through evolution.

4 Necessary patterns for living things to continue to exist can not be memorized as evaluation axes by learning, but by evolution.

4.1 Evaluation axes are created not by learning, but by evolution.

The reasons are shown in following (1)~(3).

(1)There are basic necessary patterns for living things to continue to exist, which should be memorized by nature like eating food in living things with a simple structure and like seeking flourish in living things with a more complex structure. The patterns must be memorized so as to accompany actions to approach and get the states when they are stimulated.

(2)Necessary patterns can be memorized by evolution.(from section 3)

(3)Evaluation axes are not created by learning after birth. Here I suppose that patterns memorized by learning can not be connected to cause actions directly without any evaluation and that patterns memorized by learning can not be transmitted to offsprings.

Under the assumption patterns memorized by learning can not cause actions directly, so these patterns can not be evaluation axes from the definition of value in section 2.1. Moreover even if some patterns, which are very valuable for living things, are memorized by learning in a living thing, they are supposed not to be memorized in gene.

By learning hierarchical neural network tends to memorize new patterns diagonal to already memorized patterns impressively. Here neural network produces a new axis to memorize the new patterns. So this kind of neural network tends to memorize a wide range of patterns.

Evaluation axes can be said to be patterns memorized in gene which correlate with continuous existence or flourish for generations.

4.2 Evaluation axes are made memorize the essential patterns of the necessary concrete patterns.

Living things, which memorize patterns with correlation to necessary patterns for existence as evaluation axes, can continue to exist according to the degree of the correlation. Living things, which memorize essential patterns as precisely as possible, can continue to exist with the highest probability, so the essential patterns are memorized by evolution from the mechanism of section 3. Here an essential pattern means a common pattern of a same kind of necessary concrete patterns.

5 Part B is made important and can contribute as a part of mind like emotion in model 2

5.1 Many types of responses by part C with multiple components make part B large and important through evolution.

The enlargement of both part B and each component C_i $i=1,..,n$ of C in fig.2 can contribute to the enhancement of probability for the living thing to continue to exist. But the enlargement of part B can work to all the C_i $i=1,..,n$ and strengthen their functions more efficiently than the enlargement of a component C_i. More living things with enlarged part B rest than the living things with enlarged C_i, so part B can be enlarged faster and made important through evolution.

On the other hand in the case of model 1, which has only one component for part C, to enhance probability to exist, the part B and the part C can be strengthened equally. So this kind of model with simple structure for response can not easily develop part B through evolution.

5.2 Many types of responses by part C with multiple components make part B important for perception of value and make part C separate from such the perception.

A component C_i $i=1,..,n$ of C is not always stimulated to work when part A is stimulated. So each component C_i $i=1,..,n$ can not be said to perceive the information received from part A. Part B is always stimulated and strengthens the information from part A transmitting to part C when part A is stimulated. So part B can be said not only to perceive the information received from part A, but also to cause strong emotion like desiring and avoiding from sense of crisis to the living thing.

5.3 Through evolution neural networks in living things can have possibility to develop various evaluation axes.

Through evolution neural networks in the living things can have possibility to develop various evaluation axes which are valuable for the living things to continue to exist. Because if these newly created evaluation axes can contribute for the living things to continue to exist, the axes must continue to exist with living things with a high probability. Then the multiple evaluation axes give wider range of choices for actions to each input patterns. These axes can give many various emotions like desiring, avoiding from sense of crisis, hoping, fearing, etc. to the living things and can contribute for the formation of mind of the living things. For example they are not only the axes to seek necessary states like eating food, but also can be the axes to seek natural circumstances, natural beauty, truth, etc..

5.4 Priority among multiple evaluation axes in a living thing should be made through evolution.

Priority among multiple evaluation axes in living things is necessary to heighten probability for existence. The most necessary state memorized in an evaluation axis must have highest priority. So this kind of priority can be made through evolution.

If there are multiple evaluation axes, there are pairs of part A_i and part B_i $i=1,...,k$ in the model of fig.2. Part A_i and part B_i are components of part A and part B respectively. Part B_i amplifies and transmits informations only from A_i to part C.

Then large part B_j, which can give strong outputs to part C, can mean high priority, when we consider competition among part B_i of part A_i $i=1,...,k$.

5.5 Part B can contribute as a part of mind like emotion.

This can be caused by 5.1~5.4.

6 Discussion

As shown in section 2.2 part C in Model 2 consists of multiple components and the living things can do various responses like movement for various directions, hearing some information, telling to information, etc.. These actions can have generalized meaning to approach to a nearer position to get necessary states in a meaning that they most heighten the probability to get the states at each action. So even in the complex model actions taken may be able to be determined in advance to a large extent and may be projected like in the simple model.

References

[1]Perry, R.B.(1954)Realms of value, Harvard university press
[2]Perry, R.B.(1926)General theory of value, Longmans green and company

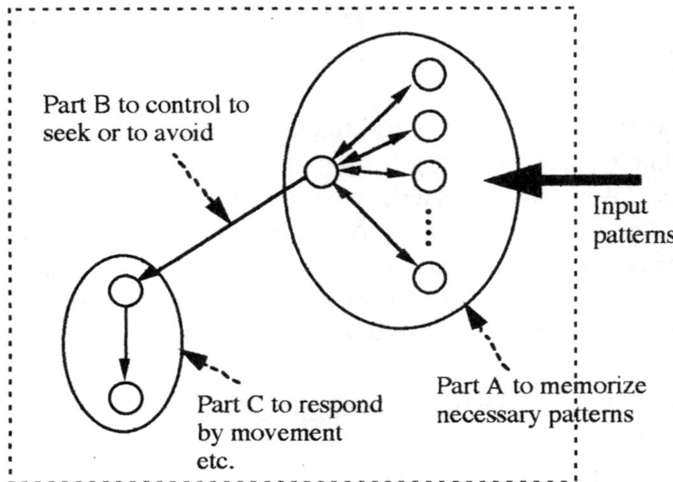

fig.1 Neural network where response is very simple. Small circles mean a cell or a set of cells.

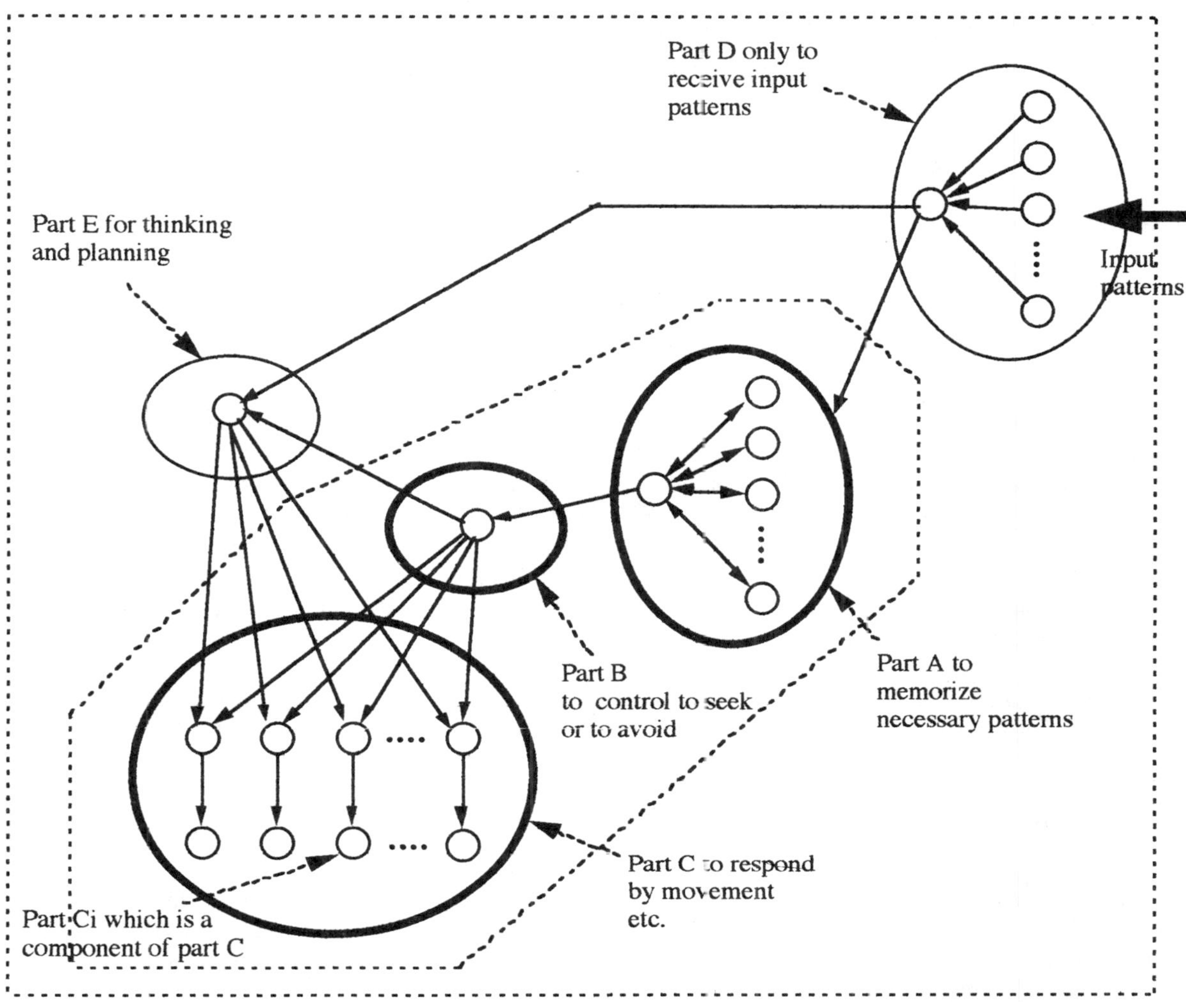

fig.2 Neural network where response is a vector and there can be too many patterns of response. Then what response should be taken can not be easily determined in advance. Small circles mean a cell or a set of cells.

The Use of Neural Networks for Detecting Cancerous
Cells Based on the One-class Problem Approach

Nabeel A. Murshed[‡], Flávio Bortolozzi[†] and Robert Sabourin[††]
[‡†]Centro Federal de Educação Tecnológica do Paraná (CEFET-PR) -
Pontifícia Universidade Católica do Paraná (PUC-PR), Paraná - Brasil.
[‡†]email: murshed@dainf.cefetpr.br
[††]École de Technologie Supérieure, Montréal - Canada.
e-mail: sabourin@gpa.etsmtl.ca

Abstract. We investigate the use of neural networks for detecting cancerous cells in microscopic images of breast cancer. Network training is performed using positive patterns (cancerous cells) *only*. This is a divergent from the common approach in which the neural networks are trained with positive and negative patterns. Four neural networks were studied: Back-propagation (BKP), Fuzzy ARTMAP, General Regression (GR), and Radial Basis Functions (RBF). Each network was trained with 383 patterns of cancerous cells and tested with 54 patterns of cancerous cells and 105 non-cancerous cells. Experimental analysis were performed with the Neural Works Professional II/Plus Simulator. Results of the experiments show that the performance of the Fuzzy ARTMAP network is superior to that of the other networks.

Key Words: Classification of cancerous cells, two-class problem approach, one-class problem approach, Back propagation, Fuzzy ARTMAP, General Regression Neural Network, and Radial Basis Functions.

1 Introduction

At the Laboratory de Sistemas Adaptativos (LSA) of the Centro Federal de Educação Tecnológica do Paraná (CEFET-PR) and at the Laboratory de Redes Neurais of the Universidade Católica do Paraná (PUC-PR), research has been conducted for developing a computer-based system for the analysis and classification of cancerous cells. One of the objectives of this research is to develop a classifier module based on neural networks, such that the classifier be able to detect cancerous and non-cancerous cells based on its *knowledge of the cancerous cells only*. This implies that the classifier network must be trained with patterns of cancerous cells (positive patterns) only. This approach is called the ***one-class problem approach***. It is defined bellow[9].

> *"If the objective of the pattern recognition system is to recognize a certain class of similar objects (positive patterns), then the pattern recognition system should be trained with prototypes from this class only"*.

This is similar to the way human beings perform pattern recognition. We all know that children and adults alike are capable of identifying positive patterns (e.g., airplanes) without being taught to identify negative patterns (e.g., cars, building, etc.). Moreover, a child or an adult is capable of identifying a negative pattern (e.g., cars) as ***not being an airplane*** without an *a priori* knowledge of the class of cars. A child or an adult, of course, could be trained to identify airplanes and cars as well. In such a case we have a two-class problem. But, if the objective is to identify the class of airplanes, then we have a one-class problem and, thus, there is no need to train the child or the adult with negative patterns.

The advantages of using the one-class problem approach is that network training is accomplished in a time shorter than when using the ***two-class problem approach***, in which the network is trained with positive and negative patterns. This is obvious since the network, in the one-class approach, needs to learn the features in one class only. Whereas, in the two class problem approach the network needs to learn the features in two classes. The training phase could even get complicated when dealing with complex and large data sets. Another advantage of the one-class problem approach is that the design of real-time systems can be simplified, when using the appropriate neural network, since collecting negative patterns for training is not required. For example consider the case of developing a computer-based signature verification system. In such system, obtaining *a good quantity* of signature forgeries for training is impossible. Thus, by adopting the one-class problem approach the system can be trained, for each writer, with genuine signatures of this writer and tested with genuine signatures of this writer and of other writers. Using other writers signatures for training requires special treatment to select the signatures that are similar to those of the writer in question [4]. This puts some burden on the system. Another example is the case of developing a computer-based inspection system for detecting defects in biscuits. In such application, the defect is random and rare and, thus, obtaining enough samples of defect biscuits is not possible. Again, by adopting the one-class problem approach the system can be trained with patterns of non-defected biscuits. Then during its normal operation, the system should ***compare*** the shape of the biscuit under examination to those learned during the training phase. However, this depends on the ability of the classifier network to perform such task. In the next subsection we will define the problem of detecting cancerous cells and it will be seen that this problem can be solved by adopting the one-class problem approach.

1.1 Problem definition

A typical sample of microscopic binary images of cells taken from cancerous tumor is shown in figure 1a. The objects contained in such sample is divided into circular cells, artifacts and superposed cells. Circular cells are nucleus with quasi-circular shape, of medium size and connected contour. These cells are considered by the pathologist as being good cells for further analysis. Artifacts are particles of circular shape and relatively smaller than the cancerous cells. The superposed cells are of random deformed shapes. These two types of cells are not used for analysis. With this composition, it is clear that the objective of a computer-based classification system is to analyze the cytological sample and separate the circular cells (cancerous cells) from the rest of objects contained in the image. Ideally, the system should identify all the cancerous cells (Fig. 1b). However, in most practical cases a small percentage of classification error could be accepted (Fig. 1c), since the pathologist could perform a visual inspection or even use another alternative techniques.

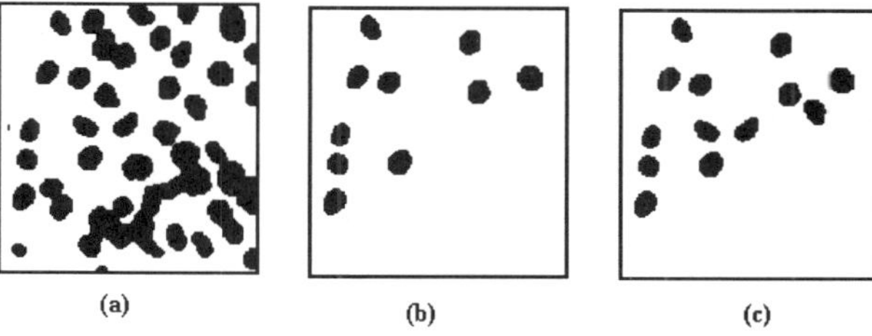

Figure 1. Typical sample of microscopic binary images of breast cancer. a) Image to be analyzed ; b) ideal classification results; c) practical classification results. The binary images are obtained by applying Otsu's algorithm[12] and techniques of mathematical morphology on the original gray-level images[6].

From the above description, it can be seen that the problem of detecting cancerous cells can, indeed, be soled by the one-class problem approach. In another work [10] we have demonstrated that the Fuzzy ARTMAP is *an* appropriate network for detecting cancerous cells based on the one-class problem approach. In this work we investigate the use of other models of neural networks for detecting cancerous cells based on the one-class problem approach, and compare their results with that of the Fuzzy ARTMAP. The neural networks studied are: Back-propagation (BKP), General Regression (GR), and Radial Basis Functions (RBF). The following section describes the experimental protocol. Section 3 presents some discussions and conclusions. Bibliographical references are given in section 4.

2 Experimental Protocol

2.1 Definition of the experimental data

Experimental protocol was performed using two sets of data collected from tumor of breast cancer. The first set contained 383 cancerous cells, and the second set contained 159 cells, 54 of which is cancerous cells and 105 is composed of superposed and deformed cells. The first set were used for training *only* and the second set were used for evaluation. The artifacts, the circular cells of smaller size, were removed from the samples by applying a simple separation process based on the area. That is, only objects of area bigger than 350 pixels were considered for the classification process. The experimental study consisted of three parts: defining the feature vector, selecting the optimum feature sub-vectors and the final experiments. All experiments were performed with the Neural Works Professional II/Plus Simulator running on an IBM DX4 compatible PC.

2.2 Feature vector

From the set of selected objects (cancerous, superposed and deformed cells), 7 parameters were extracted. These parameters were: perimeter, area, factor of compactness, minimum radius, maximum radius, circularity and diameter. The equations for calculating these parameters from binary images can be found in[5]. For the sake of clarity, the seven parameters will be labeled, respectively, as x_0, x_1, x_2, x_3, x_4, x_5, x_6. Typical values of these parameters are: (99.59800, 655.00000, 1.20517, 9.21954, 19.104973, 0.48257, 739.08837) for the class of cancerous cells and (123.29651, 896.00000 , 1.35015, 8.54400, 23.70653, 0.36040, 1011.02771) for the class of non-cancerous cells. As it can be observed from these samples, the feature space is not homogeneous. Hence, if the entire feature vector is applied to the network, the high-value features will have a stronger effect on NN learning than the small-value features will, when a normalization process is performed. To render the feature space homogeneous, the feature vector was divided into 6 sub-vectors (FS0, FS1, FS2, FS3, FS4, FS5) each of which contains a different set of features. These sets are: x_0x_4, x_1x_6, x_2x_3, x_2x_5, $x_2x_3x_5$ and $x_0x_2x_3x_4x_5$. The division criteria was based on the similarity between feature values.

2.3 Selecting the optimum feature sub-vectors

A selection process was performed prior to the final experiment, the objective of which was to determine the most optimum sub-vectors that would produce the best results. The selection process was performed by training and evaluating six networks of each model, each with different sub-vector. The training and test sets for the parameter selection process were, respectively, 76 cancerous cells and 31 (10 cancerous cells and 21 superposed and deformed cells). The architecture of each network is detailed in table 1.

The results of the selection process, in terms of the False Acceptance Rate (FAR) and False Rejection Rate (FRR) for the six networks of each model are shown in table 2. These errors describe, respectively, the percentage of negative cases accepted by the network as being cancerous cells, and the percentage of positive cases accepted as being non cancerous cells. Each value in the last raw is the average of the two errors. From table 2, it can be observed that the feature sub-vectors (FS2, FS4 and FS5) produced the lowest errors, in the case of the Fuzzy ARTMAP. These sub-vectors were then used for the final experiment.

Network	Topology (input, hidden/prototypes, output)	Learning Rule	Learning Parameters
BKP	$(m, 2, 1)$	QuickPro	LR=0.5, QR=0.9, PA=1.0 and DF=0.1
GR	$(m, 120, 1)$	GR	cluster radius=0.005
RBF	$(m, 120, 1)$	Delta	LR=0.9, Momentum=0.6
FMAP	$(m, 150, 1)$	Fuzzy ARTMAP	$\beta = 1$, $\alpha = 0.01$ and $\rho = 0.99$

Table 1. Summary of networks' architecture. FMAP denotes Fuzzy ARTMAP. The letter m indicates the dimension of the input vector. LR, QR, PA, and DF indicate, respectively, learning rate, quadratic rate, parabolic approximation and decay factor.

Error	Network	FS0	FS1	FS2	FS3	FS4	FS5
FAR(%)	BKP	100.00	100.00	100.00	100.00	100.00	100.00
	GR	100.00	100.00	100.00	100.00	100.00	100.00
	RBF	100.00	100.00	100.00	100.00	100.00	100.00
	FMAP	14.29	33.33	4.76	14.29	4.76	4.76
FRR (%)	BKP	0.00	0.00	0.00	0.00	0.00	0.00
	GR	0.00	0.00	0.00	0.00	0.00	0.00
	RBF	0.00	0.00	0.00	0.00	0.00	0.00
	FMAP	30.00	20.00	0.00	20.00	10.00	10.00
Et (%)	BKP	50.00	50.00	50.00	50.00	50.00	50.00
	GR	50.00	50.00	50.00	50.00	50.00	50.00
	RBF	50.00	50.00	50.00	50.00	50.00	50.00
	FMAP	22.14	26.66	2.38	17.14	7.38	7.38

Table 2. Evaluation results for the selection process.

2.4 The final experiments

The structure of the final neural networks-based classification system is depicted in figure 2. It is composed of three classifier networks and one decision stage. Each classifier network was trained and tested, separately, with one combination of parameters, as indicated in figure 2. The final decision of the system is based on a majority decision rule defined bellow:

- Consider an unknown cell as being cancerous, if at least two of the three networks agreed upon such decision and as being non-cancerous, otherwise.

The intermediate classification results, made by each classifier network, are shown in table 3. The final results of the system after applying the majority decision rule are shown in table 4.

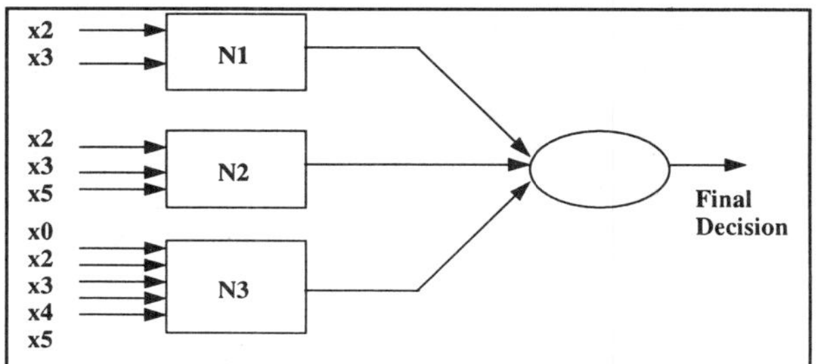

x2, x3 → N1

x2, x3, x5 → N2

x0, x2, x3, x4, x5 → N3

N1, N2, N3 → Final Decision

Figure 2. Block diagram of the neural network-based classification system for detecting cancerous cells

Error	Network	FS2	FS4	FS5
FAR (%)	BKP	100.00	100.0015	100.00
	GR	100.00	100.00	100.00
	RBF	100.00	100.00	100.00
	FMAP	18.00	15.00	12.00
FRR (%)	BKP	0.00	0.00	0.00
	GR	0.00	0.00	0.00
	RBF	0.00	0.00	0.00
	FMAP	3.70	7.41	5.55
Et (%)	BKP	50.00	50.00	50.00
	GR	50.00	50.00	50.00
	RBF	50.00	50.00	50.00
	FMAP	10.85	11.21	8.78

Table 3. Intermediate classification results.

Network	FAR (%)	FRR (%)	Et (%)
BKP	100.00	100.00	50.00
GR	100.00	100.00	50.00
RBF	100.00	100.00	50.00
FMAP	5.00	1.85	3.42

Table 4. Final classification results.

3 Discussion and Conclusions

In this paper we have presented an experimental study for investigating the use of neural network for detecting cancerous cells, based on the one-class problem approach. This approach states that if the pattern recognition system is required to detect cancerous cells, for example, then it needs to be trained with positive patterns *only*(cancerous cells). This is a divergent from the common approach in which the system would be trained with both positive and negative patterns. We have demonstrated that when adopting the one-class problem approach, one need not be concerned about obtaining negative data set for training, which, otherwise, could be a difficult task to accomplish. Another advantage is that the system can be designed to operate in real time.

The experimental study consisted in training and testing three neural networks: BKP, GR and RBF and comparing their results to those of the Fuzzy ARTMAP obtained in [11]. Training was performed with 383 cancerous cells *only*, and test was performed with 159 cells, 54 of which is cancerous cells and 105 is composed of superposed and deformed cells. The feature vector contained seven parameters which describe the shape of a circular object. Due to the difference in magnitude between these parameters, the feature vector was divided into six sub-vectors each of which contained a different combination of parameters. Such division was necessary in order to make the input space to a classifier network as homogeneous as possible. A selection process was then conducted to select the most optimum feature sub-vectors. This was done by training and testing each network with different sub-vector. The results of the selection process are demonstrated in table 2. From those results three sub-vectors were selected as the optimum sub-vectors and were used for the final experiments. During these experiments, three classifiers of the same type of network were trained and tested, each with different sub-vector. Training and test, for both the selection process and the final experiments, were performed based on the one-class problem approach as defined above. Results of the final experiments are demonstrated in tables 3 and 4.

3.1 General Comments

It should be noted that the selection approach adopted in our experiments turned out to be very efficient, since the performance of the BKP, GR and RBF networks were the same. In other situations when dealing with a multi-class problem, such selection approach might not be efficient. The reason for selecting three sub-vectors as being the optimum sub-vectors is clearly justified, since the average error for each sub-vector was less than 10%; and this number marks the limit for the acceptable errors in most applications. In general, when dealing with a huge data set and the feature space is of a higher dimension, things might be very complicated and one would have to investigate different alternatives for selecting the optimum features.

3.2 Comments on the Results

As it can be observed from tables 3 and 4 , the performance of the Fuzzy ARTMAP network is superior to that of the other networks studied here. The reason for this can be explained by analyzing the decision-making capability of each network. On the one hand, the decision-making capability of the Fuzzy ARTMAP is based on some sort of intelligence. An input pattern is first compared to a learned exemplar, and the output (the network decision) is then given based on the result of this comparison. This can be seen from the following equation of the mapfield[3]:

$$
x^{ab} = \begin{cases} y^b \wedge w_J^{ab}, & \text{if the } J\text{th } E^a \text{exemplar neuron is active and } E^b \text{is active} \\ w_J^{ab}, & \text{if the } J\text{th } E^a \text{exmplar neuron is active and } E^b \text{is inactive} \\ y^b, & \text{if } E^a \text{ is inactive and } E^b \text{is active} \\ 0, & \text{if } E^a \text{ is inactive and } E^b \text{is inactive} \end{cases}
\tag{1}
$$

It can be observed from equation 1 that if the Fuzzy ARTMAP is trained with patterns from one class only along with the respective association, 1 for example, then the network will learn this association for each pattern pair that are presented during the training process. This association is encoded, during learning, in the weight vector w_J^{ab} that connects the exemplar neurons of the ART^a to the neurons of the mapfield. When learning occurs, the weight connection from the *winning* exemplar neuron to the mapfield is set to '1', and the weight connections from the neighboring exemplar neurons to the mapfield is set to '0'. During test, or normal operation, when an unknown pattern is presented to the network, the output, x^{ab}, of the mapfield would either be equal to the weight vector, w_J^{ab} , if the unknown input is found to be similar to a previously learned exemplar, or equal to 0 otherwise. This feature of the Fuzzy ARTMAP neural network makes it ideal for implementing the one-class problem approach.

On the other hand and in comparison with the Fuzzy ARTMAP, the other networks studied here (BKP, GR and RBF) do not have an intelligent decision-making capability. Conceptually speaking, the decision-making capability of the BKP network is based on forward signal propagation from one layer to another without any sort of analysis. During training, based on the one-class problem approach, the BKP network classifies all training patterns in an open region. During test, when an unknown pattern is presented, the network *blindly* classifies it in the same region, without performing any analysis. Though the other networks (GR and RBF) use some sort of clustering techniques, the output is generated in a way similar to that of the BKP network. This feature of the BKP, GR and RBF neural networks make their use inappropriate for implementing the one-class problem approach.

As seen from table 3, the intermediate results in terms of the FRR is acceptably low, whereas, the FAR error is somewhat high. These errors can be minimized by investigating the use of a better set of parameters and/or a better method for selecting the optimum parameters. However, the use of the majority decision rule is proved to be very effective, as it can be seen from table 4. This is because one set of parameters may not succeed to identify a particular cell, whereas, the other two sets may succeed.

3.3 Conclusions

From the analysis presented above and from the results shown in tables 3 and 4, we may conclude that

- the problem of detecting cancerous cells, as defined above, can, indeed, be solved by the one-class problem approach;
- of the neural networks studied here, the Fuzzy ARTMAP neural network is the appropriate choice for detecting cancerous cells, based on the one-class problem approach; and
- the majority decision rule, when applied to multi-classifier system, could improve system's performance.

However, we are very well aware that further studies are required to fine-tune the system. Our future work will focus on obtaining a large database, optimizing the parameters selection process and comparing our results to that of some expert pathologists and of other systems. We will also continue our investigation in using the one-class problem approach in other pattern recognition problem.

4 References

[1] The American Cancer Society. " Facts on breast cancer ", 1987.

[2] G. Brug. "Pattern recognition , image processing, related data analyses and expert systems integrated in medical microscopy, "*Proc. Int. Conf. Pattern Recognition*, pp.286-293. 1988.

[3] G. A. Carpenter, S. Grossberg, N. Markuzon, and J. H. Reynolds. "Fuzzy ARTMAP: A neural network architecture for incremental supervised learning of analog multidimensional maps". IEEE Tran. Neural Networks. Vol. 3, No. 5, pp. 698-713, 1992.

[4] H. Cardot, M. Revenu, B. Victorri, and M. Revillet. An artificial neural network achitecture for handwritten signature authentication, SEPT, 42 rue des Coutures, 14000 Caen, France, 1992.

[5] M. Coster and Y.L Chermant. Precis d'analise d'images. 1. ed. França: Presses du CNRS, 1989.

[6] S. B. Filho, " Um quantificador da ploidia tumoral através da citofotometria '. **Master thesis.** Centro Federal de Educação Tecnológica do Paraná (CEFET-PR). 1994.

[7] F. Giroud. "Cell nucleus pattern analysis : geometric and densitometric featuring, automatic cell phase identification". *Biol.Cell*, 44, p. 177 - 188, 1982.

[8] J.A. Leonard, M. A. Kramer and L. H. Unger. " Radial Basis Functions for Classifying Process Faults", IEEE Control Systems, April 1991.

[9] N. A. Murshed. "A natural approach to signature verification". **Master thesis.** Centro Federal de Educação Tecnológica do Paraná (CEFET-PR). 1995.

[10] N. A. Murshed, F. Bortolozzi and R. Sabourin, "Off-line signature verification, without a priori knowledge of class w2. A new approach, " *Proc. Int. Conf. Image Analyses and Recognition,* Vol. I, pp. 191-196, Montreal, 1995.

[11] "_______________" A Fuzzy ARTMAP-Based Classification System for Detecting Cancerous Cells, Based on the One-Class Problem Approach. Proceedings of the ICPR'96 -The 13th International Conference on Pattern Recognition. Viena, Austria, 1996. To appear.

[12] N. Otsu. "A threshold selection method from gray-level histograms". *IEEE Trans. Syst. Man. Cybernetics*, Vol. SMC-   9, NO. 1, pp. 62-66, 1979.

[13] D. E. Rumelhart and J. L. McClelland, editors, " Parallel Distributed Processing: Explorations in the Microstrucure of   Cognition ". Vol. I, *Foundations*. MIT Press.

[14] D. F. Specht. " A General Regression Neural Network ", IEEE Transaction on Neural networks, vol. 2, no. 6, pp. 568-576.

A Neural Network Approach to Threshold Selection

C. H. Li   P. K. S. Tam
Department of Electronic Engineering
Hong Kong Polytechnic University
Hung Hom, Hong Kong
chli@en.polyu.edu.hk enptam@hkpucc.polyu.edu.hk *

Abstract

The article describes an approach to histogram thresholding using neural network. A neural network is employed for selecting the appropriate thresholding algorithm for a particular histogram. The misclassification error and an accuracy criteria has been used to compare the neural network approach with classical thresholding method. The neural approach has lower errors than the classical thresholding algorithms and achieves near optimal performances.

1   Introduction

In various applications of image processing such as template matching and morporlogical operations, the number of gray levels of the image has often to be reduced. Such operations are often achieved efficiently through the use of the thresholding operation. Research work in threshold selection is extensive and a detailed review can be found in Ref. [1]. However, there is no consensus on which algorithm is superior and which algorithm is suitable for applying to a particular situation. In fact, most of the classical thresholding algorithms seem to perform better in specific situations than others. In this article, a probabilistic model for gray-level histogram is adopted and several misclassification error criteria are employed for comparing the performance of the different histogram thresholding algorithms. Four well-known and widely applied algorithms, viz., the Otsu method [2], the maximum entropy method [3], the minimum error thresholding algorithm by Kittler and Illingworth [4] and the minimum cross entropy algorithm [5] will be compared using the probabilistic model.

In this work, the problem of the evaluation of histogram thresholding is tackled by systematically generating a large collection of sample histograms using distributions with known parameters and applying the misclassification error criteria for evaluating the performance of the different thresholding algorithms.

2   Histogram Distribution Model

The gray-level histogram will be modeled as a combination of two probability distributions

$$h(x) = \rho_1 p_1(x) + \rho_2 p_2(x). \tag{1}$$

*This research work is supported in part by the Hong Kong Research Grant Council under project number: HKP98/95E.

where ρ_1 and ρ_2 are the proportions of the two classes of objects, and $p_1(x)$ and $p_2(x)$ are the probability distributions of the two classes respectively.

The simulated histograms must have similar statistics as the actual histograms encountered in thresholding operations. Out of the major statistical distributions commonly encountered, Gaussian distributions will be the most important one for modelling purposes. The central limit theorem states that the distribution of the sum of a large number of independent random variables will approach a normal distribution as the number of random variables increases [6]. In this section, the probability distributions are assumed to be Gaussian. The probability density functions will be denoted as $p_i(x)$ where $i = 1, 2$ respectively for the foreground and the background,

$$p_i(x) = \frac{1}{\sqrt{2\pi}\sigma_i} \exp(-\frac{(x - \mu_i)^2}{2\sigma_i^2}) \tag{2}$$

where μ_i and σ_i are the means and the standard deviations of the Gaussian distribution respectively.

The observed gray-level histogram is $h_n(x)$ which is modelled as a noisy realization of an underlying noise-free gray-level distribution. More specifically, each entry in the histogram will be considered as a random variable which is the sum

$$h_n(x) = h(x) + \sigma_n y \sqrt{h(x)} \tag{3}$$

where σ_n is the standard deviation controlling the amount of random fluctuations, and y is an i.i.d. Gaussian random variable with unit standard variance. The histograms generated with this method correspond closely to histograms captured from real-world environment.

3 Evaluation criteria

In order to compare the performances of different thresholding algorithms, the misclassification error is employed. The misclassification error when t is selected as the threshold is given by:

$$E(t) = \rho_2 \int_{-\infty}^{t} p_2(x)dx + \rho_1 \int_{t}^{\infty} p_1(x)dx. \tag{4}$$

In simulations, the discrete version of the above formula is implemented,

$$E(t) = \rho_2 \sum_{x=0}^{x<t} p_2(x) + \rho_1 \sum_{x=t}^{x=L} p_1(x). \tag{5}$$

With a total of N sample histograms, the average misclassification error for any chosen algorithm is defined as,

$$\bar{E} = \frac{\sum_j E_j}{N}, \tag{6}$$

where E_j is the misclassification error $E(t)$ for the j-th sample histogram.

The use of a single criterion is prone to bias of various kinds. An additional criteria, the accuracy, will be employed in order to make a fair comparison. The accuracy $A(t)$ is defined as the ratio between the minimum misclassification error and the misclassification error of the algorithm on the histogram,

$$A(t) = E(t_o)/E(t), \qquad (7)$$

where $E(t_o)$ is the minimum misclassification error and t_o is the optimal threshold, defined by the threshold which minimizes the misclassification errors. This accuracy will takes its maximum value of one when the threshold t selected by the thresholding algorithm gives the minimal possible classification error. With a total of N sample histograms, the average accuracy for any chosen algorithm is defined as,

$$\bar{A} = \frac{\sum_j A_j}{N}, \qquad (8)$$

where A_j is the accuracy for the j-th sample histogram.

4   The neural network approach

The neural network approach relies on the fact that different histogram thresholding algorithms perform better in specific situations than others, and the classification errors can be lowered by applying a suitable algorithm for a particular histogram. However, the association between the particular algorithm and the optimal thresholding algorithm to be used is highly complex.

In this paper, the supervised training of a back-propagation network is used to perform the association. The training phase trains the network to learn an association between the statistical descriptors of the histograms and the thresholding algorithms to be employed. A number of statistical parameters had been investigated, e.g. the n-th order moments and the centralized moments. Experimental results indicate that the two parameters: coefficient of skewness and coefficient of kurtosis, provide good results.

A three layer feed-forward network is employed for the classification of training features. The input layer consists of the neurons which accepts the shape descriptors of the histograms. The coefficients of skewness and kurtosis are fed to the input layer. There are two hidden layers, each consisting of eight neurons which are completely connected to neurons of the adjacent layers. The output layer contains neurons which represent the individual thresholding algorithms. In this simulation the number of algorithms selected is four, thus there are four neurons in the output layer. The back-propagation algorithm is used for updating the weights in the network.

In summary, the training phase of the neural network approach consists of the following steps :

1. Generate a sample histogram with known random parameters.

2. Threshold the histogram using different algorithms.

3. Calculate misclassification errors for the thresholds calculated for each thresholding algorithm.

4. Select the optimal algorithm as the one with the smallest misclassification error.

5. Calculate the coefficients of skewness and kurtosis of the histogram.

6. Train the network to learn the association between the input histogram feature and those of the optimal algorithm.

The application phase of the neural network apprcach consists of the following steps :

1. Generate the histogram using the input data.

2. Calculate the coefficients of skewness and kurtosis of the histogram.

3. Choose the thresholding algorithm determined by the neural network.

5 Results and Discussions

In this paper, 1000 training sample histograms are generated under the following conditions :

- ρ_1 is uniformly sampled from the interval $(0.01, 0.99)$, $\rho_2 = 1 - \rho_1$

- μ_1 is uniformly sampled from the interval $(71.5, 121.5)$,

- μ_2 is uniformly sampled from the interval $(135.5, 185.5)$,

- σ_1 are uniformly sampled from the interval $(5, 30)$, $\sigma_2 = \sigma_1$.

The testing histograms are generated under the following condition:

- ρ_1 varies from 0.01 to 0.99 in steps of 0.01, $\rho_2 = 1 - \rho_1$

- σ_1 varies from 5 to 30 in steps of 0.252, $\sigma_2 = \sigma_1$

- μ_1 is uniformly sampled from the interval $(71.5, 121.5)$,

- μ_2 is uniformly sampled from the interval $(135.5, 185.5)$,

The testing samples consists of 99 different values of ρ and 99 different values of σ. For each set of values of ρ and σ, five set of values for μ_1 and μ_2 are generated. Thus, the total testing sample comprised of 49005(99x99x5) histograms.

The interval for μ_1 and μ_2 are chosen such that μ_1 and μ_2 are separated from each other and away from the maximum and minimum gray values of 255 and 0. The intervals for standard deviations σ_1 and σ_2 are chosen to cover situations of minimal overlapping to high overlapping of gray levels between the foreground and the backgrcund. The proportions of the background against the foreground are in ratios ranging from 1:99 to 99:1, which should cover common occurring situations.

The performances of the different thresholding algorithms on these testing histograms are shown in Figure 1. The misclassification errors of the algorithms are shown as gray values where darker pixels correspond to smaller errors. Thus it can be seem that different thresholding algorithms have different error patterns.

Comparing the results on the average misclassification errors $\bar{E}$, the error of the neural network approach is half the errors of other major thresholding algorithms except for the maximum entropy method. In fact, the average misclassification error of the neural network approach is very close to the lower bound on the misclassification error.

Comparing the results on the average accuracy, the proposed method is very close to the optimal result, achieving a 96% accuracy. This average accuracy is much higher that the best performing classical algorithm, the minimum error method, which achieves a 69% accuracy. It is also of interest to note that the maximum entropy algorithm does not perform as good under

Table 1: Average misclassification errors of different algorithms (a) cross entropy, (b) maximum entropy, (c) minimum error, (d) Otsu's method, (e) proposed approach and (f) lower bound on errors

	(a)	(b)	(c)	(d)	(e)	(f)
$\bar{E}(\%)$	12.2	6.2	11.7	11.5	4.9	4.7

Table 2: Average accuracy of different algorithms (a) cross entropy, (b) maximum entropy, (c) minimum error, (d) Otsu, (e) proposed approach and (f) upper bound on accuracy

	(a)	(b)	(c)	(d)	(e)	(f)
$\bar{A}(\%)$	58.0	61.0	69.0	62.5	96.1	100

the criteria of average accuracy than the average misclassification errors. The reason is that the average misclassification error is easily dominated by sample histograms with large errors. The average accuracy defined in this paper normalizes the performances of thresholding algorithm so that each sample histogram has even contribution to the average.

To conclude, a new composite approach to thresholding using a neural network has been developed. The method include the training of a neural-network to select the thresholding algorithm to be applied to a particular histogram. The performance of the proposed approach, based on a combination of several error criteria, is shown to be superior to those of the classical thresholding algorithms and achieves near optimal results.

References

[1] C. A. Glasbey. An analysis of histogram-based thresholding algorithms. *CVGIP : Graphical models and image processing*, 55(6):532–537, 1993.

[2] N. Otsu. A threshold selection method from gray-level histogram. *IEEE Trans. Syst. Man, Cybern.*, 9:62–66, 1979.

[3] J. N. Kapur, P. K. Sahoo, and A. K. C. Wong. A new method for grey-level picture thresholding using the entropy of the histogram. *Computer Vision, Graphics and Image Processing*, 29:273–285, 1985.

[4] J. Kittler and J. Illingworth. Minimum error thresholding. *Pattern Recognition*, 19:41–47, 1986.

[5] C. H. Li and C. K. Lee. Minimum cross entropy thresholding. *Pattern Recognition*, 26:617–625, 1993.

[6] A. Papoulis. *Probability, random variables, and stochastic processes.* McGraw-Hill, 3 edition, 1991.

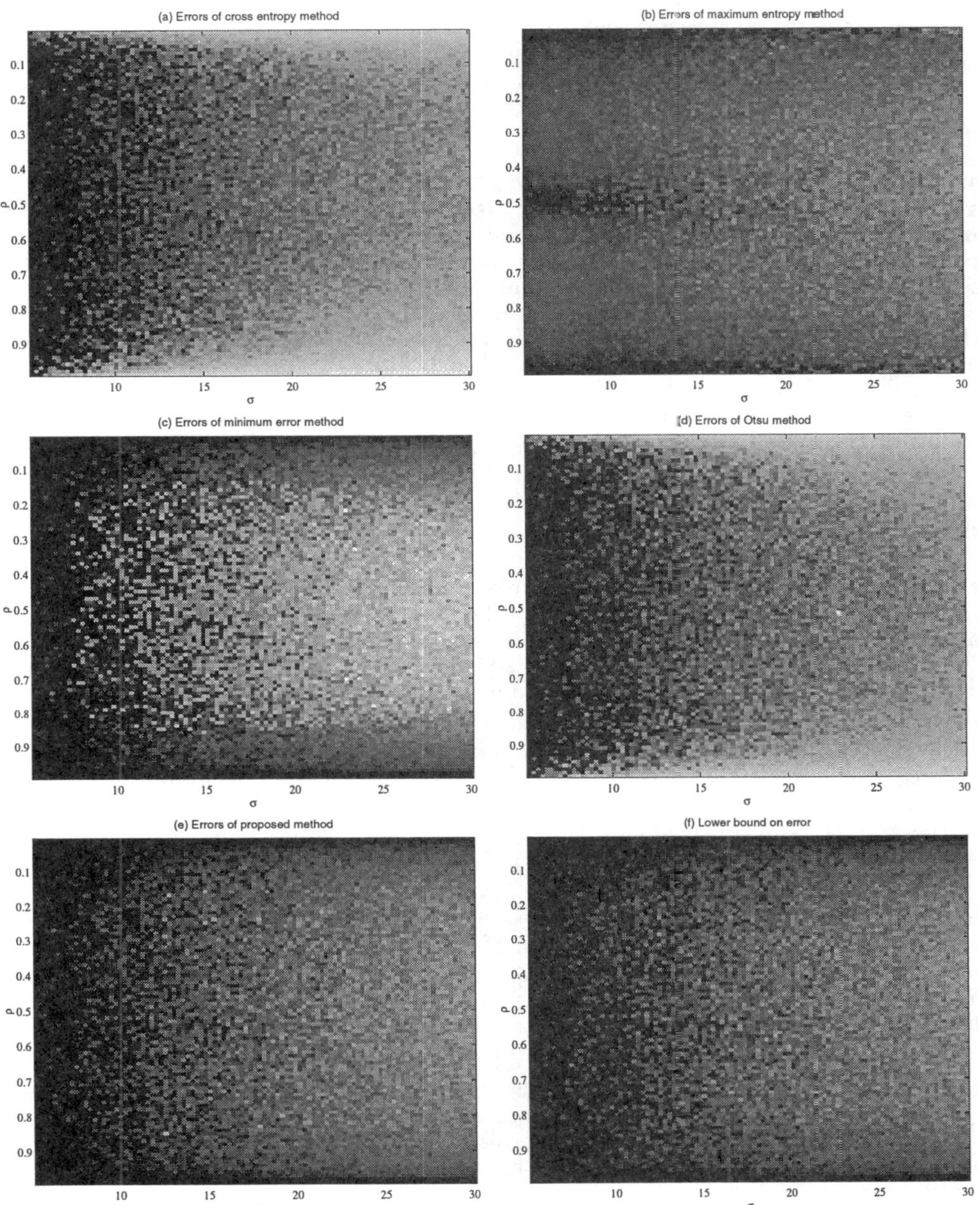

Figure 1: Error plots of thresholding method (a) cross entropy, (b) maximum entropy, (c) minimum error, (d) Otsu, (e) proposed method and (f) lower bound on error

Spatial Representation of Keywords and Documents by Optimization and Inverse Optimization

Naoto Homma†, Masumi Ishikawa‡
Department of Control Engineering and Science, Kyushu Institute of Technology
680 Kawazu, Iizuka, Fukuoka 820, Japan
† nhomma@kuri.ces.kyutech.ac.jp,　‡ ishikawa@ces.kyutech.ac.jp

Abstract—

Proposed in this paper is a method to spatially represent keywords and documents in information retrieval, which enables intermittent users to effectively retrieve documents based on keywords. Conventional studies on spatial representation of keywords is limited to their positioning based on the similarity between them. Because the given positioning of keywords does not, in general, coincide with that of a user, a bidirectional positioning is required. The bidirectional positioning of keywords and documents can be carried out by Quantification theory 3 and an inverse optimization. Since constraints in the positioning involve an unknown relevance matrix between keywords and documents, the inverse optimization in this problem is extremely difficult. A procedure which performs constraint satisfaction and learning of the relevance matrix iteratively is proposed. Selecting 19 keywords and 41 documents in neurocomputing, we apply the proposed method to evaluate its effectiveness.

1　Introduction

The present paper proposes to spatially represent keywords and documents for realizing intelligent and flexible human interfaces in information retrieval. Such interfaces facilitate efficient retrieval of documents based on keywords, because recalling of keywords is not easy especially for intermittent users. There have been various studies on spatial representation of concepts [2][3][4]. Their aim is the positioning of concepts based on some criteria such as mutual similarity. Multidimensional scaling(MDS) has also been devoted to spatial positioning of concepts or events based on constraints on distances between them.

A difficulty inherent in these approaches is that the given positioning of keywords on a plane does not, in general, coincide with that of a user. This necessitates the modification of the positioning in accordance with one's judgment. However, simply modifying the positioning of keywords does not suffice; it is also required to modify the similarity between keywords accordingly. The maintenance of the consistency between the spatial positioning and the similarity between keywords facilitates deep understanding of the relation between them.

This *bidirectional* positioning of keywords on a plane has already been proposed by the authors using Quantification theory 4 (QT4) [5] [6]. It is a combination of forward optimization and inverse optimization. The former provides the positioning of keywords based on the similarity between keywords by QT4. The latter gives the modified similarity between keywords under which the modified positioning becomes optimal. Although the proposed method is effective, it can represent only keywords on a plane.

The present paper proposes a bidirectional positioning of not only keywords but also documents on separate planes based on the relevance between keywords and documents using Quantification theory 3 (QT3) [5]. In case of QT4, it is easy to satisfy consistency conditions in positioning, i.e., the orthogonality of position vectors. In case of QT3, on the other hand, consistency conditions in positioning involve both a modified positioning and a modified relevance matrix between keywords and documents. This makes the inverse optimization extremely difficult.

To overcome this difficulty, it iteratively performs the following two procedures: constraint satisfaction keeping a relevance matrix constant, and the learning of a relevance matrix keeping the positioning constant. Selecting 19 keywords and 41 documents in neurocomputing [1], we apply the proposed method to evaluate its effectiveness.

2　Positioning of keywords and documents by QT3

The Quantification theory 3 simultaneously gives scores to keywords and documents based on a relevance matrix between them. The criterion for determining the scores is this: keywords appearing in similar set of documents have similar keyword scores, and documents having similar set of keywords have similar document scores. This is equivalent to maximizing the correlation coefficient between keyword scores and document scores. This optimization is reduced to the solution of the following characteristic equation.

The initial relevance matrix, $\boldsymbol{N}$, is defined as follows: $N_{ij} = 1$ provided the document i includes the keyword j, and $N_{ij} = 0$ otherwise. Let the normalized relevance matrix be $\boldsymbol{P}_{xy}$. Since elements of $\boldsymbol{P}_{xy}$ sums to one, it may be regarded as a probability distribution. Let the scores of documents be $\boldsymbol{x} = (x_1, x_2, ..., x_n)^T$, and those of keywords be $\boldsymbol{y} = (y_1, y_2, ..., y_m)^T$.

The correlation coefficient between scores of documents and those of keywords, $r(\boldsymbol{x}, \boldsymbol{y})$, is represented as,

$$
\begin{aligned}
r(\boldsymbol{x}, \boldsymbol{y}) &= V(\boldsymbol{x}, \boldsymbol{y})/(S(\boldsymbol{x})S(\boldsymbol{y})) \\
V(\boldsymbol{x}, \boldsymbol{y}) &= \sum_{i=1}^{n}\sum_{j=1}^{m} x_i y_j P_{xy}(i,j) - \overline{x}\,\overline{y} \\
S(\boldsymbol{x}) &= \{\sum_{i=1}^{n} x_i^2 p_x(i) - (\overline{x})^2\}^{\frac{1}{2}} \\
S(\boldsymbol{y}) &= \{\sum_{j=1}^{m} y_j^2 p_y(i) - (\overline{y})^2\}^{\frac{1}{2}} \\
p_x(i) &= \sum_{j=1}^{m} P_{xy}(i,j) \\
p_y(j) &= \sum_{i=1}^{n} P_{xy}(i,j) \\
\overline{x} &= \sum_{i=1}^{n} x_i p_x(i) \\
\overline{y} &= \sum_{j=1}^{m} y_j p_y(j)
\end{aligned}
$$

Taking the derivative of $r(\boldsymbol{x}, \boldsymbol{y})$ with respect to $\boldsymbol{x}$ and $\boldsymbol{y}$, we obtain the following equation,

$$
\sum_{k=1}^{m}\sum_{i=1}^{n} \frac{P_{xy}(i,j)P_{xy}(i,k)y_k}{p_x(i)} = r(\boldsymbol{x}, \boldsymbol{y})^2 p_y(j)y_j \quad ; j = 1, \ldots, m \tag{1}
$$

This is equivalent to,

$$
\boldsymbol{P}_y^{-1}\boldsymbol{P}_{yx}\boldsymbol{P}_x^{-1}\boldsymbol{P}_{xy}\boldsymbol{y} = \lambda\boldsymbol{y} \tag{2}
$$

where λ equals $r(\boldsymbol{x}, \boldsymbol{y})^2$, $\boldsymbol{P}_x$ is an $n \times n$ diagonal matrix whose ith diagonal element is $p_x(i)$, $\boldsymbol{P}_y$ is an $m \times m$ diagonal matrix whose jth diagonal element is $p_y(j)$, and $\boldsymbol{P}_{yx}$ is a transpose of $\boldsymbol{P}_{xy}$. Eq.(2) can be rewritten as the following characteristic equation,

$$
\boldsymbol{P}_y^{-\frac{1}{2}}\boldsymbol{P}_{yx}\boldsymbol{P}_x^{-1}\boldsymbol{P}_{xy}\boldsymbol{P}_y^{-\frac{1}{2}}\boldsymbol{z} = \lambda\boldsymbol{z} \tag{3}
$$

where $\boldsymbol{z} = \boldsymbol{P}_y^{\frac{1}{2}}\boldsymbol{y}$ and λ is an eigenvalue.

The resulting solution maximizes the correlation coefficient, $r(\boldsymbol{x}, \boldsymbol{y})$. The corresponding scores $\boldsymbol{x}$ are obtained by,

$$
\boldsymbol{P}_x^{-1}\boldsymbol{P}_{xy}\boldsymbol{y} = \sqrt{\lambda}\boldsymbol{x} \tag{4}
$$

By solving the above characteristic equation, the eigenvectors corresponding to the largest and the second largest eigenvalues, $\boldsymbol{z}^{(1)}$ and $\boldsymbol{z}^{(2)}$, are obtained. corresponding $(\boldsymbol{x}^{(1)}, \boldsymbol{x}^{(2)})$ and $(\boldsymbol{y}^{(1)}, \boldsymbol{y}^{(2)})$ provide the positioning of documents and keywords respectively,on a plane.

3 Inverse optimization

As has been mentioned in Introduction, the positioning of keywords and documents by QT3 does not, in general, coincide with that of a user. Inverse optimization realizes consistent modification of both the positioning and the relevance matrix between keywords and documents. Figure 1, corresponding to Eq.(2), indicates the relation between $\boldsymbol{P}_{xy}$ and the positioning of documents, $\boldsymbol{x}$, and keywords, $\boldsymbol{y}$. The key idea in the inverse optimization is the following. When we modify $\boldsymbol{x}$ and $\boldsymbol{y}$ to $\boldsymbol{x}'$ and $\boldsymbol{y}'$, respectively, based on a user's judgment, we also modify $\boldsymbol{P}_{xy}$ accordingly by the learning of the 5-layer neural network in Figure 1.

However, due to the following reasons, conventional back propagation (BP) learning cannot be used as it is. First, it is impossible to give target outputs to this network, because an eigenvalue, λ, which is unknown for modified $\boldsymbol{x}'$ and $\boldsymbol{y}'$, is included in the outputs in Figure 1. The use of a novel criterion function, i.e, square of the cosine of the angle between an output vector and a target output vector, solves this difficulty. Although the criterion function is different from the conventional one, it is still possible to use the error back propagation algorithm [6].

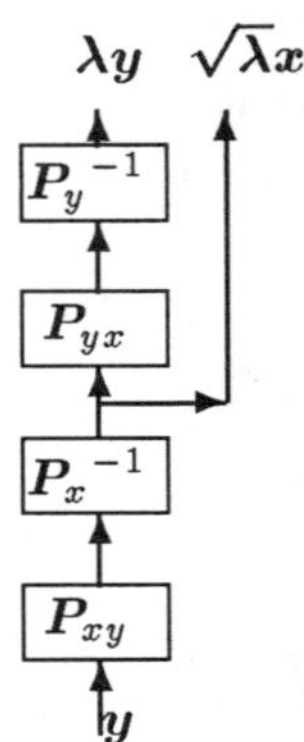

Figure 1: Network architecture used in solving QT3

Table 1: 19 keywords on neurocomputing

bp: *back propagation*	bi: *biological*	cl: *class*	he: *Hebb*
ho: *Hopfield*	in: *intelligence*	le: *learning*	na: *neural*
ne: *neuro*	no: *noise*	or: *organization*	pa: *parallel*
pc: *perception*	pt: *Perceptron*	ph: *physiological*	ru: *rule*
si: *simulation*	sy: *synaptic*	vi: *vision*	

Secondly, since connection weights in Figure 1 are interdependent, i.e., $\boldsymbol{P}_x^{-1}$, $\boldsymbol{P}_y^{-1}$ and $\boldsymbol{P}_{yx}$ are functions of $\boldsymbol{P}_{xy}$, they must be modified subject to these constraints. Furthermore, elements in $\boldsymbol{P}_{xy}$ must sum to one. If a constraint is linear as in the case of $\boldsymbol{P}_{yx} = \boldsymbol{P}_{xy}{}^{T}$, it is easy to satisfy it algebraically; simply projecting the modified connection weight vector onto the hyper-plane determined by the active constraints suffices. But in case of $\boldsymbol{P}_x^{-1}$ and $\boldsymbol{P}_y^{-1}$, it is not so easy because of their nonlinearity. The following criterion function, J, is devised to iteratively satisfy these constraints.

$$J = \sum_{i,j} \left(\hat{\boldsymbol{P}}_{xy}(i,j) - \boldsymbol{P}_{xy}(i,j)\right)^2 + \sum_{i,j} \left(\hat{\boldsymbol{P}}_{xy}(i,j) - \boldsymbol{P}_{yx}(j,i)\right)^2$$

$$+ \sum_i \left(\sum_j \hat{\boldsymbol{P}}_{xy}(i,j) - \frac{1}{\boldsymbol{P}_x^{-1}(i,i)}\right)^2 + \sum_j \left(\sum_i \hat{\boldsymbol{P}}_{xy}(i,j) - \frac{1}{\boldsymbol{P}_y^{-1}(j,j)}\right)^2 + \lambda \left(\sum_{i,j} \hat{\boldsymbol{P}}_{xy}(i,j) - 1\right)^2 \quad (5)$$

where $\hat{\boldsymbol{P}}_{xy}(i,j)$ is the consistent estimate of $\boldsymbol{P}_{xy}(i,j)$ and λ is a Lagrangian multiplier. Since Eq.(5) is quadratic, the estimates, $\hat{\boldsymbol{P}}_{xy}$, can easily be obtained by solving the corresponding simultaneous equation. Thirdly, the consistent scores, $x^\star$ and $y^\star$, must satisfy the following constraints.

$$x^{\star(i)T} \hat{\boldsymbol{P}}_x x^{\star(j)} = \delta_{ij} \tag{6}$$

$$y^{\star(i)T} \hat{\boldsymbol{P}}_y y^{\star(j)} = \delta_{ij} \quad ; i = 1, 2; j = 1, 2 \tag{7}$$

where δ_{ij} is the chronecker's delta, and $x^{\star(i)}$ and $y^{\star(i)}$ are the consistent scores corresponding to the ith largest eigenvalue. As pointed out in Introduction, it is not easy to satisfy the constraints in Eqs.(6) and (7). This is because $\hat{\boldsymbol{P}}_x$ and $\hat{\boldsymbol{P}}_y$ are obtained by learning and are unknown *a priori*. An iterative procedure is adopted here. First, constraint satisfaction of Eqs.(6) and (7) is carried out keeping $\hat{\boldsymbol{P}}_x$ and $\hat{\boldsymbol{P}}_y$ constant. Secondly, the consistent normalized relevance matrix, $\hat{\boldsymbol{P}}_{xy}$, is modified by the learning of neural networks in Figure 1 keeping the positioning, $x^\star$ and $y^\star$, constant. Repeated applications of these two procedures generate consistent estimates of scores, $x^\star$ and $y^\star$, and the normalized relevance matrix, $\hat{\boldsymbol{P}}_{xy}$, simultaneously.

4   Simulation results

The initial relevance matrix, $\boldsymbol{N}$, indicating the relation between keywords and documents, are obtained as follows. We select 41 pioneering papers on neurocomputing as a set of documents [1]. 19 keywords which often appear in these documents are collected as in Table 1.

In the first case, synonymous keywords are moved to their center of gravity. Pairs of keywords, {*neuro* (ne), *neural*(na)} and {*back propagation*(bp), *learning*(le)}, are selected as synonymous keywords. The inverse optimization is carried out by giving inputs, y, and target outputs, y, to the neural network in Figure 1. An application of QT3 to the initial relevance matrix between keywords and documents in Figure 4(a) gives the spatial positioning of keywords and documents. The result is successful; the consistent spatial positioning and the relevance matrix are obtained. QT3 is applied to the resulting modified relevance matrix for reconfirmation. It turns out that the consistent spatial positioning is successfully resproduced by QT3, thus proving the correctness of the inverse optimization.

In the second case, keywords are modified based on a user's judgment. An application of QT3 to the initial relevance matrix between keywords and documents in Figure 4(a) gives the spatial positioning of keywords and documents in Figures 2(a) and (c). The modified keywords by a user are: *biological*(bi), *learning*(le), *neural*(na), *neuro*(ne), *Perceptron*(pt) and *synaptic*(sy) as shown in Figure 2(a). Figure 2(b) illustrates the consistently modified positioning of keywords. The consistently modified positioning of documents is shown in Figure 2(d). The modified relevance matrix corresponding to the consistently modified spatial positioning of keywords is shown in Figure 4(b).

Figure 3 indicates the resulting eigenvalues in decreasing order in the second case. Each eigenvalue represents the square of the correlation coefficient between scores of keywords and documents. Figure 4 illustrates the initial relevance matrix and the modified one in the second case. Initial relevance is either 0 or 1, but modified relevance takes a continuous value. Initially, the number of relevances which have the value of 1 is 240 out of 779. The number of relevances which are larger than 0.3 after modification is 279.

Figure 5 illustrates the frequency of appearance of keywords in each document. The correlation coefficient between the frequencies and the initial relevances (0/1) is 0.611, and that between the frequencies and the modified relevance values is 0.639. The increase in the value of the correlation coefficient suggests that the modifications of the relevance matrix is made in accordance with the frequencies in this case.

Simultaneous modification of both documents and keywords is also possible. This is successfully done, but is omitted here due to space limitation.

5   Conclusions

The present paper proposes a novel method for a bidirectional positioning of keywords and documents using Quantification theory 3 (QT3) and an inverse optimization. Application to a small example demonstrates its effectiveness. It enables a customized spatial positioning of keywords and documents, which is useful as a front-end processing of information retrieval based on keywords, especially for intermittent users. Synonymous keywords can be treated without difficulty by moving them to their center of gravity on a keyword plane. In case of a polysemous keyword, multiple positions would be necessary for representing it with multiple meanings.

However, it is not powerful enough for a large number of keywords and documents. Therefore, further research remains to be done for realizing a practical front-end processing system in information retrieval. When the number of keywords increases, i.e., a few hundreds, it becomes difficult to represent all the keywords on a two-dimensional plane. Three-dimensional representation of keywords and documents might be a good candidate.

When the number of keywords and documents further increases, i.e., several thousands, a hierarchical approach would be of necessity. By introducing macroscopic keywords obtained by self-organization, we can use hierarchical positioning of keywords; higher level representation provides a birds-eye-view of the whole field with macroscopic keywords, and lower level representation provides a local view with microscopic keywords.

References

[1] J. A. Anderson and E. Rosenfeld, (Eds.) *"Neurocomputing: Foundations of research,"* The MIT Press, 1988.

[2] R. Oka, "A self-organizing network composed of symbol codes with location parameter," *Proceedings of the Workshop on Algorithmic Learning Theory*, 1990, pp. 81-94.

[3] K. Hori and S. Ohsuga, "Assisting the articulation of the mental world," *Proceedings of the 1st Japanese Knowledge Acquisition for Knowledge-Based Systems Workshop*, Tokyo, Oct. 8-10, 1990, pp. 289-300.

[4] H. Ritter and T. Kohonen, "Self-organizing semantic maps," *Biological Cybernetics*, 61, pp. 241-254, 1989.

[5] C. Hayashi, "On the prediction of phenomena from qualitative data and the quantification of qualitative data from the mathematico-statistical point of view," *Annal of the Institute of Statistical Mathmatics*, vol.6, pp. 227-338, 1952.

[6] Y. Yoshioka and M. Ishikawa, "Interactive arrangement of words on a plane by inverse optimization using neural networks," *Proc. ICONIP*, Korea, Oct. 17-20, 1994, pp.1861-1866.

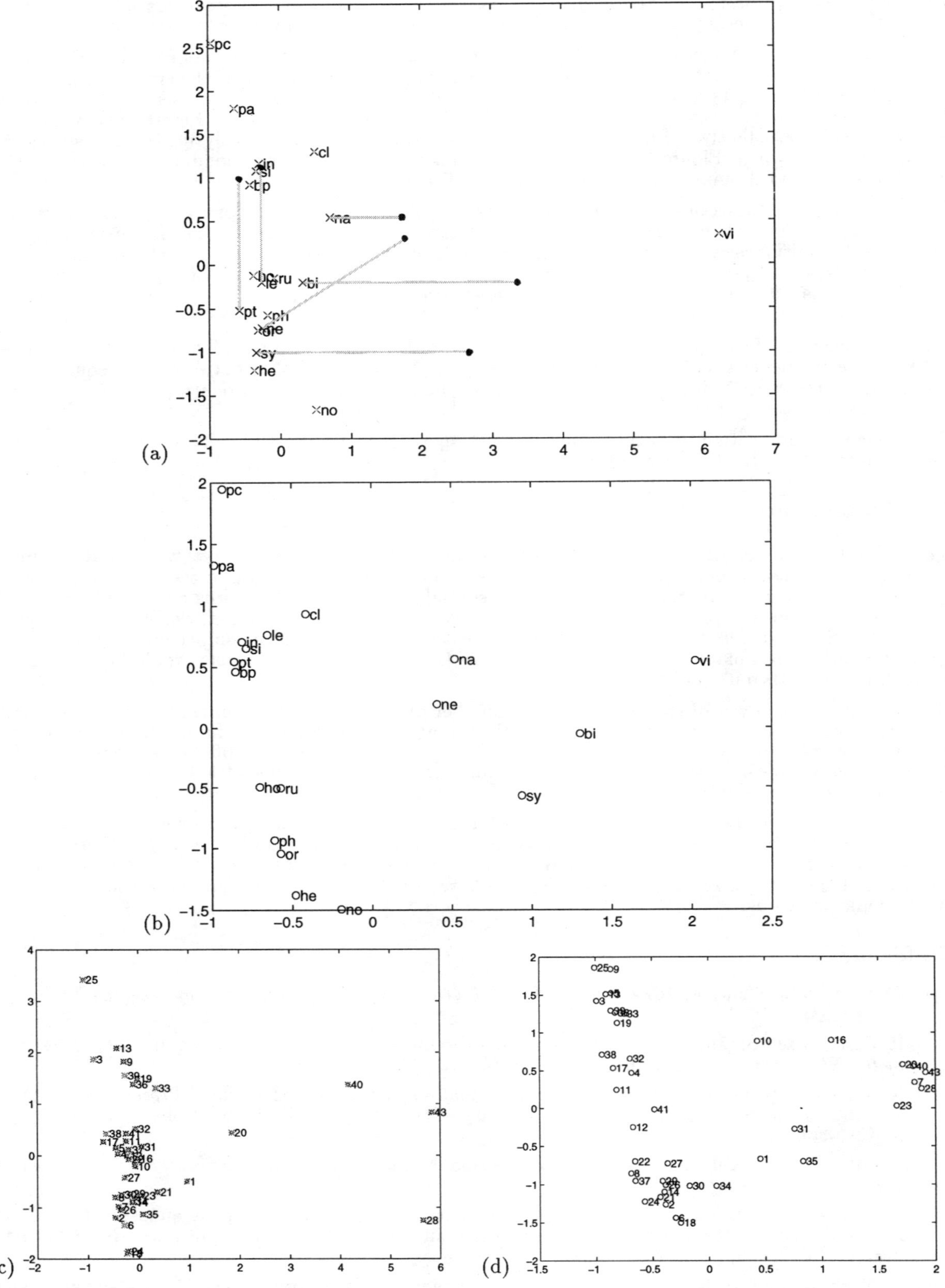

Figure 2: (a) Initial spatial positioning of keywords and modified positioning. × indicates the initial position and ● indicates the modified position by a user. (b) Consistently modified spatial positioning of keywords. (c) Initial spatial positioning of documents. (d) Modified spatial positioning of documents. Horizontal axis and vertical axis represent the eigenvectors corresponding to the largest and the second largest eigenvalues, respectively.

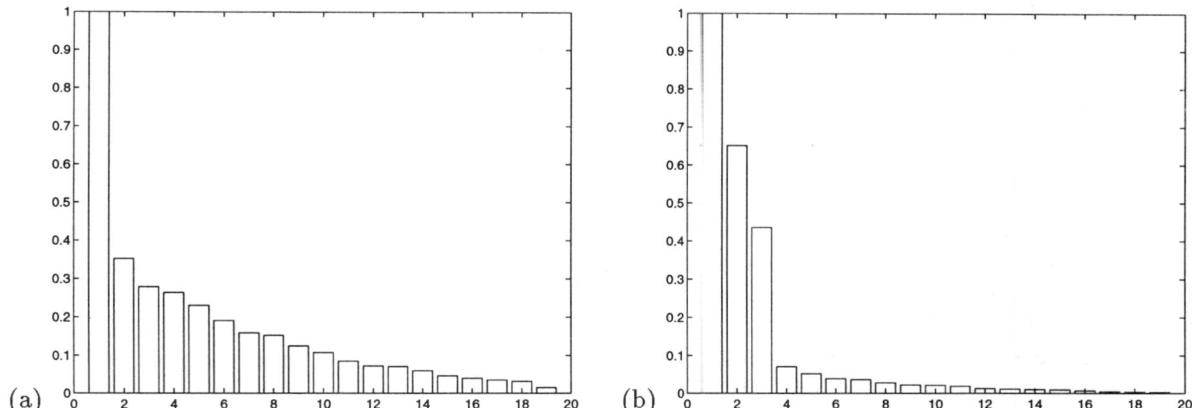

Figure 3: (a) Eigenvalues for the initial relevance matrix. (b) Eigenvalues for the modified relevance coefficient matrix. The eigenvalue of one is a trivial solution, hence does not represent the square of the correlation coefficient.

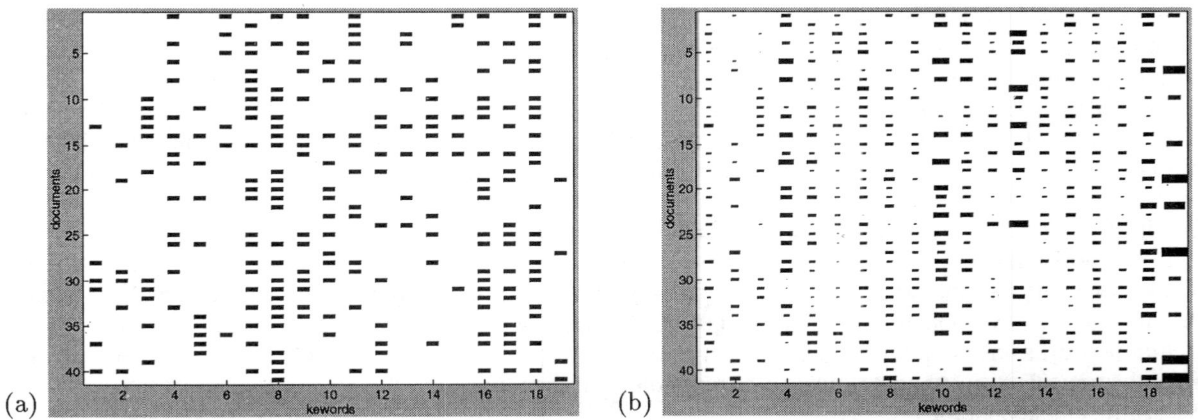

Figure 4: Relevance matrices between keywords and documents. (a) Initial relevance matrix. (b) Modified relevance matrix. The area of each rectangle indicates the value of relevance in both figures.

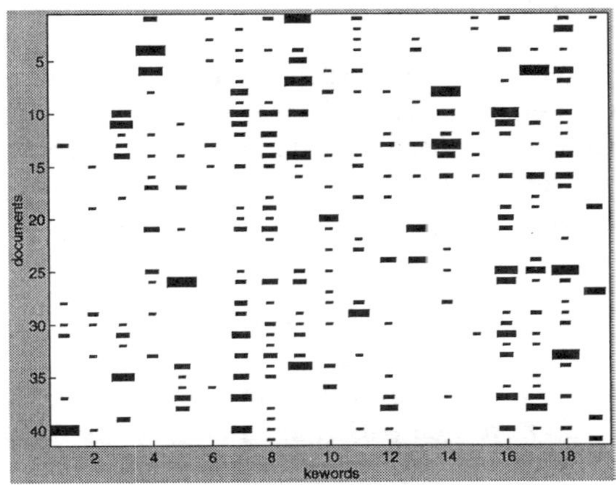

Figure 5: Frequency of appearance of keywords in each document. The smallest rectangle has the value of one.

Neural Soft-sensor for the RFCCUs' Fractionator Naphtha Endpoint

Jin Chun   Wang,   Shu Qing   Wang

Institute of Industrial Process Control, National Key Lab. of Industrial Control Tech., Zhejiang University
Hangzhou 310027,   P. R. China

Abstract— **In this contribution, an on-line neural network based soft sensor for the RFCCUs' main fractionator overhead naphtha endpoint is developed, in order to implement the closer product quality limit control scheme. According to the analysis of the process mechanism, the fractionator overhead naphtha partial pressure is calculated by the correlation of many process data.   Then, by the use of the ability of neural networks to approximate an unknown nonlinear mapping to any degree accuracy, a process soft sensor is built on the TDC-3000 Distributed Control System.**

1   Introduction

In the refinery, the residual fluidic catalyst cracking unit (RFCCU) plays an important role due to its high profits, and the main fractionator is one of the most essential devices in the RFCCUs.   The main fractionator overhead composition control is always interested in order to maintain a uniform, on-specification overhead composition with primary emphasis on the heavy end of the overhead product (i.e., naphtha endpoint). Therefore, in advance to obtaining the advanced control benefits (Lin[12] 1993), such as reduced off-specification gasoline, increased gasoline yield by operating closer to the specification limit and more consistent gasoline quality, it is necessary to get the on-time information of the naphtha endpoint.   Unfortunately, although an analyzer is available, it can not be operated correctly for long time because of its high cost and the maintenance difficulty.   So, it is essential to develop a powerful soft-sensor for the RFCCUs' fractionator product quality.

So far, it has not been reported that the naphtha endpoint can be calculated explicitly by the process variables. But, it is well known that the relationship between the naphtha endpoint and its process variables (e.g. the top temperature, the top pressure, and etc.) is apparently nonlinear and uncertain.   Hunt et al (1992)[5]pointed out that neural networks potentially provide a general framework for modeling and control of nonlinear systems. Neural networks have the following important characteristics and properties useful to the process soft sensing:
• the theoretical ability to approximate arbitrary nonlinear mappings;
• learning and adaptation;
• the ability to operate simultaneously on both quantitative and qualitative data; and
• naturally apply to multivariable systems.
ANN's thus exhibit potential as soft-sensors, i.e. sensors based on software rather than hardware (Tham et al., 1989)[11]. Recent studies show that neural networks have been widely used for dynamic modeling, inferential control and soft sensing, e.g. Willis et al, 1991[2], 1992[3]; Sunil Elanayar et al, 1994[1]; Bhat et al, 1990[5]; Pottmann et al, 1992[6]; Chen et al, 1990[8-10].

So, the neural process soft-sensor for the implementation of the advanced process control strategy is promising. This paper is organized into six sections.   Section 2 analyses the process principles of the RFCCU's main fractionator and gets the correlation of the naphtha endpoint to the process variables; Section 3 describes the steps of building a neural soft-sensor; Section 4 gives the soft-sensor's strategy; Section 5 and 6 discuss the implementation strategy and its results.

2   Process analysis

The main fractionator separates the hydrocarbon vapors from the riser reactor into five distillates: wet gas, naphtha, light cycle oil (LCO), heavy cycle oil (HCO) and slurry, and is sketched in figure 1.   It is equipped with four heat removal systems, such as the cold reflux, the top pumparound, the LCO pumparound, the HCO pumparound and the slurry pumparound, to regulate the according internal reflux.   LCO is a distillate blending stock subject to seasonal cold filter plug point limits. The naphtha/LCO split is controlled to meet a gasoline end boiling point specification.

The naphtha end boiling point is affected by many factors as follows:
• the overhead temperature.
• the overhead pressure which is uncontrollable variable, and is affected by both the operation conditions of the reactor/regenerator pressure and the wet gas compressor.
• the property of the feed stock.
• the feed flow rate to be treated.
• the reaction depth.
• the degree of heat removal.
• the steams added to the unit such as reactor stripping steam, reactor atomizing steam, sparging steam, riser fluffing steam, and the fractionator stripping steam.

For the sake of the model reduction, the naphtha end boiling point can be correlated by both the overhead temperature and the overhead naphtha hydrocarbon partial pressure through the analysis of the process, and the overhead naphtha hydrocarbon partial pressure can be calculated by the other above listing factors.

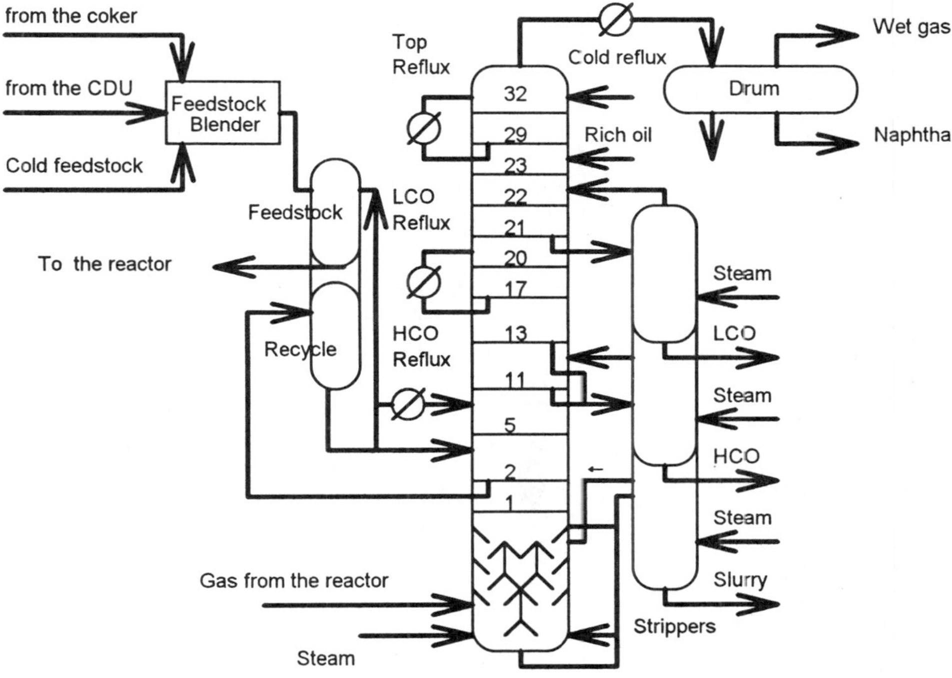

Fig.1 RFCCU's main fractionator

3 The steps of building a neural soft-sensor

The neural soft-sensor can provide a "fast" inference of a "difficult to measure" nonlinear process output from other easily measured process variables.

Much like the system identification, the procedure to determine a neural soft-sensor of a dynamical system from observed input-output data involves three basic ingredients:
•   the input-output data (the sample pattern space)
•   a set of candidate models (the model structure including the appropriate network topology)
•   a criterion to select a particular model in the set, based on the information in the data (the identification method)

The process amounts to repeatedly selecting a model structure, computing the best model in the structure, and evaluating the model's properties to see if they are satisfactory.   The cycle can be itemized as follows:
1. Design an experiment and collect input-output data from the process to be identified.

2. Examine the data; polish it so as to remove trends and outliers, select useful portions of the original data and apply filtering to enhance important frequency ranges.

3. Compute the intermediate process variables based on some of the input-output data.

4. Process data reconciliation and validation such as Narasimhan et al (1993)[7].

5. Select and define a model structure - a set of candidate system descriptions - within which a model is to be found.

6. Compute the best soft-sensor in the model structure according to the input-output data and a given criterion of fit.

7. Examine the obtained process soft-sensor's properties.

8. If the process soft-sensor is good enough, then stop; else go back to step 5 to try another model set. Possibly also try other estimation methods(step 6) or work further on the input-output data(steps 1, 2, 3 and 4).

4   Neural soft-sensor strategy

The majority of the processes in the petrochemical industry are typically the slow process.   Consider a class of multi-input single-output nonlinear dynamical systems:

$$y(t) = f(p_1(t-1),...,p_1(t-n_{p1});...;p_i(t-1),...,p_i(t-n_{pi});...;p_r(t-1),...,p_r(t-n_{pr})) \tag{1}$$

where $y(t)$ denotes the process output (product quality specification); $p_i(t)$ is the process ith input pattern; npi is the ith pattern's order; $f(\,\cdot\,)$ represents the process nonlinear mapping relationship.

The basic processing neuron of the neural soft-sensor may be considered to have two components (see Fig.2):

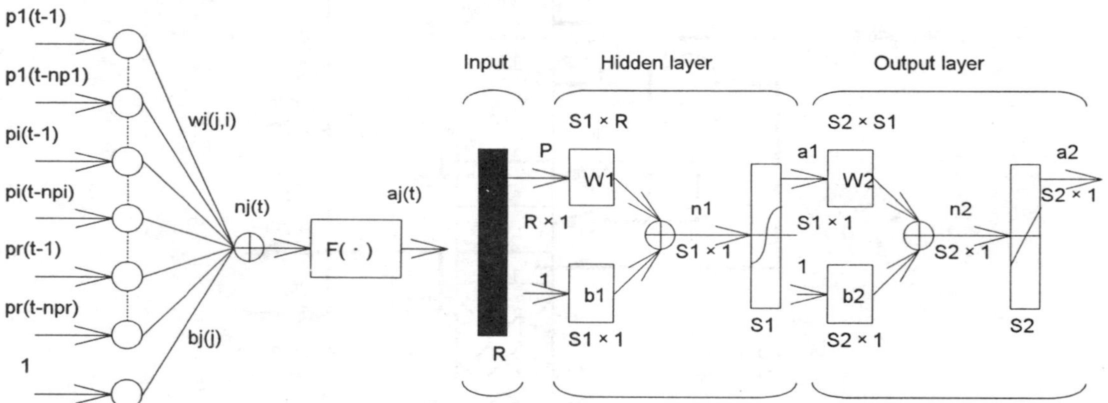

Networks with biases, a sigmoid layer and a linear layer

Fig.2 the soft-sensor's neuron   Fig.3 the neural network for the soft-sensor

1) A weighted summer

$$n_j(t) = \sum_{k=1}^{r} \sum_{i=1}^{npk} W_{(i + (k-1)np(k-1))j} \bullet p_k(t-i) \tag{2}$$

2) A transfer function

$$a_j(t) = F(n_j(t)) \tag{3}$$

where F(·) may be a linear function, a sigmoidal function or any other nonlinear function.

The neural network for the neural soft-sensor can be chosen as a network with biases, a sigmoid layer and a linear layer, depicted as Fig.3.   By definition the functional transformation of each layer of a network J can be represented by an affine transformation (weighted sum of the inputs to the later).

$$a_1(t) = J_1(p_1(t-1), \cdots, p_1(t-np_1), \cdots, p_r(t-1), \cdots, p_r(t-np_r))$$
$$y(t) = J_0(a_1(t))$$

$$(4)$$

There are many effective training algorithm used to train such networks, such as the error backpropagation (BP); the faster BP; Levenberg-Marquardt and Radial Basis Network.

As outlined above, the naphtha end boiling point can be correlated by both the overhead temperature and the overhead naphtha hydrocarbon partial pressure. Therefore, the input patterns for the neural soft-sensor of the naphtha end point are the two process variables. And the overhead naphtha hydrocarbon partial pressure (NHCPP) can be calculated by (5):

$$NHCPP = P_o \times \frac{F_n/M_n}{F_n/M_n + F_s/M_s + F_g/M_g}$$

$$(5)$$

where P_0 is the overhead pressure; F_n, F_s and F_g are the naphtha flow, the steam flows added, and the wet gas flow respectively; M_n, M_s and M_g are their molecular weight respectively.

5 Implementation

The neural soft-sensor strategy for the overhead naphtha end point is by the combination of process calculation and the ability of neural networks. It is implemented on the TDC-3000 DCS and DEC VAX/VMS (refer to Fig.4).

As shown in Fig.5, the fractionator overhead naphtha endpoint soft sensor output is mainly affected by the overhead temperature, and its curve shape is similar to the overhead temperature's. A slightly change in the naphtha endpoint soft-sensor output curve shape is due to the influence of the overhead naphtha hydrocarbon partial pressure. The results of the long-time on-line soft-sensing show that the soft-sensor output is mostly consistent with the analyzer data.

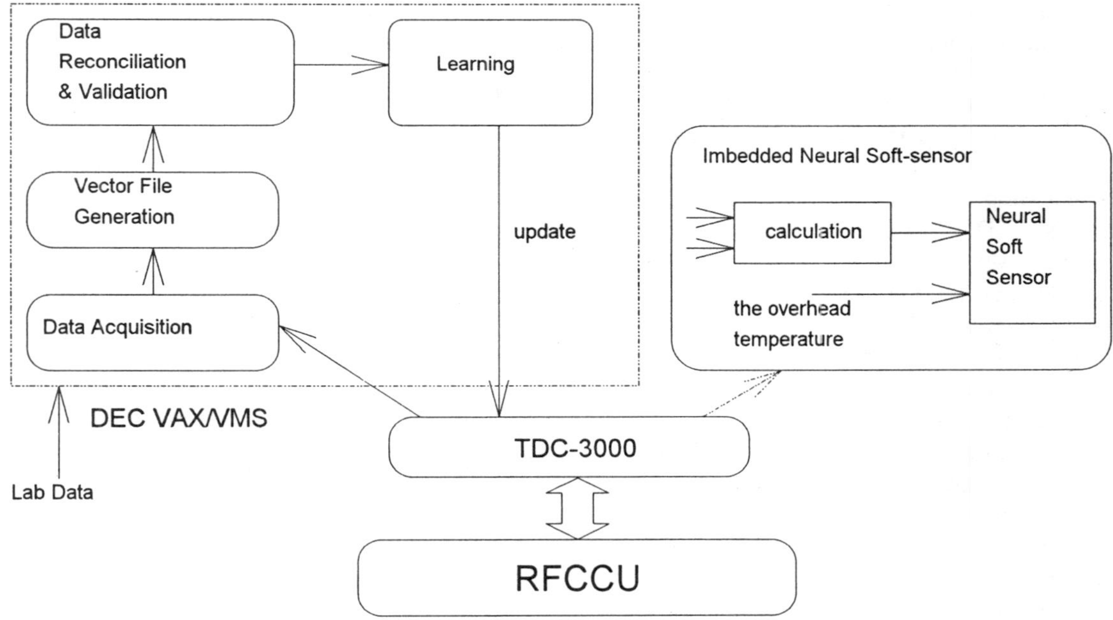

Fig. 4 the neural soft-sensor implementation

6   Conclusions

After the real industrial process is carefully analyzed to find *a prior* process knowledge and the valid process variable data are collected,   the neural soft-sensor for the RFCCU's main fractionator overhead naphtha endpoint is built and implemented.   The result is satisfactory.   It is important for the further implementation of the advanced process control for the fractionator to build successfully the neural endpoint soft-sensor.

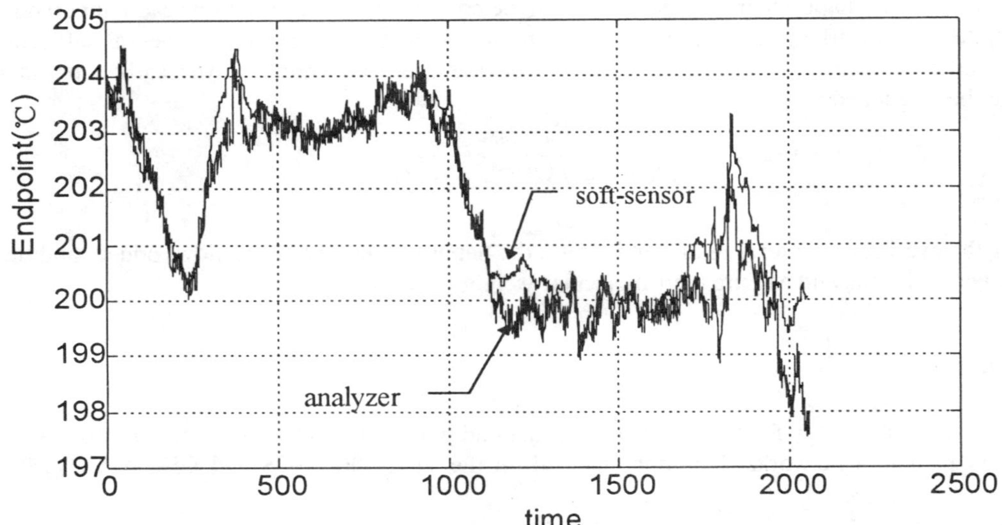

Fig. 5   the comparison of the naphtha endpoint analyzer and soft-sensor output

Acknowledgments — The support of the National Key Laboratory of Industrial Control Technology, Zhejiang University, P. R. China;   The cooperation of DCS faculty of Fujian Refinery, Fujian, P. R. China.

References

[1] Sunil Elanayar, V. T. and Y. C. Shin (1994). Radial basis function neural network for approximation and estimation of nonlinear stochastic dynamic systems.   IEEE Transactions on Neural Networks, 5(4), 594-603.

[2] Willis, M. J., G. A. Montague, C. DI Massimo, M. T. Tham and A. J. Morris (1992). Artificial   Neural networks in process estimation and control. Automatica, 28, 1181-1187.

[3] Willis, M. J., C. DI Massimo, G. A. Montague, M. T. Tham and A. J. Morris (1991). Artificial   Neural networks in process engineering. IEE Proc.-D, 138(3), 256-266.

[4] Hunt, K. J., D. Sbarbaro, R. Zbikowski and P.J. Gawthrop (1992). Neural networks for control systems—— A Survey. Automatica, 28, 1083 - 1112.

[5] Bhat, N. and T. J. McAVOY (1990). Use of neural nets for dynamic modeling and control of chemical process systems.   Computers chem. Engng., 14, 573-583.

[6] Pottmann M. and D. E. Seborg (1992).   Identification of non-linear processes using reciprocal multiquadric functions.   J. Proc. Cont., 2(4), 189-203.

[7] Narasimhan S. and P. Harikumar (1993). A method to incorporate bounds in data reconciliation and gross error detection — I. the bounded data reconciliation problem; II. gross error detection strategies. Computers chem. Engng., 17, 1115-1128.

[8] Chen, S., S. A. Billings, C. F.N. Cowan and P. M. Grant (1990). Practical identification of NARMAX models using radial basis function. Int. J. CONTROL, 52, 1327-1350.

[9] Chen, S., S. A. Billings and P. M. Grant (1990). Non-linear system identification using neural networks. Int. J. CONTROL, 51, 1191-1214.

[10] Chen, S., S. A. Billings, C. F.N. Cowan and P. M. Grant (1990). Parallel recursive prediction error algorithm for training layered neural networks.   Int. J. CONTROL, 51, 1215-1228.

[11] Tham, M. T., A. J. Morris and G. A. Montague (1989). Soft sensing: A solution to the problem of measurement delays.   Chem. Eng. Res. and Des., 67, 547-554.

[12] Lin, T. D. V. (1993). FCCU advanced control and optimization. Hydrocarbon Processing, April, 107-114.

Monitoring and Modeling of Complex Processes Using the Self-Organizing Map

Esa Alhoniemi, Olli Simula, and Juha Vesanto
Helsinki University of Technology
Laboratory of Computer and Information Science
FIN-02150 Espoo, Finland
email: `Esa.Alhoniemi@hut.fi`, `Olli.Simula@hut.fi`, `Juha.Vesanto@hut.fi`

Abstract— **In this paper, monitoring and modeling of complex processes using the SOM is considered. In a case study, a process of a pulp mill is analyzed. In addition, a new method to build a data-driven process model using hierarchical SOMs is suggested.**

1   Introduction

In monitoring of complex machines or industrial plants, the system should be described using a set of variables, which can be determined by various measurements and parameters. In many cases, these variables may be related in a strongly nonlinear way. The problem in monitoring is to find the characteristic states, or clusters of states, that determine the general behavior of the system and reflect the measurements.

The Self-Organizing Map (SOM) [1] is a nonlinear projection method that can be used to visualize the characteristic states and clusters in an efficient way. The SOM can be used to build a data-driven model without any explicit modeling of the system. Recently, the SOM has been used in fault diagnosis for detection and identification of faults in machine operation in various applications [2][3].

In this paper, a novel method to use SOMs in two hierarchical levels is proposed for estimating the future behavior of the process. The prediction of the next state is based on the information used in training of the maps.

As a case study, industrial processes of a pulp mill are considered. The pulping process consists of several process entities that interact with each other in different ways. Due to recycling of material and complex time delays analytic modeling of the system is impossible. The SOM has been applied in analysis and monitoring of different parts of this process. A case study example is presented in Section 4.

2   System Monitoring

The monitoring is based on process data measured from different parts of the system as depicted in Figure 1. The distorted and noisy data are collected from the automation system into data buffer. Parameters include input and output measurements as well as various process parameters.

In the buffer, data are preprocessed. Typical preprocessing includes data filtering or "cleaning" (removal of erroneous information), measurement vector computation, and data normalization. The normalization in SOM applications is often performed by subtracting the mean from each measurement and dividing it by the standard deviation. As a result, a distribution of zero mean and variance of unity is achieved; each measurement channel has thus equal influence in the map formation.

After preprocessing, the SOM is trained using well-known formula [1]. We have used a slightly modified algorithm, an extension, which allows the use of partial data [4][5]. This is necessary, because very often at least some of the measurement sensors are out of order and corresponding data values are missing.

There are two distinguishable ways to use the SOM in process monitoring: (1) detecting (and possibly identification of) faulty situations, or (2) observing and analyzing the behavior of process.

2.1   Fault Detection

In fault detection, the goal of the monitoring system is to reveal some clear defects occurred in the process. Sometimes only the expression of the fault is not enough - the problem may have to be identified, too. This leads to two different schema.

If fault *detection* is relevant in monitoring, the map is to be trained using measurement vectors describing normal operation only; the vectors indicating abnormal behavior of process need to be removed from the training set. In other words, the map is trained to recognize only the "normal" part of the input space.

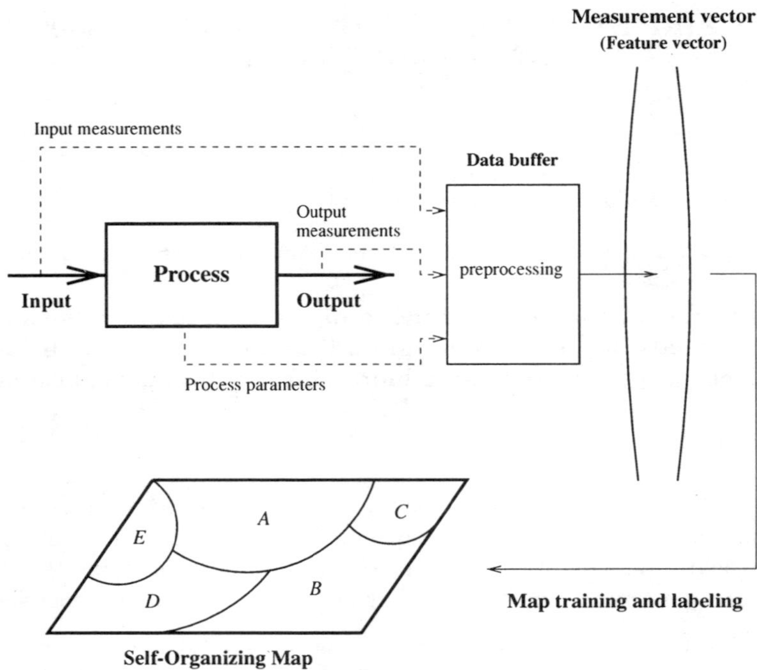

Figure 1: Training the SOM using process data.

In the monitoring, the task is to check if the map is able to recognize the measurement vector or not. This can be done using the quantization error.

Detection and identification of a fault is a more challenging task. Now the SOM should be trained using all possible data describing the process: both normal and abnormal conditions should be present in the training data set. If necessary, measurements describing simulated faults may be included in the training set. The map is trained to recognize as big part of the input space as possible. Map nodes representing fatal states of process may be marked (labeled) according to previously known samples. The monitoring is based on tracking of the operation point: the location of the point on the map indicates the process state. The quantization error may still be used, but now merely as a measure of the "familiarity" of the current situation rather than to reveal the fault.

2.2   Process Observation and Analysis

Applications for this kind of monitoring may be found among chemical processes. The main objective is not the detection of faults (although this may also be done), but rather observation of the operation point to make sure it is acceptable.

The map training and monitoring schema are similar to the ones in fault detection and identification. After training, the map nodes may be, for example, assigned different colors (by process expert) according to states on different map areas for visual state indication.

3   Process Modeling

We are here suggesting a new method for modeling complex industrial processes. In the construction, there are SOMs on two levels: (1) *state map* for process state monitoring (as described before) and (2) a *dynamics map* associated to each node of the state map. The state map is used to monitor the operating point of the process being investigated. The dynamics maps are used in prediction of the next state on state map.

Each node of the dynamics map is actually a "path" leading into the corresponding state. The dynamics of the process is thus described by means of the dynamics maps.

3.1 Training Maps on Two Hierarchical Levels

Suppose we have measurement vectors $\mathbf{x}(0)$, $\mathbf{x}(1)$, ... , $\mathbf{x}(m-1)$. The training of the system is performed as follows:

- The state map is trained using measurement vectors $\mathbf{x}(t)$. A robust process state space is built; the weight vectors are frozen.

- Next stage is training of the dynamics maps. The best-matching units (BMUs) for the training set vectors are needed: denote the BMU of vector $\mathbf{x}(t)$ by c. The training set for the dynamics map of the static map node c is formed by concatenating subsequent vectors into a single vector

$$\mathbf{x}_{hist} = [\mathbf{x}(t-\tau)^T \mathbf{x}(t-2\cdot\tau)^T \dots \mathbf{x}(t-n\cdot\tau)^T]^T. \tag{1}$$

Because the topological ordering of the dynamics maps is not important, they are plain vector quantizers. They are trained using the SOM algorithm for a short time using neighborhood, and after that, only BMUs are adapted for a long period of time.

Parameters τ and n should be selected so that it is possible to describe the process dynamics using vectors $\mathbf{x}_{hist}$. An approximation for n can be found among theory of chaotic processes: it has been shown that value of n should be at least $2d + 1$, where d is the fractal dimension [6] of the underlying dynamical process.

The structure of hierarchical maps is illustrated in Figure 2. State map nodes A, B and C are process states and dynamics map nodes a, b and c are "paths", or templates, of trajectories leading to state A.

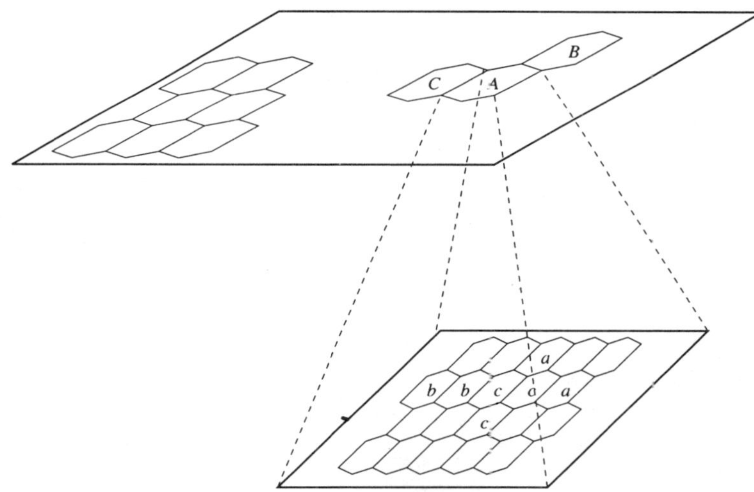

Figure 2: A hierarchical map construction: the state map and dynamics map of neuron A.

As stated before, each state map node is associated a dynamics map. In prediction, a dynamics map vector is formed using current and $n-1$ previous measurement vectors (Equation 1). This vector is compared with all dynamics map trajectory templates of all state nodes. The state map node having the best matching trajectory in its dynamics map is the predicted next state.

4 A Monitoring Example

4.1 Measurements and Preprocessing

In a monitoring experiment, a subprocess of the pulping process was investigated. The measurement period length was six days, samples were one minute averages, and there were 81 measurements, which were reduced down to 18 (see Table 1). Ignored measurements were the ones not in use, binary (0/1) ones, and measurements not directly concerning process being investigated. In the process there were seven input, three state, and two output variables. Some obviously incorrect vectors (all components equal to zero), and empty ones, were removed from the data.

	name	unit	mean	variance	min	max
a	pressure, input #1	$mbar$	44.6	50.2	16	66
b	temperature, input #1	C	82.5	0.963	80	88
c	flow, input #1	l/s	532	2074	338	677
d	pressure, input #2	mbar	60.2	81.4	0	89
e	temperature, input #2	C	37.4	0.522	32.8	40.0
f	flow, inputs #2 and #3	m^3/s	4.91	0.165	0.95	5.68
g	flow, input #4	kg/s	0.115	0.000387	0.00	0.211
h	flow, input #5	kg/s	0.026	0.000048	0.00	0.0489
i	flow, input #6	kg/s	0.000492	0.000043	0.00	0.117
j	flow, input #7	kg/s	2.99	0.0600	0.00	4.71
k	pressure, state #1	bar	16.8	0.0214	14.7	17.2
l	temperature, state #1	C	808	476	467	835
m	pressure, state #2	$mbar$	-5.00	0.0754	-8.1	0.0
n	cylinder surface, state #3	$mmVP$	4.48	21.1	-34.3	64.1
o	temperature, output #1	C	205	0.252	199	206
p	flow, output #1	kg/s	2.93	0.0460	0.25	3.31
q	temperature, output #2	C	268	28.0	219	279
r	oxygen in output #2	%	6.63	0.120	5.4	10.0

Table 1: Experiment parameter statistics.

4.2 Map Training and Results

6224 sample vectors, each consisting of 18 measurements, were used to train a SOM of 20 by 15 units. The u-matrix [7] plot, depicting the distances between adjacent units of the map, is shown in figure 3. Figure 4 shows the component planes of the map nodes visualizing the parameter values corresponding to process states.

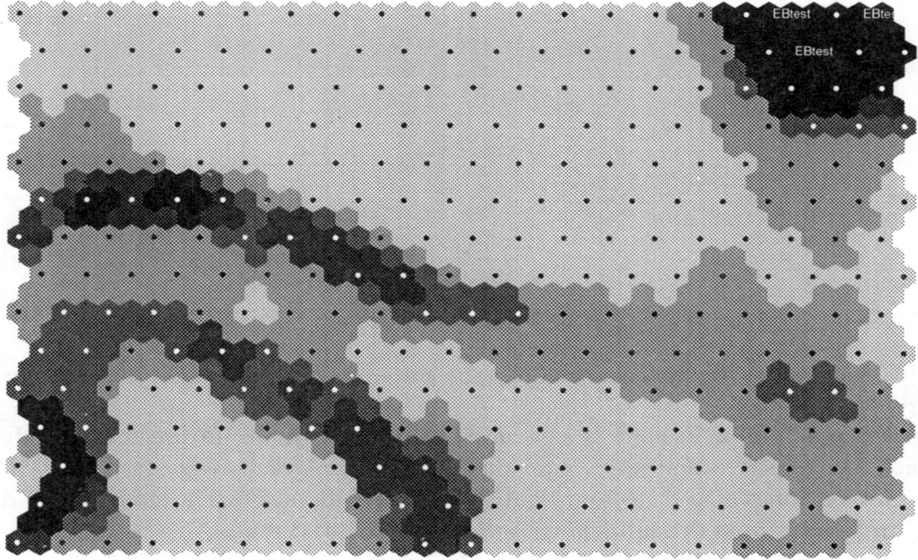

Figure 3: U-matrix representation of the example map. Dark color indicates big, and light small distance.

In this example, there was only one clearly exceptional situation: weekly test of emergency system (labeled by *EBtest*). This state is located in the top right corner of the map (see Figure 3) and can be clearly observed in the component plane representations, too.

There are also other states of the process, which can be analyzed using component distributions in Figure 4. In the bottom left corner there is an area, which describes a fault in input #1: the pressure (a) and flow (c) are small.

Next to the area described above lies a set of states, where the output (p) has the highest value. The corresponding input flows (c), (f) and (h) are big, too.

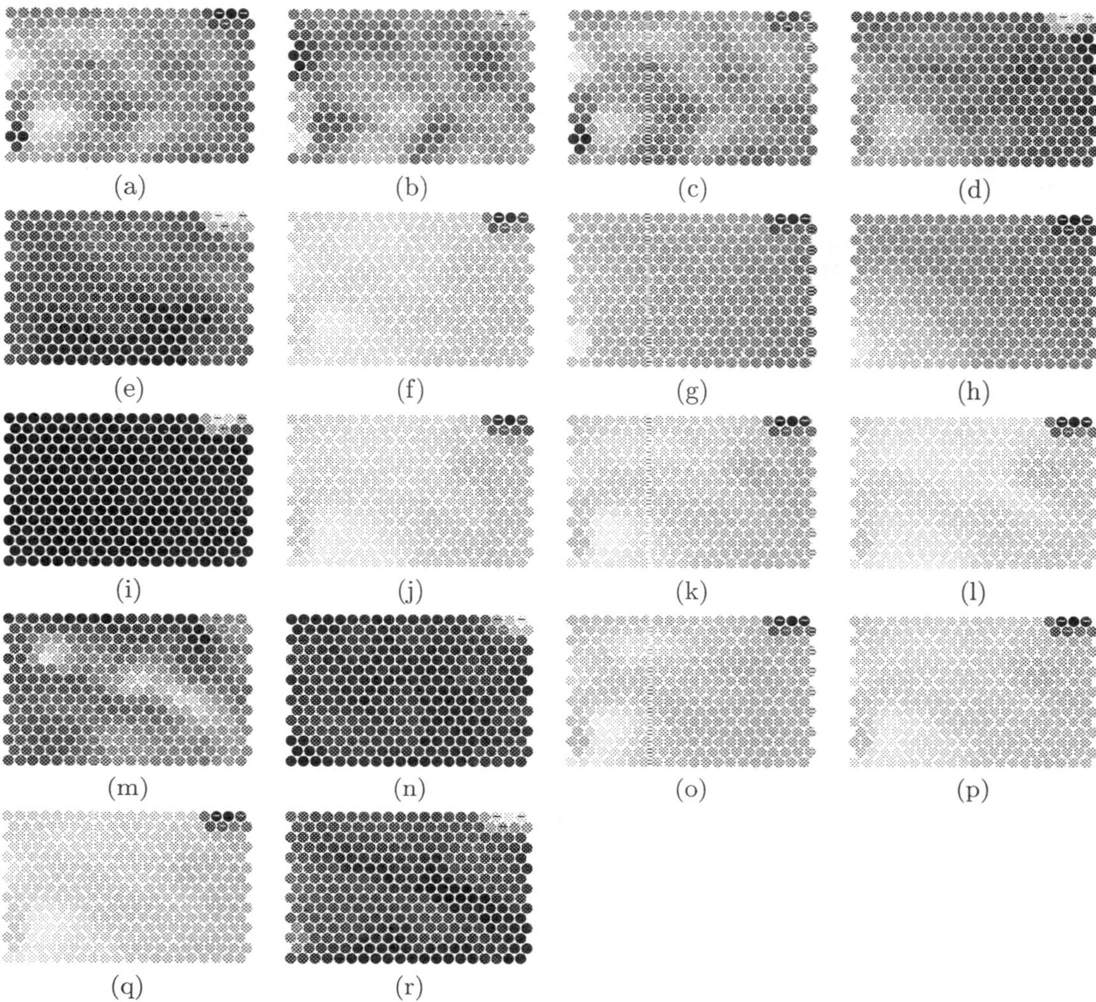

(a)   (b)   (c)   (d)

(e)   (f)   (g)   (h)

(i)   (j)   (k)   (l)

(m)   (n)   (o)   (p)

(q)   (r)

Figure 4: The component planes of the example map: dark color indicates small, and light color big value.

The system model described in Section 3 was not thoroughly used in system state prediction due to lack of process data: there were only 6224 sample vectors collected during a period of six days. This material is not enough to describe the system behavior in any way. Thus, very preliminary tests using hierarchical maps were done with this data. However, they showed positive results in the next state prediction.

5   Conclusions

The SOM has been applied in the analysis and monitoring of complex systems, e.g. industrial processes. The preliminary results show that hierarchical maps, the state map and the corresponding dynamics map, might be applicable in predicting the process states. The state estimates are entirely based on the information obtained from the training data.

The hierarchical maps can also be used in simulating the process behavior. The effect of various process parameters can be investigated using the state transitions. In addition, sensitivity of the system to various parameter changes can be simulated. A simulator tool based on the state and dynamics map is being constructed.

References

[1] Teuvo Kohonen. *Self-Organizing Maps*. Springer, Berlin, Heidelberg, 1995.

[2] Teuvo Kohonen, Erkki Oja, Olli Simula, Ari Visa, and Jari Kangas. Engineering applications of the self-organizing map. To appear in *Proceedings of the IEEE* in 1996.

[3] Olli Simula and Jari Kangas. *Neural Networks for Chemical Engineers*, volume 6 of *Computer-Aided Chemical Engineering*, chapter 14, Process monitoring and visualization using self-organizing maps. Elsevier, Amsterdam, 1995.

[4] Samuel Kaski and Teuvo Kohonen. Structures of welfare and poverty in the world discovered by the self-organizing map. Technical Report A24, Helsinki University of Technology, Laboratory of Computer and Information Science, February 1995.

[5] T. Samad and S. A. Harp. Self-organization with partial data. *Network: Computation in Neural Systems*, 3(2):205–212, May 1992.

[6] Thomas S. Parker and Leon O. Chua. *Practical Numerical Algorithms for Chaotic Systems*. Springer, 1989.

[7] A. Ultsch and H.P. Siemon. Kohonen's self organizing feature maps for exploratory data analysis. In *Proc. INNC'90, Int. Neural Network Conf.*, pages 305–308, Dordrecht, Netherlands, 1990. Kluwer.

Hydroelectric Power Plant Predictive Maintenance relying on Neural Network Acoustic Module[‡]

P. Isasi-Viñuela* ,J.M. Molina-López*, A. Navia-Vázquez**

* Departamento de Informática, Universidad Carlos III de Madrid
Madrid, Spain
** Departamento de Ingeniería, Universidad Carlos III de Madrid
Madrid, Spain

Abstract - **The analysis of sound data coming from vital components of a power plant gives additional information for the identification of potential future failures and their causes, making it possible to perform effective preventive maintenance. The use of neural networks (NN) is a novel approach that can help produce decisions when integrated in a more general system. In this paper we introduce a NN module using Kohonen Learning Vector Quantization (LVQ) Networks to discriminate sounds from the plant in order to prevent future malfunctions. This module belongs to a more general system for predictive maintenance that has been implemented and incorporated in a hydroelectric plant.**

1.   Introduction

Power plant management relies on monitoring many signals that represent the technical parameters of the real plant. Monitoring systems, in general, are able to analyze the input values and make decisions, and consequently generate alarms when the numerical value of the variables is out the range fixed by human experts. Some Artificial Intelligence (AI) techniques have been suggested in the literature to develop automatic surveillance systems for power plants [1] [2]. Using the expert knowledge of the plant operator, it is possible not only to provide valid ranges for variables but to predict future abnormal situations that could be avoided. This papers present the design of an automatic predictive system that evaluates future situations using present system variables. This system has been developed and installed in an operating plant. The main subject described in this paper is the neural network acoustic prediction module, composed of acquisition, pre-processing of the audio signal, and a predictive neural network.

The main advantages to be gained with predictive modules are productivity optimization, operation safety, and protecting equipment against damage caused by malfunctioning. The results could also be adapted to any system dependent on distributed control centers, since the general philosophy is to model the plant and predict future situations instead of merely taking precautionary measures. To achieve this objective, our project relies on advanced artificial intelligence techniques, audio and video signal processing, expert knowledge systems and neural networks modeling.

These ideas presented here have been developed in a project named MAPAIS (Spanish abbreviation of advanced system for predictive maintenance incorporating audio and video). The main goal was to develop a multimedia supervisory system taking advantage of SCADA systems (Supervisory Control and Data Acquisition), known to be effective and reliable, as well as information from audio and video transceptors. This project is an extension of a previous project called MANPRED which yielded a monitoring system (Hypervision System v.1.0) already working in the hydroelectric plant named Villalcampo I (IBERDROLA), which is located in the Zamora province of Northwest Spain. This plant has also been used for implementing and further testing of MAPAIS project.

In figure 1-1 a general view of the supervisory system is presented, consisting of the electricity generating machine group constituted by three independent generators named Group #1, Group #2 and Group #3 respectively. The plant operator is able to obtain information about any system parameter by descending a hierarchical hyperlink structure. The predictive modules have been included in a subtree of the monitoring system.

[‡] This project has been supported by CDTI (belonging to Spanish Industry Ministery) and EEC (European Economic Comunity), reference number: PASO PC067.

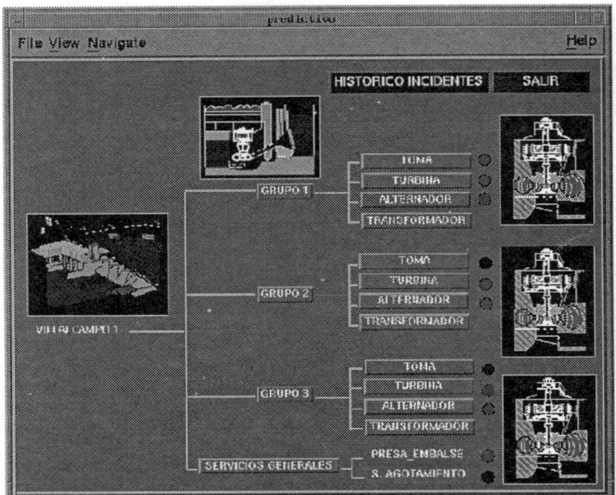

Fig. 1-1 : Monitoring System Interface.

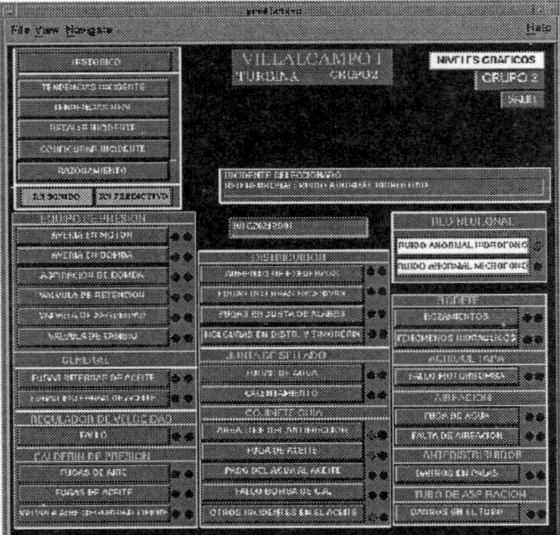

Fig. 1-2 : Predictive System Interface

Within the predictive modules of the system, the main goal of the neural network acoustic prediction module is to take advantage of sound information recorded at every energy group, acting as a future-incident-predictor in the sense that it learns to detect potentially conflictive situations. In order to obtain realistic initial information about the desired behaviour some tests have been carried out using the real plant.

The organization of the rest of the paper is as follows: the second section presents an overview of the general system, in particular the audio module, comprising acquisition and data processing. The third section describes the general classification methods taking into account to design the predictive neural network and a detailed description of the selected neural net. The real system performance at the Villalcampo plant is given in the fourth section and our conclusions are presented.

2.   The Audio Module: Global System Description

The predictive maintenance system can be decomposed in several parts, a general data flow scheme is shown in figure 2-1 . Among these, several important modules require explanation. The neural network predictive maintenance module produces predictions about future malfunctioning using a model of the plant. It relies on a neural network model generated from past data and present events. The main drawback to this approach is that abnormal incidents seldom occur, and it is therefore difficult to isolate the main variables involved in every process. The image processing module was designed to reinforce measurements from several electrical transceptors. Thus, image processing is included to assess the functioning of the power switching systems. The rule-based diagnosis module will collect all the information available from expert human controllers in order to predict problems. The neural network acoustic prediction module takes advantage of audio data recorded in different points of every energy group to generate a warning signal of future abnormal situations. Several algorithms were considered for this module, and the one with best characteristics has been incorporated in the module. This part is the main concern of this paper and it is analyzed in detail. Finally, the data fusion and decision module collects all the available data to generate an alarm and activates the interface panel shown in figure 1-2 .

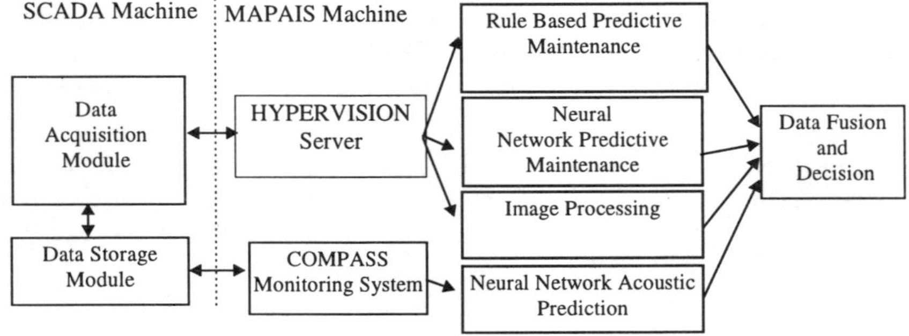

Fig. 2-1 : Data flow diagram between modules

2.1. Sound Data Acquisition

As mentioned above, an electricity-generating machine group, constituted by three independent generators named Group #1, Group #2 and Group #3 respectively, are monitored constantly. Every one of the groups can be sketched as in figure 2-2 , where part "A" represents the alternating current generator and "B" represents the hydraulic turbine (obviously, this part is underwater). Many sensors located at different points in the machinery serve to monitor the group but of main concern here are those related to sound measurements. In particular the placement of microphones M1, M2 and hydrophone H1 is marked with circles, representing microphones in the alternator and the turbine, as well as a hydrophone in the turbine.

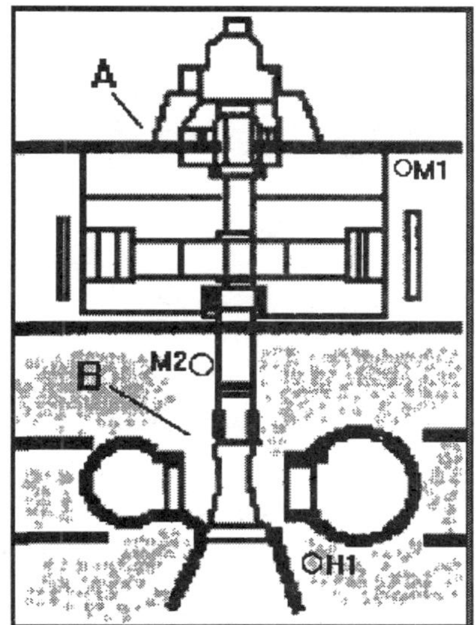

Fig. 2-2 :Sketch of a generating group, comprising an alternator (A) and a turbine (B). Sound data acquisition points are denoted as M1, M2, H1.

Generated Power	Experts Classification
5 Mw	Abnormal regime
9 Mw	Abnormal regime
13 Mw	Normal regime
20 Mw	Normal regime
25 Mw	Normal regime
30 Mw	Normal regime
31 Mw	Abnormal regime

Table 2-1 : Power situations used to obtain initial sound data.

The data acquisition equipment, which was already working in the plant and named the COMPASS Machine Monitoring System Type 3540, was considered flexible enough to perform all the preprocessing. A baseband spectrum mode was selected with a frequency span of 1Hz-5 Khz, which is considered to be adequate for our purposes. Inclusion of higher frequencies yields no improvement. Indeed, a decrease in algorithm performance could be observed due to extra high-pass noise introduced in the system.

A Hanning windowing was used and the FFT spectrum was computed using an averaging mode spanning 10 epochs in order to produce an output every 10 minutes. This time lap was considered sufficient as changes in groups tend to be slow. A typical spectrum collection is depicted in figure 2-3 , corresponding to the microphone in alternator #3.

In order to obtain initial data to use in training the malfunction prediction-module, every group was forced to work in several power production rates (Table 2-1). An expert was able to classify each situation using lateral information from other sources. In the table above the following situation is described: Group #1 is working at fixed rate and Group #3 works at different rates. Group #1 is generating background noise which corrupts measurements in Group #3. This background noise is unavoidable and therefore the system has to cope with it. This data is complex and involves relating the produced power with an expert-based classification of the situation. It is important to mention that such knowledge-based classification is carried out with the concurrent expert observation of many other variables; sound is never used exclusively by the expert in such decisions.

2.2.   *Sound Data Processing*

During the initial training, an expert continues monitoring the whole system and the sound module is presented with a teaching signal. Retraining occurs when new situations arise and new expert-assessed data is available.

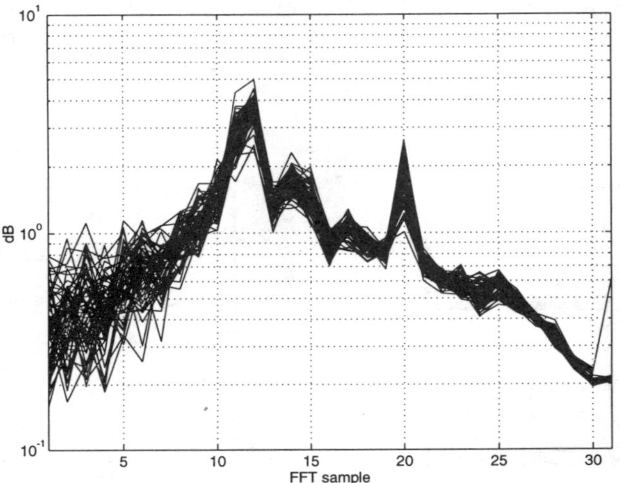

Fig. 2-3 :Ensemble of FFT spectra representing one of the normal regimes in group #3.

Before selecting the best system to carry out the task required by the acoustic module, several characteristics can be observed in the data. Every spectrum can be considered as a point in a N-dimensional space, corresponding either to "safe" situations or future abnormal situations. This way, the problem is reduced to a classification task in a N-dimensional space. Nevertheless, some special characteristics arise when analyzing the data. First of all, variance in FFT samples is not evenly distributed in the frequency range, as can be observed in figure 2-3 . This is due to the time-varying humming of water when traveling through the pipes plus a lowpass filtered component of noise from adjacent groups (data is usually recorded when several groups are working together). Nevertheless, despite of nonuniform variance, the distribution of every FFT sample can be considered as locally gaussian. It is also important to note that vectors are not evenly distributed between both classes, because "normal functioning" will be the predominant situation and "potential conflict" will seldom arise. At the same time, both events do not have the same importance because classifying a situation as conflictive when it is not is less problematic than failing to predict a potentially dangerous situation. A similar problem arises in radar detection where a false alarm is not as problematic as the non-detection case [3]. In our case this idea is reinforced by the fact that the data fusion and decision module has been designed to consider every sound-module warning. The sound module is therefore used as a warning system which is very sensitive to alterations in sound information (conservative behaviour) and forces, when activated, the system to take into account information from other variables (prediction modules).

Thus, we are operating outside of the typical Bayesian arena, because the most frequent events are not the most relevant ones. This issue must be taken into account.

3.   Neural Network Acoustic Prediction

The next step was to construct a classifier for the sound signals produced by the above mentioned working regimes. Several well-known classification methods were considered and the one that we feel that best fits our requirements has been implemented in the sound module.

A MLP (Multilayer Perceptron) is very appropriate when handling high dimensional problems because it uses hyperplanes very efficiently [4]. Nevertheless, these capabilities deteriorate when dealing with sparse data, as occurs in our application. Other possible methods, e.g., the k-NN ("k" nearest neighbours) method, would incur high computational and storage requirements. The ART algorithm (Adaptive Resonance Theory [5]) allows on-line training as new patterns are presented, but in our case such capability is of limited utility as no information is available about newly formed categories and thus we would loose generalization capabilities. These considerations led us to select LVQ (Learning Vector Quantization [6]) as the technique with the best simplicity-performance ratio. Some advantages of this method have also been pointed out by some researchers [7]. This algorithm is revisited below.

LVQ was developed by Kohonen as a method for the supervised clustering of a space into mutually exclusive classes. This is accomplished by defining a small set of centroids and yields a Voronoi tessellation of the space (i.e. boundaries are perpendicular bisector planes of lines joining pairs of neighbouring prototype vectors). An input vector "$\underline{x}$" is said to belong to the class represented by the centroid, c_i , if and only if:

$$|c_i\text{-}\underline{x}| \le |c_j\text{-}\underline{x}| \ \forall j \tag{1}$$

where |.| denotes Euclidean distance.

During the LVQ1 training phase, the centroid with minimum distance to the presented pattern is said to be the "winner", c_{winn} , and is updated using the following rule:

$$\Delta c_{winn} = \begin{cases} +\alpha(t)\left(\underline{x} - c_{winn}\right) & \text{if class is correct} \\ -\alpha(t)\left(\underline{x} - c_{winn}\right) & \text{if class is incorrect} \end{cases} \tag{2}$$

The overall behaviour of the algorithm is to place the centroids in the mass centers of the distributions. Stable solutions can be obtained if a sufficient number of centroids is available and the density functions are well behaved.

As mentioned above, not every situation has the same importance and, in order to design a conservative system (which will produce an alarm even when presented a new sound), we need to increase the probability of false alarm when predicting future incidences in order to reliably predict a real incident which could produce a disastrous effect. This can be done by constructing a "risk function" for every decision (incident/safe) using conditional probability functions when a pattern $\underline{x}$ is presented [8]:

$$R_{safe}(\underline{x}) = l_{11}\,P(safe|\underline{x}) + l_{12}\,P(incident|\underline{x}) \tag{3}$$

$$R_{incidence}(\underline{x}) = l_{21}\,P(safe|\underline{x}) + l_{22}\,P(incident|\underline{x}) \tag{4}$$

In our case we considered $l_{12} = k\,l_{21}$ $(k > 1)$, and $l_{11}=l_{22}=0$, which yields a biased decision boundary when detecting future incidents:

$$\text{"Future Incident"} \Leftrightarrow R_{incident}(\underline{x}) < R_{safe}(\underline{x}) \Leftrightarrow P(\text{"incident"}|\underline{x}) > (1/k)\,P(\text{"safe"}|\underline{x}) \tag{5}$$

The same concept can be directly translated to the evaluation of distances, by multiplying the distance to centroids of class "future incident" by k:.

$$d(c_i , \underline{x}) = \begin{cases} \left|c_i - \underline{x}\right| & \text{if } c_i \in \text{"safe"} \\ k\left|c_i - \underline{x}\right| & \text{if } c_i \in \text{"future incident"} \end{cases} \tag{6}$$

With this new distance measure we achieve a conservative system, and thereby extend the region of future risk with respect to conventional Bayesian decision boundaries.

Nevertheless, such modification can lead to misclassification of certain patterns because LVQ1 tends to place centroids in mass centers. A solution is obtained by using a modification of this basic algorithm, called LVQ2 [9], which is closer to Bayes Decision Theory, as it places centroids near the decision boundary, thereby reducing the risk of misclassification. In this case, the two nearest centroids are considered and only updated when the input vector is misclassified by the winning centroid, and the next nearest neighbour has the correct class, and $\underline{x}$ falls into a predefined window:

$$\Delta c_{winner} = -\alpha(t)\left(\underline{x} - c_{winner}\right)$$

$$\Delta c_{runner-up} = +\alpha(t)\left(\underline{x} - c_{runner-up}\right) \tag{7}$$

In general, LVQ techniques require extensive off-line training time and are unable to incorporate new data without complete retraining. These characteristics might be critical for certain applications but are acceptable in our case because the time lapses are long enough to allow re-training, and also because new situations seldom arise (only during an initial testing phase an expert assessment will be available and new, correctly-classified data, is incorporated).

4.   System Performance on Hydroelectric Plant: Final Conclusions

During a period of a week tests were carried out on the maintenance system under strict supervision from technical staff of the plant. During the test period final tuning of the system was needed due to special weather conditions under which the system was tested (heavy rainfall that overloaded the dam capacity and flood-gates had to be opened to allow run-off of the excess water). This unusual situation was serendipitous in that we were presented with a situation which allowed us to evaluate generalization capacity of the system because the network had to deal with unusual data.

Three main incidents occurred, two of them caused by data from hydrophones at turbines in Groups 2 and 3, and one caused by the microphone at turbine in Group 3. The extracted conclusions are as follows: generalization of data recorded at hydrophones is poor because of high variability in sound spectra even in non-changing environments due to excess of noise. The incident produced by data from microphone in turbine at Group 3 was identified by experts as "normal situation" and therefore included as new data for re-training together with some data collected while developing the neural network module. This phenomenon was explained as follows: due to the long period of time between initial data collection and final testing some special minor variations had occurred in the working conditions, and hence such re-training was considered as a normal final tuning.

After that, the system was considered to have reached an ideal working behaviour, this way, it was definitely included in the monitoring system on January 1996 and it is nowadays being used as a decision-making aid.

5.   References

[1]   R. Raghavan, B.H. Simon, "Advanced Plant Maintenance and Surveillance System for the Nuclear Power Plants of the Next Century", Proc. 2nd ASME JSME Nuclear Engineering Joint Conference 1993, vol. 2, pp. 693-697, 1993.

[2]   A. Loskiewicz-Buczak, I.E. Alguindigue, R.E. Uhrig, "Vibration Analysis in Nuclear Power Plant Using Neural Networks", Proc. 2nd ASME JSME Nuclear Engineering Joint Conference 1993, vol. 2, pp. 43-51, 1993.

[3]   C. Stewart, L. Yi-Chuan, V. Larson, "Vector Quantization and Learning Vector Quantization for Radar Target Classification", Proc. SPIE-The International Society for Optical Engineering, vol. 1960, pp. 115-24, 1993.

[4]   T. Rognvaldsson, "Pattern Discrimination Using Feedforward Networks: A Benchmark Study of Scaling Behaviour", Neural Computation, vol. 5, pp. 483-91, 1993.

[5]   S. Grossberg, "Competitive Learning: From Interactive Activation to Adaptive Resonance Theory", Cognitive Science, vol. 11, pp. 23-63, 1987.

[6]   T. Kohonen, *Learning Vector Quantization for Pattern Recognition*, Report TKK-F-A601, Helsinky University of Technology, Department of Technical Physics, Laboratory of Computer and Information Science, 1986.

[7]   Y. Bartal, Jie Lin, R.E. Uhrig, "Nuclear Power Plants Transient Diagnostics Using LVQ or Some Networks Don't Know That They Don't Know", 1994 International Conference on Neural Networks, vol. 6, pp. 3744-9, 1994.

[8]   Yoh-Han Pao, *Adaptive Pattern Recognition and Neural Networks*, Addison-Wesley, 1989.

[9]   T. Kohonen, "Statistical Pattern Recognition Revisited" in *Advanced Neural Computers*, R. Eckmiller (ed.), Elsevier Science Publishers B.V. (North-Holland), 1990.

Power System Fault Prediction Using Artificial Neural Networks

K C P Wong, H M Ryan, J Tindle

School of Engineering and Advanced Technology, University of Sunderland
Edinburgh Building, Chester Road, Sunderland,
SR1 3SD, United Kingdom.
patrick.wong@sunderland.ac.uk, hugh.ryan@sunderland.ac.uk,
john.tindle@sunderland.ac.uk

Abstract -- The medium term goal of the research reported in this paper was the development of a major in-house suite of strategic computer aided network simulation and decision support tools to improve the management of power systems. This paper describes a preliminary research investigation to access the feasibility of using an Artificial Intelligence (AI) method to predict and detect faults at an early stage in power systems. To achieve this goal, an AI based detector has been developed to monitor and predict faults at an early stage on particular sections of power systems. The detector only requires external measurements taken from the input and output nodes of the power system. The AI detection system is capable of rapidly predicting a malfunction within the system . Simulation will normally take place using equivalent circuit representation. Artificial Neural Networks (ANNs) are used to construct a hierarchical feed-forward structure which is the most important component in the fault detector. Simulation of a transmission line (2-port Π circuit) has already been carried out and preliminary results using this system are promising. This approach provided satisfactory results with accuracy of 95% or higher.

1.0   Introduction

Adequate fault detection is vitally important to ensure reliable power system operation. Many system fault studies are concerned mainly with a 'what if' scenario i.e. on considering what would happen after a fault occurred, identifying its location and accessing the nature and degree of damage. To date, few studies have been made concerning early fault detection (EFD) techniques which facilitate the prediction of a major fault before it actually occurs. In a typical power system, the states (voltages and currents) of most bus bar nodes are monitored and gradual changes are analysed. However, because of the complexity of recorded data, faults at an early stage cannot be easily recognised. These faults can be disguised by the complexity of power system operational data [1-6].

The aim of the EFD method is to detect and alert the operator before a catastrophic fault actually occurs. In other words, this is an early warning fault prevention method. ANNs are employed to monitor the states of some important components in power networks, such as switchgear and transformers. The ANN is trained to detect minor changes to the internal parameters modelled as power system equivalent circuits [6]. The small variations of voltages and currents resulting from internal parameters changes, at sending end and receiving ends of the power system can be derived under simulation and then presented to the ANN for training. As some of the internal parameters of the power system do not physically exist, they cannot be measured directly by simple measurement methods. Thus, the application of an intelligent technique, such as an ANN method , is obviously required. The principle of the EFD can be applied to various sections of a power system. A typical extremely simplified example will now be given.

Transmission lines in power systems carry high currents and voltages. Small changes in state, caused by partial faults, on transmission lines are often too insignificant to   trigger the conventional protection systems. However, these small scale changes may develop and eventually lead to major faults. For example, in winter, snow may gradually accumulate on transmission lines. The impedance of transmission lines could change accordingly. The circuit breaker would trip when the snow formed a short-circuit and this could "black-out" a large area. With early warning fault monitoring, the interruption of power supply could possibly be prevented. The change of impedance of the transmission line provides vital information which can be analysed by EFD technique to provide an early detection capability. This technique could alert the operator before the main fault actually occurs enabling, in some situations, appropriate action to be taken, e.g. providing power supply from another circuit and switching out the endangered line.

2.0 Artificial Neural Network

An ANN may be considered as a greatly simplified model of the human brain which can be used to perform a particular task or function of interest. The network is usually implemented using electronic components or simulated in software on a digital computer. The massively parallel distributed structure and the ability to learn and generalise makes it possible for ANNs to solve complex problems that otherwise are currently intractable. A brief description of neural network characteristics is given below. For more information, see [9-23].

2.1 Neurons and Synapses

A neuron is an information processing unit that is fundamental to the operation of an ANN. Two basic elements can be identified from a neuron; an adder and an activation function. An adder is used to sum up the input signals, weighted by the respective synapses of the neuron. The activation function limits the amplitude of the output of a neuron. It compresses the permissible amplitude range of the output signal to some finite value. [16] Synapses are simple connection that can either impose excitation or inhibition on the receptive neuron. Knowledge is acquired by the network through a learning process. The synaptic weights are used to store the knowledge. Through the learning process, the synaptic weights of the network are modified in such a way to map the input patterns to the output patterns. [16]

2.2 Structure of a Artificial Neural Network

Four popular neural network architectures are being widely used [16]. They are the single-layer feedforward network, multi-layer feedforward network, recurrent network, and the lattice structure. The standard multi-layer feedforward network is employed as the network architecture in this project, and is described below. The multi-layer feedforward network is a network of neurons and synapses organised in the form of layers. There are three kinds of layers in an ANN : the input layer, hidden layer and output layer. The function of the input layer is simply to buffer the external inputs to the network. The hidden neurons have no connections to the inputs or outputs. By including hidden layers, the network is empowered to extract higher-order statistics as the network acquires a global perspective despite its local connectivity by virtue of the extra set of synaptic connections and the extra dimension of neural interactions (Churchland and Sejnowski, 1992)[10]. Figure 1 shows the structure of multi-layer feedforward network.

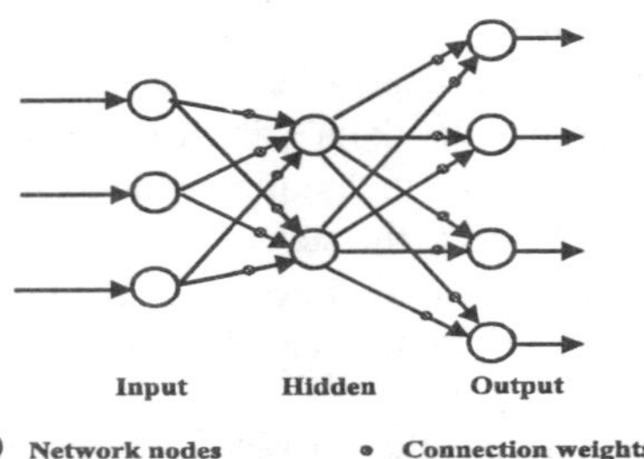

Figure 1. A 3-2-4 multi-layer feedforward network.

As ANNs basically consist of a network of neurons and synapses organised in layers, the source nodes in the input layer of the network supply respective elements of the activation pattern, which constitute the input signals applied to the neurons (computation nodes) in the second layer. The output signals of the second layer are used as inputs to the third layer, and so on, for the rest of the network.

2.3 Learning Algorithm

The procedure used to perform the learning process is called a learning algorithm, the function of which is to modify the synaptic weights of the network in an orderly fashion so as to attain a desired design objective. Many learning methods have been developed in the last few decades. Detailed information of ANN learning algorithms can be obtained from [10],[16],[19].

Two learning algorithms have been used for this project; the standard back-propagation (BP) method and the genetic learning algorithm (GA). BP has already been successfully applied by several workers to solve some difficult and diverse problems by training ANNs in a supervised manner. With regard to the BP method, a training set is applied to the input of the network, signals propagate through the network and emerge as a set of output states. An error term is derived from the difference between the desired and actual output values and synaptic weights are then adjusted in accordance with an error correction rule. As the iteration proceeds, the overall error normally approaches zero.

However, the very slow rate of learning and premature convergence are limitations of the standard BP learning method. An alternative to the BP is the GA which is an evolutionary algorithm based on the concept of natural selection and evolution. Genetic methods seek to imitate the biological phenomenon of evolutionary reproduction, described in [7], [8]. Evolutionary computing techniques are based upon Darwin's theory of evolution where a population of individuals, in this case potential solutions, compete with one another over successive generations, 'survival of the fittest'. After a number of generations, the best solutions survive and the less fit are gradually eliminated from the population [8]. As the GA's can prevent the local solutions when guided by the parallel search strategy, premature convergence can be avoided. The synaptic weights of ANNs are considered to be the chromosomes of a population. Standard crossover and mutation are employed as the reproduction operators. Each new population of weights will be transferred to the ANN for evaluation. After the fitness values are calculated, a new generation of weights will be genetically created. This process is repeated many times until the pre-defined precision is met. Figure 2 shows a representation of the GA training method.

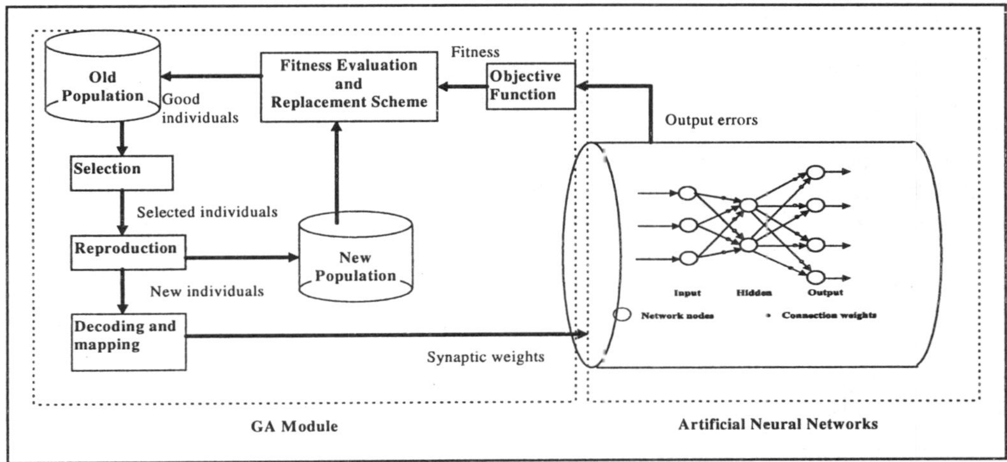

Figure 2. Block diagram representation of GA training method.

2.4 Hierarchical Distributed ANN (HDANN)

Hierarchical Distributed ANNs are advanced neural network architectures which have been developed recently[17]. HDANN consists of several level of ANNs. The outputs of lower level ANNs are connected to the inputs of higher level ANNs. A typical schematic of a HDANN is shown on Figure 3. The advantages of using a HDANN rather than a large conventional ANN are that the learning rate is faster, the number of training patterns required are smaller and the memory for storing the states of the neurons and synapses are thus smaller. Furthermore, each of the individual ANNs can be trained separately, 'the divide and conquer approach'. Hierarchical distributed artificial intelligent neural networks are being investigated within this project. Each of individual ANNs at level 3 is used to monitor a small section of a power system.

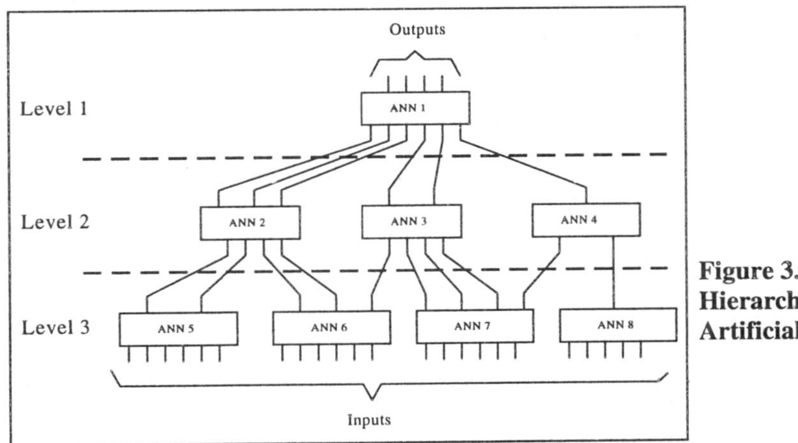

Figure 3. Hierarchical Structured Artificial Neural Network

3.0 Experiments

In order to verify the principle of the early warning fault detection system, a simple Π circuit was selected and used as a target test circuit. The ANN based pre-fault detector was used as a monitor for the detection of partial faults on a simple Π circuit. The Π circuit consists of three complex components (impedances) representing the equivalent circuit for a transmission line. The circuit is represented in Figure 4.

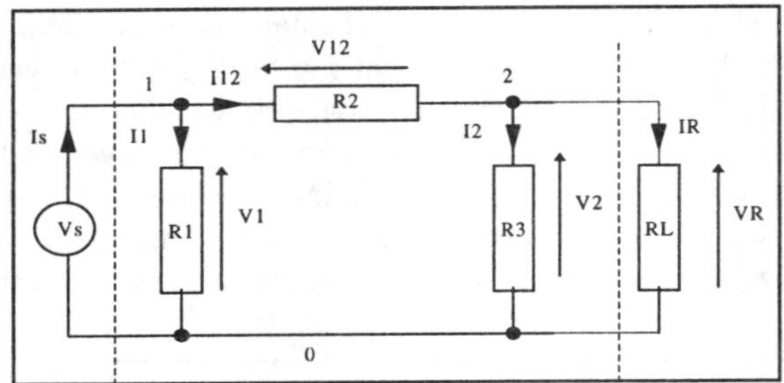

Figure 4.
The schematic diagram of the Π circuit.

For a physical transmission line, the only positions where measurements can easily made are at the junction points sending and receiving ends. Initially, only DC voltages and currents for the transmission line were considered in the feasibility study.

Training patterns for the ANNs were constructed based on the case of a constant input voltage source and a constant load. The values of the impedances in the Π circuit were varied in small incremental steps. The changes of impedance of the Π circuit affected states at both the sending and receiving ends of the transmission line. By specifying a certain degree of impedance change, for example 10% (see Table 1 and Figure 5), as a 'soft' fault, the states at both ends of the transmission line can be used to generate the training pattern for the ANN. Table 1 shows the pre-normalised training pattern for the ANN.

% of Degradation	Vs	Is	Vr	Ir	F1	F2	F3
-50% (R1)	1.0000	0.2667	0.3333	0.0333	1	0	0
-50% (R2)	1.0000	0.2000	0.5000	0.0500	0	1	0
-50% (R3)	1.0000	0.1750	0.2500	0.0250	0	0	1
-10% (R1)	1.0000	0.1778	0.3333	0.0333	1	0	0
-10% (R2)	1.0000	0.1714	0.3571	0.0357	0	1	0
-10% (R3)	1.0000	0.1679	0.3214	0.0321	0	0	1
-5% (R1)	1.0000	0.1719	0.3333	0.0333	0	0	0
-5% (R2)	1.0000	0.1690	0.3448	0.0345	0	0	0
-5% (R3)	1.0000	0.1672	0.3276	0.0328	0	0	0
Normal	1.0000	0.1667	0.3333	0.0333	0	0	0
+5% (R1)	1.0000	0.1619	0.3333	0.0333	0	0	0
+5% (R2)	1.0000	0.1645	0.3226	0.0323	0	0	0
+5% (R3)	1.0000	0.1661	0.3387	0.0339	0	0	0
+10% (R1)	1.0000	0.1576	0.3333	0.0333	1	0	0
+10% (R2)	1.0000	0.1625	0.3125	0.0313	0	1	0
+10% (R3)	1.0000	0.1656	0.3438	0.0344	0	0	1
+50% (R1)	1.0000	0.1333	0.3333	0.0333	1	0	0
+50% (R2)	1.0000	0.1500	0.2500	0.0250	0	1	0
+50% (R3)	1.0000	0.1625	0.3750	0.0375	0	0	1

Where
Vs is sending end voltage;
Is is sending end current;
Vr is receiving end voltage;
Ir is receiving end current;
F1 = 1 indicates a fault on R1;
F2 = 1 indicates a fault on R2;
F3 = 1 indicates a fault on R3.

Table 1. Training patterns for the ANNs based 'soft' fault detector.

The first column lists changes to the resistances R1 to R3, while the four columns of numbers are the sending (Vs, Is) and receiving end (Vr, Ir) voltages and currents respectively. The last three columns represent the fault states, where a fault is represented by logic '1' for resistance R1, R2 and R3 respectively. Each row of data was produced by changing the value of either R1, R2 and R3 by a small step. As can be seen for the data in each column, there is very little difference between these values. These relatively small differences in current and voltage make it very difficult for the ANN fault analyser to detect a 'soft' fault state. The solution to this problem is to pre-process the input data for the ANN. A normalisation pre-process method has been developed by the authors to maximise the differences among the data. The results from this experiment demonstrate that the pre-process (normalisation) method is essential to obtain a solution and it also helps to reduce the training process time.

3.1 Experiment Results

An ANN of structure 4-6-3 was developed for the purpose of soft fault analysis and detection, EFD. The voltages and currents of both sending and receiving end of the Π circuit (see Figure 4) are used as inputs to the ANN. The outputs of the ANN are used to indicate which impedance of the actual Π circuit exceeds the allowable tolerance limits. The results obtained were produced by an ANN, trained by the BP training method, within approximately 10,000 iterations. Figure 5 shows the results produced by the soft fault detector. As can be seen in Figure 5, the desired and all simulated results are closely matched and therefore the system may be used to accurately identify soft fault states.

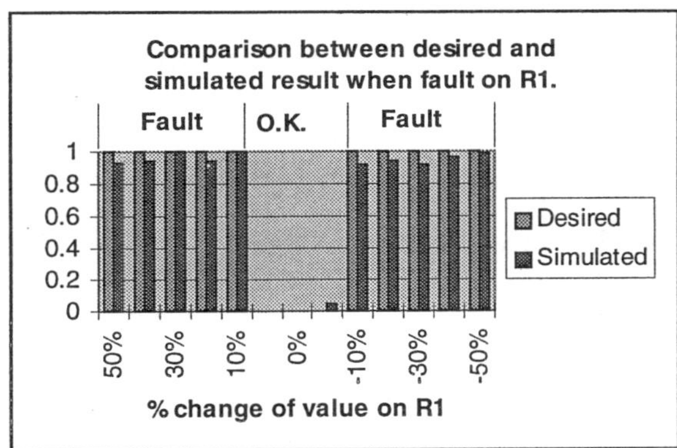

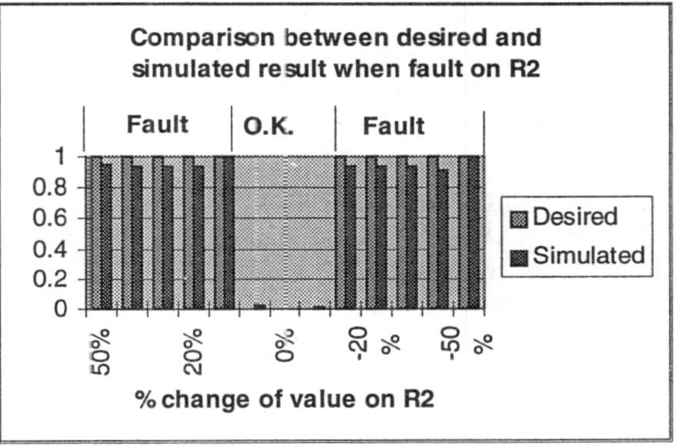

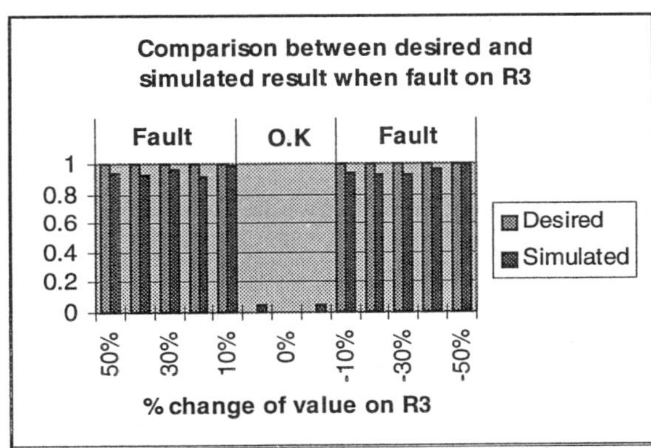

Figure 5 :
Comparison between desired and simulated results using BP.

4.0 Discussions and further work

A new concept and methods for EFD or soft fault detection has been outlined and tested. The preliminary results have been encouraging and show good potential for the algorithm to be successfully implemented in real power system environments. As fault detection is one of the important processes for reliable operation of any power system, an effective soft detection algorithm could eventually become a standard monitoring application essential for power system operational processes.

The transmission line (Π circuit) validation experiments reported have indicated the capability of the ANN based soft fault detection algorithm. During the early stages of development, the ANN 'soft' fault detection could not learn to recognise small differences within the training data. The differences among these values of voltage and current in the Π circuit were simply too small and insignificant for the detector to analyse satisfactorily. Data pre-processing is essential for this system so that an ANN can learn the set of input fault states. This approach also considerably reduces the learning time.

The DC Π circuit fault detection test results were considered to be very satisfactory. A total of 37 sets of different testing cases were used to evaluate the detector. Half of the them were not part of the training set. All test sets produced satisfactory results with an accuracy of 95% or higher.

Further work is being carried out on balanced 3-phase a.c. circuits. Multiple 'soft' faults detection methods will also be considered. Evolutionary computing techniques such as the Genetic Algorithm will be used to further improve the performance of the ANN by devising operators specific to the domain. A significant advantage of this approach is that by measuring the states of external nodes within a system, it is possible determine the state of equivalent internal circuit elements and thereby detect, at an early stage, components which are gradually moving out of acceptable tolerance range, prior to possible failure.

5.0 BIBLIOGRAPHIES

[1] Christie R D & Zadehgol H & Habib M M : "High impedance fault detection in low voltage networks", IEEE Transactions on Power Delivery, Vol.8, No.4, p1829-1836, October,1993.

[2] Eaton J R & Cohen E : "Electric Power Transmission Systems", Prentice-Hall, 1983.

[3] Kennedy T : "A System Operator's View of Evolving Applications' IEEE Computer Applications in Power Systems", Vol 8 , No2 , pp25-29 , April 1995.

[4] Parise G & Grasselli U & Luozzo V D : "Arcing fault in sub-distribution branch-circuits", IEEE Transactions on Power Delivery, Vol.8, N0.2, p580-583, April, 1993.

[5] Ryan H M, Editor : "High Voltage Engineering and Testing", IEE Peregrinus Ltd, 1994.

[6] Wong K C P & Ryan H M &Tindle J : "A Unified Model for the Electrical Power Network", University of Power Engineering Conference (UPEC), 1995

[7] Goldberg D.E. : "Genetic Algorithms in Search, Optimisation & Machine Learning", Addison-Wesley Publishing Company, INC, USA, 1989.

[8] Paul H & Tindle J : "Passive optical network planning in local access network – An optimisation approach utilising genetic algorithms. British Telcom Technology Journal, April, 1996.

[9] Butler K L & Momoh J A : "Detection and classification of line faults on power distribution systems using neural networks", Midwest symposium on circuit and systems, Vol., p368-371, 1993.

[10]Chunchland P.S. & Sejnowski T.J. : "The Computational Brain", Cambridge, MA : MIT Press, 1992.

[11]Dasgupta D & McGregor D.R. : "Designing Application-Specific Neural Networks using the Structured Genetic Algorithm", Proceeding of COGANN92 (International Workshop on Combinations of Genetic Algorithms and Neural Networks), IEEE Computer Society Press, 1992.

[12]Ebron S & Lubkeman D L & White M : "A neural network approach to the detection of incipient faults on power distribution feeders", IEEE Transactions on Power Delivery, Vol. 5, N0.2, p905-914 April, 1990.

[13]Fernando S R & Watson K L : "High impedance fault detection using artificial neural network techniques", Proceedings of the Intersociety Energy Conversion Engineering Conference : Aerospace Power Vol., No.1, p191-196, 1992.

[14]Fukuyama Y & Ueki Y : "Fault analysis system using neural networks and artificial intelligence", IEEE 1993

[15]Ghosh A K & Lubkeman D L : "The classification of power system distribution disturbance waveforms using a neural network approach", IEEE Transactions on Power Delivery, Vol.10, N0.1, p109-115, January, 1995.

[16]Haykin S : "Neural Networks, A Comprehensive Foundation", Macmillan College Publishing Company, 1994

[17]Kim K H & Park J K : "Application of hierarchical neural networks to fault diagnosis of power systems", International journal of electrical power and energy systems Vol.15, No.2, p65-70, 1993.

[18]Liu Y & Yao X : "A Population based Learning Algorithm which Learns both Architectures and Weights of Neural Networks", Proceeding of ICYCs95 Workshop on Soft Computing Vol.3 No.1, Allerton Press Inc. New York, 1996.

[19]Ranaweera D K : "Comparison of neural network models for fault diagnosis of power systems", Electric Power Systems Research, Vol.29, No.2, p99-104, 1994.

[20]Sultan A F & Swift G W & Fedirchuk D J : "Detect of high impedance arcing faults using a multi-layer perception", IEEE Transactions on Power delivery, Vol., N0.4, p1871-1877, October, 1992.

[21]Tang K.S.& Chan C.Y. & Man K.F. & Kwong S.K. : "Genetic Structure for NN Topology and Weights Optimisation" Genetic Algorithm in Engineering System: Innovations and Applications Conference publication, IEE Peregrinus Ltd, 1995.

[22]Yang H T & Chang W Y & Huang C L : "A new neural network approach to on-line fault section estimation using information of protective relays and circuit breakers" IEEE Transactions on Power delivery, Vol.9, N0.1, p220-229, January, 1994.

[23]Zhou G.Z. : "A neural network approach to fault diagnosis for power systems", Proceeding of IEEE region 10 Conference, Computing, Communication, Control and Power Engineering (TENCON '93), p885-888, 1993.

Blind Signal Processing - Adaptive and Neural Network Approaches

The invited program is also featured by 8 special sessions on current interesting topics. Each special session organizer is invited by the Program Committee and the success of each special session is completely due to the hard efforts of each organizer.

Unconstrained Optimization Criteria for Blind Deconvolution of Multichannel Linear Systems

Yujiro Inouye and Takehizo Sato

Department of Systems Engineering, Faculty of Engineering Science, Osaka University
Machikaneyama 1-3, Toyonaka,Osaka, Japan
inouye@sys.es.osaka-u.ac.jp

Abstract— **Blind deconvolution and blind equalization have been an important interesting topic in diverse fields including data communication, image processing and geophysical data processing. Recently, Inouye and Habe proposed a multistage maximization criterion and a single-stage maximization criterion for attaining the blind deconvolution of multichannel linear time-invariant systems. However, their maximization criteria should be subjected to several constraints of equations. In this paper, we present unconstrained new maximization criteria for accomplishing the blind deconvolution of multichannel linear time-invariant systems. Stochastic gradient algorithms are proposed for solving the unconstrained maximization problems. Simulation examples are included to examine the performance of the proposed algorithms.**
Keywords: Equalizers, Data communications, Cumulants

1   Introduction

Blind deconvolution and blind equalization have been an important interesting topic in diverse fields including data communication, image processing and geophysical data processing [1]-[3]. Recently, Shalvi and Weinstein presented several new criteria for blind deconvolution of single-channel linear time-invariant systems. Inouye and Habe [3] extended the Shalvi-Weinstein approach to the multichannel case. They proposed a multistage maximization criterion and a single-stage maximization criterion for attaining the blind deconvolution of multichannel linear time-invariant systems. However, their maximization criteria should be subjected to several constraints of equations. In general, unconstrained optimization criteria are generally better than constrained optimization criteria for the purpose of achieving the optimization.

In this paper, we present unconstrained new maximization criteria for accomplishing the blind deconvolution of multichannel linear time-invariant systems. Stochastic gradient algorithms are proposed for solving the unconstrained maximization problems. Simulation examples are included to examine the performance of the proposed algorithms.

We use the following notation in this paper. Let Z denote the set of all integers. Let $E\{x\}$ denote the expectation of a random variable x, and $\mathrm{cum}\{x_1 \cdots, x_n\}$ denote the nth-order (joint) cumulant of random variables $x_1, \cdots, x_n$. Let $c_{x_1, \cdots, x_n}(\tau_1, \tau_2, \cdots, \tau_{n-1})$ be the nth-order cumulant (function of $\tau_1, \cdots, \tau_{n-1}$) of jointly ($n$th-order) stationary random processes $\{x_1(t)\}, \cdots, \{x_n(t)\}$ defined by $c_{x_1, \cdots, x_n}(\tau_1, \tau_2, \cdots, \tau_{n-1}) = \mathrm{cum}\{x_1(t + \tau_1), \cdots, x_{n-1}(t + \tau_{n-1}), x_n(t)\}$. Since we are only interested in second- and fourth-order cumulants in this paper, we use the following simple notation for the variance σ_x^2 of $\{x(t)\}$, the correlation function $r_{x_1, x_2^*}(\tau)$ of $\{x_1(t)\}$ with $\{x_2^*(t)\}$, and the fourth-order cumulant $\kappa_{4,x}$ of $\{x(t)\}$ as $\sigma_x^2 := c_{2,x,x^*}(0)$, $r_{x_1, x_2^*}(\tau) := c_{2,x_1,x_2^*}(\tau)$, and $\kappa_{4,x} := c_{4,x,x^*,x,x^*}(0,0,0)$, respectively.

2   Problem Formulation

Let us consider the system shown in Fig. 1. It is a cascade connection of an unknown multichannel system preceding a multichannel equalizer. We make the following assumptions on the system and the signals involved.

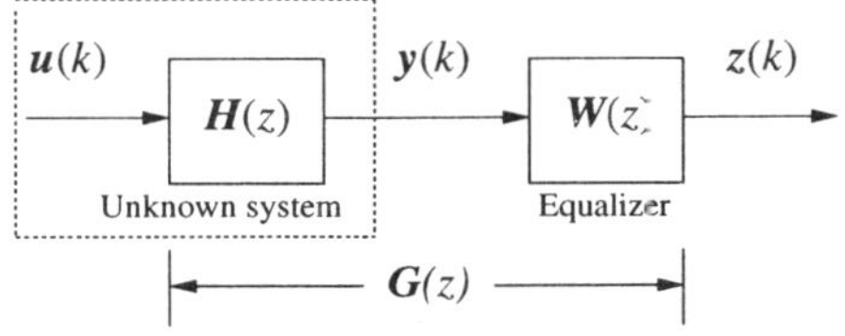

Figure 1: Unknown system and equalizer

(A1) The unknown system $\boldsymbol{H}(z)$ is described by

$$\boldsymbol{y}(t) = \sum_{k=-\infty}^{\infty} \boldsymbol{H}(k)\boldsymbol{u}(t-k) \tag{1}$$

where $\boldsymbol{y}(t)$ is a real/complex n-column output vector, $\boldsymbol{u}(t)$ is a real/complex n-column input vector, and $\{\boldsymbol{H}(k)\}$ is a real/complex $n \times n$ matrix sequence called the **impulse response**. The system is stable, that is, the impulse response satisfies the absolute summability condition

$$\sum_{k=-\infty}^{\infty} \|\boldsymbol{H}(k)\| < \infty \tag{2}$$

(A2) The transfer function defined by

$$\boldsymbol{H}(z) := \sum_{k=-\infty}^{\infty} \boldsymbol{H}(k)z^k \tag{3}$$

is of full rank on the unit circle $|z| = 1$ (this implies it has no zero on the unit circle).

(A3) The input process $\{\boldsymbol{u}(t)\}$ is a zero-mean, non-Gaussian vector process, whose component processes $\{u_i(t)\}$, $i = 1, \cdots, n$, are mutually independent. Moreover, each component process $\{u_i(t)\}$ is an independently and identically distributed (i.i.d.) process with variance $\sigma_{u_i}^2 \neq 0$ and fourth-order cumulant $\kappa_{4,u_i} \neq 0$.

(A4) The equalizer $\boldsymbol{W}(z)$ is described by

$$\boldsymbol{z}(t) = \sum_{k=-\infty}^{\infty} \boldsymbol{W}(k)\boldsymbol{y}(t-k) \tag{4}$$

where $\boldsymbol{z}(t)$ is a real/complex n-column vector, called the **equalizer output**, and $\{\boldsymbol{W}(k)\}$ is a real/complex $n \times n$ matrix sequence. It is assumed that the equalizer $\boldsymbol{W}$ is also stable.

For the blind deconvolution of the unknown system, we cannot observe the inputs, but can observe only the outputs. This implies there are inherent ambiguities in the solution to the multichannel deconvolution problem as follows: In general, we cannot identify the order of the arrangement of the components $u_1(t), \cdots, u_n(t)$ of input vector $\boldsymbol{u}(t)$, the time origin of each component $u_i(t)$, and the magnitude of each component $u_i(t)$.

Taking these ambiguities into account, the multichannel blind deconvolution problem is formulated such that it is to find a equalizer $\boldsymbol{W}$ so that the transfer function $G(z)$ of the combined system takes the form of

$$\boldsymbol{G}(z) = \boldsymbol{P}\boldsymbol{\Lambda}(z)\boldsymbol{D} \tag{5}$$

where $\boldsymbol{P}$ is a permutation matrix, $\boldsymbol{\Lambda}(z)$ is a diagonal matrix with diagonal entries $\lambda_{ii}(z) = z^{l_i}$, $i = 1, \cdots, n$ (where l_i is an integer), and $\boldsymbol{D}$ is a constant diagonal matrix. Moreover, if we know all the magnitudes of the variances of the components of the input process ahead, we can constrain to make the diagonal matrix $\boldsymbol{D}$ in (5) be equal to a diagonal matrix with the diagonal entries all being unit magnitude.

It is said that a stationary random process $\{\boldsymbol{u}(t)\}$ satisfies the **normalized whitening condition** if the all the component processes $\{u_i(t)\}, i = 1, \cdots, n$, of $\{\boldsymbol{u}(t)\}$ are white random processes with unit variance and they are mutually uncorrelated. When the random process is zero-mean, this condition is equivalent to $E\{\boldsymbol{u}(t+k)\boldsymbol{u}^*(t)\} = \boldsymbol{I}\delta(k)$, where $\boldsymbol{I}$ denotes the identity matrix and $\delta(k)$ denotes the Kronecker delta.

By the multilinearity property of cumulants, we can derive the following formula for the components of the equalizer output vector $\boldsymbol{z}(t)$ from (1) and (4) with (A1)-(A4). Let $\{\boldsymbol{G}(t)\}$ be the impulse response of the cascade system in Fig. 1. Then for any $i_1, i_2 \in \{1, 2, \cdots, n\}$,

$$r_{z_{i_1}, z_{i_2}^*}(\tau_1) = \sum_{j=1}^{n} \sum_{\tau=-\infty}^{\infty} g_{i_1 j}(\tau + \tau_1) g_{i_2 j}^*(\tau) \sigma_{u_j}^2. \tag{6}$$

For any $i_1, i_2, i_3, i_4 \in \{1, 2, \cdots, n\}$, we have

$$c_{4, z_{i_1}, z_{i_2}^*, z_{i_3}, z_{i_4}^*}(\tau_1, \tau_2, \tau_3) = \sum_{j=1}^{n} \sum_{\tau=-\infty}^{\infty} g_{i_1 j}(\tau + \tau_1) g_{i_2 j}^*(\tau + \tau_2) g_{i_3 j}(\tau + \tau_3) g_{i_4 j}^*(\tau) \kappa_{4, u_j}. \tag{7}$$

3   Blind Deconvolution

To begin with, let us assume that the input process $\{\boldsymbol{u}(t)\}$ satisfies the normalized whitening condition by dividing each component $\{u_i(t)\}$ by the square root of variance $\sigma_{u_i}^2$ to eliminate the magnitude ambiguity.

3.1 Constrained Criteria

In the previous work [3], the following two maximization criteria, the multistage maximization criterion (A) and the single-stage maximization criterion (B), were proposed and analyzed.

The multistage maximization criterion (A):

(Stage 1): Maximize $|\kappa_{4,z_1}|$ subject to $\sigma^2_{z_1} = 1$.

(Stage k): Maximize $|\kappa_{4,z_k}|$ subject to $\sigma^2_{z_k} = 1$ and $r_{z_i,z_k^*}(\tau) = 0$ for all $\tau \in Z$ and all $i = 1, 2, \cdots, k - 1$.
  Here k moves successively from 2 to n.

The single-stage maximization criterion (B):

Maximize $\sum_{i=1}^{n} |\kappa_{4,z_i}|$ subject to $r_{z_i,z_i^*}(\tau) = \delta(\tau)$ for all $i = 1, \cdots, n$ and $r_{z_i,z_j^*}(\tau) = 0$ for all $\tau \in Z$ and all distinct $i, j = 1, \cdots, n$.

Theorem 1: Under the normalized whitening condition of the input process, *i.e.*, $\sigma^2_{u_i} = 1$ for $i = 1, \cdots n$, the multistage maximization criterion (A) and the single-stage maximization criterion(B), both yield a solution to the multichannel blind deconvolution.

3.2 Unconstrained Criteria

It is generally more difficult to solve a maximization problem with constraints than to solve a constraint-free maximization problem equivalent to the original one. In the sequel, we develop constraint-free criteria for solving the multichannel blind deconvolution.

Let us assume that we know all the magnitudes of the fourth-order auto-cumulants of the components of the vector process ahead and that they satisfies the following decreasing sequence condition

$$|\gamma_1| \geq |\gamma_2| \geq \cdots \geq |\gamma_n| \tag{8}$$

where $\gamma_i := \kappa_{4,u_i}$ for $i = 1, \cdots, n$. Consider the following potential function [2] defined by

$$\phi_i(z_i) := |\kappa_{4,z_i}| + |\gamma_i| f(\sigma^2_{z_i}) \tag{9}$$

where $f(\cdot)$ is a continuous real-valued function over $[0, \infty)$ such that

$$p(x) := x^2 + f(x) \tag{10}$$

monotonically increasing in $0 \leq x < 1$, monotonically decreasing $x > 1$, and has a unique maximum at $x = 1$. Such a function, for example, is given by $p(x) = 2\alpha x - \alpha x^2, \alpha > 0$.

Corresponding to the multistage maximization criterion (A), we consider the following unconstrained criterion.

The unconstrained multistage maximization criterion (C):

(Stage 1): Maximize

$$J_1 := |\kappa_{4,z_1}| + |\gamma_1| f(\sigma^2_{z_1}) \tag{11}$$

(Stage k): Maximize

$$J_k := |\kappa_{4,z_k}| + |\gamma_k| f(\sigma^2_{z_k})$$
$$- \lambda_0 \left(\sum_{i=1}^{k-1} \sum_{\tau \in Z} |r_{z_i,z_k^*(\tau)}|^2 \right)^2 \tag{12}$$

where λ_0 is a positive constant greater than $|\gamma_1|, i.e., \lambda_0 \geq |\gamma_1|$.

Based on Theorem 1, we have the following theorem.

Theorem 2: Under the normalized whitening condition of the input process $\{u(t)\}$, the unconstrained multistage maximization criterion (C) gives a solution to the multichannel deconvolution problem.

Corresponding to the single-stage maximization criterion (B), we need another assumption for the time being that all the magnitudes of the fourth-order cumulants are identical, *i.e.*,

$$|\gamma_1| = |\gamma_2| = \cdots = |\gamma_n|. \tag{13}$$

Under this condition, we consider the following unconstrained criterion.

The unconstrained single-stage maximization criterion (D):

Maximize

$$J := \sum_{k=1}^{n} \{|\kappa_{4,z_k}| + |\gamma_k| f(\sigma_{z_k}^2)\} - \lambda_0 (\sum_{k=2}^{n} \sum_{i=1}^{k-1} \sum_{\tau \in Z} |r_{z_i,z_k^*}(\tau)|^2)^2, \tag{14}$$

where λ_0 is a positive constant.

Based on Theorem 1, we can obtain the following theorem.

Theorem 3: Under the normalized whitening condition of the input process $\{u(t)\}$ and the condition (13), the unconstrained single-stage maximization criterion (D) gives a solution to the multichannel blind deconvolution problem.

Remark 1: When all the magnitudes of the fourth-order auto-cumulants of the components of the input vector process are not the same, the criterion function (14) with λ_0 being a small positive constant can not be generally applied for achieving the multichannel blind deconvolution. In such a general case, it is not clear at the present how to choose a large number for λ_0 in the criterion function (14) to solve the multichannel blind deconvolution problem.

4   Simulation Examples

In order to see the effectiveness of the proposed criteria, we developed two stochastic gradient algorithms for solving the problem of the multistage maximization criterion (A) and the unconstrained multistage maximization criterion (C). They are omitted for page limitation. The algorithm for criterion (A) requires (multichannel) spectral prewhiting of the output process of the unknown system. We used a finite impulse response (FIR) system to approximate the equalizer.

We took following system that is a 2-input and 2-output all-pass system described by

$$\boldsymbol{H}(z) = \begin{pmatrix} \frac{0.5+z^{-1}}{1+0.5z^{-1}} & 0 \\ 0 & \frac{0.2+z^{-1}}{1+0.2z^{-1}} \end{pmatrix} \begin{pmatrix} \frac{1}{2} & -\frac{\sqrt{3}}{2} \\ \frac{\sqrt{3}}{2} & \frac{1}{2} \end{pmatrix}. \tag{15}$$

We note that $\boldsymbol{H}(z)$ satisfies the all-pass condition $\boldsymbol{H}(e^{j\omega})\boldsymbol{H}^*(e^{j\omega}) = \boldsymbol{I}$. Hence we need not perform

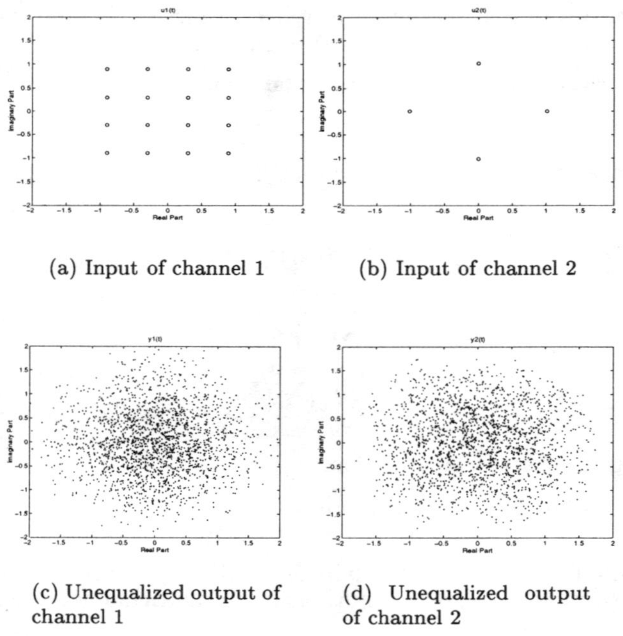

(a) Input of channel 1   (b) Input of channel 2

(c) Unequalized output of   (d) Unequalized output
channel 1   of channel 2

Figure 2: Signal constellations before equalization.

prewhiting in this case. The first channel input signal $u_1(t)$ was 16-QAM with unit variance, and the second channel input signal $u_2(t)$ was 4-PSK (phase-shift keying) with unit variance. Fig. 2 shows the channel input and output signal constellations. We used a 2-input, 2-output and 24-tap equalizer $\boldsymbol{W}(z)$.

The initial estimates $\widehat{\boldsymbol{W}}(z)$ were set to be zeros except for $\widehat{w_{11}}(12) = \widehat{w_{21}}(12) = 1$, $\widehat{w_{12}}(12) = \frac{1}{6}$ and $\widehat{w_{22}}(12) = \frac{1}{2}$. The both algorithms contain stochastic expectation. Therefore, we used 50 data points to calculate expectation. The step size was chosen to be 0.02. The positive constant λ_0 in (12) was set to be 1. As a measure of performance we used the **multichannel intersymbol interference** denoted by M_{ISI}, defined by

$$
M_{ISI} \ := \ \sum_{i=1}^{n} \frac{\left| \sum_{j=1}^{n} \sum_{t=-\infty}^{\infty} |g_{ij}(t)|^2 - |g_{i\cdot}|^2_{\max} \right|}{|g_{i\cdot}(\cdot)|^2_{\max}}
$$

$$
+ \ \sum_{j=1}^{n} \frac{\left| \sum_{i=1}^{n} \sum_{t=-\infty}^{\infty} |g_{ij}(t)|^2 - |g_{\cdot j}|^2_{\max} \right|}{|g_{\cdot j}(\cdot)|^2_{\max}}
$$

where $|g_{i\cdot}(\cdot)|^2_{\max}$ and $|g_{\cdot j}(\cdot)|^2_{\max}$ are respectively defined by

$$
|g_{i\cdot}(\cdot)|^2_{\max} \ := \ \text{Max}_{j=1,\cdots,n} \text{Max}_{-\infty < t < \infty} |g_{ij}(t)|^2 ,
$$

$$
|g_{\cdot j}(\cdot)|^2_{\max} \ := \ \text{Max}_{i=1,\cdots,n} \text{Max}_{-\infty < t < \infty} |g_{ij}(t)|^2 .
$$

It can be seen easily that the $M_{ISI} = 0$ if and only if $G(z)$ is of the form (5). The initial M_{ISI} in the logarithmic (dB) scale was 8.0411 dB.

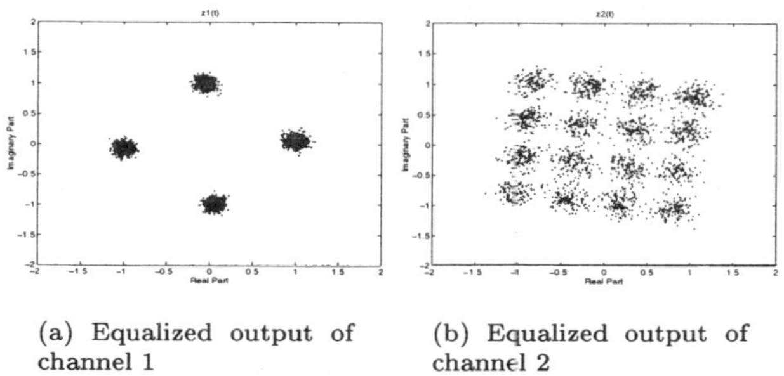

(a) Equalized output of channel 1

(b) Equalized output of channel 2

Figure 3: Signal constellations after equalization using criterion (A).

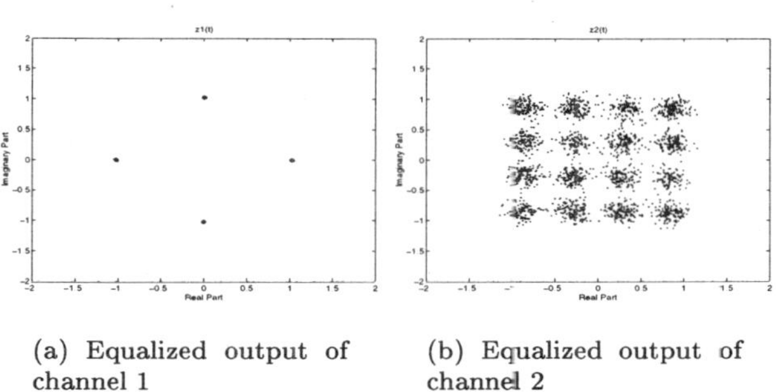

(a) Equalized output of channel 1

(b) Equalized output of channel 2

Figure 4: Signal constellations after equalization using criterion (C).

The both algorithms were tested in 10 Monte Carlo runs using 20,000 data samples at each of the two channel outputs. Fig. 3 and Fig. 4 show the equalized signal constellations obtained by using the constrained criterion (A) and the unconstrained criterion (C) with $\alpha = 10$, respectively. Since the magnitude of fourth-order cumulant of the 4-PSK signal is greater than that of the 16-QAM signal, the 4-PSK signal was recovered as the first channel output $z_1(t)$ at Stage 1 and 16-QAM as second channel the output $z_2(t)$ at Stage 2. We see that the equalized output of channel 1 using the unconstrained criterion (C) converge better than that using the constrained criterion (A), though there was no clear difference between the two equalized outputs of channel 2 using the constrained criterion (A) and using the unconstrained criterion (C).

In Fig. 5, we plotted the averaged M_{ISI}, denoted by $< M_{ISI} >$, over 10 Monte Carlo runs. By comparing the constrained criterion (A) with the unconstrained criterion (C) we found through simulations that the unconstrained criterion (C) exhibits better convergence behavior than the constrained criterion (A)

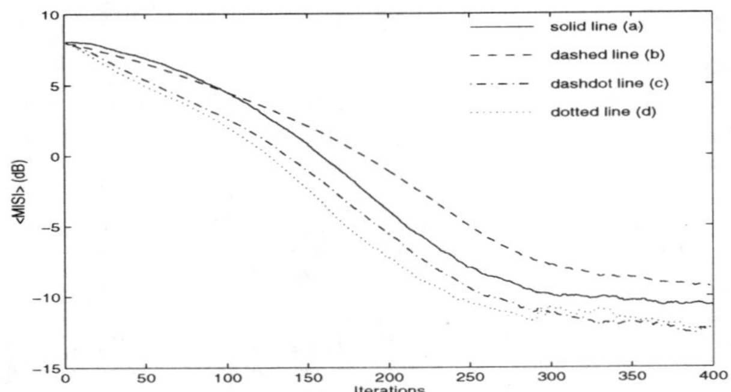

Figure 5: Performances of the algorithms of the constrained criterion (A) and the unconstrained criterion (C). The solid line (a) denotes $< M_{ISI} >$ using the constrained criterion (A), the dashed line (b) denotes $< M_{ISI} >$ using the unconstrained criterion (C) with $\alpha = 1$, the dashdot line (c) denotes $< M_{ISI} >$ using the unconstrained criterion (C) with $\alpha = 5$, and the dotted line (d) denotes $< M_{ISI} >$ using the unconstrained criterion (C) with $\alpha = 10$

except for the case of $\alpha = 1$. Therefore we had better choose the value of α greater than 1. Fig. 6 shows the magnitudes of the components of the impulse response $\{G(t)\}$ after equalization using the constrained criterion (A).

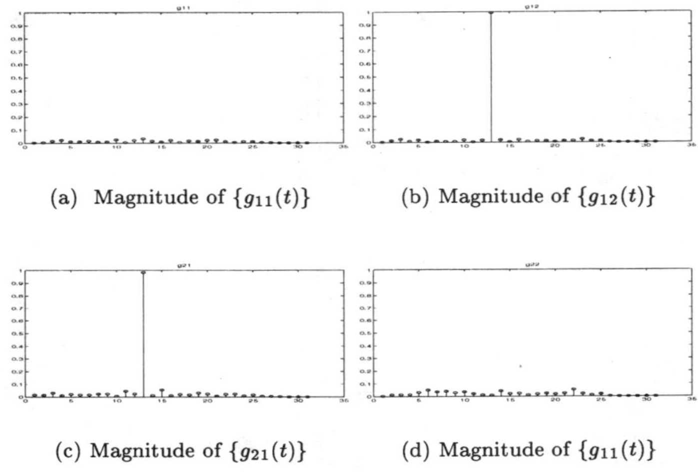

(a) Magnitude of $\{g_{11}(t)\}$ (b) Magnitude of $\{g_{12}(t)\}$

(c) Magnitude of $\{g_{21}(t)\}$ (d) Magnitude of $\{g_{11}(t)\}$

Figure 6: Magnitudes of the components of the impulse response $\{G(t)\}$ after equalization using the constrained criterion (A).

5   Conclutions

We have proposed the unconstrained multistage maximization criterion and the unconstrained single-stage maximization criterion. Simulation examples have shown to illustrate the performance of the algorithm of the constrained multistage criterion (A) and the performance of the algorithm of the unconstrained multistage criterion (C). We have not yet developed two stochastic gradient algorithms for the problems of the single-stage maximization criterion (B) and the unconstrained single-stage maximization criterion (D).

References

[1] D. L. Donoho, "On minimum entropy deconvolution", in D. F. Findley, Ed., *Applied Times Series Analysis, II*, pp. 565-608, New York; Academic Press, 1981.

[2] O. Shalvi, and E. Weinstein, "New criteria for blind deconvolution of nonminimum phase systems(channels)", *IEEE Trans. Inform. Theory*, vol. 36, pp. 312-321, Mar. 1990.

[3] Y. Inouye and T. Habe, "Multichannel blind equalization using second- and fourth-order cumulants", *Proc. IEEE Signal Processing Workshop on Higher-Order Statistics*, pp. 96-100, 1995.

A Blind Identification and Separation Technique via Multi-layer Neural Networks

A. BELOUCHRANI[*], A. CICHOCKI[**] and K. ABED MERAIM[***]
[*] Department of Electrical Engineering and Computer Sciences,
University of California, Berkeley CA 94720, U.S.A, adel@robotics.eecs.berkeley.edu
[**]FRP RIKEN, Lab. for Artificial Brain Systems,
Wako-Shi, Saitama, 351-01, JAPAN, cia@kamo.riken.go.jp
[***] Department of Electrical and Electronics Engineering,
University of Melbourne, Parkville, Victoria 3052, AUSTRALIA, a.karim@ee.mu.oz.au

Abstract— This paper deals with the problem of blind identification and source separation which consists of estimation of the mixing matrix and/or the separation of a mixture of stochastically independent sources without a priori knowledge on the mixing matrix . The method we propose here estimates the mixture matrix by a recurrent Input-Output (IO) Identification using as inputs a nonlinear transformation of the estimated sources. Herein, the nonlinear transformation (distortion) consists in constraining the modulus of the inputs of the IO-Identification device to be a constant. In contrast to other existing approaches, the covariance of the additive noise do not need to be modeled and can be estimated as a regular parameter if needed. The proposed approach is implemented using multi-layer neural networks in order to improve performance of separation. New associated on-line un-supervised adaptive learning rules are also developed. The effectiveness of the proposed method is illustrated by some computer simulations.

1 Introduction

The blind identification and source separation problem has recently become an intense area of research. It consists in estimating of mixing matrix and/or recovering original waveforms of independent sources from only an observed linear mixture of them. The first solution to the source separation problem was proposed in 1985 [3] and was based on cancelation of higher order moments assuming non-Gaussian and i.i.d source signals. Other criteria based on minimization of cost functions, such as the sum of square fourth order cumulants [4, 5, 6], contrast functions [5, 7] or likelihood function [8, 9], have been used by several researchers. Note that in the case of non i.i.d source signals and even Gaussian sources, solutions based on second order statistics are possible [10, 11]. In order to improve the robustness and the speed of convergence of the separation process several on-line adaptive learning algorithms are developed [12, 19, 20, 15, 13, 14, 1, 2, 16].

In this paper, we propose a new approach based on a recurrent Input Output (IO)-Identification where the inputs (learning signals) are a nonlinear transformation of current estimated sources $\hat{s}(t)$ (see Fig.1). This nonlinearity is taken into account here by constraining the modulus of these inputs to be a constant. Hence, this approach will be referred to as a Constant Modulus Source Separation (CMSS) [17, 18]. For our approach, we propose here a multi-layer neural network implementation in order to improve performance of separation.

This paper is organized as follows. In section 2, the problem of blind source separation is stated together with the relevant assumptions. Section 3 presents a new blind source separation technique based on a recurrent Input-Output Identification. In section 4, novel on-line un-supervised adaptive learning rules for a multi-layer neural network implementation are developed. Finally, some computer simulations illustrating the effectiveness of our approach are presented in section 5.

2 Problem Formulation

The blind source separation problem consists in recovering a set of n independent signals from $m \geq n$ observed instantaneous mixtures of these signals *without knowledge of any structure of the mixture.*

Let $\mathbf{x}(t)$ be $m \times 1$ vector of observations (sensors signals) at time instant t which may be corrupted by an additive noise $\mathbf{n}(t)$. Let, the linear mixture model is given by:

$$\mathbf{x}(t) = \mathbf{A}\mathbf{s}(t) + \mathbf{n}(t), \tag{1}$$

where the $m \times n$ unknown matrix $\mathbf{A}$ is called the 'mixing matrix' and where the n independent zero-mean signals are collected in a $n \times 1$ vector denoted $\mathbf{s}(t)$ which is referred to as the source signal vector.

The source signal vector is assumed to be (H1) an i.i.d. stationary multivariate process. The additive noise $\mathbf{n}(t)$ is assumed (H2) stationary, temporally white, zero mean complex random process with a possibly unknown covariance matrix,

$$\mathbf{R}_{nn} = E[\mathbf{n}(t)\mathbf{n}(t)^H], \tag{2}$$

where the superscript ^{H} denotes the conjugate transpose of a vector or a matrix and the notation $E[.]$ is used for ensemble averaging under hypothesis (H1). The noise is assumed to be (H3) independent of the source signals. The $m \times n$ complex matrix $\mathbf{A}$ is assumed to have (H4) full rank but is otherwise unknown. In contrast with traditional parametric methods, no specific structure of the mixture matrix is assumed.

Let us point out that this problem of blind source separation has two inherent ambiguities. First of all, there is no way of knowing the original labeling of the sources, hence any permutation of the estimated sources is also a satisfactory solution.

The second ambiguity is that it is inherently impossible to uniquely identify the source signals. This is because the exchange of a fixed scalar factor between a source signal and the corresponding column of the mixture matrix $\mathbf{A}$ does not affect the observations as is shown by the following relation,

$$\mathbf{x}(t) = \mathbf{A}\mathbf{s}(t) + \mathbf{n}(t) = \sum_{i=1}^{n} \frac{\mathbf{a}_i}{\alpha_i} \alpha_i s_i(t) + \mathbf{n}(t), \tag{3}$$

where α_i is an arbitrary non zero complex factor and $\mathbf{a}_i$ denotes the i-th column of $\mathbf{A}$. Hence, the blind source separation must be understood as the identification of the mixing matrix and/or the recovering of the source signals up to a fixed permutation and some complex factors. In the following, we propose a new separation approach based on a recurrent Input-Output Identification.

3   Recurrent Blind Input-Output Identification

Let us first start by assuming that the source signals are available. In this case, it would be a simple matter to estimate the mixture matrix $\mathbf{A}$ and the noise covariance matrix $\mathbf{R}_n$ using an Input-Output Identification. The solution will consist in evaluating the following statistics,

$$\mathbf{R}_{xx} = \frac{1}{T} \sum_{t=1}^{T} \mathbf{x}(t)\mathbf{x}(t)^H, \tag{4}$$

$$\mathbf{R}_{xs} = \frac{1}{T} \sum_{t=1}^{T} \mathbf{x}(t)\mathbf{s}(t)^H = \mathbf{R}_{sx}^H, \tag{5}$$

$$\mathbf{R}_{ss} = \frac{1}{T} \sum_{t=1}^{T} \mathbf{s}(t)\mathbf{s}(t)^H, \tag{6}$$

and computing the estimated parameters by

$$\hat{\mathbf{A}} = \mathbf{R}_{xs}\mathbf{R}_{ss}^{-1}, \tag{7}$$

$$\hat{\mathbf{R}}_{nn} = \mathbf{R}_{xx} - \mathbf{R}_{xs}\mathbf{R}_{ss}^{-1}\mathbf{R}_{sx}. \tag{8}$$

Hence, $\mathbf{y}(t) = \hat{\mathbf{s}}(t) = \hat{\mathbf{A}}^{-1}\mathbf{x}(t) = \mathbf{R}_{ss}\mathbf{R}_{xs}^{-1}\mathbf{x}(t)$ (see Figs.1-3).

In our problem, the source signals $\mathbf{s}(t)$ are of course not available, otherwise we will not have any need to perform the source separation. In this case, one can use instead of the original source signals, as depicted in Fig.1, a nonlinear version of the current estimated sources $\hat{\mathbf{s}}(t)$ as inputs to the IO-Identification device.

Hence, we could estimate the matrix $\hat{\mathbf{A}}^{-1}$ adaptively by employing a recurrent IO-Identification approach.

The nonlinear function $g(\mathbf{y}(t)) = g(\hat{\mathbf{s}}(t))$ is taken into account here by constraining the inputs of the IO-Identification device to have Constant Modulus. Hence, the proposed method will be refereed to as Constant Modulus Source Separation (CMSS). The use of the nonlinearity $g(\mathbf{y}(t))$ involves higher order statistics and ensures mutual independence of the output signals [5].

In contrast to other existing blind source separation techniques, the covariance matrix $\mathbf{R}_{nn}$ of the additive noise do not need to be modeled and can be estimated from equation (8). Moreover, the proposed algorithms are simple and robust to noise and ill-conditioned mixing matrices.

4   The Proposed Learning Algorithms

First consider, as depicted in Fig.2 and Fig.3 a multi-layer feed-forward neural network described by

$$\mathbf{y}(t)^l = \mathbf{W}(t)^l \mathbf{y}(t)^{l-1}, \; l = 1 \cdots, k; \; \mathbf{y}(t)^0 = \mathbf{x}(t). \tag{9}$$

Our purpose here is to propose an adaptive learning algorithm for the synaptic weights w_{ij}^l. Based on the approach described in the previous section, we have first developed a continuous-time adaptive learning algorithm (given here in the matrix form) for the estimation of the inverse of the statistic (5) and the statistic (6) which we denote here respectively by $\mathbf{W}_1(t)$ and $\mathbf{W}_2(t)$:

$$\frac{d\mathbf{W}_1^{-1}(t)^l}{dt} = \mu(t)\mathbf{y}(t)^{l-1}g(\mathbf{y}(t)^l)^H, \tag{10}$$

$$\frac{d\mathbf{W}_2(t)^l}{dt} = \mu(t)g(\mathbf{y}(t)^l)g(\mathbf{y}(t)^l)^H, \tag{11}$$

$$\tag{12}$$

where the nonlinearity of the activation function $g(\mathbf{y})$ is taken into account by constraining the outputs of the each layer to have a constant modulus [1] and $\mu(t)$ is a positive learning rate.

Taking into account that for any nonsingular matrix satisfying relation $\mathbf{W}(t)\mathbf{W}^{-1}(t) = \mathbf{W}^{-1}(t)\mathbf{W}(t) = \mathbf{I}$, we have

$$\frac{d\mathbf{W}(t)}{dt} = -\mathbf{W}(t)\frac{d\mathbf{W}^{-1}(t)}{dt}\mathbf{W}(t). \tag{13}$$

Hence, we obtain simple learning rules which avoids the matrix inversion

$$\frac{d\mathbf{W}_1(t)^l}{dt} = -\mu(t)\mathbf{W}_1(t)^l\mathbf{y}(t)^{l-1}g(\mathbf{y}(t)^l)^H\mathbf{W}_1(t)^l, \tag{14}$$

$$\frac{d\mathbf{W}_2(t)^l}{dt} = \mu(t)g(\mathbf{y}(t)^l)g(\mathbf{y}(t)^l)^H. \tag{15}$$

The synaptic weights w_{ij}^l are then given in the matrix form by,

$$\mathbf{W}(t)^l = \mathbf{W}_2(t)^l\mathbf{W}_1(t)^l. \tag{16}$$

Hence, the layer l will have the cascade structure shown by Fig.3.

It should be emphasized that for well conditioned problem only one single layer could be used, however, for ill-conditioned problems more layer are necessary in order to achieve improved performance. This has been confirmed by extensive computer simulations.

The above learning algorithm can easily be converted into the following discrete time[2] iterative algorithm,

$$\mathbf{W}_1^{-1}(t+1)^l = \mathbf{W}_1^{-1}(t)^l + \eta(t)\mathbf{y}(t)^{l-1}g(\mathbf{y}(t)^l)^H, \tag{17}$$

$$\mathbf{W}_2(t+1)^l = \mathbf{W}_2(t)^l + \eta(t)g(\mathbf{y}(t)^l)g(\mathbf{y}(t)^l)^H, \tag{18}$$

or taking into account equations (14), (15) the following formula gives estimate of the inverse of the cross correlation matrix (5) ($\mathbf{W}_1 = \hat{\mathbf{R}}_{xs}^{-1}$) and estimate of the autocorrelation matrix (6) ($\mathbf{W}_2 = \hat{\mathbf{R}}_{ss}$)

$$\mathbf{W}_1(t+1)^l = \mathbf{W}_1(t)^l - \eta(t)\mathbf{W}_1(t)^l\mathbf{y}(t)^{l-1}g(\mathbf{y}(t)^l)^H\mathbf{W}_1^l(t), \tag{19}$$

$$\mathbf{W}_2(t+1)^l = \mathbf{W}_2(t)^l + \eta(t)g(\mathbf{y}(t)^l)g(\mathbf{y}(t)^l)^H, \tag{20}$$

where $\eta(t) = \mu(t)T$ (T - time step).

The above algorithm can be easily transformed to normalized form

$$\mathbf{W}_1(t+1)^l = \mathbf{W}_1(t)^l - \eta(t)\frac{\mathbf{W}_1(t)^l\mathbf{y}(t)^{l-1}g(\mathbf{y}(t)^l)^H\mathbf{W}_1(t)^l}{1 + g(\mathbf{y}(t)^l)^H\mathbf{W}_1(t)^l\mathbf{y}(t)^{l-1}}, \tag{21}$$

$$\mathbf{W}_2(t+1)^l = \mathbf{W}_2(t)^l + \eta(t)\frac{g(\mathbf{y}(t)^l)g(\mathbf{y}(t)^l)^H}{1 + \eta(t)g(\mathbf{y}(t)^l)^Hg(\mathbf{y}(t)^l)}. \tag{22}$$

The recursive formula for the updating of the estimation of inverse of cross-correlation matrix $\mathbf{W}_1 = \hat{\mathbf{R}}_{xs}^{-1}$ is similar to the RLS algorithm for linear adaptive FIR filter.

5 Performance evaluation

The performance of our algorithm is characterized here in terms of interference rejection. At each time instant t, the output vector of layer k is computed by applying to its input vector the synaptic weight matrix $\mathbf{W}^k = \mathbf{W}_2^k\mathbf{W}_1^k$, i.e.

$$\mathbf{y}(t)^k = \mathbf{W}^k\mathbf{y}(t)^{k-1} = \mathbf{W}^k...\mathbf{W}^1\mathbf{A}\mathbf{s}(t) + \mathbf{W}^k...\mathbf{W}^1\mathbf{n}(t). \tag{23}$$

It should be noted that the source separation is achieved as soon as the matrix $\mathbf{P}(t) = \mathbf{W}(t)^k...\mathbf{W}(t)^1\mathbf{A}$ is close to some generalized permutation matrix [11]. The performance index used in the sequel is the following global rejection level,

$$\mathcal{I} = \sum_{i=1}^{m}(\sum_{j=1}^{n}\frac{|p_{ij}|}{\max_k |p_{ik}|} - 1) + \sum_{j=1}^{n}(\sum_{i=1}^{m}\frac{|p_{ij}|}{\max_k |p_{kj}|} - 1), \quad \text{where} \quad \mathbf{P} = [p_{ij}]. \tag{24}$$

The numerical performance evaluation presented below has been obtained in the following setting. We have simulated two i.i.d source signals respectively 4-QAM [3] and 16-QAM constellation with unit variance.

---

[1] As nonlinear function we can select e.g. $g(y) = y/|y|$. However, other nonlinearities can be used.

[2] We keep the same notation t for either the continuous or the discrete time.

[3] QAM: Quadratic Amplitude Modulation.

The p-th element of the q-th column of the mixture matrix is $\exp\{2i\pi p\alpha_q\}$. Of course, we do not use here this *a priori* information. We choose a 2×2 mixing matrix with $\alpha_1 = 0.2$ and $\alpha_2 = 0.4$. The additive noise is generated from a zero mean and temporally white Gaussian process with the following covariance matrix,

$$\mathbf{R}_{nn} = \sigma^2 \begin{bmatrix} 1 & \rho \\ \rho & 1 \end{bmatrix} \tag{25}$$

where σ^2 is the noise power and ρ is the coefficient of noise correlation. The proposed learning algorithm is performed here with a learning rate $\eta(t) = 1$.

Spatially White Noise   The noise power σ^2 is set to -30 dB corresponding to a SNR (Signal to Noise Ratio) of 30 dB and the coefficient ρ is taken equal to 0 corresponding to a white noise. Fig.4, 5 and 6 show respectively the inputs to the first layer corresponding to the observations, the outputs of the first layer and the outputs of the second layer. Herein, we see a clear improvement in performance by using the second layer. This is confirmed by Fig.7 which displays the rejection level at the outputs of the two layers during convergence in the same sample run as in Fig.5 and 6.

Spatially Colored Noise   The noise power σ^2 is set to -20 dB corresponding to a SNR of 20 dB and the coefficient ρ is taken equal to 0.9 corresponding to a colored noise. Fig.8 shows the rejection level at the outputs of the two layers during convergence. The improvement of the second layer with respect to the first one is still significant.

6   Conclusions

This paper presents a new approach for blind separation of signals based on a recurrent Input-Output Identification using as inputs a nonlinear transformation of current estimated sources. In contrast to other existing techniques, the covariance of the noise do not need to be modeled and can be estimated as a regular parameter if needed. Efficient on-line adaptive learning algorithms were developed for the implementation of the proposed approach using multi-layer networks. The main advantage over a single layer learning in the noiseless case is the handling of ill-conditioned signal mixtures thanks to the multi-layer network architecture. The validity and the performance of the proposed neural network have been illustrated by some computer simulation experiments.

References

[1] S. Amari, A. Cichocki and H. H. Yang, "A new learning algorithm for blind signal separation ," in *NIPS-95, USA*, Vol.8 MIT 1996 (in press).

[2] S. Amari, A. Cichocki and H. H. Yang, "Recurrent neural networks for blind separation of sources," in *Proc. Nolta, Las Vegas, USA*, pp. 37-42, Dec. 1995.

[3] C. Jutten and J. Hérault, "Détection de grandeurs primitives dans un message composite par une architecture de calcul neuromimétrique en apprentissage non supervisé," in *Proc. Gretsi*, (Nice), 1985.

[4] M. Gaeta and J.-L. Lacoume, "Source separation without a priori knowledge: the maximum likelihood solution," in *Proc. EUSIPCO*, pp. 621–624, 1990.

[5] P. Comon, "Independent component analysis, a new concept?," *SignalA Processing*, vol. 36, pp. 287–314, 1994.

[6] J.-F. Cardoso and A. Souloumiac, "An efficient technique for blind separation of complex sources," in *Proc. IEEE SP Workshop on Higher-Order Stat., Lake Tahoe, USA*, 1993.

[7] E. Moreau and O. Macchi, "New self-adaptive algorithms for source separation based on contrast functions," in *Proc. IEEE SP Workshop on Higher-Order Stat., Lake Tahoe, USA*, 1993.

[8] A. Belouchrani and J.-F. Cardoso, "Maximum likelihood source separation for discrete sources," in *Proc. EUSIPCO*, pp. 768–771, 1994.

[9] A. Belouchrani and J.-F. Cardoso, "Maximum likelihood source separation by the expectation-maximization technique: Deterministic and stochastic implementation," in *Proc. International Symposium on Nonlinear Theory and its Applications, Nolta'95, Las Vegas, Nevada, U.S.A.*, Dec. 1995. Invited paper.

[10] L. Tong and R. Liu, "Blind estimation of correlated source signals," in *Proc. Asilomar conference*, Nov. 1990.

[11] A. Belouchrani and K. Abed Meraim and J.-F. Cardoso and E. Moulines, "Second-order blind separation of correlated sources," in *Proc. Int. Conf. on Digital Sig. Proc.*, (Cyprus), pp. 346–351, 1993.

[12] J.-F. Cardoso, A. Belouchrani, and B. Laheld, "A new composite criterion for adaptive and iterative blind source separation," in *Proc. ICASSP*, pp. 273–276, 1994.

[13] A. Cichocki and L. Moszczynski, "New learning algorithm for blind separation of sources," *Electronics Letters*, vol. 28, pp. 1986–1987, 1992.

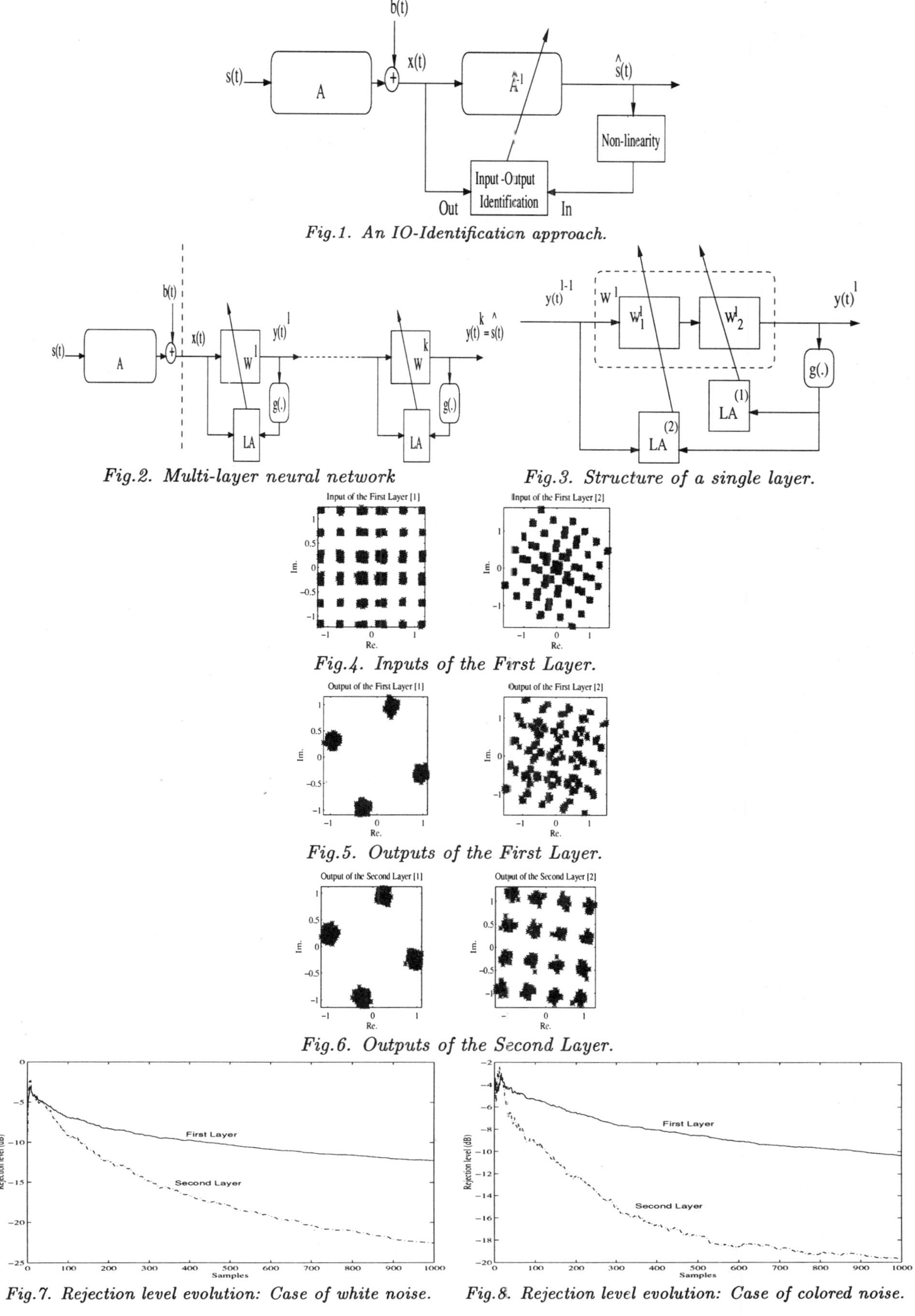

Fig.1. An IO-Identification approach.

Fig.2. Multi-layer neural network

Fig.3. Structure of a single layer.

Fig.4. Inputs of the First Layer.

Fig.5. Outputs of the First Layer.

Fig.6. Outputs of the Second Layer.

Fig.7. Rejection level evolution: Case of white noise.

Fig.8. Rejection level evolution: Case of colored noise.

[14] A. Cichocki, W. Kasprzak and S. Amari, "Multi-layer neural networks with a local adaptive learning rule for blind separation of source signals," in *Proc. Nolta, Las Vegas, USA*, pp. 61-65, Dec. 1995.

[15] A. Cichocki, R. Unbehauen, L. Moszczynski and E. Rummert "A new on line adaptive learning algorithm for blind separation of source signals," in *Proc. ISANN-94, Taiwan*, pp. 406-411, Dec. 1994.

[16] K. Matsuoka, M. Ohya and M. Kawamoto, "A neural net for blind separation of non-stationary signals," *Neural Networks*, vol. 8, pp. 411–419, 1995.

[17] A. Belouchrani and K. Abed Meraim, "Constant modulus blind source separation technique: A new approach," in *Proc. ISSPA, Gold Coast, Australia*, August 1996.

[18] J.R. Treichel and A. Paulraj, "A new approach to multi-path correction of constant modulus signals," *IEEE Trans ASSP*, vol. 31, pp. 459-471, Apr. 1983.

[19] J.-F. Cardoso and B. Laheld, "Equivalent adaptive source separation," *IEEE Tr. on SP*, 1996. To appear.

[20] A. Cichocki and R. Unbehauen, *Neural Networks for Optimization and Signal Processing*. John Wiley, 1994.

Simple One-Unit Neural Algorithms for Blind Source Separation and Blind Deconvolution

Aapo Hyvärinen
Helsinki University of Technology
Laboratory of Computer and Information Science
Rakentajanaukio 2 C, FIN-02150 Espoo, Finland
Email: `aapo.hyvarinen@hut.fi`

Abstract— **We approach the problems of blind source separation and blind deconvolution from the point of view of a single neuron. Two simple non-linear learning rules for a neuron are presented. When used for blind source separation, the first rule learns to separate one (arbitrary) source which has a negative kurtosis (i.e. is sub-Gaussian), and the second rule separates a source with positive kurtosis (i.e. a super-Gaussian source). Formulating the problem of blind deconvolution as a special case of blind source separation, we can also apply our learning rules for that problem. Then, the single unit learns to deconvolve the signal.**

These learning rules use the raw data, requiring no whitening (sphering). In addition, their convergence can be rigorously proven.

A supplementary unit that performs on-line estimation of kurtosis enables separation of any source, or deconvolution of any signal, regardless of the sign of its kurtosis. The neurons can also be combined in a network of several units that separates several sources in parallel.

1 Introduction

Several neural algorithms for blind source separation (BSS) or Independent Component Analysis (ICA) have been proposed recently [1, 2, 7, 8, 10]. In blind source separation, several unknown linear mixtures of a number of unknown independent source signals are observed. Only minimal assumptions on the distributions of the sources are made. The problem is then to find (separate) the original sources, or some of them, based on observed mixtures only. If all the sources, except perhaps one, are assumed to be non-Gaussian, the problem can be theoretically solved in a meaningful way [3].

The related problem of blind deconvolution [5] has also received some attention [2] in the neural network community. Indeed, this problem can be (approximately) formulated using the same mathematical model as BSS, the independent sources being in this case time-delayed versions of a single signal. Thus blind deconvolution can be considered a *constrained* BSS problem [3].

In this paper, we introduce one-unit neural algorithms for BSS and blind deconvolution that use directly the observed mixtures, requiring no sphering or prior knowledge on the number of sources. Using these learning rules, *a single neuron develops either into a separator* that can find one of the original, independent sources from their linear mixtures, *or into a deconvolver* that finds the original, deconvolved signal. One of the learning rules separates (or deconvolves) sub-Gaussian sources, i.e. sources of negative kurtosis, and the other separates super-Gaussian sources, i.e. sources of positive kurtosis. Because of their simplicity, the convergence of the one-unit rules can be rigorously proven.

Using a supplementary unit to estimate on-line the kurtosis of the output of the neuron, sources of any (non-zero) kurtosis can be separated, or deconvolved. Moreover, if separation of several sources is required, neural units can be combined into a system that separates all the sources in parallel. Note, however, that in applications of BSS related to, for example, noise canceling, separation of one source is often all that is needed.

This paper is organized as follows: in Section 2, the problem setting is described. The basic one-unit algorithms are introduced in Section 3. The general two-unit algorithm that uses an on-line estimate of the kurtosis of the output, is presented in Section 4. Feedback mechanisms for multi-unit systems are discussed in Section 5. Section 6 contains simulation results.

2   Problem Setting

2.1   Definition of Blind Source Separation and Blind Deconvolution

In the simplest form of BSS, we observe n scalar signals $x_k^j, j = 1...n$, where $k = 1, 2, ...$ is the time index. The signals x_k^j are different linear combinations of m ($m \leq n$) unknown sources $u_k^i, i = 1...m$. The source signals u_k^i are assumed to be stationary, zero-mean, and, above all, statistically independent, at any point of time k. Usually, all the source signals, except perhaps one, are assumed to be non-Gaussian. In contrast, several Gaussian sources are allowed in this paper. However, only non-Gaussian sources (of non-zero kurtosis, see below) can be separated.

The BSS model can be expressed in matrix form by arranging the source signals into the vector $\mathbf{u}_k = (u_k^1, u_k^2, ..., u_k^m)$, and the observed signals into the vector $\mathbf{x}_k = (x_k^1, x_k^2, ..., x_k^n)$. Then the model is as follows:

$$\mathbf{x}_k = \mathbf{A}\mathbf{u}_k \tag{1}$$

where $\mathbf{A}$ is an unknown $n \times m$ matrix whose columns are linearly independent.

Blind source separation then means estimating the original signals u_k^i, or some of them, from the mixtures x_k^j, or, equivalently, estimating a pseudo-inverse of the matrix $\mathbf{A}$. The solution of this problem is not uniquely defined: one could for example multiply one of the sources by a constant and divide the corresponding column of $\mathbf{A}$ by the same constant, getting a different solution for the same problem. Following an established convention, we define that the sources u_k^i have unit variance. Then the non-Gaussian source signals can be estimated (separated), up to their signs. Note that no order is defined between the sources in BSS.

Blind deconvolution [5] can also be formulated using equation (1). Assume that we observe a scalar signal x_k which is a convolution of an i.i.d. scalar signal u_k. Then using the time-delayed vectors $\mathbf{u}_k = (u_k, u_{k-1}, ..., u_{k-n+1})$ and $\mathbf{x}_k = (x_k, x_{k-1}, ..., x_{k-n+1})$, the convolution can be expressed as in (1), where $\mathbf{A}$ is a matrix defined by the convolving filter. This is, of course, only an approximation of the original convolving process, as in principle equation (1) should contain the signals x_k and u_k for all k, and not only a small subset of observations. The problem is then to estimate the original signal u_k. Using the results of uniqueness of BSS, it is easy to see that the original, deconvolved signal is only defined up to an arbitrary time-lag and the sign.

Since blind deconvolution can be regarded as a special case of BSS, we consider below only the problem of BSS. All results on the *one-unit BSS learning rules can also be used for blind deconvolution*. Note that one neural unit is enough to solve the problem of blind deconvolution, as then it is enough to find one of the components of $\mathbf{u}_k$.

2.2   Kurtosis

An important distinction between two classes of signals must be made. This is based on the sign of the *kurtosis* of the signal. The kurtosis of a random variable x of zero mean is defined as

$$\text{kurt}(x) = E\{x^4\} - 3(E\{x^2\})^2 \tag{2}$$

For a Gaussian random variable, kurtosis is zero; for sharper densities, it is positive, and for flatter densities, negative. Signals of negative kurtosis are also called sub-Gaussian signals, and signals of positive kurtosis are called super-Gaussian.

Our basic stochastic gradient learning rules, introduced in Section 3, cannot separate source signals of any arbitrary distribution (nor deconvolve any signal). One of the algorithms separates sources of negative kurtosis and the other separates sources of positive kurtosis.

However, it is possible to separate a source of any (non-zero) kurtosis by introducing a supplementary unit that estimates on-line the kurtosis of the source to be separated, and enables the first unit to decide which one of the basic learning rules should be used. This is discussed in Section 4.

3   Basic One-Unit Learning Rules

3.1   Separating One Source of Negative Kurtosis

Let us assume, as above, that the observed signal vector $\mathbf{x}_k$ is a linear combination of independent sources $\mathbf{u}_k$ according to eq. (1). Recall that this formulation encompasses both BSS and blind deconvolution, and that no sphering of the data is needed. Furthermore, let us assume that at least one of the sources has a negative kurtosis. Then we can separate one of those sources, in a sense explained below, using the following learning rule for the n-dimensional weight vector $\mathbf{w}$ of a neuron:

$$\mathbf{w}_{k+1} = \mathbf{w}_k + \mu_k[\mathbf{x}_k g(\mathbf{w}_k^T \mathbf{x}_k)] \tag{3}$$

where $\{\mathbf{x}_k, k = 0, 1, ...\}$ is the sequence of observed signals, the initial value $\mathbf{w}_0$ is chosen randomly, and μ_k is the learning rate, which must fulfill the conditions usual in stochastic approximation. The non-linear learning function g is a polynomial:

$$g(t) = t - t^3 \tag{4}$$

It can be proven (see subsection 3.3, or [7]) that the linear output $\mathbf{w}_k^T \mathbf{x}_k$ of the neuron converges to Cu_k^i where u_k^i is one of the source signals of negative kurtosis, and C is a scalar constant. (Note that we make here a distinction between the *linear output* $\mathbf{w}_k^T \mathbf{x}_k$ of the neuron and the *non-linear learning function* $g(\mathbf{w}_k^T \mathbf{x}_k)$.) This multiplication of the source signal by the constant C is in fact not a restriction, as the variance and the sign of the sources cannot be estimated (the variance was defined to be 1 for mathematical convenience only). Thus we can say that *the neuron learns to separate one of the sources*. If the neural unit is used for (approximate) blind deconvolution, as explained in subsection 2.1, the output of the neuron becomes, up to a constant, equal to the original signal, with an arbitrary time-lag. In this case, *the single neuron learns to deconvolve the signal*.

The learning rule (3) can be interpreted as a mixture of Hebbian and anti-Hebbian learning. Since $g(t)$ is positive for small t and negative for large t, the learning is Hebbian for small outputs $\mathbf{w}_k^T \mathbf{x}_k$ and anti-Hebbian for larger outputs.

As will be seen in subsection 3.3, the cubic (anti-Hebbian) part of the learning function g is trying to minimize the kurtosis of the linear output $\mathbf{w}_k^T \mathbf{x}_k$. This can be motivated by information-theoretical considerations [3], and has been used for multi-unit neural BSS for prewhitened mixtures in [6, 8, 10]. The linear Hebbian part of g is due to the constraint of this minimization, and prevents $\mathbf{w}$ from converging to $\mathbf{0}$.

Note also that if the algorithm is initialized with a $\mathbf{w}_0$ whose norm is very small, the linear Hebbian term will be dominant in the beginning, and the algorithm will find most probably the source whose contribution to the energy of the observed signals is the largest, i.e. the signal u^i such that the norm of the i-th column of the mixing matrix $\mathbf{A}$ is the largest. This may be very useful if BSS is used, e.g., for noise cancelling.

3.2 Separating One Source of Positive Kurtosis

To separate a source of positive kurtosis (assuming, of course, that at least one such source exists), under the same assumptions as in the preceding subsection, we use the following learning rule:

$$\mathbf{w}_{k+1} = \mathbf{w}_k + \mu_k[\mathbf{x}_k g_{\mathbf{w}_k}(\mathbf{w}_k^T \mathbf{x}_k)] \tag{5}$$

where all notation is as with algorithm (3), expect that the learning function $g_{\mathbf{w}_k}$ is defined as follows:

$$g_{\mathbf{w}}(t) = -t(\mathbf{w}^T \mathbf{C} \mathbf{w})^2 + t^3 \tag{6}$$

where $\mathbf{C}$ is the covariance matrix of $\mathbf{x}_k$, i.e. $\mathbf{C} = E\{\mathbf{x}_k \mathbf{x}_k^T\}$. The problem with this definition of $g_{\mathbf{w}_k}$ is that we need an estimate of the covariance matrix. Therefore, this learning rule is not, strictly speaking, a one-unit rule, if definition (6) is used. This problem can be circumvented by defining the $g_{\mathbf{w}_k}$ as follows:

$$g_{\mathbf{w}}(t) = -t\|\mathbf{w}\|^4 + t^3 \tag{7}$$

Then the neuron needs no supplementary information. However, if $g_{\mathbf{w}_k}$ is defined as in (7), the convergence properties cannot be proven with the same rigor as is possible with definition (6). If $\mathbf{C}$ is badly conditioned, spurious minima may appear. In most cases, however, defining $g_{\mathbf{w}_k}$ as in (7) gives no convergence problems.

The behaviour of algorithm (5) is completely analogous to algorithm (3). If used for BSS, the linear output $\mathbf{w}_k^T \mathbf{x}_k$ of the neuron converges (up to a multiplicative constant) to one of the source signals u_k^i whose kurtosis is positive. If blind deconvolution is desired, the output converges, up to a constant, to the original deconvolved signal, shifted slightly in time. The convergence of this algorithm, for $g_{\mathbf{w}_k}$ defined as in (6), is proven rigorously in [7]. An outline of the proof is presented in subsection 3.3.

Because of the influence of the norm of $\mathbf{w}$, or of $\mathbf{w}^T \mathbf{C} \mathbf{w}$, in $g_{\mathbf{w}_k}$, this learning rule is not purely a mixture of Hebbian and anti-Hebbian learning, as was the case with learning rule (5). However, the two terms in $g_{\mathbf{w}_k}$ can be interpreted in a rather similar way. The second term in $g_{\mathbf{w}_k}$ can be interpreted as a Hebbian term that tries to find a maximum of kurtosis. The first term is a anti-Hebbian-like constraint term that prevents $\mathbf{w}$ from growing infinite.

3.3   Mathematical Analysis

Here, we outline the proof of convergence of algorithms (3) and (5). The detailed rigorous proof is presented in [7]. For simplicity, we consider in the following only algorithm (3). The proof for algorithm (5) is analogous. Note that the proof is exact only in the case of BSS, because blind deconvolution is only approximately a special case of BSS.

It is now well-known [3, 4] that the minimization of the kurtosis of the linear output $\mathbf{w}_k^T \mathbf{x}_k$ is closely related to separating sources with negative kurtosis in BSS. This is because the kurtosis can be used to approximate the mutual information between the output of the neuron and the rest of the signal [3]. Note that this use of kurtosis was, in fact, first formulated in the context of blind deconvolution [9].

The connection between the kurtosis of the output and source separation can be seen clearly in the following expression:

$$\text{kurt}\,(\mathbf{w}^T \mathbf{x}) = \text{kurt}\,(\mathbf{z}^T \mathbf{u}) = \sum_i z_i^4\,\text{kurt}\,u^i \tag{8}$$

where we have defined $\mathbf{z} = \mathbf{A}^T \mathbf{w}$, used model (1), and dropped the index k for simplicity.

It is rather obvious (for a proof, see [4]) that the local minima of $\sum_i z_i^4\,\text{kurt}\,u^i$ under the constraint $\|\mathbf{z}\| = 1$ are attained exactly when $\mathbf{z} = \mathbf{e}_j$, i.e. $\mathbf{z}$ equals the j-th canonical basis vector, where j is the index of one of the sources of negative kurtosis. But then the output of the neuron $\mathbf{w}^T \mathbf{x} = \mathbf{z}^T \mathbf{u}$ equals one of the source signals of negative kurtosis.

To find the desired constrained minima in a neural learning process, we must be able to express the constraint $\|\mathbf{z}\| = 1$ in terms of the weight vector $\mathbf{w}$ and the observed signals $\mathbf{x}$. This can be done by the variance of the output, because by definition, $\|\mathbf{z}\|^2 = \mathbf{w}^T \mathbf{A} \mathbf{A}^T \mathbf{w} = E\{\mathbf{w}^T \mathbf{A} \mathbf{u} \mathbf{u}^T \mathbf{A}^T \mathbf{w}\} = E\{(\mathbf{w}^T \mathbf{x})^2\}$. Therefore, we can separate a source by finding a solution of

$$\min_{E\{(\mathbf{w}^T\mathbf{x})^2\}=1} E\{(\mathbf{w}^T \mathbf{x})^4\}$$

where we have used the fact that under the given constraint, $\text{kurt}\,(\mathbf{w}^T \mathbf{x}) = E\{(\mathbf{w}^T \mathbf{x})^4\} - 3$. The constraint $E\{(\mathbf{w}^T \mathbf{x})^2\} = 1$ may be difficult to take into account explicitly. However, we can achieve a similar result by introducing a penalty (constraint) term in the function to be minimized. Then we have the following unconstrained problem:

$$\min E\{(\mathbf{w}^T \mathbf{x})^4 - 2(\mathbf{w}^T \mathbf{x})^2\} \tag{9}$$

where the weight of the penalty term has been chosen to be 2 for algebraic simplicity; it could be any positive constant. Learning rule (3) is simply a stochastic gradient descent algorithm for this minimization problem. Note that the minimization of the fourth moment has the effect of reducing the variance, and therefore the constraint term only needs to prevent the variance from converging to $\mathbf{0}$ (in learning rule (5), the opposite is true).

It is then possible to analyze, by classical means, the properties of the function to be minimized in (9). The result is that its only local minima correspond to points where the linear output of the neuron equals (up to a multiplicative constant) one of the source signals of negative kurtosis. Moreover, the algorithm cannot diverge to infinity. This proves the convergence of (3). The convergence of algorithm (5) can be proven in a similar way.

4   General Two-Unit Learning Rule

We can combine learning rules (3) and (5) to obtain a learning rule that separates a source whose kurtosis is of the same sign as the sign of the cubic term of the learning function. Then we can use a second unit to simultaneously estimate the sign of the kurtosis of the output of the first unit [4, 9]. Thus, we get *a two-unit couple that separates a source of any (non-zero) kurtosis*, or deconvolves a signal regardless of its kurtosis.

Combining the constraint terms of learning rules (3) and (5), and denoting by $s = \pm 1$ the sign of the cubic term of the learning function g, we get the learning rule

$$\mathbf{w}_{k+1} = \mathbf{w}_k + \mu_k[s\mathbf{x}_k(\mathbf{w}_k^T \mathbf{x}_k)^3 + \mathbf{x}_k(\mathbf{w}_k^T \mathbf{x}_k)(1 - \|\mathbf{w}_k\|^4)] \tag{10}$$

In the right-most term, $\|\mathbf{w}\|^4$ might be replaced by $(\mathbf{w}^T \mathbf{C} \mathbf{w})^2$ for guaranteed convergence, as explained in subsection 3.2. To estimate the appropriate s in parallel, we need a second unit that estimates on-line the kurtosis of the output $\mathbf{w}_k^T \mathbf{x}_k$ of the first unit. This can be done simply by two separate on-line estimates of the second $(\widehat{m^2}_k)$ and the fourth $(\widehat{m^4}_k)$ moments

$$\widehat{m^2}_{k+1} = (1-\nu)\widehat{m^2}_k + \nu(\mathbf{w}_k^T \mathbf{x}_k)^2 \tag{11}$$

$$\widehat{m^4}_{k+1} = (1-\nu)\widehat{m^4}_k + \nu(\mathbf{w}_k^T \mathbf{x}_k)^4 \tag{12}$$

where ν is a small constant, and $\widehat{m^4}_0$ and $\widehat{m^2}_0$ are some rough estimates of the second and the fourth moments. Then we can use the definition of kurtosis to obtain an on-line estimate of kurtosis $\widehat{\mathrm{kurt}}_k$

$$\widehat{\mathrm{kurt}}_k = \widehat{m^4}_k - 3(\widehat{m^2}_k)^2.$$

Now, we can replace s in learning rule (10) by the sign of this estimate of kurtosis, and get the *general learning rule*

$$\mathbf{w}_{k+1} = \mathbf{w}_k + \mu_k [\operatorname{sign}(\widehat{\mathrm{kurt}}_k)\mathbf{x}_k(\mathbf{w}_k^T \mathbf{x}_k)^3 + \mathbf{x}_k(\mathbf{w}_k^T \mathbf{x}_k)(1 - \|\mathbf{w}_k\|^4)] \tag{13}$$

where $\widehat{\mathrm{kurt}}_k$ is the estimate of kurtosis given by the supplementary unit, and $\|\mathbf{w}\|^4$ may be replaced by $(\mathbf{w}^T \mathbf{C} \mathbf{w})^2$ for better convergence.

5 Multi-Unit Learning Rule

If BSS of several sources is desired, it is possible to construct a parallel multi-unit system by combining N units that learn according to the learning rules given above, and adding a feedback term to each of those learning rules.

If we know a priori that all (interesting) sources have a positive (resp. negative) kurtosis, all units can use the simple one-unit learning rule (5) (resp. learning rule (3)). If we have no such prior information, we must instead combine two-unit couples described in Section 4.

Probably the simplest kind of feedback that can be used here is a symmetric decorrelating bigradient feedback, adapted from [10]. The bigradient feedback term also contains a constraint term. As an example, let us take the one-unit learning rule (3). Assuming we have a system of N neurons with weight vectors $\mathbf{w}^i, i = 1...N$, which define the columns of the weight matrix $\mathbf{W}$, the weight matrix is updated according to the learning rule

$$\mathbf{W}_{k+1} = \mathbf{W}_k - \mu_k \mathbf{x}_k(\mathbf{x}_k^T \mathbf{W}_k)^3 + \alpha \mathbf{C}\mathbf{W}_k(\mathbf{I} - \mathbf{W}_k^T \mathbf{C}\mathbf{W}_k) \tag{14}$$

where α is a constant in the range $[0.5, 1]$, μ_k is the ordinary learning rate sequence, $\mathbf{C}$ is the covariance matrix of the inputs, and the cubic function is applied separately on every component of the vector. For details, and other ways of separating several source signals, see [7].

6 Simulation Results

To illustrate our algorithms, we used them for separating four source signals from linear mixtures. The source signals were artificially generated to allow easy visual inspection of the results. The sources were time signals of 2000 points. The first 100 points of the signals are shown in Figure 1. Signals 1 and 2 have negative kurtosis, whereas signals 3 and 4 have positive kurtosis.

A 4×4 mixing matrix $\mathbf{A}$ was randomly chosen. The mixing matrix might also have been rectangular; this would not have implied any changes in the procedure. The mixed signals are depicted in Figure 2. Next, we used a multi-unit neural network, which consisted of 4 couples of two units, each couple learning according to the general two-unit algorithm of Section 4. The feedback used was the symmetric decorrelating bigradient feedback described in Section 5. The learning rate sequence was $\mu_k = 1/(100 + k^{0.7})$, ν was chosen 0.01, and $\alpha = 0.5$. The observed signals were also scaled so that their variance was approximately 1, to prevent numerical instability.

The separated signals are depicted in Figure 3. Visual comparison of Figs. 1 and 3 confirms the validity of our algorithms in the source separation problem.

References

[1] S. Amari, A. Cichocki, and H.H. Yang. A new learning algorithm for blind source separation. In *Proc. Int. Conf. Neural Information Processing Systems*, November 1995.

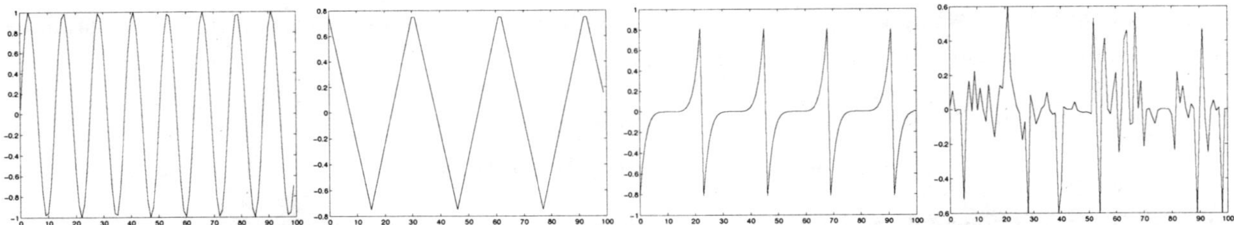

Figure 1: Original source signals used in the simulations.

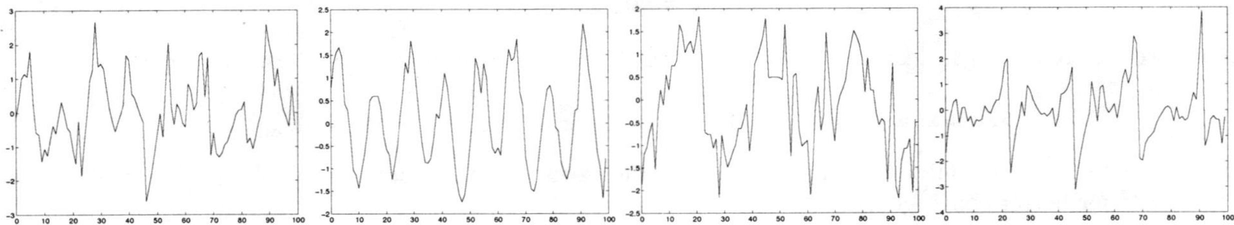

Figure 2: Linear mixtures of source signals in Fig. 1, i.e. observed data

[2] A.J. Bell and T.J. Sejnowski. An information-maximization approach to blind separation and blind deconvolution. *Neural Computation*, 7:1129–1159, September 1995.

[3] P. Comon. Independent component analysis – a new concept? *Signal Processing*, 36:287–314, 1994.

[4] N. Delfosse and P. Loubaton. Adaptive blind separation of independent sources: A deflation approach. *Signal Processing*, 45:59–83, 1995.

[5] S. Haykin. *Adaptive Filter Theory*. Prentice-Hall International, 3rd edition, 1996.

[6] A. Hyvärinen and E. Oja. A neuron that learns to separate one independent component from linear mixtures. In *Proc. IEEE Int. Conf. on Neural Networks*, Washington, D.C., June 1996.

[7] A. Hyvärinen and E. Oja. Simple neuron models for independent component analysis. Technical report, Helsinki University of Technology, Laboratory of Computer and Information Science, 1996.

[8] J. Karhunen, L. Wang, and R. Vigario. Nonlinear PCA type approaches for source separation and independent component analysis. In *Proc. IEEE Int. Conf. Neural Networks '95*, pages 995–1000, Perth, Australia, Nov 27–Dec 1 1995.

[9] O. Shalvi and E. Weinstein. New criteria for blind deconvolution of nonminimum phase systems (channels). *IEEE Trans. on Information Theory*, 36(2):312–321, March 1990.

[10] L. Wang, J. Karhunen, and E. Oja. A bigradient optimization approach for robust PCA, MCA, and source separation. In *Proc. IEEE Int. Conf on Neural Networks '95*, pages 1684–1689, Perth, Australia, Nov 27–Dec 1 1995.

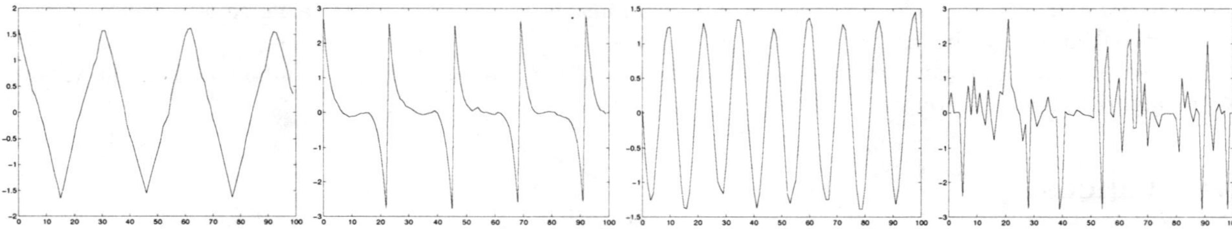

Figure 3: Separated signals, i.e. estimations of source signals in Fig. 1 based on mixtures depicted in Fig. 2

Nonlinear Blind Source Separation by Self-Organizing Maps

Petteri Pajunen, Aapo Hyvärinen, and Juha Karhunen

Helsinki University of Technology
Laboratory of Computer and Information Science
Rakentajanaukio 2 C, FIN-02150, Espoo, Finland
e-mail: Petteri.Pajunen@hut.fi

***Abstract*— In neural blind source separation most approaches have considered the linear source separation problem where the input data consist of unknown linear mixtures of unknown independent source signals. The solution is a linear transformation which makes the output vector components statistically independent. More generally we can consider nonlinear mixtures of sources. Then we can try to separate the sources by constructing mappings that make the components of the output vectors independent. We show that such a mapping can be approximately realized using self-organizing maps with rectangular map topology. We apply these mappings to the separation of nonlinear mixtures of sub-Gaussian sources.**

1 Introduction

In linear blind source separation (BSS), the goal is to separate independent sources signals from their linear mixtures using a minimum of a priori information. Such blind techniques have applications for example in array processing, communications, speech processing, and medical signal processing. Recently, BSS has become an active research area of unsupervised neural learning. Several neural algorithms that use nonlinearities instead of explicit higher-order statistics have been proposed; see [1, 2, 3, 4]. These algorithms try to find a linear transformation that makes the components of the output vectors statistically independent. The underlying data model is essentially the same as in linear Independent Component Analysis (ICA), which is studied and defined formally in the fundamental paper [5].

One natural generalization of the linear ICA and BSS is to consider the problem of finding more general, nonlinear transformations that would yield statistically independent outputs. This extension has already been considered in some papers [6, 7, 8, 9]. However, the proposed algorithms are not completely satisfying from a neural network point of view, because they are either complicated and/or require explicit computation of higher-order moments.

In this paper, we introduce a new neural approach for nonlinear blind source separation and independent component analysis. It uses self-organizing maps to construct mappings that make output vectors statistically independent. These mappings are used to separate nonlinearly mixed sub-Gaussian sources.

2 The Blind Source Separation Problem

We consider the problem of blind separation of statistically independent source signals s_k^i, $i = 1, \ldots, M$, where k is a time index. It is assumed that we only observe the instantaneous mixtures

$$\mathbf{x}_k = F(\mathbf{s}_k) \tag{1}$$

of the sources $\mathbf{s}_k = [s_k^1, s_k^2, \ldots, s_k^M]^T$, where $F : \mathbb{R}^m \to \mathbb{R}^m$ is an unknown mixing function. The problem consists of finding a mapping $G : \mathbb{R}^m \to \mathbb{R}^m$ which would give estimates of the source signals as

$$\mathbf{y}_k = G(\mathbf{x}_k). \tag{2}$$

In the linear case, the mixing function F is assumed to be an invertible linear transformation. The mixtures are obtained as a matrix multiplication $\mathbf{x}_k = \mathbf{A}\mathbf{s}_k$. The solution G exists and is also a linear transformation. The estimated sources are $\mathbf{y}_k = \mathbf{B}\mathbf{x}_k$. It can be shown that the matrix $\mathbf{B}$ cannot be uniquely determined by the independence assumption only. The ordering and the variances of the sources are arbitrary without additional constraints. However, their waveforms can be recovered in practice.

The nonlinear case, where we do not assume that the mixing function F is linear, requires obviously some constraints to make the problem tractable. Intuitively it is natural to require that the mixing function is one-to-one. If we also require continuity of F and G, it follows that F is a *homeomorphism*, i.e. a topology-preserving mapping. Now the problem is essentially geometric; the mixing function F transforms the joint density of the sources into mixture density and we should determine an inverse mapping G which does the opposite. In the nonlinear case, the indeterminacy in the mapping G is even more serious. Any componentwise function

$$\mathbf{x} = [H^1(s^1), H^2(s^2), \ldots, H^m(s^m)]^T. \tag{3}$$

of the source vector $\mathbf{s}$ keeps the components statistically independent. Thus the waveforms are in general not recoverable. However, they can be approximately recovered in practice in many situations.

3 Self-Organizing Maps and Statistical Independence

A self-organizing map [10] performs a mapping from input space to an array of nodes in the output space. The positions of the nodes are fixed and each node is represented by a reference vector in the input space. Input vectors are mapped by finding the closest reference vector with respect to some distance function. The image of the input vector is the corresponding node on the map.

The self-organizing map can be made continuous if we apply some suitable interpolation method. Then we can think of SOM as a homeomorphism from input space to the map.

The distribution of the reference vectors in the input space can be roughly described using the density

$$c \cdot p(\mathbf{x})^\alpha \tag{4}$$

where p is the density of the input vector $\mathbf{x}$ and α is the magnification factor. If $\alpha = 1$, the weight vectors are distributed approximately according to the input space density. In this case we have the important property that each weight vector on the map is equally likely the winner, that is, it lies closest to a random input vector. This implies that the joint density on the map is uniformly distributed. Since we consider rectangular maps, the final implication is that the density on the map is factorizable, i.e. the coordinates are statistically independent. Learning rules that can make the magnification factor equal to one have been recently proposed [11, 12].

4 Application of SOM to Blind Source Separation

The self-organizing map can be used to estimate the inverse of the mixing function G by taking the set of observed mixture vectors $\mathbf{x}_k$ as the input vectors to the SOM. Then the coordinates of the winner neuron on the map define the estimated source vector $\mathbf{y}_k$ for each $\mathbf{x}_k$. Using interpolation on the map this function can be made continuous.

Even though the self-organizing map can produce statistically independent output vectors, this property does not guarantee that the components of the output vectors are good estimates for the source signals. With some heuristic constraints, however, it seems that the sources can be separated at least roughly. The mixture density should be of such a shape that a rectangular map can naturally adapt to it. Furthermore this natural adaptation should provide the correct separation. One reasonable class of problems for which this description holds consists of sub-Gaussian sources that are first mixed linearly and then mildly nonlinearly distorted. Typically, sub-Gaussian signals have a probability density which is flatter than the Gaussian density. Formally stated, sub-Gaussian signals have the property $E[x^4] - 3(E[x^2])^2 < 0$. The expression on the left is called the *kurtosis* of x, and it equals zero for Gaussian signals.

Due to the flat shape of sub-Gaussian densities the linear mixture of sub-Gaussian sources gives often rise to a roughly rectangular density. The converged map in Figure 1 demonstrates this. Mild nonlinearities do not distort too much the rectangular form of the density, allowing fitting of a self-organizing map.

5 Experiments

In each experiment two sub-Gaussian source signals are considered. The source signals consisted of a sinusoid and uniformly distributed white noise.

First, the sources $\mathbf{s}_k$ were linearly mixed using a mixing matrix

$$\mathbf{A} = \begin{pmatrix} 0.7 & 0.3 \\ 0.3 & 0.7 \end{pmatrix} \tag{5}$$

The resulting vectors $\mathbf{v}_k = \mathbf{A}\mathbf{s}_k$ were distorted by a nonlinearity f applied separately to each component. This yields the mixture vectors

$$\mathbf{x}_k = [f(v_k^1), f(v_k^2), \ldots, f(v_k^m)]^T. \tag{6}$$

The resulting vectors were first whitened so that their covariance matrix becomes the identity matrix.

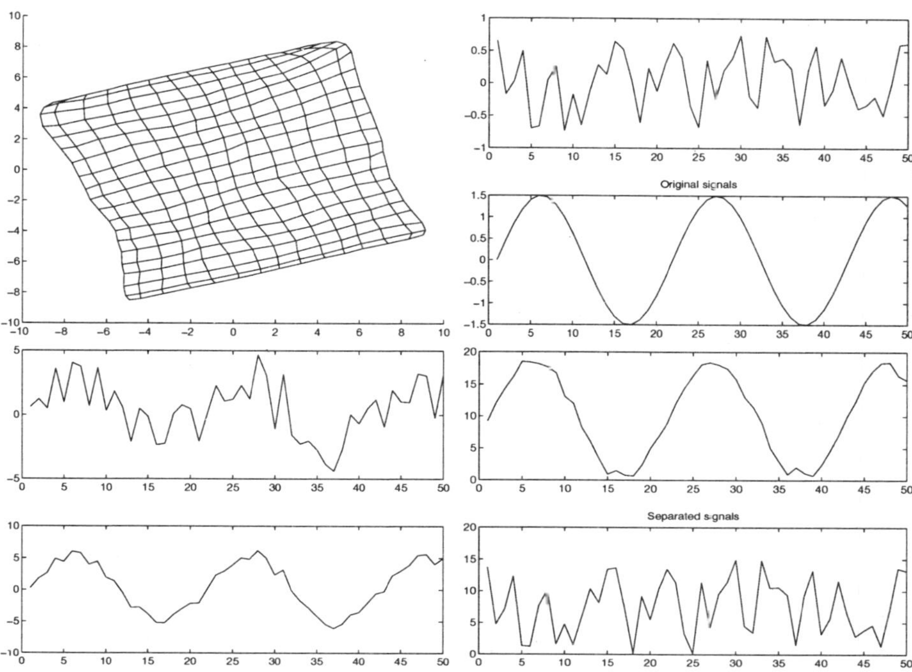

Figure 1: Results using linear mixtures; Top left: converged map. Top right: original source signals. Bottom left: mixture signals. Bottom right: separated source signals.

Fig. 1 shows the results for the linear case where $f(x) = x$ and Fig. 2 the results for $f(x) = x^3 + x$. Note that the signs of separated sources have been changed in some cases to make comparisons with original source signals easier.

In these experiments the basic SOM learning rule has been used. It is possible that the learning rules proposed in [11, 12] could improve the results since the density on the map would be closer to uniform density. Further experiments are currently being made.

6   Discussion

A method for separating sub-Gaussian sources from nonlinear mixtures is presented. First experiments show that at least in simple cases the sources can be recovered. However, the resulting estimates of source signals are often noisy. The noise in the estimated sources is partly due to the quantization error caused by a finite number of neurons. Using interpolation this can be reduced but not eliminated completely. Also the indeterminacy in the separating function G mentioned earlier can cause distortion to separated sources.

The complexity of SOM grows exponentially with the number of dimensions of the map. Thus it is not practical to consider mixtures of a large number of sources using this method.

The main problem of our approach is the requirement of sub-Gaussian sources. This requirement is mainly due to the inherent rectangular topology of the self-organizing map. Further research is currently carried out to extend this method to a larger class of problems.

References

[1] A. Cichocki and R. Unbehauen, *Neural Networks for Optimization and Signal Processing*. John Wiley, 1994. (new revised and improved edition).

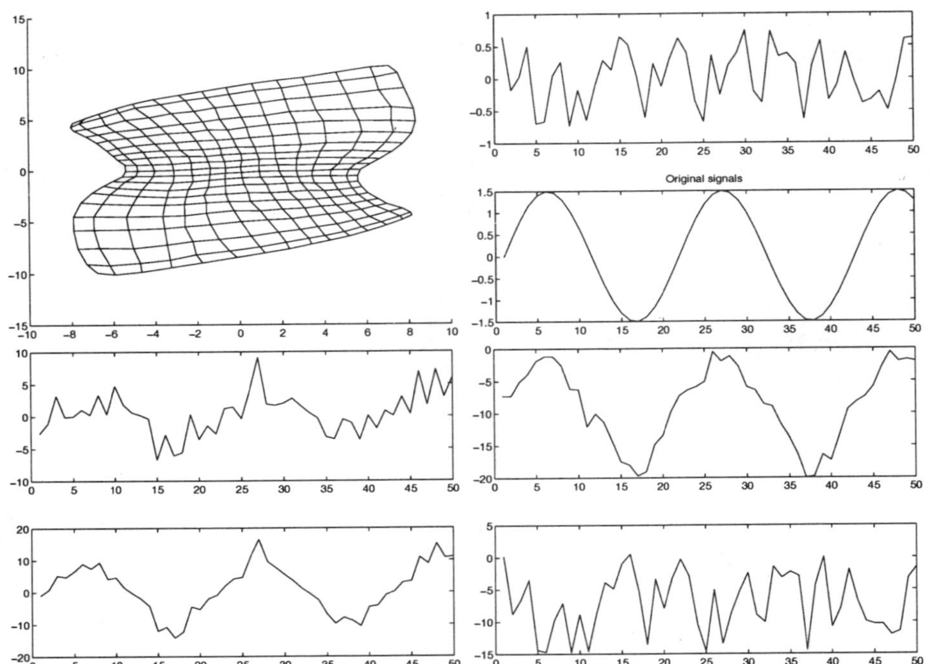

Figure 2: Results using linear mixtures distorted by $f = x^3 + x$; Top left: converged map. Top right: original source signals. Bottom left: mixture signals. Bottom right: separated source signals.

[2] J. Karhunen, E. Oja, L. Wang, R. Vigario, and J. Joutsensalo, "A class of neural networks for independent component analysis," Report A28, Helsinki Univ. of Technology, Lab. of Computer and Information Science, October 1995. Manuscript submitted to a journal.

[3] J. Karhunen, "Neural approaches to independent component analysis and source separation," in *Proc. of ESANN'96 (4th European Symposium on Artificial Neural Networks)*, (Bruges, Belgium), April 1996. to appear, invited paper.

[4] A. Bell and T. Sejnowski, "An information-maximisation approach to blind separation and blind deconvolution," *Neural Computation*, vol. 7, no. 6, pp. 1004–1034, 1995.

[5] P. Comon, "Independent component analysis – a new concept?," *Signal Processing*, vol. 36, no. 3, pp. 287–314, 1994.

[6] G. Burel, "Blind separation of sources: A nonlinear neural algorithm," *Neural Networks*, vol. 5, no. 6, pp. 937–947, 1992.

[7] G. Deco and W. Brauer, "Nonlinear higher-order statistical decorrelation by volume-conserving neural architectures," *Neural Networks*, vol. 8, no. 4, pp. 525–535, 1995.

[8] L. Parra, "Symplectic nonlinear component analysis," in *NIPS-95, Advances in Neural Information Processing Systems 8*, (Cambridge, MA), MIT Press, 1996. (in press).

[9] L. Parra, G. Deco, and S. Miesbach, "Statistical independence and novelty detection with information preserving nonlinear maps," *Neural Computation*, vol. 8, pp. 260–269, 1996.

[10] T. Kohonen, *Self-Organizing Maps*, vol. 30 of *Springer Series in Information Sciences*. Springer-Verlag, 1995.

[11] M. Herrmann, H.-U. Bauer, and R. Der, "Optimal magnification factors in self-organizing feature maps," in *Proc. of the Int. Conf. on Artificial Neural Networks*, (Paris, France), pp. 75–80, October 9-13 1995.

[12] M. Van Hulle, "Globally-ordered topology-preserving maps with a learning rule performing local weight updates only," in *Neural Networks for Signal Processing V*, pp. 95–104, IEEE Press, 1995.

Perspectives and Limitations of Self-Organizing Maps in Blind Separation of Source Signals

M. Herrmann[1], H. H. Yang[2]

RIKEN, Laboratory for Information Representation
2-1 Hirosawa, Wako-shi, 351-01 Saitama, Japan
[1] michael@sponge.riken.go.jp, [2] hhy@koala.riken.go.jp

Abstract— The capabilities of self-organizing maps (SOMs) in parametrizing data manifolds qualify them as candidates for blind separation algorithms. We study the virtues and problems of the SOM-based approach in a simple example. Also numerical simulations of more general cases have been performed. It shows that the performance is unquestionable in the case of a linear mixture only if the observed data are prewhitened and inhomogeneities in the input data are compensated. The algorithm is robust with respect to deviations from linearity, although may fail for complex non-linearly distorted signals. Due to computational restrictions only mixtures from a few sources can be resolved. Under certain conditions it is possible to separate more sources than sensors using a dimension-increasing map.

1   Introduction

The problem of extracting independent sources from sensor signals arises in many areas in science and technology. Particularly, it is an important issue in the processing of sensor information in brain science for processing data such as EEG. The goal is to find a transform (linear or non-linear) which reveals a set of statistically independent components in the measured signals [1].

Most of the blind separation algorithms are based on the theory of the independent component analysis (ICA) [2]. The idea there is to find the independent components from the mixture by optimizing some criteria. Some blind separation algorithms such as those in [3, 4, 5, 6] have the equivariant property when there is no noise in the observation of the mixture. However, the linear ICA theory only holds for the linear mixture model. Hence, blind separation algorithms for the linear mixture model generally fail to extract the independent sources from a non-linear mixture.

The present contribution investigates the perspectives of the self-organizing map (SOM) algorithm [7] in solving the blind separation problem. At first glance SOMs appear to offer a very general approach to the task of separating non-linear mixtures of originally correlated data in the presence of external noise. However, one soon encounters several insufficiencies of the original SOM, which are to be discussed in the following sections. Our goal is to show that preprocessing of the observational data and some recently proposed modifications of SOMs algorithm are suited to overcome problems arising from instabilities in the map formation or systematic inaccuracies and to at least partly meet the above expectations. Extending a recent work by Pajunen, Hyvärinen, and Karhunen [8] we concentrate here on the effect of noise and on the case of less sensors than sources, which is tackled for discrete signals using dimension-increasing maps.

The behavior of SOMs in non-linear problems has been subject of many computational studies. Due to the lack of analytical understanding it is at the moment difficult to make explicit statements about the range of applicability of SOM-based approaches to the blind separation problem. We may grant the model-free nature of SOMs with substantial robustness with respect to deviations from linearity, but numerical experiments as well as implications from the study of strongly simplified problems show also some inherent limitations of the algorithms in some cases.

2   Parametrization of data sets by self-organizing feature maps

Self-organizing maps (SOMs, [7]) comprise a class of vector quantizers that impose a prescribed topological order on the reference vectors. If the network structure is chosen to be equivalent to the topology of the sources, namely if the common Cartesian product of one dimensional spaces is used, then under certain conditions the SOM represents the inverse of the mixing transform by mapping the mixed observation signals onto a regular output grid. Each coordinate of the SOM output will represent one of the sources up to a proportionality constant and in a discretized version. Thus, although being otherwise considered as a disadvantage of SOMs, the fixed network structure is crucial in the present context. The possibility of applying self-organizing maps to blind equalization or blind separation problems has been pointed out earlier [9] and a working example has been given recently [3].

In this section we will clarify the ability of SOMs to blindly separate independent source signals more thoroughly. Later we will present an example that demonstrates perspectives as well as limitations of this method.

Suppose, a data manifold $\mathcal{X}$ is mapped onto a discrete code space $\mathcal{R}$. Here, $\mathcal{X}$ is the observation space and $\mathcal{R}$ reveals the original sources. The assumption that $\mathcal{X}$ and $\mathcal{R}$ are of same dimensionality $n_\mathcal{X} = n_\mathcal{R}$

expresses the fact that the number of sources is known and that each source is to be recovered. The map $\Omega : \mathcal{X} \to \mathcal{R}$ is defined in terms of the reference vectors $\mathbf{w_r} \in \mathcal{X}$. A nearest neighbor rule assigns $\mathbf{x} \in \mathcal{X}$ to $\mathbf{r}^* \in \mathcal{R}$ if the distance $\|\mathbf{x} - \mathbf{w_r}\|$ is minimal for $\mathbf{r} = \mathbf{r}^*$. The formation of the maps is achieved by updating the reference vectors,

$$\Delta \mathbf{w}_{\mathbf{r},i} = \epsilon_{\mathbf{r}^*} h_{\mathbf{rr}^*} (\mathbf{x}_i - \mathbf{w}_{\mathbf{r},i}), \quad i = 1, \ldots, n_{\mathcal{X}} \tag{1}$$

where $\epsilon_{\mathbf{r}^*}$ is a unit-dependend learning rate [10] and $h_{\mathbf{rr}^*}$ is a Gaussian function of the distance $\|\mathbf{r} - \mathbf{r}^*\|$ that imposes the topological structure in $\mathcal{R}$ to the reference vectors $\mathbf{w_r} \in \mathcal{X}$.

If the components of $\mathbf{x}$ are uncorrelated there exists also a stationary configuration $\tilde{\mathbf{w}}_{\mathbf{r}}$ with uncorrelated components $\tilde{\mathbf{w}}_{\mathbf{r},i}$. Whether or not such a solution will be found depends on the initial configuration $\mathbf{w}_{\mathbf{r}}^0$ and on the stability of $\tilde{\mathbf{w}}_{\mathbf{r}}$. Little is know about the general case, but the analysis of idealized models [11, 12] indicates that instabilities will indeed occur, e.g. for elongated rectangular input spaces. Analogous instabilities are to be expected if the data have correlated components.

A further important issue is neighborhood preservation in the map, i.e. nearby vectors $\mathbf{x}^{(1)}$, $\mathbf{x}^{(2)} \in \mathcal{X}$ are mapped to nearby locations $\mathbf{r}^{(1)}$, $\mathbf{r}^{(2)} \in \mathcal{R}$. Neighborhood distortions will result in mixed output of the SOM. Measures for the determination of neighborhood preservation [13] will indicated this and are, moreover, able to determine the number of sources behind a given set of observations.

3 Discrete sources

Since in the SOM-based approach continuous sources are recoverable only in a discretized manner or via interpolation, the main features of the present approach reveal itself already when the sources are restricted to discrete values. In this section the sources are chosen to be binary. Non-binary discrete signals can be treated as well, but if the sources are binary the computational effort remains small and high dimensional problems can be addressed as well. We shall first discuss a trivial example in which capabilities and possible complications are analytically understandable. Thereafter the effect of noise, non-linearities and correlations are addressed.

3.1 A simple example

We consider the case of a linear mixture of two binary sources $s_i \in \{\pm 1\}$. The observations $\mathbf{y} = \mathbf{As}$, where $\mathbf{s} = (s_1, s_2)^T$ and $\mathbf{y} = (y_1, y_2)^T$, serve as inputs $\mathbf{x} \equiv \mathbf{y}$ to a 2-by-2-unit SOM. Ideally, the map should evolve such that each unit $\mathbf{r} = (r_1, r_2)^T$ is activated by one of the four possible combinations of input signals, and that neighboring units code one value of one of the sources, i.e. $r_1 \sim s_{\pi(1)}$ and $r_2 \sim s_{\pi(2)}$, where $\pi(i)$ is a permutation of the indices. The discrete case has the advantage that the SOM formation is guided by an energy function [14].

$$E = -\frac{1}{2} \sum_{\mathbf{x}} \sum_{\mathbf{r}} h_{\mathbf{r},\mathbf{r}^*(\mathbf{x})} (\mathbf{x} - \mathbf{w_r})^2 \tag{2}$$

If for vanishing neighborhood range σ each of the $\mathbf{x}$ is matched exactly by one of the $\mathbf{w}$, there are essentially two possible configurations: an ordered one and a twisted one. From (2) we find that for any non-singular mixing the ordered configuration has lower energy. This also holds in the singular case, namely if a dimension-increasing SOM is trained by only one of the observations. More specifically, the two sources are recoverable if both the mixing matrix $\mathbf{A}$ satisfies $(a_{11}^2 + a_{21}^2)(a_{12}^2 + a_{22}^2) > 0$ and the map is one-to-one. In the singular case, however, a dilemma arises because convergence to a perfectly matching configuration is not always guaranteed. For simplicity assume $a_{11} = \cos(\phi)$, $a_{12} = \sin(\phi)$, $\phi \in (0, \pi/2)$, and $a_{21} = a_{22} = 0$. If σ is sufficiently large, the configuration $\mathbf{w}_{12} = \mathbf{w}_{21} = 0$, and $\mathbf{w}_{11} = \cos(\phi)$, $\mathbf{w}_{22} = -\cos(\phi)$ is stable, but does not match any of the observations $\mathbf{x} = \pm \cos(\phi) \pm \sin(\phi)$. For small ϕ, however, it has an even lower energy than the ideal configuration. If σ is decreased, the algorithm may get stuck in this local minimum, rather than converging to the ideal configuration. We should remark that for small ϕ one of the sources is hardly visible from a single sensor and the other source is still recovered. The latter example is depicted in Fig. 1.

A related type of instability occurs also for non-singular mixing, where also a non-matching state will be stable for large values of σ. For randomly chosen $\mathbf{A}$ the net eventually reaches the ideal configuration in most cases, although this may not happen if $\mathbf{A}$ is ill-conditioned. The occurrence of non-matching final states leads to an elevated average error rate even for zero noise, cf. Fig. 2. These effects are related to the elongation instability described for the continuous case in Ref. [12].

In the singular case (Fig. 1) another problem becomes visible. In the above example the observations are not uniquely related to the sources states if $\phi = \pi/4$, because two $\mathbf{x}$-values coincide, and recovery becomes impossible. In order to quantify this effect we distinguish three cases: none of the sources is recovered (for $\phi \approx \pi/4$), only one source is recovered (for $\phi \approx 0$ or $\phi \approx \pi/2$), or both sources are recovered (remaining ϕ values). Table 1 gives in addition to the relative frequency of these cases among 1000 trials also the analogous values in dimensions three and four for a rotation of the sources projected onto lower dimensional observation spaces. In all cases the rotation matrices[1] where determined from randomly chosen rotation angles.

The above results indicate that a dimensionally increasing map does not produce a separation in many cases. A more promising way to of recovering after information loss opens in the case of autocorrelated sources signals. By the use of time-delay coordinates as auxiliary variables the full dimension of the problem can in principle be recovered from a sensory space of lower dimension if the temporal variations are independent across the sources.

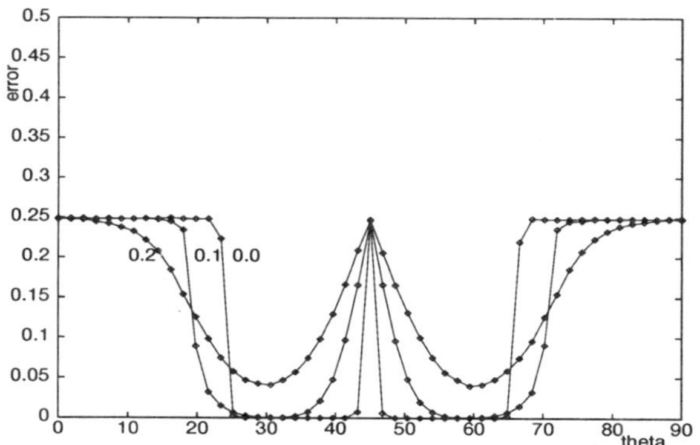

Fig. 1: *Bit error rate after separating two binary sources from a single sensory signal in dependence on the mixing angle θ. Three different noise levels are given ($a_i = 0, 0.1, 0.2$). Low error indicates that the two sources have been separated.*

Fig. 2: *Separation of two binary sources from a (non-)linear mixture with and without whitening of the inputs. The mean bit error rate is displayed as a function of the noise variance. For the chosen non-linearity (cf. 3.2) the non-linear case is easier.*

We have discussed the above example in some detail in order to illustrate the following issues, which are also supported by numerical simulations of higher dimensional problems.

- Generally SOMs are applicable to blind separation.

- Even in the most simple case various problems occur, which among others are present also in more general situations.

- In special cases recovery from singular mixtures of binary signals or separation of more sources than sensors is possible. Conditions are uniqueness and an appropriate positioning of the sensors.

- Some noise in the observation is helpful in order to escape local minima of the learning algorithm.

dimensions		sources recovered (1000 trials)				
sources	sensors	none	1	2	3	4
4	4	0	0	0	0	1000
4	3	0	57	165	476	302
4	2	277	355	228	140	0
4	1	989	10	1	0	0
3	3	0	0	0	1000	
3	2	13	186	412	389	
3	1	702	256	42	0	
2	2	0	0	1000		
2	1	112	295	593	(cf. Fig. 1)	

Table 1: *Recovery of binary signals from a varying number of sensors. The orthogonal mixing matrices were determined by randomly chosen rotation angles. Perfect recovery implies all sources to be identified each time which occurred only for the number of sources and of sensors being equal. The signals were subject to Gaussian noise with standard deviation 0.1. If the dimension of the input space is rather small recovery becomes nearly impossible due to relatively increased noise strengths as well as instabilities in the map formation.*

3.2 Whitening

The results in Table 1 show that perfect recovery is possible if the numbers of sources and sensors are equal and if the mixing is a mere rotation of the source signals. For more general mixing matrices

---

[1] The matrices are assumed to be orthogonal in order to get a convenient parametrization of the possible transformations. Because of the subsequent projection step it does not restrict generality for $n_\mathcal{X} < n_\mathcal{R}$.

(Fig. 2) the elongation instability causes an substantial mean error rate even at zero noise. When adding noise the map escapes more easily from local minima, but the portion of cases with non-unique observational signals increases. Taken together, the twofold effect of noise initially leads to a slight improvement of the performance, whereas later the error rate increases with the noise. Both, the noise-dependent deterioration and the elongation instability are absent in the case that the mixing matrix is well-conditioned. This can be achieved by a whitening transform [2], i.e. the inputs to the SOM, $\mathbf{x}$, are preprocessed from the observation vectors by $\mathbf{x} = \mathbf{V}\mathbf{y}$, where the *whitening* matrix $\mathbf{V}$ is updated via

$$\Delta \mathbf{V} = \epsilon (I - \mathbf{x}\mathbf{x}^T)\mathbf{V}. \tag{3}$$

In this way almost all instable case are avoided and noise tolerance is maintained. The noise enters the mixing transformation as

$$y_i(t) = \sum A_{ij}\left(s_j(t)\right) + \eta_i \tag{4}$$

Fig. 2 gives results again for an binary problem. Additional numerical experiments on problems with up to 16 binary sources showed that a nearly perfect retrieval is possible when the the effect of ill-conditioned mixing matrices is compensated by a whitening transform, and the neighborhood parameter is scaled by a factor of $\sqrt{n_\mathcal{R}}$. The mean bit error rate remained for all dimensions at the same level which is determined only by the noise variance $\langle \eta_i^2 \rangle = a$, $\forall i$. The effect in the continuous case is very similar for a linear mixture. If as in Fig. 2 the sources are non-linearly distorted by applying a hyperbolic tangent after linear mixing, the performance is improved due to a squeezing of the noise. Another type of a non-linear mixture

$$y_i(t) = u_i(t) + \rho \prod_{j \neq i} u_j(t), \quad \text{with} \quad u_i(t) = \sum_j A_{ij} s_j(t) + \eta_i \tag{5}$$

yields similar results.

Thus, in the binary case whitening is in principle sufficient. It produces uncorrelated input data to the SOM, which are of approximately same variance such that rectangle instabilities are prevented. In the n-ary or continuous case, however, whitening is helpful, but not sufficient, cf. below.

3.3 Biased signals

In all of the above for the sources it was assumed $s_i = \pm 1$ independently and with equal probability. For small learning rates the same results can be achieved also for temporally correlated sources. For example, we have chosen each source to be a two-state Markov chain with a transition probability matrix $\begin{pmatrix} 1 - p_i & p_i \\ p_i & 1 - p_i \end{pmatrix}$. In another set of simulations the relative frequency of the discrete values of each out of four sources was biased, i.e. the source signal were given by a two-state Markov chain with a transition probability matrix $\begin{pmatrix} 1 - p_i^- & p_i^- \\ p_i^+ & 1 - p_i^+ \end{pmatrix}$. The sources are temporally uncorrelated if $p_i = p_i^+ = 1 - p_i^-$. The bias is defined as $b_i = |(1 - p_i^-/p_i^+)/(1 + p_i^-/p_i^+)|$ or $b_i = |1 - 2p_i|$, respectively. In order to retain the performance of the algorithm a learning rate control has been adopted to compensate for the unequal probability of the input vectors. This issue concerns the magnification rate of the algorithm. In Kohonen's algorithm the density of the input data $P(\mathbf{x})$ is related to the pointer density $\tilde{P}(\mathbf{w})$ by a power law with exponent $\mu = 2/3$. This result holds generally for the one-dimensional case, but is valid also in higher dimensions if *both* distributions factorize [15]. This condition is satisfied if the maps separates the sources. Hence, the scale of the output of the map is determined by the input distribution. At least in a linear mixture equidistancy within each source can be preserved if $\mu = 0$. According to Ref. [10] such a compensation is achieved if $\epsilon_\mathbf{r} \sim 1/P(\mathbf{x})$ which results in the case of discrete input in a mere monitoring of the winning frequency, i.e. $\epsilon_\mathbf{r} \sim 1/P(\mathbf{r})$. For biasses $b < 1/2$ the performance remained virtually unchanged compared to the unbiased case. This does not happen when constant $\epsilon_\mathbf{r}$ is used. Hence, if the effects the uneven distribution of the observations are removed the separation is not influenced. Generally, it can be expected that for sufficiently small learning rate certain types of correlations among the sources and in time will be averaged out if they are not temporally long-ranged (compared to the inverse of the learning rate) and if the frequency of the inputs is homogeneous or — as by the above mechanism — homogenized. For non-linearly distorted signals the goals of achieving a separating map and a $\mu = 0$ map may, however, interfere. Here, one may affect instead $\mu = 1$ under additional the condition that the sources are evenly (or, in the continuous case, uniformly) distributed.

4 Continuous signals

The treatment of continuous signals is analogous to the discrete case, but a postprocessing stage should be included that interpolates the outputs between the winner and neighboring units. In the case of a linear mixture only two neurons per dimension are necessary for this purpose, whereas non-linearly distorted signals require more base points.

4.1 Interpolation

The main source for errors are systematic deviation of the reference vectors from the optimal parametrization of the observation data. It is, hence, sufficient to apply a component-wise linear interpolation scheme.

$$\tilde{s}_{\pi(i)} = \alpha \mathbf{r}_i^* + (1 - \alpha) \mathbf{r}_i^{(i)}, \tag{6}$$

where

$$\alpha = \frac{\langle (\mathbf{x} - \mathbf{w}_{\mathbf{r}^{(i)}}), (\mathbf{w}_{\mathbf{r}^*} - \mathbf{w}_{\mathbf{r}^{(i)}}) \rangle}{\|\mathbf{w}_{\mathbf{r}^*} - \mathbf{w}_{\mathbf{r}^{(i)}}\|} \tag{7}$$

and $\mathbf{r}^*$ is the index of the best-matching neuron and $\mathbf{r}^{(i)}$ is the index of the second best-matching one among those neurons with a differing component in the direction of the i-th recovered source, i.e. $\mathbf{r}_i^{(i)} \neq \mathbf{r}_i^*$. The effect of the interpolation depends on the size of the discretization error compared to the total error. For whitened linear mixtures interpolation reduces the error to acceptable limits, whereas in the non-linear case the systematic error is predominant. This statement extends to weakly non-linear mixtures, cf. Fig. 4.

4.2 Overdetermined problems

When the numbers of sources $n_{\mathcal{S}} \equiv n_{\mathcal{R}}$ and sensors $n_{\mathcal{X}}$ differ the SOM has a dimensional mismatch between input and output space. Maps of high-dimensional inputs onto a low dimensional output grid, i.e. $n_{\mathcal{X}} > n_{\mathcal{R}}$, are well studied [14]. The topology-induced averaging in the algorithm discards minor components for appropriate neighborhood parameters, such that only those data features that correspond to the sources are represented in the map. In standard blind separation algorithms this problem can be solved by inspecting the eigenvalues of the correlation matrix of the observations. In a SOM-based approach also non-linear principal curves can be extracted [16] such that this problem is solvable also for non-linearly distorted source signal.

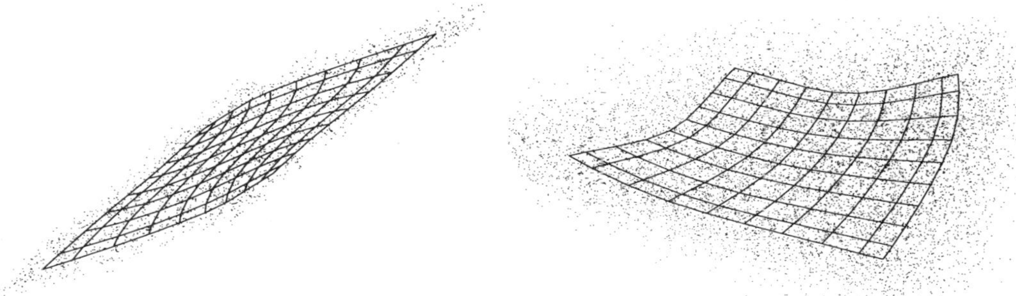

Fig. 3: *Due to correlations in the coordinates of the reference vectors even in linear mixtures of continuous signals systematic errors occur. The curvature in the coordinates of the network can be removed by pre-whitening.*

Fig. 4: *Map evolved in a problem with a quadratic non-linearity. The smoothness of coordinates has been maintained by pre-whitening and large neighborhood range. The outside points are captured by linear extrapolation.*

5 Discussion

The present paper has been devoted to the study of perspectives of the self-organizing maps in the blind separation problem. SOMs provide a non-parametric approach to a certain range of non-linear mixtures, which is algorithmically simple, adaptive and robust. Whereas instabilities and systematic inaccuracies can be prevented in many cases, the computational cost remains the weak point of this approach. This concerns learning times which are generally relatively long and the number of units which increases exponentially with the number of sources. Hence the method is generally restricted to low dimensional problems if an moderate degree of precision in recovery is required. For binary sources this problem is less serious. Thus, here we have concentrated to an analysis of this case in some detail. For this task the SOM-based approach is well-suited. This includes non-linear mixtures, noisy observations and, partially also underdetermined problems. It turned out that small noise added to the input signals stabilized the map formation and, hence, improved the separation abilities.

For continuous sources the present approach can be used as well, although due to several types of instabilities and smooth distortions (cf. Fig. 4) the range of applicability remains limited. Although non-linear problems are expressly treatable little is known about the types and strengths of non-linear distortions which can be reversed [11], such that a reliable statement about applicability can be made only for linear mixtures, but with the addition that the algorithm will be robust with respect to deviations from linearity. Non-linear distortions may be recoverable only if (1) the distortion function is one-to-one, (2) the topological features are preserved in the process of distortion, and (3) the deformation of length scales is rather homogeneous in any direction.

Nevertheless, the SOM-based approach to blind separation is suggestive and deserves, hence, further elaboration. The present contribution leaves many open question, in particular concerning the non-linear continuous case. Further work should be devoted to the task of exploiting the experiences from the discrete case. For example, the linear whitening transform, which has been shown to be useful in ill-conditioned mixtures, needs to be generalized to non-linear problems in order to recover sources from more general non-linear mixtures. Thus, in particular in combination with other algorithms, that could be used as local linear approximations in this way, SOMs may turn out useful tools in future. The presented results at least allow to evaluate a SOM-based algorithms as an alternative to linear algorithms in non-linear problems.

Acknowledgement: The authors wish to thank H.-U. Bauer, R. Der, and J. Karhunen for useful discussions.

References

[1] C. Jutten, J. Herault: Blind Separation of Sources, Part I: An Adaptive algorithm based on Neuromimetic Architecture. *Signal Processing* **24**, 1-10, 1991.

[2] P. Comon: Independent Component Analysis: A new Concept? *Signal Processing* **36**, 287-314 1994.

[3] S. Amari, A. Cichocki and H. H. Yang: A New Learning Algorithm for Blind Signal Separation. To appear in: D. Touretzky, M. Mozer, and M. Hasselmo (eds.) *Advances in Neural Information Processing Systems 8*, MIT Press, Cambridge MA, 1996.

[4] S. Amari, A. Cichocki and H. H. Yang: Recurrent neural networks for blind separation of sources. *NOLTA'95*, 37-42, Las Vegas, December, 1995.

[5] J.-F. Cardoso, B. Laheld: Equivariant Adaptive Source Separation. To appear in: *IEEE Transact. on Signal Processing*, 1996.

[6] A. Cichocki, R. Unbehauen: *Neural Networks for Optimization and Signal Processing*. John Wiley, New York, 1994.

[7] T. Kohonen: *Self-Organizing Maps*. Springer, Berlin, Heidelberg, New York, Springer Series in Information Sciences, Vol. 30, 1995

[8] P. Pajunen, A. Hyvärinen, J. Karhunen: Nonlinear Blind Source Separation by Self-Organizing Maps. Submitted to: *ICONIP*, Hong Kong, Sept. 24-27, 1996.

[9] T. Kohonen, K. Raivio, O. Simula, O. Ventä, and J. Henriksson: Combining Linear Equalization and Self-Organizing Adaptation in Dynamic Discrete-Signal Detection. *Proc. IJCNN*, San Diego, California, June 17-21, 1996, I-223-228.

[10] H.-U. Bauer, R. Der, M. Herrmann: Controlling the Magnification Factor of Self-Organizing Feature Maps. To appear in *Neural Computation*, 1996.

[11] M. Cottrell, J. C. Fort, G. Pagès: Two or three things that we know about the Kohonen algorithm. *Proc. ESANN'94*, 1994. The original paper cited there as Ref. 11, is: J.C. Fort, G. Pagès: Sur la convergence *p. s.* de l'algorithme de Kohonen généralisé. *Note aux Comptes Rendus de l'Académie des Sciences de Paris*, t. 317, Série I, 389-394, 1993.

[12] G. A. van Velzen: Instabilities in Kohonen's Self-Organizing Feature Map. *J. Phys. A: Math. Gen.* **27**, 1665-1681, 1994.

[13] T. Villmann, R. Der, M. Herrmann, T. Martinetz Topology Preservation in SOFMs: Exact Definition and Measurement. To appear in *IEEE Transact. on Neural Networks*, 1996.

[14] H. Ritter, K. Schulten, T. Martinetz: *Neural Computation and Self-Organizing Maps*. Addison-Wesley, Reading, Mass., 1992.

[15] H. Ritter, K. Schulten: On the Stationary State of Kohonen's Self-Organizing Sensory Mapping. *Biol. Cybern.* **54**, 99-106, 1986.

[16] M. Herrmann: Self-Organizing Feature Maps with Self-Organizing Neighborhood Widths. *Proc. ICNN'95, Perth, Australia*, 27 Nov - 1 Dec, 1995. p. 2998-3003.

Blind Signal Processing: Adaptive Blind Equalization Using Artificial Neural Networks

Chiu Fai Wong
School of Electrical Engineering
Rhodes 326 Cornell University
Ithaca, NY 14853
wongcf@ee.cornell.edu

Terrence L. Fine
School of Electrical Engineering
Rhodes 388 Cornell University
Ithaca, NY 14853
tlfine@ee.cornell.edu

Abstract

We attempt to use a neural network to solve the channel blind equalization problem. An equalizer is a device which by observing the channel outputs recovers the channel inputs. A blind equalizer does not require any known training sequence for the startup period. We have implemented a blind equalizer using a neural network for channel inputs of $\{-1, 1\}$. The key to our approach is a three-component error/loss function which controls the hidden layer node output, the final network output and the output layer weight parameters. The neural network is trained using a scaled conjugate gradient method which is faster than the steepest descent algorithms and is free from user-defined parameters. Our method is robust. It makes no assumption about the channel input distribution or channel frequency response and needs fewer taps than conventional blind equalizers. Compared to the popular CMA blind equalizers, our network achieves a significantly lower BER but takes longer to train.

1 Introduction

Signals transmitted through high rate digital communication channels suffer from intersymbol interference (ISI). Noise may also corrupt the signals. Figure 1 shows a typical data transmission system. A random sequence $\{x_i\}$ (where $x_i \in \{-1, +1\}$) is passed through the channel and produces a sequence of outputs $\{y_i\}$. The problem is to produce an estimate $\tilde{x}_{i-d} \approx x_{i-d}$ (or $\tilde{x}_{i-d} \approx -x_{i-d}$) given the observed channel outputs $\{y_i, y_{i-1}, \ldots, y_{i-tap+1}\}$. Therefore the purpose of a channel equalizer is to combat ISI and recover the original channel outputs.

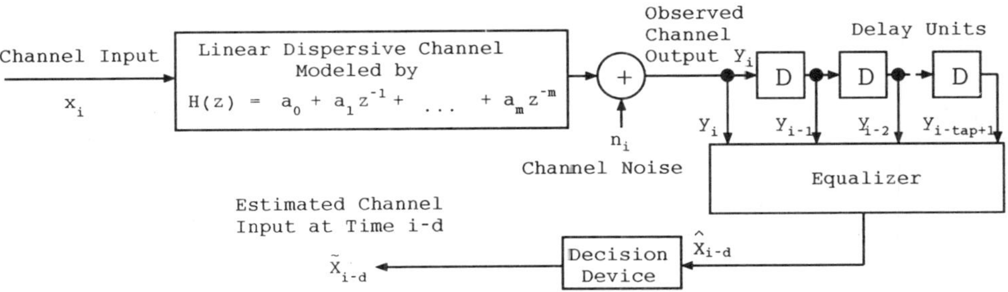

Figure 1: A Typical Data Transmission System

Conventional equalizers used in digital communication systems require an initial training period during which a known data sequence is transmitted to be used in calibrating the equalizer. Equalizers for which such an initial training data sequence is not needed during the training period are referred to as blind equalizers. The problem of blind equalization arises from the need to recover on-line the original input signal to an unknown channel based merely on the observation of the observed channel outputs and the knowledge of the channel input signal characteristics.

There are three main blind equalization techniques: the Bussgang algorithms, a polyspectra technique which utilizes the second and higher order statistics of the channel outputs to derive the amplitude and the phase spectra of the channel response and some probabilistic algorithms [9]. Linear equalizers trained with LMS type algorithms are simple to implement. However, performance degrades rapidly with channels having deep nulls and with non-minimum phase channels. A large number of taps is needed for the equalizer which consequently increases the training time because convergence is slow. Zhi Ding in [2] and Zhi Ding et al. in [1] have proved that the Bussgang algorithms in practice do not converge globally. The algorithms can be trapped in local minima and fail to remove the ISI. The polyspectra technique lacks robustness due to an inability to produce an accurate approximation of the ensemble statistics. Both the polyspectra technique and the probabilistic methods are computationally intensive.

Neural network approaches to blind equalization are discussed in Karaoğuz et al. [4],Kohonen [5], Lee and Pearson [6]. Peng et al. in [8] argued that the performance of self-organizing maps as blind equalizers was not good enough to solve the channel equalization problem especially when the ISI was large.

In this paper, we present a new approach to solve the channel blind equalization problem using an artificial neural network structure. We have compared our blind equalizer to the popular CMA equalizer and found out that our equalizer achieves a much lower BER (bit error rate) than the CMA equalizers especially for channels with severe ISI. However, the CMA equalizers can be trained faster.

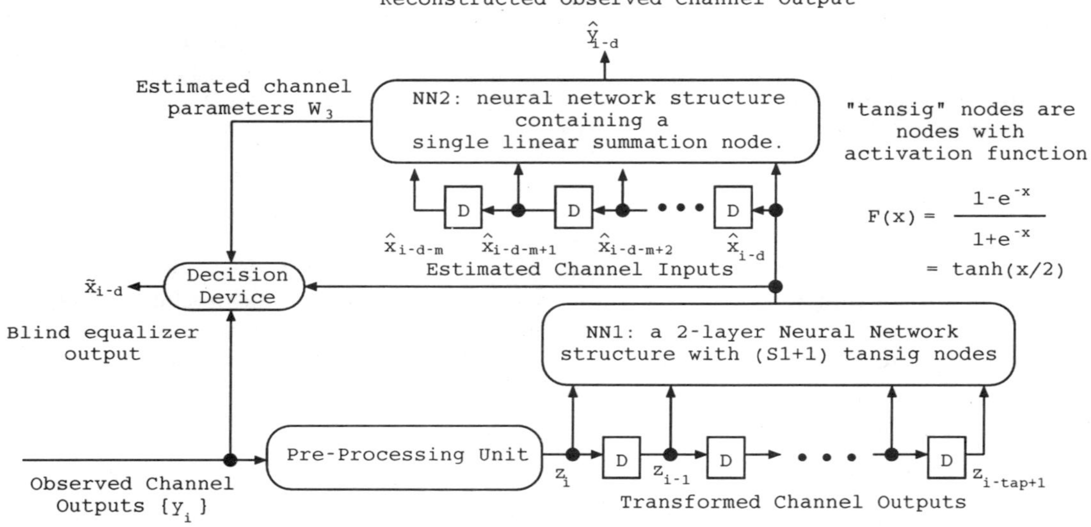

Figure 2: Neural Network Blind Equalizer (NNBE) for an mth-Order Moving Average Channel

2   A Neural Network Approach

2.1   Network Architecture for an m-th Order Channel

Figure 2 shows a neural network structure designed for an m-th order moving average channel with transfer function $\mathcal{H}(z)$ as

$$\mathcal{H}(z) = a_0 + a_1 z^{-1} + a_2 z^{-2} + \ldots + a_m z^{-m} \tag{1}$$

where $a_0, a_1, a_2, ..., a_m$ are the channel parameters. The channel input/output relationship can be described as

$$y_i = a_0 x_i + a_1 x_{i-1} + a_2 x_{i-2} + \ldots + a_m x_{i-m} \tag{2}$$

where x_i is the channel input and y_i is the channel output. The network consists of three main parts: the pre-processing unit, two cascaded neural network structures (NN 1 and NN 2) and the decoding units which include the sign operator and the decoder.

2.1.1   The Pre-processing Unit

For channels with severe ISI, the network has to learn that channel outputs that are close together are produced by different channel inputs. This increases the training time. An advantage of a nonlinear neural network approach is that we can first pass the channel outputs through a quantizer. A compander then transforms the quantized channel outputs so that they are uniformly spaced. This pre-processing materially assists the neural network convergence and reduces the training time. It is speculated that provided the channel outputs are quantized correctly (i.e. channel outputs from exactly the same channel inputs are quantized into the same level), the transformation helps the network to recognize channel outputs produced by different channel inputs by separating those channel outputs that are close together. Such an option is not available to the usual linear filter based blind equalizer.

2.1.2   The Neural Network Structures

Observe that from Figure 2, the network can be described mathematically by

$$\hat{x}_{i-d} = tansig\left(\mathbf{W_2}\left(tansig\left(\mathbf{W_1}\vec{Z}\right)\right)\right), \quad \hat{y}_{i-d} = W_{3:m+1}\hat{x}_{i-d} + W_{3:m}\hat{x}_{i-d-1} + \ldots + W_{3:1}\hat{x}_{i-d-m}. \tag{3}$$

$\mathbf{W_i}$ is the weight parameter matrix, $\vec{Z}$ is the vector representing the transformed channel outputs $\{z_{i-tap+1}, \ldots, z_{i-1}, z_i\}$ and "*tansig*" is a Matlab term for the matrix form of hyperbolic tangent. $S1$ is the number of nodes used in the first layer of NN 1 and *tap* is the number of inputs of NN 1. $S1$ is chosen so that the network is complicated enough to solve the blind equalization problem but not enough to allow over-fitting of the training data. *tap* is set to be $m+1$ because the network only needs to be fed with channel outputs $\{y_{i-d}, y_{i-d+1}, \ldots, y_{i-d+m}\}$ to estimate the channel input x_{i-d}. Other channel outputs are not produced with x_{i-d} in the channel input sequence and therefore do not contain information on x_{i-d}. In the linear approach, the number of inputs to the filter is chosen to be 3 or 4 times the channel order. It is obvious that our approach needs fewer inputs than the linear approach.

To summarize, neural network structure NN 1 is used to produce an estimate of the actual channel input x_{i-d} or $-x_{i-d}$ as $\hat{x}_{i-d}$; NN 2 is used to estimate the channel parameters through the construction of $\hat{y}_{i-d}$ which is an estimate of the actual channel output y_{i-d} from the estimated channel inputs $\{\hat{x}_{i-d-m}, \ldots, \hat{x}_{i-d-1}, \hat{x}_{i-d}\}$. Comparing equation (3) and equation (2), NN 2 imitates a transmission channel with channel parameters as elements of the weight vector $\mathbf{W_3}$.

2.1.3   The Decision/Decoding Units : the Sign Operator and the Decoder

The decoded channel inputs $\{\tilde{x}_{i-d}\}$ can be derived from two sources: the sign operator together with neural network NN 1 for channels with an signal to noise ratio (SNR) lower than 30dB or the decoder if the channel SNR is 30dB or higher. The sign operator basically decodes the channel inputs in the following manner:

$$\tilde{x}_{i-d} = \text{sign}(\hat{x}_{i-d}) = \text{sign}\left(tansig\left(\mathbf{W_2}\left(tansig\left(\mathbf{W_1}\vec{z}\right)\right)\right)\right) = \begin{cases} 1 & \text{if } \hat{x}_{i-d} > 0, \\ -1 & \text{otherwise.} \end{cases}$$

The decoder, given $\mathbf{W_3} = \{W_{3:1}, W_{3:2}, \ldots, W_{3:m+1}\}$ and $\{y_i\}$, needs to be initialized by first decoding a short length of channel inputs $\tilde{x}_{-m}, \ldots, \tilde{x}_{n-1}, \tilde{x}_n$ such that $\sum_{j=1}^{n}(y_j - y_j')^2$ is minimized where

$$y_i' = W_{3:m+1}\tilde{x}_i + W_{3:m}\tilde{x}_{i-1} + \ldots + W_{3:1}\tilde{x}_{i-m}. \tag{4}$$

After the best sequence of $\tilde{x}_{-m}, \ldots, \tilde{x}_{n-1}, \tilde{x}_n$ has been chosen, from equation (4), the channel inputs are decoded as

$$\tilde{x}_i = \text{sign}\left(\frac{y_i - (W_{3:m}\tilde{x}_{i-1} + W_{3:m-1}\tilde{x}_{i-2} + \ldots + W_{3:1}\tilde{x}_{i-m})}{W_{3:m-1}}\right). \tag{5}$$

assuming the previous channel inputs have been decoded correctly. Observe that from (5), if $\tilde{x}_i$ is decoded wrong, this error will propagate like a snowball effect. To ensure good performance, the decoder needs to be initialized from time to time.

The network can operate in two modes: the adaptive/training mode and the decoding mode. The adaptive/training mode is used when the network needs to capture the channel characteristics or to follow a time-varying channel. The network is continuously being trained and the training set is continuously being replaced with new channel outputs which reflect the current state of the channel characteristics. $\mathbf{W_1}, \mathbf{W_2}$ and $\mathbf{W_3}$ are continuously being updated in NN 1 and NN 2 and sent to the decoding units. The decoding mode is on when the network has captured the channel characteristics and adaptation is no longer needed (assuming the channel is not time-varying), training is turned off and only the decoding units are on.

2.2   The Error Function ε

The neural network blind equalizer performs three estimations: channel inputs as $\{\hat{x}_i\}$, channel outputs as $\{\hat{y}_i\}$ and the actual channel parameters as elements of the weight vector $\mathbf{W3}$. In a departure from normal neural network design, three error measures are introduced to ensure good approximations in each of these estimates.

Error function ε_1 measures the discrepancies between the estimated channel input $\hat{x}_i$ and the actual channel input x_i when all that is known about the channel input signal is that its magnitude is 1. ε_2 is designed to approximate the channel parameters by forcing a good approximation to the observed channel outputs. Hence ε_1, ε_2 are defined as

$$\varepsilon_1 = \frac{1}{4}\alpha \sum_{i=1}^{n}(\hat{x}_i^2 - 1)^2, \qquad \varepsilon_2 = \frac{1}{2}\sum_{i=1}^{n}(\hat{y}_i - y_i)^2$$

where n is the size of the training set and α is a constant used to scale ε_1.

Assuming that the channel inputs are uncorrelated and wide sense stationary (WSS), noting that $\mathrm{E}(x_i) = 0$ and $\mathrm{E}(x_i^2) = 1$ yields

$$\mathrm{E}(y_i y_{i+p}) = \mathrm{E}\left(\left(\sum_{j=0}^{m} a_j x_{i-j}\right)\left(\sum_{k=0}^{m} a_k x_{i+p-k}\right)\right) = \sum_{j=0}^{m-p} a_j a_{j+p} \mathrm{E}\left(x_{i-j}^2\right) = \sum_{j=0}^{m-p} a_j a_{j+p}. \tag{6}$$

Here, we are trying to force $\{W_{3:m+1}, W_{3:m}, \ldots, W_{3:1}\} \approx \{a_0, a_1, \ldots, a_m\}$. Using an approximation to (6) based on estimating this correlation, ε_3 is defined as

$$\varepsilon_3 = \frac{1}{2}\sum_{p=0}^{m}\left(\left(\frac{1}{n}\sum_{i=1}^{n} y_i y_{i+p}\right) - \left(\sum_{j=0}^{m-p} W_{3:m+1-j} W_{3:m+1-j-p}\right)\right)^2 .$$

From simulation, it is observed that ε_3 is orders of magnitude smaller than ε_2. Therefore, the error function ε is defined as

$$\varepsilon = \varepsilon_1 + \varepsilon_2 + \beta \varepsilon_3$$

where β is a scaling factor choosen according to [3]. For networks with correlated channel inputs, set $\beta = 0$ and use a two-component error function. In both cases, ε_1 can be made trivially small by setting $\mathbf{W_1}, \mathbf{W_2}$ large and saturating the nodes. However, ε_2 can be made trivially small only if W_1, W_2 are small and the cascade of NN1 and NN2 forms an identity mapping network. Hence, joint optimization can only be achieved by a solution to the channel equalization problem.

A scaled conjugate gradient algorithm described in [7] is used. This scaled conjugate gradient method replaces a line search for α_k by a trust region method which is free from user defined parameters. Convergence is very fast compared to the steepest descent type algorithms and even other conjugate gradient methods.

3 Simulation Results

Programs written in Matlab were run on HP700 machines to simulate the actual process of blind equalization. A 4-th order channel with transfer function $\mathcal{H}(Z) = 0.227 + 0.46z^{-1} + 0.688z^{-2} + 0.46z^{-3} + 0.227z^{-4}$ is used. This is a reputedly difficult channel because it has deep channel nulls and therefore introduces severe ISI. Two sets of simulation results are displayed. The first set shows the performance of our NNBE for channel SNR ranging from noiseless to 10dB. The second set of simulations is a comparison of our NNBE with the CMA blind equalizer.

Table 1: Simulation Results with the Three-Part Error Function					
channel SNR	Noiseless	40dB	30dB	20dB	10dB
average bit error rate (BER)	0	0.02%	2.13%	8.1%	17.5%
% of success with 0 BER	82	51	42	0	0
% of success over all simulations	82	64	63	65	58

Table 2: Simulation Results with the Two-Part Error Function					
channel SNR	Noiseless	40dB	30dB	20dB	10dB
average bit error rate (BER)	0	0	1.5%	8.3%	17.1%
% of success with 0 BER	67	52	28	0	0
% of success over all simulations	67	52	41	30	31

Table 1 and Table 2 show that the network performs much better using the three-component error function because it provides more information about the channel to the network than the two-component error function. At high SNR, the network is able to approximate the channel parameters accurately and achieves a 0 BER. Performance degrades with lower SNR. As is the case with the Bussgang algorithms, our algorithm does not converge all the time. However, if we have 10 networks running simultaneously, the chance of at least one network converging is $1 - 0.7^{10} = 0.972$ for the worst SNR. Since the network is very simple, the cost of having 10 such networks should be small.

The CMA blind equalizer described in [10] is compared with our NNBE. Fixing the training set or the training time, we compared the BER and speed of both equalizers.

Table 3: Comparing the blind equalizers with the same training set					
Equalizer	channel SNR	No Noise	40dB	30dB	20dB
NN	range of training time (s)	40 - 161	152 - 167	271 - 320	320 -343
	average BER from LMS Decoder	0	0	0	-
	average BER from Sign Decoder	0	-	-	0.002
CMA	training time (s)	3	3	3	3
	Minimum BER	0.0955	0.0905	0.091	0.1

Table 4: Comparing the blind equalizers with fixed training time					
Equalizer	channel SNR	No Noise	40dB	30dB	20dB
NN	average BER from LMS Decoder	0	0	0	-
	average BER from Sign Decoder	0	-	-	0.002
CMA	Minimum BER	0.09	0.086	0.0805	0.0905

Giving the CMA blind equalizers the same training time and more training data, our NN blind equalizer still achieves significantly lower BER.

4 Conclusion

Our blind equalizer is robust: the network performance is not strongly affected by the channel frequency response and we have solved the blind equalization problem for some non-minimum phase channels and channels with deep nulls. Furthermore, our approach can be used with correlated channel inputs as well.

When compared with the CMA blind equalizers, our blind equalizer is slower to train. However, it can achieve a very low BER using a much smaller amount of channel outputs. Besides, using fewer taps, it can decode the channel inputs much faster than the CMA blind equalizers. For channels with severe ISI, our neural network blind equalizer can be considered as an alternative choice.

References

[1] Zhi Ding. *Application Aspects of Blind Adaptive Equalizers in QAM Data Communications.* PhD thesis, Cornell University, 1990.

[2] Zhi Ding and C. Richard Johnson Jr. Existing gap between theory and application of blind equalization. *Proceedings of the SPIE*, 1565:154–65, 1991.

[3] J. E. Dennis Jr and Robert B. Schnabel. *Numerical Methods for Unconstrained Optimization and Nonlinear Equations.* Prentice-Hall series in Computational Mathematics, 1977.

[4] Jeyhan Karaogŭz and Sasan H. Ardalan. Blind adaptive channel equalization using the unsupervised cluster formation technique. *IEEE International Symposium on Circuits and Systems*, 3:223–228, 1992.

[5] Teuvo Kohonen, Kimmo Raivio, Olli Simula, Olli Venta and Jukka. Combining linear equalization and self-organizing adaptation in dynamic discrete-signal detection. *IJCNN International Joint Conference on Neural Networks*, 1:223–228, 1990.

[6] W-T. Lee and J. Pearson. A hybrid linear/nonlinear approach to channel equalization problem. *Advances in Neural Information Processing Systems 5*, 5:674–681, 1993.

[7] Martin Fodslette Moller. A scaled conjugate gradient algorithm for fast supervised learning. *Neural Networks*, 6:523–533, 1993.

[8] Marcia Peng, C. L. Nikias and John G. Proakis. Adaptive equalization for pam and qam signals with neural network. *25th Asilomar Conference on Signal, Systems and Computers*, November 1991.

[9] John G. Proakis and Chrysostomos L. Nikias. Blind equalization. *Proceedings of the SPIE*, 1565:76–87, 1991.

[10] John R. Treichler and Brian G. Agee. A New Approach to Multipath Correction of Constant Modulus Signals. *IEEE Trans. on Acoustics, Speech, and Signal Processing*, ASSP-31, NO. 2, April, 1983.

A Technique for
Higher-Order-Only Blind Source Separation*

Lieven De Lathauwer, Bart De Moor, Joos Vandewalle
K.U.Leuven - E.E. Dept.- ESAT - SISTA
Kard. Mercierlaan 94, B-3001 Leuven (Heverlee), Belgium
tel: 32/16/321085   fax: 32/16/321986
email: Lieven.DeLathauwer@esat.kuleuven.ac.be

Abstract— **We present a technique for Blind Source Separation that resorts only to the higher-order statistics of the data. In this way the algorithm is asymptotically insensitive to the effects of additive Gaussian noise. The identification of the transfer matrix is expressed as a simultaneous congruence transformation. By reformulating the problem as a simultaneous generalized Schur decomposition we restrict the unknowns to the set of orthogonal matrices. The solution can be obtained by Givens iteration, but this paper focuses on an alternative method based on bigradient optimization. This technique can be interpreted as a neural network method, in which the basic learning rule is Hebbian. Adaptivity is obtained by exponential data weighting. Cumulant matching takes the form of an extra least-squares descent algorithm.**

1 Introduction

Denote the basic statistical model for *Blind Source Separation*, or *Independent Component Analysis* (ICA), as:

$$Y = \mathbf{M}X + N \tag{1}$$

in which the observed vector Y, the source vector X and the noise vector N are zero-mean random vectors with values in $\mathbb{R}$ or $\mathbb{C}$. The components of X are mutually statistically independent, as well as statistically independent from the noise components. The goal of ICA now consists of the estimation of the transfer matrix $\mathbf{M}$ and the corresponding realizations of X, given only realizations of Y.

Blind source separation is a very fundamental problem, with a large application area. The classical example is blind Space Division Multiple Access (SDMA) in the context of wireless communications, where one aims at the separation of messages (same time slot - same frequency bin) from different users at different locations, by using an array of antennas, even if this array is badly calibrated. Indeed, if the source signals are narrow-band, then the complex envelope representation of the transmission takes precisely the form of Eq. (1) (the components of X are the source signals and the components of Y are the signals captured by the antenna array) [13]. The same separation model arises in a very natural way in seismic prospection, psychometrics, astronomy, vibro-acoustics, biomedical signal processing, etc. - see e.g. [5, 12].

Without a priori knowledge the ICA-problem cannot be solved using only second-order statistics. Usually the second-order statistics of the observation vector Y are used for a whitening of the data. In this way the transfer matrix can be estimated up to an orthogonal factor $\mathbf{U}$. In the second step $\mathbf{U}$ is then obtained from higher-order cumulants of the standardized data. Several algorithms have been presented in literature. Among the most well-known algebraic approaches are the one by Comon [4] (further analyzed in [7]), where $\mathbf{U}$ is computed by a Jacobi-type diagonalization of the standardized cumulant tensor, and the one by Cardoso [2], where $\mathbf{U}$ is found as the solution of a simultaneous eigenvalue decomposition. Solutions based on artificial neural networks (ANN) are discussed in e.g. [3].

In our paper the problem is solved using *only* the *higher-order* cumulant. This approach has the advantage that it is conceptually blind for the noise term N, when this term is Gaussian. For simplicity of notation, the exposition in this summary is restricted to fourth-order processing of real-valued data. The technique can be applied to cumulants of any order (higher than 2), as well as to complex data.

*This research was partially supported by the Belgian Program on Interuniversity Attraction Poles (IUAP-17, IUAP-50), the European Community Research program ESPRIT, Basic Research Working Group nr. 6620 (ATHOS) and the Flemish Institute for Support of Scientific-Technological Research in Industry (I.W.T.) Lieven De Lathauwer is a Research Assistant supported by the I.W.T. Bart De Moor is a Research Associate of the National fund for Scientific Research (N.F.W.O.)

The paper is organized as follows. In the next section the relation between the columns of $\mathbf{M}$ and the fourth order observation cumulant is explicited. This relation takes the form of a tensorial decomposition of the cumulant in a sum of tetrads, and the uniqueness of this decomposition is discussed. In Section 3 the estimation of the transfer matrix from the cumulant model is presented as a simultaneous congruence transformation. In Section 4 the problem is reformulated as a simultaneous generalized Schur decomposition, for which we derive a bigradient optimization computation scheme. Section 5 discusses the issue of adaptivity, which is realized by means of an exponential forgetting function. In Section 6 the algorithm is interpreted as a neural network method. In Section 7 it is explained how the solution can be used for cumulant matching. Section 8 contains a concluding discussion.

2   A Decomposition in Tetrads

2.1   Model

When the noise N is Gaussian, it does not contribute to the fourth-order cumulant of Y. This cumulant, denoted by $\mathcal{C}^{(4)}$, has a very typical structure:

$$c^{(4)}_{ijkl} = \sum_{s}^{S} \kappa_s\, m_{is} m_{js} m_{ks} m_{ls} \tag{2}$$

where κ_s denotes the fourth-order cumulant of the sth source ($1 \leqslant s \leqslant S$). In tensorial terminology each term corresponds to a fourth-order rank-1 tensor, or tetrad, equal to the outer product of four times the same column of $\mathbf{M}$. (These columns will further be symbolized by M_s ($1 \leqslant s \leqslant S$) and denoted as "steering vectors"). The contribution of a non-Gaussian noise component, and the effect of other estimation errors when $\mathcal{C}^{(4)}$ is a finite sample cumulant, is considered as a perturbation of Eq. (2).

2.2   Uniqueness

For notational convenience we assume that the transfer matrix is square and regular, and that all the sources have non-vanishing kurtosis. It can be proved [6] that these conditions are sufficient to guarantee that decomposition (2) is unique up to the following trivial indeterminacies:

- permutation of the terms
- scaling of the steering vectors with a factor α_s, combined with inverse scaling (factor α_s^{-4}) of the coefficients κ_s.

Note that different sources can have the same probability distribution, as long as they are mutually statistically independent. The conditions can be weakened for the identification of at most one non-kurtic source. It is also possible to handle the "more-sensors-than-sources" case.

3   Simultaneous Congruence Transformation

We associate to $\mathcal{C}^{(4)}$ a linear matrix transformation in the following way:

$$\mathbf{B} = \mathcal{C}^{(4)}(\mathbf{A}) \quad \Longleftrightarrow \quad b_{ij} = \sum_{kl} c_{ijkl} a_{kl} \tag{3}$$

for all index values. From Eq. (2) follows that every matrix in the range space of $\mathcal{C}^{(4)}$ can be written as a linear combination of the "steering matrices" $M_s M_s^T$ ($1 \leqslant s \leqslant S$). In other words, the transfer matrix $\mathbf{M}$ diagonalizes every matrix in the range space of $\mathcal{C}^{(4)}$ by congruence transformation. Assume that the range space is spanned by $\mathbf{T}_1, \mathbf{T}_2, \ldots, \mathbf{T_P}$ ($P \geqslant S$), then we have the following *simultaneous congruence transformation*:

$$\begin{aligned}
\mathbf{T}_1 &= \mathbf{M} \cdot \mathbf{D}_1 \cdot \mathbf{M}^T \\
\mathbf{T}_2 &= \mathbf{M} \cdot \mathbf{D}_2 \cdot \mathbf{M}^T \\
&\;\;\vdots \\
\mathbf{T_P} &= \mathbf{M} \cdot \mathbf{D_P} \cdot \mathbf{M}^T
\end{aligned} \tag{4}$$

where $\mathbf{D}_1, \mathbf{D}_2, \ldots, \mathbf{D_P}$ are diagonal. This set of equations is the higher-order-only equivalent of the *simultaneous eigenvalue decomposition* on which the ICA-algorithm by Cardoso and Souloumiac is based [2].

In the latter algorithm pre-whitening leads to a simultaneous matrix decomposition from which an orthogonal matrix has to be computed; in the current approach a general regular matrix has to be determined (up to the indeterminacies mentioned in Section 2.2), corresponding to the fact that there is no pre-whitening.

4 Simultaneous Generalized Schur Decomposition

4.1 Principle

Theoretically the transfer matrix can be computed from 2 of the equations in (4). E.g. if we can assume that $\mathbf{D_2}$ does not contain any zero elements on the diagonal, then combination of the first two equations leads to the following eigenvalue decomposition:

$$\mathbf{T_1} \cdot \mathbf{T_2}^{-1} = \mathbf{M} \cdot \mathbf{D_1} \cdot \mathbf{D_2}^{-1} \cdot \mathbf{M}^{-1} \tag{5}$$

Intuitively however, it is clear that it is preferable to solve (4) simultaneously, in order to exploit all the available information. This can be substantiated by numerical arguments [9].

The fact that the unknown transfer matrix is basically an arbitrary regular matrix, makes it hard to deal with in a proper numerical way. We reformulate the problem in terms of orthogonal unknowns by introducing a QR-factorisation $\mathbf{M} = \mathbf{Q}^T \mathbf{R}'$ and an RQ-decomposition $\mathbf{M}^T = \mathbf{R}'' \mathbf{Z}^T$, which leads to a set of matrix equations that we will denote as a *simultaneous generalized Schur decomposition* (a set of two of the equations below is called "generalized Schur decomposition" in [11]):

$$
\begin{aligned}
\mathbf{Q} \cdot \mathbf{T_1} \cdot \mathbf{Z} &= \mathbf{R_1} = \mathbf{R}' \cdot \mathbf{D_1} \cdot \mathbf{R}'' \\
\mathbf{Q} \cdot \mathbf{T_2} \cdot \mathbf{Z} &= \mathbf{R_2} = \mathbf{R}' \cdot \mathbf{D_2} \cdot \mathbf{R}'' \\
&\vdots \\
\mathbf{Q} \cdot \mathbf{T_P} \cdot \mathbf{Z} &= \mathbf{R_P} = \mathbf{R}' \cdot \mathbf{D_P} \cdot \mathbf{R}''
\end{aligned} \tag{6}
$$

(The same trick can be found in [14], for the separation of constant-modulus signals.) From these equations the orthogonal matrices $\mathbf{Q}$ and $\mathbf{Z}$ have to be determined such that $\mathbf{R_1}, \mathbf{R_2}, \ldots, \mathbf{R_P}$ are "as upper triangular as possible" (in least-squares sense). The criterion function f to be maximized can be written as:

$$f(\mathbf{Q}, \mathbf{Z}) = \|\mathrm{upp}(\mathbf{Q} \cdot \mathbf{T_1} \cdot \mathbf{Z})\|_F^2 + \ldots + \|\mathrm{upp}(\mathbf{Q} \cdot \mathbf{T_P} \cdot \mathbf{Z})\|_F^2 \tag{7}$$

in which $\|\mathbf{A}\|_F$ denotes the Frobenius-norm and $\mathrm{upp}(\mathbf{A})$ the upper triangular part of $\mathbf{A}$.

In the next section we will explain how the optimization can be realized, and in Section 4.3 we will describe how $\mathbf{M}$ can be derived, once $\mathbf{Q}$ and $\mathbf{Z}$ have been found.

4.2 Solution by bigradient optimization

The core of our method is the computation of $\mathbf{Q}$ and $\mathbf{Z}$ from Eq. (6). The maximization of the criterion function f with respect to $\mathbf{Q}$ and $\mathbf{Z}$, and the adaptive tracking of the solution (Section 5), can take various forms. In the companion paper [8] the solution is based on an iteration technique, in which $\mathbf{Q}$ and $\mathbf{Z}$ are determined as a sequence of elementary Givens rotations. Each elementary rotation makes the set $\mathbf{R_1}, \mathbf{R_2}, \ldots, \mathbf{R_P}$ simultaneously as upper triangular as possible. For a continuous-time formulation of the problem a gradient flow is considered in [9]. Here we will present a bigradient optimization algorithm [15], which is more suitable for interpretation in terms of ANN's.

At each iteration step n a small correction term, in the direction of steepest ascent of f, is added to $\mathbf{Q}(t)$ and $\mathbf{Z}(t)$. This correction term does not take into account that $\mathbf{Q}(t)$ and $\mathbf{Z}(t)$ are orthogonal matrices; orthogonality is realized by simultaneous minimization of the criterion:

$$g(\mathbf{Q}, \mathbf{Z}) = 1/2 \, \|\mathbf{I} - \mathbf{Q}^T \mathbf{Q}\|_F^2 + 1/2 \, \|\mathbf{I} - \mathbf{Z}^T \mathbf{Z}\|_F^2 \tag{8}$$

in which $\mathbf{I}$ is the identity matrix. The updating rule then takes the form:

$$
\begin{aligned}
\mathbf{Q}(t+1) &= \mathbf{Q}(t) + \mu \nabla_{\mathbf{Q}(t)} f - \gamma \nabla_{\mathbf{Q}(t)} g \tag{9} \\
\mathbf{Z}(t+1) &= \mathbf{Z}(t) + \mu \nabla_{\mathbf{Z}(t)} f - \gamma \nabla_{\mathbf{Z}(t)} g \tag{10}
\end{aligned}
$$

in which μ is a small and γ a relatively large $(0.5 \ldots 1)$ gain parameter, and in which the gradients are given by:

$$\nabla_{\mathbf{Q}} f = 2 \sum_p \mathbf{M}_p \cdot \mathbf{Z} \cdot (\mathrm{upp}(\mathbf{R}_p))^T \qquad \nabla_{\mathbf{Z}} f = 2 \sum_p \mathbf{M}_p^T \cdot \mathbf{Q} \cdot \mathrm{upp}(\mathbf{R}_p) \tag{11}$$

$$\nabla_{\mathbf{Q}} g = -\mathbf{Q} \cdot (\mathbf{I} - \mathbf{Q}^T \mathbf{Q}) \qquad \nabla_{\mathbf{Z}} g = -\mathbf{Z} \cdot (\mathbf{I} - \mathbf{Z}^T \mathbf{Z}) \tag{12}$$

4.3 Reconstruction of the transfer matrix

It is not hard to show that the pair $(\mathbf{Q}, \mathbf{Z})$ is actually an alternative representation of the transfer matrix itself. From the definition of $\mathbf{Q}$ and $\mathbf{Z}$ we have:

$$(\mathbf{Q} \cdot \mathbf{Z}) \cdot \mathbf{R}''^T = \mathbf{R}' \tag{13}$$

The orthogonal matrix $\mathbf{Q} \cdot \mathbf{Z}$ will be denoted as $\mathbf{V}$. The lower triangular part of Eq. (13) is a system of linear equations in the unknown coefficients of $\mathbf{R}''$:

$$\begin{bmatrix} v_{P,P-1} & v_{PP} \end{bmatrix} \begin{bmatrix} r''_{P-1,P-1} \\ r''_{P-1,P} \end{bmatrix} = 0$$

$$\begin{bmatrix} v_{P-1,P-2} & v_{P-1,P-1} & v_{P-1,P} \\ v_{P,P-2} & v_{P,P-1} & v_{P,P} \end{bmatrix} \begin{bmatrix} r''_{P-2,P-2} \\ r''_{P-2,P-1} \\ r''_{P-2,P} \end{bmatrix} = \begin{bmatrix} 0 \\ 0 \end{bmatrix} \tag{14}$$

$$\vdots$$

Note that a scaling of the rows of $\mathbf{R}''$ does not affect this homogeneous set of equations, which is consistent with the fact that the steering vectors can only be determined up to a scalar multiple. By substitution of $\mathbf{R}''$ in Eq. (13) $\mathbf{R}'$ can be found.

5   Adaptivity

When the data are slowly time-varying, the algorithm can be made adaptive by considering the weighted observations $Y(t), \alpha Y(t-1), \alpha^2 Y(t-2), \ldots$ instead of $Y(t), Y(t-1), Y(t-2), \ldots$ ($0 < \alpha \lesssim 1$), in which the slowly decaying exponential function serves as a forgetting mechanism.

For long datasets a consistent estimate of the fourth-order moment is obtained as:

$$\hat{\mathcal{M}}^{(4)}(t) = (1 - \alpha')(\tilde{\mathcal{M}}^{(4)}(t) + \alpha' \tilde{\mathcal{M}}^{(4)}(t-1) + \alpha'^2 \tilde{\mathcal{M}}^{(4)}(t-2) + \ldots) \tag{15}$$

in which $\alpha' = \alpha^4$ and $\tilde{\mathcal{M}}^{(4)}(t)$ is the tetrad corresponding to $Y(t)$: $\tilde{m}^{(4)}_{ijkl}(t) = y_i(t)y_j(t)y_k(t)y_l(t)$. It is clear that this estimate can be updated as:

$$\hat{\mathcal{M}}^{(4)}(t+1) = (1 - \alpha')\tilde{\mathcal{M}}^{(4)}(t+1) + \alpha' \hat{\mathcal{M}}^{(4)}(t) \tag{16}$$

A consistent estimate of the covariance, $\hat{\mathbf{C}}^{(2)}(t)$, is found and updated in a similar way:

$$\hat{\mathbf{C}}^{(2)}(t+1) = (1 - \alpha'')\tilde{\mathbf{C}}^{(2)}(t+1) + \alpha' \hat{\mathbf{C}}^{(2)}(t) \tag{17}$$

in which $\alpha'' = \alpha^2$ and $\tilde{\mathbf{C}}^{(2)}(t)$ equals $Y(t)Y(t)^T$. The fourth-order cumulant estimate at time $t+1$, $\hat{C}^{(4)}(t+1)$, can be computed from its classical definition, or equivalently, by the following updating rule:

$$\begin{aligned}
\hat{c}^{(4)}_{ijkl}(t+1) = {} & \alpha' \hat{c}^{(4)}_{ijkl}(t) + (6\alpha'' - 4\alpha' - 2)\,\tilde{m}^{(4)}_{ijkl}(t+1) + (\alpha' - \alpha'')\,(\tilde{c}^{(2)}_{ij}(t+1)\hat{c}^{(2)}_{kl}(t) + \hat{c}^{(2)}_{ij}(t)\tilde{c}^{(2)}_{kl}(t+1) \\
& + \tilde{c}^{(2)}_{ik}(t+1)\hat{c}^{(2)}_{jl}(t) + \hat{c}^{(2)}_{ik}(t)\tilde{c}^{(2)}_{jl}(t+1) + \tilde{c}^{(2)}_{il}(t+1)\hat{c}^{(2)}_{jk}(t) + \hat{c}^{(2)}_{il}(t)\tilde{c}^{(2)}_{jk}(t+1))
\end{aligned} \tag{18}$$

This expression can also be considered as the updating rule for $\mathbf{T_1}(t), \mathbf{T_2}(t), \ldots, \mathbf{T_P}(t)$, if these matrices are chosen as the cumulant slices of $C^{(4)}(t)$ corresponding to fixed indices k and l.

For the Givens-solution scheme of [8] it is not necessary to start a complete iteration every time step, considering the fact that we are only dealing with a weak non-stationarity. Simulations show that e.g. one sweep of rotations per time step produces sufficiently accurate results.

6   Neural Network Architecture

The bigradient algorithm can be interpreted in terms of a two-layer ANN as follows. First of all, to deal with the multidimensional character of the data to be processed, the different layers of the ANN should be considered as a stack with PS levels, each level containing S neurons. The ith input to the $((p-1)P+j)$th input level consists of the matrix element $(\mathbf{T_p}(t))_{ij}$. The weight vector of the nth neuron of the first layer is the nth column of $\mathbf{Q}(t)$, independent of the level. In this way the output of the nth neuron at the $((p-1)P+j)$th level of the first layer equals $(\mathbf{Q}(t)^T\mathbf{T}_p(t))_{ij}$. Summarized, the first layer computes $\mathbf{Q}(t)^T\mathbf{T_1}(t), \mathbf{Q}(t)^T\mathbf{T_2}(t), \ldots$ from the inputs $\mathbf{T_1}(t), \mathbf{T_2}(t), \ldots$ In a similar way the weights of the neurons in the second layer are the elements of $\mathbf{Z}(t)$; the output of the network are the matrices $\mathbf{R_1}(t), \mathbf{R_2}(t), \ldots$ The left part of Fig. 1 is a schematic representation of this ANN for the case where $P = S = 2$.

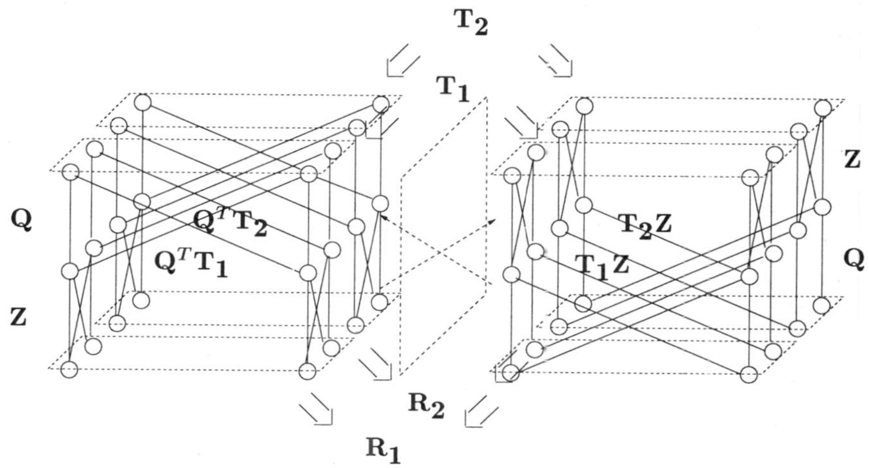

Figure 1: Schematic representation of an ANN for simultaneous generalized Schur decomposition.

It is easy to verify that the first correction term in the learning rule of Eq. (10) is in fact a Hebbian term: $\mathbf{Z}(t)$ is updated with a sum of products, each obtained by multiplication of the values at the in- and output of the connection. As far as the criterion f is concerned, the updating of $\mathbf{Z}(t)$ can be implemented as a simple, uniform, local learning rule. This doesn't hold true for $\mathbf{Q}(t)$. However by a mathematical trick the size of the network might be traded for simplicity of the learning rule. Fig. 1 shows the principle: in the right part of the figure the ordering of the multiplication with $\mathbf{Z}(t)$ and $\mathbf{Q}(t)$ is reversed with respect to the left part. In this way $\mathbf{Q}(t)$ can be updated by a Hebbian rule too. The new values $\mathbf{Q}(t+1)$ and $\mathbf{Z}(t+1)$ are immediately fed back to the weights for the first layer.

7 Least-squares Cumulant Matching

The least-squares criterion associated to the upper triangularity in Eq. (6) and the least-squares criterion associated to the fit in Eq. (2) are only asymptotically equivalent, although simulations show that they are quite close in practice. The simultaneous generalized Schur solution could be used as an interesting starting value for an additional least-squares descent algorithm that matches both sides of Eq. (2). For this extra optimization step one can use closed-form expressions for the gradient and Hessian of the criterion function. We stress the importance of the initial value, obtained by simultaneous generalized Schur decomposition: the cumulant matching criterion is a multivariate polynomial function, of degree 8 in the unknown transfer matrix entries, and shows a lot of irrelevant local optima.

8 Discussion and Conclusions

We presented a new technique for Blind Source Separation that resorts only to the higher-order cumulants of the observations. The transfer matrix estimate that is obtained shows exactly the same uniqueness properties as in the classical ICA-algorithms [2, 4], which also exploit second-order information in a prewhitening step. Higher-order-only Blind Source Separation has the advantage that it is asymptotically insensitive to additive Gaussian perturbations of the data. When dealing with finite sample cumulants, the accuracy of higher-order-only versus classical approaches is subject to a trade-off, caused by the fact that higher-order statistics are harder to estimate than second-order statistics [1, 10].

Our approach is based on the observation that the data cumulant can be expanded as a sum of tetrads. This implies that all the matrices in the range space of this cumulant tensor, considered as a supersymmetric matrix-to-matrix mapping, satisfy a simultaneous congruence transformation. For the numerical computation of this set of matrix equations we proposed a new representation of the transfer matrix: it turns out that any matrix, of which the columns are fixed up to multiplication with a scalar, can be represented by a pair of orthogonal matrices, obtained by QR- and RQ-factorisation. In this new format the simultaneous congruence transformation takes the form of a simultaneous generalized Schur decomposition, that can be computed by bigradient optimization. The technique can be interpreted as an ANN method, in which the basic learning rule is Hebbian. Adaptivity can be realized by exponential data weighting. The result can be considered as an approximate solution of *other* cumulant-based identification criterions, e.g. least-squares cumulant matching.

The derivation established in this paper is in fact the higher-order-only equivalent of the well-known combined second/higher-order ICA-algorithm by Cardoso and Souloumiac [2]. Simultaneous congruence transformation and simultaneous eigenvalue decomposition play exactly the same role. However, without prewhitening *a pair* of orthogonal matrices has to be determined, instead of a single simultaneous eigenmatrix. The equivalent of simultaneous diagonalization turns out to be simultaneous *triangularization*. For a solution method based on Givens-iteration, like in [2], the reader is referred to [8]. The concepts of this paper also lead to a higher-order-only equivalent ([9]) of the ICA-algorithm by Comon [4].

The technique can also be generalized for higher-order tensors without symmetry properties [6]. The unsymmetric version of the algorithm can be used for Factor Analysis of multiway datasets.

References

[1] C. Bourin and P. Bondon, "Efficiency of high-order moment estimates," *Proc. IEEE SP / ATHOS Workshop on Higher-Order Statistics*, Girona, Spain, June 12-14, 1995, pp. 186-190.

[2] J.-F. Cardoso and A. Souloumiac, "Blind beamforming for non-Gaussian signals," *IEE Proceedings-F*, vol. 140, no. 6, pp. 362-370, 1994.

[3] A. Cichocki and R. Unbehauen, *Neural Networks for Optimization and Signal Processing.* N.Y.: John Wiley, 1993.

[4] P. Comon, "Independent Component Analysis, a new concept?" *Signal Processing*, Special Issue *Higher Order Statistics*, vol. 36, no. 3, pp. 287-314, April 1994.

[5] P. Comon *et al.* (Ed.), *Proc. IEEE SP / ATHOS Workshop on Higher-Order Statistics.* Girona, Spain, June 12-14, 1995.

[6] L. De Lathauwer, B. De Moor and J. Vandewalle, "Canonical decomposition of a fourth-order tensor," *IMA Conf. on Linear Algebra and Its Applications*, Manchester, U.K., July 10-12, 1995.

[7] L. De Lathauwer, P. Comon, B. De Moor and J. Vandewalle, "Higher-order power method - application in Independent Component Analysis," *Proc. NOLTA'95*, Las Vegas, USA, December 10-14, 1995, vol.1, pp. 91-96.

[8] L. De Lathauwer, B. De Moor and J. Vandewalle, "Independent Component Analysis based on higher-order statistics only," *Proc. SSAP-96, 8th IEEE SP Workshop on Stat. Signal and Array Processing*, Corfu, Greece, June 24-26, 1996.

[9] L. De Lathauwer, *Signal Processing by Higher-Order Tensors*, Ph.D. thesis, K.U.Leuven, E.E.Dept.-ESAT, Belgium (in preparation).

[10] J. Fonollosa, "Sample cumulants of stationary processes: asymptotic results," *IEEE Trans. on Signal Processing*, vol. 43, no. 4, pp. 967-977, April 1995.

[11] G.H. Golub and C.F. Van Loan, *Matrix computations.* Johns Hopkins University Press, 1991.

[12] J.L. Lacoume (Ed.), *Higher Order Statistics. Proc. of the International SP Workshop on Higher Order Statistics.* Chamrousse, France, July 10-12, 1991.

[13] K.S. Shanmugam, *Digital and Analog Communication Systems.* N.Y.: John Wiley & Sons, 1985.

[14] A.-J. van der Veen and A. Paulraj, "An analytical constant modulus algorithm," *IEEE Trans. Signal Processing*, vol. 44, no. 5, May 1996.

[15] L. Wang, J. Karhunen and E. Oja, "A bigradient optimization approach for robust PCA, MCA, and source separation," *Proc. IEEE Int. Conf. on Neural Networks*, Perth, Australia, Nov. 1995, pp. 1684-1689.

Performance surfaces of blind source separation algorithms

S J Flockton, D Yang, and G J Scruby
Royal Holloway, University of London,
Egham, Surrey TW20 0EX, England
E-mail : S.Flockton@rhbnc.ac.uk

Abstract—Many source separation methods use a two-stage procedure of first equalising the second order statistics of the data by a whitening process and then seeking a separation matrix for this whitened data. The second part of this procedure is in fact a question of finding the rotation matrix that maximises (or minimises, as appropriate) a higher order statistics performance criterion. We illustrate the shape of the performance surface for some typical examples and draw conclusions about the possible efficacy of adaptive search procedures on these surfaces.

1   Introduction

There are a number of different threads in blind source separation algorithms. One of the distinctions between classes of algorithms relate to the assumptions made about the number and type of sources. Another distinction can be drawn between the type of algorithm used to find candidate solutions to the problem. On the one hand there are batch-type methods which involve a fairly explicitly derived single solution to the problem; on the other there are adaptive algorithms in which an iterative search is made for a stationary point. Many performance surfaces have more than one stationary point. In some cases these all correspond to alternative solutions to the problem; in others some of the stationary points correspond to true solutions but some do not. A further complication is that the solutions may not correspond to stationary points of the type being searched for, but the desired solution may be found by specific shifts from the stationary points.

It is clear that one cannot say anything with certainty about the performance capabilities of an adaptive algorithm unless one has some knowledge of the nature of the performance surface being searched and of the type of movement across this surface that is induced by any particular update rule. In this paper we discuss the shape of the performance surface that must be searched in the second stage of a two-stage separation method. We confine the major part of our discussion to two particular contrast functions.

2   Separation methods

Many of the methods proposed for separating instantaneous mixtures of statistically independent signals perform the separation by a two-stage process. In the first stage the data are rotated and scaled in such a way that the resulting signals are mutually orthogonal and have unit variance. The data then have no preferred directions in terms of their second order statistics. They are not, however, in general separated. Indeed since there are no preferred directions in terms of second order statistics one could not tell whether or not they were separated as a result of whitening, and the symmetry of the whitened data means that there is a continuum of different whitened data sets which are all equally valid. The second stage of the separation involves finding the appropriate rotation of the coordinate system that must be performed in order to achieve separation. One needs some criterion to decide when separation is achieved and the most widely used such criteria are 'contrast functions' based on higher order statistics of the whitened data.

2.1   Contrasts discussed in this paper

Even though the whitening and separation can be concatenated into a single algorithm, it is convenient from a theoretical point of view to discuss two-stage algorithms. In his well-known paper Comon [1] uses this type of approach to derive the result that the sum of the squares of the fourth order cumulants of the whitened sources, i.e.

$$J^2(y) = \sum_{i=1}^{n} \mathrm{cum}^2(y_i{}^4) \tag{1}$$

can be used as a contrast function provided not more than one of sources has a zero fourth order cumulant. It has also been shown, by Moreau and Macchi [2], that under more restricted conditions the slightly simpler function

$$J^1(y) = \sum_{i=1}^{n} \left|\mathrm{cum}(y_i{}^4)\right| \tag{2}$$

can be used as a contrast function.

Moreau and Macchi also suggested the use of composite contrasts containing cross-cumulant terms, such as

$$J^2_{\alpha\beta\gamma}(y) = \alpha \sum_{i=1}^{n} \mathrm{cum}^2(y_i{}^4) - \sum_{i \neq j=1}^{n} \left[\frac{\beta}{2} \mathrm{cum}^2(y_i{}^2 y_j{}^2) + \gamma\, \mathrm{cum}^2(y_i y_j{}^3) \right] \tag{3}$$

and

$$J^1_{\alpha\beta\gamma}(y) = \alpha \sum_{i=1}^{n} \left| \mathrm{cum}(y_i{}^4) \right| - \sum_{i \neq j=1}^{n} \left[\frac{\beta}{2} \left| \mathrm{cum}(y_i{}^2 y_j{}^2) \right| + \gamma \left| \mathrm{cum}(y_i y_j{}^3) \right| \right]. \tag{4}$$

They derived adaptive algorithms to optimise $J^1_{\alpha\beta\gamma}(y)$ provided γ is zero and demonstrated some examples of their performance. Though authors such as Wang, Karhunen and Oja [3] have discussed single stage adaptive algorithms that do not have an explicit whitening stage, these often consist of a whitening algorithm embedded in a separation one, so the work on the shape of performance surfaces described in this paper is still of relevance.

In the rest of this paper we look at the shape of the performance surfaces for various of the above contrasts, first of all in the two source case, and then the three source case.

3   Two source case

3.1   Simplified contrast

We discuss first of all the form of the simplified contrast, $J^1(y)$. The fourth order cumulant is given by

$$\mathrm{cum}(y^4) = \mathrm{E}(y^4) - 3\,\mathrm{E}^2(y^2) \tag{5}$$

which, for whitened signals with zero mean, reduces to

$$\mathrm{cum}(y^4) = \mathrm{E}(y^4) - 3. \tag{6}$$

In order to find the shape of the performance surface we need to find out how this varies as the coordinate axes are rotated about the origin. We can find the form of this variation by the following simple reasoning.

The vector representing a single point in the whitened signal will have a particular length and be oriented at a particular angle, to the x-axis. Let us look at the variation in the contribution of this one point to the fourth order cumulant as the coordinate axes are rotated through 2π radians. Since we are only interested in the form of the variation we can without loss of generality look at a point of unit radius which lies on one of the original axes. The contribution of a point at unit distance from the origin to the fourth moment will be equal to

$$contr1 = \cos^4\theta + \sin^4\theta \tag{7}$$

where θ is the angle by which the coordinate axes have been rotated. This expression can be simplified to

$$contr1 = \frac{1}{4}(\cos(4\theta) + 3) \tag{8}$$

This is the contribution to the contrast from just one point. The total fourth moment is equal to this term integrated over the probability distribution of the length of the vector and over all possible θ. However the summation of a number of sinusoids of the same frequency, though different amplitudes and phases, can only result in a sinusoid of the same frequency, though of indeterminate amplitude and phase. Hence we deduce that the form of the variation of the contrast $J^1(y)$ with rotation of the coordinate axes, must be of the form $|\cos(4\theta - \delta) + \text{constant}|$ where δ is the angular shift required to bring one of the coordinate axes in line with one of the maxima of the contrast.

3.2   Comon's contrast

The behaviour of $J^2(y)$ is a little more complicated, owing to the squaring. Following the same method yields the following for the contribution to the cumulant squared from just one signal point:

$$contr2 = \frac{1}{32}(\cos(8\theta) - 36\cos(4\theta) + 163) \tag{9}$$

Clearly the variation of this contribution with θ is dominated by the 4θ term, so a similar argument leads one to expect a similar shape to the previous case.

3.3   Moreau and Macchi's composite contrast, $J^1_{\alpha\beta\gamma}(y)$

It is more difficult to generalise about contrasts that include cross-terms in them, so for our discussion of Moreau and Macchi's function we will use examples. The signals used to produce the figures are the same as

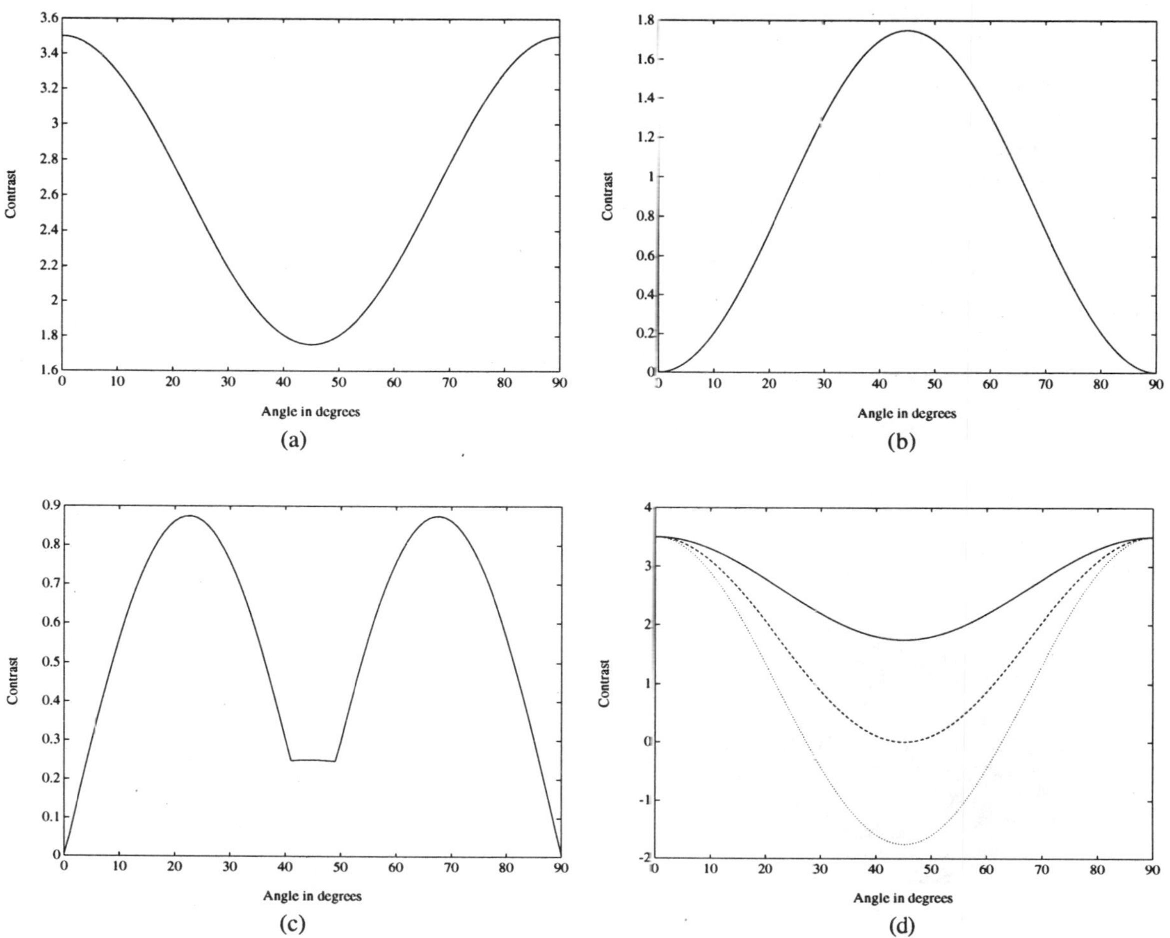

Figure 1. The three terms that go to make up $J^1_{\alpha\beta\gamma}(y)$ and the combinations used in Reference [2]: (a) the autocumulant term; (b) the symmetric cross-cumulant; (c) the odd-odd cross-cumulant (d) composite performance criterion used in [2]: solid line, $\beta = 0$; dashed line, $\beta = 2$; dotted line, $\beta = 4$.

used in [2], namely a sine wave with period 17 and a binary ± 1 random signal. Figure 1 (a) shows the variation of the first term of equation 3 (for $\alpha = 1$) as a function of angle of rotation of the coordinate axes. It can be seen that the variation is indeed of the form of a sinusoid with four maxima per unit rotation and with a DC shift. Since the signals were not mixed, the maxima of the function lie at 0, $\pi/2$, π, and $3\pi/2$.

The cumulant terms appearing in the square brackets of equation (2) are shown in Figures 1 (b) and 1 (c). Each of them, as expected, goes to zero at angles of 0 and $\pi/2$, i.e. when the two signals are unmixed, and are in general non-zero elsewhere. Moreau and Macchi showed results using an adaptive algorithm based on a performance surface that is a weighted sum of the functions shown in Figure 1 (a) and (b), and showed that subtracting a scalar multiple of the function shown in (b) from that in (a) slightly increased the convergence speed of the algorithm. The reason for this slight increase can be seen in Figure 1 (d), which shows the performance surface for the three values of ß for which Moreau and Macchi show results. The increased depth of the dip and consequent emphasising of the maxima on either side of the dip should indeed increase convergence speed.

It is interesting to look also at the third cross-cumulant (which Moreau and Macchi were unable to use in their adaptive algorithm as they could not derive an appropriate adaptation rule) in the same manner as the other terms. The particularly noteworthy feature of the shape of the function is that, whilst the global minima are zero at the angular variation corresponding to unmixed signals, there is a local minimum also which does *not* correspond to unmixing. This is consistent with the observation in [4], reported in [5], that using adaptation equations based on the cancellation of the third term in $J^2_{\alpha\beta\gamma}(y)$ can give spurious solutions, but they can be 'removed' by looking also for simultaneous cancellation of the second term. Note the slightly strange appearance of the middle section of Figure 1 (c), where there is an almost straight section. It transpires that this is a result of summing moduli of the cumulants, rather than their square, as used in (3); the graph of the sum of the squared cumulants is of the same general form, but is smooth throughout.

4   Three source case

In this section we extend our observations to the three source case, showing the nature of the performance surface of Comon's contrast function (1) for two different methods of describing the rotation of the coordinate system.

In two directions there is only one plane in which rotation can take place, so it is easy to see how to cover all possible rotations as functions of a single angle variable. When one moves to three dimensions, however, the problem of covering the entire space of possible rotations exactly once is more difficult. The standard formulation in mechanics is to use Euler angles, which represent rotation first about the z-axis, then about the transformed y-axis, and finally about the newly transformed z-axis. To cover all possible transformations the first and last rotations must span 2π radians while the middle rotation must have a span of π radians. Figure 2 shows the performance surface as a function of the first and third rotations for various fixed values of the second

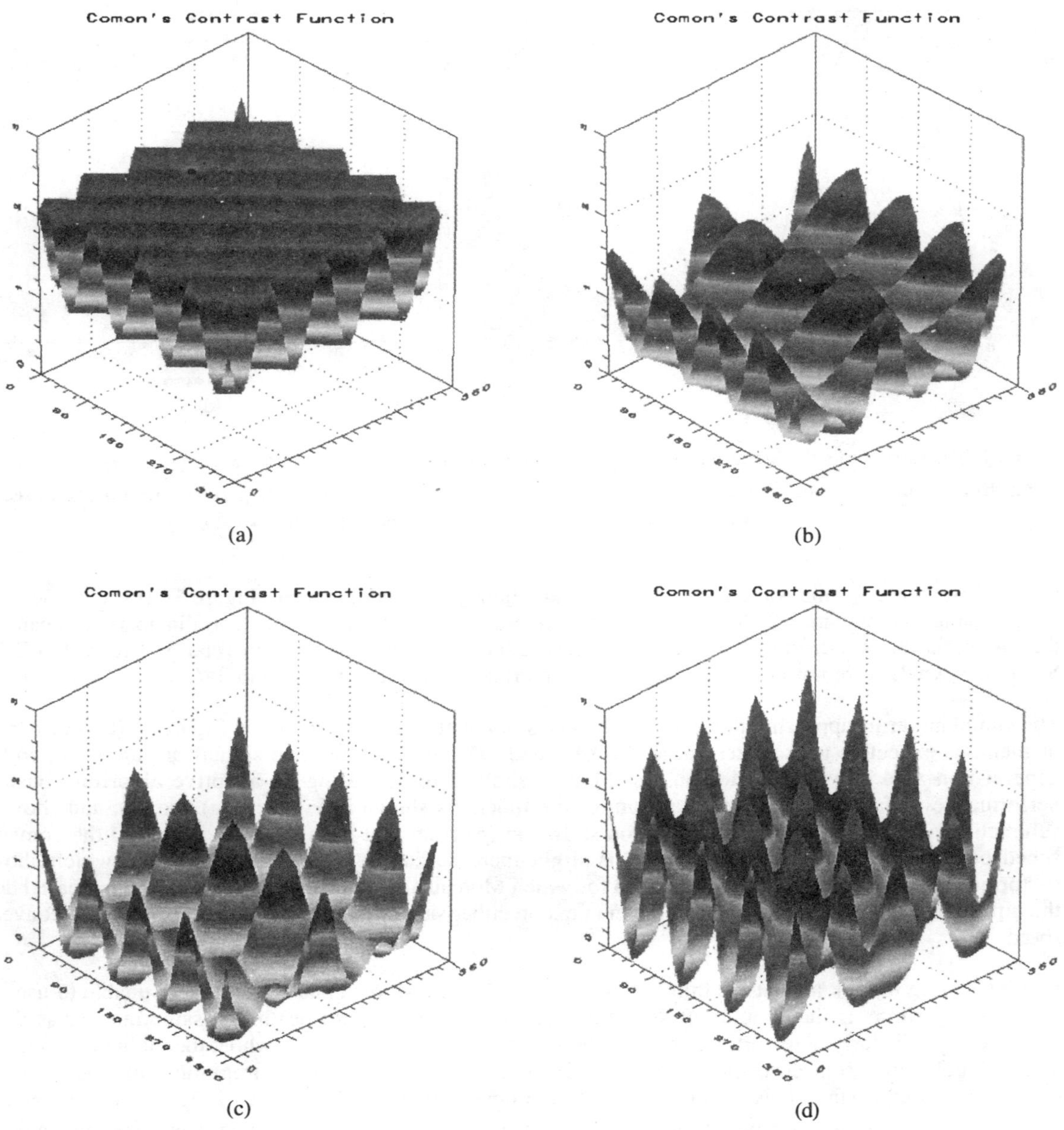

(a)　　　　　　　　　　　　　　　　　(b)

(c)　　　　　　　　　　　　　　　　　(d)

Figure 2. Variation of Comon's contrast as a function of the first and third Euler angle rotations of the coordinate system for values of the intermediate rotation equal to: (a) 0°; (b) 30°; (c) 60°; (d) 90°.

rotation.

By considering the number of permutations and allowing for sign reversal it can be seen that there must be 24 possible distinct equally good solutions to the separation problem. It is instructive to identify the features of the performance surface corresponding to these solutions. In Figure 2 we show the performance surface for a mixture of uniform, Gaussian and super-Gaussian sources. In Figure 2 (a) there are eight parallel lines of equal height which correspond to eight solutions. The reason that the peaks are spread into lines is that, for the special case of the second rotation equal to zero, the first and third rotations are the same thing, so any combination of them that sums to an integer multiple of $\pi/2$ will serve to separate the signals. As the intermediate rotation is increased to 30° and 60° the maximum height decreases and the long folds begin to form into distinct peaks. When the intermediate rotation reaches 90° these 16 distinct peaks have risen to match the height of the original folds and represent the rest of the available solutions. This shows that performance of an adaptive algorithm based on this description of coordinate transformation will vary depending on whether convergence is taking place towards one of the distinct peaks or one of the folds.

In Figure 3 we present a similar set of performance surfaces, but this time expressed in the form of Givens

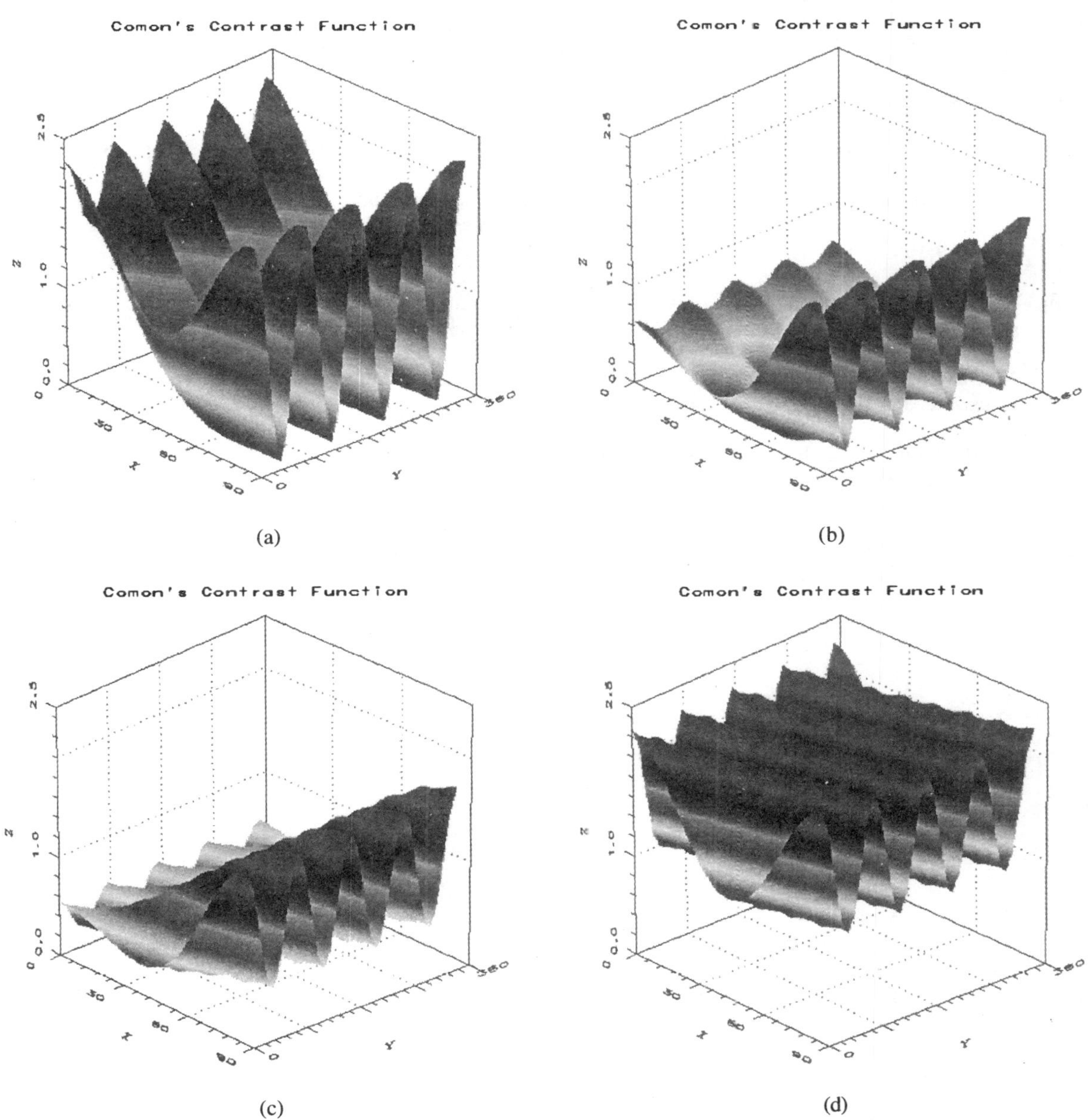

Figure 3. Variation of Comon's contrast as a function of first and third Givens rotations of the coordinate system for values of the intermediate rotation equal to: (a) 0°; (b) 30°; (c) 60°; (d) 90°.

rotations about the z-, then y-, and finally x-axes. The third rotation is shown only over the range 0 to $\pi/2$ to make the figures clearer. This means that only 12 of the 24 possible solutions actually occur in the figures, but the rest of the figure will be symmetric with that shown here. It is interesting to note that the performance surface shows the same general shape as before, except that the degenerate solutions now occur for a value of $\pi/2$ for the intermediate rotation, rather than for a value of 0 for the Euler formulation. This is of course because in the formulation used for this figure a value of $\pi/2$ for the intermediate rotation brings the first and third planes of rotation into coincidence with each other.

5   Summary and Conclusions

We have demonstrated the way in which a number of performance criteria used for separation of instantaneous mixtures of vary as the coordinate system is rotated in the signal space. This has led to an improved understanding of the reasons for the behaviour experimentally observed in [2] and [4], and provides a platform from which to consider the development of other adaptive algorithms. Although not shown here, we have also looked at the performance surface of the three source case reported in [2] which demonstrated clearly the improvement to be obtained by the use of the second term in (3) or (4). However we have also shown, by presenting graphs of the form of the third term of (3) and (4), that extension of the algorithm in [2] to include non-zero values of γ would have the undesirable effect of potentially introducing local minima into the performance surface and hence the possibility of convergence to spurious solutions.

References

[1]   P. Comon, "Independent component analysis, a new concept?," *Signal Processing* 36 pp. 287-314 1994

[2]   E. Moreau and O. Macchi, "New self-adaptive algorithms for source separation based on contrast functions," *Proceeding IEEE Signal Processing Workshop on Higher Order Statistics, Lake Tahoe*, pp. 215-219 1993.

[3]   L. Wang, J. Karhunen, and E. Oja, "A bigradient optimization approach for robust PCA, MCA, and source separation," *Proceeding ICNN-95 Perth*, pp. 684-1689 1995

[4]   X. Oliva Galvan, "Blind separation of sources: some adaptive algorithms," *Tech. Rep., Lab. CEPHAG, Grenoble*, Jan. 1993.

[5]   A. Mansour and C. Jutten, "Fourth-order criteria for blind sources separation", *IEEE Transactions on Signal Processing* 43 (8) pp. 2022-2025 1995

A General Independent Component Analysis Framework Based on Bayesian-Kullback Ying-Yang Learning *

Lei Xu[1] and Shun-ichi Amari[2]
1. Computer Science and Engineering Department, The Chinese University of Hong Kong
2. Frontier Research, The Institute of Physical and Chemical Research, Japan

Abstract— **A general Independent Component Analysis (ICA) framework is proposed based on the recent Bayesian-Kullback Ying-Yang learning scheme (Xu, 1995&1996). It unifies the information maximization (INFORMAX) approach (Bell and Sejnowski, 1995) and the minimum mutual information (MMI) approach (Amari, Cichocki, and Yang, 1996). Moreover, an interesting constrained ICA probelm is studied with a theorem given.**

1 Introduction

Independent Component Analysis (ICA) has recently received many attentions due to its application in blind source separation (Common, 1994; Bell & Sejnowski, 1995a&b, NOLTA, 1995; Amari, Cichocki & Yang, 1996). Blind source separation problem arises not only in several branches of intelligent cognitive system, e.g., the so called *cocktail-party* problem that addresses hearing system's ability of separating the sounds by different speakers, and the problem of separating and locating different oders in a complicated environment by olfactory system, but also in many engineering flieds such as radar or water sonar system, digital communication, and biomedical signal analysis.

Currently, there exist two types of information theory related ICA approaches. One is the minimization of mutual information or the so called contrast function defined as the Kullback-Leibler divergence between the joint and the product of marginal densities of the linear system outputs (Jutten & Herault, 1991; Comon, 1994; Amari, Cichocki & Yang, 1996). For this type, the key problem is how to estimate the marginal densities and either Gram-Chalier expansion (Amari, Cichocki & Yang, 1996) or Edgeworth expansion (Comon, 1994) is used for this purpose. The other type is the maximization of information transmitted from the linear system followed by a prespecified nonlinear *sigmoid monotonic function* transformation.

This paper proposes a general ICA framework based on Bayesian-Kullback Ying-Yang learning, which unifies the information maximization approach (Bell and Sejnowski, 1995) and the minimum mutual information approach (Amari, Cichocki, and Yang, 1996). Sec. 2 briefly describes the problem of Independent Component Analysis (ICA). Sec. 3 introduces the recent proposed Bayesian-Kullback Ying-Yang learning scheme (Xu, 1995&1996). Sec. 4 proposes a general ICA framework based on the Bayesian-Kullback Ying-Yang learning scheme and shows how it unifies the two information theory related ICA approaches. In Sec.5, an interesting constrained ICA probelm is studied with a theorem given. Finally, we conclude in Sec.6.

2 ICA Problem and Two Existing Approaches

Currently, a widely used formulation for the ICA problem is given as follows.

There are n channels of unknown source signals $\mathbf{s} = [s_1, \cdots, s_n]^T$ which are mutually independent with $E\mathbf{s} = 0$. The observations from n sensors are given as $\mathbf{x} = A\mathbf{s}$ with A being an $n \times n$ unknown nonsingular mixing matrix. The objective is to find a so-called de-mixing matrix W such that $W = A^{-1}$ and $\mathbf{y} = W\mathbf{x} = \mathbf{s}$ such that the unknown source signals $\mathbf{s}$ can be recovered. In a summary, we have the information passage

$$\mathbf{s} \rightarrow \mathbf{x} = A\mathbf{s} \rightarrow \mathbf{y} = W\mathbf{x} = WA\mathbf{s}, \tag{1}$$

Obviously, without knowing either $\mathbf{s}$ or A, it is impossible to find $W = A^{-1}$ generally. However, if $\mathbf{s}$ is nongaussian and if we can find a matrix W such that the components of $\mathbf{y}$ are mutually independent, we are possible to obtain $y_i = c_i s_i$ which recovers s_i up to a unknown constant and a permutation of indices. The existing approaches for this purpose is to design an adaptive algorithm for learning the de-mixing matrix W from a set of i.i.d. observations $\mathbf{x}_t, t = 1, \cdots, N$ that correspond to the i.i.d. samples $\mathbf{s}_t, t = 1, \cdots, N$.

One major information theory related approach is selecting a W to minimize of the dependency among the components of y (Jutten & Herault, 1991; Comon, 1994; Amari, Cichocki & Yang, 1996). The dependency measure used is called the mutual information or the so called contrast function defined as the Kullback-Leibler divergence between the joint and the product of marginal densities of the linear

---

*This project was supported by Ho Sin-Hang Education Endowment Fund for Project HSH 95/02 and by the HK RGC Earmarked Grants CUHK250/94E.

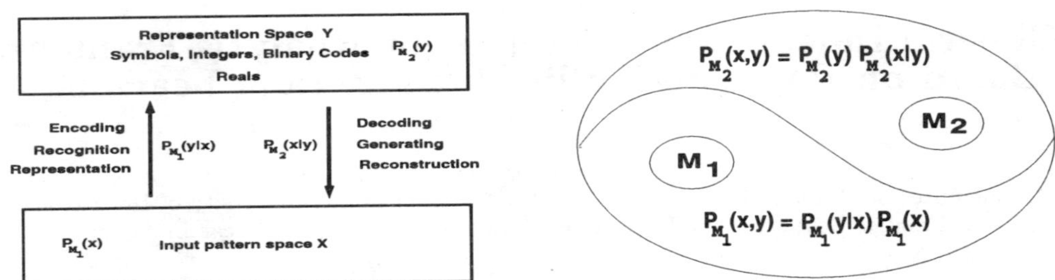

Figure 1   The joint spaces X, Y and the YING-YANG Machine

system outputs:

$$KL(W) = \int P(\mathbf{y}) \ln P(\mathbf{y}) / \prod_{i=1}^{n} p_i(y_i) d\mathbf{y} \tag{2a}$$

where $\mathbf{y} = [y_1, \cdots, y_n]^T$ and $p_i(y_i)$ is the marginal density of y_i. The key problem here is how to estimate the marginal densities. Either Gram-Chalier expansion (Amari, Cichocki & Yang, 1996) or Edgeworth expansion (Comon, 1994) is used on approximating $p(y_i)$, which results in an adaptive algorithm

$$\Delta W = \alpha(I - g(\mathbf{y})\mathbf{y}^T)W, \tag{2b}$$

that will converge at $E[g(\mathbf{y})\mathbf{y}^T] = I$, where $g(\mathbf{y}) = [g(y_1), \cdots, g(y_n)]$ and $g(y)$ is a prespecified *odd nonmonotonic* function.

One other type is the maximization of output entropy from the linear system $\mathbf{y} = W\mathbf{x}$ followed by a prespecified nonlinear *sigmoid monotonic function* transformation $f(\mathbf{y}) = [f(y_1), \cdots, f(y_n)]$, that is, to select W to maximize

$$H(W) = -\int P(f(\mathbf{y})) \ln P(f(\mathbf{y})) df(\mathbf{y}) \tag{3a}$$

which results in an adaptive algorithm

$$\Delta W = \alpha[[W^T]^{-1} + (1 - 2f(\mathbf{y}))\mathbf{x}^T)], \tag{3b}$$

that will converge to $2E[f(\mathbf{y})\mathbf{y}^T] = I$, where $f(y)$ is $f(y) = (1 + e^{-y})^{-1}$ or other sigmoid function (Bell & Sejnowski, 1995).

3   Bayesian-Kullback Ying-Yang Learning

As shown in Xu (1995a & 96a), both the supervised and unsupervised learning problems are summarized into the problem of estimating joint density $P(x, y)$ of patterns in the input space X and the representation space Y as shown in Fig.1. Under Bayesian framework, we have two representations for $P(x, y)$. One is $P_{M_1}(x, y) = P_{M_1}(y|x)P_{M_1}(x)$, implemented by a model M_1 called *YANG*/(male) part since it performs the task of transferring a pattern/(a real body) into a code/(a seed). The other is $P_{M_2}(x, y) = P_{M_2}(x|y)P_{M_2}(y)$, implemented by a model M_2 called *YING* part since it performs the task of generating a pattern/(a real body) from a code/(a seed). They are complement to each other and together implement an entire circle $x \rightarrow y \rightarrow x$. Here we have four components $P_{M_1}(x)$, $P_{M_1}(y|x)$, $P_{M_2}(x|y)$ and $P_{M_2}(y)$ with each having several choices. Any combination of the choices of the four components forms a potential YING-YANG pair, which belongs to one of four types of marital status: (a) *marry*, i.e., YING and YANG match each other; (b) *divorce*, i.e., YING and YANG go away from each other; (c) YING chases YANG, YANG escapes; (d) YANG chases YING, but YING escapes. The four types can be described by a combination of minimization (chasing) and maximization (escaping) the following Kullback divergence :

$$KL(M_1, M_2) = \int_{x,y} P_{M_1}(y|x)P_{M_1}(x) \log \frac{P_{M_1}(y|x)P_{M_1}(x)}{P_{M_2}(x|y)P_{M_2}(y)} dx dy, \tag{5}$$

or its variant $KL(M_2, M_1)$. The minimization/maximization can be implemented by alternatively minimizing/ maximizing one model with the other temporarily fixed. The four types of marital status together with the fact that each of $P_{M_1}(x)$, $P_{M_1}(y|x)$, $P_{M_2}(x|y)$ and $P_{M_2}(y)$ can have several choices provide a large number of potential YING-YANG pairings. Although not all of them provide sensible learning models, a quite number of them indeed lead us to useful learning models. This scheme is called *Bayesian-Kullback YING-YANG* learning scheme since it bases on the two complement YING and YANG Bayesian representations and the Kullback divergence for measuring their marital status. Furthermore, each pairing that is sensible for learning purpose is called *Bayesian-Kullback YING-YANG Machine* or *YING-YANG* machine shortly.

This scheme can unify several existing major unsupervised and supervised learning methods. As shown in Xu(1995a &96a), one of its special case reduces to the EM algorithm related learnings, to Amari's *Information geometry* theory and the *em* algorithm, to Hinton & Zemel's MDL autoencoder. to multisets modeling learning (Xu, 1995a)–a unified learning framework for clustering, PCA-type learnings and self-organizing map. Its one other special case reduces to maximum information preservation. More interestingly its another special case reduces to the recent proposed Helmholtz machine by Hinton and Dayan et al with new understandings. The scheme includes also maximum likelihood learning (least square learning in particular). Moreover, this scheme has also been extended to temporal patterns with a number of new models for signal modeling, including the extensions of Hidden Markov Model (HMM), AMAR models, as well as the extensions of Helmholtz machine or maximum information preservation to temporal processing (Xu, 1995b). Another applications of this scheme is that a theory with the corresponding criteria has been obtained for determining the number of models in a finite mixture (e.g., Gaussian mixture) or in a mixture-of-experts and for determining the dimension of subspace in *principal component analysis*, both of which are well known important problems that remain unsolved for decades (Xu, 1996b).

4   A General ICA Framework

Considering the information passage eq.(1), $\mathbf{s}$ is hidden and it generates $\mathbf{y}$ via $\mathbf{s} \to \mathbf{y}$, which we regard as the Ying part M_2. While, the passage $\mathbf{y} \to \mathbf{s}$ along an inverted direction in eq.(1) is regarded as the Yang part M_1. We consider the case of $Ying - Yang$ marrying each other because the joint density $p(\mathbf{s}, \mathbf{y})$ should be as close as possible.

Let us to regard $\mathbf{s}$ in eq.(1) as y in eq.(5), $\mathbf{y}$ in eq.(1) as x in eq.(5), We can get

$$KL(M_1, M_2) = \int_{\mathbf{s}, \mathbf{y}} P_{M_1}(\mathbf{s}|\mathbf{y}) P_{M_1}(\mathbf{y}) \log \frac{P_{M_1}(\mathbf{s}|\mathbf{y}) P_{M_1}(\mathbf{y})}{P_{M_2}(\mathbf{y}|\mathbf{s}) P_{M_2}(\mathbf{s})} d\mathbf{y} ds, \qquad (6a)$$

According our desire $\mathbf{y} = \mathbf{s}$, we design

$$P_{M_1}(\mathbf{s}|\mathbf{y}) = \delta(\mathbf{s} - \mathbf{y}) = \delta(\mathbf{y} - \mathbf{s}) = P_{M_1}(\mathbf{y}|\mathbf{s})$$

For the true source distribution, we have $P(\mathbf{s}) = \prod_{i=1}^{n} P(s_i)$ with $\mathbf{s} = [s_1, \cdots, s_n]^T$. So, Our design for P_{M_2} should be any density function satisfying $P_{M_2}(\mathbf{s}) = \prod_{i=1}^{n} P_{M_2}(s_i)$.

Moreover, we let $P_{M_1}(\mathbf{y})$ is the transformation of the source density $P(\mathbf{s})$ or observation signal $\mathbf{x}$ via the forward passage $\mathbf{y} = WA\mathbf{s}$ of eq.(1):

$$P_{M_1}(\mathbf{y}) = P(\mathbf{s})/det[WA] = P(\mathbf{x})/det[W], \qquad (6b)$$

Putting these designs into eq.(6a), we have

$$KL(M_1, M_2) = \int_{\mathbf{y}} P_{M_1}(\mathbf{y}) \log P_{M_1}(\mathbf{y}) / \prod_{i=1}^{n} P_{M_2}(y_i) d\mathbf{y}, \qquad (7a)$$

Since the minimization of $KL(M_1, M_2)$ is equivalent to $KL(M_1, M_2) + C$ for any constant C, we can generalize this equation further into

$$KL(M_1, M_2) = \int_{\mathbf{y}} [P_{M_1}(\mathbf{y}) - \prod_{i=1}^{n} g_i(y_i)] d\mathbf{y} + \int_{\mathbf{y}} P_{M_1}(\mathbf{y}) \log \frac{P_{M_1}(\mathbf{y})}{\prod_{i=1}^{n} g_i(y_i)} d\mathbf{y}, \; g_i(r) = c_i p_i(r), c_i > 0 \quad (7b)$$

where $c_i > 0$ is a constant and $p_i(r)$ is a density function, thus $g_i(r)$ is an positive integrable function due to $\int_{-\infty}^{\infty} g_i(r) dr = c_i$

As will be shown by Theorems 1-4 given in the next section, we can fix $g_i(r)$ at an interagable positive function that satisfies very mild condition. Moreover, the first term in eq.(7b) is a constant. As a result, the minimization of $KL(M_1, M_2)$ in eq.(7b) becomes the minimization of the following $J(W)$ with respect to M_1 (i.e., W), that is

$$J(M_1(W)) = \int_{\mathbf{y}} P_{M_1}(\mathbf{y}) \log \frac{P_{M_1}(\mathbf{y})}{\prod_{i=1}^{n} g_i(y_i)} d\mathbf{y}, \qquad (7c)$$

We suggest to use it as a general framework for getting W to perform ICA, which will be justified by Theorems 1-4 given in the next section.

To get the learning algorithm for implementing $\min_W J(M_1(W))$ with $W = [\mathbf{w}_1, \cdots, \mathbf{w}_n]^T$, from $\mathbf{y} = W\mathbf{x}$ and eq.(6b), we write eq.(7c) into

$$J(M_1(W)) = \int_{\mathbf{x}} P(\mathbf{x}) \log \frac{P(\mathbf{x})}{det[W] \prod_{i=1}^{n} g_i(\mathbf{x}^T \mathbf{w}_i)} d\mathbf{x} = -\log det[W] - \int_{\mathbf{x}} P(\mathbf{x}) \log \prod_{i=1}^{n} g_i(\mathbf{w}_i^T \mathbf{x}) d\mathbf{x}, \quad (7d)$$

$$\frac{\partial J(M_1(W))}{\partial W} = -[W^T]^{-1} - \int_{\mathbf{x}} P(\mathbf{x}) [\frac{g_1'(\mathbf{w}_1^T \mathbf{x})}{g_1(\mathbf{w}_1^T \mathbf{x})} \cdots, \frac{g_n'(\mathbf{w}_n^T \mathbf{x})}{g_n(\mathbf{w}_n^T \mathbf{x})}]^T \mathbf{x}^T d\mathbf{x}$$

which gives the following batch algorithm eq.(7d) and adaptive algorithm eq.(7e) respectively:

$$\delta W = -\frac{\partial J(M_1(W))}{\partial W} W^T W = \{I + \sum_t [\frac{g_1'(\mathbf{w}_1^T \mathbf{x}_t)}{g_1(\mathbf{w}_1^T \mathbf{x}_t)} \cdots, \frac{g_n'(\mathbf{w}_n^T \mathbf{x}_t)}{g_n(\mathbf{w}_n^T \mathbf{x}_t)}]^T \mathbf{y}_t^T \} W \qquad (7e)$$

$$\delta W = \{I + [\frac{g_1'(\mathbf{w}_1^T\mathbf{x})}{g_1(\mathbf{w}_1^T\mathbf{x})} \cdots, \frac{g_n'(\mathbf{w}_n^T\mathbf{x})}{g_n(\mathbf{w}_n^T\mathbf{x})}]^T\mathbf{y}^T\}W \tag{7f}$$

Obviously, in the special case $g_i(y_i) = P_{M_1}(y_i)$, the marginal density of $P_{M_1}(\mathbf{y})$, eq.(7c) will reduce to exactly eq.(2a), and we get the minimum mutual information approach (Amari, Cichocki, and Yang, 1996).

Moreover, let $f_i(r) = \int_{-\infty}^r g_i(u)du$ and $\mathbf{z} = f(\mathbf{y})$, we do transform $\mathbf{y} \to \mathbf{z}$ in eq.(7c), by noticing the Jacobia $det[\frac{\partial \mathbf{y}}{\partial \mathbf{z}^T}] = \prod_{i=1}^n g_i(y_i)$, we get

$$J(M_1(W)) = \int_{\mathbf{Z}} P_{M_1}(\mathbf{z})\log P_{M_1}(\mathbf{z})d\mathbf{z}.$$

If we further assume each $f_i(r) = f(r)$ is sigmoid monotonic function, then we have reached the information maximization approach (Bell and Sejnowski, 1995).

The above statements also give the direct connection between the maximum entropy approach (Bell & Sejnowski, 1995a) and the minimization of the mutual information (Amari, Cichocki & Yang, 1996). That is, they become equivalent when $f_i(r) = \int_{-\infty}^r P_{M_1}(y_i)dy_i$.

5   An Interesting Constrained ICA Scheme and A Theorem

We further consider a useful constrained case of the ICA problem eq.(1) with a source density $P(\mathbf{s}) = \prod_{i=1}^n p_i(s_i)$ and a mixing matrix A such that $AA^T = I$. That is, the source has been mixed via a rotation matrix without energy dissipation.

We modify the scheme of $\min_W J(M_1(W))$ in eq.(7d) into a constrained minimization $\min_{W, WW^T=I} J(M_1(W))$. To do so, we can either use a Lagrange term into eq.(7d) or project $W + \gamma\delta W$ back to the manifold of $WW^T = I$ by Gram-Scmidt Orthogonalization procedure in each iteration of eq.(7e) or eq.(7f). Other more powerful approach may also be possible. Here, we will not discuss the implementation in detail, but show that such a constrained ICA scheme can be realized rather easily by gaussian type functions $g(r)$.

Theorem   Assume that that $AA^T = I$ with A unknown and that $E(\mathbf{s}) = 0$ and $E(\mathbf{ss}^T) = \Lambda_s = diag[\lambda_1, \cdots, \lambda_n]$ known and $\lambda_1 \neq \cdots \neq \lambda_n$. Given a set of gaussian functions $g_i(r) = exp(b_{i0} + b_{i1}r - 0.5\lambda_i^{-1}r^2), i = 1, \cdots, n$; then for $J(W)$ given by eq.(7c) or eq.(7d), any W such that $WW^T = I$ and $\nabla_W J(W) = 0$ will satisfies $W = PDA^{-1}$, where P is a permutation matrix, and D is a diagonal matrix with either -1 or $+1$ entry.

Proof: From $\mathbf{y} = WA\mathbf{s}$ and eq.(6b), eq.(7c) will become

$$J(W) = \int_{\mathbf{s}} P(\mathbf{s})\log\frac{P(\mathbf{s})}{det[WA]\prod_{i=1}^n g_i(\mathbf{v}_i^t\mathbf{s})}d\mathbf{s} =$$

$$= \int_{\mathbf{s}} P(\mathbf{s})\log P(\mathbf{s})d\mathbf{s} - \log det[V] - \int_{\mathbf{s}} P(\mathbf{s})[\sum_{i=1}^n \log g_i(\mathbf{v}_i^t\mathbf{s})]d\mathbf{s} = J(V), \tag{8}$$

where $V = WA, \quad V = [\mathbf{v}_1, \cdots, \mathbf{v}_n]^T$.

Since $\nabla_W J(W) = \nabla_V J(V)A^t$ and A is nonsingular and $VV^T = WAA^TW^T = WW^T = I$, we have that $\min_W J(W) = 0$ with constraint $WW^T = I$ is equivalent to $\min_V J(V) = 0$ with constraint $VV^T = I$, from which we get

$$[V^T]^{-1} = -\int_{\mathbf{s}} P(\mathbf{s})[\frac{g_1'(\mathbf{v}_1^T\mathbf{s})}{g_1(\mathbf{v}_1^T\mathbf{s})} \cdots, \frac{g_n'(\mathbf{v}_n^T\mathbf{s})}{g_n(\mathbf{v}_n^T\mathbf{s})}]^T\mathbf{s}^T d\mathbf{s}, \quad with \ VV^T = I, \tag{9}$$

From $g_i(r) = exp(b_{i0} + b_{i1}r - 0.5\lambda_i^{-1}r^2)$ we have $\frac{g_i'(r)}{g_i(r)} = b_{i1} - \lambda_i^{-1}r$, we put this into eq.(9) and remember that the components of $\mathbf{s}$ are independent, we have

$$[V^T]^{-1} = \Lambda_s^{-1}V\Lambda_s, \Lambda_s \ is \ diagonal.$$

That is, we have $V\Lambda_s V^T = \Lambda_s$ with $VV^T = I$, where Λ_s is a diagonal matrix with different positive entries. Therefore, it must be $V = I$. So, $WA = I$ and the theorem is proved.   **Q.E.D.**

6   Conclusions

A general ICA framework is proposed. It unifies the information maximization approach (Bell and Sejnowski, 1995) and the minimum mutual information approach (Amari, Cichocki, and Yang, 1996). A theorem has also given to show that the ICA problem can be solved even by simple gaussian type nonlinear functions under certain constraints.

Acknowledgment   We thank Dr. H.H.Yang for helpful discussions and comments.

References

Amari, S., Cichocki, A. & Yang, H.H. (1996), " A New Learning Algorithm for Blind Signal Separation", *Advances in Neural Information Processing Systems 8* (to appear), David S. Touretzky, Michael C. Mozer & d Michael E. Hasselmo, eds, MIT Press: Cambridge, MA.

Bell, A.J., & Sejnowski, T.J.(1995a), " An information- maximization approach to blind separation and blind deconvolution", *Neural Computation 7*, 1995, pp1129-1159.

Bell, A.J., & Sejnowski, T.J.(1995b), " Fast blind separation based on information theory", Proc. 1996 Intl Symp. on Nonlinear Theory and Its Applications (NOLTA 95), Las Vegas, USA, Dec 10- 14, 1995, pp43-47.

Common, P. (1994), "Independent component analysis, a new concept ?", *signal Processing 36*, 1994, pp287-314.

Jutten C. & Herault, J. (1991), "Blind Separation of Sources, part I: an adaptive algorithm based on neuromimetic architecture", *Signal Processing 24*, 1991, pp1-10.

NOLTA, (1995), Special session on signal blind separation, Proc. 1996 Intl Symp. on Nonlinear Theory and Its Applications (NOLTA 95), Las Vegas, USA, Dec 10- 14, 1995.

Xu, L. (1995a), YING-YANG Machine: a Bayesian-Kullback scheme for unified learnings and new results on vector quantization, Keynote talk, in *Proc. Intl Conf. on Neural Information Processing (ICONIP95)*, Oct 30 - Nov. 3, 1995, pp977-988.

Xu, L.(1995b), YING-YANG Machine for Temporal Signals, Keynote talk, in *Proc Intl Conf. on Neural Networks and Signal Processing 1995*, Vol.I, pp644-651, Nanjing.

Xu, L. (1996a), A Unified Learning Scheme: Bayesian-Kullback YING-YANG Machine, *Advances in Neural Information Processing Systems 8* (to appear), David S. Touretzky, Michael C. Mozer & d Michael E. Hasselmo, eds, MIT Press: Cambridge, MA.

Xu, L. (1996b), "Bayesian-Kullback YING-YANG Learning Scheme: Reviews and New Results", to appear on Proc. Intl Conf. on Neural Information Processing (ICONIP96).

Xu, L, Yang, H., and Amari, S (1996), "Maximum equalization by entropy maximization and mixture of cumulative distribution functions", in preparation.

Special Session II
Hardware Implementations

The invited program is also featured by 8 special sessions on current interesting topics. Each special session organizer is invited by the Program Committee and the success of each special session is completely due to the hard efforts of each organizer.

An on-chip parallel processor for neural networks

Ken-ichi Tanaka and Kazuo Kyuma
Neural & Parallel Processing Technology Department
Advanced Technology R&D Center, Mitsubishi Electric Corporation
Amagasaki, Hyogo 661, JAPAN
tanakake@mec.crl.melco.co.jp

Abstract— **A parallel processor which is suitable for neural networks and parallel algorithm computations has been developed. The processor employs SIMD architecture and was designed based on microprocessor technology. Twelve DSP-like cores, a nonlinear function unit and a control unit are integrated on a chip. The function of the processor is programmable so that a lot of neural network and parallel algorithms can be efficiently executed by loading a software onto the processor. To take full advantage of the processor power and realize practical applications with it, two types of board combined with their software development environments that can be plugged into VMEbus and PCI bus have also been developed.**

1 Introduction

A lot of neural network learning and optimization algorithms use iteration to solve a problem. This fact implies intensive computational power is required when we use those algorithms in a practical situation. Since an algorithm based on a neural network can be parallelizable in nature, we can overcome this difficulties if we use a special hardware that can accelerate parallel computations. From the early stage of neural network research, many people have been working on a hardware implementation of the neural network. Neural processors developed so far are roughly divided into two categories, a model specific processor and a model independent processor. The architecture of the model specific processor is optimally designed to have the maximum efficiency for a specific neural network model. Ni1000 by NESTOR/INTEL[1] and ZISC036 by IBM[2] belong to this category. Both of them dedicate to RCE model and are primarily used for a pattern recognition application. On the other hand, the architecture of the model independent processor is very similar to that of a general purpose parallel processor. Most of the neural processors belong to this category employ SIMD architecture with a systolic array configuration. CNAPS-1064 by ASI[3], HNC100 by HNC[4] and NEURO4 by Mitsubishi[5] are good examples. The key feature of those processors is flexibility. The function of the processor can be changed by loading an appropriate software so that they can be used for a wide range of applications including ordinary parallel algorithms as well as neural network algorithms. However this feature requests to provide a software development environment of the processor on which lots of development cost and time has to be spent in addition to the hardware development. In this paper we describe an overview of the NEURO4 processor system from both hardware and software points of view.

2 Neural processor

We have developed an on-chip parallel processor for neural networks, called NEURO4. The architecture of the NEURO4 is a SIMD parallel microprocessor with a systolic array configuration. As shown in Fig.1, the NEURO4 has twelve PU(Processing Unit)s, an NFU(Nonlinear Function Unit), and a CU(Control Unit). All of these units are integrated on a chip. Figure 2 shows a picture of the NEURO4. Floating point numbers in the NEURO4 are represented using 24bits: 1 for the sign, 6 for the exponent, and 17

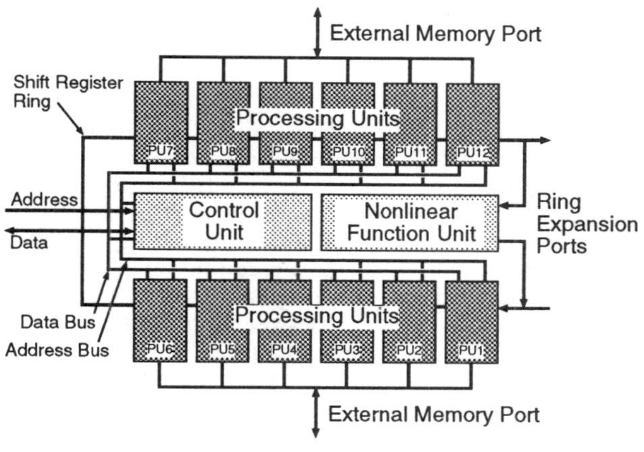

Fig.1   NEURO4 processor block diagram

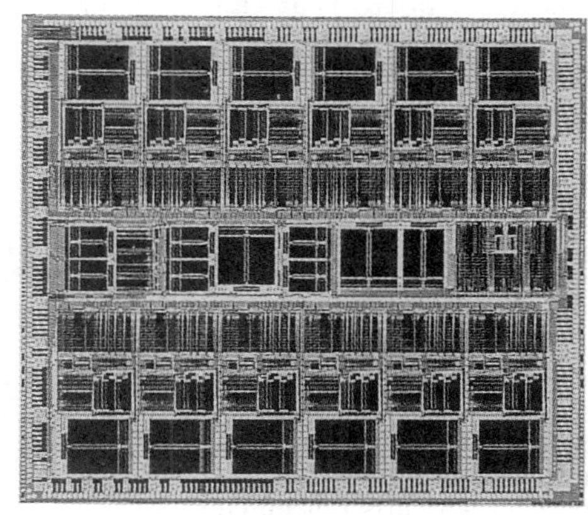

Fig.2   Picture of NEURO4 processor

for the fraction. Integer numbers are also represented using 24bits. The processor contains a format conversion circuit that converts data between 24-bit NEURO4 format and 32-bit IEEE standard format. Therefore, NEURO4 can be directly connected to the most of the processors now available in the market. Throughout this paper one word means 24 bits. Each PU consists of two arithmetic units(adder and multiplier), registers, and its own local memory. The size of the local memory is 1K words/PU and it is expandable up to 64K words/PU if an off-chip memory is available. Two external memory ports can be used to expand the local memory. The PUs can communicate with each other through the shift register ring. By connecting ring expansion ports, multi-chip configuration can be realized. The adder and multiplier constitutes pipe stages. An addition and multiplication instructions can be overlapped in execution. This architecture is quite useful in the case of product-sum operation which is often encountered in the neural network algorithm. The processor achieves the peak performance of 1.2GFLOPS at the clock frequency of 50MHz. In addition to this feature, the NEURO4 has a special hardware circuit to accelerate the learning speed of a multi-layered neural network by eliminating waste operations. The circuit controls the arithmetic units so as to automatically skip the addition operation of negligible small values until an effective operation is found. This function is useful to update weights of the multi-layered neural network and becomes more effective as the learning process converges. In the case of the three layered neural network trained by the back-propagation algorithm, the total learning time was typically decreased to the one third.

The CU generates and broadcasts control codes for each unit on the chip. The CU can also broadcast addresses and data to PUs using the address bus and data bus. The CU consists of a sequencer part, an arithmetic part, and an internal instruction memory. The sequencer part is pipelined into three stages: instruction fetch, decode, and execution. Most of the instructions can be executed in a single clock cycle because the three stages operate in parallel. The arithmetic part manipulates and holds broadcast addresses and data to control the program flow. The size of the internal instruction memory is 1K words and it is expandable up to 128K words outside. There is no time penalty between the internal and the external instruction memory.

The NFU calculates nonlinear functions, which are often used in neural networks, at high speed. The conversion is executed through the shift register ring. The NFU transforms floating-point data entered from one end of the shift register ring and outputs the data to the other end of the ring. The internal operation consists of a table look-up scheme that is pipelined to five stages and enables high speed transformation. The table is implemented by RAM. By changing the contents of the table, we can use the NFU to calculate not only a sigmoid function for neural networks but also other functions, such as sine and cosine functions. The NFU also contains a noise generator which is implemented by a linear feedback shift register to be used for the probabilistic models, such as Boltzmann and Gaussian machines. Chip characteristics are summarized in Table.1.

Table 1   Chip characteristics

Process technology	0.5μm CMOS(1poly, 3Al)
Chip size	17.4mm × 15.4mm
Local memory	24bit × 1K × 12
Number of processing units	12(SIMD architecture)
Accuracy	24bit floating point/integer
Peak performance	1.2GFLOPS(@50MHz)
External memory	24bit × 64K × 12
Ring extensions (max)	1.4M chips
Power dissipation	4.0W(@50MHz, Vcc=3.3V)
Number of transistors	3.4M

3   Neural processor systems

To take full advantage of the processor power and realize practical applications with it, we have developed two types of board that can be plugged into VMEbus and PCI bus. Both boards work as a back-end processor of a host processor and they are designed to be expandable – multiple board configurations are easy to set up.

The VMEbus version, called NEURO4_VME consists of four NEURO4s, a DSP, memory blocks for the NEURO4 and the DSP, and a VMEbus interface circuit. All of these units are mounted on a standard double-high VMEmodule which takes two slots in a VME system. Figure 3 shows a picture of the NEURO4_VME. The board has a total of 768K word external memory, i.e. 16K word/PU and it delivers 3.17GFLOPS peak performance at 33MHz clock rate. The ring expansion port of the NEURO4 is connected to that of the adjacent NEURO4 to make the multi-chip configuration having a total of 48 processing units in a single ring. The expansion port is also connected to the connector located on the front panel to realize the multiple board configurations which offers scalable peak performance up to 15 boards. The DSP on the board provides high throughput data transfer between the VMEbus and the NEURO4 using its built-in DMA circuit. The DSP has a large main memory of 4M words on which the program for the DSP is loaded. The main memory is also used as a buffer area for the application which handles large amount of data, such as image and CAD data. The DSP can also be used for the scalar operation which is not efficiently executed by the parallel processor. The VMEbus interface supports an Address 32/Data 32/64 (A32/D32/D64) VMEbus slave mode including BLT block data transfer. From the hardware configuration point of view, two types of operation mode, host mode and stand-alone mode, can be selected. In the host mode, NEURO4_VME runs in conjunction with the host processor. We have selected an AXPvme 160 CPU board(Alpha 21066) as the host processor because of its high speed data transfer capability. The target operating system of the AXPvme 160 is DEC OSF/1 AXP UNIX. In the stand-alone mode, which is suitable for an embedded application, the DSP acts as the host processor by providing the program which serves the host function.

The PCI bus version, called NEURO4_PCI, consists of a NEURO4, an external memory block, and a PCI bus interface circuit. All of these units are mounted on a full size PCI card which can be plugged into a PCI slot of the PC and other computers. The device driver software for Windows NT has already been developed. Figure 4 shows a picture of the NEURO4_PCI. The board has a total of 768K word external memory, i.e. 64K word/PU and it delivers 792MFLOPS peak performance at 33MHz clock rate. The ring expansion port is available at the connector located on the edge of the board. This enables us to realize multiple board configurations and offers scalable peak performance up to 4 boards. The PCI bus interface meets the PCI specification Rev.2.1 and supports both master and slave device functions.

Fig.3   Picture of NEURO4_VME

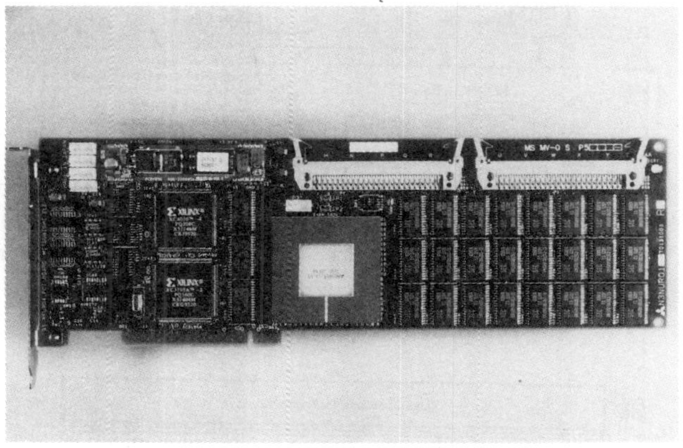

Fig.4   Picture of NEURO4_PCI

4   Software development environment

Since the basic operation of the NEURO4 is the same as the microprocessor, we have to write a software to calculate neural network algorithms. For this purpose, we have developed a software development environment for the neural processor systems. Figure 5 shows an overview of the software development environment. Software tools available for developing an application program is listed in Table 2. All of the tools have been developed and implemented on the standard operating systems: Unix and Windows NT as shown in Fig.6. Unix is the target OS of the NEURO4_VME and Windows NT is the target OS of the NEURO4_PCI, respectively.

As shown in Fig.5, the NEURO4 has basically two kinds of languages: assembly language and C language. In C language programming environment the SIMDizer[6] acts as a preprocessor to a C compiler of the host processor. It is a key tool of our software environment. The SIMDizer automatically detects areas in C source code that can be effectively executed by the NEURO4 processors, dividing the program into NEURO4 board and host processor sections. Compiling the NEURO4 and host sections by a language processing system of each processor, two executable files are obtained. Those two files are loaded on to the NEURO4 board and the host processor, and then the program execution conducted in conjunction with the communication between the processors over the system bus. An assembly coded function can also be called from the user C program. A macro assembler, linker and archiver are available. For debugging, a command-line based and GUI based assembler level debuggers have been developed. In addition to the hardware-level debugger, a software simulator which can simulate all the functions of the board including data transfer between the NEURO4 and the host has also been developed. The user can debug and evaluate the program without using a real hardware. The same user interface is used for the assembler level debuggers and the software simulator to make it easier to use. Figure 7 shows a sample view of the GUI debugger. A vector library includes C callable functions of the neural network algorithms, such as back-propagation learning algorithm, LVQ, LVQ2, etc.. It also includes basic vector calculation functions, such as vector addition, inner-product, vector-matrix multiplication, nearest neighbor classifier, convolution, and wavelet to support a user defined algorithm. A board control library consists of the functions which take care of the interface and data transfer between the NEURO4 and the host processor.

We have conducted several benchmark tests by using the NEURO4_VME. As for the neural network example, the four color problem which is a well-known combinatorial optimization problem was solved by Hopfield model. The calculation speed of the NEURO4_VME was 120 times faster than that of Sun Sparc 10. As for the parallel computation example, a finite-difference representation for the heat diffusion equation was solved. The speed of the NEURO4_VME was 40 times faster than that of Sun Sparc 10.

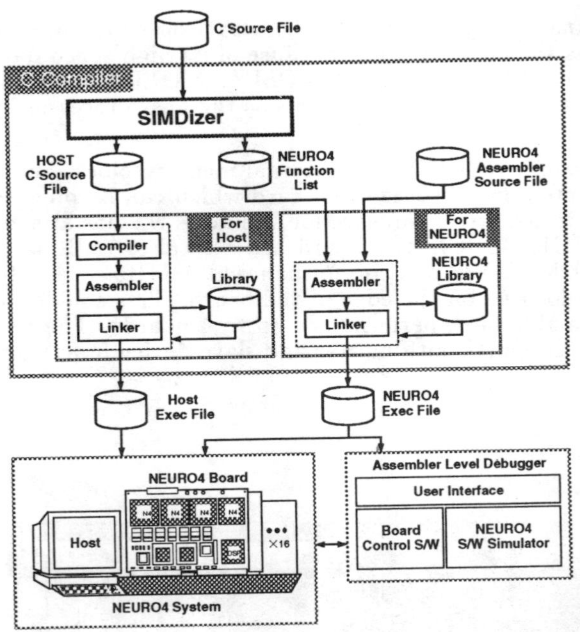

Fig.5   Overview of NEURO4 software development environment

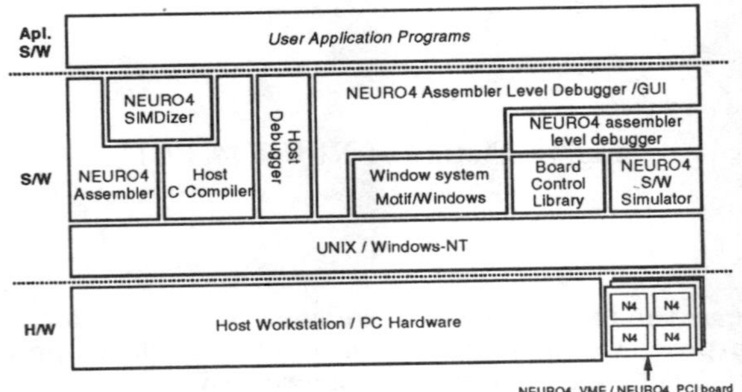

Fig.6   Software architecture of NEURO4 system

Table 2.   Software tools for neural processor system

- SIMDizer
- Macro Assembler
- Linker
- Archiver(Librarian)
- Assembler Level Debugger/GUI
- Software Simulator
- Vector Library
- Board Control Library

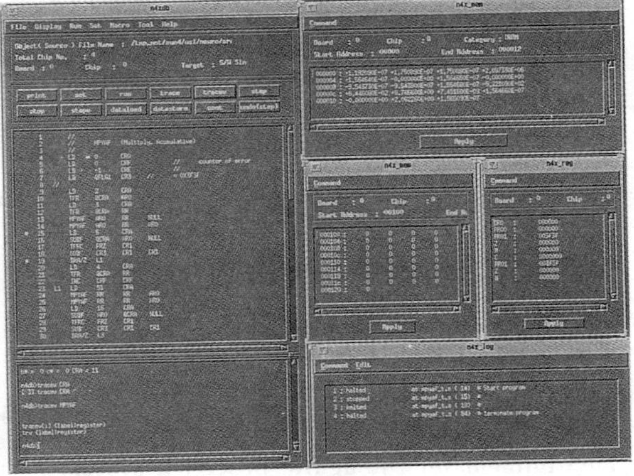

Fig.7   Sample view of GUI debugger

5   Conclusions

The 12PU SIMD parallel microprocessor for neural networks has been developed. The architecture of the processor is suitable for vector/matrix computations as well as neural network computations. To utilize the NEURO4 processor for the practical application, two types of board, NEURO4_VME and NEURO4_PCI combined with their software development environments have also been developed. The high performance of the system enables us to realize several applications which require intensive computational power.

References

[1] Nestor Inc., http://www.nestor.com/ni1000.htm.

[2] G. Lebesnerais *et al.*, "The Zero Instruction Set Computer: ZISC036", *Proc. Int. Conf. Artificial Neural Network*, Paris, vol. A9, pp.13–17, October 1995.

[3] Adaptive Solutions Inc., http://www.asi.com/hw/hw.html.

[4] HNC Inc., *SNAP Technical Description*, HNC Inc. 1993.

[5] Y.Kondo *et al.*, "A 1.2GFLOPS Neural Network Chip Exhibiting Fast Convergence", *ISSCC Digest of Technical Papers*, pp.218–219, 1994.

[6] V.Konda *et al.*, "A SIMDizing C Compiler for the Mitsubishi Electric Neuro4 Processor Array", *Proc. of First SUIF Compiler Workshop*, Stanford Univ., Jan.11–13, 1996.

Neural　Network　Implementation　with Analogue-Digital Mixed Neural Chip URAN

Il-Song Han
Korea Telecom Multimedia Lab
17 Woomyun-dong, Suhcho-ku, Seoul, 137-792Korea
ishan@basic.kotel.co.kr

ABSTRACT

This paper introduces the way of neural network hardware implementation with the neural chip URAN. The analogue-digital mixed operation allows the massive synapse array and the biological neuron function in CMOS VLSI. Application tasks are utilized as examples to demonstrate the ways that the URAN can be used in multi-layer perceptrons. The multi-layer perceptron with the URAN is evaluated for both of speech recognitions and character recognitions. The recognition result of more than 98% is shown for the Korean printed character recognition. Results of using the URAN for hand-written digit recognition and the 100 spoken word recognition highlight the potential superiority of implementing applications with the URAN. Finally, with the URAN of simulating the probabilistic RAM(pRAM) based neural network, the intelligent multimedia applications using neural network are to be available for various real world environments.

1. Introductions

Neural networks have the potential of being implemented in VLSI hardware in a parallel way in respects of its relatively fast speed, huge network size and effective cost comparing to software simulation. The URAN has been developed as one of those VLSIs, which is based on the controllable MOSFET resistance. With the URAN of analogue-digital mixed operation, the accuracy as well as the capacity has been improved by using the MOSFET resistance for the synapse weight emulation.

The URAN's adaptability to various applications has been evaluated for the multi-layer perceptron and the pRAM. The implementations for both the hand-written and the printed character recognition is proposed for the use of the URAN in the modular structure as well as the general multi-layer perceptron. The multi-layer perceptron with the URAN is proved for the successful speech recognition under the 8-bit precision of synaptic connections and the linear neuron with conventional back propagation learning. It is also possible to implement the probabilistic RAM(pRAM) principle with the URAN, where the pRAM itself was developed from earlier motivation of biological modelling of synaptic noise and is almost unique in being able to function both stochastic and non-linear aspects.

2. Analogue-Digital Mixed MOSFET Operation of URAN

There have been improvements in analogue or analogue-digital mixed VLSI chips. Based on the pulse-stream operation, the analogue-digital mixed neural network circuits are suggested for the accuracy improvement with the use of linear MOSFET resistance for basic synapse.

Most of the circuit in URAN is conceptually operated in an analogue way. Except the decoder for the synaptic weight access, circuit operation over the chip is based on the switching of MOSFET and the specially designed static MOSFET resistance cell of synapse. With URAN's synapse circuit of linear voltage-controlled bipolar current source, the synaptic multiplication with weight value is done with the switching transistor, in a similar way of analogue-sampled data type. And as they are almost virtually static except switching transistor controlled by neural input, the computation speed becomes higher and even can be improved substantially with the advanced fabrication process. The basic circuit of artificial synapse unit is built with 9 transistors including weight memory as in Fig. 1.　The conversion linearity of weight value to current amount is attained by the compensated synaptic MOSFET channel resistance in the triode region, and proved to have more than 8 bit from the measured linear characteristic of   0.25% in an equivalent total harmonic distortion. The silicon cell size including interconnection area in conventional 1.0μ standard single poly double metal CMOS technology is reduced to less than 900 μm^2 in size.

3. Multi-Layer Perceptron with the URAN

The URAN chip of Table 1 is tested for implementing the Korean speech recognition and character recognition.

Table 1. Specification of the URAN

No. of Connections	135,424
Speed	200 giga CPS
Connection Accuracy	8-bit
No. of Modules	16
No. of Inputs/Outputs	92/92
Supply Voltage	+/- 3V
Operation	Analog-Digital Mixed

For the case of the character recognition, the modular configuration of the URAN is thoroughly utilized to yield the desired performance using multiple parallel networks. Two kinds of the recognition are also tested for the effect of the limited computation accuracy. One is the printed Korean character recognition and the other is hand written digit recognition. Those implementation is based on the multiple 16x16 modules. With the special consideration on the given modularity and the 8-bit accuracy of the URAN, the URAN is proved to be suitable for the binary pattern recognition from the overall performance shown in Table 2.

Table 2. Recognition Rate of OCR with the degraded accuracy

	8-bit	7-bit	6-bit	5-bit
Printed Korean Font I	99.43 %	99.43 %	99.29%	98.72%
Printed Korean Font II	98.93 %	99.00 %	98.65%	98.22%
Handwritten Digit	97.38 %	97.33 %	97.15%	93.63%

The modular configuration does not show any severe problem in the learning phase from the case of the hand-written digit recognition. In the case of speech recognition, the modular configuration is proved to be efficient to identify the more vocabulary than 100 words for its fast operation in either the learning phase or the recognition phase. The speech recognition using the URAN is tested in many ways for the optimal implementation using the multi-layer perceptron only, VQ-MLP with HMM and VQ-MLP with DTW. The speaker independent 100 word recognition is implemented using VQ-MLP with HMM for the portable environment of using the notebook with the designed hardware. Here, the MLP is implemented in the parallel modular structure based on the URAN. The overall performance in noisy audio environment is more than 96% of the successful recognition.

4. pRAM Implementation with the URAN

The pRAM has been known as an efficient way of building artificial neural networks for physiological nets in hardware, which is proved to have the generalization properties of noisy learning and neuron number minimizing than other model. It is based on the fact that a living neuron receives its input from other neuron by means of packets composed of neuro transmitter chemicals released with a   certain probability(not necessarily 0 or 1) at the synapses when a nerve impulse arrives. There is a distribution of chemical transmitter in the synaptic cleft with probability where the chemical transmitter is taken up with the efficiency by the post-synaptic terminal. The basic structure of pRAM is modeled with the probability for the noisy characteristic. With the use of packet of electric charge as both synaptic signal and inherent noise, the principle of pRAM is easily implemented with the URAN. The implementation is based on the charge packet control by proper switching of current sources correspondent to the synaptic connection strength and the noise level. As the charge packet from the current source is used, the capacitor is used as an accumulator at the neuron function part to yield unlimited synaptic connection and unlimited timing. The basic operation principle is used and proved in URAN chip to realize the large scale and high speed general neural network with the resonable accuracy.

The circuit in Fig. 2 is developed for the pRAM implementation and the connection weight has the accuracy of 8 bit. The noise circuit of Fig. 2 can also be replaced by the same one as the synapse circuit with the random signal from externals if required. With the control of the equivalent pulse activation, the proper probability due to noise is effective in neural computation. The speed in neural computation is also improved by the simple switch operation for the neural multiplication function as shown in previous works. The general flexibility is also inherently attained by the independent characteristic of each circuit cell for the inter-chip interface. It is possible to integrate the large number of pRAM units in analogue-digital mixed operation as each unit is relatively equivalent to a simple gate in respect to its area or complexity, while it is still possible in the low cost digital CMOS technology.

4. Conclusion

Ways of using the URAN are suggested to realize the recognition tasks, such as the voice, the printed character or the hand-written character, in either the multi-layer perceptron or the modular parallel configurations. For the potential real world applications, multi-layer perceptrons using the URAN have been shown to be efficient for implementing general cases of recognition.

The way of implementing the pRAM principle is also suggested for realizing the very large scale neural system/VLSI of both stochastic and biological aspects of biological neural network. As it is operated by the electronic pulse stream mechanism of the URAN, the pRAM algorithm and application is extended their use easily in the fast and massive neural chip of the URAN. The underlying principle of implementing the analog-digital mixed pRAM is also applicable to any other model in which the special transfer characteristic is necessary for the hardware implementation using the URAN.

References

1. Il-Song Han, "Neural Network VLSI of Pulse Operation for Reduced Power Consumption," IEE-ASIC, 1995

2. Il Song Han and Ki-Hwan Ahn, "Neural Network VLSI Chip Implementation of Analog-Digital Mixed Operation for more than 100,000 Connections" MicroNeuro'93, pp. 159-162, 1993

3. Il-Song Han, "Analog Circuit for a Nerual Network," Proc. of ICANN'91, pp. 1577-1580, 1991

4. M. Brownlow, L. Tarassenko, A. F. Murray, A. Hamilton, I S Han, H. M. Reekie, "Pulse Firing Neural Chips Implementing Hundreds of Neurons," NIPS2, pp. 785-792, 1990

5. KTRL Tech Report 95-55, 'A Study on the Basic Technology for the Applications of Neuro-chips,' 1995

6. Il-Song Han and T. G. Clarkson, "Neural Hardwares Realized with Neural VLSI URAN," WCNN '95, 1995

7 T. G. Clarkson, Y. Guan, J. G. Taylor, and Gorse, "Generalization In Probabilistic RAM Nets," IEEE trans. Neural Network, pp. 360-363, 1993

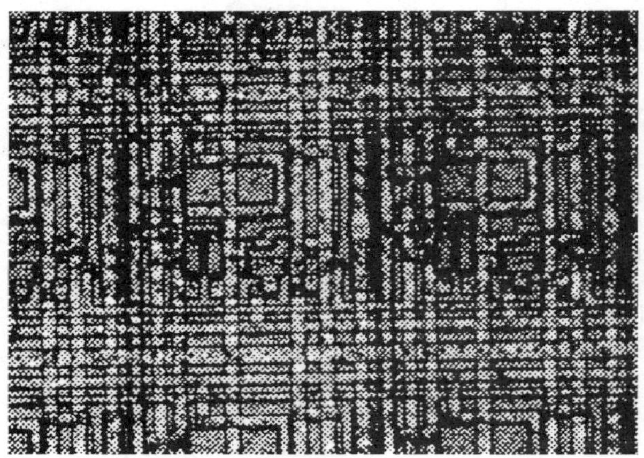

Fig. 1. Unit Synapse of URAN

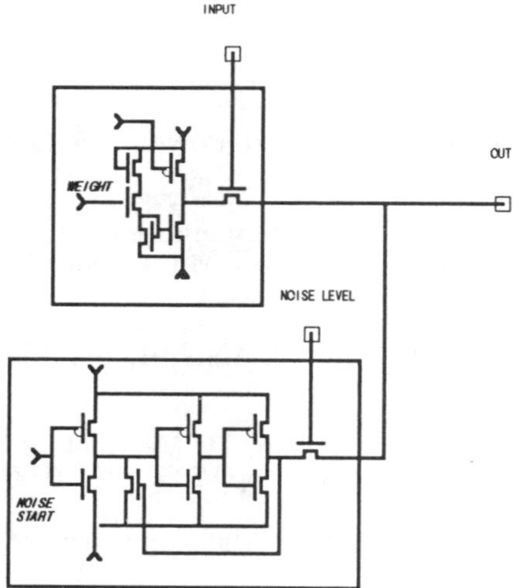

Fig. 2. pRAM Implementation with URAN

A PDM Digital Neural Network System with 1,000 Neurons Fully Interconnected via 1,000,000 6-bit Synapses

Yuzo Hirai† and Moritoshi Yasunaga‡
Institute of Information Sciences and Electronics, University of Tsukuba
1-1-1 Ten-nodai, Tsukuba, Ibaraki 305, Japan
e-mail: † hirai@is.tsukuba.ac.jp, ‡ yasunaga@is.tsukuba.ac.jp

Abstract— **We are developing a PDM (Pulse Density Modulating) digital neural network system. It consists of one thousand digital neurons fully interconnected via one million 6-bit digital synapses. Each neuron operates asynchronously and the system solves one thousand simultaneous nonlinear first order differential equations in a parallel and continuous way. We are fabricating one kind of VLSI chips using $0.7\mu m$ CMOS gate array with 250,000 gates. Each chip carries eighteen neurons and fifty-one synapses for each neuron. About 85% of the gates in a gate array, which is an extremely efficient number, can be used. The system consists of 1,120 chips with 3.3V power supply. The power consumption is expected to be 1,500W.**

1 Introduction

Since mid 80s, many neural chips have been fabricated in analog, optoelectronic and digital circuits. (Typical examples are listed in [1].) Most of them are dedicated to feedforward neural networks, and only a few are to feedback neural networks. One of the difficulties in developing feedback neural networks is that it requires to solve a set of simultaneous nonlinear differential equations in a parallel and continuous way. So far several examples including an analog VLSI system [2] and a *PDM* digital VLSI system [3] for small neural networks have been reported.

A project of developing a hardware system for a large scale, feedback neural network is running in our laboratory. The circuit design basically inherits from the prototype system with 54 neurons fully interconnected [3], but the size of the system scales up to one thousand neurons fully interconnected via one million synapses. Since it is not possible to fabricate the system of this size in a single chip, it is anticipated that more than one thousand chips will be connected. The problems we have to solve in this situation are as follows:

1. Fully parallel operation over more than one thousand chips,

2. Faithful analog data transmission between chips, and

3. The number of signal lines between chips.

For easy implementation of the fully parallel operation, asynchronous operation is preferable to synchronous operation because synchronous operation needs to supply a common clock to all chips. For faithful analog data transmission, digital coding is preferable to purely analog transmission because of the immunity to noise and process parameter variations between chips. Since the number of pins of a chip is limited, pulse density coding is preferable to binary digital coding because single lines are sufficient to transmit digitally coded analog data as our real neurons do. Only pulse density coding solves all of the above problems. Besides, the circuit size of synaptic wights, which is one of the most critical factors in hardware implementation, is moderate as described below. Therefore, we chose PDM (Pulse Density Modulating) digital circuits to implement a large scale, feedback neural network.

2 Model of Neural Network

Mathematical model of the feedback neural network we are implementing in the system is described by the following one thousand simultaneous nonlinear first order differential equations:

$$\mu_i \frac{dy_i^*(t)}{dt} \;=\; -y_i^*(t) + \sum_{j=1}^{N} w_{ij} y_j(t) + I_i(t) \tag{1}$$

$$y_i(t) \;=\; \varphi[y_i^*(t)] \tag{2}$$

$$\varphi[a] \;=\; \begin{cases} a & \text{if } a > 0 \\ 0 & \text{otherwise,} \end{cases} \tag{3}$$

where μ_i is a time constant of the ith neuron, $y_i^*(t)$ is an internal potential of the ith neuron at time t, w_{ij} is a synaptic weight from the jth neuron to the ith neuron, and $I_i(t)$ is an external input to the ith neuron. $\varphi[a]$ is an analog threshold output function which will saturate at some maximum value.

In our system, the differential equation is solved by the following integral form:

$$y_i^*(t) = \int_0^t \left\{ -y_i^*(\tau) + \sum_{j=1}^N w_{ij} y_j(\tau) + I_i(\tau) \right\} \frac{d\tau}{\mu_i} + y_i^*(0), \tag{4}$$

where $y_i^*(0)$ is an initial value.

The right hand side of the equation represents an internal potential of a neuron. If it is positive, the output is transmitted by a pulse stream whose frequency is proportional to the constantly varying, instantaneous internal potential. The integration is carried out by an up/down counter. Excitatory pulses from excitatory synapses are spatially summed by a set of *OR* gates and are fed to the up input of the counter, and inhibitory pulses from inhibitory synapses are also spatially summed by a separate set of *OR* gates and are fed to the down input. Internal pulse stream whose frequency is proportional to the *absolute value* of the internal potential is generated. The negative feedback in the first term of the integrand in Eq.(4) is realized by feeding back the internal pulses to the *up* input of the up/down counter when the internal potential is *negative* and by feeding back to the *down* input when it is *positive*.

3   Mapping Neural Networks into PDM Digital Circuits

In this section, neuron circuits which are composed of synapse circuits, dendrite circuits and cell body circuits are described. These circuits consist of fully digital circuits and operate in a parallel, asynchronous and continuous manner.

3.1   Neuron circuits

Neuron circuits in a chip are schematically shown in Figure 1. Each neuron consists of synapse circuits, excitatory and inhibitory dendrite circuits and cell body circuits. To simplify the illustration, only three neurons and three synapse circuits for each neuron are shown in the figure.

The actual number of cell bodies and that of synapses for each neuron to be contained in a chip are eighteen and fifty-one, respectively. Since we will fabricate only one kind of chips, most of the chips in the system will be used only for synapse circuits, and cell body circuits in these chips are not used. The number of unused circuits should be minimized as well as the total number of chips in the system. The actual numbers of neurons and synapses in a single chip are optimized in this sense.

For each neuron there are two groups of input signal lines and two groups of output signal lines. Input lines designated as "From neuron outputs" on the left side of the figure receive outputs from other neurons and are broadcasted to all neurons in a chip via synapse circuits. The other input lines designated as "excitatory and inhibitory dendrite" in the upper part of the figure are *dendrite extension terminals* and are used to increase the number of synapses for each neuron.

One group of output signal lines is for direct outputs from excitatory and inhibitory dendrite circuits. By connecting dendrite *output* lines to the corresponding dendrite *input* lines in another chip, the number of synapses for each neuron can be increased without supplying a common clock. Output signal lines from cell body circuits transmit pulse streams to the other neurons. For each chip, either cell body outputs or direct dendrite outputs can be selected by a set of *selectors* shown in the figure.

Output pulse stream from a neuron is broadcasted to a synapse of each neuron. A synapse consists of a synaptic weight register and a rate multiplier. It transforms input pulse frequency to the frequency proportional to the synaptic weight. The MSB of synaptic weight register specifies whether the synapse is excitatory or inhibitory. If it is zero, the synapse is excitatory and the synaptic output pulses are sent to the excitatory dendrite circuit. If it is one, the synapse is inhibitory and the synaptic output pulses are sent to the inhibitory dendrite circuit. Excitatory and inhibitory synaptic output pulses are spatially summed by separate OR-circuits and are integrated by the cell body circuits.

3.2   Synapse circuits

For the hardware implementation of neural networks, one of the key issues is the circuit size of synapses because for a fully interconnected neural network, the number of synapses increases in proportion to the square of the number of neurons. By using analog circuits, the circuit size of synapses can be very small, but the precision will be a crucial problem. Binary digital multiplier is precise, but it is prohibitive to use one for each synapse because of the large circuit size.

In the PDM digital implementation, moderate circuit size can be achieved. Synapse circuit transforms an input pulse frequency to the frequency which is proportional to the synaptic weight as shown in Figure 2. This transformation is carried out by a 6-bit rate multiplier. Additional sign bit specifies the type of a synapse which is either excitatory or inhibitory. Rate multiplier consists of a counter with 2^N states, where N is the depth of the counter. When an input pulse comes, the current state transits to the next one. The N-bit rate value, which represents the absolute value of a synaptic weight, specifies at which

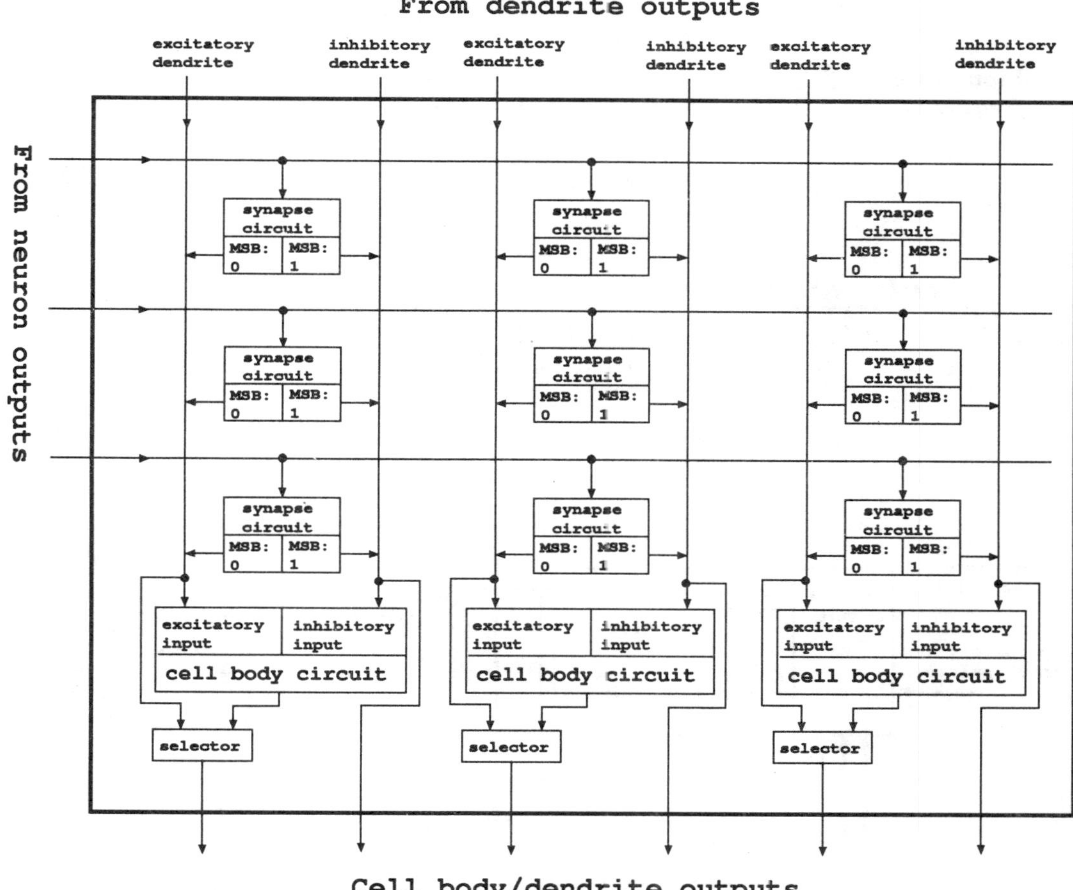

Figure 1: Neuron circuits in a chip. To simplify the illustration only three cell body circuits and nine synapse circuits are shown in this figure. Control lines and read/write lines for various registers are omitted from this figure.

state an output pulse is produced. The output pulse frequency is given by

$$f_{\text{output}} = \frac{\text{rate value}}{2^N} f_{\text{input}}. \tag{5}$$

Therefore, the magnitude of synaptic weight representable by a rate multiplier is always less than one. This limitation is overcome by scaling the output frequency by the factor of either 1 or 2, which is programmable in a cell body circuit. In the present system, we use a 6-bit rate multiplier with an additional sign bit for each synapse.

3.3 Dendrite circuits

Excitatory and inhibitory dendrite circuits spatially sum output pulses from synapse circuits by OR gates. When more than one pulse comes simultaneously, they are counted as one pulse. Although linear summation cannot be taken place in such a case, theoretical analysis shows that the summation characteristic is similar to the positive part of hyperbolic tangent function. This has been confirmed by 54 neuron prototype system [1]. This came from the fact that since each neuron was driven by an individual clock, input pulses to different synapses of a single neuron became out of phase even if their frequencies were identical. In the present system, one thousand neurons are driven by one thousand individual clocks and they operate in a fully asynchronous manner.

3.4 Cell body circuits

Cell body circuits consist of an up/down counter and two rate multipliers, one for producing output pulses and the other one for changing time constant, as shown in Figure 3. Output pulses from excitatory synapses are fed to the *up* input of the counter and those from inhibitory synapses are fed to the *down* input. The precision of the counter is 11-bit with an additional sign bit. It acts as an integrator. The 12-bit rate multiplier transforms the counter value including the sign to a pulse stream whose frequency is

Synapse circuit

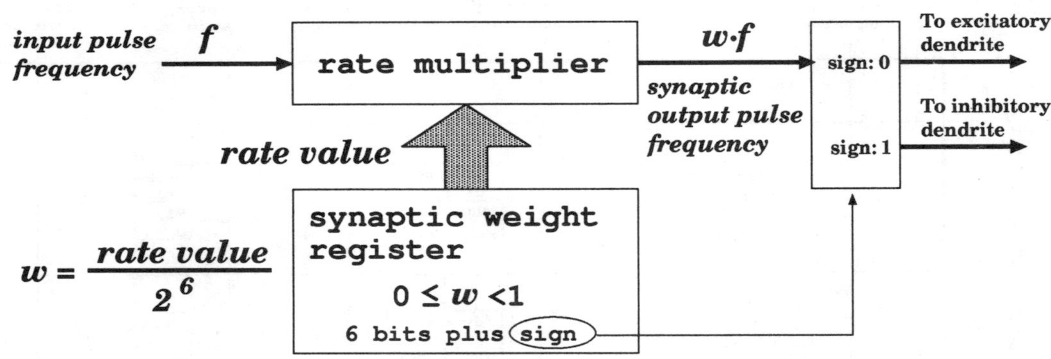

$$w = \frac{rate\ value}{2^6}$$

Figure 2: Structure of a synapse circuit.

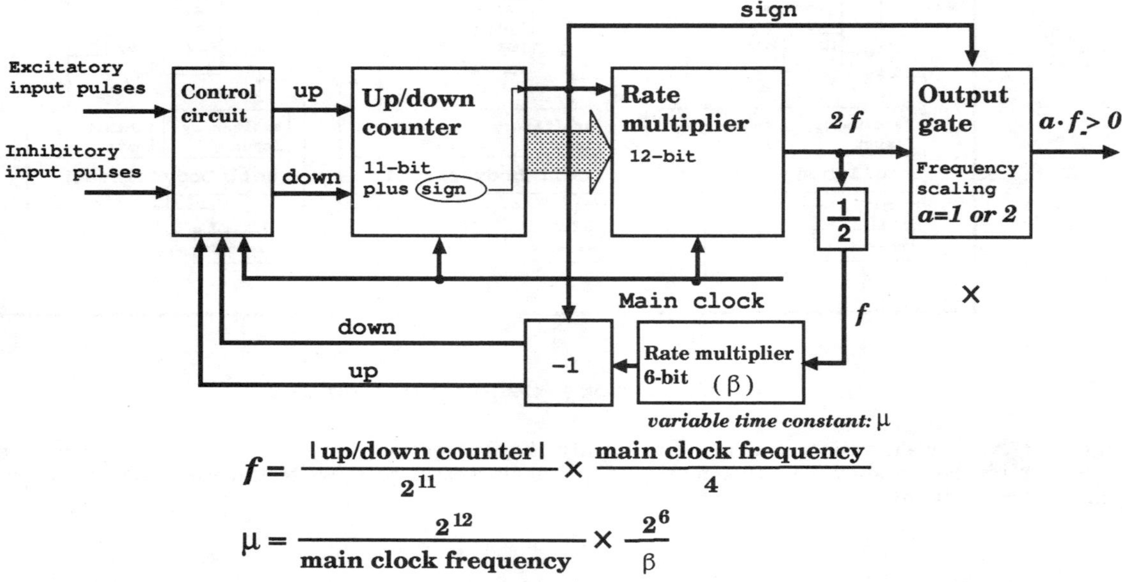

$$f = \frac{|\,up/down\ counter\,|}{2^{11}} \times \frac{main\ clock\ frequency}{4}$$

$$\mu = \frac{2^{12}}{main\ clock\ frequency} \times \frac{2^6}{\beta}$$

Figure 3: Cell body circuits

proportional to the value. By changing the polarity of the pulses when the counter value is negative, the frequency of the output pulses from the rate multiplier becomes proportional to the absolute value of the counter. This output frequency is taken as a scaled up frequency to increase the synaptic weight by the factor of two. An ordinary pulse frequency is obtained by halving the output frequency. Therefore, the maximum ordinary output frequency is a quarter of the clock frequency driving the 12-bit rate multiplier. Neuron output is transmitted only when the counte value is positive.

The reason why the absolute value of the counter is transformed to an internal pulse stream is that as seen in Eq.(4), there is a negative feedback term in the integrand. The ordinary output pulses from the rate multiplier are fed to the *down* input of the counter when the content is *positive* and are fed to the *up* input when it is *negative*. The 6-bit rate multiplier inserted in this feedback path is used to change the time constant. From Eq.(4), we obtain the following:

$$y_i^*(t) = \int_0^t \left\{ -\frac{y_i^*}{\mu_i}(\tau) + \sum_{j=1}^N \frac{w_{ij}}{\mu_{ij}} y_j(\tau) + \frac{I_i(\tau)}{\mu_i} \right\} d\tau + y_i^*(0), \tag{6}$$

where μ_i^{-1} is a scaling factor given by the 6-bit rate multiplier and is defined by

$$\mu_i^{-1} = \frac{\beta}{2^6} < 1, \tag{7}$$

where β is the rate value. If we set β to zero, the negative feedback is disabled and the neuron operates as a simple integrater. By setting each scaling factor μ_{ij}^{-1} of each weight w_{ij} to μ_i^{-1} and by scaling the

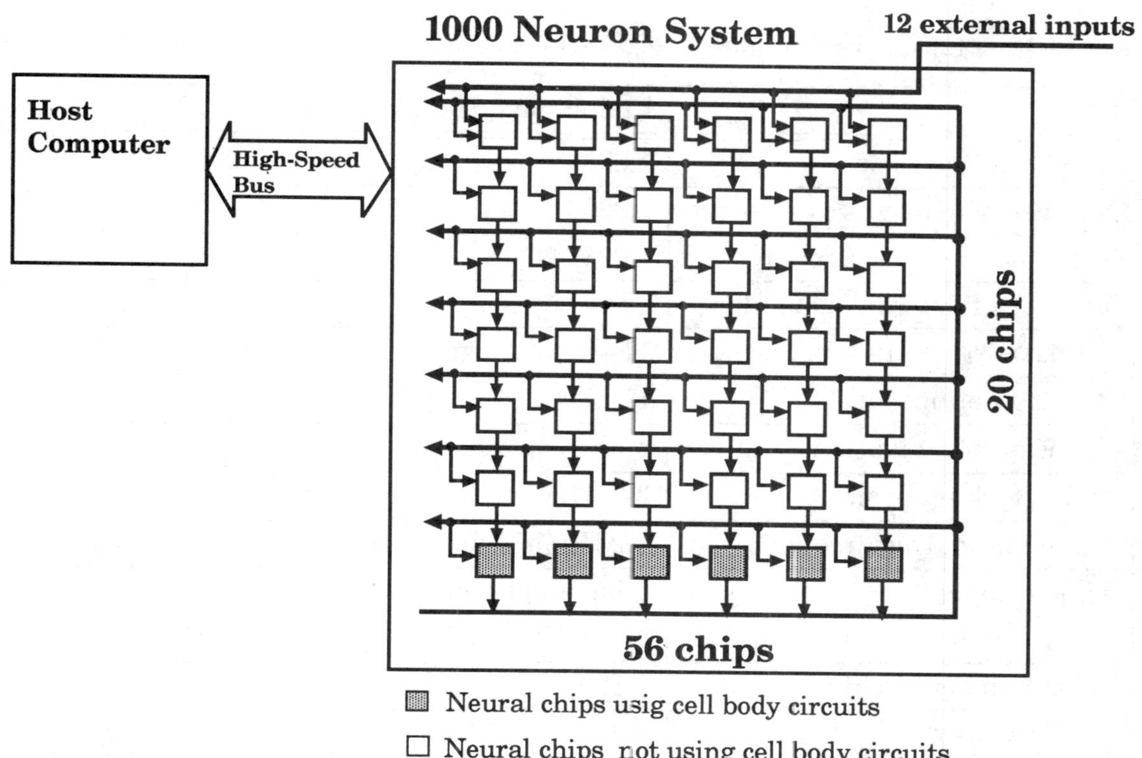

Figure 4: System configuration of 1000 neuron system.

external input value accordingly, the time constant $\widehat{\mu}_i$ is given by

$$\widehat{\mu}_i = \frac{2^{12}}{f_{main}} \frac{2^6}{\beta} \tag{8}$$

where, f_{main} is the clock frequency driving the 12-bit rate multiplier and β is the rate value of the 6-bit rate multiplier.

It should be noted that from Eq.(6), the ratio between the scaling factors μ_i^{-1} and μ_{ij}^{-1}, which is given by

$$r_{ij} = \frac{\mu_{ij}^{-1}}{\mu_i^{-1}} = \frac{w_{ij}}{\beta}, \tag{9}$$

can be interpreted as the scaling factor of synaptic weight.

4 Neural VLSI and the System

We are fabricating one kind of VLSI neural chips using $0.7 \mu m$ CMOS gate array with 250,000 gates. Each chip carries eighteen neurons and fifty-one synapses for each neuron, so that in total there are 918 synapses in a chip. About 85% of the gates in a gate array, which is an extremely efficient number, can be used.

As illustrated in Figure 4, $56 \times 20 = 1120$ chips are connected. The chips arranged in the bottom row, which are designated by shaded squares, are used for both cell bodies and synapses. The other chips designated by open squares are used only for synapses. By simply connecting dendrite extension terminals and cascading chips without supplying a common clock, large scale neural networks can be made.

There are $56 \times 18 = 1,008$ neurons and $20 \times 51 = 1,020$ synapses for each neuron, so that there are 1,028,160 synapses in total. The actual number of neurons fully interconnected is $1,008$. Since twelve synapses remain for each neuron, they will be used to receive some external signals from sensors such as a microphone. Since sensory analog signals must be transformed to pulse streams whose frequencies are proportional to the instantaneous analog values, we are planning to fabricate another VLSI chip using FPGA for this transformation.

The system will be controlled by a host computer via high-speed bus. Synaptic weights and control data are downloaded from the host system. No learning mechanism is implemented in this version. The contents of the up/down counters in the cell body circuits can be read and written from the host system.

Table 1: Preliminary specifications of the 1000 neuron system.

Item	Preliminary Specifications
Number of neurons	1,008
Number of synapses per neuron	1,020
Total number fo synapses	1,028,160
Number of external signal lines	12
Precision of internal potential	11-bit plus sign
Precision of output	11-bit
Precision of synaptic weight	6-bit plus sign
Main clock frequency	32 MHz
Maximum output frequency	16MHz in $2f$ mode or 8 MHz in ordinary mode
Time constant	6-bit programmable $128 \times \frac{64}{\beta}\mu$sec, for $0 \leq \beta < 64$
Total number of chips	1,120
Power supply	3.3 V
Power consumption	about 1,500 W

Preliminary specifications of the 1000 neuron system are summarized in Table 4.

5   Conclusions

A project of developing a neural network hardware system with 1,000 neurons fully interconnected via 1,000,000 synapses is described. We employ asynchronous PDM digital circuits because they provide a means for easy cascadability, moderate circuit size for synapses and relaxation of wiring problem. The system will be finished by this September. We will implement large scale neural networks in this system and will examine the performance.

Acknowledgement

We would like to express our special thanks to Mr. Yoshihiro Kuwabara and Mr. Tatsuo Ochiai of Hitachi Microcomputer System LTD. for their active participation in developing this system.

This work is supported by Proposal-Based Advanced Industrial Technology R&D Program of NEDO.

References

[1] Hirai, Y., *VLSI Neural Network Systems.* Reading, Birkshire: Gordon and Breach Science Publishers, 1992

[2] Mueller, P. *et al.*, "Design and performance of a prototype analog neural computer," *Proc. 2nd Inter. Conf. on Microelectronics for Neural Networks*, Munich, Oct. 16–18, 1991, pp. 347–357.

[3] Hirai, Y. *et al.*, "A digital neuro-chip with unlimited connectability for large scale neural networks," *Proc. IJCNN*, Washington D.C., June 18–22, 1989, pp. Vol.II/163–169.

An Amplitude and Shift Invariant Micropower Template Matcher

Richard Coggins, Marwan Jabri, Raymond Wang and Steve Avery
Systems Engineering and Design Automation Laboratory
Department of Electrical Engineering J03,
University of Sydney, 2006, Australia.
Email: richardc@sedal.usyd.edu.au

Abstract— Template matching is an essential function required by many data compression and classification systems. In this paper a very low power implementation of template matching is described targeted for use in an implantable cardiovertor defibrillator (ICD). The template matching scheme is tolerant to amplitude variations, inter and intra sample phase variations. A combination of micropower analogue and low power digital techniques yields a system capable of adaptive classification and compression of the intracardiac electrogram (ICEG) while meeting the size and area requirements of the implantable system. The system is fabricated in $1.2\mu m$ nwell CMOS.

1   Introduction

Implantable cardioverter defibrillators (ICDs) were introduced into the world market in the early 1980s and have had considerable success in treating people with heart conditions likely to lead to sudden cardiac arrest. ICDs treat the heart by monitoring the electrical activity of the heart muscle and then applying appropriate levels of electrical stimulation if abnormal conditions are detected. Despite the considerable success of ICDs they suffer from a number of limitations including an inability to detect and treat some abnormal heart rhythms, limited data recording capabilities and increased size and power consumption compared to conventional pacemakers.

Researchers have shown that morphological based classification is required to distinguish some dangerous arrhythmia from normal conditions [14, 9]. Due to variations in tissue growth, disease progression, drug therapy and metabolism it is desirable that morphology classifiers are adaptable. Previously we have shown how micropower analogue MLPs can be trained to separate such arrhythmia [4]. However, MLPs are best suited to learning the boundary between classes whereas a template matching scheme allows a measure of the probability density of the morphological types to be estimated. This leads to the following advantages.

- By characterising normal morphology, blind separation from abnormal classes can be achieved [3].

- Template information may be exploited to create a compressed representation of the ICEG for storage in the ICD [3].

Chip "in-loop" approaches have been exploited by adaptive analogue designs for a number of years now [13]. In this paper, this approach is exploited to adapt the parameters which null out the differences in phase and amplitude between a sampled analogue template and a digital template. For classification, as in the case for MLPs, this allows some imprecision of the analogue computation to be compensated for. For data compression however, where the transformed template is later digitised, part of the analogue processing is outside of any feedback loops and higher precision is required.

In order to implement parameter adaptation, the data sequencing and the encoding stages for data compression, digital state machines and data paths are also required. In order to achieve the lowest power consumption in these parts of the system adiabatic logic techniques are used [5, 1]. Adiabatic logic is used to implement the digital logic so as to decrease energy consumption. It does so by attempting to reclaim and recycle energy used to charge node capacitances in the circuit through the use of a clocked power supply. The only losses experienced by adiabatic logic are due to potentials across resistive components, which result in I^2R losses. By causing the clock to run sufficiently slowly, these potentials are minimised, as is the energy loss of the circuit. Since the bandwidth of the ICEG is approximately 50Hz the computation rate, and hence the clock rate, is relatively slow leading to significant energy savings. In this paper, only the analogue circuit functions will be described.

Section 2 shows how template matching may be exploited for adaptive classification and compression of the ICEG. Section 3 describes the technique used to achieve amplitude and shift invariant template matching. Section 4 describes the system implementation. Section 5 summarises the work and discusses areas for further research.

2   Adaptive Classification and Compression

The ICEG is clearly a periodic non-stationary signal. There are several mechanisms for its non-stationary behaviour:

- The ICEG is a measure of the heart pumping blood in a normally synchronous manner. This leads to a periodic (seasonal) non-stationary mean.

- The ICEG is subject to longer term deterministic cycles, such as daily cycles in metabolism, exercise etc.

- There are also influences which may introduce longer term trends in the ICEG such as tissue growth in the heart muscle, the continued progress of heart disease and aging.

- Transient non-stationarities may be caused by temporary influences such as temporary drug treatments, diseases, behavioural and environmental changes.

- Sampling the ICEG introduces sampling jitter.

- Beat detection suffers from variations in amplitude, shape and rate depending on the technique used.

Classifiers in ICDs currently use timing features (heart rate) as the means of classification which as mentioned in the Section 1 does not fulfill all requirements. However, when timing and morphology are combined a much more powerful classifier results [9]. Further, timing information can be exploited to adapt the morphology classification for the blind separation of abnormal rhythms from normal ones [3]. In particular, at low rates morphology can be safely characterised as normal and any templates detected in this range along with a measure of variation can be used to characterise the normal region of morphology space. Such adaptation overcomes the long term variations in the ICEG.

Recording of ICEGs in ICDs is currently very limited due to the amount of memory available and the power/area cost of implementing all but the simplest compression techniques. Micropower template matching however, enables large amounts of the signal to be encoded as template indices plus amplitude parameters. However, effective compression of the ICEG requires adaptation to the short term non-stationary behaviour of the ICEG. In particular, short term amplitude variations, lag variation, phase variation and ectopic beats reduce the achievable compression. The impact of ectopic beats can be reduced by increasing the number of templates. This can often be achieved without increasing the code book search complexity by using associated timing features. However, the amplitude and shift variations require short term adaptation of the template matching in order to minimise the residual error and hence raise the compression ratio at fixed distortion. [10, 3] describe compression algorithms based on this approach.

Hence, adaptive template matching is a common ingredient for effective classification and compression of the ICEG. The following sections outline the template matching principle we adopt and its implementation.

3   Amplitude and Shift Invariant Matching

In this section an approach to template matching which is tolerant to amplitude, sampling jitter and sample shifts is described. In order to facilitate analogue implementation, a backward prediction procedure is used rather than the usual forward prediction. This approach allows the incoming analogue template to be manipulated in the analogue domain while being compared to a digital template prior to digitisation. Consider the long term backward prediction problem described by,

$$r_b(n) = \tilde{x}(n - \alpha) - b_0 x(n) - b_1 \frac{\{x(n + 1) - x(n - 1)\}}{2} \tag{1}$$

where $r_b(n)$ denotes the backward residuals and b_0 and b_1 are the amplitude and phase coefficients respectively and α is the time lag of the current beat to the previous. b_0 is scaling the current beat to match the previous beat and hence is an amplitude term. b_1 is scaling the central difference of the current beat. To see why this is a phase term consider the Taylor expansion of $x(t + \phi)$ to the first derivative term around t,

$$x(t + \phi) = x(t) + \phi x'(t) \tag{2}$$

where ϕ is a small phase shift of $x(t)$. When ϕ is due to sampling jitter,

$$-\frac{T}{2} \leq \phi \leq \frac{T}{2} \tag{3}$$

where T is the sampling period. Hence, provided that $x(t)$ is sampled according to the Nyquist criterion ϕ is sufficiently small for the first derivative term to adequately account for the sampling jitter.

It now remains to determine b_0, b_1 and α. b_0 and b_1 can be determined by minimising the squared error between the current and the previously recorded template which in this case has a closed form solution in terms of correlation coefficients. α is usually determined by maximising the correlation between the templates to be matched. In Section 4 an alternative iterative procedure suited to analogue implementations is described.

4   Implementation

4.1   Architecture

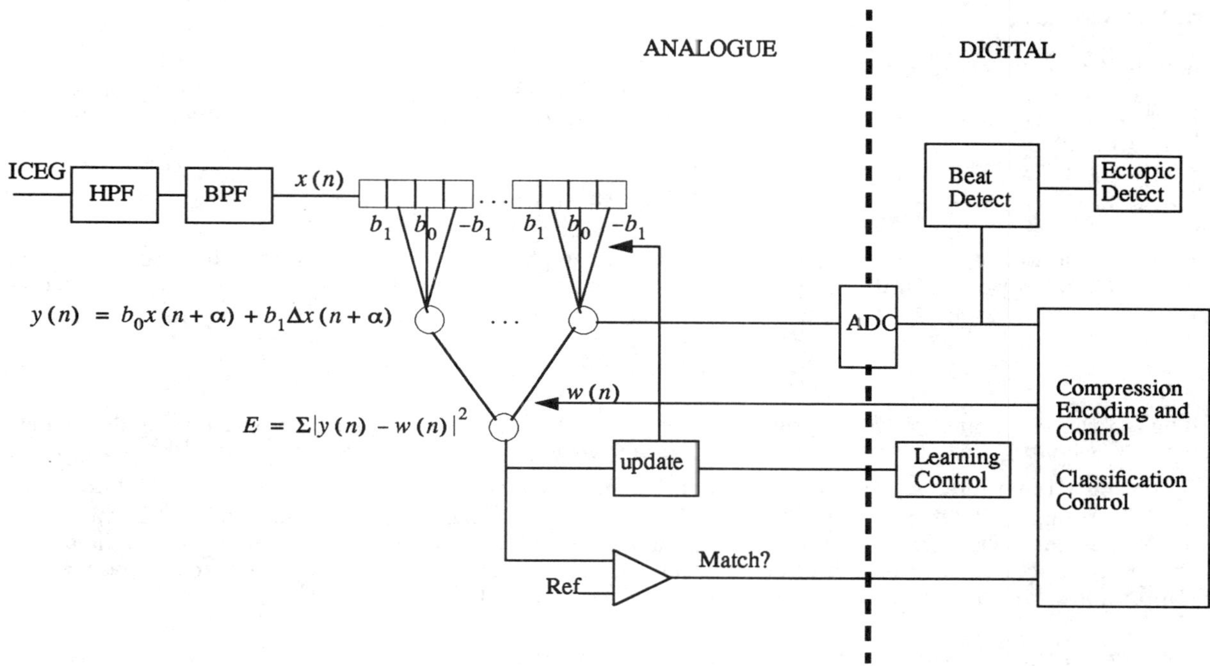

Figure 1: Overview block diagram of the template matching system showing the split between analogue and digital functions.

Figure 1 shows the main functional blocks and the split between analogue and digital implementation. This paper is primarily concerned with the analogue block. The analogue subsystem functions as follows. The ICEG is first high pass filtered to remove the DC and then is bandpass filtered to prevent aliasing and enhance the high frequency component for beat detection. (This is the filtering approach already existing in an ICD and therefore not implemented by us). This then feeds the discrete time analogue delay line, which is continuously sampling the signal at 250Hz. The analogue samples are then transformed by a two layer network. The first layer implements the linear prediction by adjusting the amplitude b_0 and the phase of the analogue vector. Note that the phase consists of two components, the coarse part α corresponding to sample lags and the fine part b_1 corresponding to intra sample lags. The second layer calculates the distance between the linearly predicted vector and the template $w(n)$ to be matched. The update block facilitates the change in the prediction parameters based on the matching error E. A comparator is provided so that a match to within a given threshold may be detected.

The digital blocks perform the following functions. The beat detect block represents an automatic sensitivity tracking algorithm for beat detection. The ectopic detector is a simple timing classifier used to change the template to that for an ectopic beat. The learning control block implements the learning algorithm. Since only two parameters are to be learned and they are approximately orthogonal, sequential line searches may be used to adapt them. The remaining digital control and data path is for the encoding of the compressed data and control of which templates are used during classification and compression. This block is interfaced to a static RAM memory for storage of the compressed ICEG and the template library.

4.2 Precision

An important consideration for the analogue approach is the precision requirements for the different parts of the system. The most critical parts are those which lie outside feedback loops in the system since errors in these parts are directly reflected in the decompressed signal. In particular, the analogue processing of the signal up to the point of A/D conversion has a direct impact on the performance of the system, since any errors up to this point are undetectable by the decoder. That is, the precision of the signal $y(n)$ in Figure 1 should be matched to the A/D converter. However, the precision of the computation of E is not as critical, since errors here simply mean that the prediction parameters will have some error which will degrade the compression algorithm in terms of rate achieved but not quality. In particular, if low quality is adequate then less precise computation of E can be tolerated (the extreme case being classification where only the type of morphology is distinguished). A good choice for the prediction mapping precision (and ADC) is 7 bits plus sign as this allows for storage of templates in standard memory architectures but still with good fidelity. The prediction parameters have been tested using 6 bit precision on signals standardised to 9 bits plus sign in a subjective evaluation.

4.3   Learning

The first step in the learning process is to determine α, the coarse phase lag. This can be achieved by shifting the delay line and evaluating the error until a minimum is reached. Once the coarse phase lag α has been determined the logistic function to be learned to compensate for amplitude and phase variations is given by,

$$E = \sum_{i=1}^{N} (b_0 x_i + b_1 \Delta x_i - w_i)^2 \tag{4}$$

where the subscript i implicitly incorporates the coarse phase α. This is a quadratic in b_0 and b_1. b_0 and b_1 can be optimised separately provided cross terms in E are negligible. Here the cross terms are given by,

$$\sum_{i=1}^{N} 2b_0 b_1 x_i \Delta x_i = b_0 b_1 (x_{N+1} x_N - x_1 x_0) \tag{5}$$

Thus, if the end points of the N point window have approximately the same value (as is usually the case for ICEG beats) then the cross terms in E are negligible and b_0 and b_1 can be optimised separately.

So the only remaining issue is how to optimise a single parameter. A simple linear search takes at most 2^b evaluations of E where b is the number of bits. A search based on bisection takes $b + 2$ evaluations. Techniques involving gradient descent and conjugate gradient lead to more complex learning logic with minor reductions in the number of evaluations. Therefore, bisection is the best compromise between the number of evaluations and the complexity of the learning state machine.

4.4   Analogue Storage and Digital Memory Requirements

The analogue storage of the system is restricted to the analogue delay line (the long term storage of the vectors $w(n)$ being digital). The length of the delay line and voltage range are the important factors here. Suffice to say, the delay line does not require refreshing since the storage time is only a few milliseconds. The length of the delay line and dimension of the template matching is 30 samples as most diagnostic information in a heart beat appears in this size window. This dimension could be lengthened or shortened according to the design trade offs encountered. In general increasing the dimension will yield a more powerful system capable of matching larger vectors and therefore increasing the potential compression ratio (an option can also be added to match only a subset of the dimensions including truncation and subsampling).

Digital memory is required to store the templates (code book) to which the incoming signal is to be compared. A single beat period may be as long as 2 seconds for bradycardia (longer if there is asystole) implying a storage of 500 bytes. To support ectopic beats an additional 1kbyte is required.

4.5   The Analogue Circuits

In order to minimise the energy per computation the analogue circuits are biased at the largest current that corresponds to weak inversion. This can be made precise by considering the specific current and inversion coefficient defined in the EKV model [6]. The specific current is given by,

$$I_S = 2n\beta U_T^2 \tag{6}$$

where U_T is the thermal voltage, n is the slope factor and β is the transconductance parameter. The drain current is modelled as the sum of forward and reverse currents. The inversion coefficient IC is defined by the ratio of the forward current to the specific current. Weak inversion is defined by $IC < 0.1$.

Referring to Figure 1 the first layer of the network function is performed by linearised transconductors [7]. The bias of the transconductors is controlled by seven bit current referenced DACs in order to implement the coefficients b_0 and b_1. Sign is implemented by switching the differential current outputs. Subtracting the template $w(n)$ in the (notional) second layer is achieved using 7 bit plus sign differential current mode DACs. It remains then to form the sum of squares to produce E. The squaring function must meet the following design constraints:

- The squaring function should have current inputs and outputs in order to avoid linear current to voltage conversion at low currents.

- The squared current must be normalised to the original linear range to avoid excessive power consumption.

- The squaring function should avoid the MOS square law approach [11, 2, 8, 16] as this will lead to very long transistors being required to achieve strong inversion operation at low currents or current scaling which could cost significant power.

- The voltage range available is 2.8V rail to rail.

The choices available then are restricted to weak inversion circuits. A log followed by voltage doubling followed by anti-log does not yield the required current normalisation. Therefore, the circuit used relies on the translinear principle [12, 15]. Here, loops of PN junctions are used to form a normalised squared current which is summed to form the final normalised output. The translinear loops are implemented with P transistors in separate N-wells to avoid the body effect. Results from the fabricated circuits will be available at the time of the conference.

5   Conclusion

The advantages of our approach can be seen to be that it provides hardware support for both classification and compression. The analogue block can be used to implement several different classification and compression algorithms depending on how the template matching capability is utilised. Classification is essentially performed in analogue providing the opportunity for low power classification performance and low power compression performance of regular rhythms. Control and encoding stages exploit the potential of adiabatic logic to trade computation bandwidth for energy. These advantages are traded off against the difficulty of providing analogue precision in some parts of the system and the unusual (inductor based) power supply and clocking schemes required for adiabatic logic families. By providing significant compression capability in an ICD, a larger data base of natural onset cardiac arrhythmia should become available, leading to improved designs of adaptive classification and compression systems.

Acknowledgements

The authors acknowledge the funding for the work in this paper provided by the Australian Research Council and Telectronics Pacing Systems, Ltd.

References

[1] S. Avery, S. Reemeyer, and M. Jabri. Impact of circuit activity on adiabatic energy consumption in implantable devices. In *submitted to 1996 International Symposium on Low Power Electronics and Design*, 1996.

[2] Klass Bult and Hans Wallinga. A class of analog CMOS circuits based on the square-law characteristic. *IEEE Journal of Solid-State Circuits*, SC-22(3):357–365, 1987.

[3] R.J. Coggins. *Low Power Signal Compression and Classification for Implantable Defibrillators*. PhD thesis, University of Sydney, Sydney, Australia, 1996.

[4] R.J. Coggins, M.A. Jabri, B.G. Flower, and S.J. Pickard. A hybrid analog and digital vlsi neural network for intracardiac morphology classification. *IEEE Journal of Solid-State Circuits*, 30(5):542–550, May 1995.

[5] A.G. Dickinson and J.S. Denker. Adiabatic dynamic logic. *IEEE Journal of Solid-State Circuits*, 30(3), 1995.

[6] C.C. Enz, Krummenacher F., and E.A. Vittoz. An analytical mos transistor model valid in all regions of operation and dedicated to low-voltage and low-current applications. *Analog Integrated Circuits and Signal Processing*, 4(4), 1994.

[7] F. Krummenacher and N Joehl. A 4Mhz CMOS Continuous Time Filter with On Chip Automatic Tuning. *IEEE Journal of Solid-State Circuits*, 23(3):750–758, June 1986.

[8] O. Landolt, E. Vittoz, and P. Heim. Cmos self biased euclidean distance computing circuit with high dynamic range. *Electronics Letters*, 28(4):352–353, 1992.

[9] P.H.W. Leong and M.A. Jabri. Matic – an intracardiac tachycardia classification system. *Pacing and Clinical Electrocardiography*, September 1992.

[10] G. Nave and A. Cohen. Ecg compression using long term prediction. *IEEE Trans on Biomedical Engineering*, pages 877–885, 1993.

[11] V.A. Pedroni. Highly linear high-density vector quantiser and vector-matrix multiplier. *Electronics Letters*, 30(12):945–946, 1994.

[12] E. Seevinck. *Analysis and Synthesis of Translinear Integrated Circuits*. Elsevier, 1988.

[13] S.M. Tam, B. Gupta, H.A. Castro, and M.A. Holler. Learning on an analog vlsi neural network chip. In *IEEE International Conference of Systems, Man and Cybernetics*, pages 701–703, 1990.

[14] R.D. Throne, J.M. Jenkins, and L.A. DiCarlo. A comparison of four new time-domain techniques for discriminating monomorphic ventricular tachycardia from sinus rhythm using ventricular waveform morphology. *IEEE Trans on Biomedical Engineering*, 38(6):561–570, June 1991.

[15] C. Toumazou, F.J. Lidgey, and D.G. Haigh, editors. *Analogue IC Design: the current mode approach*. Peter Peregrinus, 1990.

[16] G.T. Tyson, S. Fallahi, and A.A. Abidi. An 8b cmos vector a/d converter. In *Proceedings of the International Solid State Circuits Conference*, pages 38–39, 1993.

REAL-TIME LEARNING OF CHAOS DYNAMICS USING A HIGH-PERFORMANCE SIMULATOR ON A NEURO-COMPUTER

Yuji Sato[*1], **Yoshihiro Kuwabara**[*2], **Ryuichi Oka**

Real World Computing Partnership,Tsukuba-shi, Ibaraki 305, Japan
*1: Presently at Central Research Laboratory, Hitachi, Ltd., Kokubunji-shi, Tokyo 185, Japan
*2: Hitachi Microcomputer Sys., Kodaira-shi, Tokyo 187, Japan
E-mail: yuji@crl.hitachi.co.jp

Abstract - We developed a simulator for evaluating models in which multiple recurrent neural networks interact during the training process. The back propagation through time learning algorithm is used for the recurrent neural networks. This simulator can execute at high speed on a neuro-computer with a maximum training capability of 1.26 GCUPS. We have demonstrated real-time learning of the Lorenz attractor. From the evaluation of the Lorenz attractor training, we estimate the simulation speed to be from 10 to 100 times faster than simulations run on a workstation. As the next step in this study, we plan to apply this simulator to the evaluation of training models for clustered recurrent neural networks using more complex problems.

1.   Introduction

We have shown [1] that a digital neural network with high-speed learning circuits can be integrated onto a wafer-scale integrated circuit. However, this learning circuits only uses the Back Propagation (BP) algorithm [2] and is not flexible enough for solving practical problems in real time. Therefore we have developed a high-performance, general purpose neuro-computer [3] which supports a range of learning algorithms, and has a maximum on-chip learning speed for the BP algorithm of 1.26 GCUPS (Giga Connections Updates Per Second). The architecture and design of the hardware is summarized in Table1.

This paper reports on the development of a high-performance simulator implemented on the above neuro-computer for recurrent neural networks. We have demonstrated real-time learning of chaos dynamics using this simulator. The Lorenz orbit used as the training signal is normally a non-periodic orbit that undergoes continuous chaotic change. Accordingly, a recurrent neural network is normally in the learning process. Here, it is demonstrated that the output of a recurrent neural network that has a learning process represents changes from a fixed point to a limit cycle and then changes again to the Lorenz attractor. That is to say, it is demonstrated that the hidden order of chaos dynamics can be learned using a simulator on the neuro-computer. Here, we give a brief general description of the simulator on the neuro-computer, describe learning algorithm for recurrent neural networks, and present the results of a evaluation using the Lorenz orbits.

2.   System Overview

2.1   System architecture

The simulator system configuration is outlined in Fig. 1. The system consists of a workstation, which provides the user interface, and a neuro-computer for high-speed training of neural networks. The neural network structure, learning parameters, training data and external input data are specified by using the workstation. That data is transferred to the neuro-computer via a SCSI bus. In the neuro-computer, up to 512 physical neurons are trained in parallel. The learning curve, the neural network output, and the status of each neuron can be presented by the workstation. The network structures that can be specified include fully-connected networks, layered networks, output layer to input layer feedback networks, and structures in which several of these types of networks are connected arbitrarily.

In the neuro-computer, general purpose neural functions are achieved by a micro-programming architecture. Each neuron executes the same instruction from a programmable control storage at each clock cycle, using SIMD (Single Instruction stream Multiple Data stream) processing, and thus any neural functions may be implemented by simply rewriting the micro-program. The execution unit of each neuron is optimized for traditional neural functions, notably BP, Hopfield, and Learning Vector Quantization (LVQ), and has a local memory for on-chip learning. High-speed on-chip learning is achieved through massively parallel-pipelined computation.

2.2   Neuron chip architecture

The configuration of a single neuron is shown in Fig. 2. Each neuron consists of an execution unit for neural functions and a local memory for on-chip learning. This circuit was designed in such a way that one neuron can not only execute high-speed on-chip learning with the BP algorithm, but also is general enough to implement any neural function. The critical circuit elements required for the BP algorithm are the multiplier, adder and accumulator. For general-purpose operation, the multiplier and adder must also operate independently. To fulfill these requirements, we adopted a three-bus architecture, with latches on the input and output sides of the multiplier to enable the multiplier and adder to operate in the same clock cycle for pipelined operation. The synapses are made from binary digital circuits, and are mainly composed of a weight storage (8 bits x 1 Kwords or 16 bits x 512 words), a multiplier (16 bits x 10 bits or 32 bits x 16 bits) and a general register file (32 bits x 20 words). The general register file is used to store the learning rate, momentum constant and output rate. It is also useful for storing the weight of virtual neurons so that more than one virtual neuron can be emulated by a single physical neuron. This register file stores weight changes (8 bits) as well as weights (16 bits). The cell body is composed of an ALU (adder: 32 bits + 32 bits or 64 bits + 64 bits), a stack register and shift registers, which are used for multiplying. Each neuron's output and input data consist of 10 bits (or 16 bits).

The neuron chip architecture is shown in Fig. 3. Eight digital neurons are integrated on each neuron chip using 1.0-μm CMOS technology. Each neuron executes the same instruction from the control storage at each clock cycle, based on SIMD processing. A parity check circuit detects faults in the instruction, data input/output and address lines to increase the reliability of on-line processing.

3.   Training Data

We used the Lorenz orbit to verify a functional validation and performance evaluation. In a closed autonomous system with three degrees of freedom, the Lorenzian equation is as follows.

$$\frac{dx}{dt} = 10(x - y) \qquad \frac{dy}{dt} = -y + (28 - z)x \qquad \frac{dz}{dt} = -\frac{8}{3}z + xy \qquad (1)$$

The orbit obtained by converting this equation to discrete time series data by Euler's law is shown in Fig. 4. While Fig. 4 shows part (2000 data points) of an orbit that continues infinitely, it shows the complex, irregular oscillation. The value of the maximum Lyapunov exponent of the unraveled orbit of the Lorenzian equation is 0.90, indicating the unstable chaotic state of the unraveled orbit. For example, the time waveforms for two unraveled orbits whose initial values differ by just one percent are shown in Fig. 5. The two unraveled orbits diverge by an exponential function over time, and after a certain time the two orbits exhibit completely different temporal behavior. That is to say, at a certain time, even if the values of the state variables (x, y and z) are known, the error with respect to those values increases over time, and after a certain amount of time it becomes impossible in principle to predict the former unraveled orbit.

Chaos dynamics are not simple random motions, but have a hidden order. For example, if the chaotic orbits of a Lorenzian equation are drawn in three-dimensional phase space, the result will necessarily converge over time within a region known as the Lorenz attractor, regardless of the initial values. Afterwards, the motion continues perpetually. An example of the Lorenz attractor projected onto three two-dimensional planes, x-y, y-z and z-x, is shown in Fig. 6.

4.   Learning Algorithm

Several supervised learning methods have been proposed for recurrent neural networks [4, 5]. The basic method we apply here is back propagation through time (BPTT) algorithm [5], which has a low computational overhead.

4.1   Neuron status (Discrete-time model)

$$S_i(t + 1) = \sum_{j=1}^{n} w_{ij} y_j(t) + \sum_{j=1}^{m} b_{ij} I_j(t), \qquad y_i(t) = f(S_i(t)) \qquad (2)$$

Here, $S_i(t)$ and $y_i(t)$ $(i=1,...,n)$ represent the internal state and the output of the units, $f(\ )$ is a linear function or a sigmoid function, and $I_j(t)$ $(j=1,...,m)$ represent the external inputs to the network.

4.2   Error evaluation function

The error evaluation function, E, is the sum with respect to training pattern p of the cumulative squared error of the output of neuron i from t_0 to t_1, y_i, and the training data, T_i.

$$E = \sum_{p} \sum_{t=t_0}^{t_1} \sum_{i_{output}} \left(y_i(t) - T_i(t) \right)^2 / 2 \tag{3}$$

4.3   Updating the connection weights

The adjoint coefficient, q_i, is obtained with the following adjoint equations.

$$q_i(t-1) = \sum_{j=1}^{n} q_j(t) w_{ji} f'\left(S_i(t) \right) + \delta_i(t), \tag{4}$$

$$q_i(t_1) = 0, \qquad (i = 1,..., n)$$

by using the output error as the input

$$\delta_i(t) = \left(y_i(t) - T_i(t) \right) f'\left(S_i(t) \right), \quad \text{(output units)},$$
$$= 0, \qquad\qquad\qquad \text{(hidden units)}.$$

After obtaining the adjoint coefficient, q_i, by retracing back to time t_0, the change in connection weight between neurons i and j, Δw_{ij}, can be computed as follows.

$$\partial E / \partial w_{ij} = \sum_{p} \sum_{t=t_0}^{t_1} q_i(t) f\left(S_j(t) \right) \tag{5}$$

$$\Delta w_{ij}(t+1) = -\eta \partial E / \partial w_{ij} + \alpha \Delta w_{ij}(t) \tag{6}$$

Here, η is the learning rate, and α is the momentum coefficient.

4.4   Teacher Forcing

This system also supplies a technique called "teacher forcing [6]" is required in some learning tasks. It replaces that actual output of the network with the desired output;

$$S_i(t+1) = \sum_{j=1}^{n} w_{ij} T_j(t) + \sum_{j=1}^{m} v_{ij} I_j(t), \qquad y_i(t) = f\left(S_i(t) \right) \tag{7}$$

If the actual outputs $y_i(t)$ are made equal to $T_i(t)$ by learning, the solution of (7) is same to that of the non-forced system (2). Although the stability of the non-forced solution is not theoretically guranteed, they were found to be stable in most of the computer simulations [4, 6].

4.5   Method for Learning Non-periodic Orbits

In order to learn non-periodic orbits, the error evaluation interval is restricted to a certain length, TB, and within that interval variations of every TF ($<$TB) are made [7]. The learning procedure is described below.

(a)   The cumulative mean square error of the recurrent neural network output with respect to the training signal is obtained over the time period from time T to time (T+TB).

(b)   Connection weights of the recurrent neural network are updated by BPTT algorithm described in the former section.

(c)   The hidden unit output after time TF is calculated using the new connection weight values and the initial hidden unit values.

(d)   Increment the time T by TF and return to step a.

        The above method is a real-time learning rule for infinitely continuing non-periodic time series data. Because the object of learning is infinitely continuing non-periodic time series data, it is impossible to complete the learning of the training signal waveform itself; rather, the temporal development rule that generates the training signal is what is learned.

5 .   Experiments

The network configuration used in this learning experiment is shown in Fig. 7. It consists of three modules allocated to interconnected neural networks corresponding to the three outputs, x, y and z. The neural networks have 17 neurons (2 dynamic units and 15 sigmoid units). These three modules mutually interact through their output signals. The learning curve for this network is shown in Fig. 8. We can see that although the network output corresponding to the weight changes is discontinuous and the error function temporarily increases to large values, the error function values decreases gradually over a long period of time. An orbit output by the recurrent neural network during learning is shown in Fig. 9. At a relatively early stage after learning begins, there is convergence on fixed point. As learning proceeds, a limit cycle appears. With further learning, the Lorenz attractor is observed. Moreover, the simulator allowed us real-time learning of chaos dynamics. The simulation speed to be from 10 to 100 times faster than simulations run on a workstation .

6 .   Conclusions

We developed a high-performance simulator on a neuro-computer for recurrent neural networks. The back propagation through time learning algorithm is used for the recurrent neural networks. From the evaluation in which Lorenz attractor learning was used, the neuro-computer implementation of the simulator is expected to be from 10 to 100 times as fast as a workstation implementation. Moreover, the simulator system allows us real-time learning of chaos dynamics. Future work must verify the cooperative learning function in detail using this simulator.

Acknowledgments

The authors would like to express their gratitude to Mr. T. Ochiai, Mr. Y. Abe, and Mr. A. Miura of Hitachi Microcomputer System LTD., for their cooperation in fabrication, and to Dr. J. Shimada of Real World Computing Partnership for giving us the opportunity to do research in the field of artificial neural network.

References

[1] M. Yasunaga et al., "A Self-Learning Neural Network Composed of 1152 Digital Neurons in Wafer-Scale LSIs," Proc. of IJCNN'91, vol. 2, pp. 1844-1849, 1991.

[2] D. E. Rumelhart et al., "Parallel Distributed Processing," Vol. I and Vol. II, MIT Press, 1986.

[3] Y. Sato et al., "Development of a High-Performance, General Purpose Neuro-Computer Composed of 512 Digital Neurons," Proc. of IJCNN'93, pp. 1967-1970, 1993.

[4] R. J. Williams, D. Zipser, "Experimental analysis of the real-time recurrent learning algorithms," Connection Science, 1, pp. 87-111, 1989.

[5] B. A. Pearlmutter, "Learning state space trajectories in recurrent neural networks," Neural Computation, 1, pp. 263-269, 1989.

[6] K. Doya, "Bifurcations in the Learning of Recurrent Neural Networks," Proc. of Inter. Sym. on Circuits and Systems, pp. 2777-2780, 1992.

[7] M. Sato et al., "Learning chaotic dynamics by recurrent neural networks," Proc. Inter. Conf. on Fuzzy Logic & N. N., pp. 601-605, 1990.

Tab. 1. Summary of the neuro-computer

Circuit	Completely Digital
Architecture	Micro-programming Architecture Horizontal Microinstruction Format Nanomemory for Parameters Time-Sharing Digital Bus
Complexity	512 Physical Neurons/System 4096 Virtual Neurons/System 1024 Synapses/Neuron
Performance	1.26 GCUPS (MAX) 12.8 GCPS (MAX)
Learning Algorithm	General Purpose (BP, HF, LVQ etc.)
Neuron Output	10 bits / 16 bits
Synapse Weight	8 bits / 16 bits
Clock Rate	25 MHz
Process	1.0 µm CMOS
Interface	SCSI
Host	3050, SUN etc.

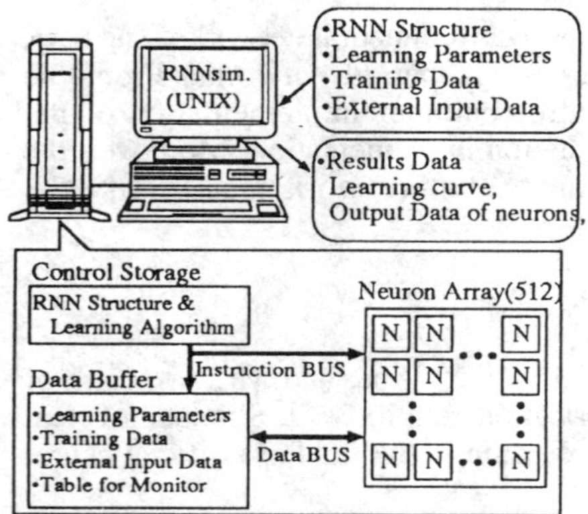

Fig. 1 System configuration of the simulator system.

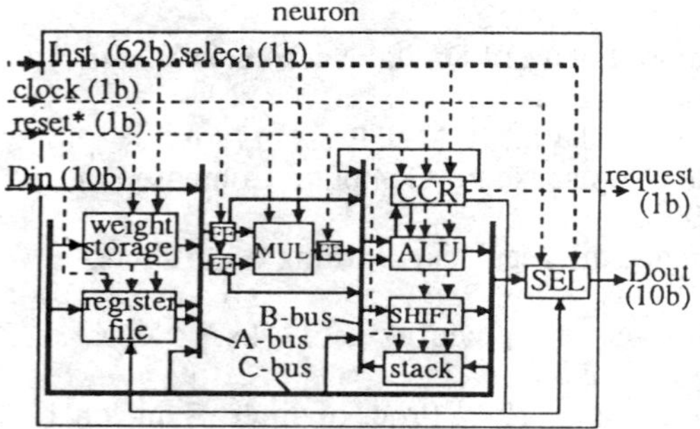

Fig. 2 Block diagram of a single neuron with general purpose neural functions and learning circuits.

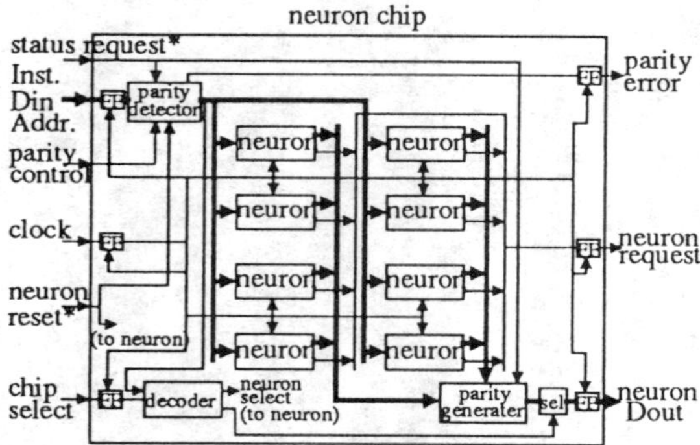

Fig. 3 Configuration of one neuron chip. One neuron chip is composed of 8 neurons and parity circuits.

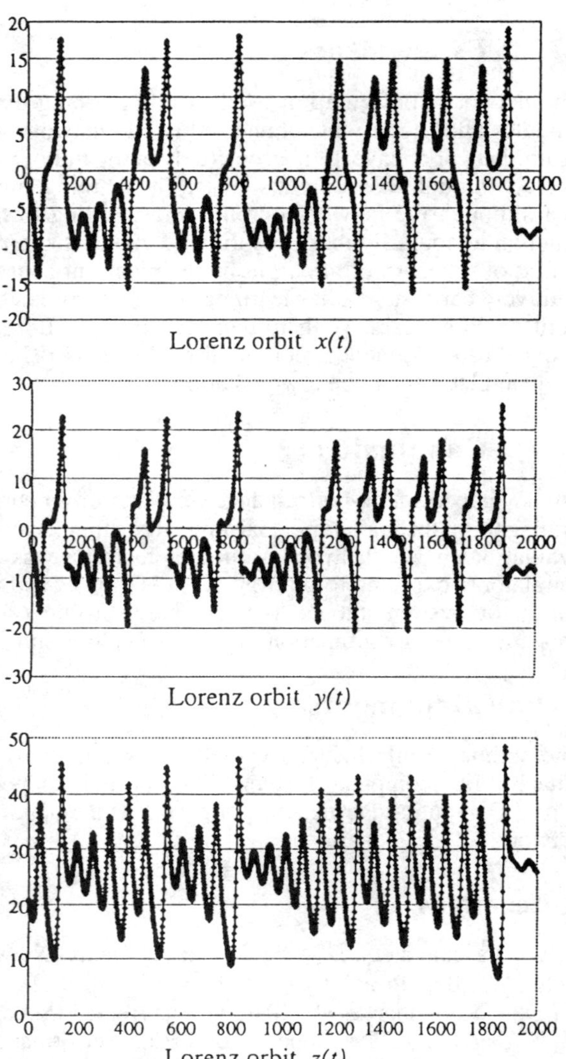

Fig. 4 Lorenz orbit $x(t)$, $y(t)$, $z(t)$. (dt=0.01, t=0 to 20)

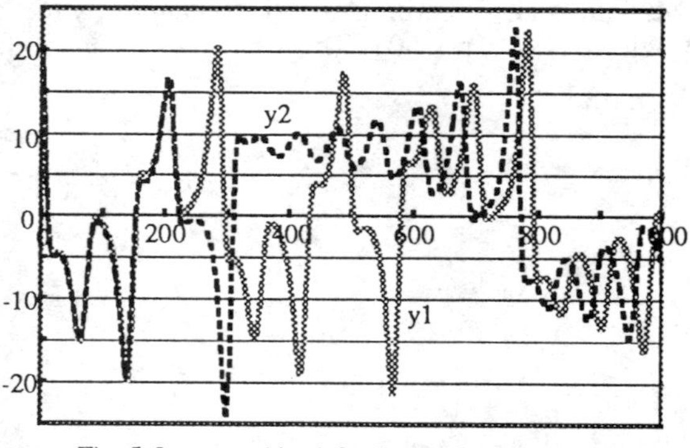

Fig. 5 Lorenz orbit $y1$ & $y2$. (dt=0.01, t=0 to 10)

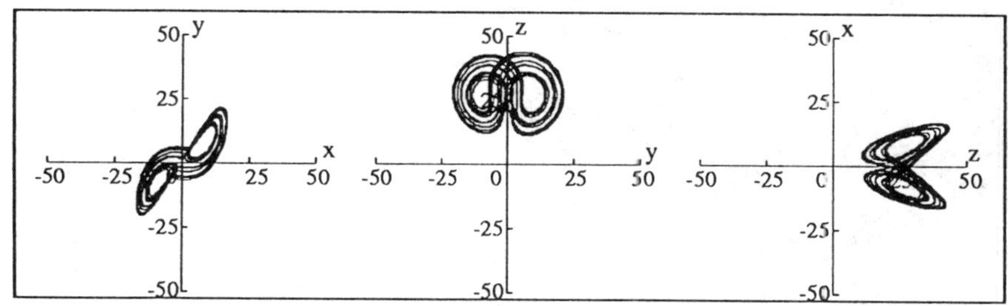

Fig. 6 Lorenz attractor

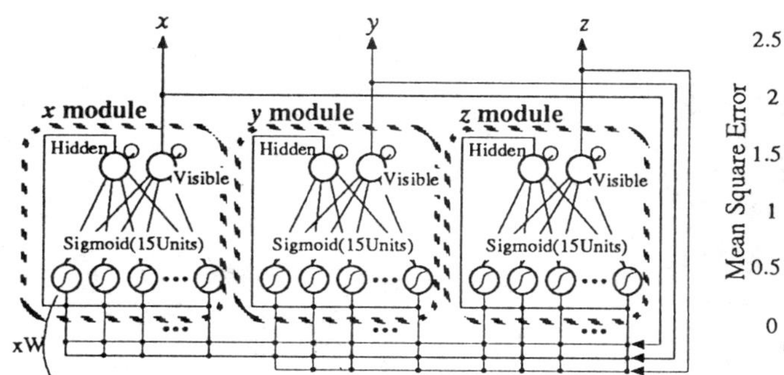

Fig. 7 Structure of neural network used in learning.

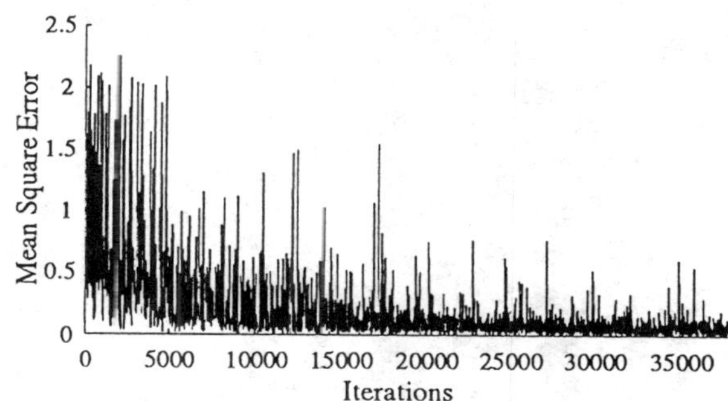

Fig. 8 Learning curve for learning the Lorenz attractor

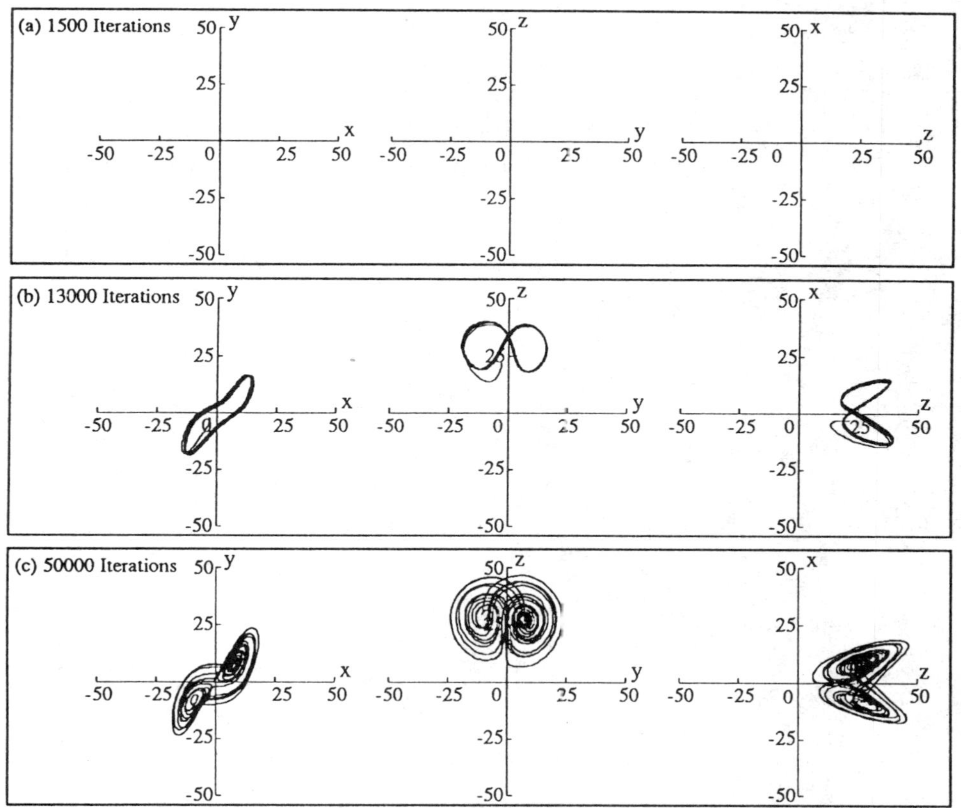

Fig. 9 Strange attractor outputs by recurrent neural network outputs after training.

Special Session III
Spatio-temporal Coding of Neural Networks

The invited program is also featured by 8 special sessions on current interesting topics. Each special session organizer is invited by the Program Committee and the success of each special session is completely due to the hard efforts of each organizer.

PSYCHOPHYSICAL AND NEURAL RESPONSES TO VISUAL FLOW COMPOSED OF TWO DIRECTIONAL MOVING COMPONENTS

Hide-aki Saito, Eiki Hida, Yosuke Kurachi, Hiroshi Ohno,
Kei-ichi Odajima and Minoru Tsukada
Tamagawa University, Faculty of Engineering.
Department of Information and Communication Technology,
6-1-1 Tamagawa-gakuen, Machida, Tokyo 194, Japan
Fax:+81-427-39-8858

ABSTRACT

We studied properties of the perception of coherent wide-field movement when elements moving in two directions were superimposed. We also studied responses of neurons in macaque MST area (where the wide-field movements were known to be analyzed) to the same stimuli, and examined the psychology-physiology correspondence. It is found that we percept two different coherent movements at the same time when the numbers of elements moving in two directions are even. This perceptual property and the previously found tolerance to directional noise in visual flow discrimination could be well interpreted by a neural circuit model which learns to make a simple computation on the responses of MST cells.

Key words: perception of visual flow, spatio-temporal stimuli, neural coding

INTRODUCTION

To stabilize visual images as well as to control the posture and locomotion, it is prerequisite for the animal to discriminate the visual flow caused by self movement in the presence of independently moving objects (which are regarded as motion noise for visual flow discrimination). In the previous work (Hida et al., 1993), we have shown that the human discrimination of wide-field visual flow is highly tolerable for directional noise caused by incoherent movement of the texture elements. That is, the correct response for the discrimination of direction of coherent motion reachs to 90% at 30% coherency. On the other hand, the magnitude of the directionally selective response of cells in MST (*Medial Superior Temporal*) area increased monotonically as the coherency of movement direction of texture elements increased. To assess the participation of directionally selective MST cells in the discrimination performance of the field movement, we introduced *'Direction Index'* (DI) defined by the equation

$$DI=(Rp-Rn)/Rp$$

where Rp and Rn stand for the magnitudes of the presponses to the motions to preferred and null directions, respectively (Hida et al., 1993). However, it soon arizes a question that how this works when two coherent motions are superimposed. In such a case, DI will reduce to zero, and therefore the system cannot get the signal to discriminate the direction of field motion.

In the present study, we investigated both the discrimination performance of human subjects and the response properties of MST cells to the field motion in which two coherent movements are superimposed. We will show that human can percept two directions at the same time and that DI can be computed from MST-responses by a simple neural network in that situation if we assume that the network might learn to find a combination of preferred cells and null cells which gives the maximum Rp-Rn difference.

MATERIALS AND METHODS

Stimuli employed in both psychophysical and physiological experiments were wide-field motion patterns in which two coherent movements of texture elements in different directions in the same speed were superimposed. The stimuli were generated in a computer workstation (IRIS Crimson, Silicon Graphics Co.), and displayed on a monitor screen. Eight elemental motion patterns separated 45

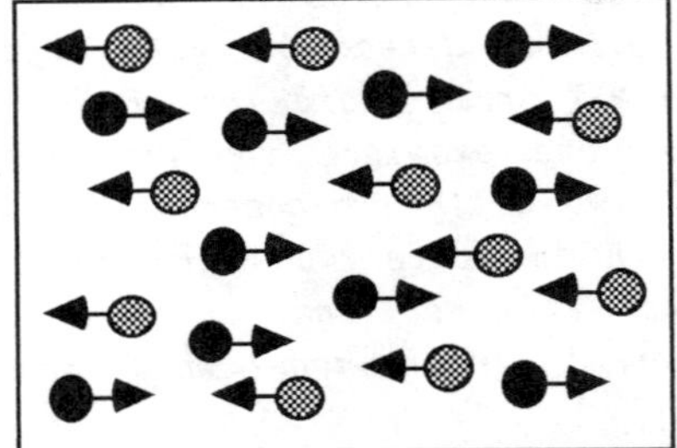

Fig. 1. SUPERIMPOSED
MOTION PATTERN

degrees in direction were prepared and 28 different motion patterns (see Fig. 2) were made by superimposing 2 out of 8 elemental motion patterns. An example in which the two directions are opposite is given in Fig.1. The actual shape of texture elements (pixels) was an octagon. The size of the motion field and that of single pixel was 45.0 and 1.4 degrees in visual angle, respectively. The speed was in the range of 11- 88 degrees/ sec within which a good apparent motion could be perceived. In the psychophysical experiments, each superimposed motion pattern selected at random from 28 patterns was shown to the human observers for 1 sec. They were requested to report the directions of coherent field motions. In the physiological experiments, the responses of cells in MST area of anesthetized paralyzed monkeys (*Macaca fuscata*) to the superimposed motion patterns were recorded and compared with the responses to the elemental (single directional) motion.

RESULTS

Psychophysical performance is shown in Fig.2. Except for the combinations in which the two directions were both oblique (columns C and F), observers could percept two directions correctly at almost 90% level. As to why the perceptual performance was low for the oblique combination, we think that the brain-ability to percept oblique movement would be low due to less frequent experiences of such movements relative to right-left and up-down movements caused by eye movements.

Examples of response properties of MST cells to the same stimuli are given in Fig.3. The responses of MST cells to the coherent movement in the preferred direction of each cell were generally inhibited by the superposition of coherent movement of another direction. The strength of inhibition differed cell to cell: strong in the cell A, medium in cell B and no inhibition in cell C. We found no cell in which the response was remarkably fascilitated by the superposition of two coherent movements.

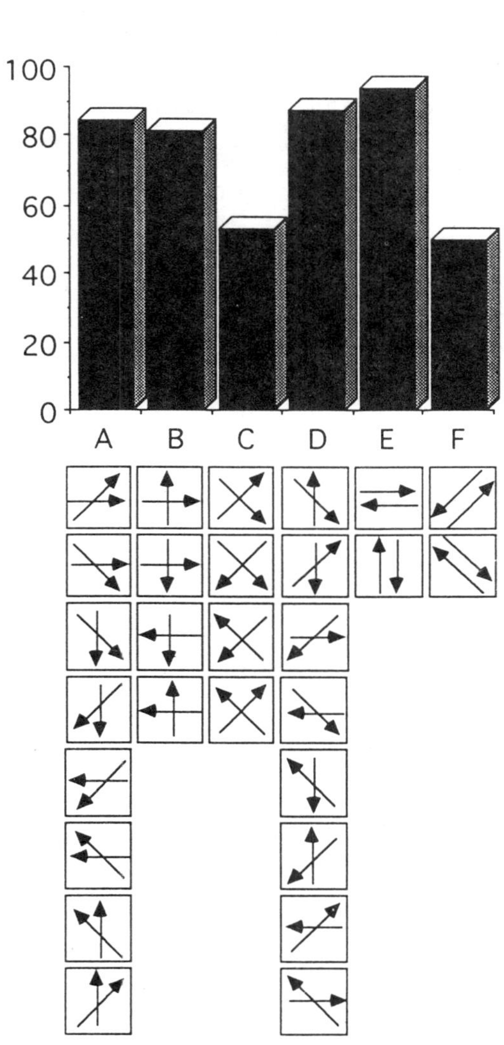

Fig.2. Perception of two directions of superposed coherent movements. Ordinate indicates percentage of correct responses.

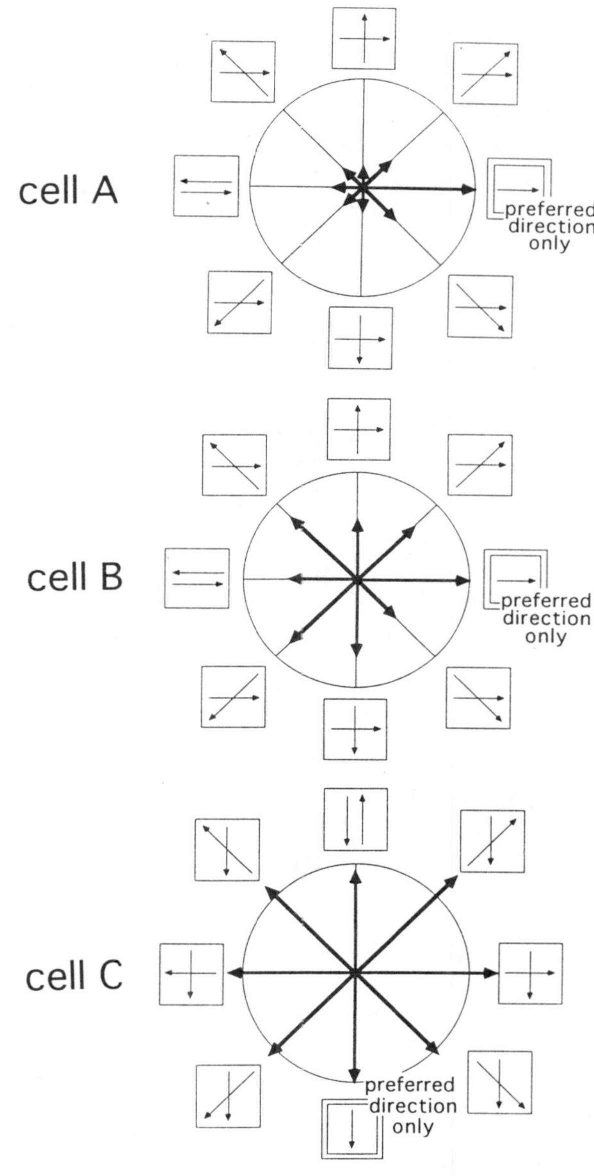

Fig.3. Response properties of MST cells to superposed coherent movements. The radius of the circle indicates the magnitude of the responses to the single coherent movement in preferred direction.

DISCUSSION

As a neural network which can provide a correct directional signal consistently under different conditions in which random noise or another coherent movement is superimposed on a single coherent movement, we propose a model shown in Fig. 4. In this model, direction signals are detected by sets of directionally selective cells which are different in the preferred direction. We assume that initially networks to compute Rp-Rn are constructed between any combinations of the two sets which have opposite preferred directions and have received different magnitude of inhibition by the superposition of another coherent movement to the coherent movement in the preferred direction. Among these networks, those which provide a small output will die out through synaptic competition at the target cells which compute (Rp-Rn)/Rp.

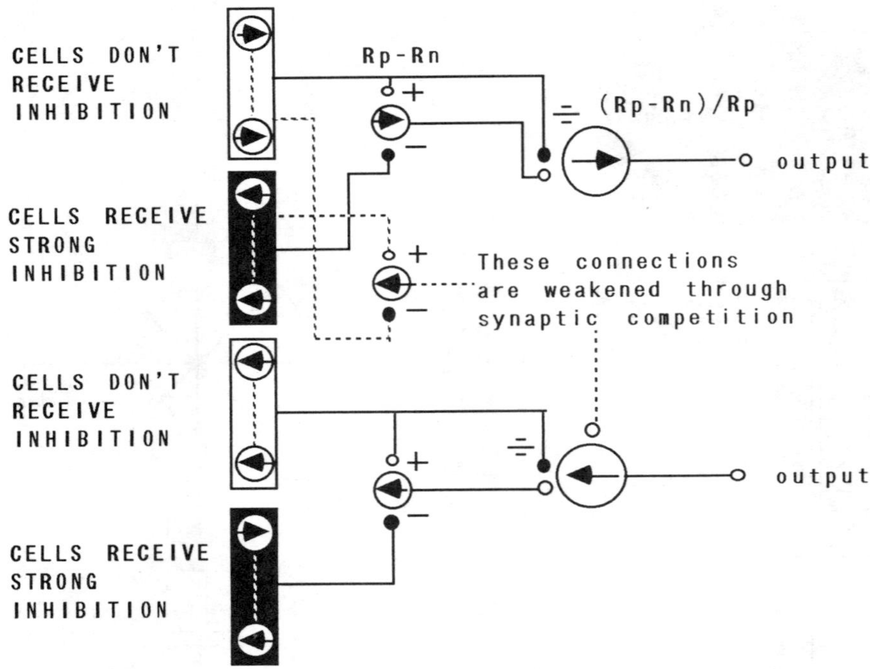

Fig. 4. A neural network to compute DI

REFERENCES

Hida, E., Saito, H., Mizuno, M. and Tsukada, M.
Neural substrate for a high degree of noise tolerance in visual flow discrimination in macaque dorsal MST area. Proc. IJCNN'93, 61-64, 1993

ACKNOWLEDGEMENTS

This study was supported by grant in aid (#05267105) for scientific research from Ministry of Education, Science and Culture of Japan.

Long-Term Potentiation and Neural Coding as a Single Dynamical Process*

Michael Stiber[†], Ricci Ieong
Department of Computer Science
The Hong Kong University of Science and Technology
Clear Water Bay, Kowloon, Hong Kong
stiber@cs.ust.hk, ricci@cs.ust.hk

***Abstract*— Because we think of learning and computation in terms of separate *a priori* categories, we naturally consider them as separate processes in neural networks. Our preconceptions do not translate into imperatives for Nature, however. We present an overview of work carried out by the HKUST Biocomputing Group which shows that some learning mechanisms must be considered as inseparable parts of the synaptic coding process, leading to the consideration of coding in the presence of learning-mediated changes.**

1 Introduction

Modification of neural networks in response to life experience is of central importance in living organisms. Without such a capability, they would be forced to react to their changing environment using only hard-wired reflexes. In higher organisms, this adaptation or learning process extends to the construction of basic architectural components for sensory input processing, as has been shown in the development of visual cortex in kittens, for example [1]. It is certainly what enables what at a high level we call "learning" and "memory".

Artificial neural network research presupposes experience-mediated synaptic modification occurs according to some *learning algorithm*, and much effort is spent in developing and analyzing the relative strengths and weaknesses of various algorithms from practical performance and theoretical computational points of view. One assumption underlying all such work is that the learning algorithm, while coupled to the network which it modifies, can be treated as an independent module of the overall system: in other words, its operation can be understood without reference to the details of the network.

Candidate physiological mechanisms have been identified only relatively recently. Notable among these are long-term potentiation (LTP) [2] and inhibitory LTP (ILTP) [3]. These involve changes in excitatory and inhibitory synapses, respectively, in response to stereotypical stimuli. These changes cause subsequent postsynaptic potentials' amplitudes to be increased, and this can extend for a significant period of time.

An important question is: what effect does a learning mechanism have on the information processing function of a single neuron or network? In the case of ANNs, this is a well-posed problem *by design*. One of the major contributions of such work has been the rigorous and precise explication of the computational properties of networks of simple processing elements coupled to certain classes of learning algorithms. Results are usually interpretable in terms of the parameters of the network transfer function being adjusted to minimize some error metric computed from the data used during the learning process.

The HKUST Biocomputing Group has been concerned recently with the issue of the meaning of learning in terms of *synaptic coding*: the transformation of presynaptic spike trains into postsynaptic spike trains across a single synapse. Because neurons are nonlinear dynamical systems, their responses to even simply-described spike trains (for example, *pacemaker* inputs where all spikes are separated by an invariant interval I) are complex [4]. This has important consequences for any learning algorithm which might be applied [5].

This is one consequence of the *bifurcation behavior* of such a nonlinear dynamical system [6]. In such systems, as some parameter is gradually changed (in the case of a neuron in the presence of a pacemaker presynaptic discharge, the presynaptic rate or the synapse strength), the output may change by either a small or a large amount. Large changes in postsynaptic discharge generally occur at discrete values of the parameter — *bifurcation points*, so-called because they are parameter values at which two distinct dynamical behaviors come together. Such behavior has been illustrated in terms of synaptic coding by our collaborators and ourselves in both living preparations and simulations [4, 7, 8, 9, 10, 11, 12]. Our current

____
*This work was sponsored by the Hong Kong Research Grants Council (UST 187/93E, 527/94M, and 668/95E).
[†]Current address: Department of Molecular and Cell Biology, 195 Life Science Addition, University of California, Berkeley, CA 94720 USA stiber@cicada.berkeley.edu

work has included analysis of coding across a single synapse in the presence of a synaptic potentiation process; this can be undertaken by extension from the observed coding in the absence of LTP [13].

2   Methods

The living preparation includes the recognized prototype of an inhibitory synapse: the crayfish slowly adapting stretch receptor organ or SAO [4]. A Hodgkin-Huxley-like model was adapted for duplication of experiments on the SAO [14, 8, 9, 12]; its basic equations are presented in Appendix A.

Presynaptic spike trains were delivered to both the SAO and the model and the times of each presynaptic and postsynaptic spike was recorded: s_k and t_i for spikes numbered k and i ($k, i = 0, 1, \ldots$), respectively. From these, certain time intervals and cross intervals were computed, the most relevant here being the presynaptic intervals $I_k = s_k - s_{k-1}$ (identically equal to a fixed I for pacemaker driving), postsynaptic intervals $T_i = t_i - t_{i-1}$, and *phases* $\phi_i = t_i - s_*$ (the cross interval from a postsynaptic spike back to the most recent presynaptic spike). This assimilation of the spike trains to a point process [15] has proven sufficient for analysis of the dynamical behaviors of this system.

It will be sufficient for the purposes of this paper to distinguish between two broad classes of dynamical responses displayed by the neuron: *phase locking* and non-locked behaviors. In phase locking (or simply "locking"), a fixed, repeating temporal relationship exists between the postsynaptic discharge and the pacemaker input. p presynaptic spikes occur in the same period of time as q postsynaptic ones, and a locking is thus said to occur at a *p:q ratio*. Intervals $\langle T_i, T_{i+1}, \ldots, T_{i+q-1} \rangle$ and phases $\langle \phi_i, \phi_{i+1}, \ldots, \phi_{i+q-1} \rangle$ repeat in exactly the time taken up by p inputs, pI.

A variety of non-locked behaviors are also exhibited; we can lump them all together in one category here without affecting our conclusions (this is some indication of the very early stage of the work of incorporation of ILTP into the dynamical coding model).

3   An Example: Pacemaker Inhibition

Figure 1 presents results of 2800 simulations: 1550 performed without ILTP and 1250 with. In all cases, pacemaker input was used. The figure is an *Arnol'd map* or *two-dimensional bifurcation diagram*: a plot of some measure of system behavior versus two parameters. In this case, the parameters are presynaptic rate (normalized as N/I) and synaptic strength. The measure used is computed from the recorded phases and intervals, with locations in the plane corresponding to parameter combinations that produced ratio 1:2, 2:3, 1:1, 3:2, and 2:1 lockings identified and colored gray for the non-ILTP simulations (white regions correspond to non-locked behaviors and lockings at other ratios). The result is a group of 5 vertical *tongues*, "anchored" at the X-axis (zero synaptic strength) at $N/I = p/q$, and broader (occupying a nonzero range of the rate domain) for physiologically meaningful values of synaptic strength. These tongues show that contiguous regions of the parameter plane produced lockings at particular ratios, a familiar result from the periodically-driven pacemaker literature [16].

3.1   ILTP Effects

For any combination of parameters, under pacemaker driving, the ILTP simulation will approach an asymptotic value of synaptic strength after some time. ILTP simulations were performed and the resultant behaviors analyzed within the epochs for which synaptic strength had become acceptably stationary. These simulations were used to locate presynaptic rates which were bifurcation points bounding one of the five locking ratios previously mentioned. Each ILTP simulation is indicated by a '+' in the figure, located at the coordinates corresponding to its presynaptic rate and asymptotic synaptic strength. Parameter settings were combinations of $\mathcal{G} = \{0.01, 0.2575, 0.505, 0.7525, 1.0\}$ and $\gamma = \{1, 25.75, 50.5, 75.25, 100.00\}$; for all, $\bar{P}_{\text{syn,f}} = 5 \times 10^{-6}\text{cm/s}$ and $\alpha = 0.505\text{s}$ (see Appendix A for a discussion of model parameters). Simulations corresponding to equal amounts of neurotransmitter release are connected by solid lines.

These preliminary results suggest that, for fixed parameters and presynaptic pacemaker rate, the effects of presynaptic-discharge-only induced ILTP are equivalent to a rotation and scaling of the non-ILTP Arnol'd map, with angle of rotation determined primarily by the amount of neurotransmitter released. In the new coordinate system, widths of locking tongues are increased for simpler ratios above (and including) 1:1. Thus, LTP causes an increase of simple synchronization *in a rate-dependent manner*.

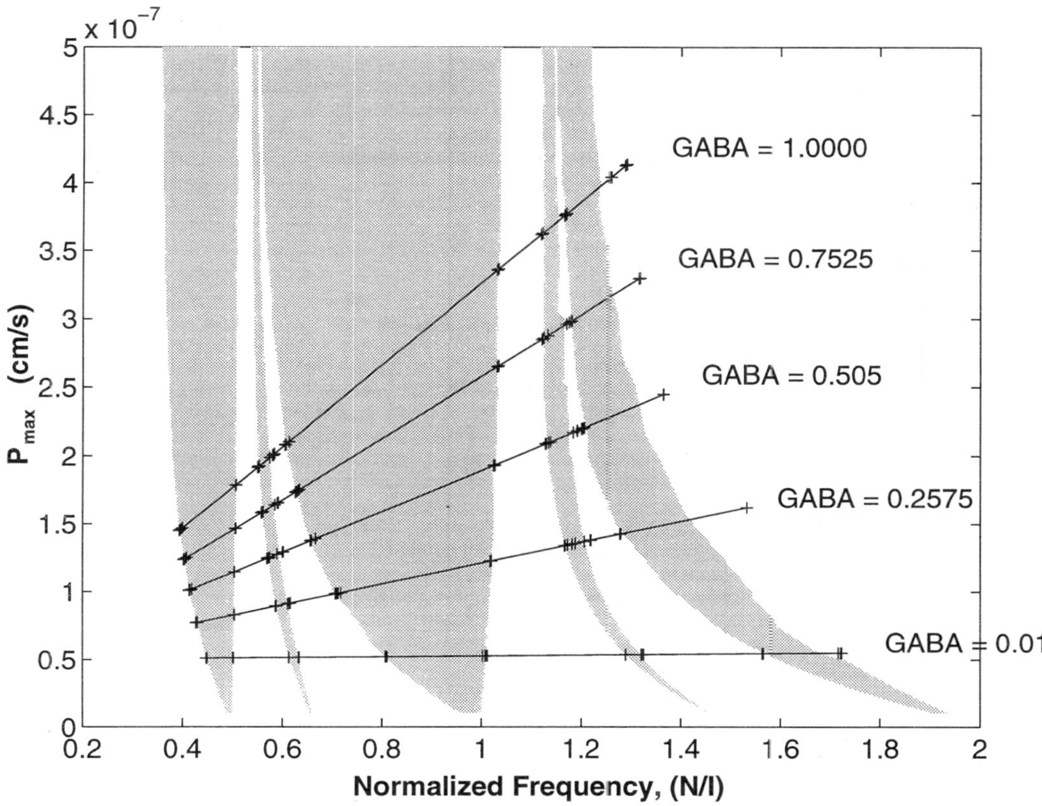

Figure 1: Comparison of behaviors produced by the simulation for both constant synaptic strength and ILTP. Gray regions correspond to lockings at ratios 1:2, 2:3, 1:1, 3:2, and 2:1 for constant synaptic strength. Each ILTP simulation's asymptotic synaptic strength is labeled with a '+'; simulations that involved release of equal amounts of neurotransmitter are connected by lines.

Table 1: Typical values for model time constants.

m	0.3ms	r	2s
h	5ms	τ_+	0.25ms
n	6ms	τ_-	0.5ms
l	1.7s	α	0.5s

4 Discussion

Understanding the physiological and molecular mechanisms which underly synaptic modification requires an experimental paradigm in which one can reliably induce a potentiating response at desired times and test the results of such potentiation while minimizing disturbance of it. Figure 2(A) illustrates this approach, in which LTP is treated as a binary action produced only by a stereotypical, discrete potentiating stimulus and unaffected by other, test stimuli. This is fine as far as it goes, but it would be unrealistic to expect nervous systems to perform learning as such a discrete behavior. We therefore must be careful not to confuse an experimental setup developed to dissect LTP into understandable parts with the action of LTP *in vivo*.

An alternative approach is taken in the ANN community, shown in (B), where the learning mechanism does indeed receive the same inputs as the neural network and operate while the network is. However, it is typically assumed that the system can be decomposed into two parts: the network (feedforward or recurrent) and the learning method (supervised or unsupervised). Even given this decomposition, network dynamics (including bifurcation behavior) complicate learning algorithm design [17].

Decomposing a dynamical system into independent subparts is a reasonable approximation if a sufficient difference exists among the time constants of these parts. We typically break such a system into two

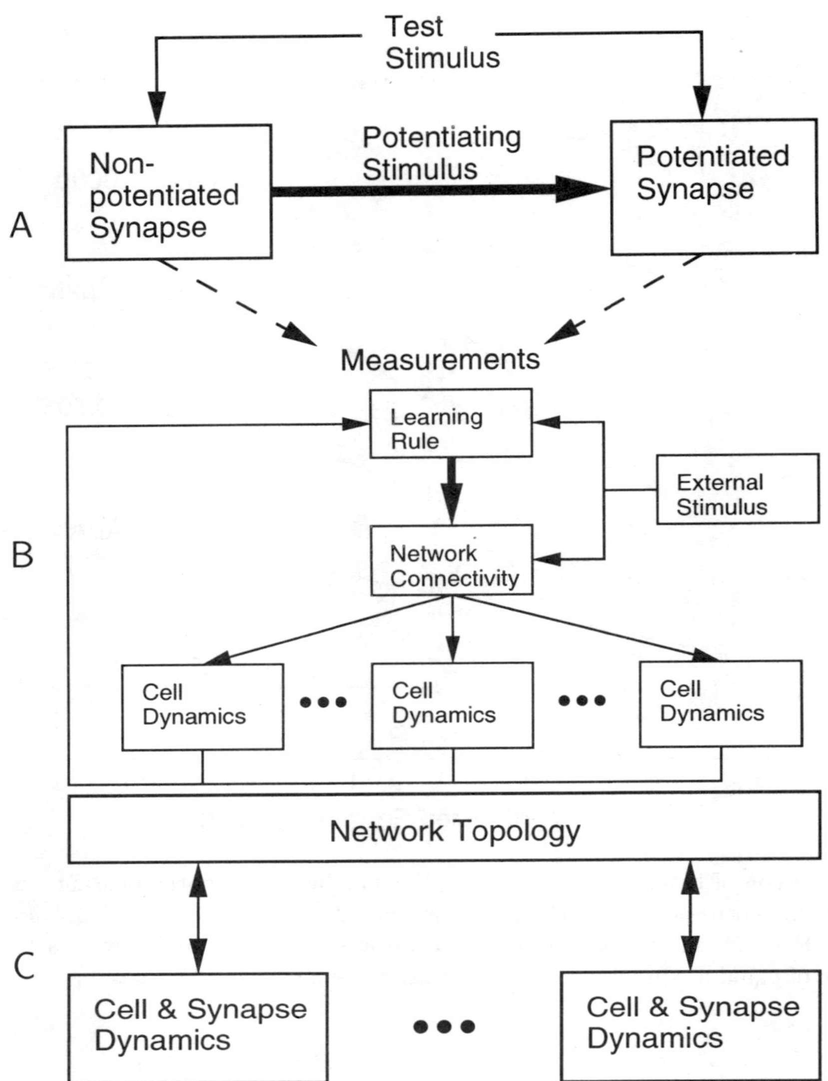

Figure 2: Schematic block diagram showing three approaches to analyzing learning in neural networks: physiological mechanisms (A), ANN (B), and dynamical coding (C).

parts: a *slow subsystem* and a *fast subsystem*, though in principle one is not limited to two. From the point of view of the fast subsystem, the slow variables are treated as constants (since over the time scale of change in the fast subsystem, they change little). Decomposing a neural network into a slow learning subsystem and a fast network processing system presupposes that the time scale of change in the learning algorithm is much different than that in the neurons themselves. However, this is not the case in real neurons or physiological models. Table 1 lists typical values for various time constants in our model.

The time that the cell produces its next spike depends not only on the time of arrival of the last IPSP, but also on the times of arrival of a few previous ones, for a length of time which can be considered its dynamical memory. As can be inferred from the table (and from previous results with time-varying inputs [18, 19, 20, 21]), this dynamical memory is at least as long the time *constant* α associated with ILTP, which is on the order of 2–5 times I. We cannot separate out the ILTP equations as a separate, slow learning subsystem. Instead, we must consider the process of input pattern coding into output pattern via the intact synapse/cell system, as schematized in Figure 2. In this approach, LTP is an inseparable part of coding.

A   The Model

A physiological model was modified from the lobster SAO model developed by Edman and collaborators [14, 12]. The lumped membrane model has two voltage-dependent permeabilities, P_{Na} and P_{K}, three leakage permeabilities, $P_{\mathrm{L,Na}}$, $P_{\mathrm{L,K}}$, and $P_{\mathrm{L,Cl}}$, two active pumping pathways, $I_{\mathrm{p,Na}}$ and $I_{\mathrm{p,K}}$, a fixed bias I_{bias}, and the membrane capacitance, C_m, and voltage, V_m. Inputs cause fixed-duration changes in the synaptic permeability, P_{syn}, to Cl^- [22]. Equations (1–5) describe the basics of all currents except the synaptic one, and also their summation to produce variation in the membrane potential, with A the cell membrane area, I_{X} the ionic current for ion X, $\bar{P}_{\mathrm{X}}$ its maximum permeability, F the Faraday constant, R the universal gas constant, T absolute temperature, and m, h, l, n, and r gating variables. The pumping mechanism exchanges 3 Na^+ ions for 2 K^+ in (5), where $\bar{J}_{\mathrm{p,Na}}$ is the maximum Na^+ pump capacity, K_m a constant, and the factor of 1/3 is the net effect of the 3:2 pump ratio.

$$\frac{dV_m}{dt} = -(I_{\mathrm{Na}} + I_{\mathrm{K}} + I_{\mathrm{L,Na}} + I_{\mathrm{L,K}} + I_{\mathrm{L,Cl}} + I_{\mathrm{p}} + I_{\mathrm{bias}} + I_{\mathrm{syn}})/C_m \tag{1}$$

$$I_{\mathrm{Na}} = A\bar{P}_{\mathrm{Na}}m^2hl\frac{V_mF^2}{RT}\frac{[\mathrm{Na}^+]_o - [\mathrm{Na}^-]_i\exp(FV_m/RT)}{1-\exp(FV_m/RT)} \tag{2}$$

$$I_{\mathrm{K}} = A\bar{P}_{\mathrm{K}}n^2r\frac{V_mF^2}{RT}\frac{[\mathrm{K}^+]_o - [\mathrm{K}^+]_i\exp(FV_m/RT)}{1-\exp(FV_m/RT)} \tag{3}$$

$$I_{\mathrm{L,X}} = AP_{\mathrm{L,X}}\frac{V_mF^2}{RT}\frac{[X]_o - [X]_i\exp(FV_m/RT)}{1-\exp(FV_m/RT)} \tag{4}$$

$$I_{\mathrm{p}} = \frac{AF}{3}\frac{\bar{J}_{\mathrm{p,Na}}}{\left(1+\frac{K_m}{[\mathrm{Na}^+]_i}\right)^3} \tag{5}$$

The synapse contributes current in response to each presynaptic arrival at time s_k according to equations (6–8), after Tsukada and collaborators [23]. In this model, potentiation depends solely on the arrival times of the presynaptic discharge. Each IPSP has associated with it a permeability composed of a fixed part, $\bar{P}_{\mathrm{syn,f}}$, and a modifiable part, $P_{\mathrm{syn,m}}$, that varies based on previous IPSP arrival times. The latter is set to zero for simulations without ILTP; it varies along time for ILTP-inclusive simulations, asymptotically reaching a maximum for pacemaker inputs [13]. ILTP parameters also include a growth rate, γ, amount of transmitter released, $\mathcal{G}$, and a decay time constant, α.

$$I_{\mathrm{syn}} = A\frac{V_mF^2}{RT}\frac{[\mathrm{Cl}^-]_o - [\mathrm{Cl}^-]_i\exp(FV_m/RT)}{1-\exp(FV_m/RT)} \times \sum_{k=1}^{n}P_{\mathrm{syn}}(s_k)\left(e^{(s_k-t)/\tau_+} - e^{(s_k-t)/\tau_-}\right) \tag{6}$$

$$P_{\mathrm{syn}}(s_k) = \bar{P}_{\mathrm{syn,f}} + P_{\mathrm{syn,m}}(s_k) \tag{7}$$

$$P_{\mathrm{syn,m}}(s_k) = \left(1-\frac{1}{\gamma}\right)P_{\mathrm{syn,m}}(s_{k-1}) + \frac{\mathcal{G}\bar{P}_{\mathrm{syn,f}}}{\gamma} \times \sum_{\ell=0}^{k-1}\epsilon^{(s_\ell-s_k)/\alpha} \tag{8}$$

References

[1] J. Movshon and R. Van Sluyters, "Visual neural development," *Ann. Rev. Psychol.*, vol. 32, pp. 477–522, 1981.

[2] T. Bliss and T. Lømo, "Long-lasting potentiation of synaptic transmission in the dentate area of the anesthetized rabbit following stimulation of the perforant path," *J. Physiol.*, vol. 232, pp. 331–56, 1973.

[3] S. Charpier, Y. Oda, and H. Korn, "Long-term enhancement of inhibitory synaptic transmission in the central nervous system," in *Long Term Potentiation 2* (M. Baudry and J. Davis, eds.), pp. 151–68, Cambridge, MA: MIT Press, 1995.

[4] J. P. Segundo, E. Altshuler, M. Stiber, and A. Garfinkel, "Periodic inhibition of living pacemaker neurons: I. Locked, intermittent, messy, and hopping behaviors," *Int. J. Bifurcation and Chaos*, vol. 1, pp. 549–81, Sept. 1991.

[5] M. Stiber and J. Segundo, "Learning in neural models with complex dynamics," in *Proc. IJCNN*, (Nagoya, Japan), pp. 405–8, 25–29 Oct. 1993.

[6] P. Bergé, Y. Pomeau, and C. Vidal, *Order Within Chaos: A Deterministic Approach to Turbulence.* New York: Wiley, 1986.

[7] J. P. Segundo, E. Altshuler, M. Stiber, and A. Garfinkel, "Periodic inhibition of living pacemaker neurons: II. Influences of driver rates and transients and of non-driven post-synaptic rates," *Int. J. Bifurcation and Chaos*, vol. 1, pp. 873–90, Dec. 1991.

[8] M. Stiber and J. P. Segundo, "Dynamics of synaptic transfer in living and simulated neurons," in *Proc. ICNN*, (San Francisco), pp. 75–80, 1993.

[9] M. Stiber, L. Yan, J. Segundo, and J.-F. Vibert, "Is there and alphabet for synaptic coding?," in *Third Japanese Workshop on Neural Coding*, (Wakayama, Japan), Sept. 1994.

[10] T. Nomura, S. Sato, S. Doi, J. Segundo, and M. Stiber, "Global bifurcation structure of a Bonhoeffer — van der Pol oscillator driven by periodic pulse trains. comparison with data from a periodically inhibited biological pacemaker," *Biol. Cybern.*, vol. 72, pp. 55–67, 1994.

[11] T. Nomura, S. Sato, S. Doi, J. Segundo, and M. Stiber, "A modified radial isochron clock with slow and fast dynamics as a model of pacemaker neurons. global bifurcation structure when driven by periodic pulse trains," *Biol. Cybern.*, vol. 72, pp. 93–101, 1994.

[12] M. Stiber, K. Pakdaman, J.-F. Vibert, E. Boussard, J. Segundo, T. Nomura, S. Sato, and S. Doi, "Complex responses of living pacemaker neurons to pacemaker inhibition: a comparison of dynamical models," *Biosystems*, in press, 1996.

[13] R. Ieong and M. Stiber, "Long-term potentiation effects on synaptic coding," in *CNS*96*, (Boston), submitted, 1996.

[14] A. Edman, S. Gestrelius, and W. Grampp, "Transmembrane ion balance in slowly and rapidly adapting lobster stretch receptor neurones," *J. Physiol.*, vol. 377, pp. 171–91, 1986.

[15] D. Cox and V. Isham, *Point Processes.* London: Chapman and Hall, 1980.

[16] V. Arnol'd, *Geometrical Methods in the Theory of Ordinary Differential Equations.* New York: Springer-Verlag, 1983.

[17] K. Doya, "Recurrent networks: Supervised learning," in *The Handbook of Brain Theory and Neural Networks* (M. Arbib, ed.), pp. 796–800, MIT Press, 1995.

[18] J. Segundo, M. Stiber, E. Altshuler, and J.-F. Vibert, "Transients in the inhibitory driving of neurons and their post-synaptic consequences," *Neurosci.*, vol. 62, no. 2, pp. 459–80, 1994.

[19] M. Stiber, R. Ieong, R. Chandramani, J. Segundo, and J.-F. Vibert, "Synaptic coding of inhibitory transients: comparison of model and living preparation," in *CNS*95*, (Monterey, California), July 1995.

[20] M. Stiber and R. Ieong, "Hysteresis and asymmetric sensitivity to change in pacemaker responses to inhibitory input transients," in *Int. Conf. on Brain Processes, Theories and Models. W.S. McCulloch: 25 Years in Memoriam* (R. Moreno-Diaz and J. Mira-Mira, eds.), (Grand Canary, Spain), pp. 513–22, MIT Press, Nov. 1995.

[21] M. Stiber, R. Ieong, and J. Segundo, "Responses to transients in living and simulated neurons," *IEEE Trans. Neural Networks*, submitted, 1996.

[22] K. Ozawa and K. Tsuda, "Membrane permeability change during inhibitory transmitter action in crayfish receptor cell," *J. Neurophysiol.*, vol. 36, no. 5, pp. 805–16, 1973.

[23] S. Shinomoto, M. Crair, M. Tsukada, and T. Aihara, "The stimulus dependent induction of long-term potentiation in CA1 area of the hippocampus. II. Mathematical model," tech. rep., Department of Information-Communication Engineering, Tamagawa University, Tokyo, Japan, 1992.

Neural Coding of Auditory Information in Animal Brain Revealed by Optical Imaging

Kohyu Fukunishi, Ryo Tokioka, Nobuyuki Murai
Hitachi Advanced Research Laboratory, Hitachi, Ltd.
Hatoyama, Saitama 350-03 Japan

Abstract— Neural coding aspects in the guinea pig auditory cortex for tones, clicks and vocalizations are reviewed in a physiological investigation by observing their spatiotemporal neural activities using an optical recording system with a 12 x 12 photodiode array. Dynamic neural behaviors are in the cortical field in response to complex sounds such as clicks and vocalizations, in contrast to static and stable responses to tones, the simplest sounds. Of special significance, when an animal hears a natural vocal call the temporal encoding pattern in the auditory cortex is possibly related to the tonal information included in the onset sound of the call. The empirical neural network of the auditory neural responses is estimated by applying a pattern time series analysis.

1   Introduction

To understand how auditory information is processed in mammal brains is a very interesting matter not only from a neuroscience viewpoint, but also from an engineering viewpoint. The requirement for auditory human-interface in information processing equipment is increasing for easier user access to a computer system. However, application of vocal recognition and vocal synthesis to auditory human-interface is very limited in spite of a development history of over 40 years. This is because general methods of vocal recognition and vocal synthesis have still not been found. Recently it has been said that information gleaned from a biological auditory system might give us insight that would lead to breakthrough in this area.

However, there is still remarkably little understanding of auditory information processing mechanisms, especially of the higher level functions, carried out in the brain, despite the huge amount of experimental data [1]. These data have principally been obtained based on physiological experiments investigating a neuron's response property to a special auditory stimulus using a microelectrode. It may be difficult to reorganize the functional brain from the large amount of experimental data on neuron characteristics. Recently, however, neural dynamic association and connection as well as temporal neural coding have been considered to be promising for general neural information processing in the brain [2]. These new trends in brain research are derived by analyzing neural response data by multiunit recording instead of unit recording.

Optical recording which measures neural activity using multiple optical sensors has been applied to observe spatiotemporal neural behavior in the auditory cortical field [3]. Generally, the advantage of this recording method is its possibility to quantitatively analyze the functional mechanism of information processing in mammal brains. Here, we review our experiments and analysis of observation of spatiotemporal neural activities in the guinea pig auditory cortex during the emission of sounds such as tones and vocalizations using optical recording with voltage-sensitive dye [3, 4, 5, 7, 8, 9].

2   Optical Imaging

A 128-channel optical recording system with a 12 x 12 photodiode array as the multiple optical sensors installed in a specially designed and manufactured optical system was used in the experiments (Fig. 1). The fluorescent dye RH 795 was adopted for transferring the neural membrane potential response to an optical signal response. All signals were amplified and fed into a computer in parallel with a time resolution of 10 kHz to prevent time-delay nonlinear effects in data processing among signals. The results from subsequent control trials were subtracted from those of trials in which stimuli were used and averaged for 20-100 trials to improve the signal-to-noise ratio. Recently, this averaging process has become almost unnecessary due to the development of a new system.

The experiments were carried out on anesthetized mature male guinea pigs controlled with a respirator. The acoustic stimuli were controlled so as to synchronize with the ECG and respiration in order to avoid the artifacts from heart beat and respiration.

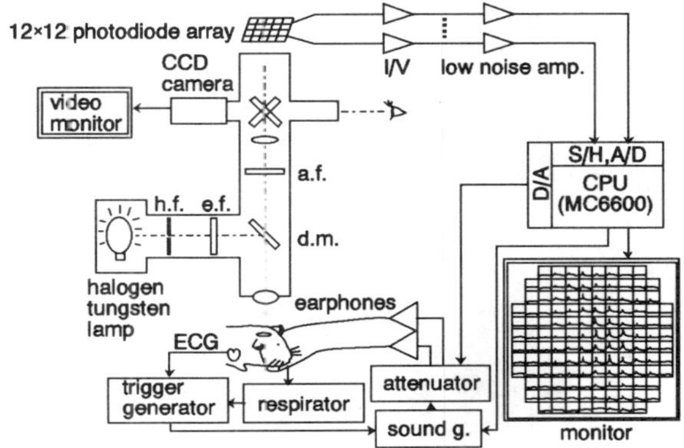

Figure 1: The optical recording system with a 12 x12 photodiode array for auditory physiological experiments.

The auditory stimuli used were pure tones as simple sounds, clicks as an artificial complex sound and species-specific vocalizations. Two different vocal calls, a "scream" and a "whistle", were classified among a several vocal calls by evaluating the sound feature of a call itself and the animal behavior while listening to the call.

3 Neural Population Coding

3.1 The simplest sound coding

Pure tone bursts without an abrupt onset might be the simplest spectral sound. The response to the pure tone burst in an auditory cortex (field A) in guinea pigs is known to show isofrequency bands in the dorso-ventral direction located over the rostra-caudal axis, as low-frequency responses in the rostral and high frequencies in the caudal, by the microelectrode experiments. Optical imaging of the response

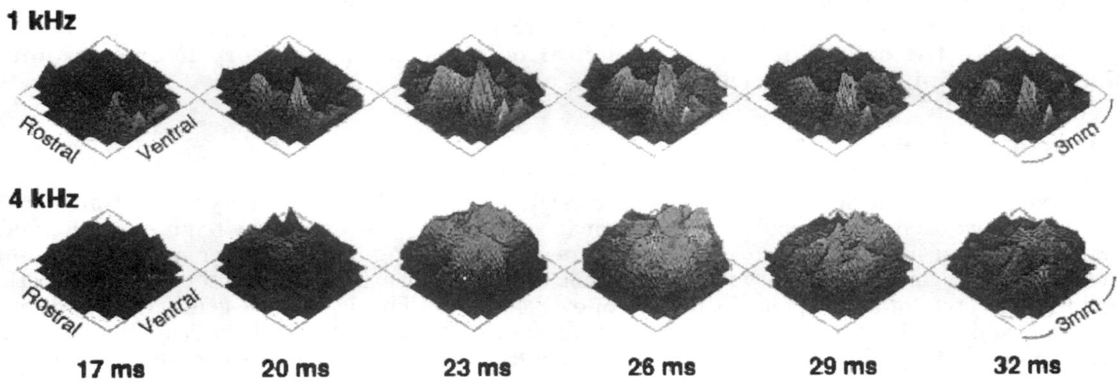

Figure 2: Spatiotemporal response pattern for tone bursts of 1kHz and 4kHz in the guinea pig primary auditory cortex (3mm ^{2} of field A, spatial resolution of 0.22mm).

to the tone bursts showed results slightly different to those of the above electrical physiology results, as illustrated in Fig. 2. The three-dimensional picture denotes a spatiotemporal neural response pattern for each tone, where the height indicates the response amplitude, in 3-mm^2 of the auditory cortex (field A). The response area for a low-frequency (1 kHz) tone is located in the rostral, and for a high-frequency tone in the caudal, which is similar to the results by the electrode experiment. However, the response area for each frequency, the tonotopic response area, consists of some response neural groups instead of the neuron's isotopic frequency band for the tone. Furthermore, the tonotopical area remained stable at the same cortical position for an increased stimulus intensity with the same frequency, but expanded peripherally in the response area [3, 9]. Thus, spatiotemporal neural response visualization by optical imaging in the animal auditory cortex for tone stimuli has revealed a neural population coding pattern for the simplest sound and the sound intensity.

4 Temporal Coding

4.1 Complex sound processing

The click, pulse sound, in which sounds in a wide range of frequencies are emitted at a constant intensity at the same time, is an artificial complex sound for an animal. The spatiotemporal response pattern to clicks was dynamic in that the response areas moved within a wide area of the primary cortical field in a boomerang-shaped pattern; from rostral to caudal, and back again to rostral in the

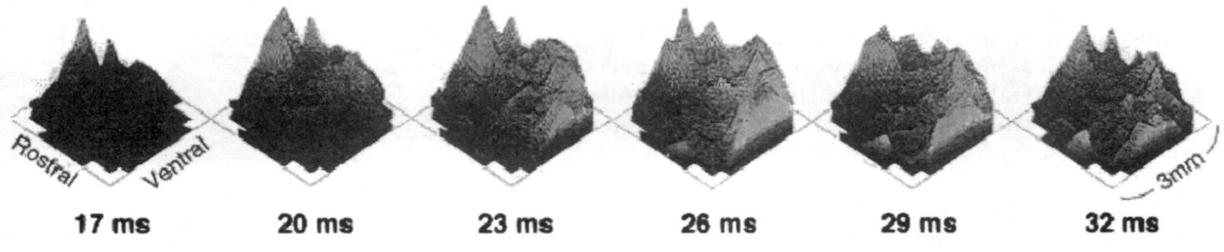

Figure 3: Spatiotemporal response pattern in the animal auditory cortex (A) for a click sound.

auditory cortex (dominantly, field A) as depicted in the three-dimensional illustration (Fig. 3). Thus, the spatiotemporal response pattern of the cortical neurons for click revealed temporal processing evidence that the complex signal is processed sequentially over the auditory cortical field. This dynamic neural behavior to this complex sound is quite different to the static and stable neural response to tones [3].

The results show that the spatiotemporal patterns of responses to clicks possibly move across the response area for tones from higher frequencies to lower frequencies in the ventral auditory field by overlapping the observed response pattern to click and tones, as illustrated in Fig. 4. The tone response area, tonotopic response, in the auditory cortex signifies a coded memory pattern by the neural population for tones. The overlapped picture suggests a functional neural processing structure of the temporal neural processing of complex sounds in the relation with the tonotopic response, like as recalling sound frequency memories.

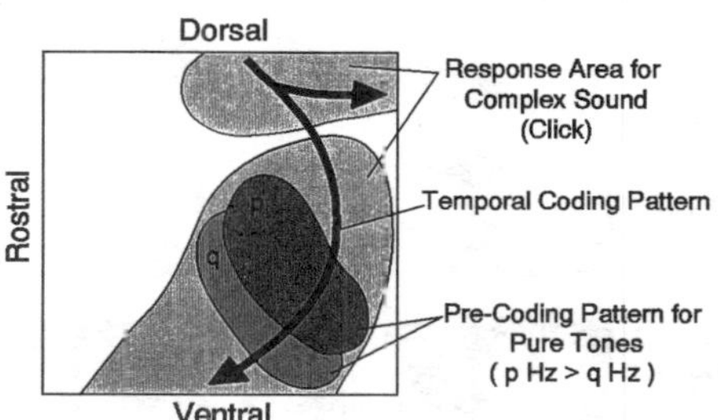

Figure 4: Topographic image of temporal coding for a click over the tonotopical area of the auditory cortex.

4.2 Natural sound processsing

Understanding how normal communication signals are encoded by auditory neurons is the ultimate target of this auditory physiological study. Vocalizations of guinea pigs, which were recorded and analyzed by their spectrum, were classified in relation to their behavior [6, 8]. The sound wave and the spectrum of the

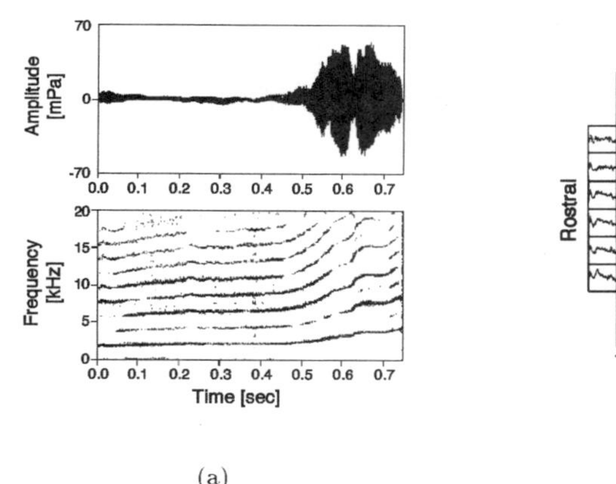

(a)

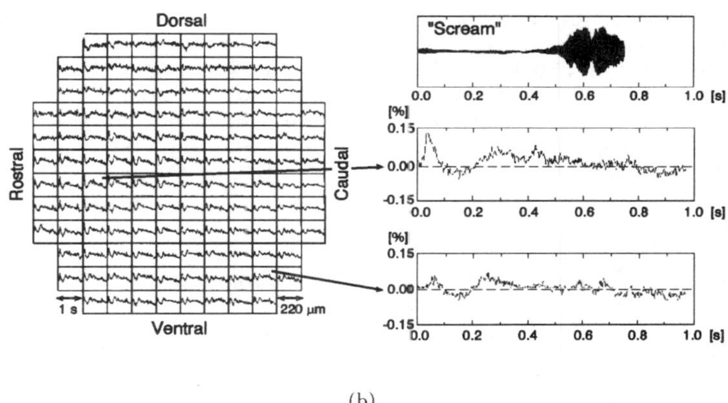

(b)

Figure 5: (a) Sound wave and spectrum patterns of guinea pig "scream" vocalization. (b) Spatial response pattern by time courses to the vocal call, and typical responses.

"scream" are depicted in Fig. 5a. The spatiotemporal response pattern in 3-mm^2 of the auditory cortex (field A) of a guinea pig that heard a "scream" lasting about 750ms elicited stronger excitatory responses during the first 50ms and inhibitory responses during the next 150ms than the responses during the time interval from 500 to 750ms, of the strong loudness and varying sound pressure in the "scream" stimulus, as shown in Fig. 5b. The neural responses elicited later, when the stimulus was more intense and its sound frequency was modulated sharply, were less dynamic than those elicited earlier. This evidence suggests that neural encoding for vocalization is closely related to the neural behavior of the stronger response phases exhibited when the onset of a vocal call is heard.

The topographic patterns of neural activities generated in response to tone bursts of 1, 4 and 16kHz and the vocal "scream" for one animal are compared at each latency during the onset response, as denoted in Fig. 6. The topographic neural activity pattern from the "scream" sound stimulus showed that excitatory responses propagated briefly on the tonotopical area according to the dominant sound frequencies appearing in the voice even though the sound spectrum structure did not change rapidly during the first 50ms of the stimulus. When the guinea pig heard the skewed "scream" sound of which the lower frequency components were eliminated by a low-frequency cut filter, the tonotopic response corresponded to the lower frequency tones was lost. Thus, we can confirm that the auditory information for a vocal call is probably processed temporally over the tonotopical area in the auditory cortex (field A) according to the tone information appearing successively in the onset sound.

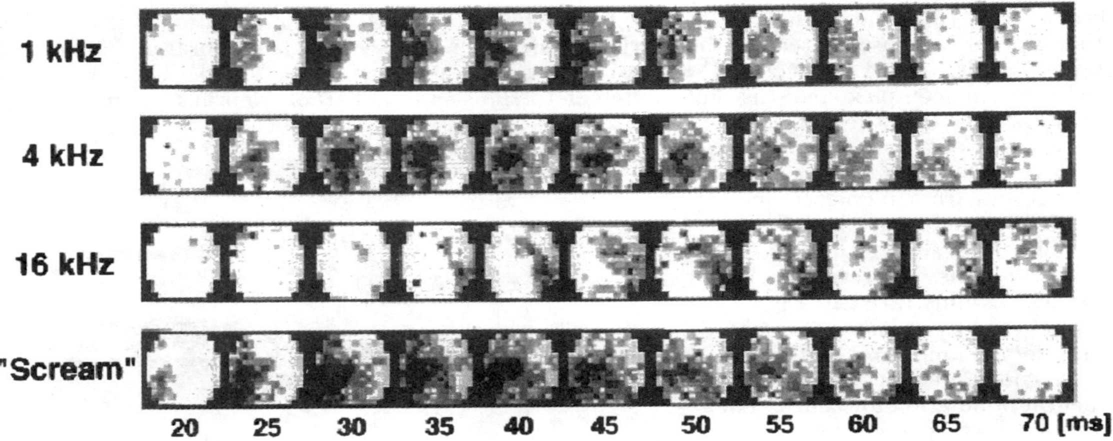

Figure 6: Comparison of the topographic pattern of neural activities for "scream", and tone bursts of 1kHz, 4kHz and 16kHz during the first 70ms.

5 Neural Binding Structure

Simple cross-correlation analysis of the click responses in each sensed region of a 128-region optical imaging indicates the existence of functional modules about 0.3~0.5mm in diameter in the cortical field [3, 4]. However, a correlation analysis applied to the identification of the dynamics of a complex system with feedback loops may derive insufficient and distorted dynamic features, as discussed in our recent article [5, 7]. There, experimental data was manipulated by applying pattern time series analysis using a multivariable autoregressive (MAR) model to analyze the optical imaging data. This method showed neural oscillations of 20-50Hz in the click-induced evoked responses in the auditory cortical field which was similar to work involving the visual cortex of monkeys and cats, etc., using microelectrodes. Furthermore, the forward and backward neural functional binding effects at the oscillation frequencies identified by this method suggest that the anxiety connoted by the neural binding between the cortical regions - estimated by conventional correlation and coherency analysis - may be imaginary in some cases.

Thus, both spatiotemporal measurements and dynamic analysis of spatiotemporal data offer one hopeful new approach to better understand the dynamic neural system of the auditory brain.

References

[1] A. N. Popper and R. R. Fay, *The Mammalian Auditory Pathway: Neurophysiology*. Berlin: Springer, 1992.

[2] G. Buzsaki *et al.*, *Temporal Coding in the Brain*. Berlin: Springer, 1994.

[3] K. Fukunishi *et al.*, Dynamic characteristics of the auditory cortex of guinea pigs observed with multichannel optical recording, *Biological Cybernetics*, vol. 67, pp. 501-509, September 1992.

[4] K. Fukunishi *et al.*, Spatio-temporal observation of guinea pig auditory cortex with optical recording, *Japanese Journal of Physiology*, vol. 43 suppl. 1, pp. 91-96, 1993.

[5] K. Fukunishi and N. Murai, Cortical neural networks revealed by spatio-temporal neural observation and analysis on guinea pig auditory cortex, for auditory, *Proc. Int. Joint Conf. on Neural Networks*, Nagoya, Oct. 25-29, 1993, pp. 73-76.

[6] K. Fukunishi *et al.*, Vocal coding pattern of guinea pig auditory cortex by optical imaging, *Society for Neuroscience Abstracts*, vol. 20, p. 324, 1994.

[7] K. Fukunishi and N. Murai, Temporal coding of the guinea pig auditory cortex revealed by optical imaging and its pattern time series analysis, *Biological Cybernetics*, vol. 72, pp. 463-473, August 1995.

[8] K. Fukunishi *et al.*, The coding of species-specific vocalization in guinea pig auditory cortex revealed by optical imaging with dye, *in preparation*.

[9] H. Uno *et al.*, The tonotopic representation in the auditory cortex of the guinea pig with optical recording, *Neuroscience Letters*, vol. 150, pp. 179-182, March 1993.

Dynamic population representations of visual and somatosensory cortex

Hubert R. Dinse , Dirk Jancke, Amir C. Akhavan, Thomas Kalt,
Martin Giese, *Gregor Schöner

Institut für Neuroinformatik, Theoretische Biologie, Ruhr-Universität Bochum,
*Centre de Recherche en Neurosciences Cognitives, CNRS, Marseille, France

hubert@neuroinformatik.ruhr-uni-bochum.de

Abstract

We present an analysis of the dynamics of neural population behavior recorded in cat and rat primary visual and somatosensory cortex. The time resolved population representations provide an accurate representation and reconstruction of the stimulus location and reveal global nonlinearities following two-point stimulation. They allow the analysis of short-term dynamics of entire population of cells and the analysis of motion trajectories. The approach requires that all cells of the sampled population must be stimulated by identical common stimuli in a non RF-centered mode. As the approach uses the parametric space, it specifies the meaning of the activation of single cells independently of the constraints of cortical maps. As the data reflect the response properties of an entire population of cells, their behavior provide rather direct links to psychophysical data.

Introduction

During the recent years, experimental evidence was accumulated that receptive field (RF) organization is characterized by complex spatio-temporal properties. A remarkable and highly idiosyncratic dynamic behavior was shown for neurons of visual [1-7], auditory [8-10] and somatosensory [11,5] cortex that made an uniform functional interpretation in terms of implications for information processing fairly difficult. Apart from the obvious similarities of the various RF dynamics, there are also clear differences across modalities which mainly concern the absolute timing of these dynamics. In addition, using voltage sensitive dyes in combination with optical imaging techniques, cortical representational maps were shown to possess comparable spatio-temporal dynamics [12-16].

In addition, the existence of cooperative effects in cortical information processing gained increasing interest in both psychophysical and neurophysiological research. Among others, cooperativity can be assumed to result in essential nonlinear effects. In presence of strong cooperative effects, classical descriptions of cortical functions in terms of single RFs appear more and more incomplete. An attempt to treat aspects of cooperativity experimentally was the introduction of the concept of neuron assemblies [17,18] and population coding [19-22].

Population coding in a sensory domain allows in an operationally defined way the measurement, description and analysis of a population of neurons to a common task or common stimulus [23]. It can be regarded as the projection of many single cells' responses to a common stimulus into a space representing the parameter of interest. By means of the construction of a neural activity distribution over the functional space (as normally done for single cell RF mapping), the analysis becomes independent of the constraints of anatomical descriptions. However, the method requires a special experimental paradigm: All cells of the population must be stimulated by identical stimuli independently of the spatial arrangement of the single cells' RFs in the sensory field (non RF-centered approach). This procedure seems biologically plausible as it appears conceivable that under natural conditions, most of the neurons are unlikely to be stimulated in a RF-centered mode.

Here we apply the population technique for neurons recorded in cat visual and rat somatosensory cortex to describe effects of distance dependent interactions of "composite" stimuli of different spatio-temporal delays and to moving stimuli of different velocities. All stimulus configurations are based on highly complex spatio-temporal interactions. The population approach enables us to analyze on a level of population of cells the global properties of spatio-temporal dynamics of representations and global nonlinearities.

Materials and Methods

Recording and stimulation. The activity of single neurons was recorded extracellularly in cat visual and rat somatosensory cortex. According to the non-centered RF approach, to all neurons the same and identical set of stimuli was applied independent of the location of the individual RF. We used so-called elementary stimuli and composite stimuli composed of 2 elementary stimuli simultaneously applied at various separation distances and temporal delays. In the visual system, small squares of light were flashed or moved with different velocities, in the somatosensory systems, tactile stimuli at different locations on the paw were used. In addition, in both systems, the location of the receptive fields of each individual cell was measured using the response plane (visual cortex) or handplotting techniques (somatosensory cortex).

Construction of population code. For a given stimulus, the contribution of each cell to the population response is its normalized firing rate. To achieve an interpolated and smooth activation distribution, spatial lowpass filtering was performed by weighting individual firing rates with a Gaussian profile. Thus, the contribution of each cell is given as a Gaussian profile in the parameter space centered at its RF-center location and with a height proportional to its actual firing rate. To correct for sampling density, the interpolated population activation distribution is divided by a distribution equally constructed from equal individual cell activations of 1. The result is an interpolated population activation distribution taking into account irregularities in the sampling density. Application of a time slice technique allows the reconstruction of the population representation in time windows of variable width. We used 10 ms temporal resolution for the visual, and 3 ms for the somatosensory cortex.

Results

Dynamics of population representations and reconstruction of stimulus position.
The population representation allowed the reconstruction of the actual location and position of single elementary stimuli with high precision (fig. 1/2). Using the time-slice technique it is possible to visualize and analyze the temporal evolution of the population representation in discrete time windows (fig. 1/2). In general, we observed in both modalities a gradual and coherent evolution of the population response (composed of a large number of single cell responses) to an elementary stimulus over time and space. This is remarkable in view of the complex spatial-temporal structure of the single cells' receptive field. The precise representation was present during the entire duration of the response. While the duration of temporal evolution was about 50 ms for the visual system, we found about 10 ms for the somatosensory system.

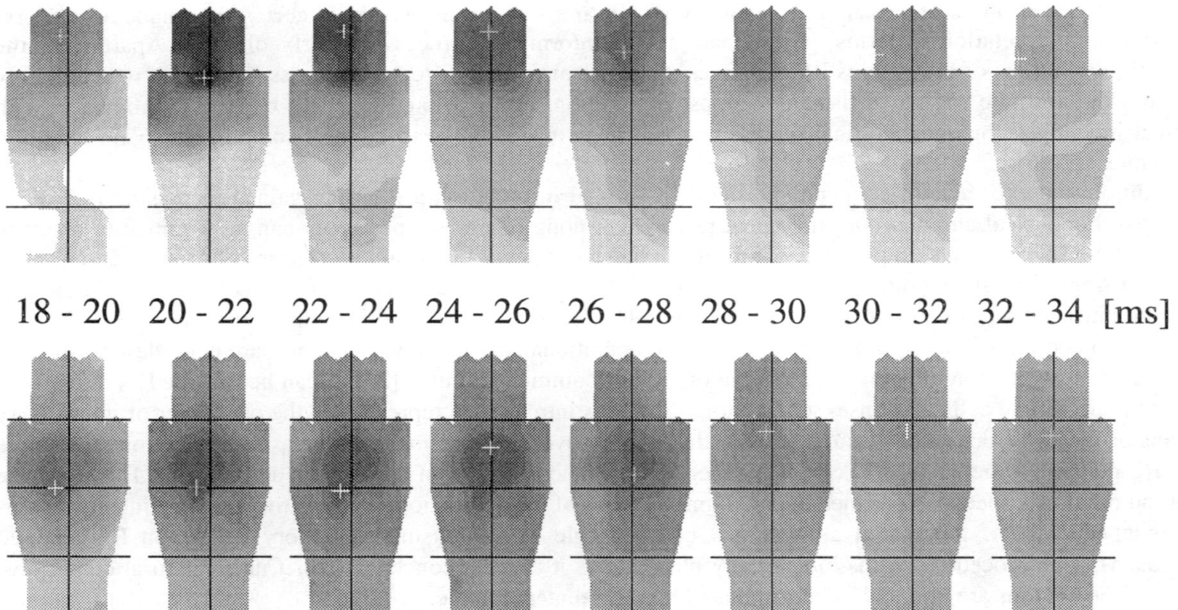

Fig. 1. Somatosensory cortex. Temporal evolution of the population representation of two different so-called elementary stimuli (top: distal aspects of digits; bottom: middle pad) using the time-slice technique displaying a coherent build-up and decay of neural activity (rat somatosensory cortex, SI). Time steps after stimulus onset are indicated on top. The parametric space (skin surface on the hindpaw) is shown. Population activity is gray-coded. Time and location of maximal activity is indicated.

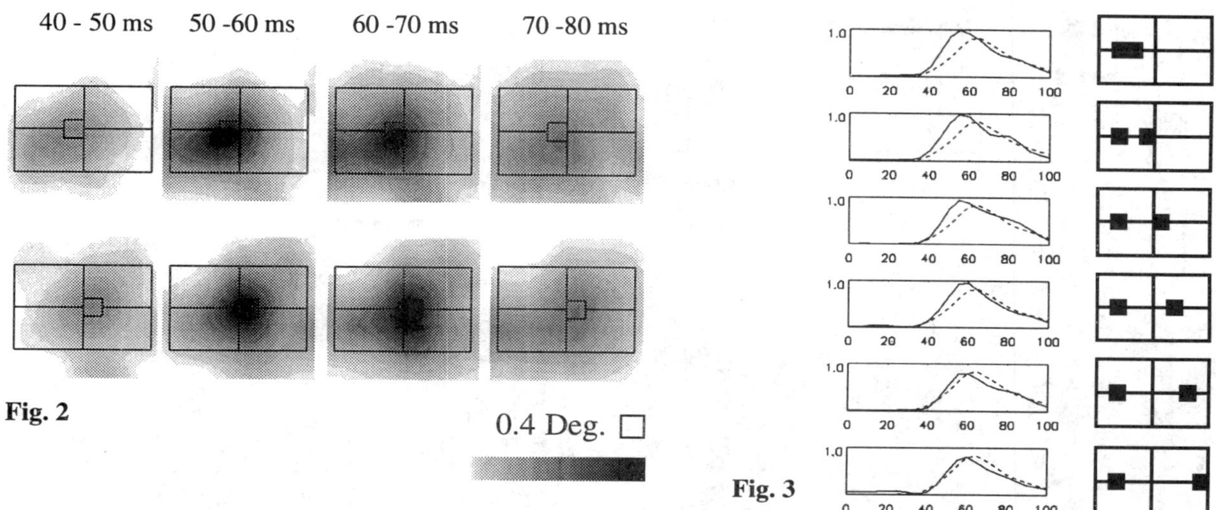

Fig. 2

0.4 Deg. □

Fig. 3

Fig. 2. Visual cortex. Temporal evolution of the population representation of two different so-called elementary stimuli using the time-slice technique displaying a coherent build-up and decay of neural activity (cat viusal cortex, area 17). Time steps after stimulus onset are indicated on top. The parametric space (central visual field) and the position of each elementary stimulus is shown (0.4 deg. visual field). Population activity is gray-coded and was normalized for each single stimulus.
Fig. 3. Visual cortex. Time course [ms] of the maximum population activity at the position of the left stimulus (solid line) in the composite stimulus paradigm. Dashed lines illustrate the time course of maximum activity at the position of the left square when presented alone. Separation between the squares increases from top to bottom (small column).

Dynamic interaction effects.

When composite stimuli were presented, we found a distance dependent global nonlinear behavior of the entire neural population of neurons with respect to the amplitude of representation and to the location of population representation. Global nonlinear interactions were analyzed by comparing the measured population responses to composite stimuli in a time resolved way with the calculated linear superposition of the corresponding elementary stimulus representations. The most striking interaction effect is a distance dependent strong inhibition of the population response (fig. 3/5). A closer inspection of the above described overall inhibition with respect to a finer temporal resolution reveals two separable interaction effects: an early excitation and late inhibition (cf. figs. 3/4). When the composite stimuli were applied with delays between 35 and 70 ms (somatosensory cortex), excitatory and inhibitory interaction effects turned out to be dependent on both temporal delay- and spatial separation distance.

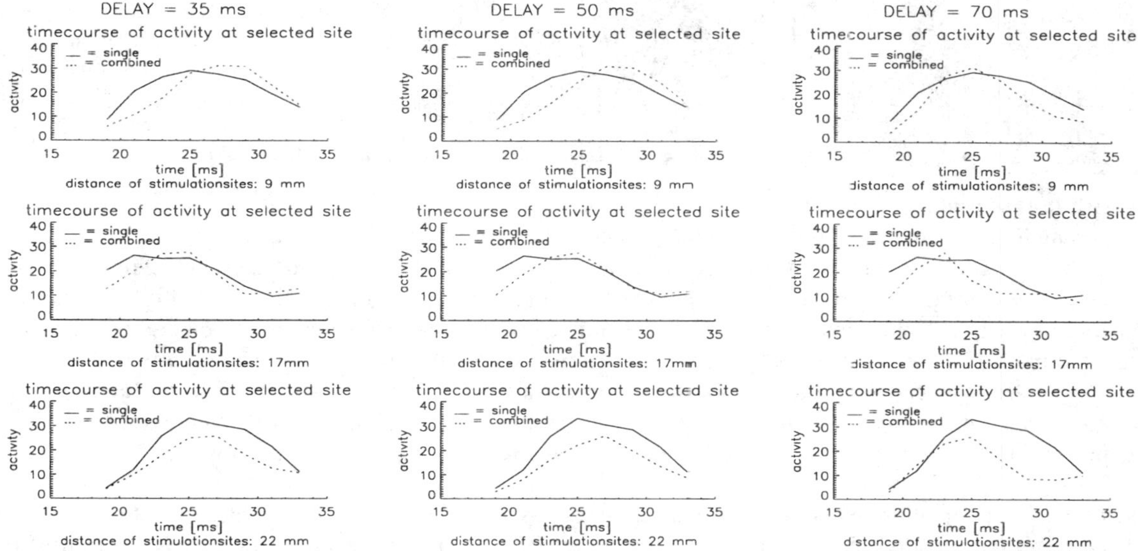

Fig. 4. Somatosensory cortex. Effects of spatio-temporal delays on the time course [ms] of the maximum population activity at different positions of the stimulus when presented alone (solid line) compared to the composite stimulus paradigm (dotted line). Separation between the stimuli increases from top to bottom. Temporal delay is indicated at the top of each column.

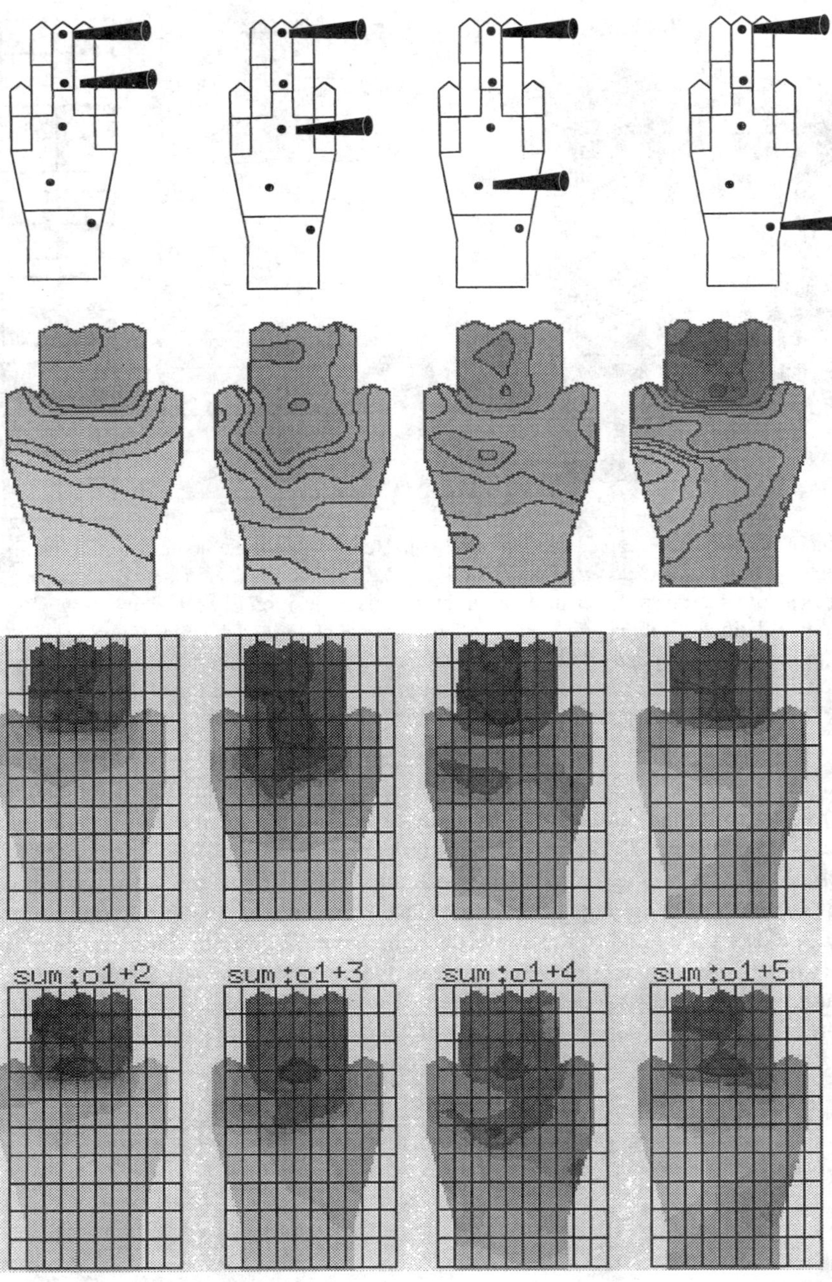

Fig. 5. Somatosensory cortex. Nonlinear effects induced by composite stimuli (schematically shown in top row) on the amplitude and location of the population representations in rat somatosensory cortex revealed by comparison with the calculated linear superposition of single corresponding elementary stimuli (bottom row). The parametric space (skin surface on the hindpaw) is shown. Population activity is gray-coded. Second row illustrates the aspects of nonlinear suppression of the amplitude of the population representation. To visualize the degree of suppression, the amplitudes of calculated superposition and the measured activity are equally normalized and thus directly comparable. To illustrate nonlinear effects on the localization and position of the maximal population response (third row) that can be characterized as an attraction towards the tips of the digits, amplitudes are normalized for each individual example shown.

Representation of motion.

The representation of moving stimuli in primary visual cortex has been subject of many studies of individual cells and their spatio-temporal receptive field structure. However, it has been impossible to reconstruct from individual cell responses the cortical representation of moving stimuli, and thus to link spatial information and movement information. This is important to assess the influence of cooperative interactions on the representation of moving stimuli. The responses of all neurons to a moving stimulus (presented for all neurons at identical retinal coordinates independent of their RF locations) were analyzed in short time slices and represented as levels of activation on the retinal space, with each neuron contributing at the location of its RF center. The peak of this time-dependent population representation can be tracked and directly compared to the stimulus motion on the retina (fig. 7).

We found that the population response follows the stimulus on the retina with a velocity dependent delay (fig. 6/7). At 8.8 deg/s the peak position in the population representation closely matches the current position of the stimulus with near zero delay. For faster speeds a phase lag, for slower speeds a phase advance is observed. We interpret this finding as evidence for contributions of dynamic cooperativity to the representation of moving stimuli in primary visual cortex.

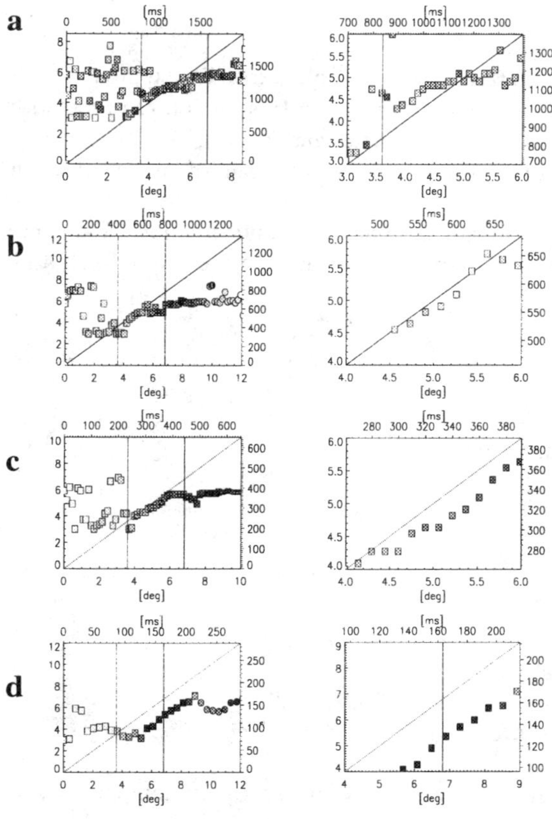

Fig.6.

The ordinate illustrates the reconstructed spatial and temporal position of the maximal amplitude of the population representation in timesteps of 20 ms (a,b) and 10 ms (c,d) in terms of time (ms) at the top of each diagram and space (visual degree) at the bottom of each diagram of a stimulus moving from left to right in the visual field. The abscissa shows the actual position of the moving stimulus in time and space (left and right sides of the diagrams, respectively). The velocities tested are (from top to bottom): 4.4, 8.8, 15.0, 42.0 deg/s. The grey level of each square indicates the strength of the population activity distribution. The circles indicate the position of the maximal activity distribution after stimulus offset. Vertical lines indicate left and right borders of the parametric space. The right column shows the results in a finer temporal and spatial resolution.

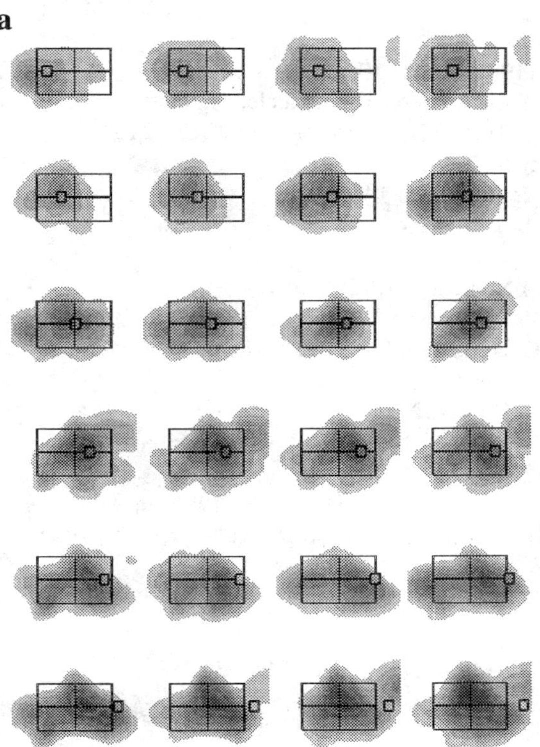

Fig. 7 a.

Dynamic population representation of a stimulus moving from left to right in the visual field at 15 deg/s. Sequence of single population representations resolved at timesteps of 10 ms duration running from top left to bottom right. The parametric space (central visual field) and the actual position of the moving stimulus (0.4 deg. visual field) is shown for each time step. Population activity is gray-coded.

Fig. 7 b.

Dynamic population representation of a stimulus moving from left to right in the visual field at 42 deg/s. Same convention as Fig. 7.

Fig. 7

Conclusion

General aspects
- We present an analysis of cortical spatio-temporal dynamics based on the population coding approach
- Our approach enables us to construct a collective neural activation distribution (population representation) over an functional parameter space, in our case the retinal spatial coordinates and the skin.
- Since the approach uses the parametric space, it specifies the meaning of the activation of single cells independently of the constraints of cortical maps
- All cells of the sampled population must be stimulated by identical common stimuli in a non RF-centered mode, which seems biologically plausible: under natural conditions, most of the neurons are unlikely to be stimulated in a receptive field centered mode.

Specific aspects - the population coding approach allows
- accurate reconstruction of stimulus location
- analysis of short-term dynamics of entire population of cells
- analysis of global nonlinearities following two-point stimulation
- analysis of motion trajectories

References

[1] Jones PP, Palmer LA (1987) J Neurophysiol 58: 1187-1211

[2] Dinse HR, Krüger K, Best J (1990). Concepts in Neuroscience (CINS) 1: 199 - 238

[3] Dinse HR, Krüger K, Mallot HP, Best J (1991) in: Krüger J (ed) Neuronal Cooperativity (Springer) pp 67-104

[4] Dinse HR, Spengler F, Godde B, Hartfiel B (1993) in: Aertsen A (ed) Brain Theory: Spatio-temporal aspects of brain functions. Elsevier, pp 209-230

[5] Eckhorn R, Krause F, Nelson JI (1993) Biol. Cybern 69: 37 - 55

[6] DeAngelis GC, Ohzawa I, Freeman RD (1993) J Neurophysiol: 69: 1091-1117

[7] Dinse HR (1994) Physica D 75: 129-150

[8] Aertsen A, Johannesma P (1981) Biol Cybern 42: 133-143

[9] Eggermont JJ, Aertsen A, Hermes DJ, Johannesma PIM (1981) Res 5: 109-121

[10] Dinse HR, Schreiner CE (1996) in: The auditory basis of speech perception, Keele, England

[11] Nicolelis MAL, Lin RCS, Woodward DJ, Chapin JK (1993) Proc Natl Acad Sci 90: 2212-2218

[12] Fukunishi K, Murai N, Uno H (1992) Biol Cybern 67: 501-509

[13] Taniguchi I, Horikawa J, Moriyama T, Nasu M (1992) Neurosci Lett 146: 37 40

[14] Uno H, Murai N, Fukunishi K (1992) Neurosci Letters 145: 23-26

[15] Fukunishi K, Murai N (1996) Biol Cybern in press

[16] Grinvald A, Lieke E, Frostig RD, Hildesheim R (1994) J Neurosci 14, 2545-2568

[17] Palm G (1984) Neuronal assemblies, Springer

[18] Aertsen A, Gerstein G, Johannesma P (1986) in: Palm G, Aertsen A (eds) Brain Theory. Springer, pp 7-24

[19] Georgopoulos AP, Kettner RE, Schwartz AB (1988) J Neurosci 8: 2928 - 2937

[20] Georgopoulos AP, Taira M, Lukashin A (1993) Science 260: 47-52

[21] Lee C, Rohrer WH, Sparks OL (1988) Nature 332: 357 - 360

[22] Lehky SR, Seijnowski TJ (1990) J Neurosci 10: 2281 - 2299

[23] Jancke D, Akhavan AC, Erlhagen W, Giese M, Steinhage A, Schöner G, Dinse HR (1996) in: von der Malsburg C, von Seelen W (eds) ICANN '96. International Conference on Artificial Neural Networks, in press

Supported by the Deutsche Forschungsgemeinschaft, Nos. Di 334/5 -1, /5 - 3 and Scho 336/4-2

Spatial-Temporal Representation of Complex Sounds in Auditory Cortex

Christoph E. Schreiner, Sarah Wong, Ben Bonham, Norman Ge, Srikantan Nagarajan

Keck Center for Integrative Neuroscience, Sloan Center for Theoretical Neuroscience, University of California, San Francisco, CA 94143-0732, USA; chris@phy.uscf.edu

Abstract - **Cortical neurons have a wide range of functional properties that are related to the coding of acoustic spectra. In particular, cortical neurons in primary auditory cortex (AI) have been found to be independently sensitive to the bandwidth, the spectral energy distribution, and the overall intensity of the signal, in addition to their frequency selectivity. Several largely independent spectral parameter 'maps' of these simple acoustical stimuli have been observed in AI. An understanding of spatial-temporal relationships between activation of different, overlaying 'maps' and coding properties is essential for the comprehension of the neural code of communication sounds such as speech and provides an essential framework for the extraction and generation of higher auditory processes such as the sound categorization, and condition-independent word recognition. The spatio-temporal representation of simple sounds and speech sounds in cat auditory cortex is discussed with regard to the underlying parameter maps and implications for the role of ensemble coding of complex signals.**

1   Introduction

The functional organization of many sensory cortical areas is characterized by systematic changes of response properties of neurons along the cortical surface dimensions. The exploration of the range and spatial distributions of physiological response properties has provided crucial information for unraveling principles and mechanisms underlying cortical processing, for example in the visual cortex [1], and in the auditory cortex of echolocating bats [2]. An initial emphasis on topographic patterns in physiological and anatomical investigations of cortical areas provides an essential framework from which more detailed studies of the local and global processing properties and mechanisms can emerge. Recently, a number of studies have been published that utilize a spatial mapping approach to define basic organizational and functional principles in auditory cortex of a variety of mammals.

Detailed single and multiple neuron mapping studies of the coding of simple signals in the primary auditory cortex of cats and monkeys have revealed that there are remarkably similar principles for the representation of various, non species-specific acoustic signals [3-10]. These experiments have revealed that there are <u>spatially organized and superimposed</u> representations of, at least, i) signal frequency, ii) stimulus bandwidth, iii) sound intensity, iv) frequency modulation direction and rate, and v) sound source location within the primary auditory cortical field in these species. These observations suggest that behaviorally very different mammalian species like cats and monkeys use the same general neurological strategies to encode and represent the wide variety of complex acoustic spectra, at this first level of cortical representation.

A principal component analysis of eight basic receptive field parameters from several animals revealed an orthogonality or virtual independence in the distribution of several receptive field parameters. We studied CF, threshold, non-monotonicity, best level (strongest response level), Q-10dB, Q-40dB, onset latency, and binaurality. Four groups of parameter ('factors') emerged that were statistically independent between groups and covaried within groups. The four factors accounted for more than 65% of the total variance in the data. One factor was closely associated with the CF of the recording sites; a second factor was related to sharpness of tuning measures; a third factor was closely associated with response threshold and best level; and a fourth factor reflected the distribution of binaural response classes. Latency and non-monotonicity were associated with more than one of these factors. The most important conclusion is that response properties extracted from frequency response areas represent at least four different and independently varying aspects of AI receptive fields. Although these do not provide a complete description of the receptive field, they do give a clear picture of spatial organization. The general independence of the four factors is reflected in different spatial distribution patterns analogous to the distribution of basic response properties of neurons in the primary visual cortex (e.g., ocular dominance, orientation selectivity, spatial frequency). This organization suggests that primary auditory cortex can be considered a generalized processor of auditory information, based on spectral, temporal and sound localization cues.

Self-organizing feature map algorithms, such as that proposed by Kohonen [11], provide a mathematical means to project several independently varying input parameters. This mapping provides an economic representation of data by preserving neighborhood relationships within each of the stimulus dimensions and, simultaneously, by minimizing the required wire length between locations with similar receptive field properties [12]. Simulation of the development of auditory cortical maps using this type of model replicates to a large degree the spatial distribution properties of receptive field parameters observed in physiological experiments [13].

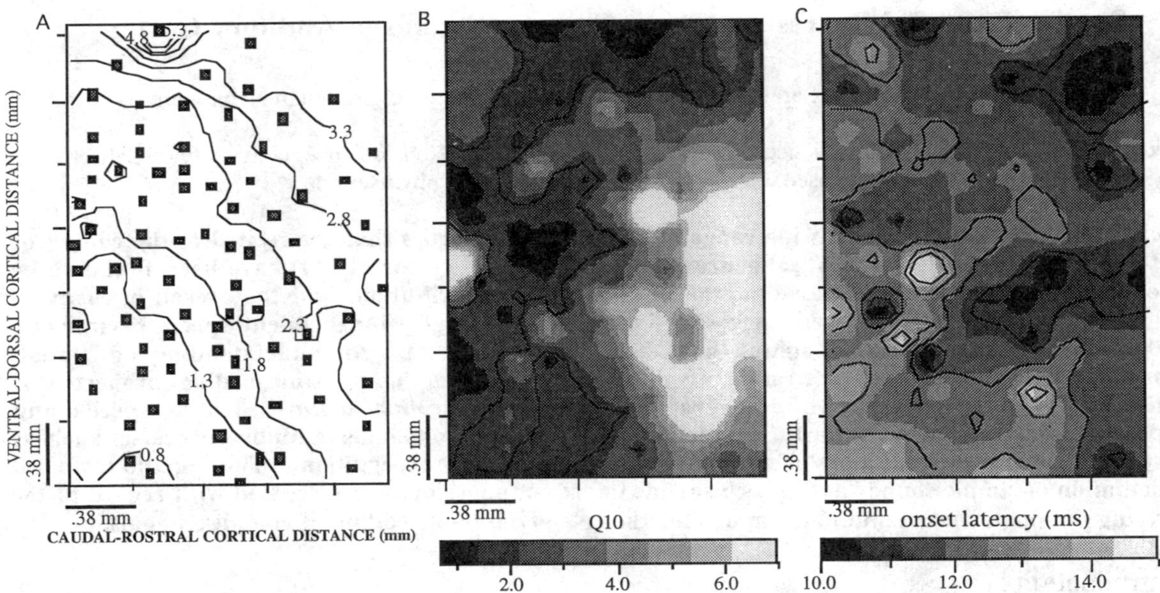

Figure 1. Cortical representations of best frequency, Q10, and onset latency for binaural, closed-field pure-tone stimulation from AI. The values used to reconstruct the representations were derived from pure-tone tuning curves obtained at each penetration site within the low-frequency region of AI. A) Tonotopic organization of the recorded region of AI extends from 0.8 to 5.3 kHz. Each point marks a penetration site. The lines correspond to interpolated iso-frequency contours. B) The Q10 representation, depicting the sharpness of neural tuning, reveals regions of very sharply tuned neurons (depicted as the white areas) and regions of broadly tuned neurons (depicted as the darker areas). The largest region of high Q10 values has generally been considered to be the center portion of an isofrequency contour. C) The representation of neural onset latency reveals patches of longer onset latencies which appear to be scattered and are not highly correlated with broadness of tuning. However, longer latencies tend to be encountered in regions with lower frequencies.

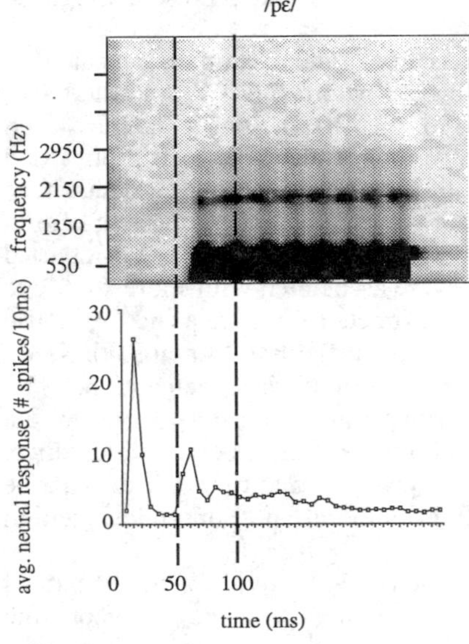

Figure 2. Spectrogram of a Klatt-synthesized /pe/ and grand averaged neural response to /pe/. The spectral energy content of /pe/ falls below 3 kHz while the voiced onset time (VOT) is 60 ms. Data from neural spike responses were analyzed in 50 ms windows, which are denoted by the dotted lines. The averaged neural response manifests two peaks in neural activity which correspond with the onset of the consonant and the onset of voicing for the vowel.

2   Representation of Speech Signals in Auditory Cortex

Fundamental to a study of complex signal coding is the investigation of the mechanisms by which these signals are analyzed and represented by the central auditory nervous system in terms of two important features, spectral content and temporal character. While it is well known that spectral or frequency content of an acoustic signal is represented in the cortex by bandpass filters with systematically varying center frequencies and bandwidths [3, 6, 7], less is known about the simultaneous coding of the spectral variety contained in complex signals, such as speech or other communication signals, and the timing of those events.   Numerous psychophysical studies have demonstrated the constraints the time context imposes on the detection, discrimination, integration, and segmentation of acoustic events.   Accordingly, it is necessary to describe these temporal processing capacities in detail at each level of the auditory system to understand and model the coding principles of the central auditory system.

One possible strategy of encoding complex sounds in the cortex is by the temporal-spatial discharge pattern of distributed neuronal populations across the cortical field [14-15].   There has been increasing evidence that distributed coding schemes operate in other sensory or motor cortical regions [e.g., 16-18]. In a recent study of the representation of species-specific vocalizations in the primary auditory cortex of marmosets [19], we obtained evidence that behaviorally relevant vocalizations are indeed represented by spatially distributed neuronal discharges and that behaviorally distinguishable sounds are represented by clearly distinct, only partially overlapping populations of neurons.   Studies of the cortical encoding of speech signals with clearly defined phonetic features in AI of primates have provided evidence that some of the major phonetic distinctions are reflected in the activity of cortical neurons [20-21]. These findings indicate that phonetic distinctions can be preserved in the activity distribution of primary auditory cortex.

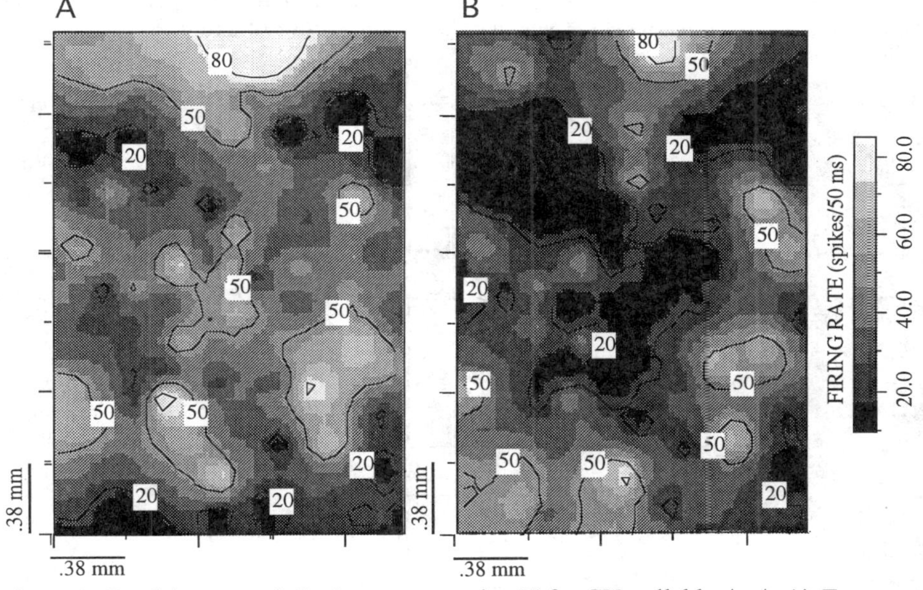

Figure 3: Spatial-temporal discharge pattern in AI for CV syllable /pe/. A) Topographic representation of firing rate integrated over the first 50 ms of the syllable response. The lighter the shading, the higher the firing rate (see scale). Localized regions of activation correspond to the spectral content of the speech syllable and the spatial distribution of receptive field parameters for simple sounds (See Figure 1). B) The integrated firing rate for the second 50 ms time segment (50-100ms) of the response to /pe/. The distribution reveals higher activation in low frequency regions (lower-left corner; see Figure 1) corresponding to the response to voicing (VOT = 60ms).   In addition, regions of high evoked activity correspond to the sharply tuned frequency regions of the map appropriate for the formant frequencies of the vowel.

The cortical representation of synthesized CVs (e.g., /pe/) were obtained by mapping the multiple unit responses from locations in the low-frequency region of cat primary auditory cortex. Animals were anesthetized with Ketamine. For each recording location we determined the pure-tone frequency-response area and the responses to the syllables at different sound intensities and under different background noise conditions. Figure 1 illustrates for one exemplary case the sites of the recordings and, superimposed, shows the course of the iso-frequency contours that were interpolated from the tuning curve at each location. The covered frequency range includes the frequency range for the frequency transitions and formant frequencies for the second and third formant of the syllables. The distributions of the sharpness of tuning of the response areas and the minimum onset latencies are shown as well.

The response to the syllable across all recording locations is characterized by brief transients at the beginning of the consonants and at the beginning of voicing (see Figure 2). Here, we show the spatial distribution of the response strength separately for only two time windows: For the first 50 ms, e.g., containing the response to the consonant in /pe/, and the next 50 ms, containing the separate onset response for the voicing in /pe/. Figure 3 shows the CV response distributions across the map shown in Figure 1. The maps show a complex distribution of activity in both time windows. There is a distinct pattern of activity for the CV /pe/ due to the beginning of voicing. The spatial pattern is not unlike that during the first 50 ms, however, distinct differences can be observed. First, a high activity region in the center of the first 50 ms map has disappeared. Although it is not clear yet, what causes this decrease in activity, it is potentially related to the difference in the 2. and 3. formant position at the beginning of the consonant versus the beginning of the voicing. Second, a new region of high activity has appeared in the lower left corner of the map, likely corresponding to the presence of the first formant during this portion of the stimulus.

Comparison between the activity distribution during the first and second 50 ms segments shows that differences between the spectra and even different portions of the spectra are reflected in differences in the spatial-temporal pattern at the level of the auditory cortex. Speech properties and phonetic differences, then, are encoded in a distributed fashion in the firing rate and temporal occurrence over large populations of neurons.

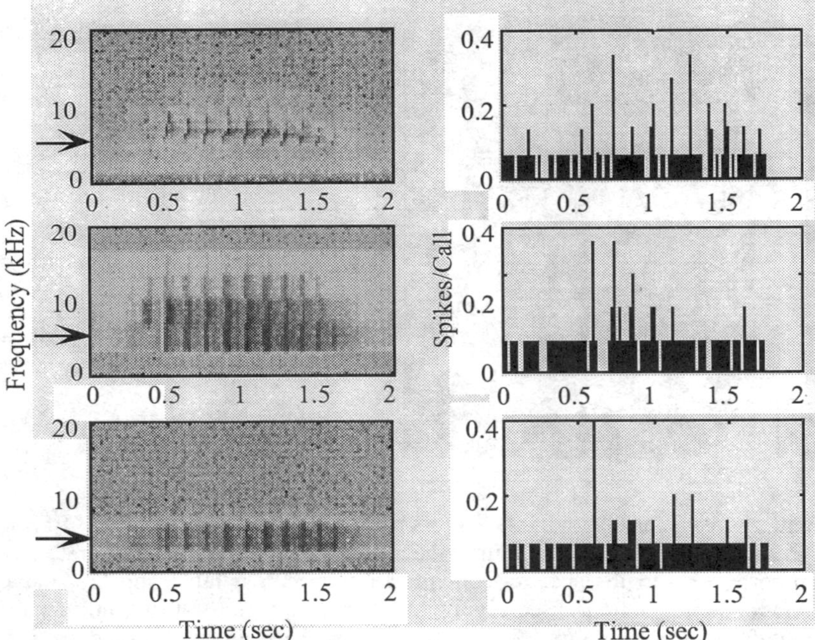

Figure 4: Effects of spectral content by maintained temporal modulation on the temporal discharge pattern. On the left side, three spectrograms of a marmoset vocalization are shown. The upper spectrogram is the unaltered natural call. The middle spectrogram has been synthesized to contain only four bands of 1 octave width, each with the same average power as in the original call and with the same temporal modulation as in the original call in the corresponding frequency band. The spectrogram at the bottom left contains only one octave band around the center frequency of the neuron (5 kHz, see arrow) with fully maintained temporal modulation waveform. On the right side, the post-stimulus time histograms of the neuron are shown for these three stimuli. In the upper histogram, the response to the natural call displays distinct increases in firing rate that are highly synchronized with each repeated phrase in the call. The modified calls show a much less robust time-locking and overall diminished response strength of the response to the modulation despite the fact that the temporal envelope in each band was a very closely matched between the natural and the synthesized calls.

3　Spectral Effects on Temporal Coding

The capacity of cortical neurons to follow details in the temporal envelope of sounds reflects an essential aspect of cortical processing that has important consequences for the encoding of complex signals that often consists of sequences of shorter segments. Studies using different acoustic signals ranging from clicks to repeated tone bursts and sinusoidally amplitude modulated tones and noises have revealed that the ability of most primary auditory cortical neurons to respond to modulation frequencies is limited to rates below 20 Hz [22-23].

Details of the cortical responses to temporal envelope profile depend on a variety of parameters. Most prominent among them is the dependence on the spectral composition of the signal that carries the temporal information in its envelope. This is illustrated in the changes observed in the response of a cortical neuron to a natural vocalization when the spectral composition of the vocalization was manipulated without changing the temporal envelope [24]. Figure 4 shows the spectra for three different versions of a vocalization. The top shows the natural vocalization (twitter call of a marmoset monkey) and the evoked cortical response. Note several distinct response peaks that are temporally tightly linked to specific properties of the stimulus envelope. In the next version of the vocalization, the spectral content is replaced by four noise bands while the temporal envelope remains the same. In the response to this sound, fewer peaks can be seen. Finally, in the bottom of Figure 4, the carrier signal consists of a single noise band that is modulated by the temporal envelope extracted from the original call. In this case, hardly any temporal structure is reflected in the cortical response (with the exception of the onset response) although the depth and frequency of the amplitude modulation was very similar to the previous two cases. Since the discrimination and classification of complex signals depends crucially on the temporal sequence of spectral transitions, this demonstration underscores the relevance of the preservation of temporal changes in the spatial/spectral maps of complex sounds.

4　Discussion

The spatial distribution of receptive field parameters and the responses to speech sounds have been demonstrated for the primary auditory cortex of cats. It is concluded that observed receptive field parameter representations in primary auditory cortex are largely compatible with features of self-organizing mapping algorithms for a low-dimensional output space and a higher dimensional input space. This includes the emergence of global parameter gradients with overlaid patchiness that are a natural consequence of topology preserving algorithms. The present results, in combination with a recent study of the neural representation of species-specific vocalization of marmosets monkeys [19], provides an impression of the cortical activation pattern for complex signals that reflect the underlying organization obtained with simple sounds. These studies reveal that the spectro-temporal pattern in the acoustics of vocalizations is reflected in the spatial-temporal firing pattern of distributed neuronal populations in AI of these animals. Neuronal responses to a complex sounds are distributed very widely across AI. At the same time, the responses evoked by a vocalization distributed over several, discrete cortical patches are synchronized to specific stimulus events. However, the occurrence and precision of the temporal patterning and coherence is strongly influenced by the spectral properties of the signals (see Figure 4). As a result, at any major transition during the course of the signal, a temporally coherent activation of specific neuronal sub populations of the cortical field is present. The cells that respond to a given stimulus share some but not all of their neuronal membership with other neuronal populations. These results suggest that AI represents species-specific vocalizations and complex signals such as CV sounds in general by temporally coherent and spatially dispersed cortical cell assemblies that represent each individual vocalization in a specific way. The formation of such representational structures within AI neuronal populations reflects the anatomical and functional organization of AI that is also evident in the spatial organizations seen for simple stimulus responses. In addition, the cortical coding may contain the effects of specific spectral as well as temporal integration and normalization processes. The advantages of such a generalized representation for the classification, categorization, and discrimination of complex sounds may lie in its potential for segregating different streams of information in subsequent cortical stations without sacrificing the context of the input. In addition, the effects of different interfering acoustic conditions, such as various background noises, on these tasks may be reduced by the spatial representation of preprocessed and enhanced spectral and temporal stimulus profiles.

Acknowledgment

Supported by the Office of Naval Research (N00014-94-1-0547) and the National Institute of Deafness and other Communicative Disorders (CD02260).

References

[1] Lund,J.S. "Mapping strategies of monkey primary visual cortex". In: *Sensory Processing in the Mammalian Brain: Neural Substrates and Experimental Strategies*. J.S. Lund (ed) New York: Oxford Univ. Press, 1990; pp. 209-225.

[2] Suga, N. "Neuroethology and speech processing: complex-sound processing by combination-sensitive neurons". In: *Auditory Function- Neurobiological Bases of Hearing*, G.M. Edelman, W.E. Gall, W.M. Cowan (Eds.), John Wiley & Sons , 1988, pp.672-720.

[3] Schreiner, C.E. and Mendelson J. R., "Functional topography of cat primary auditory cortex: distribution of integrated excitation", *J. Neurophysiol* 64:1442-1459,1990.

[4] Schreiner, C.E. , Mendelson, J.R., and Sutter, M. "Functional topography of cat primary auditory cortex representation of tone intensity". *Exp. Brain Res*. 92:105-122, 1992.

[5] Merzenich,M.M., Schreiner,C.E., Recanzone,G., Beitel,R, and Sutter,M "Topographic organization of cortical field AI in the owl monkey (*Aotus trivirgatus*)". *Assoc. Res. Otolaryngol. Abstr.*, 14:44, 1991a

[6] Schreiner, C.E. and Sutter, M.L. "Topography of excitatory bandwidth in cat primary auditory cortex: single-neuron versus multiple-neuron recordings". *J. Neurophysiol*. 68:1487-1502, 1992.

[7] Heil,P., Rajan,R., and Irvine,D.R.F. "Sensitivity of neurons in cat primary auditory cortex to tones and frequency-modulated stimuli. II: Organization of response properties along the 'isofrequency' dimension". *Hearing Res*. 63:135-156, 1992.

[8] Heil,P., Rajan,R., and Irvine,D.R.F. "Topographic representation of tone intensity along the isofrequency axis of cat primary auditory cortex". *Hearing Res*. 76:188-202, 1994

[9] Mendelson, J.R., Schreiner, C.E., Sutter, M. and Grasse, K. "Functional topography of cat primary auditory cortex: representation of frequency modulation". *Exp. Brain Research* 94:65-87, 1993.

[10] Sutter and Schreiner, Topography of intensity tuning in cat primary auditory cortex: single-neuron versus multiple-neuron recordings. *J Neurophysiol*, 73:190-204, 1995.

[11] Kohonen, T., *Self-organization and associative memory*. Berlin: Springer Verlag, 1984

[12] Mitchison G: A type of duality between self-organizing maps and minimal wiring. *Neural Comp*, 7:25-35, 1995.

[13] Ge, N.N., Schreiner C.E. and Read, H. "Simulations of self-organizing feature maps in primary auditory cortex (AI)". *Soc. Neurosci. Abstr*. 22, 1996.

[14] Creutzfeldt, Hellweg, and Schreiner, "Thalamocortical transformation of responses to complex auditory stimuli", *Exp. Brain Res*. 39:87-104, 1980.

[15] Pelleg-Toiba, R. and Wollberg, Z. "Discrimination of communication calls in the squirrel monkey: "call detectors" or "cell ensembles"". *J. Basic Clin. Physiol. Pharmacol*. 2:257-272, 1991.

[16] Georgopoulos, A., Lurito,J., Petrides,M., Schwartz,A., Massey,J. "Mental rotation of the neuronal population vector". *Science* 243: 234-236,1989.

[17] Gochin,P.M., Colombo,M., Dorfman,G.A., Gerstein,G.L., Gross,C.G. "Neural ensemble coding in inferior temporal cortex". *J. Neurophysiol*. 71:2325-2337, 1994

[18] Merzenich, M.M., Grajski, K.A., Jenkins, W.M., Recanzone, G.H., and Peterson,B. "Functional cortical plasticity. Cortical network origins of representational changes". *Cold Spring Harbor Symp. Quant. Biol.*, 55, 873-887, 1991.

[19] Wang, X, Merzenich, M.M., Beitel, R, and Schreiner C.E. "Representation of a species-specific vocalization in the primary auditory cortex of the common marmoset: temporal and spectral characteristics". *J. Neurophysiol*. 74:2685-2706, 1995

[20] Steinschneider, M., Arezzo,J.C., and Vaughan, H.G. "Tonotopic features of speech-evoked activity in primate auditory cortex". *Brain Res*. 519:158-168, 1990..

[21] Eggermont JJ. "Representation of a voice onset time continuum in primary auditory cortex of the cat". *J. Acoust. Soc. Am.*, 98:911-20, 1995.

[22] Schreiner, C.E. and Urbas, J.V. (1988). "Representation of amplitude modulation in the auditory cortex of the cat. II. Comparison between cortical fields. *Hearing Research* 32:49-64, 1988.

[23] Eggermont, J.J. "Rate and synchronization measures of periodicity coding in cat primary auditory cortex". *Hearing Research* 56:153-167, 1991.

[24] Shannon RV; Zeng FG; Kamath V; Wygonski J; Ekelid M. "Speech recognition with primarily temporal cues".*Science* 270:303-4, 1995.

Special Session IV
Neural Networks for Signal Processing and System Modeling

The invited program is also featured by 8 special sessions on current interesting topics. Each special session organizer is invited by the Program Committee and the success of each special session is completely due to the hard efforts of each organizer.

Neural Networks for Computer-Human Interfaces: Glove-TalkII

S. Sidney Fels†
† ATR Media Integration & Communications Research Laboratories
Seika-cho, Soraku-gun, Kyoto, Japan, 619-02; fels@mic.atr.co.jp

Abstract— Glove-TalkII is system which has an adaptive interface built with neural networks. Glove-TalkII maps hand gestures continuously to 10 control parameters of a parallel formant speech synthesizer. The mapping allows the hand to act as an artificial vocal tract that produces speech in real time giving an unlimited vocabulary and unlimited control of fundamental frequency and volume. The best version of Glove-TalkII uses several input devices (including a CyberGlove, a ContactGlove, a 3-space tracker, and a foot-pedal), a parallel formant speech synthesizer and 3 neural networks. The gesture-to-speech task is divided into vowel and consonant production by using a gating network to weight the outputs of a vowel and a consonant neural network. The gating network and the consonant network are trained with examples from the user. The vowel network implements a fixed, user-defined relationship between hand-position and vowel sound and does not require any training examples from the user. Volume, fundamental frequency and stop consonants are produced with a fixed mapping from the input devices. One subject has trained to speak intelligibly with Glove-TalkII. He speaks slowly with speech quality similar to a text-to-speech synthesizer but with far more natural-sounding pitch variations. Characteristics of the neural networks both enhance and detract from control intimacy.

1   Introduction

Adaptive interfaces are an important and natural class of applications for neural networks. Many real devices require considerable skill and learning time by the operator to control. The utility of such "high-bandwidth" devices is dependent on the interface available to the operator. A poorly designed interface may impede learning to use the device and the skill level obtainable with the device. Ideally, interfaces should be designed to match the skills of each individual user. By making the interface *adaptive* the interface can change its behaviour to match the user's abilities. Glove-TalkII is a system which implements an adaptive interface between gestures and a formant speech synthesizer using neural networks.

At an abstract level, the role of an interface is to maps users' actions into parameters which control a device. Roughly, a user's actions can be categorized as discrete or continuous; likewise, the device parameters that are controlled are either discrete or continuous. These behaviours provide four distinctive mappings that are performed by an interface as illustrated in table 1.   For the gesture-to-speech task, Glove-TalkII considers a users' gestures as continuous and maps these to a representation of speech (formants and voicing) that is continuous. The neural networks in Glove-TalkII allow the user to learn to speak using an articulatory model while the actual synthesizer uses a very different model. By using an adaptive interface the mapping allows the user to work in an input space that is independent of the device's control space, thereby allowing it to incorporate a user's existing skills and intuition. This aspect of adaptive interfaces makes them attractive; however, the same principle may be used when designing static ones.

Techniques for mapping gestures-to-speech form a spectrum based on the granularity of speech which will be produced as shown in figure 1. Glove-TalkII is a continuous-to-continuous mapping which allows

User Actions	Device Actions	Example
Discrete	Discrete	Button presses are mapped to a set of specific actions such as letters on a keyboard.
Discrete	Continuous	Sequences of button presses are mapped to a set of motions of a character such as found in many martial-arts video games.
Continuous	Discrete	Hand gestures are mapped to words such as in Glove-Talk [4].
Continuous	Continuous	Hand gesture are mapped to formants or articulator motions such as in Glove-TalkII [5]

Table 1: The four different mapping types found in interfaces

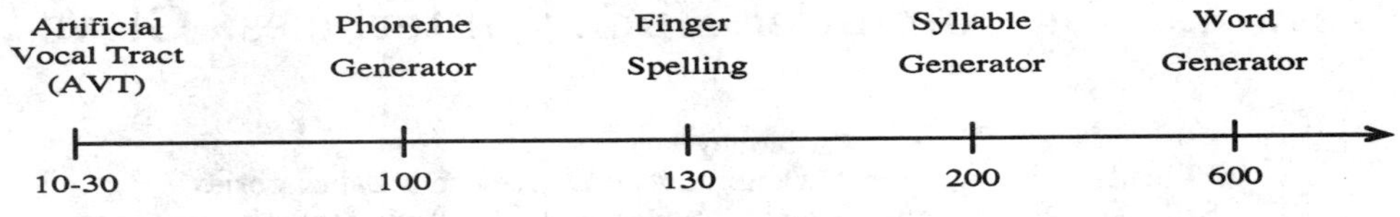

Figure 1: Spectrum of gesture-to-speech mappings based on the granularity of speech.

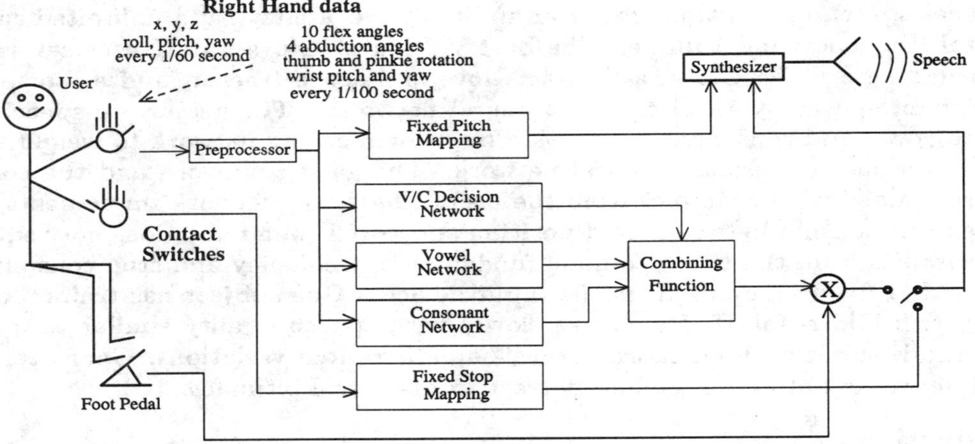

Figure 2: Block diagram of Glove-TalkII: input from the user is measured by the CyberGlove, polhemus, keyboard and foot pedal, then mapped using neural networks and fixed functions to formant parameters which drive the parallel formant synthesizer [12].

the user to control an articulatory model of speech. Thus, it is an Artificial Vocal Tract (AVT) system as shown in figure 1. Systems to the right of artificial vocal tracts are continuous-to-discrete mappings. In these systems, the goal of the interface is to *recognize* users' gestures into discrete categories which then perform a specific function in the device. Examples of these kind of systems which use neural networks to learn the mapping can found in [4] and [6]. Thus, when designing an interface, the type of mapping will dictate the types of neural network that should be used.

Glove-TalkII also can be thought of as a musical instrument except that Glove-TalkII produces vocal sounds which the user *plays* to sound like speech. For musical instruments, an important quality is "control intimacy" [9]. As Moore says,

> *Control intimacy* determines the match between the variety of musically desirable sounds produced and the psychophysiological capabilities of a practiced performer. It is based on the performer's subjective impression of the feedback control lag between the moment a sound is heard, a change is made by the performer, and the time when the effect of that control change is heard.

The notion of control intimacy for musical instruments may be generalized to *intimacy* for any interface [3]. Intimacy deals with the subjective match between the behaviour of a device and the operation of that device. The neural networks in Glove-TalkII adapt to the user's gestures to facilitate intimacy with the interface. Once trained, the system runs in real-time which is critical for a high level of control intimacy. The adaptation is performed *off-line* in lock step fashion with the user's own adaptation which reduces control intimacy. It is an open issue as to the effect *online*[1] adaptation would have on control intimacy.

2   Glove-TalkII: Converting Gestures-to-Formants using Neural Networks

The Glove-TalkII system converts hand gestures to speech, based on a gesture-to-formant model. The gesture vocabulary is based on a vocal-articulator model of the hand. By dividing the mapping tasks into independent subtasks, a substantial reduction in network size and training time is possible (see [2]).

Figure 2 illustrates the whole Glove-TalkII system. Important features include the three neural networks

---

[1] *Online* training here refers to the system adapting while the user is using the interface.

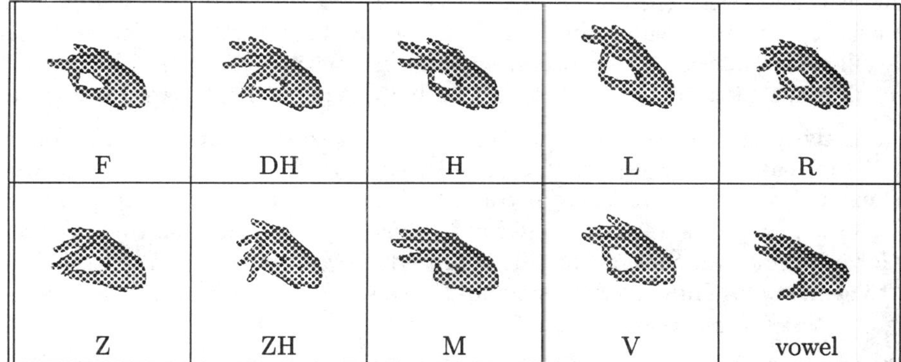

Table 2: Examples from the initial articulatory mapping showing some of the static gesture-to-consonant pairs. Note, each gesture corresponds to a static *non-stop* consonant phoneme generated by the text-to-speech synthesizer and the neural networks provide the continuous interpolation.

labeled vowel/consonant decision (V/C), vowel, and consonant. The V/C network is trained on data collected from the user to decide whether he wants to produce a vowel or a consonant sound. Likewise, the consonant network is trained to produce consonant sounds based on user-generated examples based on an initial gesture vocabulary. In contrast, the vowel network implements a fixed mapping between hand-positions and vowel phonemes defined by the user. Nine contact points measured on the user's left hand by a ContactGlove designate the nine stop consonants (B, D, G, J, P, T, K, CH, NG), because the dynamics of such sounds proved too fast to be controlled by the user. The foot pedal provides a volume control by adjusting the speech amplitude and this mapping is fixed. The fundamental frequency, which is related to the pitch of the speech, is determined by a fixed mapping from the user's hand height. The output of the system drives 10 control parameters of a parallel formant speech synthesizer every 10 msec. The 10 control parameters are: nasal amplitude (ALF), first, second and third formant frequency and amplitude (F1, A1, F2, A2, F3, A3), high frequency amplitude (AHF), degree of voicing (V) and fundamental frequency (F0). Each of the control parameters is quantized to 6 bits.

Once trained, Glove-TalkII can be used as follows: to initiate speech, the user forms the hand shape of the first sound she intends to produce. She depresses the foot pedal and the sound comes out of the synthesizer. Vowels and consonants of various qualities are produced in a continuous fashion through the appropriate co-ordination of hand and foot motions. Words are formed by making the correct motions; for example, to say "hello" the user forms the "h" sound, depresses the foot pedal and quickly moves her hand to produce the "e" sound, then the "l" sound and finally the "o" sound. The user has complete control of the timing and quality of the individual sounds making it a continuous-to-continuous mapping. The initial articulatory mapping scheme between gestures and speech is created before the system is created. This is used by the user as a basis for generating training data. The mapping is based on a simplistic articulatory phonetic description of speech [7]. The X, Y^2 coordinates of the user's hand (measured by the polhemus) are mapped to something like tongue position and height[3] producing vowels when the user's hand is in an open configuration (see table 2 for a typical vowel configuration). Manner and place of articulation for non-stop consonants are determined by opposition of the thumb with the index and middle fingers such as shown in table 2. The ring finger generally controls voicing. Only *static* articulatory configurations are used as training points for the neural networks, and the interpolation between them is a result of the learning but is not explicitly trained. Ideally, the transitions should also be learned, but in the text-to-speech formant data we use for training [8] these transitions are poor, and it is very hard to extract formant trajectories from real speech accurately.

2.1 The Vowel/Consonant (V/C) Network

The V/C network decides, on the basis of the current configuration of the user's hand, to emit a vowel or a consonant sound. For the quantitative results reported here we used a 10-5-1 feed-forward network with sigmoid activations [10]. The 10 inputs are ten scaled hand parameters measured with a CyberGlove: 8 flex angles (knuckle and middle joints of the thumb, index, middle and ring fingers), thumb abduction angle and thumb rotation angle. The output is a single number representing the probability that the hand

---

[2]X is measured as distance in front of user and Y is measured as distance to the left and right of the user.

[3]In reality, the XY coordinates map more closely to changes in the first two formants, F1 and F2 of vowels. From the user's perspective though, the link to tongue movement is useful. See [5] for details.

configuration indicates a vowel. The output of the V/C network is used to gate the outputs of the vowel and consonant networks, which then produce a mixture of vowel and consonant formant parameters. The training data available includes only user-produced vowel or consonant sounds. The network interpolates between hand configurations to create a smooth but fairly rapid transition between vowels and consonants.

For quantitative analysis, typical training data consists of 2600 examples of consonant configurations (350 approximants, 1510 fricatives [and aspirant], and 740 nasals) and 700 examples of vowel configurations. The consonant examples were obtained from training data collected for the consonant network by an expert user. The vowel examples were collected from the user by requiring him to move his hand in vowel configurations for a specified amount of time. This procedure was performed in several sessions. The test set consists of 1614 examples (1380 consonants and 234 vowels). After training,[4] the mean squared error on the training and test set was less than 10^{-4}.

During normal speaking the V/C network did not make any perceptual errors. The decision boundary feels quite sharp, and provides very predictable, quick transitions from vowels to consonants and back. Also, vowel sounds are produced when the user hyperextends his hand. Any unusual configurations that would intuitively be expected to produce consonant sounds do indeed produce consonant sounds.

2.2 The Vowel Network

The vowel network is a 2-11-8 feed forward network. The 11 hidden units are normalized radial basis functions (RBFs) [1] which are centered to respond to one of 11 cardinal vowels available from the text-to-speech synthesizer. The outputs are sigmoid units representing 8 synthesizer control parameters (ALF, F1, A1, F2, A2, F3, A3, AHF). The radial basis function used is:

$$o_j = e^{-\frac{\sum (w_{ji} - o_i)^2}{\sigma_j^2}} \tag{1}$$

where o_j is the (un-normalized) output of the RBF unit, w_{ji} is the weight from unit i to unit j, o_i is the output of input unit i, and σ_j^2 is the variance of the RBF. The normalization used is:

$$n_j = \frac{o_j}{\sum_{m \in P} o_m} \tag{2}$$

where n_j is the normalized output of unit j and the summation is over all the units in the group of normalized RBF units. The centres of the RBF units are fixed according to the X and Y values of each of the 11 vowels in the predefined mapping. The variances of the 11 RBF's are set to 0.025.

The weights from the RBF units to the output units are trained. For the training data, 100 identical examples of each vowel are generated from their corresponding X and Y positions in the user-defined mapping, providing 1100 examples. Noise is then added to the *scaled* X and Y coordinates for each example. The added noise is uniformly distributed in the range -0.025 to 0.025. In terms of unscaled ranges, these correspond to an X range of approximately $\pm$ 0.5 cm and a Y range of $\pm$ 0.26 cm.

Three different test sets were created. Each test set had 50 examples of each vowel for a total of 550 examples. The first test set used additive uniform noise in the interval $\pm$ 0.025. The second and third test sets used additive uniform noise in the interval $\pm$ 0.05 and $\pm$ 0.1 respectively.

The mean squared error on the training set was 0.0016. The MSE on the additive noise test sets (noise = $\pm$ 0.025, 0.05 and 0.01) was 0.0018, 0.0038, 0.0120 which corresponds to expected errors of 1.1%, 3.1% and 5.5% in the formant parameters, respectively. This network performs well perceptually. The key feature is the normalization of the RBF units. Often, when speaking, the user will overshoot cardinal vowel positions (especially when she is producing dipthongs) and all the RBF units will be quite suppressed. However, the normalization magnifies any slight difference between the activities of the units and the sound produced will be dominated by the cardinal vowel corresponding to the one whose centre is closest in hand space.

2.3 The Consonant Network

The consonant network is a 10-14-9 feed-forward network. The 14 hidden units are normalized RBF units. Each RBF is centred at a hand configuration determined from training data collected from the user corresponding to one of 14 static consonant phonemes. The target consonants are created with a text-to-speech synthesizer. Figure 2 defines the initial mapping for each of the 14 consonants. The 9 sigmoid output units represent 9 control parameters of the formant synthesizer (ALF, F1, A1, F2, A2,

---

[4]The V/C network, the vowel network and the consonant network are trained using conjugate gradient descent and a line search.

F3, A3, AHF, V). The voicing parameter is required since consonant sounds have different degrees of voicing. The inputs are the same as for the manager V/C network.

Training and test data for the consonant network is obtained from the user. Target data is created for each of the 14 consonant sounds using the text-to-speech synthesizer. The scheme to collect data for a single consonant is:

1. The target consonant is played for 100 msec through the speech synthesizer;
2. the user forms a hand configuration corresponding to the consonant;
3. the user depresses the foot pedal to begin recording; the start of recording is indicated by the appearance of a green square;
4. 10-15 time steps of hand data are collected and stored with the corresponding formant parameter targets and phoneme identifier; the end of data collection is indicated by turning the green square red;
5. the user chooses whether to save the data to a file, and whether to redo the current target or move to the next one.

Using this procedure 350 approximants, 1510 fricatives and 700 nasals were collected and scaled for the training data. The hand data were averaged for each consonant sound to form the RBF centres. For the test data, 255 approximants, 960 fricatives and 165 nasals were collected and scaled. The RBF variances were set to 0.05.

The mean square error on the training set was 0.005 and on the testing set was 0.01 corresponding to expected errors of 3.3% and 4.7% in the formant parameters, respectively. Listening to the output of the network reveals that each sound is produced reasonably well when the user's hand is held in a fixed position. The only difficulty is that the R and L sounds are very sensitive to motion of the index finger.

3 Qualitative Performance of Glove-TalkII

One subject, who is an accomplished pianist, has been trained extensively to speak with Glove-TalkII. We expected that his pianistic skill in forming finger patterns and his musical training would help him learn to speak with Glove-TalkII. After 100 hours of training, his speech with Glove-TalkII is intelligible and somewhat natural-sounding. He still finds it difficult to speak quickly, pronounce polysyllabic words, and speak spontaneously.

During his training, Glove-TalkII also adapted to suit changes required by the subject. Initially, good performance of the V/C network is critical for providing good control intimacy needed for the user to learn to speak. If the V/C network performs poorly the user hears a mixture of vowel and consonant sounds making it difficult to adjust his hand configurations to say different utterances. For this reason, it is important to have the user comfortable with the initial mapping so that the training data collected leads to the V/C network performing well. In the 100 hours of practice, Glove-TalkII was retrained about 10 times. Four significant changes were made from the original system analysed here for the new subject. First, the NG sound was added to the non-stop consonant list by adding an additional hand shape, namely the user touches his pinkie to his thumb on his right hand. To accommodate this change, the consonant and V/C network had two inputs added to represent the two flex angles of the pinkie. Also, the consonant network has an extra hidden unit for the NG sound. Second, the consonant network was trained to allow the RBF centres to change. After the hidden-to-output weights were trained until little improvement was seen, the input-to-hidden weights (i.e. the RBF centres) were also allowed to adapt. This noticeably improved performance for the user. Third, the vowel mapping was altered so that the I was moved closer to the EE sound and the entire mapping was reduced to 75% of its size. Fourth, for this subject, the V/C network needed was a 10-10-1 feed-forward sigmoid unit network. Understanding the interaction between the user's adaptation and Glove-TalkII's adaptation remains an interesting research pursuit.

4 Conclusions

The initial mapping in Glove-TalkII provides a guide for the user during training and is loosely based on an articulatory model of speech. An open configuration of the hand corresponds to an unobstructed vocal tract, which in turn generates vowel sounds. Different vowel sounds are produced by movements of the hand in a horizontal X-Y plane that corresponds to movements of the first two formants which are roughly related to tongue position. Consonants, other than stops, are produced by constricting the index, middle, or ring fingers or flexing the thumb, representing constrictions in the vocal tract. The smooth transition properties of non-stop consonants are a function of the neural network architectures and the training data. Stop consonants are produced by contact switches worn on the user's left hand. F0 is controlled by hand height and speaking intensity by foot pedal depression. Glove-TalkII learns the user's interpretation of this initial mapping. The V/C network and the consonant network learn the mapping from examples generated by the user during phases of training. The vowel network is trained on examples computed from the user-defined mapping between hand-position and vowels. The F0 and volume mappings are non-adaptive.

One subject was trained to use Glove-TalkII. After 100 hours of practice he is able to speak intelligibly. His speech is fairly slow (1.5 to 3 times slower than normal speech) and somewhat robotic. It sounds similar to speech produced with a text-to-speech synthesizer but has a more natural intonation contour which greatly improves the intelligibility and naturalness of the speech. Reading novel passages intelligibly usually requires several attempts, especially with polysyllabic words. Intelligible spontaneous speech is possible but difficult.

Using Glove-TalkII, the subject was able to express his emotional state. To do this, it is hypothesized, the subject must have formed a high degree of intimacy with the device. The adaptive nature of the neural networks, as well as their structure, contributed to this intimacy. Further, the relatively small networks could be simulated fast enough for real-time performance which is necessary for good control intimacy. While not discussed in this paper, since neural networks were used it was possible to obtain the inverse mapping using backpropagation [11] to compute the required partial derivatives; that is, for some speech the system could be inverted to determine the gestures required to say it [2]. Two drawbacks with the neural networks in the interface are the significant amount of training data required and the *off-line* learning procedure, both of which reduce intimacy with the device. It may be possible to use an *online* training method to solve both problems; however, the user and interface adaptation interaction will have to be studied further.

When designing adaptive interfaces it is important to embed as much knowledge as possible into the system to simplify the adaptive parts. By dividing the task into parts which do not require adaptation from those that do it should be possible to reduce neural network sizes (or simplify other types of adaptive models) and hence training data requirements. There is a relationship between usefulness of a device and the amount of tolerance the user has for providing training data. If used carefully, neural networks show promise for continuous-to-continuous and continuous-to-discrete mappings found in some interface applications.

5   Acknowledgements

Thanks go to Peter Dayan, Geoff Hinton, Sageev Oore and Mike Revow for their contributions. The Glove-TalkII research was funded by the Institute for Robotics and Intelligent Systems and NSERC. The intimacy framework research is supported by ATR International.

References

[1] D. Broomhead and D. Lowe. Multivariable functional interpolation and adaptive networks. *Complex Systems*, 2:321–355, 1988.

[2] S. S. Fels. Glove-TalkII: Mapping hand gestures to speech using neural networks, August 1994. Dissertation.

[3] S. S. Fels. Intimacy as a basis for interface analysis. Work in progress., April 1996.

[4] S. S. Fels and G. Hinton. Glove-Talk: A neural network interface between a data-glove and a speech synthesizer. *IEEE Transaction on Neural Networks*, 4:2–8, 1993.

[5] S. S. Fels and G. Hinton. Glove-TalkII: Mapping hand gestures to speech using neural networks. In G. Tesauro et. al., editor, *Advances in Neural Information Processing Systems*, volume 7, Denver, 1995. The MIT Press.

[6] J. Kramer and L. Leifer. The 'Talking Glove': A speaking aid for nonvocal deaf and deaf-blind individuals. In *Proceedings of RESNA 12th Annual Conference*, pages 471–472, 1989.

[7] P. Ladefoged. *A course in Phonetics (2 ed.)*. Harcourt Brace Javanovich, New York, 1982.

[8] E. Lewis. A 'C' implementation of the JSRU text-to-speech system. Technical report, Computer Science Dept., University of Bristol, 1989.

[9] F. R. Moore. The dysfunctions of MIDI. *Computer Music Journal*, 12(1):19–28, Spring 1988.

[10] D. E. Rumelhart, G. E. Hinton, and R. J. Williams. Learning internal representations by back-propagating errors. *Nature*, *323*:533–536, 1986.

[11] D. E. Rumelhart, J. L. McClelland, and the PDP research group. *Parallel distributed processing: Explorations in the microstructure of cognition. Vols. I and II*. MIT Press, Cambridge, MA, 1986.

[12] J. M. Rye and J. N. Holmes. A versatile software parallel-formant speech synthesizer. Technical Report JSRU-RR-1016, Joint Speech Research Unit, Malvern, UK, 1982.

Cross-Validation with LULOO

Paul Haase Sørensen & Magnus Nørgård
Department of Automation, B326
Technical University of Denmark
DK-2800 Lyngby, Denmark
Phones: (+45) 45253581, (+45) 45253565
Fax: (+45) 45881295
Emails: phs,pmn@iau.dtu.dk

Lars Kai Hansen & Jan Larsen
CONNECT, Department of Mathematical Modelling B349
Technical University of Denmark
DK-2800 Lyngby, Denmark
Phones: (+45) 45253889, (+45) 45253923
Fax: (+45) 45880117
Emails: lkhansen@ei.dtu.dk jl@imm.dtu.dk

Abstract— **The leave-one-out cross-validation scheme for generalization assessment of neural network models is computationally expensive due to replicated training sessions. Linear unlearning of examples has recently been suggested as an approach to approximative cross-validation. Here we briefly review the linear unlearning scheme, dubbed LULOO, and we illustrate it on a system identification example. Further, we address the possibility of extracting confidence information (error bars) from the LULOO ensemble.**

1　Introduction

Consider nonlinear regression in which the output y is regressed nonlinearly on the input vector x, this report concerns a neural network implementation, in which the output is predicted by $\widehat{y} = F(x; w)$ where $F(\cdot)$ denotes the nonlinear mapping of the neural net and w is the vector of network parameters.

The *conditional input-output distribution*, i.e., the probability distribution of the output conditioned on a test input, is a basic objective for neural net modeling. A main source of uncertainty, when estimating the parameters of the conditional distribution, is the random selection of training data. The associated risk of overfitting is of major concern in neural network design. The use of *system identification* design tools in neural net learning has been pioneered by [9], who derived estimators for the expected generalization error of regularized networks. These estimates, however, depend on a number of assumptions that can be quite hard to justify. Hence, it would be highly desirable to be able to perform an additional data-driven *consistency check* offered by the cross-validation technique.

The idea of cross-validation [13], [15] is based on training and testing on disjunct subsets resampled from the database, forming the *cross-validation ensemble* of models. The leave-one-out (LOO) ensemble of networks trained on all subsets leaving out one training example is an attractive — though computationally expensive — vehicle for generalization assessment of a neural network model. For the conventional neural net approaches unlearning of examples is not possible, and one basically has to train the full ensemble of networks, making the approach computationally unfeasible.

Recently it was suggested to approximate the evaluation of the ensemble using *linear unlearning* of individual examples [4]. It is assumed that unlearning of a single example only affects the network weights slightly. Under this hypothesis we estimate the change in the network parameters within the quadratic approximation of the network cost function. Using the ensemble we derive an estimator for the test error of a regularized network which in fact is similar to an estimate due to [16], but different from the conventional estimators as FPE [1], Wahba's GCV, and GPE [9]. The proposed method is further related to NCV [10] which approximates leave-v-out cross-validation. We finally discuss the possibility of exploiting the ensemble of networks for obtaining error bars on future examples.

The leave-one-out test error is compared to that obtained through linear unlearning on a benchmark case showing the viability of the approach.

2   Linear Unlearning

The network cost function is assumed to be a sum of the loss function $E(\boldsymbol{w})$ (additive in the example losses denoted ϵ [1].) and a regularization term $R(\boldsymbol{w})$, as shown by

$$C(\boldsymbol{w}) = E(\boldsymbol{w}) + R(\boldsymbol{w}) = \sum_{\alpha=1}^{N} \epsilon\left(y_\alpha, \widehat{y}_\alpha, \boldsymbol{w}\right) + R(\boldsymbol{w}) \tag{1}$$

where y_α is desired the output[2] (target) and N is the number of training examples, i.e., input-output pairs: $\boldsymbol{D} = \left[(\boldsymbol{x}_1, y_1), \cdots, (\boldsymbol{x}_N, y_N)\right]$. Training on the full set of examples provides a parameter vector denoted by $\widehat{\boldsymbol{w}}$; hence,

$$\frac{\partial C\left(\widehat{\boldsymbol{w}}\right)}{\partial \boldsymbol{w}} = \boldsymbol{0}. \tag{2}$$

Likewise, a leave-one-out ensemble of network parameters, $\{\widehat{\boldsymbol{w}}_\beta\}_{\beta=1}^{N}$, is obtained by training on the N subsets, $\boldsymbol{D}_\beta$, containing $N-1$ examples:

$$C_\beta(\boldsymbol{w}) = \sum_{\alpha=1, \alpha\neq\beta}^{N} \epsilon\left(y_\alpha, \widehat{y}_\alpha, \boldsymbol{w}\right) + R(\boldsymbol{w}), \tag{3}$$

hence,

$$\frac{\partial C_\beta\left(\widehat{\boldsymbol{w}}_\beta\right)}{\partial \boldsymbol{w}} = \boldsymbol{0}. \tag{4}$$

We suggest to estimate the variation of the parameter vectors of the leave-one-out ensemble, $\Delta\boldsymbol{w}_\beta \equiv \widehat{\boldsymbol{w}}_\beta - \widehat{\boldsymbol{w}}$, by using a Taylor expansion of equation (4). Since

$$C_\beta(\boldsymbol{w}) = C(\boldsymbol{w}) - \epsilon\left(y_\beta, \widehat{y}_\beta, \boldsymbol{w}\right), \tag{5}$$

$\Delta\boldsymbol{w}_\beta$ satisfies

$$\boldsymbol{J}_\beta \Delta\boldsymbol{w}_\beta - \boldsymbol{g}_\beta + o(\|\Delta\boldsymbol{w}_\beta\|) = \boldsymbol{0}. \tag{6}$$

where $o(\cdot)$ is the vector order function. We further have defined the the *Hessian* of the regularized cost function, $\boldsymbol{J}_\beta$, and the *gradient* of the example loss, $\boldsymbol{g}_\beta$, by[3]:

$$\boldsymbol{J}_\beta = \frac{\partial^2 C_\beta\left(\widehat{\boldsymbol{w}}\right)}{\partial \boldsymbol{w} \partial \boldsymbol{w}^\mathsf{T}}, \qquad \boldsymbol{g}_\beta = \frac{\partial \epsilon\left(y_\beta, \widehat{y}_\beta, \widehat{\boldsymbol{w}}\right)}{\partial \boldsymbol{w}}. \tag{7}$$

Solving equation (6), with the additional assumption that the regularized Hessian is non-singular, we find the N weight vectors in the ensemble given by:

$$\widehat{\boldsymbol{w}}_\beta = \widehat{\boldsymbol{w}} + \boldsymbol{J}_\beta^{-1} \boldsymbol{g}_\beta + o(\|\Delta\boldsymbol{w}_\beta\|). \tag{8}$$

With this Linear Unlearning LOO (LULOO) ensemble in hand, we can get approximations of various interesting quantities which help us in validating the network model.

2.1   Average Generalization Error Estimate

A common measure of the quality of a neural model is the expected generalization error[4] (see e.g., [6], [9]) defined as the expected loss on a test sample, further taking the expectation w.r.t. to the training set distribution[5]:

$$\langle E_{\text{test}}(\widehat{\boldsymbol{w}})\rangle_D = \left\langle \langle \epsilon(y, \widehat{y}, \widehat{\boldsymbol{w}})\rangle_{(x,y)} \right\rangle_D = \int \left[\int \epsilon(y, \widehat{y}, \widehat{\boldsymbol{w}}) \cdot p(\boldsymbol{x}, y)\, d\boldsymbol{x}\, dy\right] p(\boldsymbol{D})\, d\boldsymbol{D}. \tag{9}$$

where $\langle\cdot\rangle_{(x,y)}$ is the expectation w.r.t. to the joint input-output probability density $p(\boldsymbol{x}, y)$, and $p(\boldsymbol{D})$ is the joint probability density of the training data. $\langle\cdot\rangle_D$ denotes the expectation w.r.t. to all training sets of size N [6].

Since $p(\boldsymbol{x}, y)$ is unknown we seek for an estimate of $\langle E_{\text{test}}\rangle_D$, like the leave-one-out test error given by,

$$E_{\text{LOO}} = \frac{1}{N} \sum_{\beta=1}^{N} \epsilon\left(y_\beta, \widehat{y}_\beta, \widehat{\boldsymbol{w}}_\beta\right). \tag{10}$$

---

[1] Most learning problems come with a natural loss measure, e.g., the squared error measure $\epsilon\left(y, \widehat{y}\right) = \left(y - \widehat{y}\right)^2$, where the desired target is denoted y and the network output is denoted $\widehat{y}$

[2] For simplicity we consider single output networks only. However, without further ado, the theory is valid for multiple output networks.

[3] Here we implicitly assume that the cost function is twice continuously differentiable.

[4] Also known as the expected test error or the expected prediction risk.

[5] By assumption all expectations exist, i.e., $E_{\text{test}} < \infty$.

[6] Note, for notational convenience, we do not explicitly distinguish between the particular realization of the data set and the data set regarded as a random variable.

Theorem 1 *An $o(1/N)$ approximation of the LOO test error (10) is given by*

$$\widehat{E}_{\mathrm{LOO}} = \frac{1}{N} \sum_{\beta=1}^{N} \left[\epsilon\left(y_\beta, \widehat{y}_\beta, \widehat{w}\right) + g_\beta^\top J_\beta^{-1} g_\beta \right].$$ (11)

Proof From (6) it is easy to verify that $\Delta w_\beta = O(1/N)$, where $O(\cdot)$ is the Landau order function. For consistency, the approximation of the LOO estimator should not include terms of $O(1/N^i)$, $i \geq 2$. Thus expanding the LOO test error (10) linearly in Δw_β and using (7), (8) we get the desired result. Note that $o(1/N)$ is the order function, i.e., if $a(N) = o(1/N)$ then $a(N)/N \to 0$ as $N \to \infty$. □

Since only one data example is left out when resampling, we generally expect the $o(1/N)$ approximation to be fairly good — even for moderate training set sizes. Only in the case of a network which is linear in the parameters and trained with a quadratic cost function[7], it is possible to obtain an exact expression (see further [16] and section 3.1).

3   Mean Square Error Learning

Our scheme can be applied to any cost function and network type requiring the cost to be twice continuously differentiable in the weights. Here we consider the standard case of a regression net trained with the mean square error measure. Let $F(x, w)$ be the network function, then the loss is the squared error between the output and the predicted output, as follows:

$$\epsilon\left(y_\alpha, \widehat{y}_\alpha, w\right) = \left(y_\alpha - F(x_\alpha, w)\right)^2.$$ (12)

Introducing the gradient of the network function, $h_\beta = \partial F(x_\beta, \widehat{w})/\partial w$ we use (7) and find

$$g_\beta = -2\left(y_\beta - F(x_\beta, \widehat{w})\right) h_\beta.$$ (13)

3.1   The LOO Test Error

If (13) is inserted in (11) we get:

$$\widehat{E}_{\mathrm{LOO}} = \frac{1}{N} \sum_{\beta=1}^{N} \left(y_\beta - F(x_\beta; \widehat{w})\right)^2 \left[1 + 4h_\beta^\top J_\beta^{-1} h_\beta\right].$$ (14)

Furthermore, it is often well motivated to invoke the so-called Gauss-Newton approximation for mean square error based problems (see e.g., [8]), in which,

$$J = \frac{\partial^2 C(\widehat{w})}{\partial w \partial w^\top} = \frac{\partial^2 E(\widehat{w})}{\partial w \partial w^\top} + \frac{\partial^2 R(\widehat{w})}{\partial w \partial w^\top} \approx 2 \sum_{\alpha=1}^{N} h_\beta h_\beta^\top + \frac{\partial^2 R(\widehat{w})}{\partial w \partial w^\top}$$ (15)

Within this approximation the estimator takes a particular simple form. Using, $J_\beta = J - 2h_\beta h_\beta^\top$, and the matrix inversion lemma (see e.g., [8]) we find:

$$J_\beta^{-1} = J^{-1} + \frac{2J^{-1} h_\beta h_\beta^\top J^{-1}}{1 - 2h_\beta^\top J^{-1} h_\beta}.$$ (16)

Inserting this expression into the estimate (14) we get the remarkable simple result,

$$\widehat{E}_{\mathrm{LOO}} = \frac{1}{N} \sum_{\beta=1}^{N} \left(y_\beta - F(x_\beta; \widehat{w})\right)^2 \frac{1 + 2h_\beta^\top J^{-1} h_\beta}{1 - 2h_\beta^\top J^{-1} h_\beta}.$$ (17)

With a pointer to classical test error estimators, (17) may be interpreted as a modified "example based" FPE. Thus the term, $2h_\beta^\top J^{-1} h_\beta$, corresponds to the effective number of parameters divided by the training set size for the particular example β. With this construction one may hope that the statistical properties of the input distribution are reflected in the estimator. In the conventional asymptotically estimators the properties of the input distribution are eliminated from the theory by invoking the limit of large training sets. For further reference, see [9] and [6].

3.2   Prediction Confidence Intervals

The conditioned generalization error in the case of mean square error learning is given by

$$\sigma_e^2(x) = E\left\{e^2 | x\right\} = E\left\{(y - F(x, \widehat{w}))^2 | x\right\}$$ (18)

which equals the conditional error variance. The prediction confidence interval is thus

$$y \in [\widehat{y} \pm c \cdot \sigma_e]$$ (19)

---

[7] That is, $\epsilon = (y - \widehat{y})^2$ and $R(\mathbf{w}) \propto \mathbf{w}^\top \mathbf{w}$. Furthermore, (10) should be expanded quadratically in $\Delta \mathbf{w}_\beta$.

where c is a suitably constant. If the error is Gaussian distributed, $c = 1.96$ corresponds to a 95% confidence interval.

One might hypothesize that the individual predictions for a test input x could be used to obtain sensible error bars; however the LOO technique is not directly applicable for estimating the confidence interval, i.e., it is not possible to obtain a plain empirical estimate. Consequently, we turn to an asymptotic $(N \to \infty)$ expression.

Error bars were mentioned in [2] who formulated the classical result see [12], p. 193 in a neural network context. The conditional error variance is approximated by:

$$\sigma_e^2(\boldsymbol{x}) = \sigma_n^2 + \boldsymbol{h}(\boldsymbol{x})^\top \langle \delta \boldsymbol{w} \delta \boldsymbol{w}^\top \rangle_D \boldsymbol{h}(\boldsymbol{x}) \tag{20}$$

where $\boldsymbol{h}(\boldsymbol{x}) = \partial F(\boldsymbol{x}, \widehat{\boldsymbol{w}})/\partial \boldsymbol{w}$ and $\delta \boldsymbol{w} = \widehat{\boldsymbol{w}} - \boldsymbol{w}^\circ$ is the weight fluctuations around the true weights $\boldsymbol{w}^\circ$ which minimizies the generalization error.

From the theory of the so-called Jackknife estimator (see e.g., [3], [12]), it is known that in order to estimate the covariance matrix of the weight fluctuations from the LOO ensemble, we need to multiply the LOO fluctuations $\Delta \boldsymbol{w}_\beta$ in (6) by a factor of $\sqrt{N-1}$, thus

$$\langle \delta \boldsymbol{w} \delta \boldsymbol{w}^\top \rangle_D \approx \sum_{\beta=1}^{N} (\Delta \boldsymbol{w}_\beta - \overline{\Delta \boldsymbol{w}})(\Delta \boldsymbol{w}_\beta - \overline{\Delta \boldsymbol{w}})^\top \tag{21}$$

where $\overline{\Delta \boldsymbol{w}} = N^{-1} \sum_{\beta=1}^{N} \Delta \boldsymbol{w}_\beta$.

An estimate of the noise variance[8] σ_n^2 can be obtained by various standard methods, see e.g., [6], [10], [12], or by using

$$\widehat{\sigma_n^2} = N^{-1} \left(E(\widehat{\boldsymbol{w}}) + \frac{1}{2} \text{Trace}[\boldsymbol{H} \cdot \langle \delta \boldsymbol{w} \delta \boldsymbol{w}^\top \rangle_D] \right), \quad \boldsymbol{H} = \frac{\partial^2 E}{\partial \boldsymbol{w} \partial \boldsymbol{w}^\top}(\widehat{\boldsymbol{w}}) \tag{22}$$

4 Example

The leave-one-out cross validation scheme has been evaluated on data obtained from a non-linear simulation model of a pneumatic servo mechanism. A detailed description of the system can be found in [14].

The servo mechanism consists of a linear compressed air cylinder lifting an inertial weight. The cylinder is fed from a system of servo valves which open proportional to a control signal. The servo valve opening characteristics are approximately linear, so that the main nonlinear behavior is due to the cylinder itself. The cylinder chamber's compression dynamics are position dependent and the servo valve flow characteristic is nonlinear. The sampling period of the control system is selected to 0.1 seconds. Furthermore, measurement noise is present in the position measurement data. We seek a neural network model of the position servo, where the system input is the servo valve control input and the output of the system is the piston position.

In order to train a neural network model of the servomechanism, an experiment has initially been performed to collect a set of data. Since the servomechanism contains an integration, the experiment was carried out in closed-loop using a manually tuned PI-controller. A small random signal was added to the control signal to ensure identifiability. A data set of 3000 samples was generated. The relatively large data set is necessary in order to make sure that all of the operating range of the system was contained in the data. Fig. 1 displays the entire data set.

In figure 2 we show how the individual test errors (squared residuals) entering the test error estimate (17) correlate with the results of a full leave-one-out procedure, i.e., the result of training $N = 500$ networks on the corresponding subsets of the training set. To illustrate the capacity of the LULOO ensemble for representing the distribution of predictions on test inputs we show in figure 3 the ensemble error bars evaluated on a portion of the test set.

5 Conclusion

This paper suggested to use linear unlearning of examples to approximate the computationally expensive leave-one-out cross-validation technique. Numerical studies on a system identification problem demonstrates the viability of this approach. We have also investigated the LULOO ensemble error bars.

Acknowledgments

This research was partly supported by the Thomas B. Thriges Foundation and the Danish Natural Science and Technical Research Councils through the Computational Neural Network Center (CONNECT). JL furthermore acknowledge the Radio Parts Foundation for financial support.

---

[8] We assume that the noise variance is homogeneous.

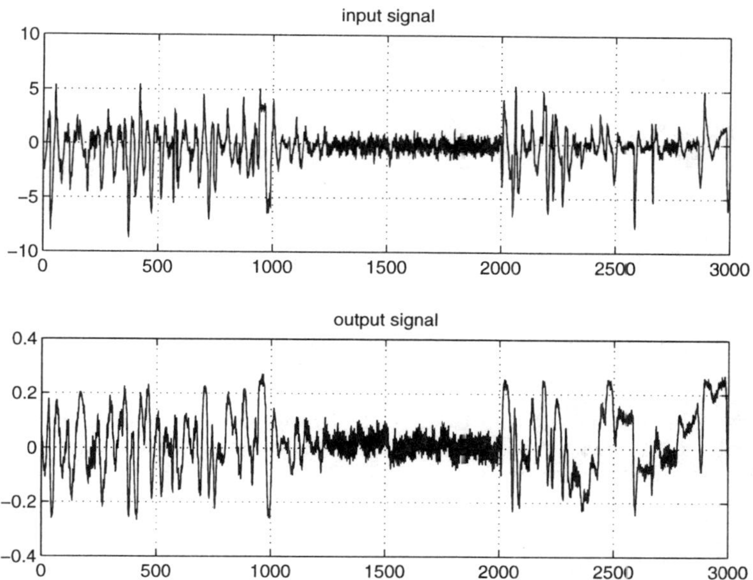

Figure 1: The entire data set used for the identification of the servo system.

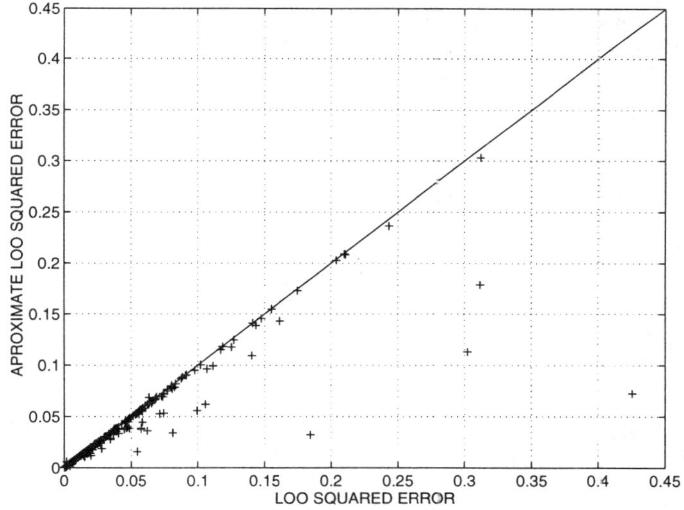

Figure 2: Correlation of individual squared errors (losses) in the leave-one-out (10) with the linear unlearned leave-one-out estimates (17) on the training set.

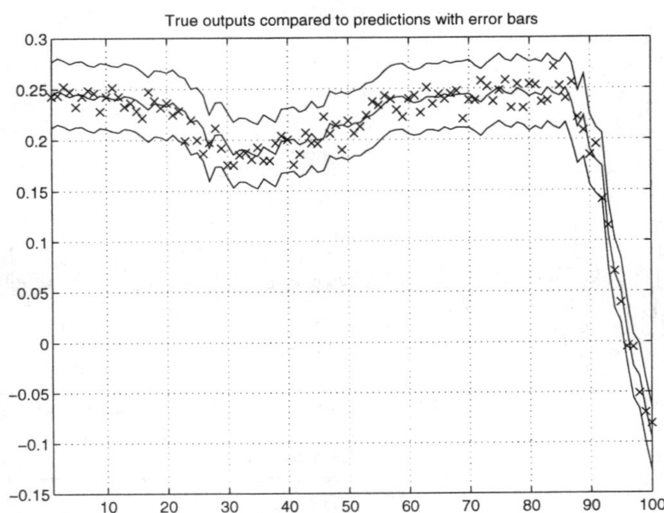

Figure 3: We show the predictions and the LULOO ensemble error bars on part of the test set. Crosses mark the test data values, the central solid line is the prediction and the standard deviation confidence interval is between the two solid lines

References

[1] H. Akaike: "Fitting Autoregressive Models for Prediction," *Annals of the Institute of Statistical Mathematics*, **21**, 243–247, (1969).

[2] W.L. Buntine & A.S. Weigend: "Bayesian Back-Propagation," *Complex Systems*, **5**, 603–643, (1991).

[3] T. Fox, D. Hinkley & K. Larntz: "Jackknifing in Nonlinear Regression," *Technometrics*, **22**(1), 29–33, (1980).

[4] L.K. Hansen and J. Larsen: "Linear Unlearning for Crossvalidation" *Advances in Computational Mathematics*, to appear (1996).

[5] A. Krogh & J. Vedelsby: "Neural Network Ensembles, Cross Validation, and Active Learning," in G. Tesauro *et al.*(eds.), *Advances in Neural Information Processing Systems 7*: MIT Press, Cambridge, Massachusetts, 1995.

[6] J. Larsen & L.K. Hansen: "Generalization Performance of Regularized Neural Network Models," in J. Vlontzos, J.-N. Hwang & E. Wilson (eds.), *Proceedings of the IEEE Workshop on Neural Networks for Signal Processing IV*, Piscataway, New Jersey: IEEE, 42–51, (1994).

[7] J. Larsen & L.K. Hansen: "Empirical Generalization Assessment of Neural Network Models," in F. Girosi, J. Makhoul, E. Manolakos & E. Wilson (eds.). *Proceedings of the IEEE Workshop on Neural Networks for Signal Processing V*, Piscataway, New Jersey: IEEE, 30–39, (1995).

[8] L. Ljung: *System Identification: Theory for the User*, Englewood Cliffs, New Jersey: Prentice-Hall, (1987).

[9] J. Moody: "Note on Generalization, Regularization, and Architecture Selection in Nonlinear Learning Systems," in B.H. Juang, S.Y. Kung & C.A. Kamm (eds.) *Proceedings of the first IEEE Workshop on Neural Networks for Signal Processing*, Piscataway, New Jersey: IEEE, 1–10, (1991).

[10] J. Moody: "Prediction Risk and Architecture Selection for Neural Networks" in V. Cherkassky, J. H. Friedman & H. Wechsler (eds.) *From Statistics to Neural Networks: Theory and Pattern Recognition Applications*, Series F, **136**, Berlin, Germany: Springer-Verlag, (1994).

[11] N. Murata, S. Yoshizawaand & S. Amari: "Network Information Criterion — Determining the Number of Hidden Units for an Artificial Neural Network Model," *IEEE Transactions on Neural Networks*, **5**(6), 865–872, (1994).

[12] G.A.F. Seber & C.J. Wild: *Nonlinear Regression*, New York, New York: John Wiley & Sons, (1989).

[13] M. Stone: "Cross-validatory Choice and Assessment of Statistical Predictors," *Journal of the Royal Statistical Society B*, **36**(2), 111–147, (1974).

[14] Sørensen, P.H., P.K. Sinha, K. Al-Mutib : "Identification of a Pneumatic Servo Mechanism using Neural Networks." *Proc. Int. Conf. on Machine Automation*, Tampere, Finland, Vol.2, pp. 499-512, (1994).

[15] G.T. Toussaint: "Bibliography on Estimation of Misclassification," *IEEE Transactions on Information Theory*, **20**(4), 472–479, (1974).

[16] G. Wahba: "Spline Models for Observational Data," *CBMS-NSF Regional Conference Series in Applied Mathematics*, SIAM **59**, (1990).

[17] A.S. Weigend, B.A. Hubermann & D.E. Rumelhart: "Predicting the Future: A Connectionist Approach," *International Journal of Neural Systems*, **1**(3), 193–209, (1990).

Aspects of Adaptive Learning Algorithms for FIR Feedforward Networks

Andrew D. Back[†‡], Ah Chung Tsoi[†]

† Department of Electrical and Computer Engineering, University of Queensland
Brisbane, Qld 4072. Australia
‡ Frontier Research Program RIKEN, Institute of Physical and Chemical Research
Hirosawa 2-1, Saitama 351-01, Wako-Schi, Japan.
{back,act}@elec.uq.edu.au

Abstract— Various algorithms have been proposed for adapting the parameters in FIR feedforward networks. In the published literature, there appears to be some confusion over the ways in which the adaptive algorithms are derived. In a previously published paper, we have demonstrated that slight variations in the learning algorithms can result in significantly different performances in some applications. In this paper, we show the factors involved in deriving two such algorithms, discuss their underlying assumptions, and examine their performance in a system identification task.

1 Introduction

As a means of modelling time-correlated signals in a nonlinear framework, multilayer perceptrons (MLPs) with synapses described by filters have recently been proposed [1, 2, 21]. These approaches replace the traditional constant synaptic weights with finite impulse response (FIR) filters and infinite impulse response (IIR) filters commonly used in digital filter theory [5].

An algorithm for training networks having FIR synapses was first published by Wan [21]. A slightly different training algorithm for the same network as well as the case for IIR synapses was published independently around the same time by Back and Tsoi [1, 2].

There are some subtle differences between these algorithms which can result in significantly different behaviour. Such differences in behaviour have been observed particularly in long-term prediction problems [3]. The main aim of this paper is to examine in detail the way in which the on-line learning algorithms for the FIR MLP are derived. By making explicit where the training algorithms differ, we seek to highlight the underlying assumptions involved in their derivations. As a means of demonstrating their performance, we present simulation results which indicate quite different convergence characteristics. Some comments will be made as to the cause of this.

2 Derivation of Learning Algorithms for FIR MLP Networks

In this section, we consider the derivation of learning algorithms for dynamic FIR MLP network architectures. The derivation for the nonlinear case is quite similar to the linear case. However, there are subtle variations in the nonlinear algorithms which in some cases, lead to markedly different behaviour [3].

The FIR MLP network considered is defined as

$$z_k^l(t) = f\left(\hat{x}_k^l(t)\right) \tag{1}$$

$$\hat{x}_k^l(t) = \sum_{i=1}^{N_l} \hat{y}_{ik}^l(t) \tag{2}$$

$$\hat{y}_{ik}^l(t) = c_{ik}^l v_{ik}^l(t) \tag{3}$$

$$v_{ik}^l(t) = B_{ik}^l(q^{-1}) z_i^{l-1}(t) \tag{4}$$

Let the instantaneous error be

$$J(t;\theta) = \frac{1}{2} \sum_{k=1}^{N_L} e_k^2(t) = \frac{1}{2} \sum_{k=1}^{N_L} \left(y_k(t) - z_k^L(t)\right)^2 \tag{5}$$

where $y_k(t)$ is the desired output at time t. The weights in an FIR MLP are updated according to

$$b_{ikj}^l(t+1) = b_{ikj}^l(t) + \Delta b_{ikj}^l(t) \tag{6}$$

$$c_{ik}^l(t+1) = c_{ik}^l(t) + \Delta c_{ik}^l(t) \tag{7}$$

$$\Delta b_{ikj}^l(t) = \eta \delta_k^l(t) \beta_{ikj}^l(t) \tag{8}$$

$$\Delta c_{ik}^l(t) = \eta \delta_k^l(t) v_{ik}^l(t) \tag{9}$$

where

$$
\begin{aligned}
\beta_{ikj}^{l}(t) &= \frac{\partial \hat{x}_k^l(t)}{\partial b_{ikj}^l(t)} \\
&= z_i^l(t-j) \\
\delta_k^l(t) &= -\frac{\partial J(t;\theta)}{\partial \hat{x}_k^l(t)} \\
&= \begin{cases} e_k(t) f'(\hat{x}_k^l(t)) & l = L \\ f'\left(\hat{x}_k^l(t)\right) \sum_{p=1}^{N_{l+1}} \delta_p^{l+1}(t)\chi_{kp}^{l+1}(q) & 1 \le l \le L-1 \end{cases} \\
f'(\hat{x}) &= df(\hat{x})/d\hat{x} \\
\chi_{kp}^{l+1}(q) &= \frac{\partial \hat{x}_p^{l+1}(t)}{\partial z_k^l(t)}
\end{aligned}
\tag{10}
$$

Thus, it is necessary to evaluate $\delta_k^l(t)$ and the synaptic sensitivity derivative $\chi_{kp}^l(q)$ in order to compute the weight updates using the gradient descent algorithm. The $\delta_k^l(t)$ term is the usual backpropagated error [16].

Previously, various expressions have been derived for $\chi_{kp}^l(q)$. Wan derived the *Temporal Backpropagation*[1] algorithm for the FIR MLP by setting $\chi_{kp}^l(q) = B_{kp}^l(q^{-1})$ [21]. Back and Tsoi derived an algorithm for the FIR MLP by setting $\chi_{kp}^l(q) = b_{kp0}^l$ [2]. This raises the question - which method is correct ? In [3] it was shown that for a particular chaotic time series prediction problem, the latter approach yielded superior performance.

In the past, calculation of $\chi(q)$ has been performed using a network sensitivity formula [7], where

$$
\chi_{kp}^{l+1}(q) = c_{kp}^{l+1} \frac{\partial v_{kp}^{l+1}(t)}{\partial z_k^l(t)}
\tag{11}
$$

$$
= c_{kp}^{l+1} \frac{\partial B_{kp}^{l+1}(q^{-1}) z_k^l(t)}{\partial z_k^l(t)}
\tag{12}
$$

$$
= c_{kp}^{l+1} B_{kp}^{l+1}(q^{-1})
\tag{13}
$$

At first, this appears to be correct and that nothing more can be said about such a derivative. There is however, more to this computation than first meets the eye.

Suppose we wish to calculate the derivative above *instantaneously*. That is, for a given derivative $\partial y(t)/\partial x(t)$, we wish to find the value instantaneously at time t for the weight update based on the instantaneous error measure in (5). Then, by definition

$$
\frac{\partial y(t)}{\partial x(t)} = 0
\tag{14}
$$

if a small change in $x(t)$ at time t does not induce any corresponding change in $y(t)$ at time t also. For the case where $y = z_p^l(t-i)$ and $x = z_k^l(t)$, this situation applies. Hence we conclude that

$$
\frac{\partial z_k^l(t-i)}{\partial z_k^l(t)} \overset{t}{=} \begin{cases} 1 & i = 0 \\ 0 & i = 1, ..., n_b \end{cases}
\tag{15}
$$

where $\overset{t}{=}$ indicates an instantaneous equality at time t. If the derivative is calculated such that any effects in $x(t)$ are considered in $y(t)$ cumulatively over time in(14), then the usual network sensitivity result is obtained.

Hence, the synaptic sensitivity derivative may be described as

$$
\chi_{kp}^{l+1}(q) = \begin{cases} c_{kp}^{l+1} b_{kp0}^{l+1} & \text{Algorithm 1} \\ c_{kp}^{l+1} B_{kp}^{l+1}(q^{-1}) & \text{Algorithm 2} \end{cases}
\tag{16}
$$

where Algorithm 1 refers to the instantaneous result and Algorithm 2 refers to the previous network sensitivity result.

Remarks.

1. Algorithm 1 corresponds to the exact instantaneous sensitivity derivative which has appeared previously in [2].

2. We can arrive at the same result by regarding $z(t)$ and $z(t-k)$, $k = 1, ..., M$, as instantaneously independent.

3. Algorithm 2 corresponds to Wan's *Temporal Backpropagation* algorithm [21].

---

[1] In these original derivations, synaptic gains were not used. In this paper we include synaptic gains, but still attribute the algorithms to their originators. Synaptic gains for these architectures were introduced in [4].

4. It is interesting to note that the derivative in (15) appears to be of the pseudolinear regression (PLR) type [13]. Normally this is not a good choice to make due to convergence problems [10]. What is the rationale for its applicability here ?

In the classic linear adaptive IIR filter, the recursive prediction error (RPE) algorithm is generally regarded as the best choice [13]. To compute $\partial \hat{y}(t-k)/\partial \theta(t)$ where $\theta(t)$ is the parameter vector at time t, the approximation is made that the denominator is constant, ie

$$\theta(t) \approx \theta(t-1) \approx \cdots \approx \theta(t-k) \tag{17}$$

To apply the same approximation in computing $\partial z_k^l(t-i)/\partial z_k^l(t)$, it would be necessary to make the approximation that

$$z(t) \approx z(t-1) \approx \cdots \approx z(t-k) \tag{18}$$

This would allow the approximation

$$\frac{\partial z(t-i)}{\partial z(t)} \approx q^{-i}\frac{\partial z(t)}{\partial z(t)}$$
$$= q^{-i} \tag{19}$$

Hence, in this case, it would follow that $\chi(q)$ could be found as in Algorithm 2.

Clearly this assumption is unlikely to hold except for signals which are varying slowly relative to the sampling rate, or where the signal is coming from a saturated node within the network. Hence we expect better performance to be found using Algorithm 1.

It should be noted that we propose Algorithm 1 based on the concept of using it to obtain a more accurate estimate of the instantaneous sensitivity gradient used to update all synaptic filters which are in layers lower than the output layer. It is clear that it also allows reduced memory and lower computational complexity, however it is stressed that the intention of introducing this algorithm is not one of simplification, but of accuracy. The experiments in the next section lend support to this. This is in contrast to other simplification algorithms which may lead to a small degradation in the performance of the filter, since their purpose is primarily for simplification [9].

The final learning algorithms for the FIR MLP are given in (20)-(20).

$$\Delta b_{ikj}^l(t) = \eta \delta_k^l(t) z_i^{l-1}(t-j)$$
$$\Delta c_{ik}^l(t) = \eta \delta_k^l(t) B_{ik}^l(q^{-1}) z_i^{l-1}(t)$$
$$\delta_k^l(t) = \begin{cases} e_k(t) f'(\hat{x}_k^l(t)) & l = L \\ f'(\hat{x}_k^l(t)) \sum_{p=1}^{N_{l+1}} \delta_p^{l+1}(t) \chi_{kp}^{l+1}(q) & 1 \le l \le L-1 \end{cases} \tag{20}$$
$$\chi_{kp}^{l+1}(q) = \begin{cases} c_{kp}^{l+1} b_{kp0}^{l+1} & \text{Back-Tsoi FIR Algorithm} \\ c_{kp}^{l+1} B_{kp}^{l+1}(q^{-1}) & \text{Wan Temporal Backpropagation} \end{cases}$$

3 Example

As a means of testing the performance of the two algorithms, we consider some system identification problems. For the example presented here, we focus on the simplest possible system to ensure the differences due to the algorithms can be observed. Hence we perform a linear system identification experiment. This can be considered as an FIR MLP with 2 layers, and 1 hidden layer with linear activation units (this is a special case of the more standard MLP architecture, with the hidden unit activations being assumed to be linear rather than the usual sigmoidal. In this case, the resulting network is linear). The system to be identified has the same structure. The filter order is $n_b = 2$ and $\eta = 0.002$. The system to be identified has a pair of complex zeros at $(r = 0.85, \theta = 120°)$, and two real zeros at $(r = 0.9994, r = 0.9577)$, and is described by

$$G_1(q^{-1}) = 1.0 + 0.85q^{-1} + 0.7225q^{-2}$$
$$G_2(q^{-1}) = 1.0 - 1.957q^{-1} + 0.9577q^{-2} \tag{21}$$

To test each algorithm, we used a white gaussian noise input of unit variance and zero mean. We conducted Monte-Carlo tests using 200 runs of differently seeded training samples and initial coefficients, each being 20000 points to obtain the results reported. The last 500 points of each run were used to calculate the normalized mean square error $(NMSE)^2$ and variance. In this way, an indication is obtained of how well the model has approximated the system.

The experiments reveal several interesting characteristics about the algorithms. Firstly, it was observed that Algorithm 1 tended to frequently converge to much lower mean square error results than Algorithm 2. The average values of NMSE and variance for the experiment are shown in Table 1. For this example, the NMSE and variance results of Algorithm 1 were about 30% better than those from using Algorithm 2 when measured over all runs, and more than 20× better when measured over convergences to a global minima. This improvement has been observed in practice also, for example, in a chaotic time series

---

[2] The NMSE is calculated as $NMSE = \frac{1}{\hat{\sigma}^2 N}\sum_{n=1}^{N}(d(n) - y_L(n))^2$, with estimated variance $\hat{\sigma}^2$ of the desired output $d(t)$.

Table 1: Simulation Results for an FIR System Identification Task

Algorithm	All Runs		Conv. to Local Point	
	NMSE	Variance	NMSE	Variance
Alg. 1	0.135	0.408	0.000025	0.000079
Alg. 2	0.203	0.622	0.000577	0.001748

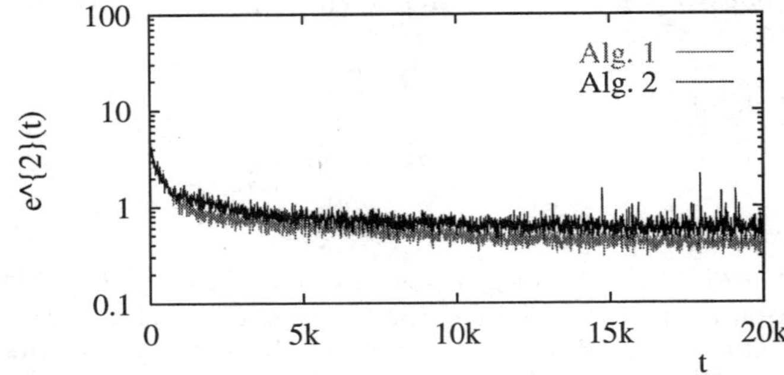

Figure 1: Convergence of $e^2(t)$ for Algorithms 1 and 2 in Experiment 1. Table 1 gives specific performance figures. Note the similar learning characteristics, but the lower error obtained using Algorithm 1.

prediction problem reported previously [3]. Figure 1 shows the averaged squared error performance of the algorithms.

The second interesting aspect about behaviour of the algorithms is that they appear to follow quite different convergence paths. Figure 2 shows the convergence of the b_0 and b_1 parameters in a typical example. The conditions for each of the simulations were identical, the only difference being due to the algorithms. It can be observed that the parameter trajectories begin at the same point and appear to track each other closely to start with. Relatively soon however, Algorithm 2 completely diverges to another point some distance away from either minima. This situation was very common in simulations. While Algorithm 1 was also sometimes observed to diverge in the same way, it occurred much more often with Algorithm 2. Even when the two algorithms both converged towards a global minima, as indicated in the second set of results in Table 1, Algorithm 1 typically gave NMSE and variance results more than an order of magnitude lower than that obtained using Algorithm 2.

A third observation concerning the algorithms, is that it was noted that Algorithm 2 also had a tendency to exhibit a form of 'bursting' behaviour, where the errors jumped sporadically to some high values during learning. This is shown in Figure 3.

It was also noted that Algorithm 1 is capable of using a higher learning constant η without encountering instability problems during the estimation process.

Referring to Figure 2, Algorithm 1 obtained a NMSE $= 1.4 \times 10e - 8$ and Algorithm 2 obtained a

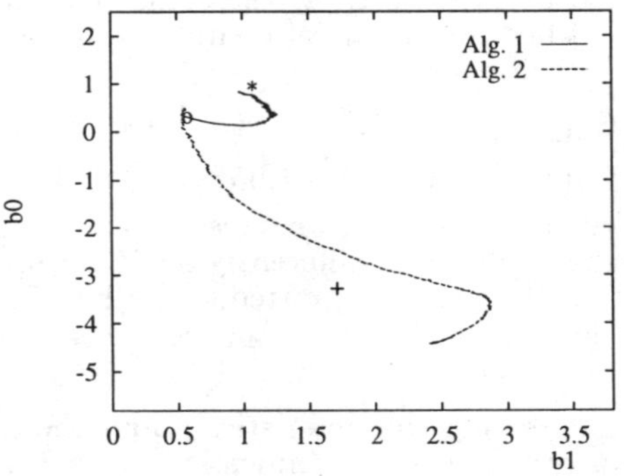

Figure 2: Convergence behaviour of $\hat{b}_0(t)$ and $\hat{b}_1(t)$ for Algorithms 1 and 2, in Experiment 1, are shown. Two (global) minimum points are associated with the model. The starting point for each algorithm is marked with a 'o'. A '*' at (1.029, 0.874) marks the minimum closest to Algorithm 1, and a '+' at (1.6557,-3.2403) marks the minimum closest to Algorithm 2. These are based on the final time-step of each algorithm, assuming $\hat{b}_2$ to be fixed. It can be clearly seen that Algorithm 2 has diverged from the local minima closest to its starting point, and has not reached the second local minima either.

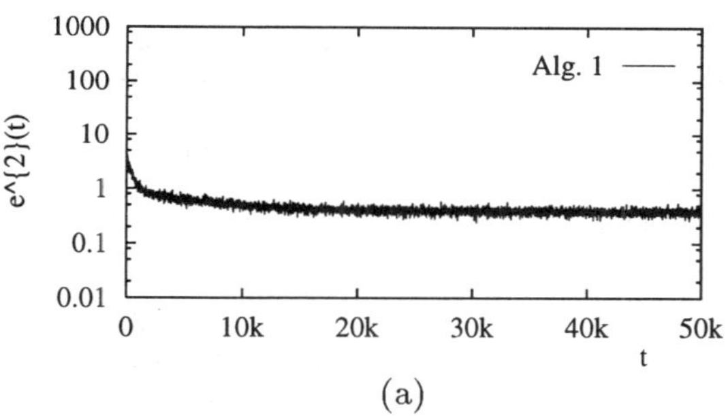

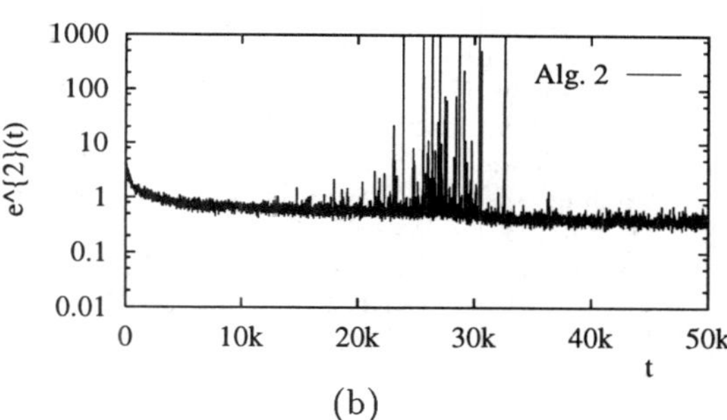

Figure 3: (a) Convergence of Algorithm 1 in Example 1 taken over 50k iterations. (b) An example of 'bursting' type behaviour occurring in the adaptation using Algorithm 2. In this case, the instability is only momementary and occurs in the adaptation loop, not as a result of instabilities in the recursive model structure itself.

$NMSE = 3.5 \times 10e - 2$. Note that it is not strictly correct to plot the MSOE contours here due to the time-varying nature of the other model parameters. For each time instant, the MSOE surface viewed in $\{b_0, b_1\}$ coordinates will be different as we move through parameter space. Hence we do not attempt to show the time-based parameter trajectories on the MSOE surface.

4   Discussion

It appears that Algorithm 1 obtains significantly improved performance for the following reasons. When an update occurs in the parameter space, there will be some small error associated with each algorithm. It is likely that one algorithm will be worse than the other. If there was a unique global minimum, this may not matter, since as long as the algorithm approximately followed the true gradient, it would converge to within some small region of the true minimum point.

In the case where there are multiple minima, the situation may be somewhat different. It is clear that from any point in parameter space, there will be a different path to the closest minimum point in the MSOE surface. Hence, if an algorithm makes a slightly incorrect step at each point, then it is conceivable that it may stray far enough away to then be drawn to converge towards another minimum, further away from the one closest to the starting point.

Hence, this suggests that for gradient descent algorithms such as these, both of which approximate the true gradient on the MSOE surface, there is a possibility that divergence and consequently poorer convergence performance may result. This problem is made more acute by the presence of the multimodal MSOE surface, resulting in the fact that a small bias in the algorithm may lead to divergence to some point far from optimal. Hence it indicates that it is most important to reduce such possible bias in these algorithms in order to ensure proper convergence.

5   Conclusions

In the foregoing analysis, we have derived FIR MLP learning algorithms based on different methods of computing the synaptic sensitivity derivative.

To compute the synaptic sensitivity derivative of a time-varying signal with respect to another time-varying signal, the assumption that $z(t) \approx z(t-1) \approx \cdots \approx z(t-k)$ may not be necessarily valid. This is in contrast to the 'trick' often used in adaptive filter algorithms where an approximation is made that $\theta(t) \approx \theta(t-1) \approx \cdots \approx \theta(t-k)$.

In the derivation of the algorithms, we approximate the true gradient direction given by the derivative of a cost function over time with respect to the parameter vector. There are a number of different methods by which the algorithms can be derived. These variations are based on different assumptions which we have described in this paper. Hence, we have indicated why one algorithm is more likely to give better results than the other.

Acknowledgements

The first author gratefully acknowledges support from the Australian Research Council and the Frontier Research Program RIKEN. The second author acknowledges partial support from the Australian Research Council.

References

[1] A.D. Back and A.C. Tsoi, "A Time Series Modelling Methodology Using FIR and IIR Synapses", Proc. Workshop on Neural Networks for Statistical and Economic Data, Dublin, DOSES, Statistical Office of European Communities, F. Murtagh (Ed.), pp. 187-194, 1990.

[2] A.D. Back and A.C. Tsoi, "FIR and IIR Synapses, a New Neural Network Architecture for Time Series Modelling". Neural Computation, vol 3. no. 3, pp. 375-385, 1991.

[3] A.D. Back, E.A. Wan, S. Lawrence, A.C. Tsoi, "A unifying view of some training algorithms for multilayer perceptrons with FIR filter synapses", Neural Networks for Signal Processing 4, J. Vlontzos, J. Hwang and E. Wilson (Eds), IEEE Press, pp. 146-154, 1994.

[4] A.D. Back and A.C. Tsoi, "Nonlinear system identification using multilayer perceptrons with locally recurrent synaptic structure", Neural Networks for Signal Processing 2 Proc. of the 1992 IEEE Workshop, S.Y. Kung, F. Fallside, J. Aa. Sorenson, C.A. Kamm (Eds), IEEE Press, New York, pp. 444-453, 1992.

[5] C.F.N. Cowan and P.M. Grant. Adaptive Filters. Prentice-Hall Englewood Cliffs, 1985.

[6] P.L. Feintuch, "An adaptive recursive LMS filter", Proc IEEE, pp. 1622-1625, 1976.

[7] A. Fettweis, "A general theorem for signal-flow networks, with applications", Arch. Elek. Übertragung, Vol 25, pp. 557-561, 1971.

[8] S. Haykin, Neural Networks. MacMillan, 1994.

[9] T.C. Hsia, "A simplified adaptive recursive filter design", Proc. IEEE, vol 69, pp. 1153-1155, 1981.

[10] C.R. Johnson and M.G. Larimore, "Comments on and additions to 'An adaptive recursive filter', " Proc. IEEE, vol. 65, no. 9, pp. 1399-1402, 1977.

[11] C.R. Johnson, "Adaptive IIR Filtering: Current Results and Open Issues", IEEE Trans. Inform. Theory, vol. 30, no. 2, pp. 237-250, 1984.

[12] A. Lapedes, and R. Farber, "Nonlinear Signal Processing using Neural Networks: Prediction and System modelling", Tech Report LA-UR87-2662, Los Alamos National Laboratory, 1987.

[13] L. Ljung, and T. Söderström, Theory and Practice of Recursive Identification, Cambridge, Massachusetts: The MIT Press, 1983.

[14] D. Parikh, N. Ahmed, and S.D. Stearns, "An Adaptive Lattice Algorithm for Recursive Filters", IEEE Trans. Acous., Speech, Signal Proc., 28, 110-111, 1980.

[15] P.A. Regalia, Adaptive IIR Filtering in Signal Processing and Control. Marcel Dekker, Inc: New York, 1995.

[16] D.E. Rumelhart, G.E. Hinton, R.J. Williams, "Learning internal representations by error propagation", in Parallel Distributed Processing, Vol 1: Foundations, D.E. Rumelhart and J.L. McClelland and the PDP Research Group, The MIT Press: Cambridge MA, 1986.

[17] J.J. Shynk, "Adaptive IIR Filters", IEEE ASSP Magazine, pp. 4-21, 1989.

[18] S.D. Stearns, G.R. Elliott and N. Ahmed, "On adaptive recursive filtering", Proc. 10th Asilomar Conference Circuits, Systems & Computers, pp. 5-11, Nov. 1976.

[19] G.B. Thomas and R.L. Finney. Calculus and Analytic Geometry, 5th Ed. Reading, MA: Addison-Wesley, 1979.

[20] A. Waibel, T. Hanazawa, G. Hinton, K. Shikano, K. Lang, "Phonemic recognition using time delay neural networks". IEEE Trans on Acoustics, Speech, and Signal Processing. Vol 37, No 3, pp 328 - 339, 1989.

[21] E.A. Wan, , "Temporal backpropagation for FIR neural networks", Proc. Int. Joint Conf. Neural Networks, San Diego, , vol I, pp 575-580, 1990

[22] S.A. White, "An Adaptive Recursive Digital Filter", Proc. Ninth Asilomar Conf. Circuits, Systems and Computers, Pacific Grove CA, pp. 21-25, 1975.

[23] B. Widrow and J.M. McCool, "Comments on 'An Adaptive Recursive LMS Filter'" Proc. IEEE, Vol. 65, No. 9, pp. 1402-1404, 1977.

[24] B. Widrow and S.D. Stearns, Adaptive Signal Processing. Prentice-Hall: Englewood Cliffs, NJ, 1985.

Estimation of taste component concentrations in a batch fermentation process

Thomas Enders, Viktor Denk

Lehrstuhl für Fluidmechanik und Prozeßautomation
Technische Universität München
85350 Freising
thomas.enders@lfp.blm.tu-muenchen.de

Abstract— **Fermentations produce a wide range of metabolites, often in small concentrations that are difficult to measure. In order to obtain an alternative to direct measurements, a software sensor based on neural networks with internal FIR filters has been developed for the estimation of diacetyl and its precursors during beer production. Only comparatively easily ˝measurable physical and chemical parameters are used as inputs. Results demonstrating the feasibility of this approach will be shown.**

1   Introduction

Diacetyl is a taste component in beer which causes an off-flavor when its concentration is higher than a threshold of about 0.1 mg/l. The result is the familiar smell and taste of fresh butter, which is, however, undesirable in beer.

Diacetyl is an indirect byproduct of the yeast metabolism. The yeast produces a number of substances (precursors) during the main phase of the fermentation which then convert to diacetyl through a relatively slow chemical reaction mainly controlled by temperature and pH. During the maturation process, diacetyl is actively converted by the yeast to a substance that does not cause an off-flavor. Figure 1 shows a typical course of a fermentation with diacetyl in relation to other important ˝parameters.

During fermentation and maturation, both diacetyl and its precursors are present in the wort. Therefore, the interesting parameter to be measured or estimated is the diacetyl concentration after conversion of all precursors. In this paper, *diacetyl concentration* refers to the concentration after complete conversion of all ˝precursors.

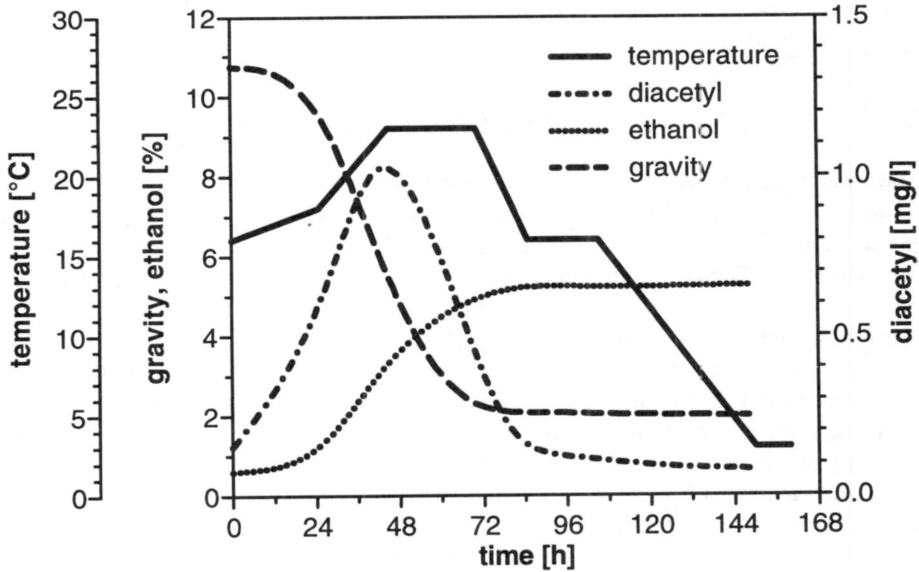

Figure 1. Important parameters during a beer fermentation

In practical operation, the determination of the diacetyl concentration is of great importance, because the next process phase (cold storage) is not started before the diacetyl concentration drops below the threshold of 0.1 mg/l mentioned above.

2 Measurement

The current state of the art in measurement technology for diacetyl and many other taste components is off-line laboratory analysis. In the case of diacetyl, conversion of the precursors to diacetyl (90 minutes at 60 °C) is necessary, followed by analysis with a gas chromatograph using the headspace method. This method was also used to obtain the data shown here.
Major drawbacks of this measurement method are the high cost due to expensive laboratory equipment, and manual sample pretreatment and handling. In addition, there is a delay of several hours before results are available. Therefore, on-line (closed-loop) control methods can not make use of this important parameter. A typical situation in practical operation is to take samples in the morning, process the samples during the day and have the results available on the next day. This frequently leads to a prolonged production time while waiting for the measurement data proving the diacetyl to be below "the threshold value.
The existing laboratory equipment cannot be adapted easily to on-line operation in the rough industrial environment (automated sampling and pretreatment, low maintenance, etc.) and alternative methods for on-line measurement are currently not available. Developments based for example on enzyme reactions failed due to a lack of specificity for diacetyl in presence of similar substances "(as in beer).

3 Estimation

A possible alternative to direct measurement is estimation. Readily measurable process parameters are used to obtain partial knowledge of the current state of the fermentation. This information is then taken and fed into the software sensor to estimate the current diacetyl "concentration (see figure 2).

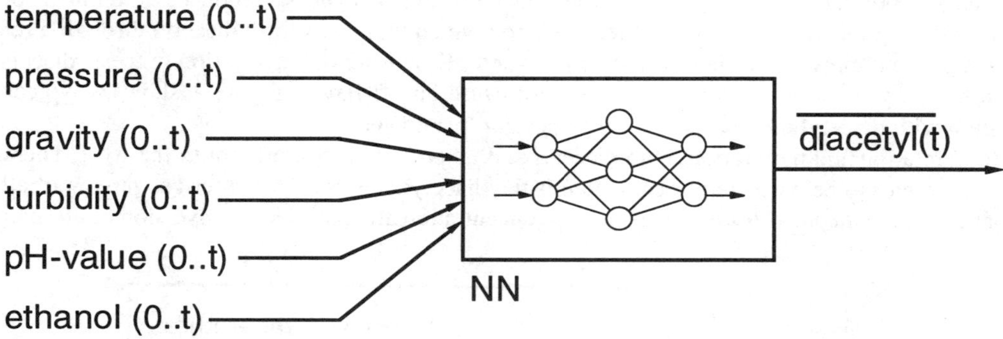

Figure 2. Inputs used for diacetyl estimation.

To be able to estimate the diacetyl concentration, the software sensor needs a model of the dynamic properties of the process with respect to the diacetyl development. The "metabolic pathways that lead to diacetyl production are fairly well understood (see above), but the dynamics of this biological process are unknown, especially in a production environment. Therefore, neural networks are used to deduce these properties from available measurements.
Due to the complex nature of the process, a complete state description of the process would include hundreds of parameters, many of which involve intracellular biochemical concentrations which are even more difficult to obtain than the diacetyl concentration. As the point of the software sensor is to estimate the diacetyl concentration from simple measurements, these parameters are not determined, and only partial state information is available. This suggests the inclusion of all available measurements "from the start of the batch up to the current point in time to allow the software sensor to make the best possible use of the available data, i.e. to reconstruct part of the unknown process state internally.
There are many ways to make this information accessible for the "neural network. Here, internal FIR filters were incorporated in the neural network. Starting from a multilayer perceptron, each weight was replaced by an FIR filter (tapped delay line). In addition, all feedforward connections in the network were included (see the example in figure 3).
Supervised training with the sum of squared errors as error "measure was used to adapt the neural network. Gradient information was obtained with the IC-1 (instantaneous "cost, instantaneous gradient) algorithm [1], weight updates were calculated with the RPROP algorithm [2].

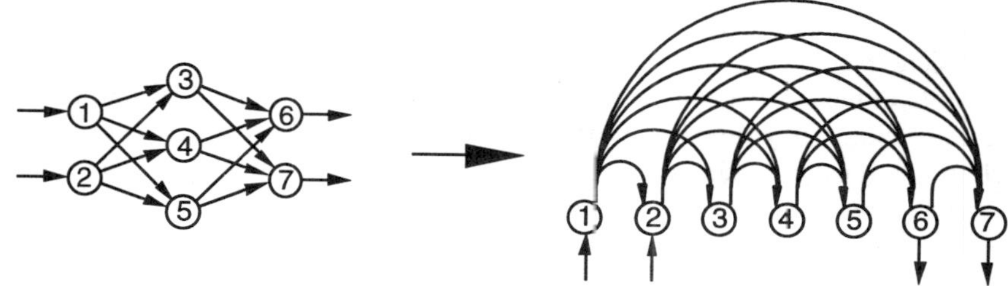

Figure 3. Example for the network structure used in the software ˜sensor.

4   Results

The choices for gradient calculation with the IC-1 algorithm and weight updates with RPROP were based on accumulated experience. For the problem at hand, IC-1 and RPROP yielded good results in terms of training time and convergence stability.

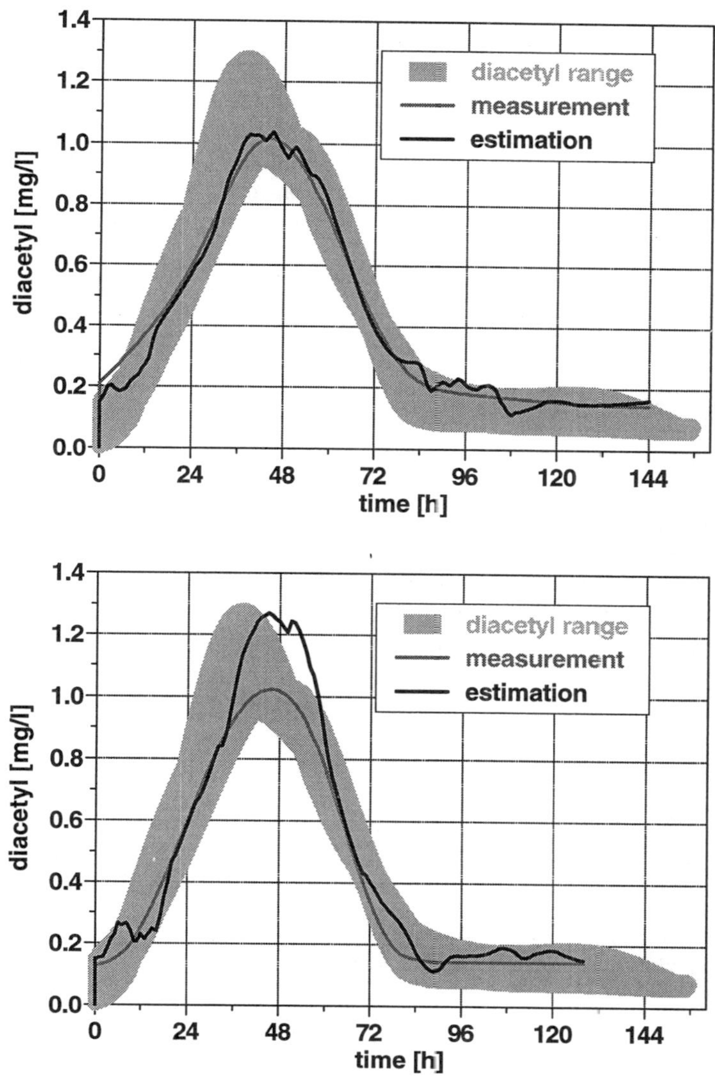

Figure 4: comparison of measurement, estimation, and variability ˜of diacetyl concentrations

The results reported here were obtained with data from the project on closed-loop control and optimization of the fermentation [3]. Experiments were run in a pilot scale plant (150l per batch) and in an industrial plant (250000l per batch). Figure 4 gives two seperate examples of a comparison between measurement (not used during training), the corresponding estimation, and the normal range of diacetyl concentrations in production. For these examples, data from the production fermenter was used.

These and other results indicate sufficient accuracy of the estimation for practical purposes. Important considerations are the time of the diacetyl maximum (the height of the maximum is less relevant), and the time when diacetyl drops below the threshold value of 0.1 mg/l. This information can be used to switch to the maturation phase and to the cold storage phase, respectively. Natural variation and the necessary safety margins lead to delays in the process by up to one day. The software sensor is able to reduce this uncertainty (see below) and thus reduce the necessary total process time (see applications below).

5 Applications

In order to judge the applicability of a software sensor properly, it has of course to be noted that an estimation can never be a full replacement for a real measurement. In many cases, however, the accuracy and reliability of a software sensor is sufficient for practical applications.

With the current situation of measurement technology in mind, there are a number of possible applications. In process supervision, the software sensor can be used to obtain better knowledge of the course of the process through ongoing observation of the diacetyl concentration. Laboratory analyses to confirm the level of diacetyl being below the threshold value can then be run at the point in time suggested by the software sensor. This reduces the number of necessary analyses and prevents wasted process time. Breweries without the necessary laboratory equipment receive a means to determine the end of the maturation phase based on the current state of the process (which was not available before).

In connection with modeling, closed-loop control, and optimization of the overall process [3], the software sensor leads to further improvements by supplying low-cost on-line diacetyl concentration estimates. These values can then be used for closed-loop control of this taste component, resulting in more consistent end product quality. The process optimization uses the software sensor in the adaptive process model to include diacetyl in its long-term predictions of the further course of the process. In turn, this model is used to optimize the course of the fermentation for each batch individually and to obtain the desired quality in the shortest possible time. Finally, the predictions of the total process time for each batch allow for better production scheduling.

6 Future Work

With the work presented here, the feasibility of the software sensor for diacetyl was shown using measurements from actual production runs and a pilot plant. The next steps will be to determine whether some of the parameters (especially the ethanol concentration) are dispensable, while the necessary accuracy can still be maintained. In addition, the robustness of the software sensor against problems in real-world applications (missing data, unexpected disturbances, confidence measures for the estimates), deviating estimates such as in the second part of figure 4, and the integration of the software sensor in the closed-loop control and optimization project will be investigated further.

References

[1] A.D. Back, E.A. Wan, S. Lawrence and A.C. Tsoi, "A unifying view of some training algorithms for multilayer perceptrons with FIR filter synapses", *Neural Networks for Signal Processing 4, Proc. of the 1994 IEEE Workshop*, J. Vlontzos, J. Hwang and E. Wilson (Eds.), IEEE Press, pp. 146-154, 1994.

[2] M. Riedmiller, H. Braun, "A Direct Adaptive Method for Faster Backpropagation Learning: The RPROP Algorithm", *Proceedings of the IEEE International Conference on Neural Networks*, San Francisco, CA, March 1993

[3] Th. Enders, U. Hege, U. Peters, V. Denk, "Neural Networks and Fuzzy Logic for Modeling, Control, and Optimization of a Batch Fermentation Process", *Proceedings of the World Congress on Neural Networks*, Washington DC, July 17-21, 1995, Vol. 2, pp. 652-655.

This project was supported by the science foundation of the German brewing industry under contract no. R318 and by the Fleischmann Foundation.

The invited program is also featured by 8 special sessions on current interesting topics. Each special session organizer is invited by the Program Committee and the success of each special session is completely due to the hard efforts of each organizer.

Two-Dimensional Object Recognition Based on a Modified Genetic Algorithm

S. K. LIM, H. C. SIM, K. C. WONG†
Centre for Graphics and Imaging Technology,
School of Applied Science,
Nanyang Technological University,
Nanyang Avenue,
Singapore 639798

†*Email : askcwong@ntuvax.ntu.ac.sg*

Abstract— **This paper presents a novel framework of a model-based object recognition system based on a modified Genetic Algorithm (GA) for recognising two-dimensional arbitrary shapes subjected to Euclidean transformation and partial occlusion. A reference table comprising of model-scene vertex pairs is generated by comparing the angles of the extracted model and scene vertices. Having identified a pool of model-scene vertex pairs encoded in the genes, a modified GA is developed to search for significant chromosomes where each chromosome comprises of a clique of compatible genes depicting the instance of an object model. A geometric compatibility constraint is devised to facilitate the assembly process of the compatible genes in a chromosome. A fitness function is proposed to evaluate the confidence measure of the transformation values computed from the compatible genes for mapping the model to the scene. A remapped fitness function and novel grouping mechanism are derived to increase the survival of the significant chromosomes and yet avoid premature convergence. The effectiveness and robustness of the proposed GA-based recognition system are verified with experimental results.**

1   Introduction

Recognition of 2D arbitrary shapes from an unconstrained environment based on a single gray-intensity image is a non-trivial task. This is because the acquired image is generally very noisy as a result of complex surface markings, uncontrolled lighting condition and occlusion caused by other irrelevant shapes. Hence, the number of model-scene combinations to be considered is huge and grows exponentially as the number of features increases. Some researchers attempted to solve the correspondence problem using GA. Nagao et al. [4] developed a method based on GA for extracting 2D arbitrary shapes. One of the major limitation of their method is that a scaling factor bound must be pre-specified based on the prior knowledge of the given scene. Furthermore, the pixels of extracted edges are employed as key features of which this type is abundant and omnipresent in the image. As a result, the process of establishing the model-to-scene corresponding pixels is computationally expensive. Hill and Taylor [2] applied GA to extract the delineation of left ventricular boundaries using ultrasound images of the heart. A flexible template model is described by a total of ten model parameters of which each set represents an instantiation of transformed model encoded in a chromsome. GA is applied to seek for potential hypotheses associated to high fitness function by exploiting different groups of model parameters encoded in the chromosomes. We envisage the method is restricted to simple objects, as very long chromosomes are required for encoding the model parameters. Furthermore, it is a non-trivial task to manually select appropriate range for large number of model parameters. We also anticipate that the result of the interpretation and convergence rate of the chromosomes are very sensitive to the initial values of the model parameters. Our proposed recognition system does not have the shortcomings of the abovementioned GA-based recognition systems.

Our aim is to develop a recognition system for identifying and localising arbitrary 2D shapes undergone Euclidean transformation, subjected to clutter scene and partial occlusion. To accomplish this task, a matching paradigm based on a modified GA is proposed and implemented. The modified GA is proposed and integrated into the recognition framework for seeking significant chromosomes where each chromosome comprises of a clique of compatible genes depicting the instance of an object model. Effective schemes such as remapping fitness function and grouping mechanism are proposed and developed to further enhance the performance of the GA-based recognition system. Having generated a pool of potential hypotheses associated to the significant chromosomes, a simple clustering and verification process are employed to identify the best hypothesis. Generally, the success rate of the GA-based recognition system for identifying and localising 2D shapes is relatively high.

2 Contributions

Our contributions lie in the development and integration of a modified genetic algorithm into the framework of a recognition system. Some of the main contributions of the proposed system can be summarized as follow :

- A gene represents a feasible model-scene vertex correspondence of which the angles of the vertices are matched up to a certain threshold. Using this representation, the search space is curtailed to only the correspondences associated to feasible model and scene vertices. The size of such search space is generally much smaller than the search space formed by exhaustive combinations of model and scene vertices or search space formed without using priori knowledge of effective visual clues.

- An effective fitness function of a chromosome is devised by incorporating both the size of clique length and the goodness of the model-to-scene transformation among the genes within a clique. A clique of a chromosome is formed by grouping 3 or more genes whose transformation values are geometrically compatible.

- To avoid the majority of the insignificant genes taking over a large proportion of the roulette wheel, an effective remapped fitness function is devised and integrated into the genetic-based search methods for increasing the exploration of the minority but significant chromosomes in the population at the early generations. A sigmoid function with designated parameter values is devised for increasing the exploration of chromosomes of clique length 3 and above in the early generations.

- To balance between exploration and exploition of chromosomes, an adaptive grouping mechanism is developed to confine the evolution of chromosomes within narrower regions measured with the model-to-scene rotation transformations. This will increase the rate of forming longer cliques with consensus rotation transformations.

- The predicted performance merits of the proposed system have been verified by experimental results. Test scene images acquired under different configurations and working conditions are employed to investigate the convergence rate of the total fitness value, adaptability of the remapped fitness function and reliability of the pose estimation for different signal-to-noise ratio.

3 Framework of the Proposed 2D Recognition System

Three modules namely, generation of model-scene vertex pairs, establishment of plausible model-scene vertex correspondences using a modified GA and verification process are implemented and integrated to our recognition system. The operations of these modules will be presented in the following subsections.

3.1 Generation of Model-Scene Vertex Pair Reference Table

The spatial relationships of the vertex features are used as bases for the constraint of search space of the transformation between the model and scene object. To maximise the utilisation of visual cues and increase the robustness of the recognition system, virtual vertices are also employed in the matching process. A virtual vertex is formed by extending the straight line segments to intersect another straight line segment or extended straight line segment.

Every pair of model and scene vertices whose difference in their angles is less than a certain predefined threshold value, is stored in a reference table which we called Model-to-Scene Vertex Pair Reference Table (MSVPRT). Each of the model-scene vertex pairs in the MSVPRT will be copied and employed as a gene of a chromosome in the population.

3.2 Establishment of Plausible Model-Scene Correspondences Using a modified GA

In this section, we will explain the formulation of the recognition problems into a structure which facilitates the exploition of the modified GA. The operations of population, evaluation and reproduction modules for establishing plausible model-scene feature correspondences depicting the instance of an object model are presented.

3.2.1   Population Module

Each chromosome is designated to represent a group of model-scene correspondences depicting an instance of an object model. As the number of geometrically compatible genes increases, it characterises the likelihood of an instance of the target object. Thus the probability of acquiring more compatible genes in a chromosome of longer fixed length will be higher than those shorter ones. However, the generation of longer chromosome will result in increased computations while too short a chromosome will introduce many unreliable hypotheses with weak evidence. Experimentally, a length of 8 designated for our application has been realised to be reasonably effective for eliminating many unreliable hypotheses without introducing too much computation overhead.

During the creation of chromosomes using the genes in the MSVPRT, a checking mechanism is implemented to ensure that the genes within a chromosome should not be conflicting each other. Two genes are said to be conflicting if an identical vertex feature is found in these genes. Obviously, conflicting genes should not be employed for the creation of a valid chromosome as a model vertex should not be matched to more than one scene vertex for an instance of an object model.

In this implementation, the size of the population is fixed at 1000. This means that there is a total of 1000 chromosomes representing 8000 genes at each generation. Our population size of 1000 chromosomes are sufficient to accomplish the recognition tasks in all the experiments and also likely for most of the practical scenes.

3.2.2   Evaluation Module

In this section, the formulation of the fitness function of a chromosome is described in detail. As each chromosome is designated to represent an instance of the object model, the information encoded in the genes must reflect how well their derived transformation values for mapping the model to the target scene. Furthermore, the quality of the estimated pose for a hypothesis should also be embedded in the fitness function.

Intuitively, if the correspondences in a chromosome belong to an instant of the model object, the transformation values in terms of scaling, rotation and translation should be homogeneous when these values are derived from any two genes within the chromosome. This forms the basis for the derivation of the fitness function of a chromosome. The fitness function is developed and integrated to the modified GA in a way to facilitate the assembly process of genes that have similar transformations in a chromosome. In the subsequence, a clique is referred to a collection of genes in a chromosome which have similar transformation and the number of such genes in the clique is termed as clique length. Next, the formation and growing process of a clique is described.

Geometric Compatibility for Formation of Clique

A clique is formed by grouping genes of which the differences in model-to-scene transformation values for rotation, scaling and translations are smaller than some pre-specified threshold values. The genes of a chromosome will be selected to form a clique only if the Euclidean transformation values computed from their associated combination triplets of model-scene vertex correspondences are equal up to a maximum allowable error.

Fitness Function

The aim of the fitness function is to assign a value to the clique of a chromosome so that the fittest chromosome will be procreated in the next generation. The proposed fitness function given in Eq. 1 has two components : one component assesses in term of clique length while the other assesses in term of normalised average transformation accuracy of triplet genes in the clique.

$$fit(ch_k) = \lambda \frac{\| U_k \|}{\| ch \|} + (1 - \lambda) \frac{\Delta\Theta + \Delta A + \Delta D_x + \Delta D_y}{4} \tag{1}$$

where λ : contribution bias between clique length and total transformation accuracies

     $\| U_k \|$: clique length

     $\| ch \|$: the chromosome length

$\Delta\Theta$: the accuracy of rotational transformation
ΔA : the accuracy of scaling transformation
ΔD_x : the accuracy in horizontal translation transformation
ΔD_y : the accuracy in vertical translation transformation

A pair of genes in the clique will give a transformation value in term of rotation, scaling and translation. The accuracy of the transformation refers to the average differences in transformation values computed from every possible pair of genes in the clique of the chromosome. We set λ at 0.7 to give more bias to the clique length for this implementation.

Remapped Fitness Function

In our framework, the generation of the initial population of chromosomes are formed by randomly grouping of genes from the MSVPRT. Therefore, the initial population is likely to comprise of many more chromosomes of two or less compatible genes within a chromosome than those of three or more compatible genes. Under this situation, the majority of the insignificant genes would take over a significant proportion of the roulette wheel using a normal selection rule. Hence, the few significant chromosomes of three or more compatible genes would unlikely to survive in the population of the subsequent generation. This results in either a random searching process or a slow total fitness covergence rate. To overcome this problem, a remapped fitness function is devised based on the following requirements :

- The geometric compatibility constraint is implemented to seek for at least three compatible genes. Hence, a significant increase in the mapped fitness value between a chromosome with clique length of 2 or less and a chromosome with clique length of 3 or more is necessary.

- Chromosomes with clique length of 6 or more are likely to describe the same instance of a target 2D shape, hence the difference in their mapped fitness values should be relatively small.

Having considered the above requirements, the following sigmoid curve is devised as a remapped fitness function $refit$:

$$refit(ch_k) = \frac{1}{1 + Aexp[-B(fit(ch_k) - C)]} \tag{2}$$

with the following designated parameters : $A = 80$ $B = 20$ $C = fit(2)/B$ where $fit(2) = 0.175$ is the fitness value computed using Eq. 1 with $\lambda = 0.7, \| U_k \| = 2$ and $\| ch \| = 8$. Generally, this designed function gives acceptable results for many experiments in recognising 2D shapes.

3.2.3   Reproduction Module

After undergoing the evaluation module, each chromosome in the population will be assigned a remapped fitness value according to Eq. 2. The remapped fitness value of a chromosome determines the probability of the chromosome being selected as a parent for the reproduction of offsprings for the next generation. A *roulette wheel selection scheme* [3] is used for the selection process. A single point crossover is implemented where the crossover site is selected to be at the end of the longest clique (x) of a parent chromosome and at (chromosome length - x) of the other parent chromosome. Genes are swapped between the opposite ends of the parent chromosomes. This crossover technique combines the good genes of both parent chromosomes into a single offspring to increase the probability of forming longer clique. The mutation operator is applied to remove conflicting genes in the chromosome. Conflicting genes refer to identical vertices found in a chromosome.

Proposed Grouping Mechanism

Logically if the selection process is performed among chromosomes with homogeneous model-to-scene rotations, the chances of converging to the optimum solutions will be faster. Hence we applied this heuristic into our genetic algorithm by introducing a grouping algorithm. The search space is divided into four equal quadrants of $90°$ each. Each chromosome is categorised into one of these quadrants according to the rotation value computed from the genes of its clique. Selection is performed within each group of quadrant until the same number of chromosomes in the quadrant are reproduced into the new generation. In order not to reduce the diversity of the GA search, this grouping algorithm is implemented to be initiated only after half of the chromosomes in the population have formed clique with a minimum length of 3.

3.3 Verification Process

As the cliques of many chromosomes carry similar transformation values, a clustering process is used to group the chromosomes with homogeneous transformation values. The strongest chromosome of each cluster is used to form a hypothesis for verification. A simple model-scene vertex correlation method is implemented to compute the confidence measure of the plausible hypotheses. The hypothesis with the highest confidence measure is deemed to be the optimal solution. The match result is shown by super-imposed the model on the scene using the transformation of the hypothesis with the highest confidence measure.

4 Experimental Results

4.1 Experiment 1 - Complex Image of a Cartoon Mouse Face

Images of a 2D flat cartoon mouse face and the test scene are shown in Fig. 1(a) and (c), respectively. It should be noted that both the model and test scene have highly complex surface marking. As a result, many curve contours were extracted from the images of the model and test scene shown in Fig. 1(b) and (d) respectively. The length and orientation of the straight lines extracted by applying polygonal approximation on the edge contours are highly sensitive to the quality of the images and low level processes, hence many of the vertices extracted from the curve contours were either prone to error or missing due to the undersampling effect of scaling. The aim of this experiment is to study both the computational efficiency and robustness of the system for dealing with scene comprising of huge number of error-prone vertices computed by polygonal approximation.

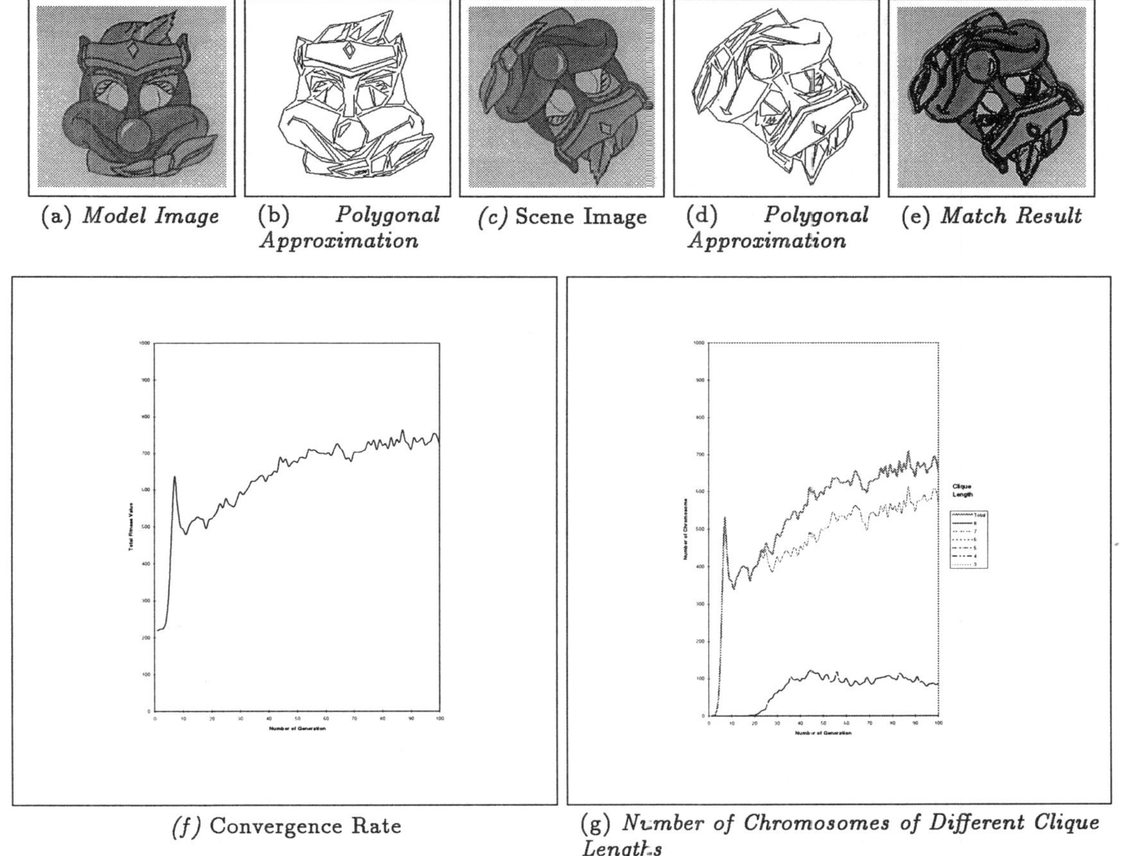

(a) *Model Image* (b) *Polygonal Approximation* (c) Scene Image (d) *Polygonal Approximation* (e) *Match Result*

(f) Convergence Rate

(g) *Number of Chromosomes of Different Clique Lengths*

Figure 1: Recognition of a Complex Face Image

Fig. 1(f) shows that the convergence rate of the chromosomes in the population. At the end of 100 generations, there are about 55% and 10% of the population are chromosomes with clique length of 3 and 4 respectively (see Fig 1(g)). The remaining portion of chromosomes are insignificant. No chromosomes of clique length of 5 or above was found in the population. There are two reasons for the slow convergence rate and low total fitness value of the population. First, this is because many of the vertices extracted from the curve contours for forming the model-scene correspondences were inaccurate. The second reason is the total number of model-scene correspondences is very much greater than the maximum allowable number of model-scene correspondences (i.e. 8000 genes) evoluted among a population for each generation. More explicitly, there are 62389 model-scene correspondences stored in the MSVPRT. Hence, the probability of generating chromosomes of long clique length is low.

Upon termination of the GA iteration, 9 clusters of homogeneous cliques are found in the last generation. The best chromosome of each cluster formed a hypothesis for verification. The final match generated by the hypothesis with the highest confidence measure is shown in Fig. 1(e). The quality of the match can be easily verified from the small misalignment of the superimposed model.

4.2 Experiment 2 - A Real Complex Scene

The aim of this experiment is to study the performance and practicability of the system for recognising real objects subjected to Euclidean transformation and occlusion. The real object model employed in this experiment is a pair of scissors with reflective metallic surface (see Fig. 2(a)). In order to maintain the stability of reference model, the spurious edge contours caused by shadow of the pair of scissors were manually removed from the approximated polygons computed from the edge map. Fig. 2(b) shows the cleanup version of the model represented by approximated polygons. To test the robustness of the system, the pair of scissors was subjected to Euclidean transformation with occlusion and surrounded by many real objects (see 2(c)). Many of the long straight line segments of the pair of scissors computed from the edge map of the scene were broken due to the occlusions by other objects (see Fig. 2(d)).

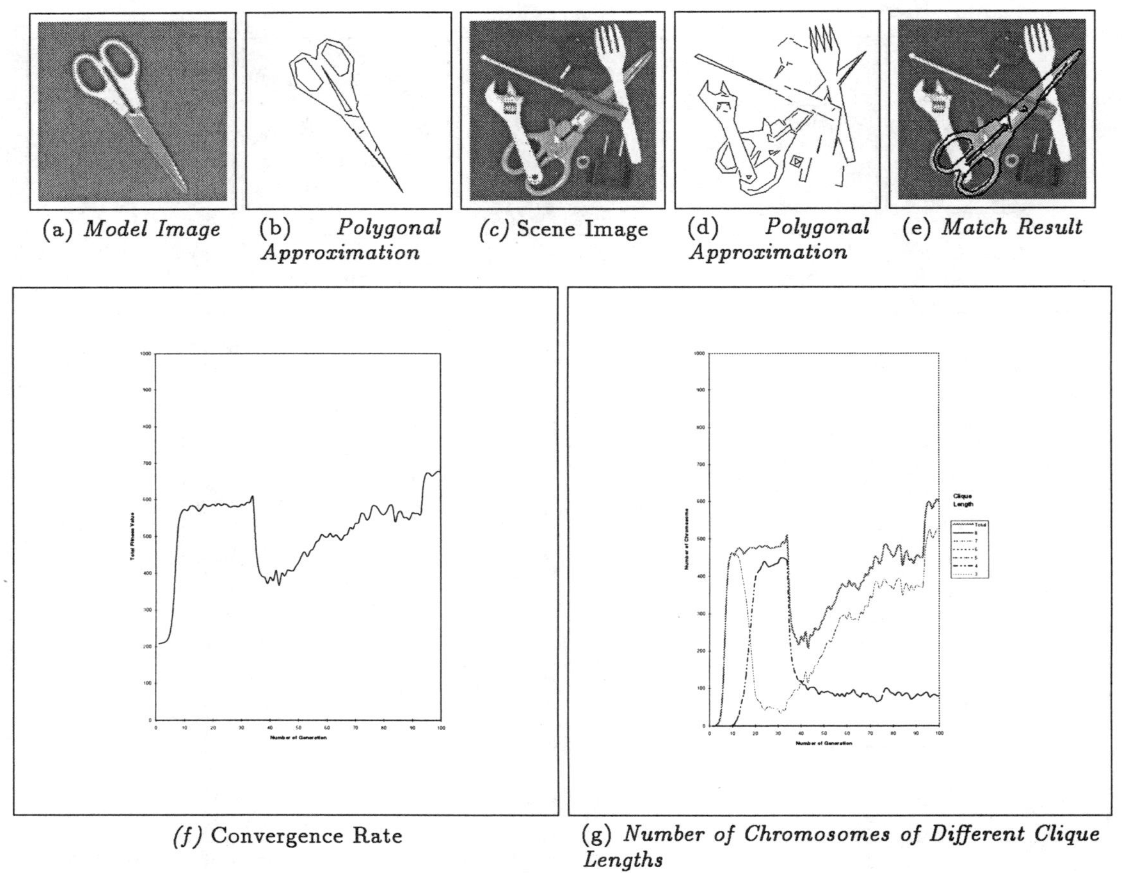

(a) *Model Image* (b) *Polygonal Approximation* (c) Scene Image (d) *Polygonal Approximation* (e) *Match Result*

(f) Convergence Rate (g) *Number of Chromosomes of Different Clique Lengths*

Figure 2: Recognition of a Real Complex Scene

Fig. 2(f) shows that the convergence rate of the total fitness value of the population. Between the 10th and 33th generations, the total fitness value of the population remains almost constant. This is because the almost same set of chromosomes of clique length of 3 and 4 were evolved in the population during this generation period (see Fig. 2(g)). All the chromosomes in the population have short clique length (i.e. less than 5). This is because many of the model-scene vertex correpondences in the reference table were formed by spurious and irrelevant straight line segments extracted from the scene. At the 34th generation, the total fitness value of the population exceeds 500. At this point, the grouping process starts to confine the evolution of chromosomes within each quadrant. Fig. 2(f) shows that the total fitness value of the entire population is reduced significantly at a rapid rate compared to the previous experiment. This is because almost all the chromosomes of clique length of 3 and 4 were being categorized into the same quadrant during the grouping process. As a result, nearly half of the chromosomes of clique length of 3 and 4 were destroyed after the crossover operations were applied within the quadrant. After the grouping process, the total fitness value of the chromosomes in the population gradually increases and ends at the 100th generation with a total fitness value greater than the plateau value between the 10th and 35th generations.

Eight hypotheses are generated from the last (100th) generation. The verification process detects 7 additional feasible scene vertices for the hypothesis with the highest confidence measure. The superimposed image generated from this hypothesis is shown in Fig. 2(e). In this experiment, the scissor was sucessfully identified and located from the complex scene image using the proposed GA-based matching strategies.

5 Conclusions

In this paper, we have described a model-based recognition system for recognising 2D arbitrary shapes undergone Euclidean transformation, surrounded by irrelevant features and subjected to partial occlusion. The framework of the proposed 2D model-based recognition system using a modified GA has been presented. The main contributions of the proposed paradigm have been summarized. The establishment of cliques of model and scene vertex correspondances have been achieved using the proposed paradigms based on a modified genetic algorithm. A simple clustering process has been integrated into the system for grouping of chromosomes of consensus model-to-scene transformation. Generally, manageable number of potential hypotheses associated to the best chromosome of each cluster are generated after the clustering process. Finally, the confidence measures of the plausible hypotheses are computed using a simple model-scene vertex correlation method. The hypothesis associated to the highest confidence measure is selected as the final match.

The performance merits of the proposed system have been verified by experiments comprising of images subjected to Euclidean transformation and partial occlusion. A number of observations have been drawn and explained for the experiments. The accuracy of the estimated pose is acceptable for practical applications. This has been demonstrated by superimposing the transformed model onto the scene image using the estimated pose of the hypothesis with the highest confidence measure.

References

[1] D. E. Goldberg, Genetic Algorithms in Search, Optimization and Machine Learning, *Addison-Wesley, Reading, Mass.*, 1989.

[2] A. Hill and C. J. Taylor, Model-based image interpretation using genetic algorithms *Image and Vision Computing*, Vol 10, No. 5, June 1992, pp 295-300

[3] J. H. Holland, Adaptation in Natural and Artificial Systems, *Ann Arbor: The Univerisity of Michigan Press*, 1975.

[4] Tomoharu Nagao, Takeshi Agui and Hiroshi Nagahashi Extraction of two-dimensional arbitrary shapes using genetic algorithm, SPIE, Vol 2094, pp 74-82, 1993

A Markov Chain Analysis of Premature Convergence in Genetic Algorithms

Yee Leung†, Yong Gao‡ and Zongben Xu‡

† Department of Geography and Centre for Environmental Studies
The Chinese University of Hong Kong, Hong Kong
‡ Institute for Information and System Sciences, Faculty of Science
Xi'an Jiaotong University, Xi'an, P.R.China

Abstract— **In this paper a concept of degree of population diversity is introduced to quantitatively characterize and theoretically analyze the problem of premature convergence in genetic algorithms (GAs) within the Markov chain framework.Under the assumption that the mutation probability is zero, the search ability of the GAs is discussed. It is proved that the degree of population diversity converges to zero with probability 1 so that the search ability of a genetic algorithm (GA) decreases and premature convergence occurs. Moreover, an explicit formula for the conditional probability of allele loss at a certain bit position is established to show the relationships between premature convergence and the GA parameters such as population size,mutation probability and some population statistics. The formula also partly answers the questions of to where a GA most likely converges . The theoretical results are all supported by the simulation experiments.**

1   Introduction

Genetic algorithms(GAs) are search and optimization algorithms based on the principles of natural evolution [1]. In applying GAs to solve large-scale and complex real-world problems, the most frequent difficulty encountered is problem of premature convergence [2],[3]. While many heuristic methods have been proposed to combat premature convergence in GAs [4],[5],[6],[7], a critical problem is the identification of premature convergence and the characterization of its extent. The term "population diversity" has been qualitatively used in many papers to study premature convergence [9],[10],[11]. It is widely recognized that the decrease of population diversity leads directly to premature convergence. However, so far there exists no effort in performing quantitative analysis of population diversity, let alone to use it as a tool to prevent premature convergence.

In this paper, we formally propose a concept of degree of population diversity and quantitatively characterize and theoretically analyze the problem of premature convergence in GAs using the theory of Markov chain. Under the assumption of zero mutation probability , the search ability of GAs (in particular, the function of the crossover operator) is discussed. It is proved that the degree of population diversity converges to zero with probability 1 so that the search ability of genetic algorithms decreases constantly and premature convergence occurs. The relationships between premature convergence and the GA parameters such as population size, mutation probability and relevant population statistics are also studied in light of an explicit formula for the conditional probability of allele loss at a certain gene position. The proposed formula is also employed to partly answer the question of to where a GA most likely converges.

2 Canonical Genetic Algorithms and Their Population Markov Chain

Without loss of generality, we consider the GAs with binary string representations of length l and fixed population size N. We further assume that the algorithms use proportional selection, one-point crossover and usual bit mutation. Each individual in the population corresponds to an element of the space $S = \{0,1\}^l$ which is called the individuals space. The population space is denoted as S^N and we call S^2 the parents space. For the sake of convenience, we write the population $\vec{X} \in S^N$ in both the vector and matrix forms as follows:

$$\vec{X} = (X_1, X_2, ..., X_N)^T = \begin{pmatrix} x_{11}\ x_{12}...x_{1l} \\ x_{21}\ x_{22}...x_{2l} \\ .... \\ x_{N1}\ x_{N2}...x_{Nl} \end{pmatrix},$$

where $X_i \in S$ is the ith individual of $\vec{X}$, while x_{ij} is the jth component of X_i. The fitness function $f : S \longrightarrow R^+$ can be derived from the objective function of the optimization problem by a certain decoding rule.

A canonical genetic algorithm (CGA) can in essence be given as follows.

CGA

Step 1:　Set $k = 0$ and generate initial population $\vec{X}(0)$;

Step 2:　Independently select N pairs of individuals from the current population for reproduction;

Step 3:　Independently perform crossover to the N pairs of individuals to generate N new intermediate individuals;

Step 4:　Independently mutate the N intermediate individuals to get the next generation

$$\vec{X}(k + 1) = (X_1(k + 1), \cdots, X_N(k + 1));$$

Step 5:　Stop if some stopping criterion is met. Else, set k=k+1 and go to Step 2.

It is easy to see that the sequence of populations $\{\vec{X}(k),\ k \geq 0\}$ is a time-homogeneous Markov chain with the state space S^N (henceforth it is called the population Markov chain). Similar to Rudoph [12], it can be proved that if the mutation probability $p_m \geq 0$, the population Markov chain $\{\vec{X}(k), k \geq 0\}$ is homogeneous, irreducible and aperiodic. Hence it can reach any state infinite times with probability 1 regardless of the initial state. Theoretically this means that the CGAs will never converge and premature convergence cannot occur provided that the mutation probability is larger than zero.

3 Degree of Population Diversity and its Markov Chain Analysis

In this section, we first propose and define a concept called "degree of population diversity" as a way to formalize the notion of population diversity which has never been rigorously characterized in the literature. We then use the concept to study , in conjunction with the basic GA operators, the problem of premature convergence in CGAs within the Markov chain framework.

Definition 3.1　Let $\vec{X} = (X_1, \cdots, X_N) \in S^N$ be a population. The degree of population diversity of $\vec{X}$, denoted by $\lambda(\vec{X})$, is defined as the number of the components of the vector $\sum_{i=1}^{N} X_i$ whose values are not equal to 0 and N. Accordingly , $\beta(\vec{X}) = l - \lambda(\vec{X})$ is called the degree of maturity of the population $\vec{X}$.

A schema $\mathbf{L}$ ([5]) is a subspace of the individual space S and can be represented as

$$\mathbf{L} = \{X = (x_1, \cdots, x_l) \in S; \; x_{i_k} = a_{i_k}, 1 \le i_k \le l, 1 \le k \le K\},$$

where $K \; (1 \le K \le l)$ is called the order of $\mathbf{L}$, $\{i_1, \cdots, i_K\}$ are called the defining components (defining gene positions), and $\{a_{i_k}, 1 \le k \le K\}(a_{i_k} \in \{0, 1\})$ are the values of the defining components (defining alleles) . To signify $\mathbf{L}$ by its defining components and their corresponding values, we may denote $\mathbf{L}$ as $\mathbf{L}(a_{i_1}, \cdots, a_{i_k})$. It is obvious that a schema of order K contains 2^{l-K} different individuals.

Definition 3.2   Let $\vec{X} = (X_1, \cdots, X_N) \in S^N$ be a population with the degree of population diversity $\lambda(\vec{X})$ and the degree of maturity $\beta(\vec{X}) = l - \lambda(\vec{X})$. Let $i_k, 1 \le k \le \beta(\vec{X})$ be the components at which all the individuals of $\vec{X}$ take the same values, say $a_{i_k} \in \{0, 1\}$, $1 \le k \le \beta(\vec{X})$. We call the schema $\mathbf{L}(a_{i_1}, \cdots, a_{i_{\beta(\vec{X})}})$ the minimum schema containing $\vec{X}$ and denote it by $\mathbf{L}(a_{i_1}, \cdots, a_{i_{\beta(\vec{X})}}; \vec{X})$ or simply $\mathbf{L}(\vec{X})$ if there is no confusion.

To evaluate the effect of population diversity on CGA performance , we first assume that the mutation probability is zero. The following theorem characterizes the search ability of CGAs with the mutation probability $p_m = 0$.

Theorem 3.1 Let $\{\vec{X}(k), k \ge 0\}$ be the population Markov chain with $p_m = 0$ and let $\vec{X}(0) = \vec{X}_0$.

(a)   For each $Y \in \mathbf{L}(a_{i_1}, \cdots, a_{i_{\beta(\vec{X}_0)}}; \vec{X}_0)$, there exists an $n \ge 0$ such that

$$P\{Y \in \vec{X}(n) / \vec{X}(0) = \vec{X}_0\} > 0 \tag{1}$$

(b)   For each $Y \notin \mathbf{L}(a_{i_1}, \cdots, a_{i_{\beta(\vec{X}_0)}}; \vec{X}_0)$ and every $n \ge 0$,

$$P\{Y \in \vec{X}(n) / \vec{X}(0) = \vec{X}_0\} = 0. \tag{2}$$

Remark 1 Theorem 3.1 shows that the search ability of CGAs with $p_m = 0$ is confined to the minimum schema containing the current population in which there are $2^{\lambda(\vec{X})}$ different individuals. So,the smaller the degree of population diversity, the lesser the feasible solutions the CGAs can search.In particular, when $\lambda(\vec{X}) = 0$, CGAs with $p_m = 0$ have no search ability any more.

Theorem 3.1 tells us that if the global optimum lies in the minimum schema containing the initial population, it is possible for CGAs to find it. However, as demonstrated later, the selection and crossover operators have a serious effect on maturation——their employment may decrease the degree of population diversity and degrade the search ability of the CGAs. So, although the global optimal solution is in the minimum schema containing the initial population, it may be excluded outside the search range by the selection and crossover operators which are ironically searching for it.

Theorem 3.2 Let $\{\vec{X}(k), k \ge 0\}$ be the population Markov chain of a CGA with $p_m = 0$ and $\mathbf{B}$ be the set of homogenous populations.

(a) $\{\vec{X}(k), k \ge 0\}$ converges to the set of homogenous population $\mathbf{B} = \{(X, \cdots, X); X \in S\}$ with probability 1, i.e.,

$$P\{\lim_k \vec{X}(k) \in \mathbf{B}\} = 1. \tag{3}$$

(b) The degree of diversity of the sequence of populations decreases monotonically with probability 1, decreases strictly monotonically with positive probabilities, and converges to 0 with probability 1, i.e.,

$$P\{\lambda(\vec{X}(k+1)) \le \lambda(\vec{X}(k))\} = 1, \; k \ge 0 \tag{4}$$

$$P\{\lambda(\vec{X}(k+1)) < \lambda(\vec{X}(k))\} > 0, \; k \ge 0 \tag{5}$$

$$P\{\lim_k \lambda(\vec{X}(k)) = 0\} = 1. \tag{6}$$

Theorem 3.2 suggests that CGAs with $p_m = 0$ converge to homogoneous populations with probability 1 and the convergence is monotone in terms of the degree of population diversity. The difficulty is, however, that the limiting homogeneous populations may correspond to the local optimal solutions, non-extremal solutions as well as the global optimal solutions. Hence, to show the effectiveness of CGAs (especially that of the selection and crossover operators), the question of to where a CGA most likely converges should be answered. We now proceed to establish some explicit formulas concerning the conditional probabilities of the population Markov chain. These formulas will partly answer the above question and, on the other hand, will give a formula of the probability of allele loss at a certain gene position. In the following, we no longer assume that the mutation probability is 0. Let us first introduce some notations in the following definition:

Definition 3.3 Given a population $\vec{X} = (X_1, \cdots, X_N)$, $X_i = (x_{i1}, \cdots, x_{il})$, $i = 1, \cdots, N$, for any positive integer $1 \leq m \leq l$, let

$$I_0^m = \{i \in \{1, 2, \cdots, N\}; \ x_{im} = 0\}$$

$$I_1^m = \{i \in \{1, 2, \cdots, N\}; \ x_{im} = 1\}$$

and write

$$f_0^m(\vec{X}) = \sum_{i \in I_0^m} f(X_i), \quad f_1^m(\vec{X}) = \sum_{i \in I_1^m} f(X_i).$$

We call

$$a_m = \frac{f_0^m(\vec{X})}{\sum_{j=1}^N f(X_j)}, \quad b_m = 1 - a_m = \frac{f_1^m(\vec{X})}{\sum_{j=1}^N f(X_j)},$$

respectively the fitness ratio of zero and one allele individuals at the mth gene position.

Theorem 3.3 Let $\{\vec{X}(k), \ k \geq 0\}$ be the population Markov chain of a CGA , then for every $1 \leq m \leq l$, we have

$$P\{\vec{X}(1) \text{ loses allele 1 at gene m}/ \ \vec{X}(0) = \vec{X}\} = (a_m + (1 - 2a_m)p_m)^N, \tag{7}$$

$$P\{\vec{X}(1) \text{ loses allele 0 at gene m}/ \ \vec{X}(0) = \vec{X}\} = (b_m + (1 - 2b_m)p_m)^N. \tag{8}$$

The following corollary shows the relationship between premature convergence and the population size, the mutation probability and the population statistics a_m.

Corollary 3.1 For the CGAs, the probability for allele loss to occur at a gene position (hence premature convergence at the gene position) is inversely proportional to the population size N, and directly proportional to $|a_m - \frac{1}{2}|$ and $|p_m - \frac{1}{2}|$. Particularly, for fixed N, the above probability get its minimum at $a_m = \frac{1}{2}$ and $p_m = \frac{1}{2}$.

From theorem 3.1, we can also get the following corollary which partly answers the question of to where a CGA most likely converges.

Corollary 3.2 Let $\{\vec{X}(k), \ k \geq 0\}$ be the population Markov chain with $\vec{X}(0) = \vec{X}$. Denote by $\mathbf{L}(1)$ and $\mathbf{L}(0)$ the two competing schemas,

$$\mathbf{L}(1) = \{X; \ x_m = 1\}, \ \mathbf{L}(0) = \{X; \ x_m = 0\}, \ 1 \leq m \leq l.$$

If $a_m > b_m$ and $0 \leq p_m < \frac{1}{2}$, then

$$P\{\vec{X}(1) \subset \mathbf{L}(0)/ \ \vec{X}(0) = \vec{X}\} > P\{\vec{X}(1) \subset \mathbf{L}(1)/ \ \vec{X}(0) = \vec{X}\}. \tag{9}$$

4   Experimental Results

To substantiate our theoretical results, a series of simulations is carried out to apply CGAs with parameters N (population size), p_m (mutation probability), and p_c (crossover probability) to a function optimization problem.

The simulation results are in support of our theoretical analysis in that the rate of decrease of the degree of population diversity is in inverse proportion to the population size and is proportion to $|p_m - \frac{1}{2}|$. We also observe that the larger the population size, the better is the performance of the algorithms. A moderate mutation probability, e.g. $p_m = 0.01$, also contributes to good performance while too large a mutation rate degrades the performance. It is also observed that the smaller the population size, the more notable is the effect of the mutation probability on the algorithm's performance. In addition, though the performance of the CGA with 0.5 mutation probability is not very bad , the convergence rate is obviously slower than the case of a lower mutation probability, e.g. $p_m = 0.005$ and $p_m = 0.01$. Details of the experiment are left out because of the limited space.

5   Conclusion

We have introduced in this paper a concept of degree of population diversity and quantitatively characterized and theoretically analyzed the problem of premature convergence in CGAs using the theory of Markov chain. Under the assumption that the mutation probability is zero, we have proved that the degree of population diversity converges to zero with probability 1 so that the search ability of a genetic algorithm decreases over time resulting in premature convergence. An explicit formula for the conditional probability of allele loss at a certain gene position has been established to show relationships between premature convergence and the CGA parameters——population size N, mutation probability p_m and population statistics a_m. The formula also partly answers the question of to where a genetic algorithm most likely converges. A series of simulations have also been conducted to validate our theoretical analysis.

Acknowledgment. This project is supported by the earmarked grant CUHK 321/95H of the Hong Kong Research Grants Council and the National Science Foundation of P.R.China.

References

[1] J.H.Holland, *Adaptations Natural and Artificial Systems*. Ann Arbor:University of Michigan Press,1975.

[2] L.Davis, *Handbook of Genetic Algorithms*.New York: Van Nostrand Reinhold, 1991.

[3] D.B.Fogel, "An introduction to simulated evolutionary optimization," *IEEE Trans. on Neural Network*,vol.5,no.1,pp.3-13,1994.

[4] H.G.Cobb and J.J.Grefenstette, "Genetic algorithms for tracking changing environment," in *Proc. of the fifth International Conference on Genetic Algorithms*, pp.523-530, 1993.

[5] K.A.De Jong, *An Analysis of the Behavior of a Class of Genetic Adaptive Systems*. Doctoral Thesis, Department of Computer and Communication Sciences, University of Michigan, Ann Arbor,1975.

[6] D.Goldberg, *Genetic Algorithms in Search, Optimization, and Machine Learning*. New York: Addison-Wesley,1989.

[7] J.J.Grefenstette, "Genetic algorithms for changing environments," in *Parallel Problem Solving from Nature 2*. R.Manner and B.Manderick,Eds. North Holland: Elsevie Science Publishers,pp.137-144,1992.

[8] M.Srinivas and L.M.Patnaik, "Adaptive probabilities of crossover and mutation in genetic algorithms", *IEEE Trans. on Systems, Man and Cybernetics*, vol.24,no.4,pp.656-667,1994.

[9] D.C.Mattfeld, H.Kopfer, and C.Bierwirth, "Control of parallel population dynamics by social-like behavior of GA-individuals", in *Parallel Problem Solving from Nature-PPSN III*,Berlin: Springer-Verlag,pp.16-25,1994.

[10] R.E.Smith, S.Forrest, and A.S.Perelson," Population diversity in an immune system model:implications for genetic search," in *Foundations of Genetic Algorithms.2*,L.D.Whitley, Ed. San Mateo,CA: Morgan Kaufmann,pp.153-166,1993.

[11] Y.Yoshida and N.Adachi, "A diploid genetic algorithm for preserving population diversity-Pseudo-Meiosis GA", in *Parallel Problem Solving from Nature-PPSN III*, Y.Davidor, H.-P.Schwefel, and R.Manner, Eds.Berlin:Spinger-Verlag,pp.36-45,1994.

[12] G.Rudoph,"Convergence analysis of canonical genetic algorithms," *IEEE Trans. on Neural Networks*,vol.5,no.1, pp.96-101,1994.

Phenotypic Forking GA with Moving Windows

Shigeyoshi Tsutsui[*1], Ashish Ghosh[*2] and Masato Takiguchi[*1]

*1 Department of Management and Information Science
Hannan University
5-4-33 Amamihigashi, Matsubara, Osaka 580 Japan
tsutsui@hannan-u.ac.jp
*2 Department of Industrial Engineering, College of Engineering
Osaka Prefecture University
1-1 Gakuen-cho, Sakai, Osaka 593 Japan

Abstract--- The *phenotypic forking GA (p-fGA)* which divides the whole search space into sub-spaces using the information of the convergence status of the population and the solutions obtained so far had already been developed. In that work, a *neighborhood hypercube* was defined around the best individual at the time of forking in the *phenotypic feature space* with the best solution as the center of that hypercube; and that sub-space was searched in *exploitation mode*. The rest of the search space was *explored*. In this investigation, we extend this concept by moving the center of the neighborhood hypercubes with generations. Here, the position of the center of the hypercube is updated every generation such that it becomes the current best solution; thereby *dynamically modifying the sub-spaces* for exploration and exploitation. This enhances the scope of tracing the optimum solution and gives more flexibility for choosing the size of the hypercube. Empirical results on complex function optimization problems show that the new method finds the global optimum in less number of trials than the original p-fGA.

1 Introduction

There are many GA-hard problems that are difficult to be solved by the conventional GAs such as multi-modal problems and deceptive functions [3], [10]. Many kinds of modified GAs, such as CHC [2], mGA [4], delta coding [6], niche methods [1] and fGA [8], [9] aimed to solve these problems are proposed in the literature.

The *forking GA (fGA)* divides the search space into sub-spaces depending on the status of convergence of the present population and the solutions obtained so far; and uses a multi-population scheme, which includes one parent population with a *blocking mode* (or *exploration mode*) and one or more child populations with a *shrinking mode* (or *exploitation mode*) generated by *population forking*. Depending on the type of the search space to be divided two types of fGAs are proposed. One of them is the *genotypic fGA* (g-fGA) which divides the genotypic search space and the other is the *phenotypic fGA* (p-fGA) which uses phenotypic parameter domain for space division. In the g-fGA, each population searches in a sub-space defined by a *salient schema* in the genotypic search space. In the p-fGA, the corresponding sub-space is defined by a *neighborhood hypercube* around the then best individual in the phenotypic parameter space.

In the p-fGA, since the position of a neighborhood hypercube is fixed after it is created, efficiency of searching the optimal point in the neighborhood hypercube becomes lower when it is located near the edge of the hypercube or just outside of it. Thus the size of the hypercube plays a major role in detecting the actual position of the optima and time needed for the same. In the present work an attempt is made to solve these problems by updating the position of the center of the neighborhood hypercube every generation. The current best solution is set to be the center of the neighborhood hypercube; thereby *dynamically modifying the sub-spaces* for exploration and exploitation. This enhances the scope of tracing the optimum solution and gives more flexibility for choosing the size of the hypercube.

The empirical results on complex function optimization problems show that the new method finds the global optimum in less (by 20-30 %) number of trials than the original p-fGA.

2 Population Forking

During the process of evolution, if the population is converged to a smaller diversity, the process may be forked to

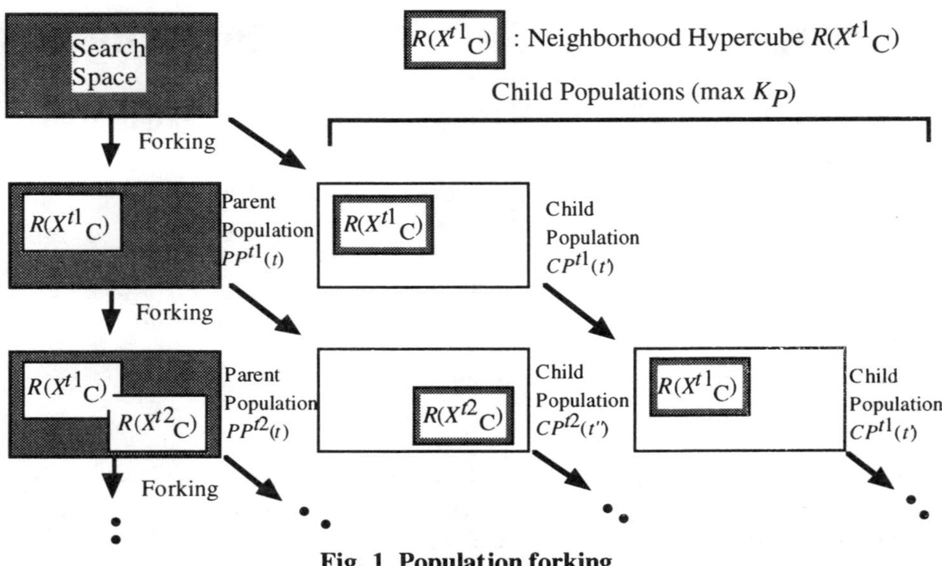

Fig. 1 Population forking

allow searching concurrently in two different sub-populations. Thus the whole search space is divided into sub-spaces depending on the status of convergence of the present population and the solutions obtained so far; and search is continued independently in these sub-spaces. We call this method *population forking*. The population is forked into a *parent population* $PP^{t1}(t)$ and a *child population* $CP^{t1}(t')$ covering the sub-spaces as shown in Fig. 1.

If the conditions for forking is satisfied again in the parent population, the second child population is formed. A maximum of K_p (≥ 1) child populations are allowed. The parent population and the child populations are evolved in time sharing mode. Sharing of computation time by the two populations is defined by the BS_{ratio} on the generation counter. For example, the $BS_{\text{ratio}} = p : q$ means we perform p generations for the parent population followed by q generations for the child population; and this sequence continues.

Individuals are not exchanged between the child populations. But when an individual with the new best value is found in a child population, it is copied to the parent population. As a result, the best individual obtained so far is always included in the parent population. If the number of child populations is more than K_p, the oldest child population is discarded.

3   Phenotypic Population Forking

In the p-fGA, a subspace (child population) is defined by a neighborhood hypercube in the phenotypic search space around the current best solution as described bellow.

Let the phenotypic parameter of a problem be $X = (x_1, x_2, ..., x_n)$. Let us consider a situation where there is no updating of the current best solution by a new individual for some consecutive generations. We represent the current best individual by its phenotypic parameter vector $X^t{}_C = (x^t{}_{1,c}, x^t{}_{2,c}, ..., x^t{}_{n,c})$. Then, the neighborhood hypercube $R(X^t{}_C)$ around $X^t{}_C$ may be defined as $R(X^t{}_C) = \{x_1, x_2, ..., x_n \mid (x^t{}_{i,c} - s_i/2) \leq x_i \leq (x^t{}_{i,c} + s_i/2), i=1,2, ..., n\}$, where $S = (s_1, s_2, ..., s_n)$ defines the size of the neighborhood hypercube $R(X^t{}_C)$ and $s_i > 0$.

Conditions for the phenotypic population forking are as follows:

(i) the current best evaluated value has not been updated by a new individual for a specified number ($K_H>1$) of generations, and

(ii) the number of the individuals located inside the neighborhood hypercube $R(X^t{}_C)$ is more than the specified number $N \times K_R$ ($0 < K_R \leq 1.0$).

If the conditions of forking are satisfied, we make the initial population fork into a parent population $PP^{t1}(t)$ which evolves outside $R(X^{t1}{}_C)$, and a child population $CP^{t1}(t')$ which evolves inside $R(X^{t1}{}_C)$ (refer Fig. 1).

3.1 Exploration and Exploitation of Sub-spaces

After the population forking has occurred, individuals which are located inside $R(X^{t1}_C)$, except the best individual, will be deleted from the parent population $PP^{t1}(t)$ and we call this as *blocking mode*; individuals are randomly regenerated to keep the parent population size fixed. Thus the diversity of $PP^{t1}(t)$ may be recovered so as to escape from being trapped in local optima. Fig. 2 shows an example of the blocking mode in the p-fGA. In this figure, there are two phenotypic parameters, x_1 & x_2 in the range $0.0 \leq x_1, x_2 \leq 25.5$ and coded by 8 bits. We assume $X^{t1}_C = (10.0, 6.0)$. Let the *resolution* of parameter x_i be represented by Δx_i. Then $\Delta x_1, \Delta x_2$ are both 0.1 ($= (25.5-0.0)/(2^8 -1)$). We consider the case where the parent and the child populations have the same resolution. The *neighborhood hypercube size S* can be determined from the number of bits used to represent each of the parameters in the child population and the resolution. If six bits are used to represent both x_1 & x_2 in the child population, then S becomes ($(2^6-1)\times0.1, (2^6-1)\times0.1$) = (6.3, 6.3); and thus $(10.0-3.1) \leq x_1 \leq (10.0+3.2)$ & $(6.0-3.1) \leq x_2 \leq (6.0+3.2)$ as shown in Fig. 3. Exploration in the parent population is then continued.

An individual with parameter values $x_1 = 10.1$, $x_2 = 5.1$, for example, is being re-encoded in $R(X^{t1}_C)$ with 6 bits for each parameter; total length of a string in the child population being 12. Thus, the search space of the child population is $1/16 (= 2^{12}/2^{16})$th of the original search space. As the string length of the chromosomes is reduced, we call this shrinking mode. The child population is then exploited to detect the actual optimum.

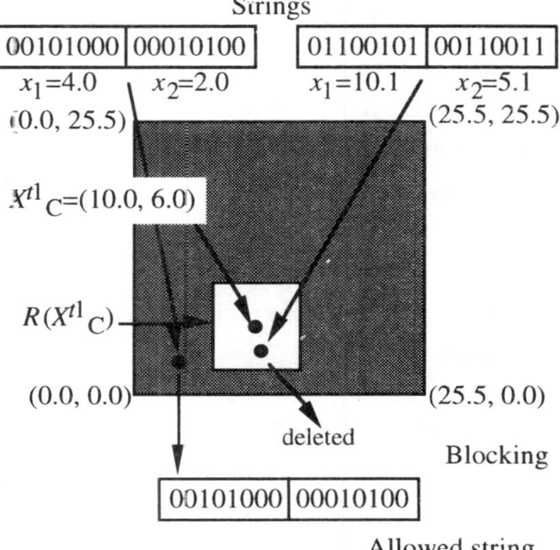

Fig. 2 Blocking mode

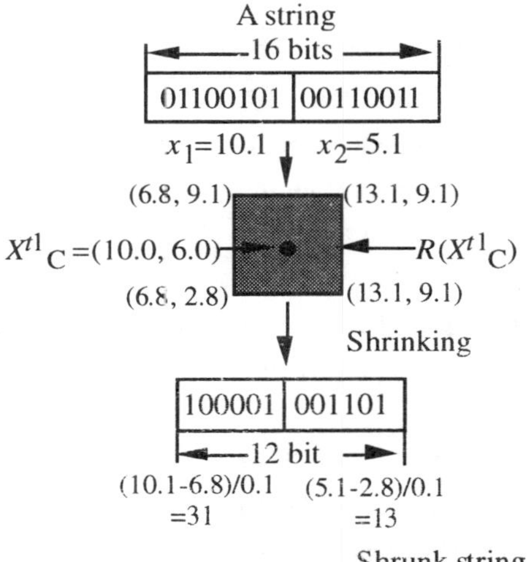

Fig. 3 Shrinking mode

3.2 Variable Resolution p-fGA

The p-fGA described above uses the same resolution Δx_i for the parent and the child populations. Hereafter, we call this p-fGA as the *fixed resolution p-fGA (fp-fGA)*. We may use different Δx_i values for the parent and the child populations. This type of GA may be called as *variable resolution p-fGA (vp-fGA)*. Thus the vp-fGA provides more flexibility to define the size of the neighborhood hypercube. Let us consider the case where we want to increase the size of the neighborhood hypercube with the fp-fGA. This can only be attained by increasing

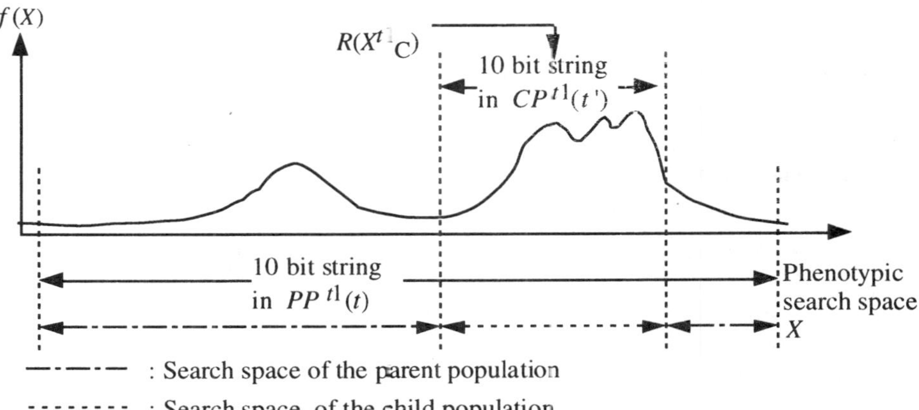

Fig. 4 Variable resolution searching in the vp-fGA

the number of bits to represent strings of the child population. However, if we increase one bit to represent x_1, for example, then the value of s_1 increases from 6.3 to 12.7; thus almost doubling its size. In the vp-fGA, each Δx_i is recalculated for a given S and a given number of bits to represent members of the child population. Thus, we can take any value for S, although it may be that the string length of the members of the child populations becomes longer than that of the fp-fGA.

With the vp-fGA we basically can achieve *variable resolution searching* as follows (Fig. 4):

(a) parent population is searched with a lower resolution and detect the near optimal solution fast,

(b) in the child populations searching is performed with a higher resolution, depending on the problem, resulting in the efficient detection of the global optimum or local optima, since searching proceeds in a smaller phenotypic search space.

4 Moving Window p-fGA (mp-fGA)

In the original p-fGA, the neighborhood hypercube is defined around the best individual obtained at the time of forking. Hence, the search sub-spaces remains fixed during the rest portion of the algorithm. Thus, detection of the actual position of the optimum becomes largely dependent on the size of the neighborhood hypercube. If the neighborhood hypercube is small, we may miss the actual location of the optimum or the optimum itself. In other words, the optimum may not be detected in the child populations. On the contrary, if the size of the neighborhood hypercube is more, we may get the actual optimum; but searching becomes very high. Thus, the choice of the neighborhood hypercube becomes a bottleneck of the p-fGA. In the present investigation, we move the neighborhood hypercube with time. The center of the hypercube is updated every generation to be the current best optimum; thereby dynamically varying the search space for the parent and the child populations. This gives us more scope to detect the actual optimum in the child populations; thereby increasing the chance of detecting the actual optimum in less number of trials.

5 Empirical Results and Discussion

In this section, performance of the mp-fGA is compared with that of the original p-fGA empirically.

5.1 Performance of the p-fGA and the mp-fGA

The performance of the p-fGA and the mp-fGA were tested on the following two test functions.

(i) *FMS (Frequency Modulation Sounds) parameter identification problem:* f_{fms} . This problem was used to evaluate the p-fGA in [9] and the objective is to determine the 6 parameters $(a_1, w_1, a_2, w_2, a_3, w_3)$ of the FM sound model represented by

$$y(t) = a_1 \sin(w_1 t\theta + a_2 \sin(w_2 t\theta + a_3 \sin(w_3 t\theta))), \tag{1}$$

with $\theta = 2\pi/100$. The function f_{fms} is defined as the summation of square errors between the evolved data and the model data as follows:

$$f_{fms} = \sum_{t=0}^{100} (y(t) - y_0(t))^2 ; \tag{2}$$

where model data are given by the following equation:

$$y_0(t) = 1.0 \times \sin(5.0t\theta - 1.5 \times \sin(4.8t\theta + 2.0 \times \sin(4.9t\theta))). \tag{3}$$

Each parameter is represented by an 8- bit Gray code in the range - 6.4 to 6.35 and a resolution of 0.05 is used. The total length of a string is $8 \times 6 = 48$ bit.

(ii) *Modified Griewank Function:* $f_{Giewank}$ [7]. The function is defined as follows:

$$f_{Griewank} = \sum_{i=1}^{5} x_i^2 / 4000 - \prod_{i=1}^{5} \cos(x^i / \sqrt{i}) + 1 . \tag{4}$$

Each parameter x_i is represented by a 10-bit Gray code in the range -51.2 to 51.1 with a resolution of 0.1. The total length of a string is $10 \times 5 = 50$ bit.

Maximum number of trials were set to 200,000 for both of the f_{fms} & $f_{Griewank}$, 30 simulations were done for each experiment. Searching continued until the global optimum was found or the maximum number of trials was reached. A population size $N = 50$, Hamming power $\alpha = 0.05$, normal mutation rate $P_{nm} = 0.02$, high mutation rate $P_{hm} = 0.2$, $K_H = 60$ and $BS_{ratio} = 1:1$ were commonly used for these experiments. The parameters $K_R = 0.8$ & 0.3 were used for the functions f_{fms} & $f_{Griewank}$, respectively. Two point crossover operator was applied.

We evaluated these models by measuring their #OPT (number of runs in which the algorithm succeeded in finding the global optimum) and MNT (mean number of trials to find the global optimum in those runs where it did find the optimum). Fig. 5 shows #OPT for restricted number of trials. Table 1 summarizes the results after 200,000 trials. The mp-fGA performed better than the p-fGA for both of the functions f_{fms} & $f_{Griewank}$. For the function f_{fms}, the mp-fGA found global optimal 30 times and the p-fGA found 28 times. Further, MNT of the mp-fGA (40,559.3) is smaller than that of the p-fGA (49,917.1). Similar trend was also seen for the function $f_{Griewank}$ (#OPT=28, MNT = 66,099.7 for the p-fGA; #OPT=30, MNT=46,428.6 for the mp-fGA). Thus, the mp-fGA enhances the performance by reducing the MNT (by approximately 20-30 %).

The performance improvement of the mp-fGA can be explained from the #OPT/C (number of runs which found the global optimum in the child populations). For the function f_{fms}, #OPT/C of the p-fGA = 12, #OPT/C of the mp-fGA = 16. Similar results were also found for the function $f_{Griewank}$ (#OPT/C=21 for the p-fGA; #OPT/C = 23 for the mp-fGA). Thus, the mp-fGA found the global optimum more number of times in the child populations than that of the p-fGA; and thus required less number of trials for detecting the global optimum. Results with other hypercube sizes also corroborated the earlier finding.

5.2 Result for the Variable Resolution Method

In this experiment, we tested the vp-fGA with moving windows

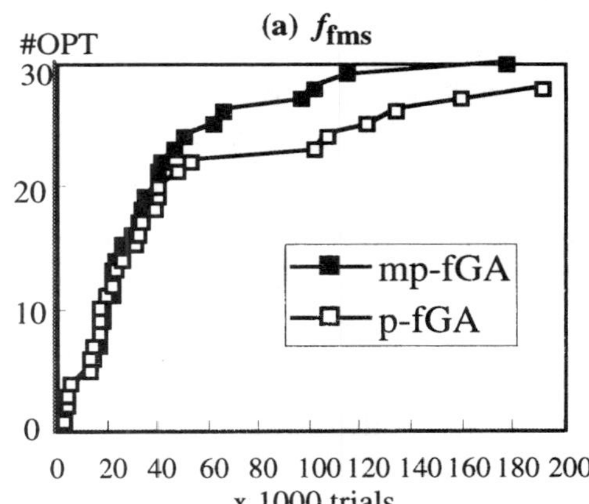

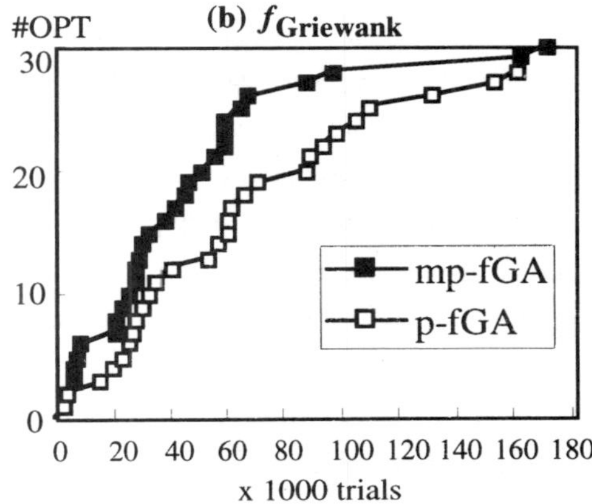

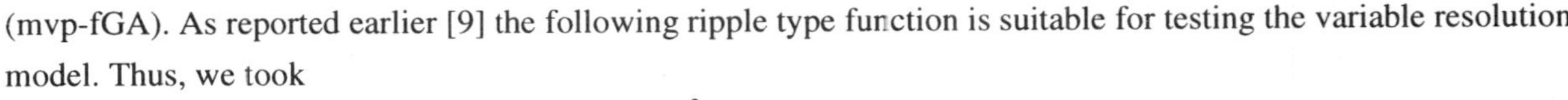

Fig. 5 #OPT for restricted number of trials

Table 1   The mp-fGA vs. the p-fGA

GA	Function	f_{fms}	$f_{Griewank}$
mp-fGA	#OPT	30	30
	MNT	40,559.3	46,428.6
	#OPT/C	16	23
p-fGA	#OPT	28	28
	MNT	49,917.1	66,099.7
	#OPT/C	12	21

(mvp-fGA). As reported earlier [9] the following ripple type function is suitable for testing the variable resolution model. Thus, we took

$$f_{ripple} = \sum_{i=1}^{5} e^{-2\ln 2\left(\frac{x_i - 0.1}{0.8}\right)^2} (\sin^6(5\pi x_i) + 0.1 \times \cos^2(500\pi x_i)), \tag{5}$$

where, each x_i is in the range of $0.0 \le x_i \le 100.0$, $i = 1, 2, .., 5$. The function f_{ripple} has many main peaks of different sizes surrounded by high frequency of small peaks and have the maximum value at $x_1 = x_2 =, .., x_5 = 0.1$ with functional value 5.5. Let us consider that the problem is to find the optimal point with a resolution of 0.0001 for each x_i. Thus, we assume that the GA is able to find the optimal solution if the parameters $x_1, x_2, .., x_5$ of the best individual are within the range [(0.1 - 0.0001) , (0.1 + 0.0001)].

The parameter $K_R = 0.5$ and $BS_{ratio} = 2:1$ were used. Each run continued until the global optimum was found or a maximum of 100,000 trials was reached. Other parameters were the same as in Section 5.1. Coding conditions are as follows: the neighborhood hypercube size $s_i = 1.5$ is used for each i; to represent each parameter x_i, 12 bits and 11 bits were used in the parent and the child populations, respectively. Thus, the resolution Δx_i of the parent and the child populations were 0.02442 (= 100.0/(2^{12}-1)) and 0.0000723(= 0.15/(2^{11}-1)), respectively.

#OPTs of the mvp-fGA and the vp-fGA were both 30 (100%). With respect to MNT, the mvp-fGA showed higher performance (17,743.4) than that of the vp-fGA (25,564.6). Fig. 6 shows #OPT for restricted number of trials for both the mvp-fGA and the vp-fGA. Thus, it is evident that the concept of moving window is also effective for the vp-fGA.

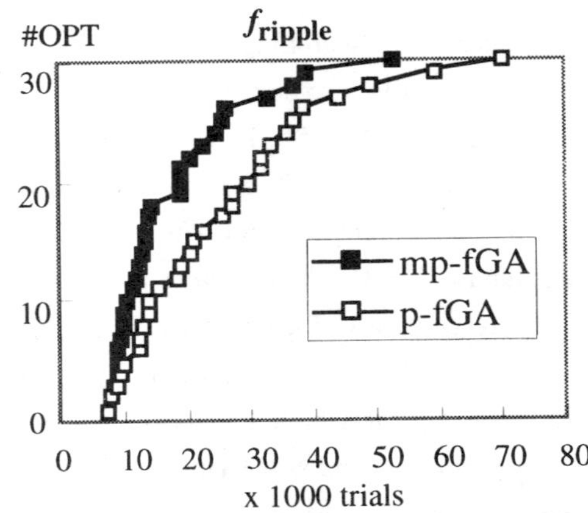

Fig. 6 #OPT for restricted number of trials

6 Conclusions

The concept of phenotypic forking GA (p-fGA) is extended in this article. In the original p-fGA, a neighborhood hypercube or a search sub-space was defined around the best individual at the time of forking with the then best solution as the center of that hypercube. In the present work, we extend this concept by moving the center of the neighborhood hypercubes with generations. Here, the position of the center of the hypercube is updated every generation such that it becomes the current best solution; thereby dynamically modifying the sub-spaces for exploration and exploitation. This enhances the scope of tracing the optimum solution and gives more flexibility for choosing the size of the hypercube. Empirical results on complex function optimization problems show that the new method finds the global optimum in less (by approximately 20-30%) number of trials than the original p-fGA.

Acknowledgments

This research is partially supported by the Ministry of Education, Science, Sports and Culture under Grant-in-Aid for Scientific Research on Priority Areas number 264-08233105.

References

[1] K. Deb and D. E. Goldberg "An investigation of niche and species formation in genetic function optimization," *Proc. Third Inter. Conf. on Genetic Algorithms*,1989, pp. 42-50.

[2] L. J. Eshelman, "The CHC adaptive search algorithm: How to have safe search when engaging in nontraditional genetic recombination," *Foundations of Genetic Algorithms* (pp. 265-283). San Mateo, CA: Morgan Kaufmann, 1991.

[3] D. E. Goldberg, *Genetic algorithms in search, optimization and machine learning*, Reading, MA: Addison-Wesley, 1989.

[4] D. E. Goldberg, K. Deb and B. Korb, "Messy genetic algorithms revisited: Studies in mixed size and scale, *Complex Systems*, vol. 4, pp. 415-444, 1990.

[5] J. J. Grefenstette, L. Davis and D. Cerys, *GENESIS and OOGA: Two GA systems*, Melrose, MA: TSP Publication, 1991.

[6] K. Mathias and D. Whitley "Changing representations during search: a comparative study of delta coding," *Evolutionary Computation,* vol. 2, no. 3, pp. 249-278, 1994.

[7] A. Torn and A. Zilmskas, *Global optimization* (p. 186). Berlin: Springer-Verlag (Lecture Notes in Computer Science), 1989.

[8] S. Tsutsui and Y. Fujimoto, "Forking genetic algorithm with blocking and shrinking modes," *Proc. Fifth Inter. Conf. on Genetic Algorithms*, 1993, pp. 206-213.

[9] S. Tsutsui and Y. Fujimoto "Phenotypic forking genetic algorithms," *Proc. IEEE Inter. Conf. on Evolutionary Computation*, 1995, pp. 566-572.

[10] D. Whitley, "Fundamental principles of deception in genetic search," *Foundations of Genetic Algorithms,* pp. 221-241, San Mateo, CA: Morgan Kaufmann, 1991.

Equilibrium Selection Using Genetic Programming[*]

Shu-Heng Chen†, John Duffy‡, Chia-Hsuan Yeh⋆
† Department of Economics, National Chengchi University
E-mail: chchen@cc.nccu.edu.tw
Taipei, Taiwan
‡ Department of Economics, University of Pittsburgh
E-mail: jduffy+@pitt.edu
Pittsburgh, U.S.A.
⋆ Department of Economics, National Chengchi University
E-mail: g3258501@grad.cc.nccu.edu.tw
Taipei, Taiwan

Abstract— **We use genetic programming techniques developed by Koza (1992) to model the behavior of a population of heterogeneous agents playing a simple coordination game with multiple equilibria. We compare the results from our computational experiments with results obtained from a number of controlled laboratory experiments conducted by Van Huyck et al. (1994) where human subjects played the same coordination game. We find that the behavior exhibited by our population of artificially intelligent players is remarkably similar to the behavior of the human subjects who played the same versions of the coordination game. In particular, the artificial agents always coordinate on the same equilibrium as was chosen by the human subjects in all versions of the game. We conclude that our genetic programming–based learning algorithm may be a useful and empirically plausible equilibrium selection mechanism in environments with multiple equilibria.**

1   Introduction

Economists are increasingly searching for ways in which to reduce the multiplicity of equilibria that can arise in even the simplest of economic models. A popular selection criterion has been to choose only those equilibria that are stable with respect to some kind of disequilibrium "learning" process. However, this selection criterion leaves open the question of what *type* of disequilibrium scheme should be used to model the learning process.

In this paper we propose the use of genetic programming techniques developed by Koza (1992) as a reasonable and empirically plausible model of the learning process. We illustrate our argument by way of an example, a simple coordination game with multiple equilibria.

This coordination game has been previously studied by Van Huyck et al. (1994), who examined how human subjects behaved when playing this game in a controlled laboratory setting. The game has two Nash equilibrium, one of which is a corner solution and the other is an interior equilibrium. Depending upon the parameterization of the game, the interior equilibrium may be either stable or unstable under myopic best response learning dynamics, a commonly used, benchmark learning algorithm. The corner equilibrium is always unstable under these same dynamics. Van Huyck et al. wanted to see whether the prediction of the myopic best response dynamics accurately characterized the behavior of human subjects playing this coordination game. They reported results from two parameterizations one in which the interior equilibrium was predicted to be stable under the myopic best response dynamics and another where the interior equilibrium was predicted to be unstable under these same dynamics. These authors found that in both cases, the human subjects always coordinated on the interior equilibrium after a few rounds of play; that is, the interior equilibrium was judged to be stable under both parameterizations of the model, thus casting doubt on the predictive ability of the myopic best response algorithm.

In this paper we use Koza's (1992) genetic programming (GP) techniques in place of the myopic best response algorithm as a way of modelling learning in the coordination game environment. Genetic programming has several advantages over the myopic best response algorithm as well as other learning algorithms that have appeared in the economics literature. First, GP involves a heterogeneous population of decision rules (agents) as opposed to the single, representative–agent type learning algorithms that are more typically encountered. Given the substantial heterogeneity of behavior observed (at least initially) in the coordination game as well as in other games, this feature of GP makes it especially well suited as a model of learning behavior in these environments. Second, GP is capable of evolving much more sophisticated forecast rules than is possible using the more standard learning algorithms. For this reason, we regard GP as a more robust model of learning behavior. Finally, as we show in this paper, the behavior of the GP–based algorithm is remarkably similar to the behavior of the experimental subjects who play the same versions of the coordination game. Thus we argue that GP is an *empirically plausible* model of adaptive behavior, making it all the more reasonable as an equilibrium selection device.

---

[*]This research was initiated while Duffy was visiting National Chengchi University during the summer of 1995. This paper is an abbreviated version of Chen, Duffy and Yeh (1996). Research support from NSC grant No.84-2415-H-004-001 is gratefully acknowledged.

The paper proceeds as follows. In the next section we describe the coordination game environment and in section 3 we describe our implementation of GP in this environment. Section 4 presents the results of our simulations and section 5 presents conclusions and extensions. We note that space considerations prevent us from summarizing all of our results and analysis from this project. For a more detailed and complete description of our results and analysis, the reader is referred to Chen, Duffy and Yeh (1996).

2   The Analytical Framework

Van Huyck et al. (1994) studied the following generic coordination game. Let $e_{i,t}, ..., e_{n,t}$ denote the set of actions taken by n players at time t. Let e_t denote this action set, and let M_t denote the mean of e_t. The game $\Gamma(\omega)$ is defined by the following *payoff function* and *action space* for each of the n players, who are indexed by i:

$$\pi_{i,t} = c_1 - c_2|e_{i,t} - \omega M_{i,t}[1 - M_{i,t}]| \tag{1}$$

where $\omega \in (1,4]$, $e_{i,t} \in \mathbf{E} = [0,1]$, and c_1 and c_2 are positive parameters. We use the notation $e_{-i,t}$ to denote $\{ e_{1,t}, ..., e_{i-1,t}, e_{i+1,t}, ..., e_{n,t} \}$. Assume that the payoff functions and feasible actions are common knowledge.

Since at the beginning of time t, M_t is not known, individual i's decision about his optimal choice for $e_{i,t}$ must be based on his *expectation* of M_t, which we shall denote by $\hat{M}_{i,t}$. Given $\hat{M}_{i,t}$ and the payoff function $\pi_{i,t}$, individual i's *expected payoff* at time t ($\hat{\pi}_{i,t}$) can be expressed as follows:

$$\hat{\pi}_{i,t} = c_1 - c_2|e_{i,t} - \omega \hat{M}_{i,t}[1 - \hat{M}_{i,t}]| \tag{2}$$

Given $\hat{M}_{i,t}$, $e_{i,t}^*$ is the action that maximizes $\hat{\pi}_{i,t}$. We have that:

$$e_{i,t}^* = \omega \hat{M}_{i,t}(1 - \hat{M}_{i,t}) \tag{3}$$

Once $e_{i,t}^*$ is decided, M_t is determined as follows.

$$M_t = \frac{\sum_{i=1}^n e_{i,t}^*}{n} \tag{4}$$

Given M_t, the actual payoff received by player i at time t ($\pi_{i,t}$) is:

$$\pi_{i,t} = c_1 - c_2|e_{i,t}^* - \omega M_t[1 - M_t]| \tag{5}$$

An action combination e^* constitutes a strict equilibrium if it satisfies the following *mutual best–response condition*:

$$\pi_i(e_i, e_{-i}^*) < \pi_i(e_i^*, e_{-i}^*) \tag{6}$$

for all $e_i \in [0,1]$ and for all i. An observed action combination is a mutual best–response outcome if it satisfies (6). An action combination is a *symmetric equilibrium* if it satisfies condition (6) and assigns the same action to all players. Notice that *all the strict equilibria of $\Gamma(\omega)$ are symmetric*. Hence, it is convenient to denote the equilibria by the ordered pair (e, M). The requirement that $\omega \in (1,4]$ results in two strict equilibria: a *corner equilibrium* $(0,0)$ and an *interior equilibrium* $(1-\frac{1}{\omega}, 1-\frac{1}{\omega})$.

Given the coordination game described above, Van Huyck et al. (1994) address the issue of equilibrium selection by considering the predictions of a class of representative–agent type models with different adaptive schemes. They find that, given $\Gamma(\omega)$, the long–run behavior will crucially depend on the adaptive scheme that is used to model the behavior of the representative agent. For some adaptive schemes, M_t will converge to interior equilibrium, $1 - \frac{1}{\omega}$. For other schemes, M_t will converge to a *chaotic attractor*. To see the possibility of the later, consider the *myopic best–response dynamic* examined by Van Huyck et al. in which

$$\hat{M}_{i,t} = M_{t-1} \quad \forall\, i \tag{7}$$

$$e_{i,t}^* = \omega M_{t-1}(1 - M_{t-1}) \quad \forall\, i \tag{8}$$

Equations (7) and (8) together state that all players expect that the mean choice of action will remain unchanged from its previous level M_{t-1} and they react to this expectation in an optimal way. Given equations (7), (8) and (4), the *realized* mean choice of action M_t evolves according to the simple *logistic map*:

$$M_t = \frac{\sum_{i=1}^n e_{i,t}^*}{n} = \omega M_{t-1}(1 - M_{t-1}). \tag{9}$$

The dynamic properties of the logistic map are well known. The long–run behavior is determined by the choice of ω. The property known as *bifurcation* implies that different choice of ω will, qualitatively, result in quite different dynamics of M_t. For example, if ω is set to be 2.47222, then M_t will converge to 0.59551. But, when ω is set to be 3.86957, M_t will very likely converge to a chaotic attractor. This explains why, theoretically, the chaotic attractor could be a possible result of this coordination game. However, despite the theoretical possibility of the existence of chaotic attractors, in all their eight experiments with human subjects, including two of $\Gamma(2.47222)$ and six of $\Gamma(3.86957)$, M_t always converges to the interior equilibrium $1 - \frac{1}{\omega}$ and the chaotic attractor is not observed in any of these experiments.

The observed inconsistency between theory and practice demands an explanation. The explanation proposed by Van Huyck et al. is that the behavior of players cannot be characterized by the predictions of the myopic best–response dynamic but that there are other, representative agent type adaptive schemes such as the *recursive simple average adaptive scheme* that can be used to characterize the behavior of the experimental subjects. However, this explanation is not without criticism. The major criticism comes from the fact that if all players use the same *recursive simple average learning scheme*, then given the same history for M_t, these players should all have identical expectations and thus take identical actions. But, this is not what we observe in the experiments of Van Huyck et al. (See their Appendix B). On the contrary, we see that players always take different actions in the early stages of each experiment, revealing that players do not hold identical expectations. In sum, models based on the representative agent system with identical adaptive schemes are simply so unrealistic that it is hard to take any explanation from them seriously. By contrast, models based on multiagent systems are preferable in that they allow for heterogeneity and interactive exploration. This is also noticed by Van Huyck et al., who, however, consider this direction a "daunting" task.

In what follows, we shall show that modeling the coordination game using adaptive multiagent systems (MASs) is not that daunting and that adaptive MASs can provide us with the foundation necessary to understand the adaptive behavior observed in the experiments. To do this we use genetic programming techniques developed by Koza (1989, 1992) to model adaptive MASs.

3 Population Learning via Genetic Programming

Let GP_t, a population of trees, represent a collection of players' forecasting functions. A player i, $i = 1, ..., n$, makes a decision about his action for time t using a tree, $gp_{i,t}$ $(gp_{i,t} \in GP_t)$, a *parse tree* written over the *function set* and *terminal set* which are given in Table 1. The simulations we report in this paper are all based on a terminal set which includes the ephemeral random floating-point constant $\Re$ ranging over the interval [-9.99,9.99] and the mean choice of action combination lagged up to h periods, i.e., $M_{t-1}, ..., M_{t-h}$. Therefore, the forecasting functions that players may use are the linear and nonlinear functions of $M_{t-1}, ..., M_{t-h}$, $gp_{i,t}(M_{t-1}, ..., M_{t-h})$. The parameter h determines players' ability to recall the past. We set h equal to 5.

The decoding of a parse tree $gp_{i,t}$ gives the forecasting function used by player i at time period t, i.e., $gp_{i,t}(\Omega_{t-1})$ where Ω_{t-1} is the information of the past means up to M_{t-1}. Evaluating $gp_{i,t}(\Omega_{t-1})$ at the realization of Ω_{t-1} will give the mean action predicted by player i at time period t, i.e., $gp_{i,t}$. Without any further restriction, the range of $gp_{i,t}$ is $(-\infty, \infty)$. However, since the action space for each firm is only [0,1], it is not reasonable if $gp_{i,t} \notin [0,1]$. We therefore restrict $gp_{i,t}$ to [0,1] by using the *truncated linear transformation* to map $(-\infty, \infty)$ to [0,1]. [1]

The *raw fitness* of a parse tree $gp_{i,t}$ is determined by the payoff it earned at the end of time t based on equation (5). To avoid a negative fitness value, each raw fitness value is adjusted to produce an *adjusted fitness* measure $\mu_{i,t}$. This adjusted fitness measure is determined as follows.

$$\begin{aligned} \mu_{i,t} &= \pi_{i,t} + 0.25 & \text{if} \quad \pi_{i,t} \geq -0.25, \\ &= 0 & \text{if} \quad \pi_{i,t} < -0.25. \end{aligned}$$

In making this adjustment, we are assuming that forecast functions that cause players lose more than \$0.25 will be immediately deleted in the following genetic operations. Our choice of a cut–off value of "-0.25" is due to the following consideration.[2] Since at the early stage of the game, players have very limited knowledge about the market, their expectations are sort of random guessing and, as a result, it is very likely that most of them could lose money. If we only considered players (rules) with positive payoffs, then the selection process can easily become dominated by those few players who are fortunate enough to earn positive payoffs in the initial stages. After a few generations when most of players start to earn positive payoffs, this protection no longer plays any effective role. The similar consideration can also be found in Chen and Yeh (1996b).

Each adjusted fitness value $\mu_{i,t}$ is then normalized. The *normalized fitness* value $p_{i,t}$ is given in equation (10):

$$p_{i,t} = \frac{\mu_{i,t}}{\sum_{i=1}^{n} \mu_{i,t}} \tag{10}$$

It is clear that normalized fitness is a *probability measure*. Moreover, $p_{i,t}$ is greater for a better parse tree $gp_{i,t}$. Once $p_{i,t}$ is determined, GP_{t+1} is generated from GP_t by three primary genetic operators, i.e., *reproduction, crossover,* and *mutation*. All the control parameters are given in Table 1.[3]

---

[1] Chen, Duffy and Yeh (1996, 1996a) have considered a different transformation, namely, *the sigmoidal activation function*. Their results based on that transformation are different from the results in this paper in many respects, including the speed of convergence, the stability, the complexity of inferred programs. Therefore, the performance of GP may be quite sensitive to different transformations. For a detailed analysis and comparison, see Chen, Duffy and Yeh (1996).

[2] This parameter choice may play an even more interesting role. Choosing a very small value for this cut–off value, say -200, effectively nullifies the proportionate selection mechanism and makes the search completely random. Needless to say, the results in this case are very poor. See Chen, Duffy and Yeh (1996) for the details.

[3] For definitions and detailed discussion of these parameter values, see Chen, Duffy and Yeh (1996).

Table 1: Tableau for the GP–Based Learning Algorithm

Population size	500
The number of trees created by complete growth	50
The number of trees created by partial growth	50
Function set	$\{+, -, \times, \%, Exp, Rlog, Sin, Cos\}$
Terminal set	$\{\Re, M_{t-1}, M_{t-2}, M_{t-3}, M_{t-4}, M_{t-5}\}$
The number of trees created by reproduction	50
The number of trees created by crossover	350
The number of trees created by mutation	100
The probability of mutation	0.0033
The maximum depth of tree	17
The probability of leaf selection under crossover	0.5
The number of generations	1000
The maximum number in the domain of Exp	1700
Criterion of fitness	Payoffs

Table 2: Parameter Values of the
Coordination Game Used in the
GP Simulations

Parameter	CASE 1	CASE 2
ω	2.47222	3.86957
c_1	0.5	0.5
c_2	1	1
n	500	500
e_I^*	0	0
e_{II}^*	0.59551	0.74157

e_I^*: The optimal action under the strict equilibrium $(e, M) = (0, 0)$.
e_{II}^*: The optimal action under the strict equilibrium $(e, M) = (1 - \frac{1}{\omega}, 1 - \frac{1}{\omega})$.

In our GP-based simulations, we used the same parameter values for the coordination game that were considered by Van Huyck et al. (1994). These parameter values are reported in Table 2. As previously discussed, Van Huyck et al. considered two different coordination games, $\Gamma(2.47222)$ and $\Gamma(3.86957)$. We refer to these two games as CASE 1 and CASE 2 respectively. Recall that the myopic best response dynamics converge to the interior equilibrium $1 - \frac{1}{\omega}$ in CASE 1, and to a chaotic trajectory in CASE 2.

4   Results of Simulations

Simulations were conducted for CASES 1 and 2 in accordance with Tables 1 and 2. For each case, we ran five simulations. Each simulation was conducted for one thousand periods (generations). The time series of the mean choice of action M_t for one out of five simulations are exhibited in Figures 1 (corresponding to CASE 1) and 2 (corresponding to CASE 2). In addition, basic statistics such as the average and the standard deviations of M_t for all cases are given in Table 3. The results of our simulations is briefly described as follows.

We find several interesting results. First, as Figures 1-2 reveal, the value for the mean, M_t, in the GP-based coordination game quickly converges to a very small neighborhood around the strict interior equilibrium value $1 - \frac{1}{\omega}$, i.e., 0.59551 in CASE 1 and 0.74157 in CASE 2. In addition, the transition to $1 - \frac{1}{\omega}$ is remarkably brief. Consider $(0.99 - \frac{1}{\omega}, 1.01 + \frac{1}{\omega})$ as a neighborhood of $1 - \frac{1}{\omega}$, for all simulations, it takes no more than 20 generations to move into this area.

Second, while M_t does not converge to $1 - \frac{1}{\omega}$ in a strict sense, there seems to be a force at work that stabilizes the movement of M_t in a very small neighborhood of the interior equilibrium. In other words, GP-based coordination games have a self-stabilizing feature. These properties are also revealed by the standard deviations reported in Table 3. Based on the average of the price from generation 201 to 1000, i.e., $\overline{M_b}$, the $\overline{M_b}$ of almost all simulations does not deviate from $1 - \frac{1}{\omega}$ by more than 0.01%. Also, comparing $\delta_{M,a}$ with $\delta_{M,b}$ or $\delta_{M^*,a}$ with $\delta_{M^*,b}$ for each simulation, we can see that after 200 periods of learning, the stability of all GP-based coordination games has improved.

Finally, the chaotic attractor in the game $\Gamma(3.86957)$ does not occur in any simulation of CASE 2. However, by comparing $\delta_{M,b}$ or $\delta_{M^*,b}$ across CASE 1 and CASE 2 in Table 3, we find that the standard deviations of CASE 2 are slightly larger than those of CASE 1. This difference is also revealed by visually comparing Figure 1 with Figure 2.

Table 3: Results of the simulations of GP

CASE/Simulation		1	2	3	4	5
1	$\overline{M_a}$	0.5928	0.5927	0.5932	0.5929	0.5924
	$\delta_{M,a}$	0.0270	0.0270	0.0242	0.0266	0.0276
	$\delta_{M^*,a}$	0.0272	0.0272	0.0243	0.0267	0.0277
1	$\overline{M_b}$	0.5954	0.5954	0.5954	0.5954	0.5954
	$\delta_{M,b}$	0.0003	0.0003	0.0002	0.0002	0.0002
	$\delta_{M^*,b}$	0.0003	0.0003	0.0002	0.0002	0.0003
2	$\overline{M_a}$	0.7407	0.7408	0.7406	0.7408	0.7408
	$\delta_{M,a}$	0.0171	0.0174	0.0187	0.0168	0.0177
	$\delta_{M^*,a}$	0.0171	0.0174	0.0187	0.0168	0.0177
2	$\overline{M_b}$	0.7415	0.7415	0.7415	0.7415	0.7415
	$\delta_{M,b}$	0.0004	0.0004	0.0004	0.0004	0.0005
	$\delta_{M^*,b}$	0.0004	0.0004	0.0004	0.0004	0.0005

$\overline{M_a}$ = the average of M_t of a simulation (from Generation 1 to 1000).
$\overline{M_b}$ = the average of M_t of a simulation (from Generation 201 to 1000).
$\delta_{M,a}$ = standard deviation about the M_a of a simulation (from Generation 1 to 1000).
$\delta_{M,b}$ = standard deviation about the M_b of a simulation (from Generation 201 to 1000).
$\delta_{M^*,a}$ = standard deviation about the *strict interior equilibrium* $1-\frac{1}{\omega}$ (from Generation 1 to 1000).
$\delta_{M^*,b}$ = standard deviation about the *strict interior equilibrium* $1-\frac{1}{\omega}$ (from Generation 201 to 1000).

5 Conclusions and Extensions

We have considered a simple coordination game, where the actions of individual players are modeled and updated using GP techniques. We have found that our GP–based algorithm effectively mimics the behavior of the experimental subjects who played the same versions of the game. For this reason, we conclude that GP techniques may serve as a reasonable model of adaptive learning behavior. We have also argued that our GP-based algorithm is a much more robust learning algorithm than the more standard, representative agent– type learning algorithms that are frequently encountered in the learning literature, in that our GP algorithm allows for (initially) heterogeneous actions, is population–based, and is capable of a much more sophisticated decision making than is possible in these other learning algorithms.

Despite the robustness of the GP algorithm, the evolution of play in our GP-based coordination game remains quite similar to that observed in the experiments that Van Huyck et al. (1994) conducted with human subjects. The mean choice of action eventually settles down to a small neighborhood of the interior equilibrium, even in CASE 2, where the myopic best response dynamic predicts that this interior equilibrium should be unstable. There is evidence however that the coordination problem our artificial agents face in CASE 2 is somewhat more difficult than the coordination problem they face in CASE 1, as indicated by the different standard deviations in these two cases.

While these results cast some doubt on the plausibility of the myopic best response dynamic as a selection criterion, it is not yet clear that the myopic best response dynamic can be completely rejected as a way of characterizing the evolution of behavior in this simple coordination game. In particular, we have only considered a single version of the coordination game, $\Gamma(3.86957)$ where the myopic best response dynamic failed to predict convergence to the interior equilibrium. In future research, we plan to conduct further computational experiments with values for $\omega \in [3, 3.839]$. In this range of values for ω, the myopic best response dynamic converges, in the limit, to stable *cycles* of differing periodicities. The question to be addressed is whether our GP–base learning algorithm might be able to coordinate on such cycles. Research by Bullard and Duffy (1995) and Marimon and Sunder (1995) suggests that both human and artificially intelligent agents are capable of coordination on low order cycles, (e.g. 2–cycles).

References

[1] Bullard, J. and J. Duffy (1995), "On Learning and the Stability of Cycles," In *Proceedings of the First International Conference of the Society for Computational Economics.*

[2] Chen, S, J. Duffy, and C. Yeh (1996), "Equilibrium Selection Through Adaptation: Using Genetic Programming to Model Learning in a Coordination Game," working paper no. 9603, Department of Economics, National Chengchi University.

[3] Chen, S, J. Duffy, and C. Yeh (1996a), "Genetic Programming in the Coordination Game with a Chaotic Best-Response Function," in P. Angeline, T. Back, and D. Fogel (eds.), *Proceedings of the Fifth Annual Conference on Evolutionary Programming*, MIT Press, Cambridge, MA.

[4] Chen, S and C. Yeh (1996), "Genetic Programming Learning and the Cobweb Model", forthcoming in Angeline, P. and K. E. Kinnear, Jr. (eds.) *Advances in Genetic Programming 2*, MIT Press, Cambridge, MA, Chapter 22.

[5] Koza, J. R. (1989), "Hierarchical Genetic Algorithms Operating on Populations of Computer Program", in *Proceedings of the 11th International Joint Conference on Artificial Intelligence*, Morgan Kaufmann.

[6] Koza, J. R. (1992), *Genetic Programming: On the Programming of Computers by Means of Natural Selection*, MIT Press.

[7] Marimon, R. and S. Sunder (1995), "Does a Constant Money Growth Rule Help Stabilize Inflation?: Experimental Evidence," *Carnegie–Rochester Conference Series on Public Policy* 43, 111-156.

[8] Van Hyuck, J. B., J. P. Cook, and R. C. Battalio (1994), "Selection Dynamics, Asymptotic Stability, and Adaptive Behavior," *Journal of Political Economy*, Vol. 102, No. 5, pp. 975-1005.

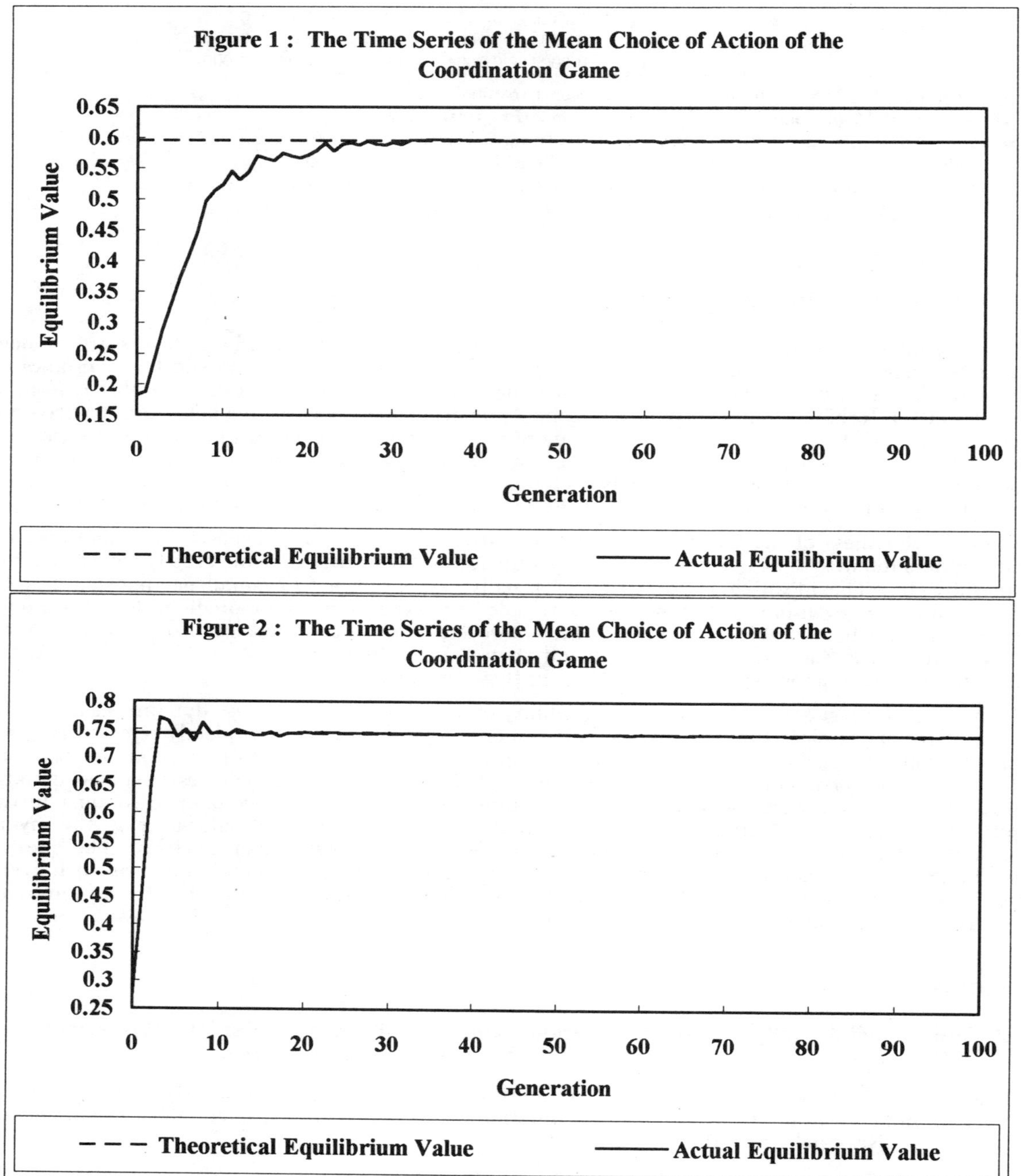

The invited program is also featured by 8 special sessions on current interesting topics. Each special session organizer is invited by the Program Committee and the success of each special session is completely due to the hard efforts of each organizer.

A Method of Combining Multiple Classifiers with Different Features

Ke Chen, Huisheng Chi
National Lab of Machine Perception and Center for Information Science
Peking University, Beijing 100871, China
Email: {chen,chi}@cis.pku.edu.cn

Abstract— In this paper, we propose a novel method of combining multiple classifiers with different features. Unlike the previous methods, the proposed method adopts the framework of linear opinion pools instead of the framework of a decision maker consulting several experts regarding some events. Accordingly, a combination scheme is obtained by training the parameters of a model of generalized finite mixture distributions based upon maximum likelihood estimation along with the EM algorithm. We apply the proposed method to text-dependent speaker identification and demonstrate its effectiveness based upon the experimental results.

1   Introduction

Recently, the combination of multiple classifiers has been viewed as a new direction for the development of highly reliable pattern recognition systems [1]. Preliminary results indicate that combination of several complementary classifiers leads to classifiers with improved performance [1]-[4]. There are at least two reasons to the necessity of combining multiple classifiers. First, for almost any one of the current pattern recognition application areas, there are a number of classification algorithms available developed from different theories and methodologies. Usually, for a specific application problem, each of these classifiers could reach a certain degree of success, but maybe none of them is totally perfect or at least anyone of them is not so good as expected in practical application. Second, for a specific recognition problem, there are often numerous types of features which could be used to represent and recognize patterns. These features are also represented in very diversified forms and it is rather hard to lump them together into one single classifier to make a decision. As a result, multiple classifiers are needed to deal with the different features [1][3].

From the viewpoint of statistics, the combination of multiple classifiers may be viewed as the combination of multiple probability distributions. In general, there are two frameworks to complete the combination [5]; one is that of a decision maker who consults several experts regarding some events and the other is that of linear opinion pool in which the decision maker forms a linear combination of expert opinions. Under these two frameworks, there have been extensive studies in the combination of multiple classifiers [1]-[5]. However, most of those techniques are merely used to combine multiple classifiers with the same input (feature). As mentioned above, multiple classifiers are needed to handle the different features for some classification problems, which makes it necessary to develop some techniques for handling the combination of multiple classifiers. After investigating the current techniques, we found that the framework of a decision maker consulting multiple experts could be directly extended to handle the aforementioned problem since a decision is made merely by combining the expert opinions based upon their own prior distribution or using a voting principle regardless of the type of input (feature) to experts. Using such techniques, some work has been done and achieved satisfactory performance [3][6]. In the framework of linear opinion pools, however, the existed techniques cannot be directly extended to handle the problem since the linear coefficients must depend upon the input (features) to each expert. In this paper, we present a novel method of combining multiple classifiers with different features under the framework of linear opinion pools. In [7][8], a scheme of combining multiple classifiers along with EM algorithm was proposed under the framework of linear opinion pools and simulations show that the combination scheme could achieve satisfactory results. Motivated by the idea, we extend the scheme to combination of multiple classifiers with different features by introducing multiple gating networks for handling different features. Accordingly, the EM algorithm is also derived based upon the proposed generalized mixture model. To demonstrate the effectiveness of the proposed scheme, we have applied it to a real-world problem, i.e. text-dependent speaker identification. Experimental results show that the performance of the combination scheme is satisfactory.

The rest of the paper is organized as follows. Section 2 presents the scheme of combining multiple classifiers with different features. Section 3 describes the maximum likelihood learning with EM algorithm. Section 4 reports experimental results and some discussions are given in section 5. Conclusions are drawn in the final section.

2   A Linear Combination Scheme for Classification with Different Features

The current problem of different features refers to that there may be more than one kind of feature which can be extracted from the same raw data. Based upon each individual feature of them, a classifier or multiple different classifiers can be trained for a classification task, which results in the existence of multiple classifiers with different features for the same classification task. The problem of combination refers to how to combine these classifiers with different features for producing a better result.

For a sample D in a training set $\mathbf{S}$ with M classes, we assume that there are P ($P > 1$) features extracted from D called $\mathbf{x}_1(D), \cdots, \mathbf{x}_P(D)$. Accordingly, we may employ N ($N \geq P$) classifiers to complete the classification task on $\mathbf{S}$ in which there are N_i classifiers trained with the feature $\mathbf{x}_i$ ($i = 1, \cdots, P$) and $\sum_{i=1}^{P} N_i = N$. Given pattern classes C_i ($i = 1, \cdots, M$), we consider such classifiers that for an input $\mathbf{x}_{p_j}(1 \leq p_j \leq P)$, a classifier e_j outputs is as follows,

$$\vec{p}_j(\mathbf{x}_{p_j}) = [p_{j1}(\mathbf{x}_{p_j}), \cdots, p_{jM}(\mathbf{x}_{p_j})]^T, \quad p_{jk}(\mathbf{x}_{p_j}) \geq 0, \quad \sum_{k=1}^{M} p_{jk}(\mathbf{x}_{p_j}) = 1. \tag{1}$$

where $p_{jk}(\mathbf{x}_{p_j})$ denotes the probability that $\mathbf{x}_{p_j}$ belongs to C_k recognized by e_j, and $\mathbf{x}_{p_j}$ denotes the feature of D used as the input of classifier e_j with its form of representation being a vector, a string or whatever else. The direct instances of these classifiers include those based upon parametric or nonparametric density estimation. Indeed, there are some classifiers, e.g. distance classifiers or neural network classifiers, which output a vector $\vec{u}_j(\mathbf{x}_{p_j}) = [u_{j1}(\mathbf{x}_{p_j}), \cdots, u_{jM}(\mathbf{x}_{p_j})]^T$ without satisfying $u_{jk}(\mathbf{x}_{p_j}) \geq 0$ and $\sum_{k=1}^{M} u_{jk}(\mathbf{x}_{p_j}) = 1$. Fortunately, these outputs can be transformed into the form in Eq. (1) after a slight modification [7] $p_{jk} = g_{jk} / \sum_{k=1}^{M} g_{jk}$, with $g(r) \geq 0$. For the multiway classification in which the output is binary($y_k \in \{0, 1\}$) with a single non-zero component, we may define a *generalized Bernoulli distribution* based upon a training pair $\{\mathbf{x}_{p_j}, \mathbf{y}\}$ where $\mathbf{y} = \{y_1, \cdots, y_M\}$ as follows

$$P_j(\mathbf{y}|\mathbf{x}_{p_j}, \vec{\theta}_j) = \prod_{k=1}^{M} [p_{jk}(\mathbf{x}_{p_j}|\vec{\theta}_j)]^{y_k} \tag{2}$$

where $\vec{\theta}_j$ is the parameter vector of classifier e_j and has been already fixed after the classifier was trained. For a fixed $\mathbf{y}$, we achieve a distribution specified by one of $p_{jk}(\mathbf{x}_{p_j}|\vec{\theta}_j)$.

Given N classifiers e_j ($j = 1, \cdots, N$) and P kinds of features $\mathbf{x}_{p_j}$ ($j = 1, \cdots, N; \ 1 \leq p_j \leq P$) and assuming that their priors are $\Phi = \{\alpha_{ij}(\mathbf{x}_i)\}$ based upon the feature $\mathbf{x}_i$ ($i = 1, \cdots, P; \ j = 1, \cdots, N$), respectively, we define a generalized finite mixture distribution for pairs $\{\mathbf{x}_i(D), \mathbf{y}\}$ ($i = 1, \cdots, P$) as follows,

$$P(\mathbf{y}|D, \Phi) = \sum_{j=1}^{N} \sum_{i=1}^{P} \beta_i \alpha_{ij}(\mathbf{x}_i) P_j(\mathbf{y}|\mathbf{x}_{p_j}, \vec{\theta}_j) = \sum_{j=1}^{N} \sum_{i=1}^{P} \beta_i \alpha_{ij}(\mathbf{x}_i) \prod_{k=1}^{M} [p_{jk}(\mathbf{x}_{p_j}|\vec{\theta}_j)]^{y_k} \tag{3}$$

where $\alpha_{ij}(\mathbf{x}_i) \geq 0$, $\beta_i \geq 0$, $\sum_{j=1}^{N} \alpha_{ij}(\mathbf{x}_i) = 1$, $\sum_{i=1}^{P} \beta_i = 1$ (each β_i is a constant and its value may be determined for a given task according to the priori knowledge.) and $\mathbf{x}_{p_j}$ refers to the feature of D used to train the jth classifier ($1 \leq p_j \leq P$).

It is worth noting that the definition of the mixture distribution relies on the fact that features $\mathbf{x}_i$ ($i = 1, \cdots, P$) are extracted from the same sample D in $\mathbf{S}$ and could be viewed as different versions of D which are also equivalents of the original D. Thus, we may deal with the problem by replacing D with an appropriate $\mathbf{x}_i$ ($1 \leq i \leq P$) in some cases. Since $P(\mathbf{y}|D, \Phi)$ is conditional on inputs $\mathbf{x}_i$ ($i = 1, \cdots, P$), those priors in Φ should be also conditional distributions on $\mathbf{x}_i$ ($i = 1, \cdots, P$). As a result, based on the result in [8], we assume that

$$\alpha_{ij}(\mathbf{x}_i) = \frac{\lambda_{ij} q(\mathbf{x}_i, \vec{\varphi}_{ij})}{\sum_{r=1}^{N} \lambda_{ir} q(\mathbf{x}_i, \vec{\varphi}_{ir})}; \quad \lambda_{ij} \geq 0, \ \sum_{j=1}^{N} \lambda_{ij} = 1, \ i = 1, \cdots, P, \ j = 1, \cdots, N. \tag{4}$$

where $q(\mathbf{x}_i, \vec{\varphi}_{ij}) \geq 0$ is a parametric function, and given by Gaussian distribution

$$q(\mathbf{x}_i, \vec{\varphi}_{ij}) = q(\mathbf{x}_i, \vec{m}_{ij}, \Sigma_{ij}) = \frac{1}{(2\pi)^{\frac{n}{2}} |\Sigma_{ij}|^{\frac{1}{2}}} \exp\{-\frac{1}{2}(\mathbf{x}_i - \vec{m}_{ij})^T \Sigma_{ij}^{-1}(\mathbf{x}_i - \vec{m}_{ij})\} \tag{5}$$

where n is the dimension of $\mathbf{x}_i$. Thus, Eq. (3) becomes a generalized finite mixture model for combining multiple classifiers with different features in which the information from the outputs of classifiers, the desire label $\mathbf{y}$ and different inputs $\mathbf{x}_i$ ($i = 1, \cdots, P$) is jointly considered for the combination. In Eq. (3), however, $\alpha_{ij}(\mathbf{x}_i)$ ($i = 1, \cdots, P; j = 1, \cdots, N$) are still unknown and we shall propose a maximum likelihood learning method to determine these priors in the next section. Suppose that those priors have been already determined, based upon Eq. (3), we can define a combination scheme, illustrated in Figure 1, that for a sample D in $\mathbf{S}$ and compute

$$P_k(D) = P(y_k = 1|D, \Phi) = \sum_{j=1}^{N} \sum_{i=1}^{P} \beta_i \alpha_{ij}(\mathbf{x}_i) p_{jk}(\mathbf{x}_{p_j}); \quad k = 1, \cdots, M. \tag{6}$$

and then make the final decision based upon the following rule,

The sample D belongs to C_k, if $P_k(D) > P_j(D)$ for all $j \neq k$. $\tag{7}$

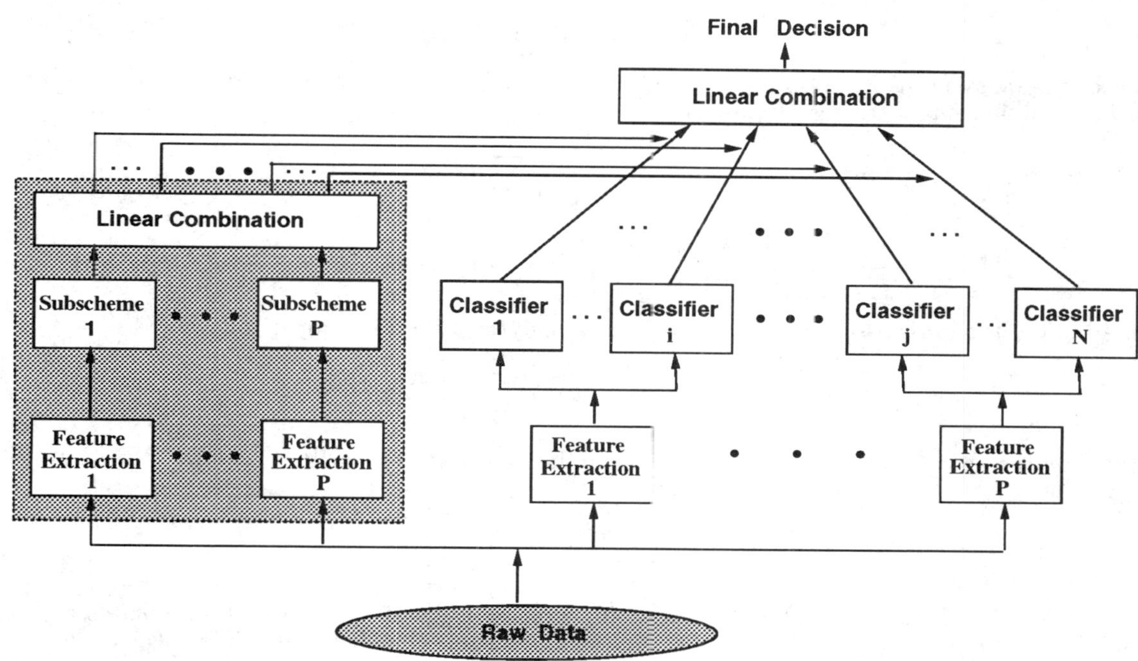

Figure 1: The linear combination scheme for classification with different features. The labels of classifiers are stipulated that classifiers with the same input feature vectors are put into a group, and all groups are arranged one by one for corresponding to different features used in all classifiers.

3 Maximum Likelihood Learning with EM Algorithm

Given a training set $\{(D^{(t)}, \mathbf{y}^{(t)})\}$ $(t = 1, \cdots, T)$, we extract P kinds features $\mathbf{x}_i^{(t)}$ $(i = 1, \cdots, P)$ from $D^{(t)}$. Using these P features, N $(N \geq P)$ classifiers can be trained. Accordingly, parameters $\Phi = \{\alpha_{ij}(\mathbf{x}_i)\}$ $(i = 1, \cdots, P; j = 1, \cdots, N)$ are learned by maximizing the log-likelihood

$$L = \sum_{t=1}^{T} \ln P(\mathbf{y}^{(t)}|D^{(t)}, \Phi) = \sum_{t=1}^{T} \ln[\sum_{j=1}^{N} \sum_{i=1}^{P} \beta_i \alpha_{ij}(\mathbf{x}_i^{(t)}) P_j(\mathbf{y}^{(t)}|\mathbf{x}_{p_j}^{(t)}, \vec{\theta}_j)] \tag{8}$$

For the log-likelihood, we may adopt EM algorithm [9] to estimate all parameters in Φ by introducing a set of indicators as *missing data* to the original training set. As a result, the corresponding EM algorithm is summarized as follows,

1. **Initialization**
   At $s = 0$, initialize randomly $\vec{\varphi}_{i1} = \vec{\varphi}_{i2} = \cdots = \vec{\varphi}_{iN}$ $(i = 1, \cdots, P)$
   subject to $\alpha_{ij}^{(s)}(\mathbf{x}_i) = \frac{1}{N}$ $(i = 1, \cdots, P;\ j = 1, \cdots, N)$.

2. **The EM procedure at $s > 0$**
   (1) **E-step**. For each pair $\{D^{(t)}, \mathbf{y}^{(t)}\}$, compute

   $$h_{ij}^{(s)}(\mathbf{y}^{(t)}|\mathbf{x}_i^{(t)}) = \frac{\beta_i \alpha_{ij}^{(s)}(\mathbf{x}_i^{(t)}) P_j(\mathbf{y}^{(t)}|\mathbf{x}_{p_j}^{(t)}, \vec{\theta}_j)}{\sum_{j=1}^{N} \sum_{i=1}^{P} \beta_i \alpha_{ij}^{(s)}(\mathbf{x}_i^{(t)}) P_j(\mathbf{y}^{(t)}|\mathbf{x}_{p_j}^{(t)}, \vec{\theta}_j)} \tag{9}$$

   Then form a set of objective functions[1]

   $$Q(\vec{\varphi}_{ij}) = \sum_{t=1}^{T} h_{ij}^{(s)}(\mathbf{y}^{(t)}|\mathbf{x}_i^{(t)}) \ln q(\mathbf{x}_i, \vec{\varphi}_{ij}); \quad i = 1, \cdots, P,\ j = 1, \cdots, N. \tag{10}$$

   $$Q(\lambda_{ij}) = \sum_{t=1}^{T} \sum_{j=1}^{N} \sum_{i=1}^{P} h_{ij}^{(s)}(\mathbf{y}^{(t)}|\mathbf{x}_i^{(t)}) \ln \lambda_{ij}; \quad i = 1, \cdots, P,\ j = 1, \cdots, N. \tag{11}$$

   (2) **M-step**. Find a new estimate for $i = 1, \cdots, P,\ j = 1, \cdots, N$

   $$\vec{\varphi}_{ij}^{(s+1)} = \arg \max_{\vec{\varphi}_{ij}} Q(\vec{\varphi}_{ij}) \tag{12}$$

---

[1]Eq. (10) is formed by using a trick that transfer the conditional distribution of Eq.(3) into an equivalent joint distribution. One may be referred to the paper [8] for details.

$$\lambda_{ij}^{(s+1)} = \arg\max_{\lambda_{ij}} Q(\lambda_{ij}) \tag{13}$$

Since the Gaussian distribution is employed in Eq. (5), the maximization in Eq. (12) becomes analytically solvable using a trick [8][10] as follows,

$$\vec{m}_{ij}^{(s+1)} = \frac{1}{\sum_{t=1}^{T} h_{ij}^{(s)}(\mathbf{y}^{(t)}|\mathbf{x}_i^{(t)})} \sum_{t=1}^{T} h_{ij}^{(s)}(\mathbf{y}^{(t)}|\mathbf{x}_i^{(t)})\mathbf{x}_i^{(t)} \tag{14}$$

$$\Sigma_{ij}^{(s+1)} = \frac{1}{\sum_{t=1}^{T} h_{ij}^{(s)}(\mathbf{y}^{(t)}|\mathbf{x}_i^{(t)})} \sum_{t=1}^{T} h_{ij}^{(s)}(\mathbf{y}^{(t)}|\mathbf{x}_i^{(t)})[\mathbf{x}_i^{(t)} - \vec{m}_{ij}^{(s+1)}][\mathbf{x}_i^{(t)} - \vec{m}_{ij}^{(s+1)}]^T \tag{15}$$

In addition, the maximization in Eq. (13) is also analytically solvable [8] as follows,

$$\lambda_{ij}^{(s+1)} = \frac{1}{T} \sum_{t=1}^{T} h_{ij}^{(s)}(\mathbf{y}^{(t)}|\mathbf{x}_i^{(t)}) \tag{16}$$

Based on the above results, we can achieve the update formula of $\alpha_{ij}(\mathbf{x}_i^{(t)})$ $(i = 1, \cdots, P, \ j = 1, \cdots, N)$ as follows,,

$$\alpha_{ij}^{(s+1)}(\mathbf{x}_i^{(t)}) = \frac{\lambda_{ij}^{(s+1)} q(\mathbf{x}_i, \vec{m}_{ij}^{(s+1)}, \Sigma_{ij}^{(s+1)})}{\sum_{r=1}^{N} \lambda_{ir}^{(s+1)} q(\mathbf{x}_i, \vec{m}_{ir}^{(s+1)}, \Sigma_{ir}^{(s+1)})} \tag{17}$$

The EM procedure proceeds until a termination condition is satisfied. After all parameters are determined, Eq. (6) and Eq. (7) can be used for combining multiple classifiers with different features.

4   Experimental Results

Speaker identification is to classify an unlabeled voice token as belonging to one of a set of N reference speaker. It is a rather difficult learning task since a person's voice changes in time. So far, the unique robust feature of a speaker has not been still available and many features have been reported to be useful to speaker identification [12]. Therefore, speaker identification becomes a typical task which needs to combine multiple classifiers with different features for robustness. To demonstrate the usefulness of the proposed method, we have already applied it to *text-dependent speaker identification* which identifies an unknown speaker with a fixed text.

In experiments, we choose isolated digits as the fixed text. The acoustic database consists of ten isolated digits from '0' to '9' uttered in Chinese and recorded in three different sessions. For each digit, ten utterances were recorded in each session for each speaker. Currently, ten male speakers are registered in the database. we adopt four common features which are often used in speaker identification, i.e. *10-order delta-cepstrum (the first-order regression coefficient of cepstrum), 14-order LPC cepstrum, 14-order Mel-scale cepstrum and 12-order LPC coefficients*. On the basis of our earlier work [11], we employ the *Hierarchical Mixture Experts* (HME) [13] as the individual classifier. For each digit, currently, four HMEs with 2-8 structure are employed and trained on the aforementioned features, respectively. During training, five utterances of each digit recorded in the first session are used to train each individual classifier. During testing, for each digit, ten utterances recorded in the second session and ten utterances recorded in the third sessions are used. Indeed, we may use last 5 utterances of each digit recorded in the first session as testing samples and identifying accuracies could be close to 100% accordingly. However, it does not indicate that the system is robust since there is little variation of speaker's voices in the same recording session. As a result, the performance of a speaker identification system should be evaluated by the data recorded in those sessions with the exception of the sessions used for training. Accordingly, the results are called Test-1 and Test-2, respectively. Results of individual classifiers on different features are shown in TABLE I-IV.

TABLE I
The identifying accuracies(%) of the HME with 10-order delta cepstrum

Text	'0'	'1'	'2'	'3'	'4'	'5'	'6'	'7'	'8'	'9'	averaging
Test-1	94.0	91.0	98.0	93.0	100.0	98.0	99.0	86.0	93.0	99.0	95.1
Test-2	85.0	84.0	95.0	89.0	97.0	80.0	82.0	89.0	89.0	91.0	88.1

TABLE II
The identifying accuracies(%) of the HME with 14-order LP-based cepstrum

Text	'0'	'1'	'2'	'3'	'4'	'5'	'6'	'7'	'8'	'9'	averaging
Test-1	91.0	94.0	82.0	91.0	95.0	97.0	94.0	87.0	93.0	99.0	92.3
Test-2	78.0	92.0	79.0	90.0	94.0	87.0	94.0	81.0	90.0	98.0	88.3

TABLE III
The identifying accuracies(%) of the HME with 14-order Mel-scale cepstrum

Text	'0'	'1'	'2'	'3'	'4'	'5'	'6'	'7'	'8'	'9'	averaging
Test-1	87.0	88.0	98.0	93.0	94.0	92.0	95.0	92.0	96.0	95.0	93.0
Test-2	84.0	93.0	93.0	82.0	93.0	82.0	82.0	75.0	92.0	77.0	85.3

TABLE IV
The identifying accuracies(%) of the HME with 12-order LPC coefficients

Text	'0'	'1'	'2'	'3'	'4'	'5'	'6'	'7'	'8'	'9'	averaging
Test-1	90.0	95.0	87.0	88.0	94.0	97.0	88.0	87.0	89.0	99.0	91.4
Test-2	81.0	93.0	86.0	80.0	92.0	84.0	83.0	82.0	80.0	88.0	84.5

Based on those trained classifiers with different features, we apply the proposed method to train the combination scheme. To train the combination scheme described in Eq. (3), we adopt three utterances of each digit recorded in the second session as training data. Currently, the values of β_i in Eq. (3) are equal, i.e. $\beta_i = 0.25$ $(i = 1, 2, 3, 4)$. For each digit, accordingly, we use other seven utterances recorded in the second session and ten utterances recorded in the third session as testing data. The corresponding results are called Comb-1 and Comb-2, respectively and shown in TABLE V. For the purpose of comparison, we also list the best identifying result on each digit obtained with individual classifiers in TABLE V. The best results are called Best-1 and Best-2, respectively, corresponding to Test-1 and Test-2.

TABLE V
The identifying accuracies(%) of the proposed combining method
along with best ones obtained by all four classifiers

Text	'0'	'1'	'2'	'3'	'4'	'5'	'6'	'7'	'8'	'9'	averaging
Comb-1	95.7	97.1	98.6	95.7	100.0	98.6	100.0	94.2	98.6	100.0	97.9
Best-1	94.0	95.0	98.0	93.0	100.0	98.0	99.0	92.0	96.0	99.0	96.4
Comb-2	91.0	93.0	95.0	94.0	97.0	87.0	98.0	89.0	97.0	98.0	93.9
Best-2	85.0	93.0	95.0	90.0	97.0	87.0	94.0	89.0	92.0	98.0	92.0

According to TABLE V, we claim that the performance of the combination is significantly better than the performance of each individual classifiers. Moreover, results of the combination are also not worse than the best ones obtained by all four classifiers.

5   Discussions

In this section, we are going to discuss some issues on the proposed method and establish a relationship to the previous work [7][8][14].

Eq. (3) describes a generalized finite mixture model for combining multiple classifiers with different features. In the model, β_i is a constant used to normalize linear coefficients based upon different features. If we can acquire prior knowledge on features used to train classifiers, we shall be able to apply the prior knowledge to the combination scheme through choosing appropriate values of β_i. Thus, the proposed mixture model may supply a method to incorporate prior knowledge of features into the combination scheme. As mentioned in section 1, the proposed method is motivated by the work of *Xu et al* [7][8]. In Eq. (3), the generalized mixture model will become the one proposed in [7] when the same feature is used in all combined classifiers $(\beta_1 = 1)$. Thus, the proposed method may be viewed as an extension of the work of *Xu et al.* Furthermore, Eq. (3) may be also extended as an alternative model for *Mixture of Experts* [14][8] to complete a task of classification with different features. This extension is explicit in Eq. (3) if we also consider each classifier as an expert network and train each expert network along with the multiple gating networks simultaneously. Accordingly, the EM algorithm can be still used for training merely by adding a set of objective functions with respect to expert networks in the E-step and completing the maximization of the set of objective functions in the M-step. The maximization can be completed with the *Iterative Reweighted Least Square* algorithm when the statistical structure of each expert network can be modeled by the *generalized linear model* theory [13].

6   Conclusions

We have already described a novel method of combining multiple classifiers with different features. In the method, a generalized finite mixture model is presented for combining multiple classifiers with different features and learning algorithms for estimating parameters are also presented by the maximum likelihood estimation in help of the EM algorithm. To demonstrate the effectiveness of the proposed method, we applied it to a typical real-world task needing to combine multiple classifiers with different features for robustness, i.e. text-dependent speaker identification. Experimental results have shown that the proposed combination scheme works well and can produce considerably better identifying accuracies. In our onging work, we shall extend the proposed generalized mixture model to *mixture of experts* for classification with different features and adopt an adaptive method for determining the normalization value, β_i, in the generalized finite mixture model instead of determining it by utilizing the priori knowledge which is often difficult to be acquired.

Acknowledgements

Authors are very grateful to D.H. Xie for his providing results of four individual classifiers which form the basis of the experiments performed in section 4. This work was partially supported by National Science Foundation of China with Grants 69571002 and 69475007 as well as the Climbing Program – National Key Project for Fundamental Research in China with Grant NSC 92097.

References

[1] L. Xu, A. Krzyzak and C.Y. Suen, "Methods of combining multiple classifiers and their applications to handwriting recognition," *IEEE Trans. Sys. Man. Cybern.*, Vol. 23, No. 3, pp. 418-435, 1992.

[2] L. Xu, A. Krzyzak and C.Y. Suen, "Associative switch for combining multiple classifiers," *Journal of Artificial Neural Networks*, 1(1), pp. 77-100, 1994.

[3] R. Battiti and A.M. Colla, "Democracy in neural nets: voting schemes for classification," *Neural Networks*, Vol. 7, No. 4, pp. 691-708, 1994.

[4] G. Rogova, "Combining the results of several neural network classifiers," *Neural Networks*, Vol. 7, No. 5, pp. 777-781, 1994.

[5] R.A. Jacobs, " Methods for combining experts' probability assessments," *Neural Computation*, 7(5), pp. 867-888, 1995.

[6] L. Wang, K. Chen and H.S. Chi, "Text-Independent Speaker identification by combining classifiers with different features," submitted to World Congress on Neural Networks, 1996.

[7] L. Xu and M.I. Jordan, "EM learning on a generalized finite mixture model for combining multiple classifiers," *Proceedings of World Congress on Neural Networks*, San Diego, pp. IV227-IV230, 1993.

[8] L. Xu, M.I. Jordan and G.E. Hinton, "An alternative model for mixture of experts," in *Advances in Neural Information Processing Systems*, 7, J.D. Cowan et al eds., MIT press, 1995.

[9] A.P. Dempster, N.M. Laird and D. B. Rubin, "Maximum-likelihood from incomplete data via the EM algorithm," *J. Royal Stat. Soc. B*, 39, pp. 1-38, 1977.

[10] L. Xu, M.I. Jordan and G.E. Hinton, "A modified gating network for the mixtures of experts architecture," *Proceedings of World Congress on Neural Networks*, San Diego, pp. II405-II410, 1994.

[11] K. Chen, D.H. Xie and H.S. Chi, " Speaker identification based on Hierarchical Mixture of Experts," *Proceedings of World Congress on Neural Networks*, Washington D.C., pp. I493-I496, 1995.

[12] T. Matsui and S. Furui, "Speaker recognition technology," *NTT Review*, Vol. 7, No. 2, pp. 40-48, 1995.

[13] M.I. Jordan and R.A. Jacobs, "Hierarchical mixture of experts and EM algorithm," *Neural Computation*, Vol. 6, pp. 181-214, 1994.

[14] R.A. Jacobs, M.I. Jordan, S.J. Nowlan and G.E. Hinton, "Adaptive mixtures of local experts," *Neural Computation*, 3, pp. 79-87, 1991.

Consciousness Machines: Theory and Applications

Yi X Zhong

Dept of Information Engineering
University of Posts & Telecom
Beijing 100088, China
e-mail: zyx @bupt.edu.cn

Abstract

A hypothesis on generative mechanism of human consciousness is presented. And then, a new model for intelligence systems, which we call the *Consciousness Machine*, is established based on the hypothesis. The essense of the model is an integration of the comprehensive information theory, fuzzy logic, neural networks as well as expert systems. As an example of the many possible applications of the model, an analysis on natural language understanding is given.

Key Words: Intelligence,   Consciousness,   Understandability
                  Comprehensive Information

1. Introduction

It is well accepted that the objective of the research in such fields as computers, artificial intelligence or expert systems, neural networks, as well as robotics etc, is to create many kinds of intelligent systems to help human beings perform some of the sophisticated functions which, in the past, could only be performed by men themselves.

Although many exciting progresses along this direction have been made, all the successes we achieveed so far are considered far away from what we would like to achieve. What we are concerned the most today is to build up machines with some sorts of consciousness because any machine without consciousness cannot be well regarded as the one with higher rank of intelligence. In accord with this criterion, all the artificially intelligent systems can be divided into two categories: intelligent systems with and without consciousness.

What we will do in the second section of the paper is to present some of the new results on the generative mechanism of human consciousness in view of the theory of comprehensive information. Meanwhile, a discussion on the relationship among the intelligence, understandability, consciousness and comprehensive information. is carried out. Based on these result, a new model of intelligent systems, which we call the consciousness machine, is then established in third section. Moreover, as an example of many possible applications of the consciousness machine, an example of natural language understanding problem is instructed in fourth section. Some remarks on
the further studies in this regard are made in the final section.

2. Analysis on Human Consciousness

It is commonly recognized that consciousness is the radical foundation for any humans to have intelligence. In other words, it would be ipossible for a man to be intelligent if he had no consciousness at all. To this regard, any artificial machines with consciousness would possibly possess higher rank of intelligence than those without consciousness.

To get deeper insight of the concept of consciousness, let us make a detailed investigation on the generative mechanism of human consciousness which may be explained from a specific example as shown shown in Fig. 1.

As we can see from Fig. 1 that the process of understanding a concept, dog, can be divided into three stages. At stage (A), only syntactic information concerning the dog can be utilized. At stage (B), both syntactic and semantic information are available. And at stage (C), all the information , the comprehensive information, concrening the dog can now be systematically utilized to form the concept. What should be strongly emphasised here is that only at stage (C) could a man be able to make a correct decision toward the object for maximizing the benefits he may obtain or minimizing the loss possibly incuured. In other words, only at stage (C) could a man be <u>fully conscious</u> toward what he is facing while he is <u>semi-conscious</u> at stage (B) and <u>little conscious</u> at stage (A).

Therefore, it is sufficiently reasonable to define the human ability to make such a correct decision as his consciousness. That is to say, <u>consciousness is an ability to make a correct, or even optimal, decision toward given objects</u>.

A more important hint we learned from the example in Fig. 1 is the mechanism through which consciousness toward an object can gradually be built up. A good **way** associated with some supporting capabilities to grow up consciousness from the unconscious state toward any specific object can be described as below.

At the stage (A), he must, first, have the <u>ability to observe</u> the object he faced, that is, he must be able to sense the <u>formal information</u> such as the shape, the size, the color, and the *general appearances* about the object. And then, he must have the <u>ability to store the information</u> on what he observed about the object. Thirdly, he must <u>able to retrieve the information</u> on that object from his memory whenever needed. Fourthly, he must <u>able to do the comparison</u> between an object he is now observing in new situation and the information about the object he retrieved from his memory so that he is able to tell whether the object he is now observing is in the same category of the object he observed before.

Up to this point, he is already able to distinguish one object from others based on the <u>utilization of formal, or syntactic, information</u>. And we define this level of the ability as the <u>shallow consciousness</u>. Obviously, systems possessing this ability **can, at most,** have <u>shallow intelligence</u>.

At the stage (B), he must be able to observe and remember the *basic behaviors* and functions the object may have. Based on these observations, he should get to a deeper understanding on what the object can, or would like to, do and what it can not do, or would not like to do. This is a high level ability which we often refer to as <u>abstraction</u>. For supporting the abstraction, he, of course, needs the abilities of observing, dynamic memory, comparison, <u>updating and prediction</u>, etc.

Up to this stage, he has had a relatively complete understanding on the object. What he can tell about the object now is not only its appearance (*what it looks like*), but also its behaviors and functions (*what it does*). In other words, he is now understand the meanings of the object (*what it is*). Because of the fact that he is able to use the functional, or semantic, information, he is already in a state of semi-conscious toward the object he is dealing with. Systems possessing this level of ability is defined as semi-conscious and will have semi-intelligence.

At the stage (C), he must not only be able to observe the object and to predict its behaviors or functions, but even more importantly, he should be able to know whether it is benefitial or harmful to himself, or to his objectives, and therefore, is able to make a correct decision and take correct actions toward the object. This means that he should have a goal in his mind and should establish related criteria for making judgements whether an object faced is benefitial or harmful to his goal. This is an ability we call the self-consciousness. The goal may be fixed either by any other persons, or by his self-learning.

However, the ability of making a value judgement with respect to his goal is the ability of utilizing the pragmatical information and is the highest level of abilities. Thus we define this ability the full consciousness. Systems possessing this level ability will have full intelligence.

Summarizing the discussions above, we can establish the inter-relationships among the intelligence, consciousness, understandability, and comprehensive information as is briefly as well as clearly expressed in Table 1.

Table 1   The inter-relationships

Degree of Intelligence	Level of Consciousness	Depth of Understandability	Type of Information
Zero	Nil	Empty	None
Primitive	Low	Shallow	Syntactic
Partial	Intermediate	Half-Depth	Syntactic + Semantic
Full	High	Deep	Comprehensive Information

3. Consciousness Machine: An Intelligent Systems Model

A possible model of intelligent systems is established on the basis of the results obtained in previous section.

It is clearly seen fron Fig.2 that the consciousness machine is an integration of artificial neural networks, expert system with comprehensive information structure as its bases. Since the comprehensive information contains great amount of fuzzy information, it is necessary to employ the fuzzy logic as its tool for supporting the approximate reasoning.

Roughly speaking, primitive intelligent problems like pattern classification and recognition, combinatorial optimization, associative restorage, algebraic coding and decoding, etc., can be performed by the neural networks array, while any fully intelligent problems should be handled by the consciousness inferencing engine.

The key component of the consciousness machine model is the comprehensive information bases. Each item of the information within the base should have the following structure as shown in Fig.3:

As an example, the item of information "DOG" will have the structure shown below:

4. Applicational Example: Natural Language Understanding

Natural Language Processing and Understanding is a typical example in the field of Artificial Intelligence research where full intelligence, thus consciousness machine, is absolutely needed and the primitive intelligance, thus the conventional expert system, is far from sufficient.

Suppose that the input of the system is spoken Chinese sentences and the task for the system is, first, to understand the meaning of the spoken sentence and then to translate the Chinese speech into written form of the Chinese sentences as is shown in Fig.5.

Employing the consciousness machine model as is shown in Fig.2, the neural networks array can be assigned to perform the task of speech recognition. The result of the neural networks array is a strem of Chinese Pinyin symbols which in turn serves as the input to the consciousness inferencing engine and the task of the consciousness inferencing engine is to translate the Chinese Pinyin symbol stream into Written Chinese sentences. This is the part where most of the intelligence lies in.

Take the sentence in Fig.5 as an example, each Pinyin word in the sentence has possibly more than one written word to correspond to, see Fig.6.

To exactly translate Pinyin to written sentence, the semantic and pragmatic information are absolutely needed. The consciousness inferencing engine should calculate the amount of comprehensive information for each possible combinations of the words and choose the one having maximal amount of the comprehensive information as the solution as is indicated by bold lines in Fig.6.

5. Concluding Remarks

The model of consciousness machine has been proved feasible as well as attractive. Also, there are many open problems to be further studied such as the expression and calculation of the comprehensive information. Fortunately, there are many possibilities to be utilized. Due to the limitation of the space we would like to discuss them in another paper.

References

1. Yi X. ZHONG, Principles of Information Science, BUPT Press, Feb., 1996
2. Yi X. ZHONG etal, Intelligence Theory and Technology, PT Press, Dec., 1992.

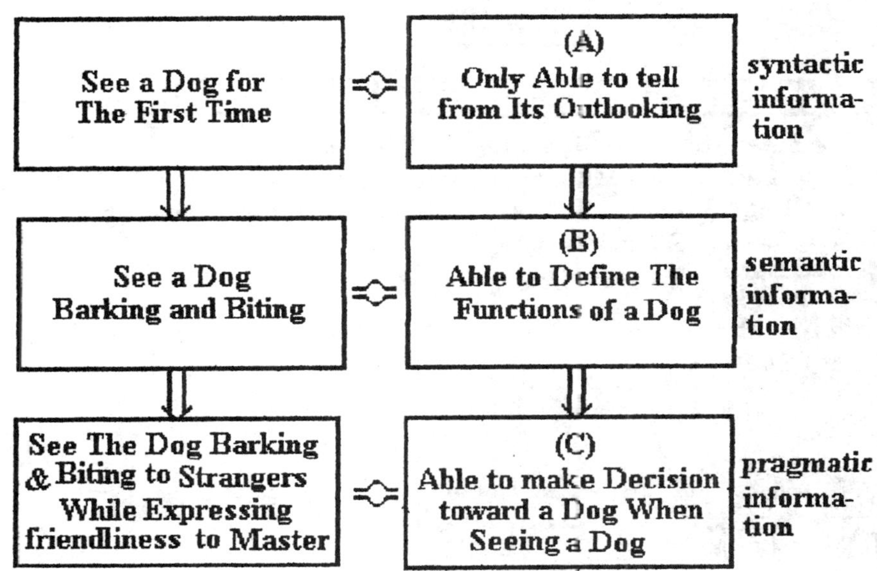

Fig.1 Understanding "Dog"

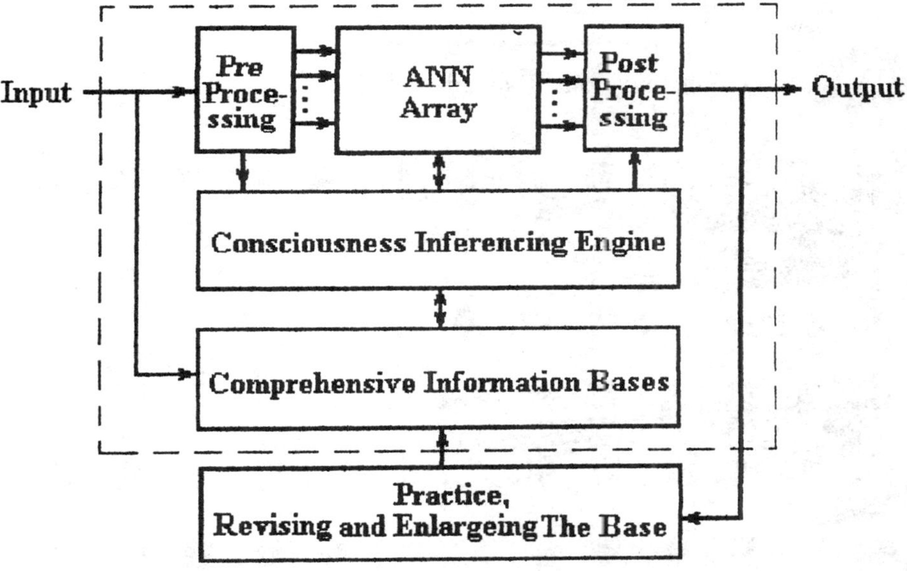

Fig.2 Consciousness Machine Model

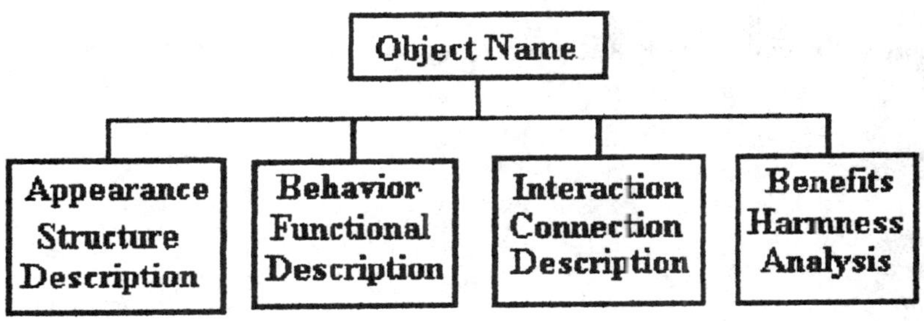

Fig.3 The Information structure in CIB Bases

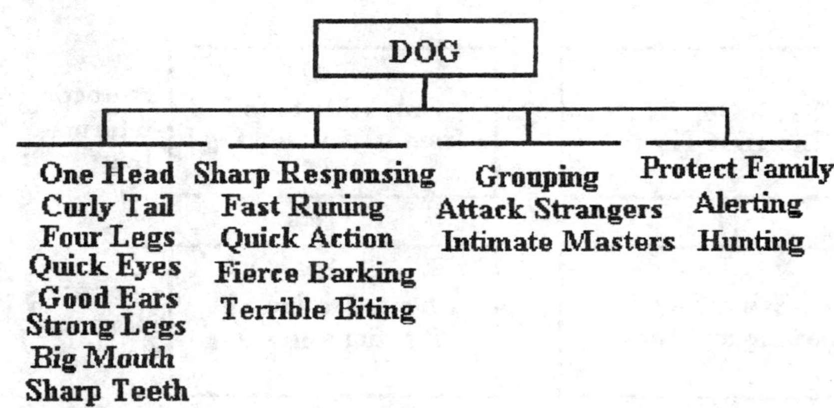

Fig.4 Example for Information Expression

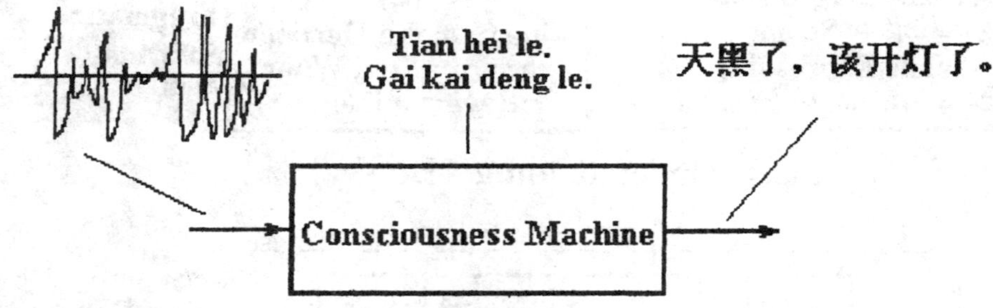

Fig.5 Applicational Example: NLU

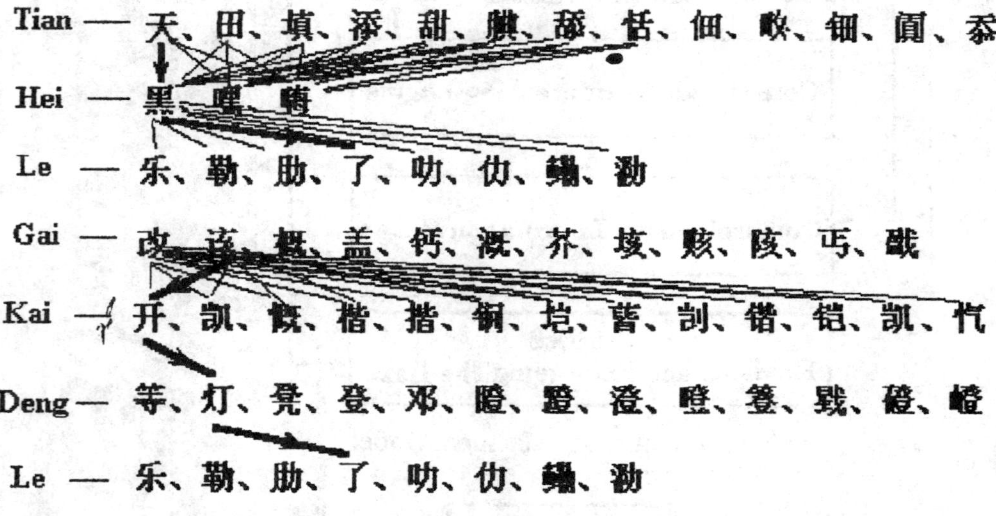

Fig.6 Intelligence Needed in translation from Pinyin to Written Sentences

Some Analysis on the Classification Capability of Neural Network Using Quadratic Sigmoidal Neurons

Baoyun Wang and Zhenya He
Department of Radio Engineering
Southeast University, Nanjing 210096
P.R. China
e-mail: lxyang @ seu. edu. cn

Abstract: The model of neurons is very important in constructing an artificial neural network. In [2], [3], Chiang, et al. proposed a new model of neuron--quadratic sigmoidal neuron. They showed that the model can endow the network with better classification capability and generalization. In this paper, we made the evaluation on the classification capability of the network using quadratic sigmoidal neurons.

1 INTRODUCTION

Neurons in an artificial neural network, as the basic processing units, receive the inputs and act the weighted inputs an activation function. To an extent, the function of the network depends upon the adopted model of neuron. Therefore, to find a suitable neuron model is very important in constructing an artificial neural network. In many references, the sigmoidal function is often used as the activation function of neuron. In order to construct more powerful neural classifier, Chiang, et. al.[2][3] proposed a new activation function called quadratic sigmoid function (QSF). Then they developed their idea and introduced an extended type of neurons called multi-threshold quadratic sigmoidal neurons. Compared to the conventional perceptrons[4]-[6] the neural networks containing quadratic sigmoidal neurons enjoy faster learning , better generalization capability and stronger recognition capability[1][2][3].

This paper mainly considers how far the improvement of the classification capability of neural network can be reached by using quadratic sigmoidal neurons. It is proved that for the three layer feed forward neural network containing single or multiple threshold quadratic sigmoidal neurons in the hidden and output layer at least k+1 hidden nodes are needed to dichotomize any dichotomy defined on the training set of 4k+7 examples.

2 QUADRATIC SIGMOIDAL NEURONS

2.1 some type of activation function

In this section, some notations about various kind of neurons and their activation functions to be used in the following will be presented.

a. multi-threshold quadratic sigmoidal neuron: suppose the input for the neuron $x = (x_1, x_2, \cdots, x_n)$, the corresponding weight vector $w = (w_0, w_1, \cdots, w_n)$, and the threshold vector $\Theta = (\theta_0, \theta_1, \cdots, \theta_n)$. The activation function of this type of neurons is

$$f(net, \Theta) = \frac{1}{1 + \exp(net^2 - g(\Theta, x))} \quad (1)$$

where

$$net = w \cdot x = w_0 + \sum_{i=1}^{n} w_i x_i \quad (2)$$

$$g(\Theta, x) = \theta_0 + \sum_{i=1}^{n} \theta_i x_i \quad (3)$$

b. single threshold quadratic sigmoidal neuron: in this kind of neurons, the threshold function $g(\Theta, x)$ of activation function is reduced to a constant θ

c. multithreshold quadratic Heaviside neuron: it takes the following extended quadratic Heaviside function as its the activation function.

$$H_q^\theta(w \cdot x, \Theta) = \begin{cases} 1, & \textit{if } g(\Theta, x) - (w \cdot x)^2 > 0 \\ 0, & \textit{if } g(\Theta, x) - (w \cdot x)^2 \leq 0 \end{cases} \quad (4)$$

d. single threshold quadratic Heaviside neuron: the threshold $g(\Theta,x)$ in activation function is reduced to a scalar.

2.2 some notations

In this subsection, some useful notations are presented, which read as

QSNN --- three layer network containing single or multiple threshold quadratic sigmoidal neurons in the hidden and output layer.

DIOH neural network --- a single-hidden-layer network *with direct input-to-output connection* and containing multiple or single threshold quadratic Heaviside neurons in the hidden and output layer.

3   MAIN RESULTS

3.1 Problem Formation

As pointed out by Chiang, et al.[3], the problem can be described as a partition on the input space into two subsets, i.e., S^+, S^-. A signal is called a positive example and has a target signal f(x) associated with it. A signal $y \in S^-$ is a negative example with target f(y)=0. For any training set $S_n = \{x^1, x^2, \cdots, x^p | x^i \in R^n\}$, we can always find a vector such that the new training set $S = \{z^1, z^2, \cdots, z^p | z^i = v \cdot x^i \in R\}$ contains no duplicated elements. So we only need to consider the dichotomy on one dimensional pattern space.

3.2 The classification capability of DIOH neural network

Assume a DIOH neural network, let $w_i = (w_{i0}, w_{i1})$ and $\Theta_i^1 = (\theta_{i0}^1, \theta_{i1}^1)$ denote the weight and threshold of the **i**-th hidden node, and $u = (u_0, u_1, \cdots, u_k)$ and $\Theta^2 = (\theta_0^2, \theta_1^2, \cdots, \theta_k^2)$ denote the hidden-to-output connection weight and threshold of output node. The output of the network is as follows

$$O(x) = H_q^\theta(u_0 + vx + \sum_{i=1}^{k} u_i H(w_{i0} + w_{i1}x, \theta_{i0}^1 + \theta_{i1}^1 x), \Theta^2) \quad (5)$$

where v denotes the direct input-output connection weight, H(.) is Heaviside function.

Theorem 1: For arbitrary $w_i, u, \Theta^1, \Theta^2$ $(i = 1, 2, \cdots, k)$, a DIOH neural network can divide arbitrary closed interval I into at most 4k+3 intervals $S^1, S^2, \cdots S^{4k+3}$, such that

$$(a)\ \ S^i \cap S^j = \phi \quad (b)\ f(x) = 1 - f(y),\ \ \forall x \in S^i,\ y \in S^{i+1},\ i = 1, \cdots, 4k+2$$

Here f(x) means the target value of network.

3.3 The classification capabilities of QSNN

Given the training set

$$S = \{z^i | z^i \in R, i = 0, 1, \cdots, 4k+2\} \quad (6\text{-}1)$$

which satisfies

$$z^i < z^{i+1} \quad \textit{and} \quad f(z^i) = 1 - f(z^{i+1}) \quad (6\text{-}2)$$

where f(.) means the target value of neural network. Before constructing a neural network to learn the training set S, we often assume some closed intervals to contain the training pattern, as follows.

$$\alpha_- < I_0 < \alpha_0 < I_1 < \beta_0 < I_2 < \gamma_0 < I_3 < \gamma_0' < I_4 < \beta_0' < I_5$$
$$< \alpha_1 < \cdots < I_{4k+6} < \alpha_+$$

The weights and thresholds of the neural network to be designed is determined by α_-, α_0, β_0, γ_0, $\cdots$, α_+. If they satisfy the following conditions (here we still adopt the notation in the proof of theorem 1)

$$q_i^-,\ q_i^+ \notin (\bigcup_{l=0}^{4k+6} I_l),\ i = 1,\ \cdots,\ k \qquad (7)$$

$$(u_0 + \sum_{i=1}^{k+1} u_i h_i)^2 \neq (\theta_0^2 + \sum_{i=1}^{k+1} \theta_i^2 h_i),\quad for\ x \in (\bigcup_{l=0}^{4k+6} I_l) \qquad (8)$$

we denote the corresponding QSNN as *QSNN-I* and obtain Theorem 3.

Theorem 2: If *QSNN-I* is used to learn the training set S in (6), then at least k+1 hidden neurons are needed.

Theorem 2 shows the degree of the improvement of the classification capability of neural network. Compared with Committee Machine, the quadratic sigmoidal neuron only improve the classification capability of neural network by a factor of 4.

4. CONCLUSIONS

This paper analyses the degree of improvement on the classification capability of neural network by using quadratic sigmoidal neuron. We believe that the result is helpful for us to find more powerful neuron model for constructing artificial neural network.

Acknowledgment: This work was supported by the Climbing Programme-National Key Project for Fundamental Research in China

References

1. E.B. Baum and D. Haussler, "What size net gives valid generalization?," Neural   Computation, 1, 151-160, (1989).
2. C.C. Chiang and H.C. Fu, " A variant of second-order multilayer perceptron and its application to function approximation," in Proc. IJCNN'92, Baltimore, III, 887-892, (1992).
3. C.C. Chiang and H.C. Fu, " Using multi-threshold quadratic sigmoidal neurons to improve classification capability of multilayer perceptrons," IEEE Trans. Neural Networks, 5, 516-519, (1994).
4. S.C. Huang and Y.F. Huang, " Bounds on the number of hidden neurons in multilayer perceptrons," IEEE Trans. Neural Networks, 2, 47-55, (1991).
5. N.J. Nilsson, Learning Machines: Foundation of Trainable Pattern Classifying Systems. New York: McGraw-Hill, (1965).
6. E.D. Sontag, " On the recognition capabilities of feed forward nets," Tech. Rep. SYCON 90-03, SYCON-Rutgers Center Syst. Contr., Dept. Mathematics, Rutgers Univ., New Brunswick, NJ, Apr. (1990).

FUZZY NEURAL COMPUTING SYSTEM USING BLOCK DESIGN[*]

Jin Fan   Fan Junbo

Institute of Neural Networks & Information Techniques

Southwest Jiaotong University, Chengdu , 610031 Sichuan China

Tel.: (028)7762923   FAX : (028)7784007   E-mail: jinfan@swjtu.edu.cn

ABSTRACT

Topological structure is of most importance to the behavior of the artificial neural networks(ANN). In this paper some fundamental definitions and theorems are given for systematical analysis of the topological structure of various neural networks. Four main parts of the architecture of a fuzzy neural computing system are outlined. Based on the block design theory of combinatorial mathematics, a novel fuzzy neural computing system is suggested, which enables us to significantly decrease the number of weights while the symmetry and balance features still hold. It is expected that a new class of hierachy structure of fuzzy neural networks for achieving attention-concentration capabilities can thus be achieved.

1.INTRODUCTION

It is well known that neural networks(NN) are characterized by their massively connective topology, through which a powerful parallel distributed processing ability can be developed. There are already a number of NNs suggested for different applications since the late 1980s. One of the most popular type is Hopfield Neural Network, which is topologically a fully-connected network[1-2]. According to the knowledge from anatomy we know that the total number of neurons in human brain system is approximately at a grade of 10^{10} ~ 10^{11}, whereas each neuron is only connected to 10^3 ~ $1\,0^5$ other neurons[3]. In fact, suppose 10^{10} ~ 10^{11} neurons are fully-connected, there would have altogether more than 10^{20} synapses(weights), which is essentially an unapproachable astronomical figure. For the same reason, from the view point of simplicity in hardware implemetation of ANN, we prefer partly-connected topology to fully-connected one.

In order to systematically analyse and compare the features of neural networks with different structures, we will firstly introduce some basic definitions, and theorems concerning topological analysis, then based on the block design theory,   a novel kind of partly-connected neural networks is suggested.

2.PRELIMINARY DEFINITIONS & THEOREMS

DEFINITION 1   For a giver neural networks, let N be the number of neurons , let w_s be the number of weights, the coupling rate of the neural network is defined as

$$C = w_s\,/\,N \tag{1}$$

DEFINITION 2   Let k be the number of the nodes(neurons) serially connected between node i and node j , then the link length l_{ij} is defined as

$$l_{ij} = k+1 \tag{2}$$

---

* This research is supported by China 863 High-Level Technology Plan Foundation

The maximum l_{ij} for a pair of arbitrary nodes i , j in a neural network is called the link length of NN , which is simply denoted by L.

DEFINITION 3   A weight vector matrix **S** is defined as

$$\mathbf{S} = \begin{vmatrix} s_{11} & s_{12} & \cdots & s_{1n} \\ s_{21} & s_{22} & \cdots & s_{2n} \\ \cdot & \cdot & \cdots & \cdot \\ s_{n1} & s_{n2} & \cdots & s_{nn} \end{vmatrix} \tag{3}$$

where

$$s_{ij} = \begin{cases} 1 & \text{if } w_{ij} = 0 \\ 0 & \text{else} \end{cases} \tag{4}$$

DEFINITION 4   The approachable rate a_{ij} is denoted by the total number of different paths from i to j. Obviously, for a layered forward NN, if there exists $a_{ij} = 0$, where i is an arbitrary node of input layer,and j is an arbitrary node of output layer, then it means any input at node i doesn't have influence on the output of node j. In this case, regular information processing couldn't be carried out.

THEOREM 1   let $\mathbf{S}^{h}$ denote the matrix product , $\mathbf{S}^{h} = \mathbf{S}^{h-1}\mathbf{S} = (\mathbf{S}^{h-2}\mathbf{S})\mathbf{S} = \cdots$, for a neural networks with weight vector matrix $\mathbf{S} = [\, s_{ij} \,]_{n \times n}$, the approachable rate a_{ij} can be determined by

$$a_{ij} = \sum_{h=1}^{n} s^{h}_{ij} \tag{5}$$

where

$$s^{h}_{ij} = \sum_{r=2}^{n} s^{h-1}_{ir} s_{rj} \tag{6}$$

Theorem 1 can easily be proved by means of graph theory[4].

Some values of C,L for different NN architectures are listed in Tab.1.

Tab.1   arameters C, L of different architectures

Parameters of Networks	*Fully-connected, n neurons*	*Cellular Networks in form n × n*	*n-cubic Networks*	*Block design of DBBD(v,b,r,k,1)*
C	n - 1	8 (or 4)	n/2	k-1
L	1	n (or 2n)	n	2

3. ARCHITECTURE OF BLOCK DESIGN NEURAL NETWORKS(BDNN)

DEFINITION 5   Let V be v-set of elements labeled by 1,2,....,v,   let $B_1, B_2, \dots, B_b$ be k-subsets of V, let r be the number of k-subsets containing an arbitrary element. The incidence system V-B will be called as[5]:

(1) Differential Balanced Block Design(DBBD). In this case, for each pair of k-subsets $B_i, B_j (1 \leqslant i \leqslant b, 1 \leqslant j \leqslant b, i \neq j)$, there are exactly λ_b elements identical. In other words, there are $k - \lambda_b$ elements to be different from each other. Its parameters can be expressed as DBBD(v,b,r,k, λ_b) .

(2)Balanced Incomplete Block Design(BIBD). In this case, for each pair of elements $i,j (1 \leqslant i \leqslant v, 1 \leqslant j \leqslant v, i \neq j)$, the number of k-subsets containing both of them is λ_e . It is expressed as

BIBD(v,b,r,k, λ_e).

(3) Symmetric Balanced Incomplete Block Design(SBIBD). This is a critical case , by which both of   the above mentioned conditions are simultaneously satisfied, i.e.

$$\lambda_b = \lambda_e = \lambda \qquad (7)$$

LEMMA 1   let k be an natural number, there always exist infinite DBBD(v,b,r,k,1) , the parameters of which can be expressed as

$$DBBD(v,b,r,k,1) = DBBD(k(k+1)/2, k+1, k, 2, 1) \qquad (8)$$

<Example 1> The 8-subsets of DBBD(v,b,k,r, λ_b) = (28,8,2,7,1) is given in Tab.2.

Tab.2   Blocks   of   DBBD(28,8,2,7,1)

B \ V	1	2	3	4	5	6	7
B1	1	2	3	4	5	6	7
B2	1	8	9	10	11	12	13
B3	2	8	14	15	16	17	18
B4	3	9	14	19	20	21	22
B5	4	10	15	19	23	24	25
B6	5	11	16	20	23	26	27
B7	6	12	17	21	24	26	28
B8	7	13	18	22	25	27	28

If each block is regarded to be a sub-NN, then the archtecture of the whole NN is illustrated by Fig.1. In each sub-NN, neurons are connected in form of SBIBD(v,k,   ) = SBIBD(7,3,1)

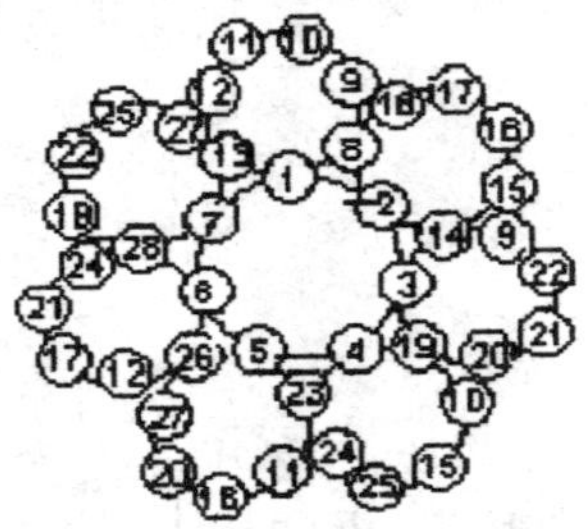

Fig. 1   Archtecture of NN derived from DBBD(28,8,2,7,1)

From this illustrative example we may conclude that :

(1) Since N=28, w_s = 8 × 14=112, the coupling rate is C=112/28=4

(2) Comparing to fully-connected scheme, the total number of weights has been significantly deduced(from 378 to 112).

(3) The link length of NN is 4.   It means the distance between arbitrary pair of nodes in NN is a rather small constant value. This feature is obviously superior to that of cellular NN.

Example 2   If we select k ~ 10^5 for DBBD(v,b,r,k,1) = DBBD(k(k+1)/2, k+1, 2, k, 1) to construct a BDNN, then it would have   N ~ $O(10^{11})$ neurons and each neuron is connected to   ~ 10^5 neurons, Obviously this case is a suitable simulation model for the real biological NN in human brain systems.

(4) ARCHITECTURE OF BDFNCS

Outline of a fuzzy neural computing system(FNCS) is given in [6]. As indicated in Fig. 2, FNCS consists of four main parts, namely (1)Pre-processing unit; (2)Sample provider;(3)Fuzzy neural networks(FNN);(4)Post-processing unit. Inspiration by the human biological brain systems, an important feature ,i.e. so called attention-concentration capabilities is introduced in   FNN.

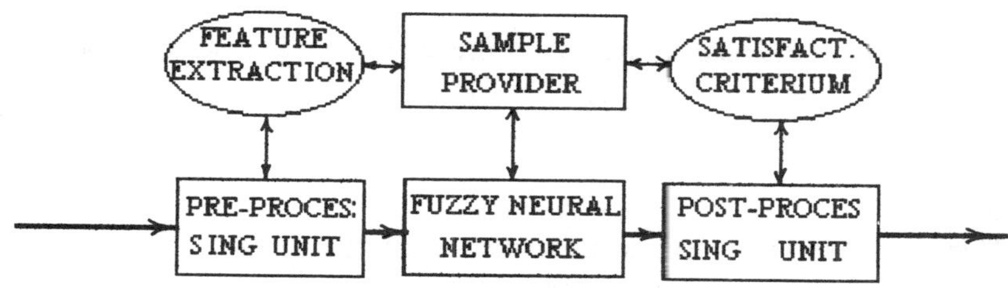

Fig. 2. Architecture of   fuzzy neural computing system

In fact , this feature can easily be achieved by using architecture based on block design.   As shown in Fig. 1, the whole NN consists of eight sub-NNs,   Usually, each sub-NN is assigned to be in charge of its own duty. Once an important   problem with larger scale appears, these eight sub-NNs are closely connected in form DBBD so that a powerful attention-concentration stage begins.

(4)PERFORMANCE OF BDNN

In order to check the performance of neural networks using block design, simulations of hand-written number recognition   were carried out using layered feedforward NN in fully-connected between adjacent layers as well as in BDNN of different schemes. The number of neurons in input layer, hidden layer and output layer are 30, 18 and 10 respectively. Simulation results are listed in Tab.3[7].

Tab.3   Performance of BDNN in hand-written number recognition

type of net-works	number of weights	reduced rate	approachable rate	coupling rate	number of iteration	error rate
regular net	720	0.0 %	18	12.4	423	5.33%
BDNN - 1	630	12.5%	5	10.9	560	4.67%
BDNN - 2	450	37.5%	9	7.8	417	3.33%
BDNN - 3	360	50.0%	1	6.2	716	5.67%

Here:

BDNN-1 : Fully-connected between input layer and hidden layer, connected in block design between hidden layer and output layer;

BDNN-2 : Fully- connected between hidden layer and output layer, 30 neurons of input layer are divided into three groups, each group is connected to hidden layer in form of block design;

BDNN-3 : Hybrid form of   BDNN-1 and BDNN-2, i.e. all neurons in three layers are connecter in form of block design.

From Tab. 3 we   may concluded that , by means of block design , the total number of weights might be significantly reduced while the error rate of hand-written number recognition is still kept in a rather low level.

CONCLUSIONS:

From the above discussion we come to the following conclusions:

(1) By means of block design , the total number of weights can be effectively reduced while symmetry and balance feature of the archtecture of NN is still kept;

(2)If a fuzzy neural computing system is constructed in form block design, an attention-concentration function may be achieved,   which is an important characteristic of   intelligent human brain system;

(3) An urgent task of our research in the near future   is to use such a noval kind of FNN to solve some practical problems.

REFERENCES

[1]Bart Kosko, Neural Networks And Fuzzy Systems, Prentice- Hall, Inc. 1992

[2] Jin Fan, Fan Junbo, Tang Yundo, Neural Networks & Neurocomputers, Southwest Jiaotong University Press, 1991

[3] Kazuyuki Aihara, Neural Computer, Tokyo Electrical University, 1988

[4]Lou Kaicheng, Graph Theory, Qinghua University Press, 1984

[5] Jin Fan, Combinatorial Design & Coding,   Southwest Jiaotong University Press, 1990

[6] Jin Fan , Fan Junbo, Principles and Features of Fuzzy Neural Computing Systems, Proceedings $C^2 N^2$, Wuhan, 1994

[7] Ye Wenxiao, Study on the Architectures of Neural Networks and the Properties Analysis of Samples, Dissertation on Master Degree, Southwest Jiaotong University, 1996

Receptive Fields Defined in Parameters Space*

Wang Yun-jiu, Chen Yu-zhi,, Qi Xiang-lin

Visual Information Processing Laboratory, Institute of Biophysics, Academia Sinica
Beijing 100101, P. R. China

Abstract — The traditional concept of receptive field (RF) in visual system is extended to RF of multi-layer network system defined in parameters space in this paper. Formulary description of RF defined in parameters space is proposed. For example of early vision, we argued that extended Gabor (EG) function is a reasonable model for primary stages of vision. We investigate the regions of parameter values in EG model and properties for information processing. A model for movement detection was constructed by means of EG function.

1. Introduction

The structure and function of visual system are well specialized and developed in some primates animals. Some experts estimated that about 80-90 percent environment information is extracted from human vision. Visual systems of animal can be considered as sophisticated systems for image recognition and intelligent systems for intuitional and non-language information processing. Because a variety of complicated information must be processed in environment of animals, the evolution of visual system adopts some strategies as follows: the low levels of visual system process information parallelly and rapidly which is accumulated mainly in evolution of animal; recognition and learning are performed by central level of visual system which results from individual experience. von Essen and Maunsell (1980) showed that about 60 percent of cortical area in macaque is directly concerned with vision[1]. Human visual system has some 10^8 transducers, only about 10^6 axons leave the retina for LGN, then about 10^{10} neurons are engaged in visual processing beyond the periphery.

Recent vision research in physiology, psychology and morphology showed that visual system of primates is network system hierarchically and divides into parvosubsystem and magnosubsystem parallelly[2]. The parvosubsystem seems to be involved with color and pattern recognition. The function of Magnosubsystem are mainly for stereo and movement vision.

Receptive fields (RF) in visual system are structural and functional units for image information processing. RF is defined classically as that region of retina which must receive illumination in order to elicit a response in a particular cell(Hartline's definition). The ability and attribution of RF in information processing depend on spatial distribution of dendrites of neurons and connective strengths among them. RFs in retina and LGN are symmetric and concentric. Hubel and Wissel[3] suggested that the structure of neural organization in visual cortex is arranged in terms of functional columns. The ocular dominate columns and preferred orientation columns are separate and perpendicular each other. Same orientation neurons are arranged in same column slide vertical to surface of cortex. A hypothesis was proposed that neurons sensitivity to different spatial frequencies are located along the same column. It is difficult to illustrate the RF maps of neurons in high level of visual system. These evidences reveal that information is processed by means of RF in parameters space and inspirit us to propose new concept of RF defined in parameters space.

---

* Project supported by the National Nature Science Foundation of China and by National Climb Science Foundation

2. Formularization of RF defined in parameters space

A neural network system consists of n layers network (Fig, 1), in each layer $M \times M$ neurons are located. (x_i^l, y_j^l) indicates the spatial coordinates of a neuron in l-th layer $(i,j=1,2,...,M)$, $(l=1,2,...,n)$, where l is the number of layers of network system. We define function $F_l(x_i^l, y_j^l, t, \alpha_l, \beta_l, \gamma_l, \cdots)$ as firing of a neuron at (x_i^l, y_j^l) and time t. Parameter space $(\alpha_l, \beta_l, \gamma_l, ...)$ are introduced at second layer and sequential layers. These parameters contain certain physiological and physical meanings (for example, spatial frequency, temporal frequency, etc.) and their valued regions. F_l is called representation at l-th layer. The RF of neuron (x_i^l, y_j^l) in l-th layer is defined as area of (x_i^{l-1}, y_j^{l-1}) at which domain the function F_{l-1} takes value. The formulas of F_l depend on the properties of multi-layer system. The information processing in this system is described as a mapping:

$$Mapping: \qquad F_{l-1} \Rightarrow F_l, \qquad (l=1,2,...,n) \qquad (1)$$

we apply it to modeling of visual system.

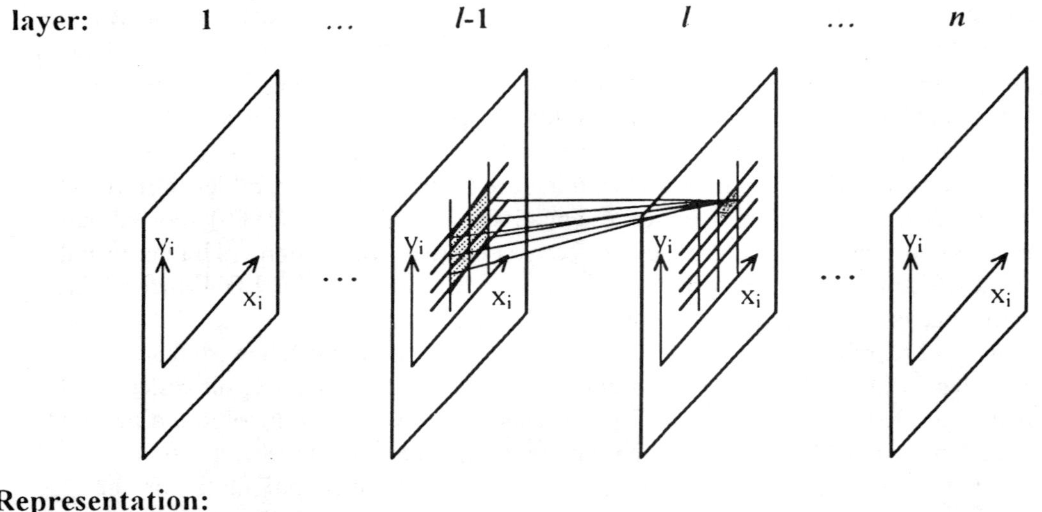

Fig. 1. The formularization representation of RF concept in parameters space. Multi-layer network system is consisted of n layers. At every layer the coordinates (x_i^l, y_j^l) are set in order to locate the position of neurons. We use F_l to denote the representation of l-th layer. The RF of one unit on layer l is defined as the relation from layer l-1 to layer l.

3. Extended Gabor functions are reasonable models in early vision

Primary information processing of vertebrate visual system can be considered as a multi-layer network system which exerts certain spatiotemporal transformation on the input image. With the viewpoint of system theory it may be expressed as following:

$$u(\xi,\eta,t) = \iiint K(x,y,t',\xi,\eta,t,\alpha,\beta,\gamma,\cdots) I(x,y,t')dxdydt' \qquad (2)$$

where $I(x,y,t')$ is a distribution of light intensity in 2-D spatial coordinate (x,y) and at time t', $u(\xi,\eta,t)$ represents the response of output (ξ,η) at time t. $K(x,y,t',\xi,\eta,t,\alpha,\beta,\gamma,...)$ is a weight function of the system which describes the properties of the multi-layer network system. Parameters $\alpha, \beta, \gamma, \ldots$ are keys to specify the weight function. We suggested[4] that the main spatiotemporal properties of major types of RF in different primary levels of primates can be described in terms of a family of extended Gabor (EG) functions as weight function in formula (2). In order to apply original Gabor function to image processing more efficiently, we here extend the spatial variable of original Gabor function from one dimension to two dimensions (x,y), add a time variable t to it, and introduce several parameters with physical and physiological meanings. We call it extended Gabor function.

The first type of EG function is defined in polar coordinates, which is expressed as follows:

$$EG_1(r,t) = W\cos(2\pi f_t t + 2\pi f_r r + \theta)\exp[-r^2/\sigma_r^2 - (t-\tau)^2/\sigma_t^2] \tag{3}$$

The second type of EG function is defined in Cartesian coordinates, which is divided to two subsystems. One is spatiotemporal separable subsystem:

$$EG_{21}(x,y,t) = W\cos(2\pi f_x x + 2\pi f_y y + \theta)\cos(2\pi f_t t)$$
$$\cdot \exp[-x^2/\sigma_x^2 - y^2/\sigma_y^2 - (t-\tau)^2/\sigma_t^2] \tag{4}$$

Another is spatiotemporal inseparable subsystem:

$$EG_{22}(x,y,t) = W\cos(2\pi f_x x + 2\pi f_y y + 2\pi f_t t + \theta)$$
$$\cdot \exp[-x^2/\sigma_x^2 - y^2/\sigma_y^2 - (t-\tau)^2/\sigma_t^2] \tag{5}$$

In Formula (3), (4) and (5), f_x, f_y (f_r) are spatial frequencies along axis x, y (r) respectively, f_t is temporal frequency, θ is initial phase, σ_x, σ_y (σ_r) and σ_t represent spatial and temporal deviation respectively. τ – time delay, W – amplitude.

If the parameters are chosen appropriately, the first type of EG function can describe the major properties of symmetrical RF in retina and LGN[5] The second type of EG function can describe various kinds of asymmetrical RF in visual cortex. Because there are spatiotemporal parameters f_x, f_y and f_t in Eq. (3-5), so the model is sensitivity to spatiotemporal frequency properties of pattern. If parameters in formula (3), (4) and (5) are chosen appropriately, RF model appears special maps with geometrical feature. Both Fourier filter theory and feature detector hypothesis in vision research may be interpreted by means of EG function model.

If temporal frequency equals zero, f_t=0 in Eq. (3), (4) and (5), the system is reduced to static system which is independent of time. The properties of this system may be corresponded to parvosubsystem in visual system. If a spatial frequency equals to zero, f_x=0 (or f_y=0), different initial phase θ correspond to different detectors, θ=0, $\pi/2$, and π to light bar, edge and dark bar detector. The ratio of spatial frequencies f_x/f_y, means that the system is sensitivity to the orientation f_x/f_y, of the input pattern.

If temporal frequency f_t is larger than zero, f_t>0 and the parameters in Eq (4) and (5) are chosen appropriately the properties of EG model may be corresponded to magnosubsystem in visual system. The values of f_t/f_x and f_t/f_y are related to components v_x and v_y of movement vector v in Eq. (5). The relationships between primary stages of visual system and characters of EG model in information processing are shown in Table 1.

We proved theoretically that EG model of visual system can achieve the lowest bounder of uncertainty relation in spatial, temporal variables and their frequencies domain[6]. If the reciprocity in multi-layer system for information processing is valid, we proposed neural wave representation in this system, and derived the partial differential equation which the neural wave is satisfied [7].

Table 1: Variables, parameters, representations and functions of EG models in primary stages of visual information processing

Anatomy of Visual System	Retina, LGN	Visual Cortex V1
Parvo-subsystem ($f_t=0$)		
representation	$EG_1(r)$	$EG_2(x,y)$
variables	r, φ	x, y
parameters	$f_r, \sigma_r, \theta, \tau$	$f_x, f_y, \sigma_x, \sigma_y, \theta, \tau$
functions	rotation invariance gradient detection in space	f_x/f_y – orientation texture detection (edge, bar, ...)
Magno-subsystem ($f_t>0$)		
representation	$EG_1(r,t)$	spatiotemporal separable system: $EG_{21}(x,y,t)$ spatiotemporal inseparable system: $EG_{22}(x,y,t)$
variables	r, φ, t	x, y, t
parameters	$f_r, f_t, \sigma_r, \sigma_t, \theta, \tau$	$f_x, f_y, f_t, \sigma_x, \sigma_y, \sigma_t, \theta, \tau$
functions	gradient detection in spatiotemporal domains	f_x/f_y – orientation $\left.\begin{array}{l} f_t/f_x - v_x \\ f_t/f_y - v_y \end{array}\right\}$ movement detect

4. Functional system Models

The multi-layer network systems which perform texture recognition, stereo vision or movement discrimination can be designed by means of EG function model. The architecture of system which exerts movement discrimination can be shown in following paragraph as an example.

The system of movement detection consists of four layers corresponding to retina, LGN, V1 and MT area in visual system (see Fig. 2). Because movement related to temporal properties, so spatiotemporal inseparable model Eq. (5) may be considered. In visual cortex V1 layer, not only the coordinate (x, y) is set in order to locate the position of neurons, but also orientation dimension (f_x/f_y), x component of velocity f_t/f_y dimension and y component of velocity f_t/f_y dimension are established. In Fig. 2, only orientation dimension f_x/f_y is shown, f_t/f_x and f_t/f_y are omitted for simplicity. Then the direction and velocity of real movement pattern may be interpreted in the MT area of visual cortex.

Fig. 3 illustrates that excitatory areas are drifted from one side to opposite side over time in inseparable model. This kind of RF is elementary units for detection of movement direction and velocity. It is also neural mechanism for movement detection in visual system.

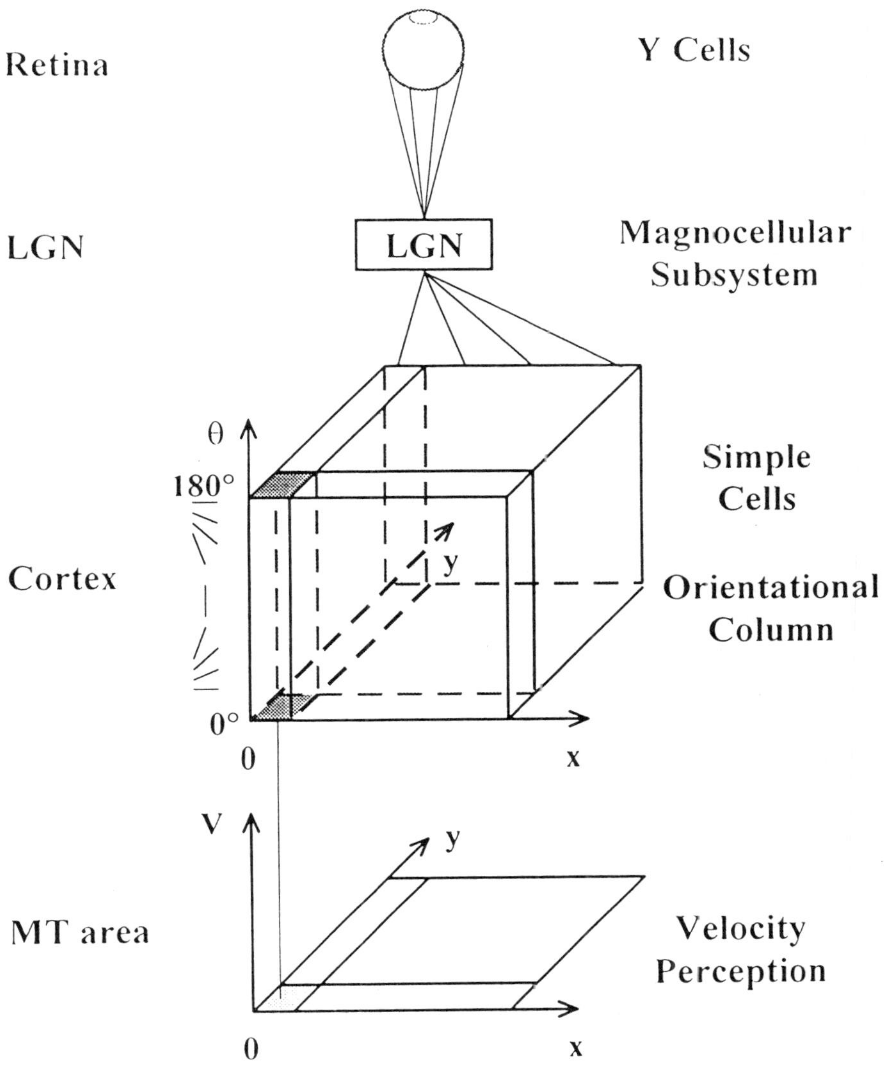

Fig. 2. Movement detection architecture simulated to magno-subsystem. Retina receives input pattern. Through LGN, the information could be expanded in visual cortex V1, then interpreted in MT area.

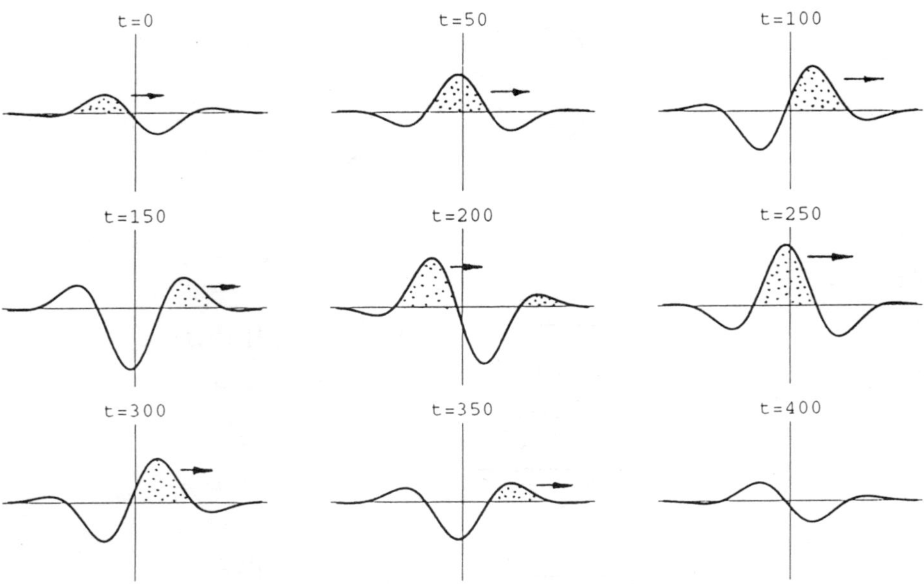

Fig. 3. RF profile of spatiotemporal inseparable system in EG model at different time. The excitatory areas are drifted from left side to right side with time. Parameters in EG model take values as following: f_x =0.5, f_t =1/200, θ=7π/12, σ_x =1, σ_t =200, τ =200

5. Discussion

The feedback connections which exist everywhere in visual system have not been considered in our model of RF defined in parameters space. Learning algorithm which is important aspect of individual development also have not been offered in this paper.

Considering EG function as a model of early vision, nonlinear output function had been introduced in order to compare the properties of the model with physiological results[4].

Reference

[1] D. C. von Essen and J. H. Maunsell, "Two dimensional maps of the cerebral cortex", *J. Comp. Neural*, 191, pp. 225-281, 1980

[2] S. Zeki and S. Shipp, "The functional logic of cortical connections", *Nature*, 335, pp. 311-317, Sept. 1988.

[3] D. Hubel and D. Wissel, "Receptive fields and functional architecture of monkey striate cortex", *J. Physiol.*, 195, pp. 215-243, 1968.

[4] Y. J. Wang, X. L. Qi and Z. H. Pan, "A mathematical model of primary information processing in vertebrate visual system, (I) Spatial properties of the model", *Acta Biophysica Sinica*, 1, pp. 123-133, 1985; "(II) Temporal properties of the model.", —— , pp. 190-198, 1985.

[5] Y. J. Wang, X. L. Qi, J. Xing and D. S. Yu, "Extended Gabor function model and simulation of some characteristic curves of RF", *Scientia Sinica (Series B)*, Vol. XXXI, No. 10, pp. 1185-1196, 1988.

[6] X. L. Qi *et al.* , "The joint spatio-temporal uncertainty principle and extended Gabor function", *Chinese Science Bulletin*, 37, pp. 408-411, 1992.

[7] Y. J. Wang *et al.* , "Neural wave representation in early vision", *Science in China (Series B)*, 36, pp. 677-684, 1993.

Neuro-Fuzzy Models and Adaptive Information System

The invited program is also featured by 8 special sessions on current interesting topics. Each special session organizer is invited by the Program Committee and the success of each special session is completely due to the hard efforts of each organizer.

Structural Learning and Bayesian Regularization in Neural Networks

Masumi Ishikawa

Department of Control Engineering and Science, Kyushu Institute of Technology

680-4 Kawazu, Iizuka, Fukuoka 820, Japan   E-mail: ishikawa@ces.kyutech.ac.jp

Abstract—

Structural learning and learning with regularization have developed more or less independently. Because of this, although several kinds of heuristic penalty terms have been proposed, only a gaussian regularizer has been exclusively used. A difficulty in the use of a penalty term or a regularizer is how to determine the relative weight of a penalty term or a regularization parameter. A Bayesian approach can solve this difficulty with ease. The present paper demonstrates the effectiveness of a Laplace regularizer, i.e., sum of the absolute values of connection weights, which has been used as a penalty term in a structural learning with forgetting (SLF). The relationship between SLF and a Bayesian approach with a Laplace regularizer is also clarified.

1   Introduction

Structural learning is a class of learning algorithms which aim at ameliorating the difficulties in backpropagation (BP) learning: prior specification of network structure and interpretation of hidden units. These algorithms roughly fall into the following four categories: the addition of a penalty term to the conventional criterion of mean square error(MSE)[6][11], the deletion of hidden units with small contribution to MSE, the deletion of connections with small contribution to MSE[7], and the incremental increase in the number of hidden units until MSE becomes sufficiently small.

Comparative studies indicate the superiority of a structural learning with forgetting (SLF)[6] proposed by the author, which fall into the first category, i.e., the addition of a penalty term to MSE. SLF is superior to other algorithms from the viewpoints of MSE, generalization ability, structural simplicity of the resulting network and computational cost.

The penalty term may also be regarded as a regularizer. Historically, structural learning and learning with regularization have developed more or less independently. A major purpose of the former is to solve the difficulties in BP learning. The latter, on the other hand, has originally developed in computer vision to cope with ill-posed problems[10], and has recently been used in learning theory to prevent over training. Because of this, although several kinds of heuristic penalty terms have been proposed [9][12][2][3][11][6], only a gaussian regularizer, i.e., sum of squares of connection weights, has been exclusively used until very recently. Exclusive use of a gaussian regularizer is due mainly to its simplicity and comprehensibility. To my knowledge, Williams first proposed other types of regularizers such as a Laplace regularizer and a Cauchy regularizer[13]. However, their effectiveness was not well demonstrated.

A difficulty in the use of a penalty term or a regularizer is the determination of the relative weight of a penalty term or a regularization parameter. Recently, information criteria such as AIC have shown their effectiveness in its determination[4]. However, they need to train a set of models from which to choose the best one. A Bayesian approach, on the other hand, can solve this difficulty with much less effort, because the training of only one model suffices.

The present paper demonstrates the effectiveness of a Laplace regularizer, i.e., sum of the absolute values of connection weights, which has been used as a penalty term in SLF. The relationship between SLF and a Bayesian approach with a Laplace regularizer is also discussed.

2   Estimation of a regularization parameter

Mean square error(MSE) and cross entropy are two frequently used criteria in learning. In case of regression tasks, MSE is often used, and in case of classification tasks, cross entropy is appropriate to use. Since examples in the following section are classification tasks, only the formulation of the latter criterion is given here. The cross entropy criterion function is defined as,

$$G(\boldsymbol{w}) = \sum_m \{t_i^{(m)} log\, y_i(\boldsymbol{x}^{(m)}; \boldsymbol{w}) + (1 - t_i^{(m)}) log(1 - y_i(\boldsymbol{x}^{(m)}; \boldsymbol{w}))\} \tag{1}$$

where $\boldsymbol{w}$ is a connection weight vector, $\boldsymbol{x}^{(m)}$ is the mth training input, $y_i(\boldsymbol{x}^{(m)}; \boldsymbol{w})$ is the output of ith output unit for mth training input, and $t_i^{(m)}$ is the corresponding target. A Laplace regularizer, E_w, is,

$$E_w = \sum_j |w_j| \tag{2}$$

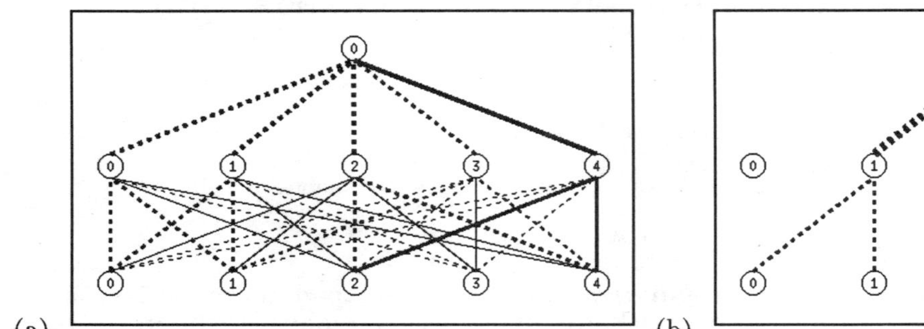 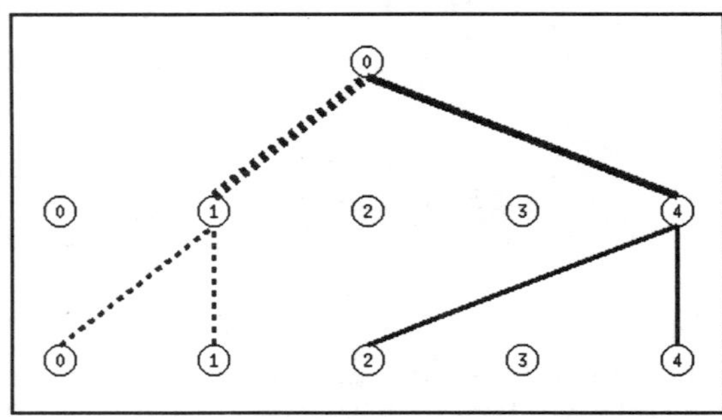

(a)   (b)

Figure 1: Resulting networks in the learning of the Boolean function, $f = (a \cup b) \cap (c \cup e)$. (a) learning with a gaussian regularizer, (b) learning with a Laplace regularizer. The input units, 0, 1, 2, 3 and 4, correspond to a, b, c, d and e, respectively. The output unit represents f. A solid line and a dashed line signify a positive connection weight and a negative one, respectively.

The total criterion function, $M(\boldsymbol{w})$, is,

$$M(\boldsymbol{w}) = -G(\boldsymbol{w}) + \alpha E_w \tag{3}$$

where α is a regularization parameter representing the relative weight of the regularizer, E_w. The maximum evidence regularization parameter, α_{MP}, is given by,

$$\frac{1}{\alpha_{MP}} = \frac{1}{k} \sum_{j=1}^{k} |w_{MPj}| \tag{4}$$

where k is the number of connections, and $\boldsymbol{w}_{MP}$ is the connection weight vector minimizing $M(\boldsymbol{w})$.

A prior distribution of connection weights under a gaussian regularizer is a normal distribution. Under a Laplace regularizer, on the other hand, a prior distribution is a Laplace or a two-sided exponential distribution. These two kinds of regularizers are exceptions which have well known prior distributions of connection weights. This simplicity is a great advantage, because other regularizers suffer from computational complexity in obtaining the optimal regularization parameters.

It is to be noted that the calculation of a Hessian matrix, i.e., the second derivatives of the criterion function, $M(\boldsymbol{w})$, with respect to connection weights, $\boldsymbol{w}$, is not required under a Laplace regularizer. Considering that the size of a Hessian matrix, $k \times k$, becomes very large in realistic problems, it is a great advantage from the viewpoint of computational cost. This is in sharp contrast to a gaussian regularizer under which the inverse of a Hessian matrix needs to be calculated. This difference is due to the fact that the second derivatives of a Laplace regularizer vanish, whereas those of the gaussian regularizer do not. Generally speaking, it is necessary to calculate a Hessian matrix unless a regularizer is linear or piecewise linear. Due to the same reason, it is shown that one of the advantages of SLF is its ability to taking into account the information on the second derivatives of MSE without explicitly calculating them[6].

Although a penalty term in SLF and a Laplace regularizer have the same form as in Eq.(2), SLF and a Bayesian approach with a Laplace regularizer are not computationally the same. SLF needs to train several models to determine the optimum amount of forgetting based on information criteria such as AIC. On the contrary, Bayesian regularization needs to train only one model. This efficient computation in Bayesian regularization can be realized by adaptive change of the regularization parameter, α. This is in contrast to the constant amount of forgetting in SLF during training.

3   Simulation experiments

The learning of a Boolean function and the classification of irises[1] are chosen to demonstrate the effectiveness of a Bayesian approach with a Laplace regularizer.

The Boolean function selected here is, $f = (a \cup b) \cap (c \cup e)$. 26 out of 32 samples are used for training and the rest are reserved for test. Figure 1 illustrates the resulting networks. It clearly indicates the superiority of a Laplace regularizer to a gaussian regularizer in terms of the simplicity of the resulting network structure. Figure 1(b) successfully represents the Boolean function, $f = (a \cup b) \cap (c \cup e)$. The network structure remains essentially the same irrespective of initial connection weights and an initial value of α. Table 1 compares the performance of various learning algorithms. Their generalization abilities are comparable because of the simplicity of the task. Figure 2(a) illustrates how the regularization parameter, α, converges to the maximum evidence value as learning proceeds. Figure 2(b) depicts M, $0.1 \times E_w$ and $-G$ as functions of α. When α is larger than 1.0, all the connections vanish due to regularization. On the other hand, as α becomes smaller, the sum of connection weights monotonically increases. The maximum evidence is obtained at $\alpha_{MP} = 0.314$.

Irises are classified into 3 categories: setosa, versicolor and virginica. Each category contains 50 samples.

Table 1: Performance comparison of the learning of the Boolean function, $f = (a \cup b) \cap (c \cup e)$. MSE and G stand for mean square error and cross entropy, respectively. Two types of regularizers, i.e., a gaussian regularizer and a Laplace regularizer, are used. Parameters in learning are: a learning rate 0.1, and a momentum 0.2.

criterion	mean square error		No. of	α_{MP}
	training data	test data	errors	
MSE	0.000075	0.000119	0	–
G	0.000025	0.000023	0	–
G+gaussian	0.005946	0.008752	0	0.083
G+Laplace	0.007954	0.007523	0	0.314

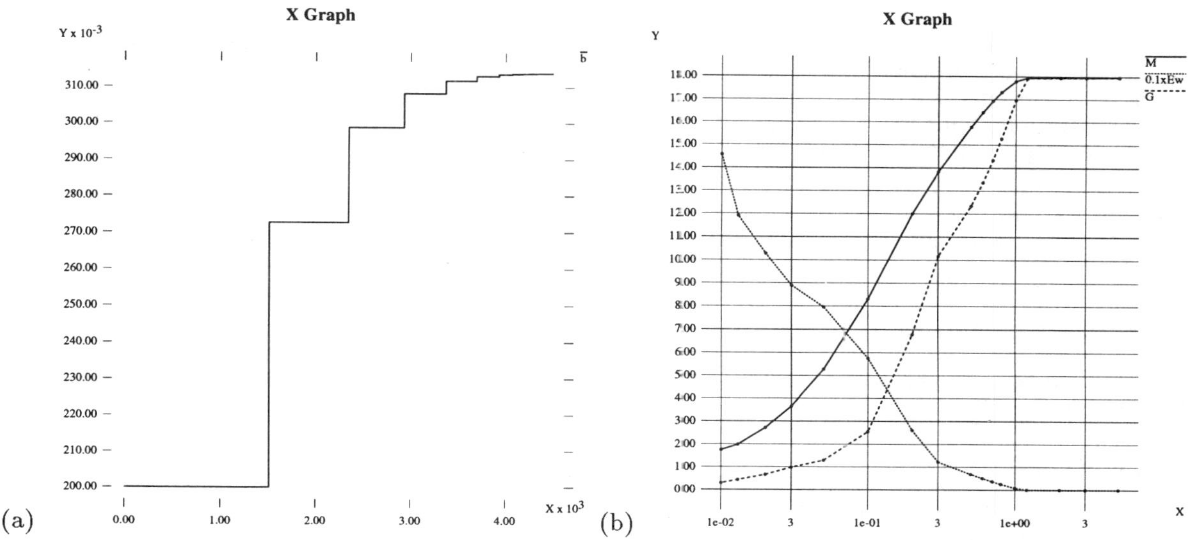

Figure 2: (a) The regularization parameter of a Laplace regularizer, α. The horizontal axis and the vertical axis represent the number of iterations and the regularization parameter, respectively. (b) M, $0.1 \times E_w$ and $-G$. The horizontal axis and the vertical axis represent α and the criteria, respectively.

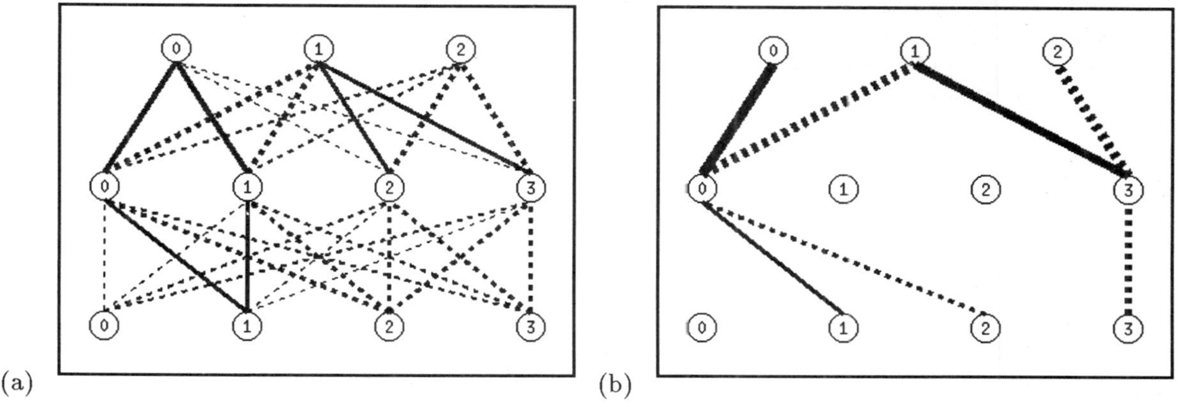

Figure 3: Resulting networks in the classification of irises. (a) learning with a gaussian regularizer, (b) learning with a Laplace regularizer.

Table 2: Performance comparison of the classification of irises. MSE and G stand for mean square error and cross entropy, respectively.

criterion	mean square error		No. of	α_{MP}
	training data	test data	errors	
MSE	0.000150	0.027417	14	–
G	0.000034	0.046051	22	–
G+gaussian	0.001766	0.025346	14	0.079
G+Laplace	0.000953	0.018946	10	0.225

Each sample possesses 4 attributes: sepal length, sepal width, petal length and petal width. A network structure used here is a 3-layer network: an input layer with 4 units, a hidden layer with 4 units and an output layer with 3 units. Seven samples in each category are randomly chosen for training, and the rest are reserved for test. Table 2 shows the performance comparison of the learning with various criteria. It clearly indicates the superiority of a Laplace regularizer to a guassian regularizer and to two BP learning methods without regularizers in terms of MSE for test data and the number of classification errors. Figure 3 illustrates the resulting networks. It is to be noted that one of the input units, i.e., sepal length, is discarded in the network, because it does not contribute to the classification.

Other examples including the learning of recurrent networks are examined to show the effectiveness of a Laplace regularizer. However, they are omitted here for space limitation.

4   Conclusions

An advantage of a Bayesian approach is that it needs to train only one model in contrast to structural learning methods. Among Bayesian methods, a gaussian regularizer, although most frequently used, proves to be less effective than a Laplace regularizer, which has been used as a penalty term in a structural learning with forgetting (SLF). It is also to be noted that the learning with a Laplace regularizer doesn't need to calculate a Hessian matrix in contrast to other regularizers.

The performance evaluation of other types of regularizers is left for further study. This is because a Bayesian method can determine the optimal regularization parameter for a given regularizer, but cannot search for the best regularizer. In other words, the search for regularizers can only be done through empirical studies.

Acknowledgements

I'd like to express my thanks to one of my graduate students, Kazuhiro Yoshida, for his contributions in this research.

References

[1] R. A. Fisher, "The use of multiple measurements in taxonomic problem," *Annals of Eugenics*, vol. 7, Part 2, pp.179-188, 1936.

[2] S. J. Hanson and L. Y. Pratt, "Comparing biases for minimal network construction with back-propagation" in D. S. Touretzky Ed., *Advances in Neural Information Processing Systems*. vol. 1, San Mateo: Morgan Kaufmann, 1989.

[3] M. Ishikawa, and H.Uchida, "A structural learning of neural networks based on an entropy criterion," *Proc.IJCNN'92*, Beijing, Nov. 3-6, 1992, pp.II375-380.

[4] M. Ishikawa, "Structural learning in neural networks," *Proc. of 3rd Inter. Conf. on Fuzzy Logic, Neural Nets and Soft Computing (IIZUKA'94)*, Iizuka, Aug. 1-7, 1994, pp.37-44.

[5] M. Ishikawa, "Neural networks approach to rule extraction," *Proc. ANNES'95*, Dunedin, Nov. 20-23, 1995, pp.6-9.

[6] M. Ishikawa, "Structural learning with forgetting," *Neural Networks,* Vol. 9, No. 3, pp. 509-521, 1996.

[7] Y. Le Cun, J. S. Denker and S. A. Solla, "Optimal brain damage," D. S. Touretzky Ed., *Advances in Neural Information Processing Systems*. vol. 2, San Mateo: Morgan Kaufmann, 1990.

[8] D. J. C. MacKay, "Probable networks and plausible predictions —— a review of practical Bayesian methods for supervised neural networks", *Network*, to appear.

[9] D. C. Plaut, S. J. Nowlan, and G. E. Hinton, "Experiments on learning by back propagation." *Technical Report*, CMU-CS-86-126, Carnegie-Mellon Univ., 1986.

[10] T. Poggio and C. Koch, "Ill-posed problems in early vision: from computational theory to analogue networks," *Proc. R. Soc. Lond.*, B-226, pp.303-323, 1985.

[11] R. Reed, "Pruning algorithms —— a survey," *IEEE Trans. Neural Networks*, vol.4-5, pp.740-747, 1993.

[12] D. E. Rumelhart, "Parallel distributed processing," Plenary Talk, *IEEE Inter. Conf. on Neural Networks*, San Diego, 1988.

[13] P. M. Williams, "Bayesian regularization and pruning using a Laplace prior," *Neural Computation*, vol. 7, pp.117-143, 1995.

[14] S. Yasui, "A new method to remove redundant connections in backpropagation neural networks: Introduction of "parametric lateral inhibition fields,"" *Proc. IJCNN'92*, Beijing, Nov. 3-6, 1992, pp.II360-367.

Analysis of EEG Signals with Wavelets and Knowledge Engineering Techniques

Saman K. Halgamuge [1,3], Christoph S. Herrmann [2], and Lakhmi Jain [3]

[1]Cooperative Research Centre for Sensor Signal and Information Processing , SPRI Building, Technology Park Adelaide, The Levels, SA 5095, Australia, *skh@cssip.edu.au*

[2] Darmstadt University of Technology, FG Intellectics, Alexandertstr. 10, 64283 Darmstadt, Germany, chris@intellektik.informatik.th-darmstadt.de

[3] University of South Australia, Knowledge-Based Intelligent Engineering Systems Group, Warrendi Road, The Levels, SA 5095, Australia, *etlcj@levels.unisa.edu.au*

Abstract—

For the task of EEG–diagnosis, it is necessary to detect certain patterns within the EEG that indicate medical phenomena. Since EEG–data is numerical, a preprocessing method has to be applied that extracts relevant patterns before the task of diagnosis can be achieved. The wavelet analysis is in several ways superior to other transforms such as the Fourier transform, since it can also detect transients such as epileptic spikes in EEG signals. From the Neural Network research point of view the major advantage of selecting Neuro-Fuzzy instead of conventional neural networks is the extensive use of transparency provided in most of the fuzzy system models but not in most of the conventional neural networks. This paper compares results of three Neuro-Fuzzy methods applied to EEG signal analysis.

1 Introduction

Analysis of EEG Signals using intelligent techniques is reported in several papers. The relation of EEG signals to the human movements and behaviour has been extensively studied in past decades, e.g. Dement and Kleitman [2] have reported their study on the cyclic variations in EEG during sleep and their relation to eye movements, Body Mobility and Dreaming in 1957. They analysed EEG Signals from 26 men and 7 woman manually. Haustein, Pilcher, Klink and Schulz [7] in their sleep research project have reported the development of a technique for analysing EEG Signals using FORTRAN language. The computing methods increase the capability of medical data analysis with respect to the speed as well as the efficiency.

The cheap and easy availability of computing power have generated tremendous interest in the application of Knowledge-Based techniques in virtually every field including medicine, science and engineering. The Knowledge-Based techniques aim to include the human like behaviour in the system such as learning, adoption, fault tolerance and self organisation in a limited sense. The main techniques used to implement such a human like behaviour include artificial neural networks and fuzzy systems. This development has a remarkable effect on analysis of EEG signals.

The interest in Knowledge-Based techniques for EEG analysis can be seen from the number of publications all around the world. Jones et. al. [11] have developed a Knowledge-Based System for automatic detection of epileptiform activity in routine clinical EEG recordings. The system's performance reported is 100% detection sensitivity for epileptiform EEGS.

The artificial neural networks (ANNS) offer human like behaviour due to their abilities such as learning, generalisation and fault tolerance. The fuzzy system also attempts to automate human like activities such as diagnosing a patient by modelling human like thinking. There is a trend to integrate fuzzy logic and ANNS to offset the weakness of one technique by the merits of another.

A number of researchers have used ANNS to analyse EEG Signals successfully. Hiraiwa, Shimo and Tokunaga [10] have reported the use of ANNS in EEG topography recognition. The EEG Signals were continuously measured through 12 - channel surface electrodes before and after a subject altered one of five Japanese syllables or moved a joystick in one of four directions. The RP (Readiness Potentials) patterns were inputted to the neural network and corresponding syllables were used as the desired output. The ANN recognised 16 out of 30 new syllable.

The application of neuro-fuzzy techniques for EEG analysis is new, although this is not the first paper written in the area. The identification of certain artifacts in EEG signal using neuro-fuzzy is reported in [9].

2 Specific Problems Related to EEG Data Analysis

For the task of EEG–diagnosis, it is necessary to detect certain patterns within the EEG that indicate medical phenomena. Since EEG–data is numerical, a preprocessing method has to be applied that extracts relevant patterns before the task of diagnosis can be achieved. Important patterns are the base rhythm, called α–rhythm, in the range from 8 to 12 Hz, sharp transients of short temporal duration (80–200ms: spikes, above 200ms: sharp waves) and so called artifacts, electric discharges that do not result from brain electric activity.

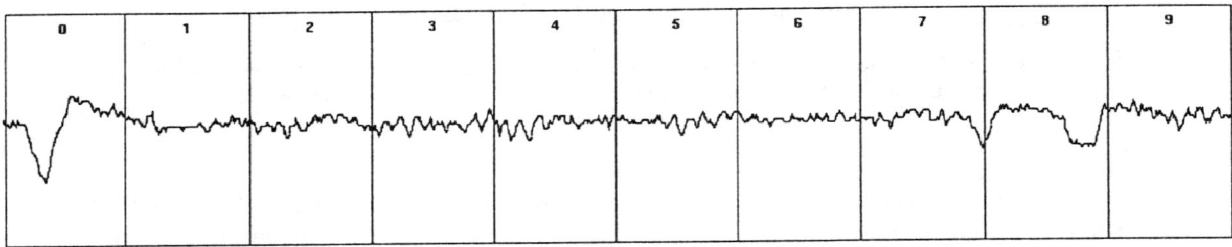

Figure 1: Ten seconds of EEG with three eye–movement artifacts in seconds 0, 7.5 and 8 as well as α–activity elsewhere.

Figure 1 depicts an EEG–trace with three patterns that are to be detected. Due to the fact that patterns that result from the same physiologic source look similar but not identical, it is necessary to use a method for the data–analysis that is fault–tolerant. Thus, neural networks and fuzzy systems are suitable candidates for this task. Our approach does not obey the strict classification of EEG–waves into the medical frequency bands δ, ϑ, α and β [13] but uses fuzzy representations instead [8].

3 Wavelet Transformation as an Effective Preprocessing Technique

The wavelet analysis is in some ways superior to other transforms, as the Fourier transform, since it can also detects transients [14]. This is of special interest for EEG analysis, due to the fact that epileptic spikes are transient waveforms and almost impossible to detect with Fourier analysis. A wavelet (literally: small wave) is a complex wave calculated according to

$$\texttt{Gauß-wavelet:} \qquad g(t) = e^{-\frac{1}{2}t^2 + j2\pi ft}$$

The result of this equation is a wave shape depicted in Figure 2 where only the real part of the complex wave is represented.

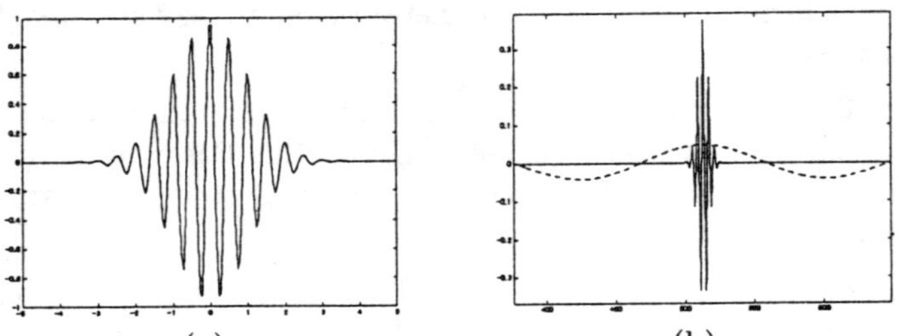

(a)   (b)

Figure 2: The real part of a basic (i.e. not shifted and not dilated) Gauß–wavelet $\texttt{Real}(g(t))$ in (a) and two dilated Wavelets in (b) (g_6 dotted and g_{10} solid)

Having such a wavelet $g(t)$, different new signals $s_a(b)$ can be derived by convolution of the EEG signal $eeg(t)$ with the wavelet (a is the wavelet dilation and b the time scale of the convoluted signal). By varying the dilation a, which results in a compression of the time scale, the shape of the wavelet is varied and the resulting signal $s_a(b)$ can be regarded as a measure of similarity between the EEG signal and the shape of the wavelet $g_a(t)$. The convolution is expressed by

$$s_a(b) = \frac{1}{\sqrt{a}} \int g^* \left(\frac{t-b}{a} \right) \cdot eeg(t) \; dt \tag{1}$$

where g^* represents the conjugate of the complex wavelet. Figure 3 demonstrates the wavelet analysis of a spiky EEG signal into two convoluted signals, representing the low and high frequency components.

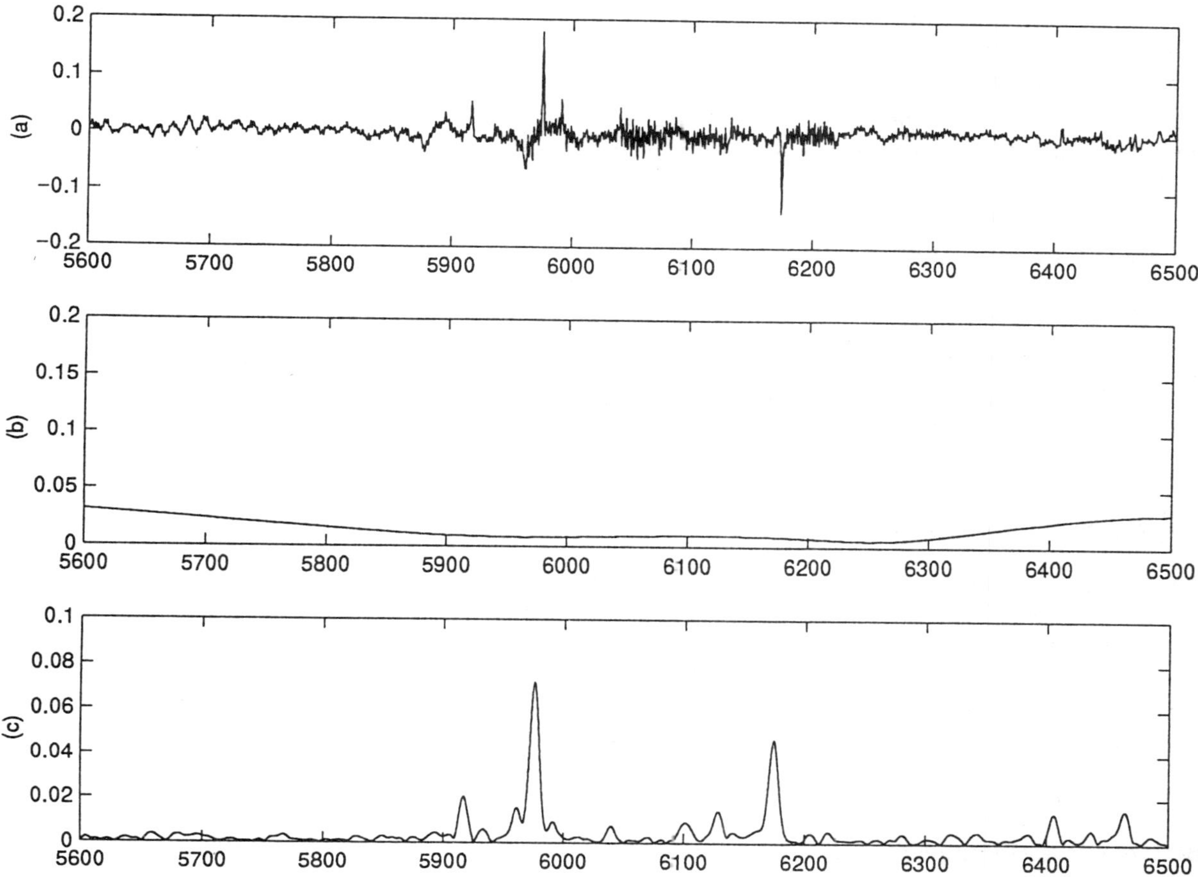

Figure 3: A spiky EEG signal (a) and two outputs of the wavelet analysis, s_6 representing slow frequency components in (b) and s_{10} representing high frequency transients in (c)

In Figure 1 (b) the peaks in signal s_{10} (sub plot c) indicates the occurrence of sharp transients (spikes) in the EEG (sub plot a), while the steadily low signal s_6 (sub plot b) indicates that the EEG does not contain low frequencies. These convolution–signals indicate the occurrence of spectral phenomena in the EEG and can now be fed into a neural network in order to learn the diagnosis of EEGs based on such phenomena.

4   Neuro-Fuzzy Techniques

From the Neural Network research point of view the major advantage of selecting Neuro-Fuzzy instead of conventional neural networks is the extensive use of transparency provided in most of the fuzzy system models and but not in most of the conventional neural networks. Furthermore, in some neuro-fuzzy methods [4] it is straightforward to remove superfluous inputs, reducing the number of input components (or features) in the application, which is not possible by using conventional neural networks.

Quite interestingly most of the applications traditionally coming from the neural network community have a higher number of inputs, and the expert knowledge or fuzzy rules, if there are any, are minimal. It is not unfair to say that those applications have no initial fuzzy systems, and therefore the major purpose is the rule generation in addition to the obvious tuning of the system. Mostly these applications are from data analysis.

It is a common practice to preprocess data before feeding to neural networks. In case of neuro-fuzzy systems it is of no use if the preprocessing completely destroys the meaning of the input, since the rules generated have to be interpretable.

The functional equivalence of FuNe I type fuzzy systems and the special type of multi-layer perceptron neural networks is shown in [3]. This method (demo version contact the first author) is basically a network oriented method containing a separate algorithm for rule generation rather than iteration of rules from all possibilities. It can be used with gradient descent type neural learning algorithms. These algorithms usually do not support the self-development of a hidden layer. The separate rule generation algorithm described in [4] solves this problem step by step.

The fact that the Classifier type fuzzy system is the most natural approximation for data clustering methods motivated many researchers to select it for neuro-fuzzy systems. Some of them are:

1. Fuzzy Rule Net [15]

2. Fuzzy Min-Max method

3. NEFCLASS [12]

4. Dynamic Vector Quantisation Variations DVQ2 and DVQ3 [5]

5. Radial/Cubic Basis Function Networks with Generalised or Modified Restricted Coulomb Energy Learning (RBFN with RCE or CBFN with MRCE) [6]

6. Fuzzy ART Map [1]

7. Fuzzy Self-Organising Map [16]

The common ground for these methods is the self-evolving character adding the complete structural and parameter generation from data. They specifically addressed the issues concerning Neuro-Fuzzy from the neural network point of view. Description of the methods, is avoided in this paper due to page limitations. The first 2 listed neuro-fuzzy classifiers and the FuNe I methods were applied in classification of EEG data. The method NEFCLASS could be applied successfully for data sets with reduced number of input components, and therefore the results are not compared in this paper.

5   Interpretation of Results

Both preprocessed and EEG signals were analysed with the neuro-fuzzy techniques. The classification of EEG signals was taken to identify the class "Bulbus artifact" (ba), critical spike wave complex (sw), and the slow wave (sl). Overlapping time windows were chosen to avoid that important features that occur in window boundaries are left undetected.

The data vectors for training the neuro-fuzzy systems contains 128 input components and 3 output classes ba, sw, and sl. The training data set with 27 data vectors (0.5 s) is considered. The test data set consists of in addition to the training set new 27 data vectors. The objective is to make sure that the system identifies the critical sharp waves in the complete 54 data vectors available.

The results summarised in Table 1 shows the identification of the more crucial spike-wave complexes with three neuro-fuzzy methods, and the comparison of the results, when the signals are preprocessed with the wavelet transformation described above is shown in Table 2.

Table 1: Identification of spike-wave complex without preprocessing

neuro-fuzzy classifier	classification rate (%)	number of rules/neurons
Fuzzy Rule Net	93.1	9
Fuzzy Min-Max	93.1	8
FuNe I	90.1	242

It must be mentioned that each rule generated by FuNe I has only two variables maintaining the readability but increasing the number of rules. And the the other two methods have less rules, but each one consisting of 128 input components, thereby reducing the readability.

The wavelet transformation seems to increase this critical classification task in all three methods, and it also reduces the number of rules generated.

Table 2: Identification of spike-wave complex after wavelet transformation

neuro-fuzzy classifier	classification rate (%)	number of rules/neurons
Fuzzy Rule Net	100	7
Fuzzy Min-Max	100	6
FuNe I	95.5	58

6 Conclusions

Similar experiments were performed for the identification of Bulbus artifact, and spike and slow waves separately. The created systems through these experiments are certainly far away from a nearly professional expert system, but it shows the capability of neuro-fuzzy systems and signal processing techniques in achieving that goal.

It is quite clear that a more comprehensive fuzzy expert system automatically created from a large data base could help a new medical expert for consultation purposes. And the more experienced senior experts can add their knowledge into the automatically created system, even test their "set of rules" with the rule base created by the neuro-fuzzy system.

7 Acknowledgements

Authors thank Dr. Nadine Tschichold-Gürman from ETH Zurich, and Dr. Detlef Nauck from Technische Univerität Braunschweig for providing their programmes to be used in this work, Frank Reine from Carl Schenck AG Darmstadt for cooperation in the wavelet analysis, and "Uniklinik Mainz" in Germany for the provision of EEG data samples.

References

[1] G. Carpenter, S. Grossberg, and D. Rosen. Fuzzy ART An Adaptive Resonance Algorithm for Rapid, Stable Classification of Analog Patterns. In *International Joint Conference on Neural Networks' 91*, Seattle, USA, 1991.

[2] W. Dement and N. Kleitman. Cyclic variations in EEG. During sleep and their Relation to Eye Movements, Body Mobility and Dreaming. *In EEG Clin. Neurophysiol*, 9, 1957.

[3] S. K. Halgamuge and M. Glesner. A Fuzzy-Neural Approach for Pattern Classification with the Generation of Rules based on Supervised Learning. In *Neuro-Nimes 92*, pages 165–173, Nanterre, France, November 1992. ISBN 2–906899–79–8.

[4] S. K. Halgamuge and M. Glesner. Neural Networks in Designing Fuzzy Systems for Real World Applications. *International Journal for Fuzzy Sets and Systems*, 65(1):1–12, 1994. North Holland.

[5] S. K. Halgamuge and M. Glesner. Fuzzy Neural Networks: Between Functional Equivalence and Applicability. *IEE International Journal on Neural Systems*, 6(2):185–196, June, 1995. World Scientific Publishing.

[6] S. K. Halgamuge, W. Pöchmüller, and M. Glesner. An Alternative Approach for Generation of Membership Functions and Fuzzy Rules Based on Radial and Cubic Basis Function Networks. *International Journal of Approximate Reasoning*, 12(3/4):279 – 298, April/May 1995. Elsevier.

[7] W. Haustein, J. Pilcher, J. Klink, and H. Schulz. Automatic Analysis Overcomes Limitations of Sleep Stage Scoring. *In Electroencephalography and Clinical Neurophysiology*, 64, 1986.

[8] C. Herrmann. Fuzzy Neural Networks in Detecting Graphoelements in EEGs. In Herrmann, H.J. and Wolf, D.E. and Pöppel, E., editor, *Supercomputers in Brain Research: from Tomography to Neural Networks*. World Scientific Publishing Company, 1995.

[9] C. S. Herrmann, S. K. Halgamuge, and M. Glesner. Comparison of Fuzzy Rule Based Classification with Neural Network Approaches For Medical Diagnosis. In *European Congress on Fuzzy and Intelligent Technologies' 95*, Aachen, Germany, August 1995.

[10] A. Hiraiwa, K. Shimohara, and Y. Tokunaga. EEG Topography Recognition by Neural Networks. *In Engineering in Medicine and Biology*, September, 1990.

[11] R. D. Jones and A. A. Dingle et.al. A PC-Based System for Automated Analysis of the EEG. In *In Proceedings of the 1st Medical Engineering Week of the World*, Taipei,Taiwan, September 1994.

[12] D. Nauck and R. Kruse. NEFCLASS - A Neuro-Fuzzy Approach for the Classification of Data. In *ACM Symposium on Applied Computing (SAC'95)*, Nashville, USA, Februray 1995. ISBN: 089791-658-1.

[13] E. Niedermeyer and F. Lopes da Silva. *Electroencephalography, Basic Principles, Clinical Applications and Related Fields*. William & Wilkins, 1993.

[14] S. J. Schiff, A. Aldroubi, M. Unser, and S. Sato. Fast wavelet transformation of EEG. *Electroencephalography and Clinical Neurophysiology*, 91:442–455, 1994.

[15] N. Tschichold-Gürman. Generation and Improvement of Fuzzy Classifiers with Incremental Learning using Fuzzy RuleNet. In *ACM Symposium on Applied Computing (SAC'95)*, Nashville, USA, Februray 1995. ISBN: 089791-658-1.

[16] P. Vuorimaa. Fuzzy Self-Organizing Map. *International Journal for Fuzzy Sets and Systems*, 1994.

FUZZY NEURAL ADAPTIVE DISCRIMINATION DIAGNOSIS SYSTEM
CONSIDERING RELATIVE IMPORTANCE AND TIME VARIATION

Jeong_Yon Shim , CHong_Sun Hwang

* Dept. of Computer Science, Korea Univ., Seoul, 136-171 KOREA
** Dept. of computer science, Yong_In Technical College, YongIn Si,
KyongKi Do, KOREA (fax: +82 335 36 9535)

Abstract

A fuzzy neural cooperate system is applied about in this paper for discrimination diagnosis considering relative importance and time variation. That system consists of a structured neural network that is based on expert knowledge associated with a fuzzy concept and relative importance. In this paper we develope the fuzzy neural Cooperate system that has dynamic structure according to time variation. We test this system with symptom data of patients.

1. Introduction

In the case of medical discrimination diagnosis, it is very often difficult to discriminate illnesses because of similar symptoms. So, for more accurate diagnosis we have to design a scrupulous knowledge processing system. When the conclusion(illness name) is elicited from several evidences(symptoms) in a human knowledge processing, all of the evidences do not contribute to the conclusion to the same degree. Namely the effect of each evidence upon the conclusion is different. In this paper we define that effect as Relative Importance (RI). Also, the number of causal data can change with lapse of time.

Therefore we design the fuzzy neural cooperate system considering two factors, (1) relative importance (2) time variation. That system has uncertain data processing, learning and perception ability.

2. Fuzzy Rule based Neural Networks

2.1 Fuzzy rules with relative importance(RI)

In inferencing medical knowledge each of the symptoms has different effects on the diagnosis. For example, when the doctor diagnoses the illess as cough, she considers relative effects of a symptom upon diagnosis. The symptom of " Nose running is severe." has more effect on the decision making than the symptom of " He feel sharp pains all over his body." We define the relative effect of symptom upon diagnosis as relative importance(: RI). An RI value is initiated by expert and its range is between 0 and 1. Initialized RI values, i.e. $R_{11.}$ $R_{12.}$ .. R_{1n}, are re_adjusted using the following operation (eq.1).

$$RW_{ij} = \frac{R_{ij}}{\sum_{j=1}^{n} R_{ij}}$$

$$\sum_{j=1}^{n} RW_{ij} = 1$$

R_{ij} : RI input value of expert's
RW_{ij} : The re_adjusted relative importance
(eq. 1)

The structure of the system under discussion will be centered around a set of "if-then" conditional statements(rules) given as follows.

$$IF\ (S1\ IS\ Q_{1,1})^{RW_{11}}\ AND\ (S2\ IS\ Q_{1,2})^{RW_{12}}\ .\ .\ .\ (S_n\ IS\ Q_{1,n})^{RW_{1n}}\ THEN\ (D_1\ IS\ F_{1)}$$

$$IF\ (S1\ IS\ Q_{2,1})^{RW_{21}}\ AND\ (S2\ IS\ Q_{2,2})^{RW_{22}}\ .\ .\ .\ (S_n\ IS\ Q_{2,n})^{RW_{2n}}\ THEN\ (D_2\ IS\ F_{2)}$$

$$.\ .$$

$$IF\ (S1\ IS\ Q_{m,1})^{RW_{m1}}\ AND\ (S2\ IS\ Q_{m,2})^{RW_{m2}}\ .\ .\ (S_n\ IS\ Q_{m,n})^{RW_{mn}}\ THEN\ (D_n\ IS\ F_{m)}$$

S_i is a fuzzy variable(a symptom), Q_i is a corresponding fuzzy set while D_i is a diagnostic illness name and F_i is the fuzzy set of the diagnostic illess name. RW_{ij} is the relative importance.

For example, ⟨table 2.1⟩ represents rhinitis pattern and ⟨table 2.2⟩ represents one of the rules based on RI values.

symptom	diagnosis		
	allergic rhinitis	nonallergic eosinohilic rhinitis	nonallergic noneosinohillic rhinitis
common age occurrence	young	.	.
stuffed nose	severe	.	.
sneezing	severe	.	.
nose itching	severe	.	.
nasal mucus	severe	.	.
not smelling	slight	.	.
turbinate anasarca	severe	.	.
secretion	watery	.	.
main cell in secretion	eosinohillic	.	.
infection	slight	.	.
aspirin nontolerance	slight	.	.

⟨table 2.1⟩ a part of rhinitis pattern

```
IF
    ( Common age of occurrence is young ) (0.14)   and
    ( Stuffed nose is severe              ) (0.07)   and
    ( Sneezing is severe                  ) (0.17)   and
    ( Nose itching  is severe             ) (0.17)   and
    ( Nasal mucus  is severe              ) (0.07)   and
    ( Not smelling is slight              ) (0.07)   and
    ( turbinate anasarca is severe        ) (0.07)   and
    ( Secretion is watery                 ) (0.08)   and
    ( Infection is slight                 ) (0.18)   and
THEN
    Acute Epilottitis.
```

⟨table 2.2⟩ one of Rihinitis pattern rules

2.2 System overview

In this chapter, we introduce the method of discrimination Diagnosis using fuzzy logic, relative importance and learning ability of neural network, NFMS[1], ⟨fig. 2.1⟩.   The input data from experts that consist of symptoms and relative importance factor are transformed in RM and FUZZIFY module. The transformed data are stored in a rule base to offer the basic frame for. inference. Actually diagnostic inference of patient's symptom data is processed through MDC and FNR. MDC(Matching Degree Calculation) module calculates the matching degree of the symptoms and the rules. FNR(Fuzzy Neural Reasoning) consists of FLRI net and RN net. In FLRI(Fuzzy Logic Relative Importance) net, the intermediate inference results using relative importance are produced . RN(Reasoning Neural) net has learning ability. After learning with intermediate values, it produces the discrimination result.

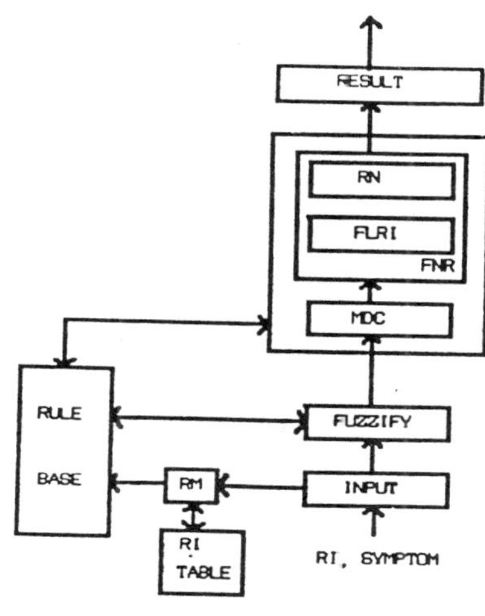

<FIG 2.1> NFMS

FNR which has the learning and reasoning ability consists of three layers, i.e. input layer, inference layer and output layer as shown in <fig2.2>. Inference layer consists of FLRI net and RN net. FLRI net is the stage of calculating the intermediate inferential values with RI values and matching degrees. RN net processes the learning step.

A learning algorithm is explained in reference[1].

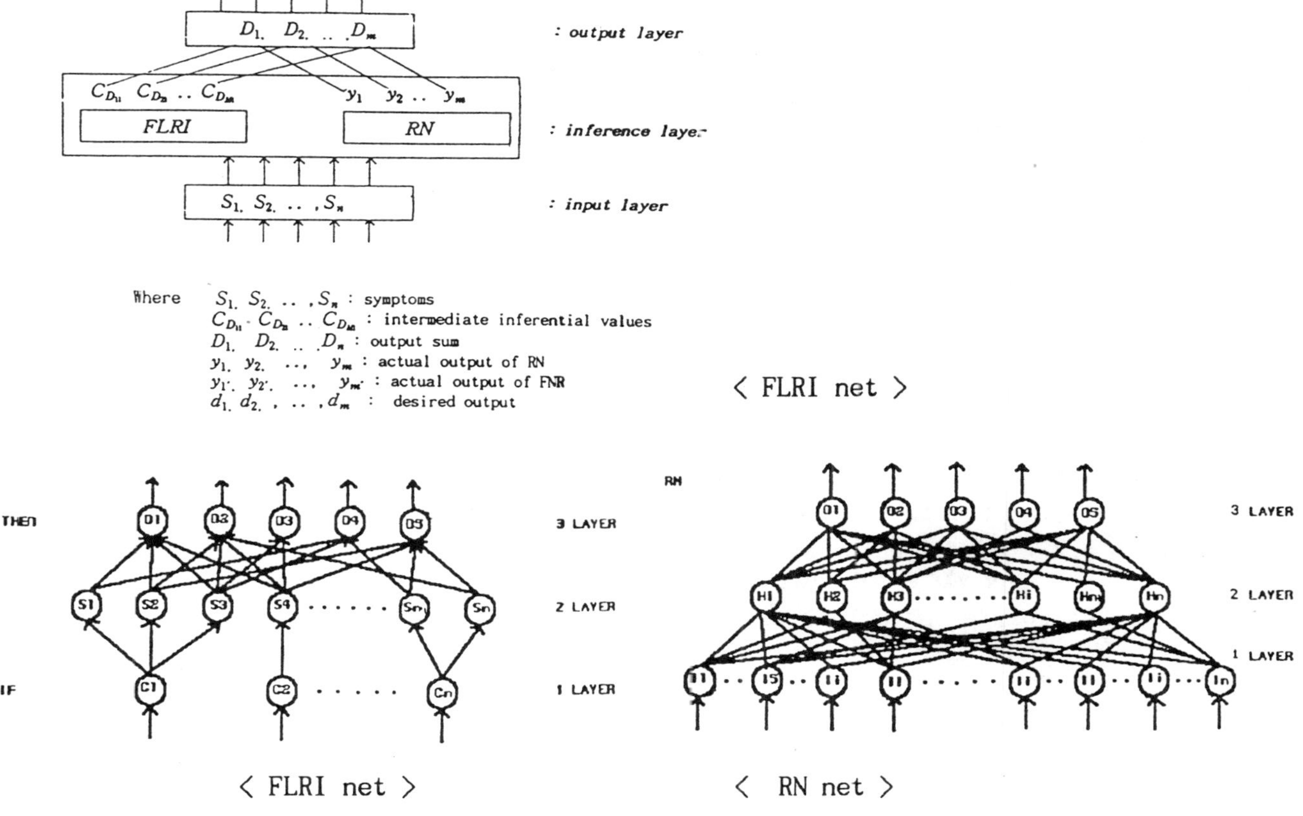

< FLRI net >

< FLRI net >   < RN net >

<fig 2.2> the structure of FNR, FLRI and RN modules

3. Fuzzy Rule based Neural Networks considering time variation.

In decision making, time factor can be a very important one. For example, in the case of medical diagnosis a doctor can't get all of the causal knowledge about patient simultaneously because several data require time for examination. Namely as depicted in ⟨fig 3.1⟩ the number of symptom data can increase with lapse of time.

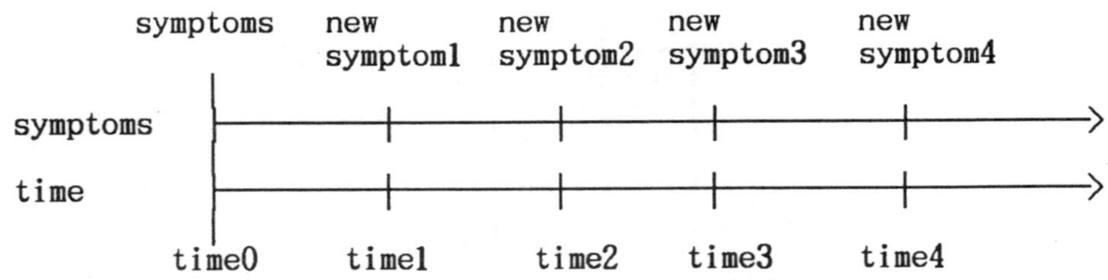

⟨ fig 3.1 ⟩ Increased symptom data over a time period

Nevertheless she can't wait for the examination result. For an efficient diagnosis and treatment, stepwise diagnosis based on time factor is needed. So, in this paper we propose fuzzy rules based neural network considering time variation.
FNR depited in ⟨fig 2.2⟩ has a dynamic structure as shown in ⟨fig 3.2⟩ according to the increased number of symptom data with lapse of time.

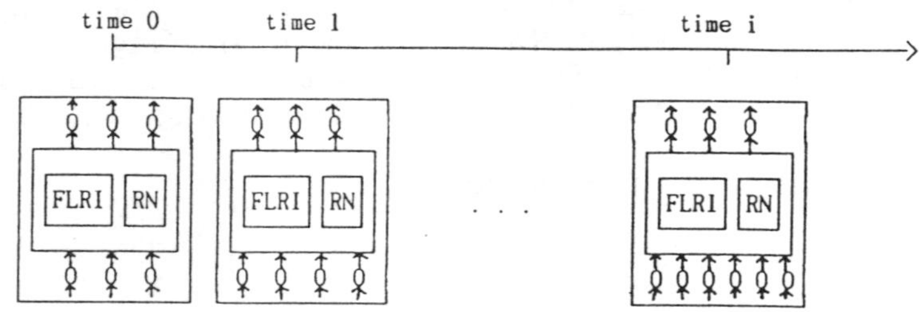

⟨ fig 3.2 ⟩ Dynamic fuzzy rule based neural network

The algorithm for above system is as follows.

□ ALGORITHM □

STEP 1 : Present the fuzzified input value, $S_1, S_2, .. , S_n$, to the input layer.

STEP 2 : IF (no. of input data is different from n)
THEN node creation or deletion;

STEP 3 : Propagate the input value to the FLRI net and RN net and calculate the intermediate value in parallel.

STEP 3.1 : FLRI net calculation.
produce the intermediate inferential data, $C_{D_{11}}\ C_{D_{21}} .. C_{D_{M1}}$.

STEP 3.2 : RN net calculation.
produce the output of RN, $y_1, y_2, .., y_m$.

STEP 4 : Calculate the actual output $y_{1'}, y_{2'}, .., y_{m'}$ of FNR.

STEP 5 : Calculate the error⟨ ε ⟩ between the desired output, $d_1, d_2, .. , d_m$ and the actual output, $y_{1'}, y_{2'}, .., y_{m'}$.

STEP 6 : Adjust the weight propagating the error backward to inference layer and input layer.

STEP 7 : go to STEP2.

4. Simulation Results

We applied this system to the problem domain of discriminating the allergic rhinitis, nonallergic eosinohillic rhinitis and nonallergic noneosinohillic rhinitis with sample symptom data. After simulating and comparing with other methods(i.e MANDANIS method of fuzzy inference, FLRI using the relative importance concept[2], BP algorithm of neural network), we conclude that Dynamic NFMS model is more efficient than other methods.

<table 4.1> shows experimental data which represents relative importance and <fig 4.1> is the compared results over time. It shows that this system discriminate the results more easily with lapse of time and it's discriminating ability is better than other system. This system can be applied more efficiently for adaptive discrimination diagnosis.

		D1		D2		D3	
		EXPERT	RI	EXPERT	RI	EXPERT	RI
common age of occurrence							
X1 age	S1 young	0.6	0.2	0	0	0	0
	S2 adult	0	0	0.2	0.1	0.3	0.1
symptoms on presentation							
X2 Stuffed nose	S3 sever	0.3	0.1	0.2	0.1	0	0
	S4 middle	0	0	0	0	0.3	0.1
	S5 slight	0	0	0	0	0	0
X3 Sneezzing	S6 severe	0.75	0.25	0	0	0	0
	S7 middle	0	0	0.2	0.1	0	0
	S8 slight	0	0	0	0	0.75	0.25
X4 nose itching	S9 severe	0.75	0.25	0	0	0	0
	S10 middle	0	0	0.2	0.1	0.75	0.25
	S11 slight	0	0	0	0	0	0
X5 Snot	S12 severe	0.3	0.1	0.2	0.1	0.3	0.1
X6 No smelling	S13 severe	0	0	1	0.5	0	0
	S14 middle	0.3	0.1	0	0	0	0
	S15 slight	0	0	0	0	0.6	0.2

< table 4.1 > Relative Importance Table
(Common age of occurrence, symptoms on presentation)

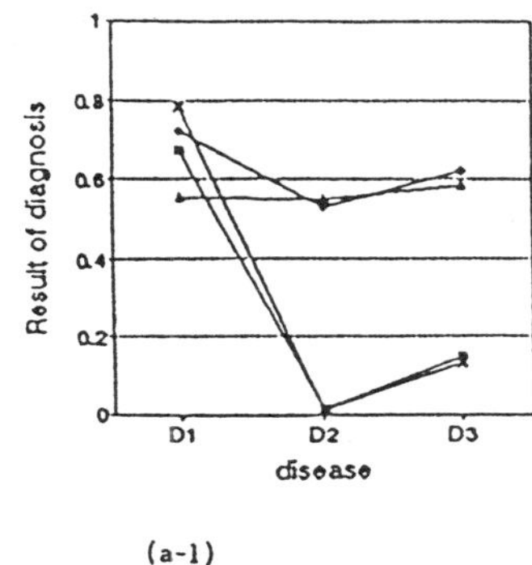

(a-1)

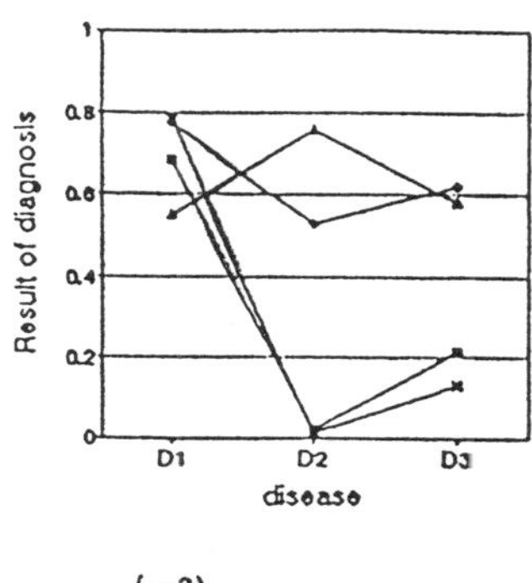

(a-2)

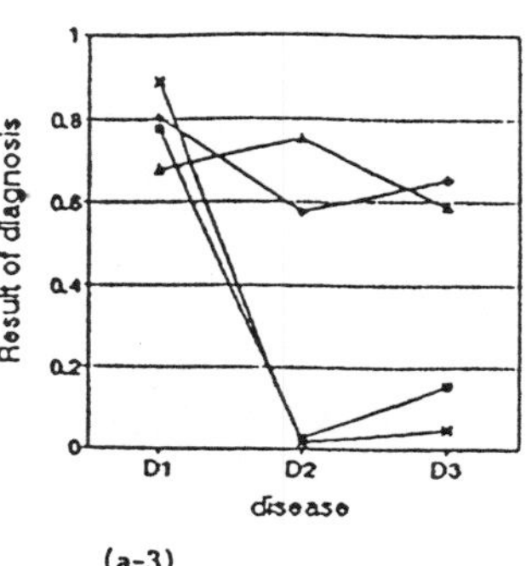

(a-3)

< fig 4.1 > The compared result according to the time factor
(a-1) time 0   (a-2) time 1   (a-3) time 2

5. Conclusion

In this paper we propose fuzzy neural cooperate system considering relative importance and time variation. This system has uncertain data processing, learning and perception ability. Also it is designed to be a flexible structure according to the variation of data with lapse of time and applicable in many domains which require adaptation.

References

[1] Jeong_Yon Shim, Young_Sik Jeong, Chong_Sun Hwang, " A DESIGN OF NEURO_FUZZY MEDICAL DIAGNOSIS SYSTEM BASED ON RELATIVE IMPORTANCE", ICONIP'94-SEOUL, pp1311-1316.

[2] Elaine Rich, Kelvin Knight, **Artificial Intelligence : second Edition**, McGraw-Hillpress, 1991.

[3] R.R.Yager, S.Ovchinnikov, R.M.Tong, H.T.Nguyen, **FUZZY SETS AND APPLICATIONS:Selected Papers by L.A. Zadeh**, A Wiley-interscience Publication, 1987.

[4] Hackerman D., "Probabilistic Interpretations for MYCIN's Certainty Factors," Workshop Proceedings of uncertainty and Probability in Artificial Intelligence, UCLA, 1985.

[5] D. Rumelhart and J. McClelland, **Parallel Distributed Processing**-Exploration in the Mirostructure of Cognition, I. Cambridge, MA: MIT Press, 1986.

[6] Hideyuki TAKAKI, " FUSION TECHNOLOGY OF FUZZY THEORY AND NEURAL NETWORKS SURVEY AND FUTURE DIRECTIONS.", Iizuka, Japan, July 20-24,1990.

[7] Akira Kawamura, Nobuo Watanabe, " A PROTOTYPE OF NEURO-FUZZY COOPERATION SYSTEM",IEEE international conference on fuzzy systems, 1992.

[8] Patrick K. Simpson, " FUZZY MIN-MAX NEURAL NETWORKS - PART I : CLASSIFICATION",IEEE transactions on neural network VOL. 3, NO. 5. SEPTEMBER 1992.

[9] Anthony V. Robins, " MULTIPLE REPRESENTATIONS IN CONNECTIONIST SYSTEMS ", International Jounal of Neural Systems, Vol. 2. NO. 4 (1992) 345 -362.

[10] Tomonori Hashiyama, Takeshi Furuhashi, Yoshiki Uchikawa, " A DECISION MAKING MODEL USING A FUZZY NEURAL NETWORK." Proceedings of the 2nd International Confernce on Fuzzy logic & Neural networks (Iizuka, Japan, July 17-22, 1992) pp. 1057 - 1060.

Special Session VIII
Applications

The invited program is also featured by 8 special sessions on current interesting topics. Each special session organizer is invited by the Program Committee and the success of each special session is completely due to the hard efforts of each organizer.

Fault-tolerance evaluation of SOM (Self-Organizing Map) using a neuro-computer: *MY-NEUPOWER*

Moritoshi Yasunaga*, Ippei Hachiya*, Moki Keiji**

*Institute of Information Science and Electronics, University of Tsukuba
Tsukuba, Ibaraki 305 JAPAN
e-mail: yasunaga@is.tsukuba.ac.jp
**Application System Engineering Dept., Hitachi Microcomputer System Ltd.

Kodaira, Tokyo 187, JAPAN

Abstract— Fault-tolerance of SOM (Self-Organizing Map) under defective neurons is evaluated using the recently developed neuro-computer *MY-NEUPOWER*. One hundred digital neurons in the MY-NEUPOWER are programmed for one-dimensional SOM array. Several neurons in the array are reprogrammed to emulate the defective neurons having stuck-at faults which impede the self-organization. By this experiment, high fault-tolerance of SOM is demonstrated, that is, the entire array of neurons can be ordered even under the condition of defective neurons. Furthermore, the presence of the extremely long meta-stable state before the global-ordering is shown. An analytical model is proposed, and the appearance of the meta-stable state and its transition probability to the global-ordering state are clarified by the model. It is also show that the period of the meta-stable state is closely related to the width of the neighborhood function.

1   Introduction

Self-organizing map (SOM) has well been studied theoretically and several applications using it have already been proposed[1]-[12]. SOM is one of the promising algorithms in neural networks. However, nothing related to its fault-tolerance, that is, robustness against defective neurons has yet been reported. By evaluating SOM's behavior under defective neurons quantitatively, it will be possible to realize a neuro-computer that can eliminate defective neurons by itself without any specialized circuits for fault-tolerance. Furthermore, this advantage can be utilized in the future neuro-computer designing and manufacturing, especially using WSI (Wafer Scale Integration) technology.

The SOM calculation including defective neurons needs high-speed hardware or neuro-computers because a long period meta-stable state emerges before a global-ordering state as discussed in this paper. The goal of this paper is to estimate SOM's fault-tolerance quantitatively using a recently developed neuro-computer (MY-NEUPOWER) and propose an analytical model including defective neurons. The MY-NEUPOWER is a massively parallel computer containing 512 neurons that are specialized processors designed based on neural functions.

At the beginning of this paper, hardware overview of MY-NEUPOWER is described. Experimental results on self-organizing under defects using MY-NEUPOWER are reported secondary. Finally, an analytical model is proposed and discussed comparing with the experimental results.

2   Hardware Overview of MY-NEUPOWER

Figure 1 shows communication architecture of MY-NEUPOWER where all neurons are connected by broadcast bus. One selected sender neuron broadcasts its output through the broadcast bus in each bus cycle. The products of the sender neuron's broadcasting output X_j and the receiver neurons' weights $W_{1j}, W_{2j}, ..., W_{Nj}$ (N is the number of neurons) are calculated simultaneously in each bus cycle. Consequently, it is possible to calculate the vector product of the neuron output vector and weight matrix in $o(N)$ time in contrast to the $o\left(N^2\right)$ time required by ordinary computers. The maximum/minimum neuron pointer circuit is located on the bus. This circuit picks up each neuron's output during broadcasting and compares the present output with the previous one pointing the newest maximum and minimum neurons.

Figure 2 shows the neuron chip configuration and the circuit diagram of one neuron. Eight digital neurons are integrated onto one chip using 1.0 µm CMOS (Complementary Metal Oxide Semiconductor) technology and each neuron is connected to the bus in the chip. Input and output of the neuron are 10 bits. A 16 x10-bit multiplier and a 32-bit ALU (Arithmetic Logic Unit) are mainly used for scalar-product calculations that are central calculations of the neural function. The weight memory stores 512 synaptic weights containing 16 bits. This memory can also be accessed as 1024 x 8-bit synaptic weights. The product of the synaptic weight and the datum on the broadcast bus, that is the sender neuron's output, is calculated by the multiplier. Output from the multiplier can be accumulated by using the ALU. The clock rate of the neuron is 25.0 MHz.

The system configuration of the MY-NEUPOWER is shown in Fig.3. One neuron board has 32 neuron chips mounted on it, so that 256 neurons are integrated into the neuron board (Fig.4). Two neuron boards are connected to the control chip, so that 512 neurons are packaged within the system. Data memory stores data that is processed directly by the neural networks. This system is connected to the host workstation by the SCSI interface. After all pattern sets and instructions are loaded into the memories, the system is cut away from the workstation to allow it to begin processing the neural algorithm by itself.

By using this hardware, we were able to calculate one million weight-updating cycles within 30 seconds for each ordering experiment, while the same calculation required more than 43 minutes with a high performance workstation (SPECint92: 139.4, SPECfp92: 222.5).

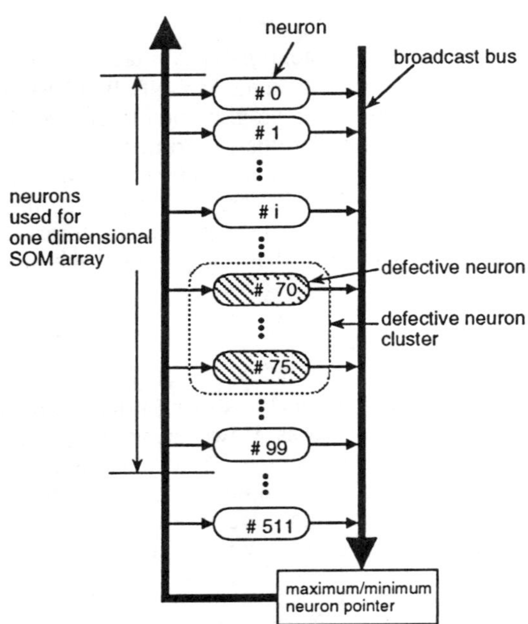

Fig.1 Broadcast bus architecture of MY-NEUPOWER.

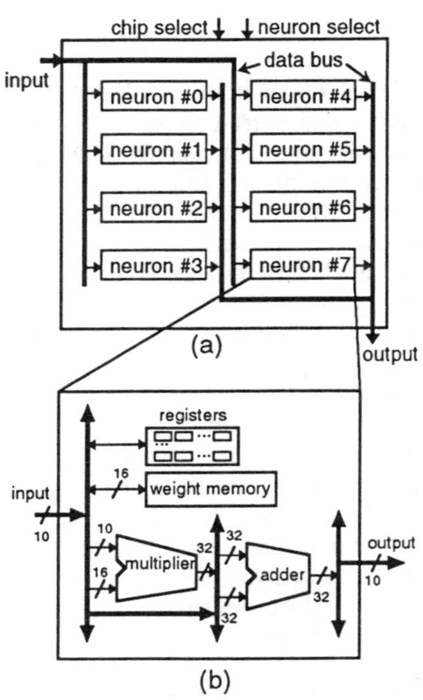

Fig.2 (a) Configuration of one neuron-chip;
(b) Block diagram of single neuron.

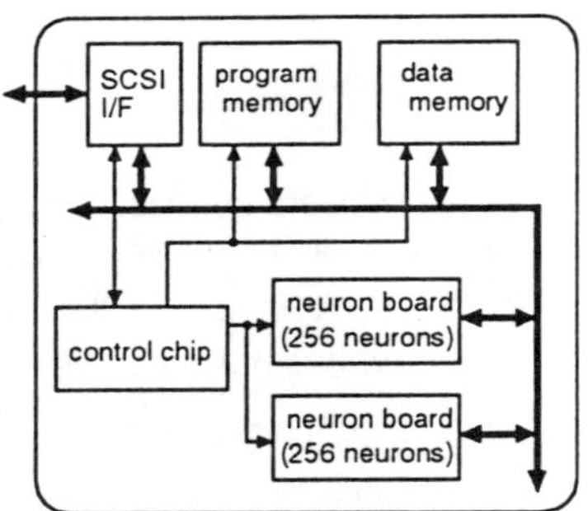

Fig.3 System configuration.

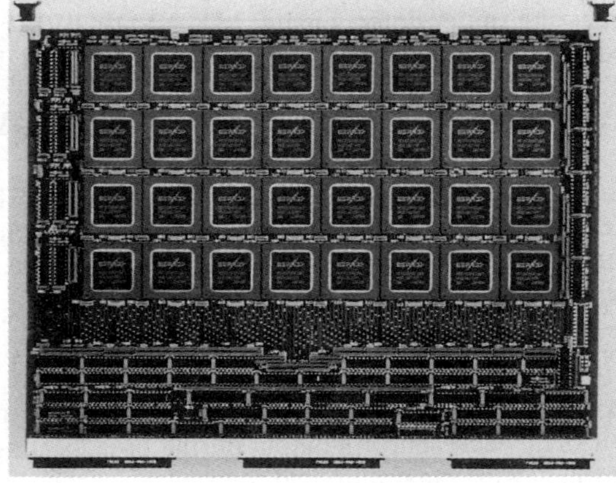

Fig.4 Photograph of neuron board.

3   Experiments on SOM with Defective Neurons

We chose the one-dimensional SOM array in which neurons were arranged in a single line, because defective neurons in it completely cut the array apart as shown in Fig.5 and this was the severest condition impeding self-organizing of the entire network. In the experiments, 100 neurons including 6 defective neurons were used

($N_d = 6$). This defective rate of 6% (6/100) was calculated from Ref.[13] in which yield data were reported for a wafer-scale neural network LSI. All defective neurons were assumed to be concentrated in one place of the line making a defective-neuron-cluster as shown in the figure to cut the array apart completely.

The MY-NEUPOWER was programmed according to the following simple SOM algorithm. First, the winner neuron w is chosen as follows:

$$\left| \xi(t) - \mu_w(t) \right| = \min_i \left| \xi(t) - \mu_i(t) \right| \, , \tag{1}$$

where $\xi(t)$ is the input signal and $\mu_i(t)$ is the synaptic weight of each neuron. Then, the winner w and its neighbor neurons $i \in N_w$ update their weights as follows:

$$\mu_i(t+1) = \mu_i(t) + \Lambda(|w-i|)\left(\xi(t) - \mu_i(t) \right) \, , \tag{2}$$

where $\Lambda(|w-i|)$ is the neighborhood function, and one of the typical functions is defined using the decreasing coefficient m as follows:

$$\Lambda(|w-i|) = 1 - \frac{|w-i|}{m} \quad if \, |w-i| < m \\ = 0 \quad\quad otherwise \tag{3}$$

Because the digital neuron in the MY-NEUPOWER uses the integer-representation architecture as described above, the quantization-effect pointed out by Ref.[8] must be considered. Evaluation of this effect on the MY-NEUPOWER is an important subject. However, including this effect makes the problem more complicated. Therefore, in this experiment, we adjusted the parameter (the shape of the neighborhood function) so that the quantization did not affect the ordering[8].

In this experiment, we only evaluated the influence of the defective neurons whose outputs were stuck at the maximum value (= 1). To emulate this stuck-at fault, 6 neurons out of 100 were chosen as shown in Fig.1 and their outputs were set to 1 forcibly. The input signal $\xi(t)$ was randomly selected in the range of $0 \le \xi(t) \le 1$. Consequently, no neurons in the defective cluster could be chosen as the winner because this fault corresponded to the maximum distance (=1) of Eq.(1).

We used the index of disorder D shown below proposed in Ref.[1] to measure the degree of ordering (self-organizing) of N neurons (#0 — #$N-1$):

$$D = \left(\sum_{i=1}^{N-1} \left| \mu_i - \mu_{i-1} \right| \right) - \left| \mu_{N-1} - \mu_0 \right| \, . \tag{4}$$

As ordering (of weights) progresses, D decreases, and $D = 0$ means the entire ordering of all weights. Figure 6 shows experimental results on the index of disorder D as a function of the number of weight-updating (learning) cycles. Four trials with different initial weights are shown in the figure. Decreasing coefficient m was fixed at $m = 11$. Therefore, the neighborhood function covered the opposite region across the defective-neuron cluster as shown in Fig.5 (a tail of the neighborhood function soaked into the opposite region). It is remarkable that self-

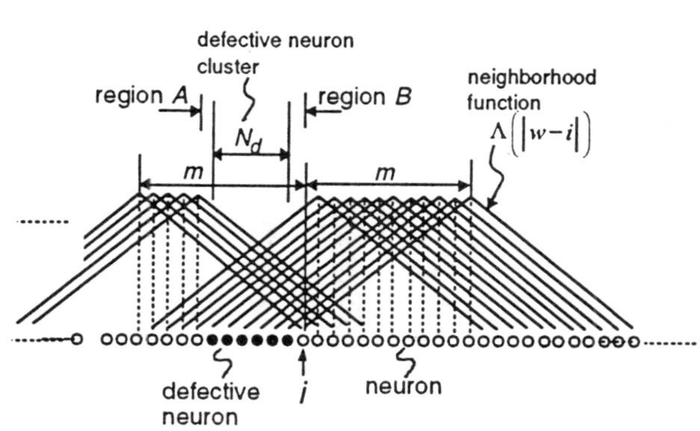

Fig.5 Neighborhood functions
     near the defective neuron cluster.

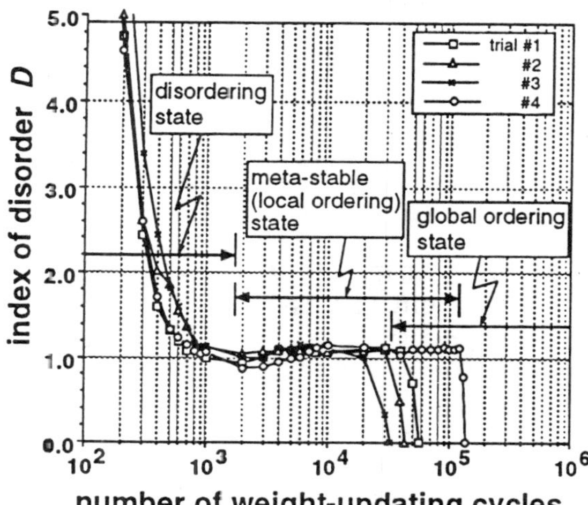

Fig.6 State transitions in ordering.

organizing of the entire network has been completed in spite of defective neurons. Furthermore, each trial shows the same ordering behavior, that is, there are three different states: disordering-, meta-stable(local ordering)-, and global-ordering-states. The global ordering suddenly occurs after the extremely long period of the meta-stable state where the index of disorder D is frozen. Snapshots of these states are shown in Fig.7. In the meta-stable state, neurons' weights in the two regions isolated by the defective neurons are almost ordered locally. Then, they suddenly transform into the global-ordering state making a monotonously decreasing array.

4   Analytical Model and Discussion

Ordering behavior described above can be analyzed as follows. As shown in Fig.5, the symmetric shape of the neighborhood function collapses near the defective-neuron cluster. Therefore, *ordering-force* from the opposite region is weaker than that in this region. This distortion of the neighborhood function delays the global ordering and neurons in each region are first ordered locally. Here, we evaluate the ratio of the ordering-forces in the both regions. Paying attention to the i -th neuron that is next to the defective-neuron cluster in Fig.5, the ordering-force Φ_B given onto this neuron in the same region is calculated by summing up the effects of the neighborhood functions in the same region as follows:

$$\Phi_B = \sum_{r=1}^{m-1} \left(1 - \frac{1}{m} r \right) = \frac{m-1}{2} \ . \tag{5}$$

On the contrary, the ordering-force Φ_A from the opposite region is calculated as follows:

$$\Phi_A = \sum_{r=N_d+1}^{m-1} \left(1 - \frac{1}{m} r \right) = \frac{m-1}{2} - \left\{ N_d - \frac{N_d(N_d+1)}{2m} \right\} \ , \tag{6}$$

where the number of neurons whose neighborhood function cover the i -th neuron is different from Eq.(5) because of the defective neuron cluster as shown in Fig.5. Ordering is random-walk process of kinks in one-dimensional array, that is, kinks in the array go right or left with the same probability at 1/2 and are finally absorbed in either the right or left edge of the array [5][6]. Because of unbalance between the ordering-forces shown by Eqs (5) and (6), the transition probability $P(m, N_d)$ of the meta-stable state to the global ordering state can be estimated using the above random-walk probability and Eqs (5) and (6) as follows:

$$P(m, N_d) = \left(\frac{1}{2} \right)^\gamma \ , \tag{7}$$

where γ is

$$\gamma = \frac{\Phi_B}{\Phi_A} = \frac{m(m-1)}{(m-N_d)\{(m-N_d)-1\}} \ . \tag{8}$$

If there is no defective neurons ($N_d = 0$), $P(m, N_d)$ equals 1/2. As the decreasing coefficient m decreases, that is, the width of the neighborhood function narrows, the transition probability $P(m, N_d)$ decreases drastically because of the γ -th power. This is why the extremely long meta-stable state exists before the global ordering state. After kinks stuck at the edges of the defective neuron cluster jump into the opposite region with

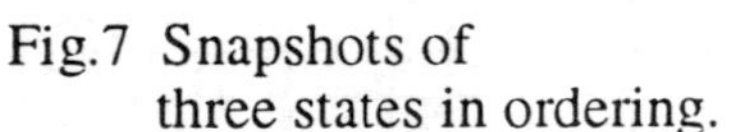

Fig.7 Snapshots of
    three states in ordering.

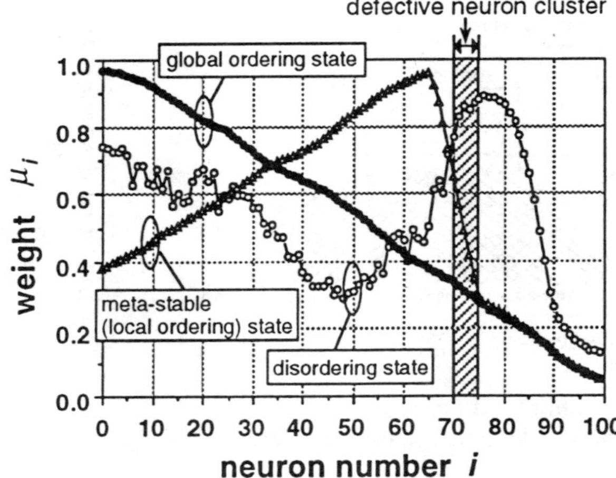

the transition probability $P(m, N_d)$, they rapidly go to the edges of the array with normal random-walk process. Fig.8 shows the experimental results on the number of cycles required for global ordering as a function of the decreasing coefficient m. As m decreases, the number of cycles increases drastically as $P(m, N_d)$ predicts.

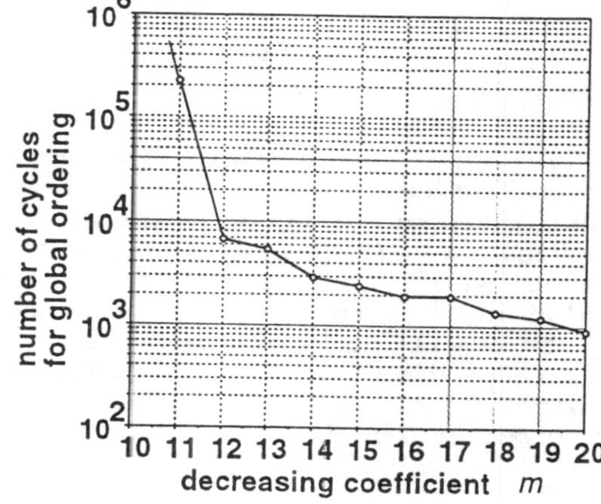

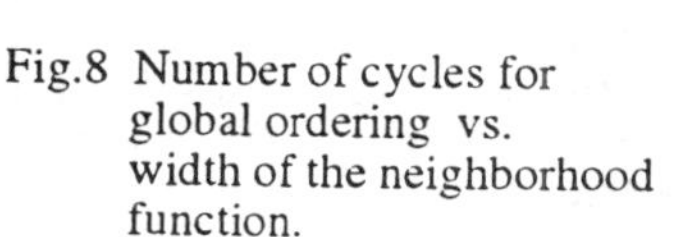
Fig.8 Number of cycles for global ordering vs. width of the neighborhood function.

5   Conclusions

Even under the condition of defective neurons having stuck-at faults, the global-ordering of one-dimensional SOM array was observed using the digital neurocomputer MY-NEUPOWER. Furthermore, the meta-stable state with a extremely long period before the global-ordering was observed. In the meta-stable state, local-orderings were achieved respectively in the regions isolated by the defective neurons. An analytical model was proposed and it clarified the appearance of the meta-stable state. The transition probability of the meta-stable state to the global-ordering state was derived from the model. Form this probability, it was shown that the period of the meta-satable state is closely related to the width of the neighborhood function. This relation was also demonstrated by the experiments using the MY-NEUPOWER.

Acknowledgments

We would like to thank Prof. Yuzo Hirai, Yoshihiro Kuwabara and MY-NEUPOWER project members at Hitachi Microcomputer System Ltd. for their helpful discussion.

References

[1] T. Kohonen, "Self-Organization and associative memory," Springer-Verlag, 1984.
[2] T. Kohonen, "The self-organizing map," Proc. of the IEEE, vol.78, no.9, pp.1464-1480, Sept. 1990.
[3] M. Cottrell and J. C. Fort, "A stochastic model of retinotopy: a self organizing process." Biol. Cybern., vol. 53, pp.405-411, 1986.
[4] H. Ritter and K. Schulten, "Convergence properties of Kohonen's topology conserving maps: fluctuations, stability, and dimension selection," Biol. Cybern., vol. 60, pp.59-71, 1988.
[5] J. Hertz, A. Krogh, and R. G. Palmer, "Introduction to the theory of neural computation," Addison-Wesley Publishing Co., 1990.
[6] T. Geszti, "Physical models of neural networks," World Scientific, 1990.
[7] E. Erwin, K. Obermayer and K.Schulten, "Self-organizing maps: ordering, convergence properties and energy functions", Biol. Cybern., vol.67, pp.47-55, 1992.
[8] P. Thiran and M. Hasler, "Self-organization of a one-dimensional Kohonen network with quantized weights and inputs," Neural Networks, vol.7, no.9, pp.1427-1439, 1994.
[9] B. Fritzke, "Growing cell structure—Self-organizing network for unsupervised and supervised learning", Neural Network, vol.7, no.9, pp.1441-1460, 1994.
[10] N. Nasrabadi and Y. Feng, "Vector quantization of image based upon the Kohonen self-organizing feature maps", Proc. of International Conference on Neural Networks, vol.I, pp.101-108, 1988.
[11] J. Lampinen and E. Oja, "Distortion tolerant pattern recognition base of self-organizing feature extraction," IEEE Trans. on Neural Networks, vol.6, no.3, pp.539-547, May 1995.
[12] J. A. Walter and K. J. Schulten, "Implementation of self-organizing neural networks for visuo-motor control of industrial robot," IEEE Trans. on Neural Networks, vol.4, no.1. pp.86-95, Jan. 1993.
[13] M. Yasunaga, N. Masuda, M. Yagyu, M. Asai, K. Shibata, M. Ooyama, M. Yamada, T. Sagaguchi, and M. Hashimoto, "A self-learning digital neural network using wafer-scale LSI", IEEE J. of Solid-State Circuits, vol.28, no.2, pp.106-114, Feb. 1993.

Identifying and Verifying Handwritten Signature Images Utilizing Neural Networks

Kai Huang, Hong Yan

Department of Electrical Engineering
University of Sydney, NSW 2006, Australia

Abstract— **This paper describes an off-line signature identification and verification method based on geometric feature extraction and neural network classification. In this method, signature images are simultaneously examined under several scales by superimposing onto them a set of feature extracting grids. Each grid is associated with a trained feed-forward feature network, which generates responses according to the similarity of the input pattern to the stored model pattern. A decision network combines all these responses to generate a collective confidence rating on whether the input is genuine. The system implemented based on this method has been tested with a database containing over 3000 genuine and forgery signature images belonging to 21 signature classes. Experimental results indicate that the system can correctly identify their classes and distinguish a large majority of forgeries.**

1　Introduction

Computerized signature identification and verification is an application in which behavior biometrics are being utilized in automated personal identity determination. Biometric verification techniques are superior in many ways compared to verifying PINs, passwords and/or access cards, since biometric properties are not easily duplicated, cannot be lost or stolen. Handwritten signature, being widely accepted socially and legally as proof of identity, is a good candidate to be processed by intelligent machines.

Research efforts in this area are best summarized in references [1, 2]. The complexity of signature verification lies in the variability of signing, affected by physical, mental conditions and other random factors. For well practiced signatures however, interpersonal variations should be much larger than intrapersonal ones. The task of a signature verification system is then to extract stable and unique features from genuine signature samples and to measure other inputs based on these features.

Recently neural network techniques have been applied to signature verification with good results [2]. Compared with classical statistical techniques, neural networks are potentially more tolerate and robust when dealing with the intricacies of real data, also incremental system updating is convenient. While it is generally accepted that local features convey more accurate and detailed characteristics of handwritten samples, global features are mostly used when classifying static signature images [3, 4]. In this paper, we present a multi-scale local feature based signature classifier, which generates confidence ratings from collective opinions at each scale. Experiment results on our signature database indicate that the method is effective.

2　Signature Database

2.1　Signature Data Collection

A total of 3528 signature images are collected to form the signature database. These images belong to 21 sets of different signatures. Each set comprises one A4 page of genuine and six A4 pages of forgery signatures. They are scanned one page at a time, at resolution of 100 dpi, 8-bit gray-scale. An A4 page is divided into 12 by 2 rectangles with dashed lines. 24 genuine signatures are signed by a volunteer and six lots of 24 forged signatures are produced by other volunteers. Each volunteer may be asked to produce one to three other people's signatures, given photocopies of the genuine signature pages. The forgeries are either freehand or traced, encompass varying skill levels (Figure 1).

2.2　Signature Image Preprocessing

The signature images are first cut out from the scanned A4 page image by a separate form processing program. The dash lines on the form are located and are used as the primary separators in the extraction of individual images. It is observed that some writers use the lower grid lines as their signature reference line, as a result part of the signature trace is cut off by the extraction program. From visual inspection, the extracted images contain most of the signature information and some loss is tolerable. It helps to force the classification system to be more robust against such situations.

Excessive white area in each image is trimmed off, and the signature is centered at gray-level centroid. Standard noise reduction and isolated peak noise removal techniques, such as median-filtering and average

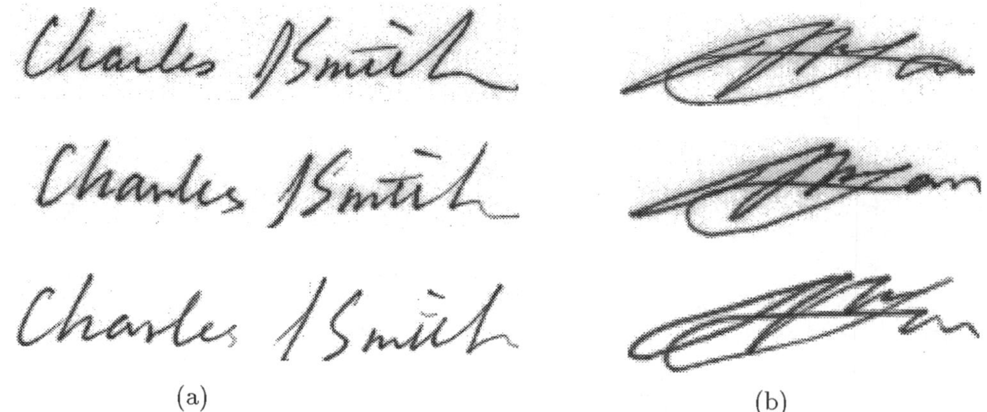

(a)   (b)

Figure 1: Examples of genuine and forgery signatures. Genuine samples are displayed on the top. The forged signatures are either simple freehand, skilled freehand or traced. (a) shows common cursive type signature samples and forgeries, (b) shows graphical type signatures.

filtering [7], are used to clean the initial image. A binarized signature mask is obtained by thresholding, followed by morphological operations [7] to fill small holes and to remove small connected components mostly generated by noisy background. It is used to mask out the gray-leveled version of the clean, centered signature image (Figure 2).

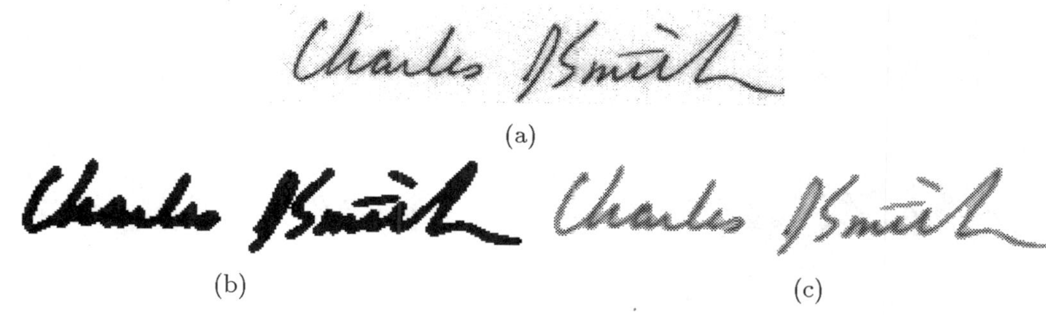

(a)

(b)   (c)

Figure 2: Preprocessing of signature image: (a) is the signature cut-out from form, (b) is the binarized mask, and (c) is the cleaned image after processing.

3 Signature Shape Feature Extraction

For a signature image S_{gray} of width w and height h, let P be a pixel inside S_{gray} (Figure 3a). The position of P is denoted by (i, j), where $0 < i < w - 1$ and $0 < j < h - 1$, and the gray level value of P is denoted by g_P, where $g_P = S_{gray}(i, j)$. The maximum and minimum gray level values of S_{gray} are denoted by g_{max} and g_{min} respectively, where $g_{max} = \max S_{gray}(i, j)$, and $g_{min} = \min S_{gray}(i, j)$, for all i and j.

3.1 Shape Features from Signature Image

The following shape features are extracted from signature images :

- Core feature F_{core}:

  Signature core is defined as the skeleton of the pen trace. The core feature is a useful structural representation of a signature, invariant with respect to pen trace thickness. It is extracted directly from the gray-level image using a 3x3 operator. A pixel is core if its gray-level value is a local peak (Figure 3b).

$$P \in F_{core}, \ if \ \sum_{k=0}^{7} step(g_P \geq g_{P_k}) \leq 6,$$

where

$$step(g_P \geq g_{P_k}) = \begin{cases} 1 & if \ g_P \geq g_{P_k} \\ 0 & otherwise. \end{cases} \tag{1}$$

- Signature outline $F_{outline}$:

  The outline feature contains most of the shape information. It is extracted from the gray-level image after thresholding, again using a 3x3 operator. A threshold $\theta_{outline}$ is set, then pixels whose gray-level intensity values are above the threshold and whose 8-neighbor count is below 8 must be on the outline (Figure 3c). That is,

$$P \in F_{outline}, \ if \ (g_P > \theta_{outline}) \ and \ (\sum_{k=0}^{7} g_{P_k} > \theta_{outline}) < 8,$$

  where

$$\theta_{outline} = g_{min} + 0.25 \ (g_{max} - g_{min}). \tag{2}$$

- High pressure region feature F_{hpr}:

  High pressure feature has been used by Ammar *et al.*[5] to detect skilled forgeries. It is extracted to indicate regions where more emphasis has been made by the signer, usually the darker area in the scanned image. A threshold θ_{hpr} is set. Pixels of gray-level intensity values larger than threshold are considered to be belong to high pressure regions (Figure 3d).

$$P \in F_{hpr}, \ if \ g_P > \theta_{hpr},$$

  where

$$\theta_{hpr} = g_{min} + 0.75 \ (g_{max} - g_{min}). \tag{3}$$

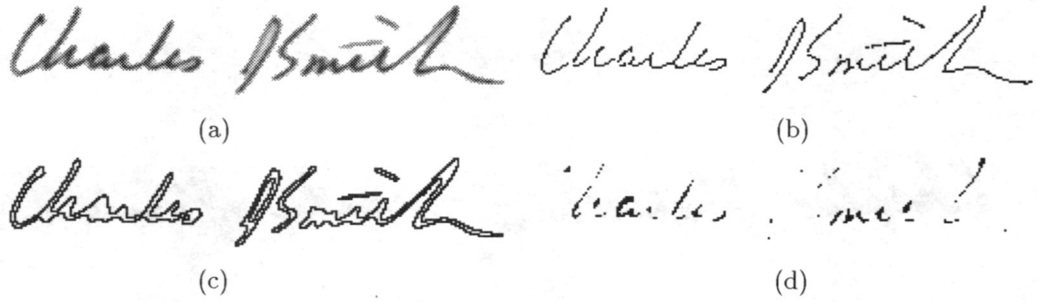

(a)   (b)

(c)   (d)

Figure 3: Shape features extracted from a signature image : (a) gray level signature image, (b) core feature, (c) signature outline, (d) high pressure region feature.

3.2   Shape Feature Alignment

To effectively reduce intrapersonal variations, the set of reference signatures as well as input test signatures need to be carefully aligned before the local feature extraction step.

The horizontal and vertical projections of the binarized ink area image are obtained for all reference samples belonging to the same signature. One set of projections are selected arbitrarily as a common reference template, and projections from others reference samples are transformed against the template to find the function which maximizes correlation, hence to better register these signature samples.

A two dimensional surface scaling function is searched by elastic matching of the horizontal and vertical projections of the fine resolution ink area image against those from the common template. A dynamic programming based technique [6] is used to correlate corresponding projections. An example of non-linear shape alignment is shown in Figure 4.

3.3   Local Shape Feature Extraction

A set of rectangular grids are overlaid on top of each signature shape representation when extracting local features (Figure 5a). A coarse grid of size 3 by 10 is used as the basis structure. The highest resolution grid is 6 by 20. A medium grid of size 4 by 15 is also used. The borders of these grids are fuzzified to reduce the effect of abrupt changes if severe misalignment occurs. Inside each grid, the number of feature pixels are counted. For feature pixels near boundary regions, a linear fuzzy weighting factor is multiplied. The extracted feature vectors are fed directly into the corresponding feature networks for classification (Figure 5b).

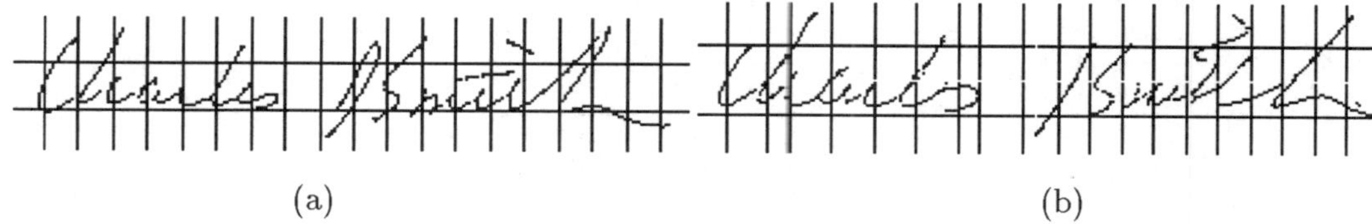

(a)   (b)

Figure 4: Non-linear shape feature alignment by elastic matching technique. The reference template is shown in (a), and the result from alignment step is shown in (b).

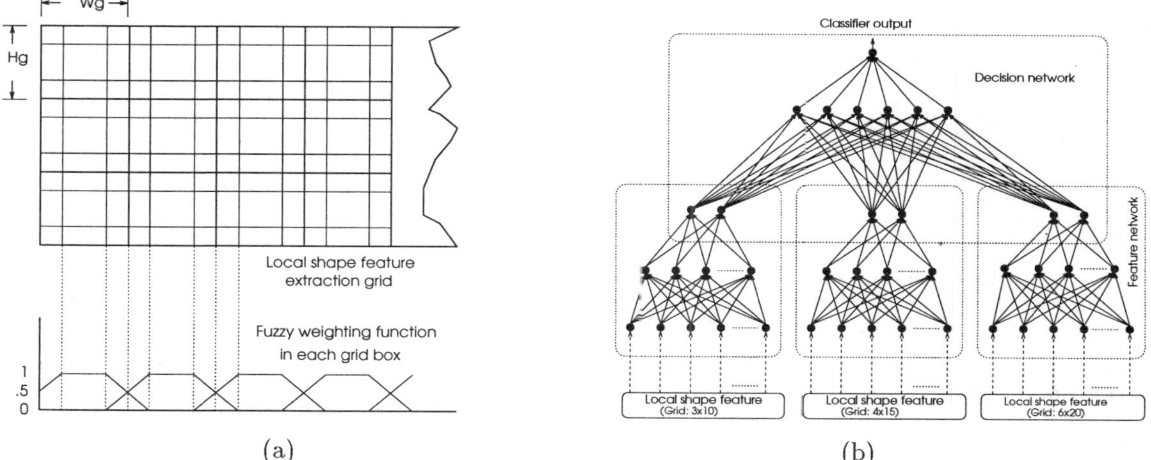

(a)   (b)

Figure 5: (a) Local shape feature extraction grid with fuzzified border regions. The regular grid location is indicated by thick border line. The extent of fuzzy region is indicated by thin border line. The linear fuzzy weighting scheme is illustrated in the lower part. (b) Neural network classifier for signature verification. It consists of several feature networks and a decision network.

4   System Implementation

The strategy of multi-scale examination is adopted in our verification system, which is in use in questioned document examination practices. The signature classifier integrates low, medium and high resolution feature networks to facilitate majority voting. A decision network is introduced to automate the process of determining the optimal voting strategy. The rationale is that when a genuine signature is presented to the system, it is likely that matches can be found at more than one scale. On the other hand, a forgery signature may appear similar to the reference at some parts under particular scale, the overall integration of similarity will tends to disqualify it as a true sample.

In the complete system, individual signature classifier is constructed for each enrolled signature class. The MLP network is trained using 8 reference samples from each signature class and samples derived from them by perturbations involving rotation, slant, perspective and scale changes. After training, the reference model is stored in the form of connection weights. The diagram which illustrates the operation is shown in Figure 6.

To identify the class of a signature, the input image is examined by all classifiers. The class label is determined as that of the classifier which gives highest output and with a high confidence value. Otherwise it is declared that the input is not registed. For verification test, only the classifier corresponding to the claimed class label is evoked. The system identifies correctly the identities of genuine samples. The verification performance of the system under targeted forgery test is about 88% when no rejection is allowed (Table 1).

Total Gen.	*Total For.*	*Total FR*	*Total FA*
504	3024	56	357
Type I	*Type II*	*Ave. FR*	*Ave. FA*
11.1%	11.8%	3	17

Table 1: Experimental result on signature database for targeted forgery test. (FA=False Reject, FA=False Accept.)

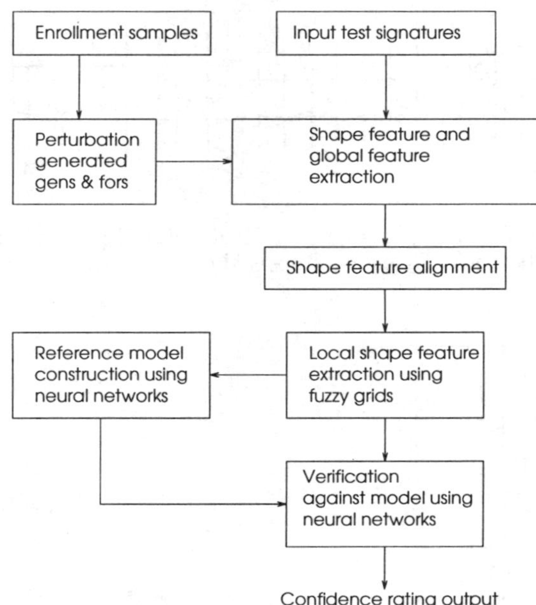

Figure 6: Signature verification system diagram. It shows the flow path for both the training phase (left portion) and testing phase (right portion) of the system.

5 Conclusion

An off-line signature recognition and verification method using neural networks has been detailed. It extracts localized, aligned signature shape features over a range of scales, and outputs an integrated confidence measure of similarity between reference model and input image. By applying neural network techniques, the complexity of system construction is greatly reduced, especially in feature comparison and collective voting stages. Further improvements of current system are to extract and utilize more effective features to enhance the discrimination power against skilled forgeries.

References

[1] R. Plamondon and G. Lorette, "Automatic signature verification and writer identification : the state of the art", *Pattern Recognition*, **22**, pp. 107-131, 1989.

[2] F. Leclerc and R. Plamondon, "Automatic signature verification: the state of the art - 1989-1993", *Int. J. of Pattern Recogn. Artif. Intell.*, **8**(3), pp. 3-19, 1994.

[3] F. Nouboud, "Handwritten signature verification: a global approach ", *Fundamentals in Handwriting Recognition*, S. Impedovo, Ed., pp. 455-459, Berlin, Heidelberg: Springer-Verlag, 1994.

[4] R. Sabourin and J. P. Drouhard, "Off-line signature verification using directional PDF and neural networks", *Proc. 11th IAPR Int. Conf. on Pattern Recognition*, 1992, pp. 321-325.

[5] M. Ammar, Y. Yoshida and T. Fukumura, "A new effective approach for off-line verification of signatures by using pressure features", *Proc. 8th Int. Conf. on Pattern Recognition*, 1986, pp. 566-569.

[6] H. Sakoe and S. Chiba, "Dynamic programming algorithm optimization for spoken word recognition", *IEEE Trans. Acoust. Speech, Signal Processing*, **ASSP-26**, pp. 43-49, 1978.

[7] R. C. Gonzalez and R. E. Woods, *Digital Image Processing*, Addison-Wesley, 1992.

Real-Time Neural Adaptive
Control of Unreliable Plants

B. Porter†, R.J.D. Hall‡

†Department of Industrial and Manufacturing Systems Engineering,
The University of Hong Kong,
Hong Kong.
e-mail: bporter@hkucc.hku.hk
‡Research Institute for Design, Manufacture, and Marketing,
University of Salford,
England.
e-mail: R.Hall@aeromech.salford.ac.uk

Abstract - **In this paper, a methodology is presented for the design of real-time neural model-reference adaptive control systems for unreliable plants subject to partial actuator failures. These general results are illustrated in the case of a particular monovariable plant for which learning occurs rapidly, both in the absence of failures and after partial actuator failure. These neural learning processes correspond to plant conditions for which no prior off-line neural training has been given, and provide simultaneous real-time adaptive control and explicit fault detection.**

1 Introduction

Many recent applications of artificial neural networks to industrial control involve the prior training of such networks. However, since such training essentially occurs off-line, the resulting controllers are irrelevant to a large class of practical automation problems for which learning must occur in real time. In particular, it is evident that controllers for unreliable plants that rely on off-line training are incapable of dealing effectively with unanticipated plant failures. Many recent developments in neural control are therefore disappointingly distant from the requirements for practical adaptive control enunciated nearly 40 years ago by Kalman [1].

In an endeavour to improve this situation, a methodology is described for the design of real-time neural model-reference adaptive control systems for unreliable plants subject to partial actuator failures. These general results are illustrated in the case of a particular monovariable plant for which learning occurs rapidly, both the in the absence of failures and after partial actuator failure. These neural learning processes correspond to plant conditions for which no prior off-line training has been given, and provide simultaneous real-time adaptive control and explicit fault detection.

It is important to note that, in the spirit of Porter [2], the neural model-reference adaptive control systems described in this paper do not require detailed knowledge of the plants under control for their design but instead use only input/output representations of such plants. This design methodology can therefore be regarded as providing a theoretical basis for the results of Showalter [3], which constitute an important early attempt to implement direct real-time neural control. The present methodology thus solves the problem of designing direct neural model-reference adaptive control systems (the difficulty of which was eloquently described by Narendra and Parthasarathy [4]).

2 Adaptive Model-Reference Neural Control

The adaptive model-reference neural control systems under investigation have the configuration shown in Fig 1. Such systems comprise the unreliable plant under control, with nominal transfer function g(z); the neural controller; the asymptotically stable reference model, with transfer function m(z); and the pre-filter, with transfer function $m^{-1}(1) \in R$. The objective of such model-reference control systems is that the plant output, $y(k)$, tracks the reference model output, $r(k)$, while the reference model output, $r(k)$, tracks the set-point command input, $v(k)$, even when partial actuator failures occur. In such failed cases, the effective transfer function of the plant becomes

$$\hat{g}(z) = g(z)\xi \tag{1}$$

where the actuator condition parameter, ξ, is such that $0 < \xi < 1$. It is assumed that there exists a proportional gain, $\hat{\kappa} \in R$, such that

$$m(z) = \frac{\hat{g}(z)\hat{\kappa}}{1+\hat{g}(z)\hat{\kappa}} . \tag{2}$$

It is evident from Fig 1 that, because of the pre-filter, it is only necessary to design the neural controller so that the plant output, $y(k)$, tracks the reference model output, $r(k)$, in all circumstances.

The neural controller is a multi-layered feedforward artificial neural network, the output from which is the input, $u(k)$, to the unreliable plant under control. This controller output can be expressed in the form

$$u(k) = NN(\theta, q)_k \quad , \tag{3}$$

where

$$\theta = \{\theta_1, \theta_2, ..., \theta_N\} \tag{4}$$

is the set of artificial neural network parameters (i.e., weights and biases) and

$$q(k) = w(k) - y(k) \tag{5}$$

is the tracking error. The design objective is to determine a real-time algorithm for changing the artificial neural network parameters such that the equivalent network gain

$$\lambda(k) = \frac{u(k)}{q(k)} \tag{6}$$

approaches the appropriate desired value, $\hat{\kappa}$, of this gain. In the case of unreliable plants, this desired gain value is equal to κ in the absence of failure but equal to κ/ξ in the presence of partial actuator failure.

The required real-time algorithm up-dates the artificial neural network parameters so as to minimise the model-following error function

$$e(k) = z^2(k) = \{r(k) - y(k)\}^2 . \tag{7}$$

This minimisation is achieved by ensuring that the changes in the error function at each sampling period are such that

$$\Delta e(k) \le 0 \tag{8}$$

with the effect that

$$\lim_{k \to \infty} e(k) = 0 . \tag{9}$$

Thus, it follows from equation (7) that, approximately,

$$\Delta e(k) = 2z(k) \, \Delta y(k) . \tag{10}$$

Therefore, in view of equations (1), (3), and (5), it is evident that

$$\Delta e(k) = -2 \sum_{j=1}^{N} \left[z(k) \, \hat{g}_{sm}(z) \left\{ \frac{\partial NN(\theta,q)}{\partial \theta_j} \right\}_k \Delta \theta_j(k) \right] \tag{11}$$

where the sensitivity model for the unreliable plant has the transfer function

$$\hat{g}_{sm}(z) = \frac{\hat{g}(z)}{1+\hat{g}(z)\,\lambda(k)} . \tag{12}$$

Equation (11) indicates (using the appropriate stability theory for systems with time-varying parameters [5]) that, in order to satisfy the conditions (8) and (9), the artificial neural network parameters should be up-dated according to the equation

$$\Delta\theta_j(k) = 2\varepsilon z(k) \,\hat{g}_{sm}(z) \left\{ \frac{\partial NN(\theta,c)}{\partial\theta_j} \right\}_k \qquad (j = 1, 2, ..., N) \quad , \tag{13}$$

where $\varepsilon \in R^+$ is appropriately small learning parameter.

However, implementation of equation (13) is not a practical proposition, since this would require explicit knowledge of the unreliable plant transfer function, $\hat{g}(z)$. But, in the case of minimum-phase plants, the results of Porter and Jones [6] indicate that the exact sensitivity model of the unreliable plant in the neural up-date equation (13) can be replaced by an approximate sensitivity model with the transfer function

$$\hat{g}_{asm}(z) = \hat{h}(T)z^{-1} \quad . \tag{14}$$

In equation (14), $\hat{h}(T)$ is the step response of the uncontrolled unreliable plant after one sampling period, T. However, it follows from equation (1) that

$$\hat{h}(T) = h(T)\xi, \tag{15}$$

where $h(T)$ is the step response of the uncontrolled un-failed plant after one sampling period, T. Since $h(T)$ can obviously be obtained directly from input/output tests on the un-failed plant, it is evident from equations (14) and (15) that use of the neural up-date equation (13) in the form

$$\Delta\theta_j(k) = 2\varepsilon z(k)h(T)z^{-1} \left\{ \frac{\partial NN(\theta,q)}{\partial\theta_j} \right\}_k \qquad (j = 1, 2, .., N) \tag{16}$$

is fully consonant with the guidelines of Porter [2] for practical control. Thus, implementation of this neural up-date algorithm in real-time ensures that conditions (8) and (9) are satisfied. In addition, the equivalent network gain defined in equation (6) is caused to approach the desired value,

$$\hat{\kappa} = \frac{\kappa}{\xi} \quad , \tag{17}$$

of this gain embedded in the reference model. Since it follows from equation (17) that

$$\xi = \frac{\kappa}{\hat{\kappa}} \quad , \tag{18}$$

it also possible to use the artificial neural network for explicit fault detection. Indeed, it is evident from equation (18) that the actuator condition parameter, ξ, can be directly obtained by monitoring the equivalent network gain, $\hat{\kappa}$, and by dividing this value into the value, κ, of this gain in the absence of failures.

3   Illustrative Example

This general approach to the real-time neural adaptive control of unreliable plants can be conveniently illustrated by considering the particular minimum-phase, second-order plant governed by the continuous-time state-space equations

$$\dot{x}(t) = \begin{bmatrix} -3, & 0 \\ 0, & -4 \end{bmatrix} x(t) + \begin{bmatrix} 4 \\ -4 \end{bmatrix} u(t) \tag{19a}$$

and

$$y(t) = [1, 1] x(t) \quad . \tag{19b}$$

It is required that the controlled plant - both before and after a 50% failure of its actuator -exhibit the behaviour of the asymptotically stable reference model governed by the discrete-time state-space equations

$$x_m(k+1) = \begin{bmatrix} 0.050, & -0.691 \\ 0.659, & 1.330 \end{bmatrix} x_m(k) + \begin{bmatrix} 0.691 \\ -0.659 \end{bmatrix} w(k) \tag{20a}$$

and

$$r(k) = [1, 1] x_m(k) \tag{20b}$$

when the sampling period is $T = 0.1s$. This reference model corresponds to the choices $\kappa = 2.0$ of the desired gain in the absence of actuator failure, and $\hat{\kappa} = 4.0$ in the presence of 50% actuator failure. The artificial neural network used as the neural controller in this case has an input layer with 1 node, a hidden layer with 6 nodes, and an output layer with 1 node.

The simulation results presented in Figs 2, 3, and 4 were obtained by using a learning parameter $\varepsilon = 10.0$ after assigning random initial values in the range ± 1.0 to the neural network parameters. The artificial neural network controlling the un-failed plant was first allowed to reach a fully learned condition by subjecting the model-reference system to 100 cycles of a square-wave command input; then, 15s after the start of the 101st cycle, the actuator was failed by 50%. In Figs 2, 3, and 4, the behaviour of the system immediately before and after partial actuator failure is displayed during the 101st to the 104th cycles; whilst the post-failure learned behaviour of the system is indicated in the final displayed cycle (which actually corresponds to the 110th cycle of the command input). It is evident from Fig 2 that the plant output (represented by the full line) diverges from the reference model output (represented by the broken line) immediately after actuator failure; but that the plant output then rapidly approaches the reference model output. In addition, it is clear from Fig 3 that the equivalent gain of the artificial neural network is initially equal to the desired value $\kappa = 2.0$ in the un-failed case; and that, after the actuator failure, this equivalent gain rapidly approaches the desired value $\hat{\kappa} = 4.0$. Finally, it is evident from Fig 4 that the actuator condition parameter is initially equal to unity in the un-failed case; and that, after actuator failure, this parameter rapidly approaches its correct value of 0.5.

4 Conclusion

In this paper, a methodology has been presented for the design of real-time neural model-reference adaptive control systems for unreliable plants subject to partial actuator failures. These general results have been illustrated in the case of a particular monovariable plant for which learning occurs very rapidly both in the absence of failures and after partial actuatur failure.

5 Acknowledgement

This research was sponsored by British Nuclear Fuels plc.

References

[1] R.E. Kalman, "Design of a self-optimizing control system", *Trans ASME*, vol. 80, pp. 468-478, 1958.

[2] B. Porter, "Issues in the design of intelligent control systems", *IEEE Control Systems Magazine*, vol. 9, pp. 97-99, 1989.

[3] B.E. Showalter, "Control applications using neural networks", *MS Thesis, MIT*, 1988.

[4] K.S. Narendra and K. Parthasarathy, "Identification and control of dynamical systems using neural networks", *IEEE Trans on Neural Networks*, vol. 1, pp. 4-27, 1990.

[5] J.L. Willems, *Stability Theory of Dynamical Systems*. London: Nelson, 1970.

[6] B. Porter and A.H. Jones, "Time-domain identification of transmission zero locations of linear multivariable plants", *IEEE Trans on Automatic Control*, vol. AC-30, pp. 1050-1053, 1985.

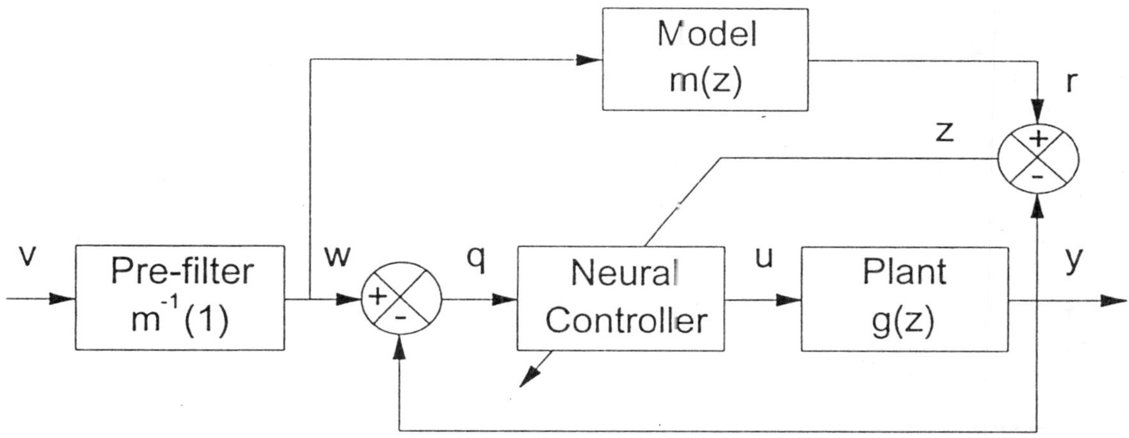

Figure 1: Reconfigurable model-reference neural control system.

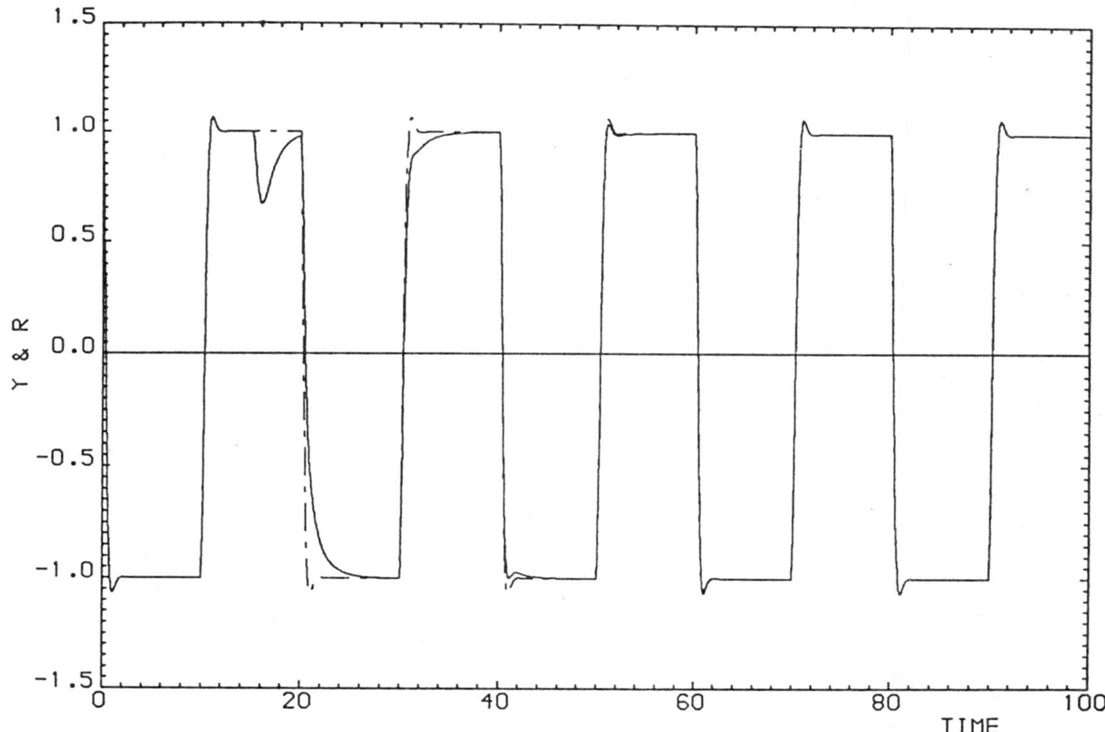

Figure 2: Outputs of plant and reference model.

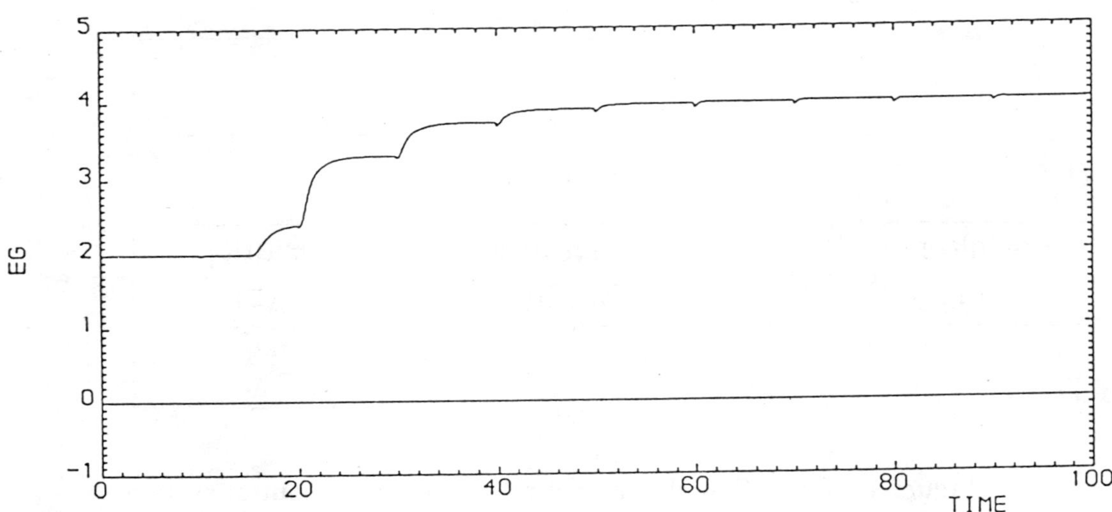

Figure 3: Equivalent gain of neural network.

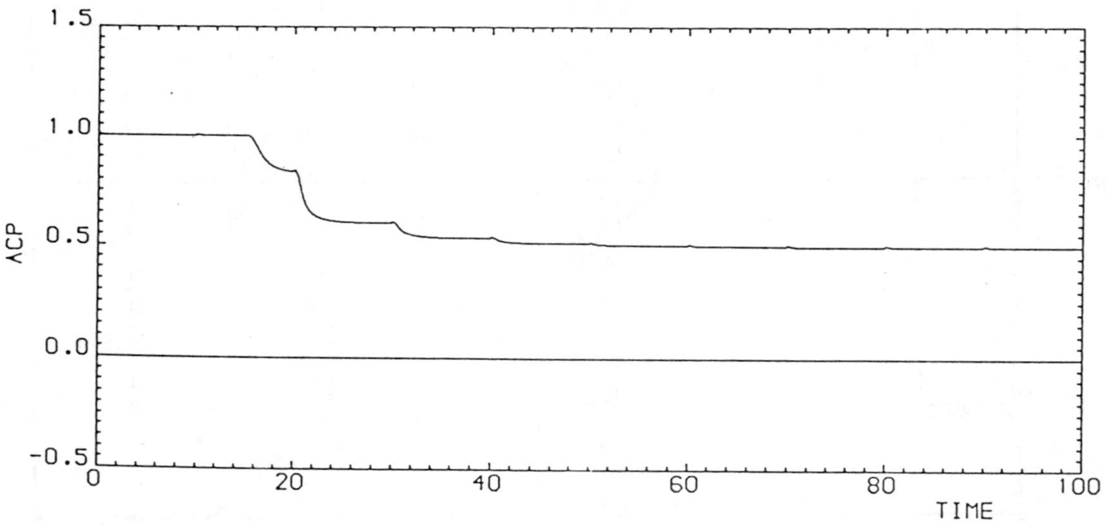

Figure 4: Actuator condition parameter.

Learning in Noisy and Drifting Environments

Anthony Kuh

Dept. of Electrical Engineering
University of Hawaii
Honolulu, HI 98822, USA
kuh@spectra.eng.hawaii.edu

Abstract— In many engineering systems, observed data is not only noisy, but the statistics of received data changes with time. When these systems are not well parameterized, using a neural network learning approach may work well. This paper studies how neural network learning algorithms perform when confronted with noisy and time varying data. We look at slowly varying changes and analytically study the performance of single layer threshold neural networks. From this analysis, we discuss approaches to studying the behavior of more complicated network architectures.

1   Introduction

This paper discusses supervised learning in noisy and changing environments. Our focus will be on the drift model where training example statistics change slowly with time. Specifically we study the behavior of a number of learning algorithms for single layer threshold networks subject to both drift and random noise. Here we consider the effects of random drift and worst case drift and show that the generalization error depends on the drift rate γ, the step size μ, the statistics of the additive noise, and the information given to the learning algorithm. We also discuss how the analysis results for single layer threshold neural networks can be extended to more complicated networks.

In many online learning situations we must account for environmental parameters that change with time and received data that is noisy. For channel equalization problems received signals are contaminated in additive noise and the channel is often time varying [4]. Radar or sonar detection involve observing noisy signals in environments that may change with time [1]. There are many other applications in signal processing, control theory, and communications where learning systems must adapt to noisy and changing system parameters.

We use a system identification model to study the behavior of various neural network learning algorithms when confronted with noisy and drifting environments. An adversary controls a target network and the way inputs are selected. The learning algorithm, also referred to as the tracking algorithm receives information from the target network and makes changes to the weights of the tracking network. We will specifically examine the drift model where the target network weights change slowly with time.

Tracking algorithms for nonstationary environments have been analyzed for linear adaptive filters, [9]. Eweda [3], analyzed the performance of the nonlinear sign algorithm in nonstationary environments. Other researchers [5, 2], studied the performance of learning algorithms for single layer threshold networks when subject to a target network with slowly changing weights.

This research extends work conducted in [5, 7] by considering learning in noisy and drifting environments. Section 2 presents a general system identification model for our learning model. Section 3 discusses analytical results for single layer threshold networks and finally Section 4 discusses how analytical results presented for the single layer case can be extended to more complicated learning models.

2   System Identification Model

We use a discrete time system identification model to model a target and a tracking neural network. Both neural networks receive the same input vector, $x(k) \in \mathcal{R}^n$. The target network, $\mathcal{N}_A$ is parameterized by a set of weights, $w(k) \in \mathcal{R}^{n_A}$ and the tracking network, $\mathcal{N}_L$ is parameterized by a set of weights, $\hat{w}(k) \in \mathcal{R}^{n_L}$. At each update, each network receives an input vector $x(k)$ and each network updates is weight vector.

We focus on the case where both target and tracking neural networks are feedforward neural networks consisting of neurons with the following characteristics:

$$y = \sigma(s), \quad s = w^T x + \theta. \tag{1}$$

Each neuron takes a linearly weight sum of its inputs x and possibly a threshold value, θ to get the synaptic strength, s. The neuron output, y is the synaptic strength passed through a monotonic increasing function $\sigma()$.

2.1   Adversary

Inputs x are chosen by the adversary from an independent and identically distributed random variable X. We use the notation $P_X(A) = P(X = A)$ where $A \subset \mathcal{R}^n$. We can also define a distance measure between two neural networks with the same number of inputs and outputs. Each neural network receives the same input x with neural network $\mathcal{N}_1$ having output y_1 and neural network $\mathcal{N}_2$ having output y_2. If outputs are binary valued, then the distance measure is the probability of error given by

$$d(\mathcal{N}_1, \mathcal{N}_2) = P_X(y_1 \neq y_2) \tag{2}$$

and if outputs are analog valued we use a mean squared error criterion given by

$$d(\mathcal{N}_1, \mathcal{N}_2) = \mathbf{E}(\|y_1 - y_2\|^2) \tag{3}$$

The adversary also updates the target weights as follows:

$$w(k + 1) = \mathcal{A}(w(k), x(k), \hat{w}(k), \gamma). \tag{4}$$

Here the weight updates depend on the previous weights, the inputs, possibly the weights of the target network, and the drift rate γ. This paper focuses on the drift model where weights change slowly with time. For this model we have that $d(\mathcal{N}_A(k), \mathcal{N}_A(k + 1)) \leq \gamma$.

We consider two types of adversary models. The first model is an average case behavior where weight updates of the target neural network are made independent of the tracking weights. This is called the random drift model. The second model model is a worst case learning behavior as the adversary adjusts weights to maximize the distance between the target and tracking neural networks. This is called the worst case drift model.

2.2 Tracker

The tracking algorithm attempts to track the target network by using information received from the tracking network to reduce the overall generalization error defined as

$$\epsilon_g = \lim_{k \to \infty} 1/k \sum_{i=1}^{k} d(\mathcal{N}_A(k), \mathcal{N}_L(k)). \tag{5}$$

The tracker receives a noisy value of the output described by $\bar{y}(k)$ and possibly other information about the target network denoted by $H(k)$. The tracking network updates are described as follows:

$$\hat{w}(k + 1) = \mathcal{L}(\hat{w}(k), x(k), \bar{y}(k), H(k)). \tag{6}$$

The tracking algorithms that we consider can be divided into conservative trackers, where tracker weights change only when the tracker output $\hat{y}(k)$ and the noisy target output $\bar{y}(k)$ differ and nonconservative trackers (trackers that are not conservative).

3 Single Layer Threshold Networks

In [5, 7] we focused on the case where both target and tracking neural networks were single layer threshold neural networks. Here we have that the target network is described by

$$y(k) = \sigma(w(k)^T x(k)) \tag{7}$$

where

$$\sigma(s) = \begin{cases} 1, & \text{if } s \geq 0 \\ -1, & \text{if } s < 0 \end{cases}. \tag{8}$$

The tracking network has the same architecture with weight vector $\hat{w}(k)$ and output $\hat{y}(k)$.

For this case the analysis is tractable and we came up with a number of analytical upper bounds on the generalization error which are described in this Section. The results focus on a conservative tracker, the Perceptron tracker [6] and a nonconservative tracker, the least mean square (LMS) tracker [8]. Here we assume that X is a Gaussian random vector with zero mean and identity covariance matrix I.

3.1 Random Drift Adversary

Consider the case when the adversary is random, unbiased, and operates independently of the tracking algorithm, [5]. The vector $w^{\perp}(k)$ is chosen randomly and uniformly in the null space of $w(k)$ independently of the tracking weight vector $\hat{w}(k)$. The weight update equation for the target network is described by

$$w(k + 1) = \cos(\gamma\pi)w(k) + \sin(\gamma\pi)w^{\perp}(k) \quad k = 0, 1, 2, \ldots \tag{9}$$

For the Perceptron algorithm we have that

$$\hat{w}(k + 1) = \begin{cases} \hat{w}(k), & \text{if } y(k) = \hat{y}(k) \\ \hat{w}(k) + x(k)y(k), & \text{if } y(k) \neq \hat{y}(k) \end{cases}. \tag{10}$$

For this case the generalization error is upper bounded by

$$\epsilon_{g_{per,r}} \leq \gamma^{2/3} \left(\frac{2n}{\pi\cos(\gamma\pi)} \right)^{1/3} \tag{11}$$

For the LMS algorithm we have that

$$\hat{w}(k + 1) = (1 - \lambda)\hat{w}(k) + \mu[s(k) - \hat{s}(k)]x(k) \qquad k = 1, 2, \cdots \tag{12}$$

For this tracker, small weight decay $\lambda > 0$ can slightly reduce the generalization error, while large weight decay term will result in a much larger generalization error rate. The best step size and weight decay is given when $\mu = 1/(n+2)$ and $\lambda = 1 - \cos(\gamma\pi)$ resulting in

$$\epsilon_{g_{\mathrm{lms},r}} \leq \gamma\sqrt{\frac{n+3}{1 + (1 - \cos(\gamma\pi))(n+1)}} \tag{13}$$

Simulations conducted in [5] showing that these bounds for the generalization error are tight when γ is small and n large. These results show that for the conservative Perceptron tracker, the generalization error is $\mathcal{O}(\gamma^{2/3})$. The LMS tracker has better generalization error as it has access to more information than the Perceptron tracker. The generalization error for this nonconservative tracker is $\mathcal{O}(\gamma)$.

3.2 Worst Case Adversary

Now consider a worst case adversary, where weight changes are made to maximize the differences between the tracking and target weights subject to a target drift rate of γ, [7]. The weight update equation for the target network is described by

$$w(k+1) = \cos(\gamma\pi)w(k) + \sin(\gamma\pi)w^-(k) \qquad k = 1, 2, \cdots \tag{14}$$

For the Perceptron tracker with $\gamma n << 1$ we have that

$$\epsilon_{g_{\mathrm{per},w}} \leq 2\sqrt{\gamma n/(\pi\cos\gamma\pi)}. \tag{15}$$

For the LMS tracker we focus on the no weight decay case where $\lambda = 0$. We have that for n large and $\gamma n << 1$ the optimal step size is given by

$$\mu_{opt} = \frac{2}{2n+3}. \tag{16}$$

and

$$\epsilon_{g_{\mathrm{lms},w}} \leq \gamma(2n + 5/2) \tag{17}$$

Simulation results conducted in [7] show that these bounds for the generalization error are relatively tight when γ is small and n large. Results for the worst case tracker are worse than the random tracker as now the conservative Perceptron tracker has generalization error that is $\mathcal{O}(\sqrt{\gamma})$. The LMS tracker has generalization error that is still $\mathcal{O}(\gamma)$, but the generalization error now depends directly on the number of inputs, n instead of $\sqrt{n}$.

3.3 Noisy Target

Here we assume that the synaptic strength of the target network is contaminated by an additive and independent Gaussian noise source $n(k)$. The tracking algorithm has access to a noisy output given by

$$\bar{y}(k) = \sigma(w(k)^T x(k) + n(k)). \tag{18}$$

For this case we discuss some observations for the random drift case and the nonconservative LMS tracker from [5]. Now there are two sources that contribute to the generalization error: drift and additive noise. A key parameter is the step size μ. If μ is set too small, then the tracking network will not be able to track the target network changes. On the other hand if the step size is set too large, the error due to the random noise is large. For step sizes with $0 < \mu < 1/(n+2)$ we can show that the generalization error is approximately

$$\epsilon_{g_{\mathrm{lms},rn}} \approx \gamma/\sqrt{\mu} + \frac{\sigma_n}{\pi}\sqrt{.5\mu n} \tag{19}$$

where σ_n is the deviation of the noise $n(k)$. We can minimize the generalization error by choosing

$$\mu = \min(\gamma\pi/(\sigma_n\sqrt{.5n}) \; 1/(n+2)). \tag{20}$$

These results are similar to analysis conducted for linear adaptive filters that are subject to random drift and additive noise, [4, 9]. Simulations conducted in [5] again show the validity of these results.

4 Arbitrary Feedforward Networks

The analysis for arbitrary feedforward tracking and target neural networks is considerably more difficult, but we can draw from the information gained in the analysis of single layer threshold networks. A major consideration is whether the tracking algorithm has knowledge about the architecture of the target neural network. In this discussion, when we refer to a size of a neural network we are referring to the total number of weights and threshold values of the neural network.

If the tracking algorithm does not have knowledge about the architecture of the target neural network it must examine some training examples in order to determine the architecture of the tracking neural network. This task is made more complicated as the training data is noisy and slowly changes with time. As with most neural network architecture design problems we must make the tracking neural network sufficiently large so that it can track the target network sufficiently well. However, the tracking neural network must not be too large or else learning will be slow and the tracking network will have poor generalization capabilities.

If target and tracking neural networks have different architectures, the tracking generalization error will clearly be higher than if the architectures are the same. We conjecture that if the tracking neural network is slightly smaller than the target network that the tracking network will have some abilities in tracking the target network. Conversely, if the tracking network is larger than the target network we conjecture that tracking abilities will be poorer than if a smaller tracking network is used.

Even if the tracking network has knowledge of the target network and uses the same architecture as the tracking network, analysis of the effects of drift and random noise is difficult. We conclude this paper by discussing some issues that must be considered when examining the behavior of multilayer neural networks.

Let us consider a one hidden layer feedforward neural network composed of h hidden units and one output unit. Inputs $x(k)$ are drawn according to Section 3·and target and tracking neural networks are identical. It is now much more difficult to measure the distance between two neural networks. Consider the random drift model and assume the target network follows equation (9). Now if the neurons are all threshold units, we have that $d(\mathcal{N}_A(k), \mathcal{N}_A(k+1)) >> \gamma$. This is because the distance will depend directly on the number of neurons and γ. For large n and h, we will likely have that $d(\mathcal{N}_A(k), \mathcal{N}_A(k+1)) \approx h\gamma$. Another major consideration is that learning algorithms for multilayer neural networks are much slower than for single layer neural networks as two or more layers of weights must be adjusted. Here the drift rates must be very small in order for a tracking neural network to have good tracking capabilities. Bounds for generalization errors for multilayer neural network will be much poorer than bounds found in Section 3.

Research in studying the behavior of multilayer neural networks in the presence of drift and random noise is ongoing. Since analysis is difficult, extensive empirical simulation studies need to be conducted.

Acknowledgements

This work was supported in part by the National Science Foundation through grant ECS-8857711.

References

[1] M. Basseville and A. Benveniste, *Detection of Abrupt Changes in Signals and Dynamical Systems*, Springer Verlag, 1986.

[2] M. Biehl and H. Schwarze. Learning drifting concepts with neural networks. *Journal of Physics, A*, 26(11):2651, 1993.

[3] E. Eweda. Optimum step size of sign algorithm for nonstationary adaptive filtering. *IEEE Trans. Acoust., Speech, Signal Processing*, 38:1897–1901, November 1990.

[4] S. Haykin. *Adaptive filter theory.* Prentice Hall, 1991.

[5] A. Kuh. Comparison of tracking algorithms for single layer threshold networks in the presence of random drift. preprint, submitted *IEEE Trans. on Signal Processing*, 1995.

[6] F. Rosenblatt. *Principles of Neurodynamics.* Spartan, 1962.

[7] X. Tian and A. Kuh. Performance bounds for single layer threshold networks when tracking a drifting adversary. preprint, submitted *Neural Networks*, 1995.

[8] B. Widrow and M. E. Hoff. Adaptive switching circuits. In *WESCON Convention Record, Part IV*, pages 96–104, August 1960.

[9] B. Widrow, J. McCool, M. Larimore, and C. Johnson Jr. Stationary and nonstationary learning characteristics of the LMS adaptive filter. *IEEE Proceedings*, 64:1151–1562, August 1976.

Author Index

F

Fan, J.B.   1364
Fels, S.S.   1299
Fernandes, M.A.   822
Fiesler, E.   275
Fine, T.L.   1217
Fishman, S.   481
Flockton, S.J.   1229
Fröhlinghaus, T.   799
Freier, B.   954
Frick, A.   766
Fry, R.L.   158
Fu, A.M.N.   389
Fujita, T.   377
Fukumi, M.   365
Fukunishi, K.   1281
Fukushima, K.   15, 405, 894
Funabiki, N.   631
Funakubo, H.   557
Fung, G.S.K.   811

G

Gallinari, P.   960
Gambardella, L.M.   921
Gandolfo, F.   938
Gao, Y.   1330
Ge, N.   1291
Ghosh, A.   1335
Giese, M.   1285
Goerke, N.   995
Gomi, H.   938
Gorse, D.   563
Guan, H.   1007
Guo, D.   502
Guo, F.X.   410
Guo, H.   410

H

Hachiya, I.   1395
Halgamuge, S.   1381
Hall, R.J.D.   1405
Han, I.S.   1247
Hansen, L.K.   1305
He, Z.Y.   845, 1361
Hecht-Nielsen, R.   41
Heinz, A.P.   926
Herrmann, C.   1381

Herrmann, M.   1211
Herrmann, R.   766
Hida, E.   1271
Hinrichs, B.E.   843
Hirai, Y.   356, 1251
Ho, D.   932
Ho, K.S.E.   1075
Hoffmann, A.   954
Homma, N.   1158
Hoshino, O.   858, 876
Hou, H.T.   1127
Howard, S.D.   970
Hsieh, W.   722
Hsu, C.   496
Huang, B.   1135
Huang, J.L.   654
Huang, K.   1400
Huang, L.   251
Hutchens, C.G.   1045
Hwang, C.S.   1387
Hyvärinen, A.   7, 97, 1201, 1207

I

Ichikawa, A.   260
Ieong, R.   1275
Ikuta, K.   894
Ingber, L.   777
Inouye, Y.   1189
Intrator, N.   29, 84
Isasi-Viñuela, P.   1175
Ishii, N.   103
Ishikawa, M.   1158, 1377
Iwata, A.   882

J

Jašić, T.   754
Jabri, M.   1257
Jagota, A.K.   592, 623, 636
Jain, L.   1381
Jancke, D.   1285
Jang, M.   989
Jeong, J.H.   283
Jin, F.   1364
Jin, L.   732
Jung, D.H.   1023

Wu, Y.S.   410

X

Xia, Y.S.   654
Xu, J.H.   932
Xu, L.   59, 216, 271, 648, 1235
Xu, Z.B.   1330

Y

Yamanoue, T.   535
Yamauchi, K.   103, 882
Yan, H.   389, 1400
Yanai,   H.F. 581
Yang, C.L.   450
Yang, D.   1229
Yang, H.H.   317, 322, 1211
Yang, S.   231
Yang, X.F.   915
Yang, Y.   337
Yao, J.T.   754
Yao, S.S.   845
Yasunaga, M.   1251, 1395
Ye, C.   948
Yeh, C.H.   1341
Yeung, D.Y.   109
Yin, H.   80
Yip, P.P.C.   827
Yoon, H.S.   587
Yu, H.Y.   771
Yu, J.B.   547
Yu, X.   294
Yuan, J.   943
Yuille, A.L.   347
Yun, T.I.   1023
Yung, N.H.C.   948

Z

Zahn, V.   401
Zeevi, A.J.   35
Zhang, B.   1012
Zhang, B.L.   216
Zhang, D.   1039
Zhang, H.Y.   742
Zhang, X.S.   551
Zhang, Y.C.   260
Zhao, J.   454
Zhao, M.S.   410
Zhao, Q.   423

Zhao, S.L.   870
Zhao, Y.N.   1012
Zhong, Y.X.   1116, 1355
Zhou, H.J.   458
Zhou, J.Z.   611
Zhu, H.   74
Zhu, S.C.   347